Biological Control of
Insect Pests and Weeds

DEDICATION

This book is dedicated to the late Professor Harry S. Smith, the mentor, inspiration, and former chief of nearly all of the chapter authors. For many years Professor Smith was recognized as one of the world's outstanding authorities on biological control. He was in charge of biological control work in California from 1913 to 1951, first in the State Department of Agriculture from 1913 to 1923, then in the University of California from 1923 until his retirement in 1951. Under his guidance the first American continental projects on biological control of weeds and on insect pathology were developed in California. Royalties from this book go to the Harry S. Smith Memorial Fund of the University of California, which is used to help students and to promote progress in the field of biological control.

Biological Control of Insect Pests and Weeds

Edited by Paul DeBach

Entomologist and Professor of Biological Control,
University of California, Riverside, California

Assistant Editor Evert I. Schlinger

REINHOLD PUBLISHING CORPORATION

NEW YORK

Preface

THIS BOOK has had a long gestation period. About thirty years ago the late Professor H. S. Smith and Professor C. P. Clausen laid plans for such a book and did considerable initial work on it. However, not until the mid-fifties was the idea decided upon of having as authors various specialists in different phases of biological control within the Department of Biological Control of the University of California. This is the result.

We think the reader will find this book to be different from the usual symposium-type, multiple-author book. It was planned for cohesiveness and continuity much as a single author would plan his book. The volume was purposely divided into sections whose chapters form a related group of subjects. Section 4, for example, is organized in the manner in which a typical project in applied biological control might be carried out; ranging from foreign exploration and importation to the final field evaluation of the effectiveness of introduced natural enemies.

Section 1 defines biological control and discusses its scope, importance, and historical development. Section 2 covers the ecological basis of biological control with emphasis on the fundamentals of population ecology and natural control and also treats of some common concepts and questions in biological control work. Section 3 lays the basis for working with and understanding the organisms employed in biological control research. It treats of their biologies, habits and identification. Section 4, as mentioned, essentially describes the 'bread and butter' work of biological control—the importation and establishment of new natural enemies. Section 5 discusses ways and means of improving the effectiveness of already established natural enemies or of preventing their effectiveness from being reduced. Sections 6 and 7 were considered separately because they deal with the specialized phases of insect pathology and biological control of weeds. In conclusion, the last chapter reviews over 220 successful cases of biological control, discusses current trends and considers future possibilities. The Table of Contents serves as an index to the various subject matter specialities. A complete index to scientific names is given at the end of the book as are over 2500 literature references. The survey of literature was completed by the various chapter authors by June, 1961.

The general outline of the book and most of the eventual authors were determined by a committee consisting of Paul DeBach, R. L. Doutt, T. W. Fisher, C. B. Huffaker, E. I. Schlinger, and E. A. Steinhaus. C. P. Clausen was originally scheduled to be editor but upon his retirement in 1959 he was succeeded by the current editor. Later, E. I. Schlinger was named assistant editor. Professor

v

25659

Clausen's contribution has been substantial through his advice and assistance to various of the chapter authors.

All chapter authors at the time of writing this book were members of the Department of Biological Control of the University of California at Berkeley and Riverside, except E. A. Steinhaus, Y. Tanada, and M. E. Martigoni who were members of the Department of Insect Pathology, University of California, Berkeley, and J. K. Holloway, who was with the U.S. Department of Agriculture, Agricultural Research Service, but had been a Research Associate in the Department of Biological Control at Berkeley for many years. The authors of the various chapters were chosen on the basis of their particular interest or specialization in the subject matter of a given chapter. Many of them are recognized internationally for their contributions to the field of biological control. Among these authors over 200 man-years of specialization in biological control is represented. Collectively they have combed all the continents in search of new and desirable natural enemies and few countries in the world have not been surveyed by them.

So many people have graciously given advice and assistance during the preparation of this book that it would be impractical to attempt to thank them all here. Professor George C. Varley of the Hope Department of Entomology of Oxford University read the manuscript critically and offered much valuable advice as well as specific suggestions and corrections. Drs. T. W. Fisher, R. van den Bosch, and B. R. Bartlett contributed an enormous amount of time of a technical editorial nature in helping to bring the original typed manuscripts to the point of publication. Mrs. Marian B. Harris of the editorial staff of the University of California, Berkeley, reviewed each of the originally submitted chapters and suggested many important changes. Typing, cataloguing, and rechecking details of the manuscript were ably carried out by Lorenne Sisson, Ruth Tibbens, Betty Radke, Marilyn Shull, Leonore Ellis, Stella Quan, and Nettie Mackey. F. E. Skinner furnished the photography in chapters 7 and 8.

Paul DeBach, *Editor*
Department of Biological Control
University of California
Riverside

The Authors

B. R. Bartlett: *Associate Entomologist in the Experiment Station, Department of Biological Control, University of California, Riverside.*

Paul DeBach: *Professor of Biological Control and Entomologist in the Experiment Station, Department of Biological Control, University of California, Riverside.*

R. L. Doutt: *Professor of Biological Control and Entomologist in the Experiment Station, Division of Biological Control, University of California, Berkeley.*

G. L. Finney: *Associate Specialist in the Experiment Station, Division of Biological Control, University of California, Berkeley.*

T. W. Fisher: *Assistant Entomologist in the Experiment Station, Department of Biological Control, University of California, Riverside.*

K. S. Hagen: *Associate Entomologist in the Experiment Station, Division of Biological Control, University of California, Berkeley.*

I. M. Hall: *Associate Professor of Insect Pathology and Associate Insect Pathologist in the Experiment Station, Department of Biological Control, University of California, Riverside.*

J. K. Holloway: *Leader, Biological Control of Weeds Investigations, U.S. Department of Agriculture, Albany, California, and Associate in the Experiment Station, Division of Biological Control, University of California, Berkeley.*

C. B. Huffaker: *Professor of Entomology and Entomologist in the Experiment Station, Division of Biological Control, University of California, Berkeley.*

M. E. Martignoni: *Associate Professor of Invertebrate Pathology and Associate Insect Pathologist in the Experiment Station, Division of Invertebrate Pathology, University of California, Berkeley.*

P. S. Messenger: *Chairman of Division, Associate Entomologist in the Experiment Station and Lecturer in Insect Ecology, Division of Biological Control, University of California, Berkeley.*

E. I. Schlinger: *Associate Professor of Entomology and Associate Entomologist in the Experiment Station, Department of Entomology, University of California, Riverside.*

E. A. Steinhaus: *Dean of Biological Sciences, University of California, Irvine.*

Y. Tanada: *Associate Insect Pathologist in the Experiment Station and Lecturer in Insect Pathology, Division of Invertebrate Pathology, University of California, Berkeley.*

A. D. Telford: *Formerly Assistant Entomologist in the Experiment Station, Division of Biological Control, University of California, Berkeley.*

R. van den Bosch: *Associate Entomologist in the Experiment Station, Division of Biological Control, University of California, Berkeley.*

Contents

Section II The Ecological Basis of Biological Control

3 Population Ecology—Historical Development

4 The Concept and Significance of Natural Control

5 Some Biological Control Concepts and Questions

Section III Biology and Systematics

6 Biological Characteristics of Entomophagous Adults

7 Developmental Stages of Parasites

8 Systematics in Relation to Biological Control

Section IV The Introduction, Culture, and Establishment Programme

9 Foreign Exploration for Beneficial Organisms

10 Quarantine Handling of Entomophagous Insects

11 Culture of Entomophagous Insects and Their Hosts

13 Insectary Facilities and Equipment

14 Methods of Colonization, Recovery, and Evaluation

Section V The Conservation and Augmentation of Natural Enemies

15 Manipulation of Entomophagous Species

16 Environmental Modification and Biological Control

17 Integration of Chemical and Biological Control

Section VI Insect Pathology

18 Microbial Diseases of Insects

19 Epizootiology of Insect Diseases

20 Mass Production of Insect Pathogens

21 Use of Micro-organisms in Biological Control

Section VII Biological Control of Weeds

22 Fundamentals of Biological Weed Control

23 Projects in Biological Control of Weeds

Section VIII Conclusion

24 Successes, Trends, and Future Possibilities

SECTION I

Introductory

CHAPTER 1

The Scope of Biological Control

PAUL DeBACH

The amount of food for each species of course gives the extreme limit to which each can increase; but very frequently it is not the obtaining food, but the serving as prey to other animals, which determines the average numbers of a species.—DARWIN

On the Origin of Species (1859).

THE PLACE OF BIOLOGICAL CONTROL IN THE BALANCE OF NATURE

THE BIOLOGICAL CONTROL of insects, mites, and weeds has received great and enthusiastic acclaim during the past 70 years, with highly successful practical results achieved in over 60 countries around the world. In spite of this, some few scientists have looked upon the method with incredulity. To these, we would point out that people fortunate enough to have witnessed a striking example of biological control taking place usually become 'true believers,' but some of those who happen later to see only the final result can be unimpressed if not downright sceptical. Seeing is believing, and very few people take the trouble or have the opportunity to 'see' biological control take place. Who today, however, would go so far as Forbes (1880),[1] who, in a purely philosophical paper, wrote: '. . . the annihilation of all the established "enemies" of a species would, as a rule, have no effect to increase its final average numbers.' Obviously failing to heed his own advice he warned, 'The main lesson taught us by these facts and reasonings is that of conservative action and exhaustive inquiry. Reasoning unwarranted by facts, and facts not correctly and sufficiently reasoned out, are equally worthless and dangerous for practical use.'

Nevertheless, the *end result* of an outstanding example of biological control is not spectacular and is likely to go unnoticed and unappreciated because the formerly abundant organism has been reduced to a rare species which is attacked by rare natural enemies. It is easy to overlook the results and to forget a problem when it has disappeared. Many striking examples of 'invisible' biological control are everywhere around us, and can be demonstrated experimentally if one goes to enough trouble, as will be shown later. An interesting insight into such a situation was made

[1] See 'Literature Cited' for citations listed according to author and date.

3

nearly 90 years ago by LeBaron (1870), who, following field studies and observations which were outstanding for the time, observed that, '. . . the oyster-shell bark louse of the apple tree has, for a number of years past, been gradually disappearing, so that it no longer occupies the rank which it has heretofore so pre-eminently held, of a first-class noxious insect. . . . Already the smoother bark, the greener foliage, and the fairer fruit proclaim to the orchardist that this deadly insect is loosening its hold upon the apple tree; and many, no doubt, have prided themselves upon the successful application of some infallible wash, or patent nostrum; but underneath all this goodly show, busily intent upon the accomplishment of her own curious economy, and heedless of the momentous results she is effecting in human interests, works unseen our infinitesimal friend, the apple-tree bark louse parasite (*Chalcis* [*Aphelinus*] *mytilaspidis*).'

The present book will show how such cryptic cases of biological control may be clearly demonstrated (chapter 15, 'Methods of Evaluation') after dealing with the historical background and the ecological and biological bases of biological control, especially of insects, mites, and weeds. Principles and practices are emphasized and specialized methodologies are detailed, but this is getting a little ahead of the story.

Animal and plant ecologists are becoming more and more interested in the basic factors influencing the distribution and abundance of organisms, including man. Frequently this is because populations of organisms so greatly affect man's economic or physical welfare that he would like to do something about it. When this occurs and a problem is investigated it becomes applied ecology, whereas otherwise it might be designated by the more academic title of 'pure' or 'basic' ecology or demography. Essentially there is no fundamental difference, and investigational procedures, hypotheses, and theories apply equally whether the problem is pure or applied. Natural control and biological control are subdivisions of ecology and each has pure and applied phases, as does ecology.

Natural Control

The study of natural control of populations of organisms is that part of ecology which seeks to explain how potential population increase is limited and more or less stabilized by environmental factors. There have been various definitions of natural control as well as proposals for substitute terms but careful consideration suggests 'natural control' as the preferred term. The word 'control' has been objected to as having various meanings, but this is true of many words in common usage that are still regularly used and understood. Dictionaries usually consider control as synonymous with regulation, limitation, or governance. Natural control can be defined simply as the maintenance of a more or less fluctuating population density of an organism within certain definable upper and lower limits over a period of time by the actions of abiotic and/or biotic environmental factors. The upper and lower limits or the average density will change appreciably only if the actions of the regulatory factors are changed, or if certain ones are eliminated or new ones are added. Natural control, therefore, is essentially permanent as opposed to chemical control which reduces populations only temporarily unless repeated indefinitely. It should be clearly understood that natural control does not necessarily imply the existence of low population densities. All animal populations regardless of their density are under some degree of natural control. Also, it is stressed that the preceding definition covers what natural control is—not how it comes about—i.e., the mechanisms of production of natural control are not explained by this definition. These controlling or regulating mechanisms are discussed and illustrated in chapters 3 and 4.

The term 'natural control' is the most common choice of authors writing on population dynamics, including Varley (1947), Thompson (1956), Solomon (1957), Lawson (1958), Milne (1958), and DeBach (1958*b*). Natural control is commonly referred to also as the 'balance of nature,' or 'natural balance' (Huffaker 1958*a*), 'population balance' (Nicholson 1933; Varley and Gradwell 1958), and 'natural regulation' (Lack 1954).

Natural control has sometimes been used by entomologists to refer to cases of naturally occurring biological control as opposed to cases of applied biological control. We feel that this usage leads to undesirable semantic complications.

Observations on natural control by Darwin were instrumental in helping him to develop the theories of natural selection and evolution. Actually, Darwin's term *Struggle for Existence* (1859, chapter 3) is what we now call natural control, as the following excerpts will indicate:

'I use the term Struggle for Existence in a large and metaphorical sense, including dependence of one being on another, and including ... not only the life of the individual, but success in leaving progeny. ...

'A struggle for existence inevitably follows from the high rate at which all organic beings tend to increase.... There is no exception to the rule that every organic being naturally increases at so high a rate, that if not destroyed, the earth would soon be covered by the progeny of a single pair.... Battle within battle must ever be recurring with varying success; and yet in the long run the forces are so nicely balanced, that the face of nature remains uniform for long periods of time. ...'

A detailed discussion of the background theories and mechanics of natural control appears in chapters 3 and 4.

Biological control is a phase of natural control, hence biological control could also be termed 'natural control,' but natural control is the broader term which includes the actions of all environmental factors, both physical and biological, in the regulation, determination, or governance of average population densities.

Biological Control

What is biological control? Again, as with the term natural control, many definitions have been proposed and considerable controversy has arisen. For reasons already given under the section on 'Natural Control,' no drawback is seen to use of the word 'control,' and in any event its status is pretty well fixed by general usage.

The author and colleagues have given this problem a great deal of study. No single definition appears satisfactory because the term biological control is used with different meanings. Accordingly, two definitions are proposed, one to apply in the fundamental ecological sense to describe the result of actions of natural enemies, as when a case of biological control is concerned; the other to cover the term when the activities of man are concerned, thereby defining the field of biological control.

Biological control, when considered from the ecological viewpoint as a phase of natural control, can be defined as 'the action of parasites, predators, or pathogens in maintaining another organism's population density at a lower average than would occur in their absence.' This definition applies to the fact of, or to a case of, biological control and also falls within the definition of natural control. It is demographic and ecological in context but note that it does not explain the mechanisms of control or regulation. That natural enemies may commonly produce control is generally conceded by most entomologists and animal ecologists. Certainly abundant proof of this exists, as will be shown in later chapters.

It will be noted that the preceding definition is a factual type in that biological control can be tested or measured experimentally. Man's activity or manipulation of natural enemies is not implicit in this definition. Also, no particular average population level is implied by the definition; it can be high or low, economically satisfactory or not. Thus, for any particular case the *degree* of biological control must be clearly delimited. Also, if parasites, predators, or pathogens are so inconsequential that the host population shows no measurable change when they are added or eliminated, then they are not regulatory and are not producing biological control even though in a different environment or under different circumstances they may do so. On the other hand, biological control can be defined from a descriptive, qualitative, and utilitarian perspective, which really describes the field of biological control. Most previous definitions have been of this nature, and one of this type is given on page 9 under the heading 'The Field of Biological Control.'

Applied biological control, as stressed in this book, is usually concerned with organisms that are pests or potential pests. The fact that an organism achieves and maintains pest status makes it obvious that climatic and other factors are reasonably favourable; thus it follows that one of the best means of modifying the environment to depress a pest's population permanently lies in the use of natural enemies. For this reason, physical factors may be of secondary concern in studies dealing with biological control, even though it is fully recognized that the distribution and abundance of many organisms may be principally limited by climatic (not climatic alone—see following citations) or other environmental factors aside from natural enemies.

Regulation of an organism's abundance below the level of economic injury is the target of the field of applied biological control. Limitation of geographical distribution is commonly basically enforced by physical factors, and therefore marginal areas of habitation are also of less concern in biological control. Physical factors determine abundance as well as distribution through their interaction with, and modifying effect on the host, its natural enemies, and other environmental factors such as refuges and food (see chapter 4; and DeBach 1958b; Huffaker 1958a). If the population levels experienced are satisfactory to man, no economic problem exists, hence the biological control investigator's interest in physical factors is more likely to be in their effect on natural enemies.

The foregoing discussion by no means provides a complete coverage of all possible factors which may play a part in natural control, nor has there been an attempt to explain the mechanisms involved in population regulation. Complicated interrelationships and various viewpoints will be involved in any particular case. Food, for instance, might be considered an abiotic factor in one case, a biotic factor in another. The abundance and quality of the food supply obviously may limit abundance and distribution. Genetically resistant host plants and host animals are ones which limit the availability or quality of the food supply. The field of artificial selection of strains of plants and animals resistant to pests is an important part of natural control, which is of great economic importance and holds much future promise but is not here considered as part of biological control. Painter (1951) has treated this field in detail. A detailed discussion of the role of various environmental factors in natural control will be found in section II, chapters 3 and 4, on population dynamics.

The field of biological control, as it is generally understood today, was initiated and developed by economic entomologists, hence the term 'biological control' is somewhat restricted in usage, particularly in this book, over the broader scope which a more general use of the word 'biological' might include. Biological control, for instance, could be interpreted to include germ warfare, antibiotics in medicine, the development of plants and animals resistant to the pathogens, parasites, or predators that attack them, or, to carry it to an extreme, even the toxic effects of chemicals on organisms.

On the other hand, certain organisms not stressed in this book, including nematodes, snails, fish, amphibians, birds, and mammals, have been used as beneficial agents in biological control projects by fundamentally entomological research institutions. Likewise, such institutions have sought to control by biological means such pest organisms as snails and lizards. Most of the information developed in this book will apply in a general way to the use of such organisms in biological control or to attempts to control such organisms biologically. However, of the more than 900,000 known animals about 700,000 are insects. The great majority of pest species are insects and most insects have natural enemies, so it follows that biological control has dealt principally with insects, as will be evident in the chapters that follow. Mites, for convenience, are usually considered as entomological problems and are so treated herein. The important disciplines of insect pathology (section VI, chapters 19 to 22) and biological weed control (section VII, chapters 23 and 24) include some specialized concepts and techniques and so are considered in separate sections, although many of the principles, theories, and examples developed throughout the book apply equally to these aspects of biological control.

Previously we have stated in effect that biological control involves regulation of an organism's population density at any given level by natural enemies. If biological control factors are responsible for population regulation of an organism below densities which would be adverse to man's interests, then this is a case of successful biological control in the economic sense. Popular usage sometimes restricts the term 'biological control' to economically successful cases. If control is achieved at somewhat higher average population densities than is economically satisfactory, this is sometimes alluded to as 'partial' biological control. In some cases biological control can be substantially successful economically for a period of time, then only partially so for a subsequent period. Here we are merely trying to evaluate the degree of biological control with an economic yardstick. It is proposed that this be done by the use of adjectives such as 'complete,' 'substantial,' or 'partial' to describe various degrees of economic success. The outstanding economic feature of successful biological control is that once achieved it is essentially permanent. No clear-cut case is known where 'complete' biological control has been attained and maintained for some years then later has failed except where natural enemies have been decimated by chemicals.

It will also be noted that man's purposeful activities do not enter into the foregoing definition of biological control. Man may utilize and manipulate biological control factors and hence favourably change the existing degree of biological control of a pest. On the other hand, biological control of an insect that feeds on a valuable crop may have been brought about naturally by indigenous parasites, predators, or pathogens. Man may not even know that such control is occurring until perhaps some of his pest control or cultural practices adversely affect natural enemies to the extent that an 'upset,'—i.e., a striking increase in the population of the host insect—occurs. Maintenance of the existing degree of biological control of potential pests can be of the utmost importance to man. This brings us to a consideration of the scope of activities which man has developed because of his interest in biological control—that is, the field of biological control as practised by applied entomologists.

THE FIELD OF BIOLOGICAL CONTROL

Study, importation, augmentation, and conservation of beneficial organisms for the regulation of population densities of other organisms comprise the field of biological control. Particular emphasis has been laid on pest insects and mites, and weeds. Each of the preceding four key words—study, importation, augmentation, and conservation—here has a particular meaning which covers a discrete phase of the field of biological control, hence a discussion of each term should help delimit the field and present a synopsis of the subject matter covered later in the book. The term 'biological control,' as frequently defined, really refers to the field of biological control—not the results—and usually stresses utilization of natural enemies by man. Franz (1961c) has emphasized this type of definition. However, a definition, which emphasizes the strictly utilitarian aspects of the science, will exclude various important basic studies which are not utilitarian in nature, and might also exclude the effects of natural enemies which have not been manipulated in some manner by man. I feel that it is extremely important to include both of these latter facets in a definition of biological control, i.e., the field of biological control. A suitable definition might be: 'the study and utilization of parasites, predators, and pathogens for the regulation of host population densities.' The use of the word 'study' (a discussion of which follows) in the definition permits the inclusion of many aspects of the field which would be left out of a definition stressing that biological control concerns only the utilization of natural enemies by man.

The literature on biological control is voluminous and much of it will be discussed in appropriate portions of this book. A few references which give a broad coverage of the subject include: Clausen (1954a, 1956a, 1958b); O'Connor (1953); Franz (1961a, b); Pemberton (1953); Rubtzov (1959); Smith (1919, 1933, 1946); Sweetman (1958) and Wilson (1960a).

Basic Studies

Under the study of biological control, phases are included which are basic to any application of the method but which do not necessarily have immediate utilitarian results as an objective, and do not involve direct attempts to utilize, manipulate, or conserve natural enemies. The first phase includes pure research into fundamental aspects of taxonomy, biology, physiology, genetics, ecology and demography, behaviour, culture methods, and nutrition. Such studies are primarily concerned with parasites, predators, and pathogens, but their hosts as well as other interacting environmental factors may enter in. Chapters 3 to 9, 19, 20, and 23, and portions of most other chapters, relate principally to basic studies.

Basic studies have a definite and highly important place in the field of biological control and should be actively supported and pursued to the fullest extent possible, even though there may be great economic pressures to concentrate on applied problems. The solution to these very problems could well lie in some unforeseeable discovery of a fundamental nature. Examples of this will be given later.

The discovery of new scientific information as an end in itself certainly needs no justification in this era. Studies of parasites, pathogens, and predators have yielded exciting biological information, for these groups in particular have many interesting biological peculiarities and adaptations. Valuable scientific data have been acquired on the nature of viruses, tissue culture, taxonomy, parthenogenesis, paedogenesis, polyembryony, sex regulation and determination, diapause, polymorphism, specialized respiration in parasite eggs and larvae, phagocytosis, obligatory hyperparasitic male development, races of parasites with specialized habits, fundamental population dynamics, effects of physical factors on natural enemies, and a multitude of other equally important subjects.

Certain of these results have later proved to be of considerable practical value. For instance, taxonomic studies finally revealed that what was once thought to be a single species of *Aphytis* parasitic on the California red scale in the Orient and elsewhere and which had been accidentally established in California, included, in fact, at least seven species having different biological adaptations, none of which actually occurred in California. As a result, it has been possible since 1957 to introduce into California at least five promising new red scale parasites which otherwise would have been assumed to have been established already.

Another fundamental discovery with practical results was the solution of the mode of reproduction in certain parasitic Aphelinidae. For years attempts had been made to introduce and establish certain species, but insectary propagation was never successful. Finally, precise biological investigation showed that unfertilized, and therefore male-producing, eggs would not develop except on a female larva or pupa of their own species, or, in some cases, an immature female of another species. These unprecedented results have made it possible to culture and colonize quite a few parasitic species which otherwise would have been 'lost.'

Sabrosky (1955) has ably discussed and illustrated the importance of taxonomy to biological control, and DeBach (1960) treats certain examples in detail. If our knowledge of the taxonomy of the parasitic Hymenoptera is as poor as Kerrich (1960) indicates, science in general and biological control in particular are suffering. He estimates, for example, that only about 10 per cent of the Ichneumonidae of tropical Asia, Africa, tropical America, and Australia are known. World wide, his figures indicate that if the parasitic Hymenoptera were known as well as are the Coleoptera, there would be about 500,000 described species of parasites whereas it appears there are fewer than 50,000. He puts forth the guess that there may be as many as 1,000,000 species of Ichneumonoidea in the world. Obviously a great increase in emphasis is needed on the systematics of the parasitic Hymenoptera.

Studies on diapause and the means of breaking it have made possible the introduction and successful colonization of parasites from one hemisphere to another. Inasmuch as the seasons are opposite, i.e.—winter in one hemisphere, summer in the other—such studies are a necessary prerequisite to successful colonization. Investigations in Hawaii on the nutritional requirements of a parasite's host (the oriental fruit fly) made it possible to rear the fly on an artificial medium which enabled mass production of the host and its parasites to be carried out and large-scale colonizations to be made.

The second phase of basic study—the ecological approach to pest control—includes ecological field studies designed to evaluate the relative importance of natural enemies with respect to other factors in the regulation of host population densities. Methods for evaluation are covered in chapter 14.

If man-induced cultural or other practices are regularly imposed on the faunal complex to be studied, it is essential that plots be obtained in which one can exclude, minimize, or otherwise permit evaluation of such factors, which of course may be adversely affecting the degree of biological control that otherwise might obtain. Such studies are an essential prelude to the development of an intelligent programme for importation, augmentation, or conservation of natural enemies. They should be the first step in any applied biological control project—in fact, in any pest control project. If adequately carried out, these studies not only will furnish to the ecologist and demographer valuable data regarding the relative roles of various environmental factors in natural control of insect or other populations, but will show which organisms actually lack potentially effective natural enemies and which organisms are abundant pests because their otherwise effective natural enemies are adversely affected by environmental factors, including those artificially imposed by man. Such information will show for a given faunal complex what degree of biological control exists naturally without any adverse or beneficial influences of man being involved. This will indicate whether or not natural enemies are lacking, are inherently ineffective, or are rendered ineffective by adverse environmental conditions.

The problems involved in attaining more complete and effective biological control of the faunal complex thus become clear-cut, and definite programmes can be undertaken to enhance biological control through the introduction of new exotic natural enemies, through the augmentation of already established natural enemies, through the conservation of already established natural enemies by modification of cultural practices or other environmental factors, and by the judicious integration of chemical with biological control.

The Importation of Natural Enemies

This term is used to cover all phases of the importation and establishment of exotic natural enemies into a new environment, and section IV—'The Introduction, Culture, and Establishment Programme' (chapters 9 to 14)—which covers this part of biological control, is organized in the manner in which a typical project in biological control might be planned. The purposeful introduction of new natural enemies is usually based on the fact that many, if not most, agricultural pests have been accidentally introduced into the area concerned, while their indigenous natural enemies have been left behind. This, however, should not be taken to exclude the possibilities of controlling indigenous pests by introducing natural enemies that occur on exotic species related to the pest. One of the most famous cases of biological control—that of the coconut moth in Fiji—resulted from the introduction of a tachinid fly from Indo-Malaya which parasitized a moth larva of a different sub-family in its native home.

In the past, importation and colonization of new natural enemies has frequently been thought of as constituting the whole field of biological control. Indeed, from the applied viewpoint the introduction and establishment of new natural enemies remains the easiest and most promising approach to pest control by biological means. Today, only a comparatively few important instances could be mentioned where biological control has been achieved or enhanced by means other than introduction of new natural enemies.

The possibilites of importation have been rigorously explored for only a relatively few pests, and it is doubtful that the last, or perhaps best, natural enemy has been imported even in those projects most assiduously attacked by the biological method, such as the gypsy moth and the European corn borer projects in the eastern half of the United States, the spruce budworm project in Canada, and the California red scale and black scale projects in California. For instance, after 60 years of more or less continuous interest in, and exploration for, natural enemies of the California red and black scales, new ones are still being found and imported. During the past few years (1956–61), at least seven species of parasites of the California red scale and four species of parasites of the black scale new to California have been introduced. This certainly indicates that for less intensively studied projects, similar if not greater opportunities exist.

The case of the codling moth is a good example of the opposite extreme. The codling moth is a major pest of many years' standing, against which intensive research efforts have been directed in attempts to develop new and improved means of chemical control. Whereas this research and the sprays applied have cost the industry many millions of dollars, virtually nothing was done up to 1960 in the United States or Canada towards importing new enemies of the pest. According to Clausen (1956a) only two parasites of the codling moth have been imported into the United States. Neither of these came from a locality in the area presumed to be the native home of the codling moth which, to judge from wild species of apples and the known distribution of the codling moth, probably extends from the Caucasus through the Himalayan foothills to China. Thompson (1944) lists nearly 120 species of parasites as being recorded from the codling moth in various parts of the world. Surely there has been ample opportunity and economic incentive to justify a major project on biological control of the codling moth. Only recently has active interest been awakened in this project. This illustrative example is not an isolated one, for although 600 or more species of insects are considered to be serious pests in the United States, Clausen (1956a) lists only 92 that have been the object of importation of new natural enemies. All this merely stresses the fact that research emphasis on biological control of pests has been insignificant in relation to the annual loss caused by these pests and as compared with the research emphasis placed on chemical control.

The extent to which importation of natural enemies might be emphasized in any given region can be illustrated by the work in the state of California. Clausen (1956a, p.10) states that, '. . . approximately one-third of the species of parasites and predators established in the continental United States have been imported by the California organizations.' At present (1961) the Department of Biological Control of the University of California (which handles work in biological control for the entire state) includes 20 trained academic members, 24 trained technicians, and 12 clerical and other workers.

Although California has strongly supported the biological control approach to pest control for some 70 years, it is doubtful that success of biological control efforts in California should be any greater for the effort expended than would be expected in the southern one-fourth of the United States, or for that matter in any other region, except to the extent that more severe climates may favour hosts over their natural enemies. However, even in severe climates cases may occur where natural enemies are better adapted to the environment than are their hosts and many outstanding examples of biological control have occurred in cool temperate countries (see chapter 24).

If California is taken as an example of what can be done in biological control, granted sufficient trained manpower and funds, does the means justify the end? That is, does intensive effort on biological control research pay off over a period of time? Before discussing the economic results in California, it should be pointed out that specialists in biological control in the state do not consider that the point of diminishing returns has been anywhere nearly approached as yet. Contrariwise, it is felt that more emphasis on biological control would be economically rewarding and, indeed, the emphasis and support is increasing each year. The following estimates on expenditures and economic results in California are for the period 1923 to 1959 when the University of California conducted the work. Previous work was done by the California Department of Agriculture and the United States Department of Agriculture. It should be noted that the enormous savings which can be attributed to the biological control of the cottony-cushion scale by the importation of the vedalia beetle from Australia do not fall within this period. Only projects resulting in notable degrees of success are included, and estimates of savings to the agricultural industry of the state are considered to be conservative even though all estimates are admittedly partly guesswork because of the many complicating factors involved. For instance, at the time the citrophilus mealybug was controlled biologically, no satisfactory chemical control method had been discovered and the mealybug was spreading to new areas. If biological control had not been attained, much greater losses might have accrued than the yearly savings claimed. These figures do not take into account the inflationary trend of the past 40 years either! Table 1 shows estimates of net savings from major biological control projects which amount to over $110,000,000.

TABLE 1. *Estimates of savings to the agricultural industry in California during the period 1923-1959 from notably successful biological control projects*

Biological control project	Degree of success	Yearly savings over previous losses plus pest control costs	Total savings to 1959
Citrophilus mealybug	Complete	$2,000,000 (since 1930)	$56,000,000
Black scale	Partial to complete	$1,684,070 (since 1940)	$31,997,330
Klamath weed	Complete	$8,960,000 (1953–1959; savings from increase in land values plus cessation of herbicidal treatment). $2,000,000 yearly since 1953 in weight gain of cattle.	$20,960,000
Grape leaf skeletonizer	Partial to complete	$75,000 for 10 years (potential saving of $1,300,000 per year).	$750,000
Spotted alfalfa aphid	Partial to complete	$5,580,000 (in 1958) (projected as $4,000,000 per year after 1958).	$5,580,000

Total savings (1923–1959) over previous crop losses plus pest control costs. $115,287,330

Total budget (1923–1959) for all work in biological control including salaries. 4,296,357

Net savings as a result of successful projects (1923–1959). $110,990,973

The estimated $2,000,000 annual savings for the citrus industry in southern California which resulted from biological control of the citrophilus mealybug is derived from figures given by Smith (1946). He showed that savings in Orange County alone has amounted to at least $1,000,000 and perhaps $1,500,000 annually since 1930. Inasmuch as Orange County has contained about one-fourth of the citrus acreage in southern California, one way to obtain an estimate of savings for the entire area would be to multiply by four. Considering various factors and still striving to remain conservative, we estimate a minimum annual savings of $2,000,000. This would amount to a total savings by the citrus industry of $56,000,000 from 1930 to 1958.

According to carefully prepared annual estimates of Howard Lorbeer, manager of the Fillmore Citrus Protective District, Fillmore, California, biological control of the black scale by an introduced parasite, *Metaphycus helvolus* (Comp.), in his district alone has resulted in a savings of $168,407 per year on an average of 7,095 acres during the period 1940 to 1954, or a total saving of $2,526,110. Mr. Lorbeer's district includes about one twenty-fifth (4 per cent) of the citrus acreage in southern California, some of which has benefited to a greater extent and some to a lesser extent than Lorbeer's district. Merely to multiply the Fillmore district's savings by 25 would be one way of obtaining an estimate of savings for the entire southern California area. To be ultraconservative, we have used a factor of 10 to obtain an estimate for the entire area. This amounts to an estimated yearly savings of $1,684,070, or a total savings to the citrus industry for the period 1940 to 1958 of $31,997,330. That this estimate is not out of line may be attested by the words of Professor H. S. Smith (1946) who wrote, 'In terms of dollars and cents the intro-duction of *Metaphycus helvolus* [which controlled the black scale] was probably just as profitable as was the biological control of *Icerya* [the cottony-cushion scale] and the citrophilus mealybug, since the black scale had a much more extensive dis-tribution.'

The biological control of the Klamath weed in northern California has brought tremendous economic savings to a large area. Similar results have subsequently been obtained in areas of other states. The Klamath weed invasion greatly reduced good forage plants over more than 2,000,000 acres. Cattle and sheep lost weight on such a diet and land values subsequently declined. In 1944, infested land would not sell for $4 an acre according to correspondence from J. K. Holloway, United States Department of Agriculture entomologist who has been active on this project, but since biological control of the Klamath weed has been achieved, any of this land is worth three to four times this amount. A conservative estimate which assumed that as a result of biological control of the Klamath weed land values only doubled, i.e., went from $4 to $8, indicates a 'savings' of $8,000,000 on 2,000,000 acres of land formerly infested. In addition, W. D. Pine, University of California Farm Advisor for Humboldt County, has estimated that $191,530 was spent in herbicides alone in Humboldt County between 1941 and 1950, or $19,153 per year. Fourteen other county governments were spending a total of about $140,000 a year on Klamath weed control alone, in excess of private funds expended for this work, according to

Mr. Holloway. Therefore, since 1953 it is evident that an estimated savings of $160,000 per year represent a bare minimum for control efforts alone. Thus, from 1953 to 1959, a minimum of $960,000 has been saved in chemical control efforts, which, added to the increase in land values, indicates an estimated minimum saving of $8,960,000 for that period.

The above figures do not include losses in weight or death of livestock. At present, estimates of losses are approximations, but C. B. Huffaker, who has conducted extensive studies on forage composition associated with biological control of this weed (Huffaker and Kennett 1959), suggests that the increased forage available has permitted a weight gain in cattle valued at roughly $2,000,000 per year since 1953, and this 'savings' will accrue each year in the future.

The total and future benefits from biological control of the grape leaf skeletonizer are very substantial but also are difficult to assess. This pest, a potential threat to the entire grape industry of California, accidentally became established in San Diego County where few commercial grapes are grown. The Bureau of Entomology of the California Department of Agriculture attempted eradication and, according to correspondence from Robert W. Harper, Chief of the Bureau of Entomology, 'For the period 1945–56 nearly $822,500 were spent by the Bureau in attempting eradication of this insect, an annual average of nearly $75,000. With the satisfactory solution to the problem which has been developed through biological control, the savings due to discontinuance of the eradication programme can be seen. Our best estimate would have been at least another 10 years of effort, with no further outward spread, to achieve total eradication.'

The ten years of effort would have cost the state about $750,000, so a saving of that amount can be credited to biological control. Had biological control not been achieved and had the skeletonizer continued to spread throughout the grape areas of the state, Mr. Harper suggests that possibly 10 per cent of the total grape acreage would need an additional treatment each year amounting to about $3 per acre. This potential saving would total about $1,300,000 per year on the basis of over 430,000 acres of grapes in the state.

The spotted alfalfa aphid was first found in California in 1954, and its rate of increase and spread was so phenomenal that alfalfa losses due to treatment cost and damage were estimated at $12,855,000 in 1955. This is taken to represent the base cost if no factor other than insecticides was involved in control, because in 1955 natural enemies had not as yet responded to the invasion but insecticides were in widespread use. The estimates on losses from this aphid were also furnished by Mr. Harper. Improved insecticidal application plus the increased response of native predators, diseases, and newly introduced parasites were credited with reducing this loss by $2,255,000 in 1956 despite the continued spread of the aphid to new areas. In 1957, state-wide losses were reduced to about $9,705,000, an additional saving of $895,000. By 1958, natural enemies (in particular the introduced parasites) had increased to the extent that it became possible in most cases to get by with one, and in many cases without any, selective insecticide application, whereas in 1955 from 6 to 10 or more non-selective insecticide applications were commonly made. Losses and treatment costs in 1958 were only $1,694,000, which again represents a large additional yearly saving of $8,011,000 and a total savings for the year of $11,161,000 as compared with 1955 losses. The total savings during 1958 indicate that continued over-all future savings could be in the neighbourhood of 10 or 11 million dollars every year in California alone.

A large proportion of the savings occurring in 1956 and 1957 is credited to native coccinellids and fungus diseases, according to R. van den Bosch, who was in charge of the biological control work. But at the same time, the introduced parasites increased rapidly, spread, and became quite stabilized by late 1957, so that during 1958 these parasites contributed significantly to the biological control of the aphid. Also, the development of the selective insecticide programme, which conserves parasites and predators, made it possible in 1958 to obtain near-maximum effectiveness from all the natural enemies and still use a chemical treatment at critical periods.

According to E. I. Schlinger (personal communication), who has made intensive population studies on this aphid and its natural enemies, field data indicate that the *introduced* parasites and the development of the selective insecticide programme (which are all that man can take credit for) were responsible for about 50 per cent of the 1958 savings. This would amount to about $5,580,000, which can be credited to induced biological control in 1958. There is every reason to believe that continued average annual savings should approximate this figure—say at least $4,000,000 per year.

Even greater savings could have been included in this table if partially successful cases of biological control had been used. Quite a few such cases are saving farmers money by reducing chemical pest control needs or by making control with chemicals easier or more efficient. These projects include the pea aphid, the yellow scale, the red scale, the purple scale, the olive scale, the citrus mealybug, the cyclamen mite, and the long-tailed mealybug.

The annual savings accruing from the biological control of the olive scale are certainly very substantial—perhaps $1,000,000 or more per year—but no estimation was included in table 1 because the effectiveness of the parasites frequently is retarded by drift of insecticides applied to neighbouring crops and because extremely low scale populations (i.e., one scale per fruit) may result in downgrading of the crop in the packing house. However, the reduction in scale populations on olive trees following the importation of parasites has certainly been about 98 to 99 per cent and, as Huffaker and Kennett (1960) also indicate, the total value gained from control of the olive scale on its many host plants in gardens, parks, and landscaped roadways may exceed that gained in olive groves. It is still too early to estimate the results in biological control of the pea aphid in California, whose imported Indian parasite was colonized during 1958–60, but the progress of the parasite by 1961 was very rapid and promising (Hagen and Schlinger 1960). The same situation exists with respect to the walnut aphid whose parasite was imported from France in 1959 and by 1961 was very abundant (van den Bosch et al. 1962). In addition, the nigra scale, formerly a very serious pest of ornamentals, has been completely controlled by *Metaphycus helvolus*. Savings in this case would be very difficult to estimate inasmuch as they would accrue largely to home owners, parks, and nurseries.

It is apparent from the figures in table 1 and the preceding discussion that the biological control method has resulted in savings to California agriculture of well over 100 million dollars in excess of the money expended. Additional savings continue to accrue and must be accredited each year because without these successful cases of biological control, insecticidal treatment still would be necessary annually and/or crop losses previously experienced would continue. Hence a bare minimum saving of over 9½ million dollars annually must be projected for each year onward from 1958. The conclusion seems inevitable that even if successes resulting from importation projects in biological control in other regions were small by comparison with those in California, it would still appear that intensive use of this method should pay for itself many times over.

Two major obstacles may hinder the development and application of a large-scale programme in many countries or states. First, the government or some major institution must finance and support the work. Industry, in the broad sense, will not provide the support it gives to pesticide development and promotion. Second, striking successes can be few and far between and support may lag because of this. Nevertheless, as previously emphasized, economic returns on research expenditures are usually high over a period of years, even though really outstanding results may occur only once or twice in a decade.

The Augmentation of Natural Enemies

This phase of biological control deals with the manipulation of natural enemies themselves in order to make them more efficient in the regulation of host population densities. The material in chapter 15 shows how man may help natural enemies through scientific planning. Game management involves some of these same ideas. The augmentation of natural enemies is a relatively new field, little explored. The major attempts at augmentation have involved the mass culture and periodic colonization of natural enemies or certain changes in cultural practices, but only the surface has been scratched.

Any attempts at augmentation and conservation should be preceded by sound, basic ecological studies of the type already discussed under the section of this chapter entitled 'Basic Studies,' and should be undertaken only if background studies indicate a reasonable chance of success or if the economic gain would be considerable. The ecological information developed by such studies will reveal or indicate the reasons why certain natural enemies fail to control their host satisfactorily, and hence will suggest lines of research for improvement of their efficiency.

Many cases are known of natural enemies being periodically decimated by extreme summer heat or winter cold. Satisfactory biological control may well be precluded by such catastrophes. There would appear to be two logical approaches to this problem. The first would be to recolonize natural enemies following adverse periods, so that a satisfactory balance between the host and natural enemies could be rapidly re-established. Such a procedure is usually termed 'periodic colonization.' The second approach would be to develop, through selective breeding, new strains of the enemies that were capable of better survival or increase during adverse periods. Before undertaking a selective breeding programme, or at least in conjunction with it, every effort should be made to ascertain whether better adapted strains occur naturally in areas other than those from which the original importations were made and, if so, to import them. Both of the foregoing procedures would involve direct manipulation of the beneficial organisms themselves and could be classed as augmentation. In other words, augmentation involves making the natural enemy better suited to the environment.

The Conservation of Natural Enemies

Another approach to the enhancement of biological control would be to modify the environment in such a way that any adverse environmental effects would be eliminated or mitigated, or simply to alter the environment better to suit certain peculiar needs or responses of the natural enemies which were previously unsatisfied. This can be termed 'conservation,' and it involves making the environment better suited to the natural enemy. As mentioned under augmentation, basic ecological studies are an essential prerequisite for intelligent attempts at conservation.

In commercial crops, as in natural environments, there are many ways in which the environment can be favourably modified to benefit desirable organisms. Adverse factors, such as air-borne dust which kills, and ants which kill or interfere with natural enemies, can be controlled. Time of ploughing, mowing, or harvesting may be adjusted to favour natural enemies. Excess shade or sunlight can sometimes be modified. Low humidities can be increased through use of cover crops. Necessary conditions can be provided and insufficient factors improved by the use of alternate host plants or host insects to furnish carbohydrate and protein foods for adult entomophagous forms, and to bring about a succession of suitable host stages which otherwise would not be present, or by providing shelters or nesting sites (Lawson 1958). The diversification of the flora and fauna in an area may be of great help, especially for general predatory feeders. The value of such a programme has been strongly stressed by Elton (1958) in *The Ecology of Invasions by Animals and Plants*. The fundamentals and possibilities of such procedures are covered in chapter 16.

In addition to the conservation of natural enemies through modification of the more or less natural environment, a major step—and usually the most important one in agricultural crops—involves the judicious use of chemical treatments. Chapter 17 is devoted to this very important subject. In any given faunal complex, be it in an undisturbed environment or in a cultivated crop, several to many potential pests will be under good biological control. Haphazard application of chemicals may so seriously disrupt the host–natural enemy interactions that 'biological explosions' or 'upsets' result from the differential toxic effect of the chemicals on the host and its enemies. Frequently the new 'pest' is worse than the original. Such happenings have been so common and so obvious during the past decade that the cause and effect involved usually are no longer questioned. Adequate experimental demonstrations, combined with detailed census data on 'biological explosions' induced by pesticides upsetting the host–natural enemy balance, also have helped to bring about widespread recognition of this problem. A good general discussion of this subject will be found in Stern et al. (1959).

It seems quite fitting that Metcalf (1959), one of the word's leading authorities on chemical insecticides, has pointed out that, 'For many years it has been recognized that the greatest single factor in preventing insects from overwhelming the rest of the world is the internecine warfare which they carry out among themselves. The entomophagous insects are generally inconspicuous and their absence is scarcely noticed until elimination by the ravages of climate or a blanket of insecticide allows the host species to increase suddenly toward its maximum biotic potential. Examples of this sort have been increasingly frequent as a result of the haphazard use of highly toxic and persistent organic insecticides and familiar cases include the outbreaks of red spider mites (Tetranychidae) following applications of DDT, Dieldrin, Sevin, etc., and cottony-cushion scale, *Icerya purchasi* Mask., after drift of DDT and malathion.'

Unfortunately, nearly all crops have one or more serious pests or diseases that lack adequate natural control factors and hence require regular periodic treatments to ensure adequate yields or quality produce. The necessity of some chemical treatments, therefore, can usually be expected, so the problem is to choose the one or several, as the case may be, that least injure the entire beneficial fauna. The use of selective insecticides, which are toxic to the pest but relatively non-toxic to beneficial species, has been demonstrated to be a valuable approach towards what may be called 'integrated control.' This term implies the use of necessary pesticides, for pests lacking adequate natural control, in a manner that permits attainment of the maximum degree of biological control of other *potential* pests present in the ecosystem. Integrated control may be approached from other directions through modification of timing, formulation, or method of application of pesticides, or through strip treatment and spot treatment which leave portions of the crop untreated at a given time to serve as reservoirs or refuges where natural enemies can survive and from whence they can move out and reinoculate the treated areas after residues have dissipated. Such measures are being increasingly recognized as an absolute necessity in certain cases, where long-term and continuous use of pesticides has led to the need for more and more pesticides until the point of diminishing returns has been reached. Coupled with this has been the rapid increase in inherited resistance of pests to insecticides and the establishment of tolerance levels for poisonous residues which seriously restrict the use of some pesticides, hence again stressing the need for a more scientific use of chemicals through integration with biological control.

Today it seems safe to say—although it would not have ten years ago—that many entomologists of broad vision would seriously consider going backward in order to modify or simplify some of our chemical pest control programmes. Each year fewer and fewer entomologists expect that so-called chemical panaceas will solve many pest problems for long.

The benefits of biological control, whether natural or induced, are gaining greater recognition and support, but the fact that no general panacea lies in biological control is also generally recognized. Continued striving for complete biological control while utilizing the scientific integration of chemical control with the biological control that already exists in a given faunal complex is now accepted by many progressive entomologists as the major truly scientific approach to pest control. It will continue to constitute the best approach to pest control in the years to come.

CHAPTER 2

The Historical Development of Biological Control

RICHARD L. DOUTT

INTRODUCTION

As POINTED OUT in chapter 1, biological control in its broadest sense is considered by some to encompass the use of antibiotics in medicine, the biotic control of vertebrate pests, weeds, and insects, and the diseases of crops (Sweetman 1958). Obviously, any attempt to cover its complete historical development would require a treatise on the history of biological science itself. Such an ambitious undertaking is not the purpose of this chapter which is, instead, a brief abstract of the early development of biological control primarily in relation to the insect pests of agricultural crops and principally up to the conclusion of the first real success—the vedalia-cottony-cushion scale project. Even so, difficult problems arise in determining the scope of the historical treatment. This is so, because this branch of applied ecology in the last half of the twentieth century is clearly an integration of knowledge, skills, concepts, and techniques drawn from many scientific disciplines.

Biological control of agricultural pests has developed with modern agriculture and has been concomitant with the accelerated acquisition and application of knowledge in biology in the last century. The fact of entomophagy has been known for a very long and indeterminate period, but the practical use of this phenomenon is much more recent and its effective application has come about with the understanding of population dynamics and the factors regulating the abundance of organisms in nature. It is therefore no fortuitous accident that the first demonstration of biological control accompanied a growing awareness that agricultural pests are mostly alien immigrants, and that the initial concepts of biological control developed contemporaneously with the realization of the need for legal restrictions (i.e., quarantine regulations) on the shipments of plants and animals.

The fusion of biological and agricultural knowledge which produced biological control occurred in the nineteenth century and that period of history is accordingly emphasized in this chapter. The first dramatic demonstration of biological control was in California, which is also the source of this book; therefore, this particular account of the history is somewhat provincial and contains much local colour. However, the first successful movement of a natural enemy from one country to another occurred in 1762, with the introduction of the mynah bird from India to

Mauritius to control the red locust (Moutia and Mamet 1946). Finally, it must be mentioned that the development of applied biological control after all is a human achievement, and the first demonstration was the experimental proof of a hypothesis that had been growing in the minds of men of science. To make the history come alive it is necessary to visualize it through the personalities who were actively engaged in its inception or who were directly affected by it.

EARLY USE OF PREDACEOUS INSECTS

Obviously no one knows precisely when man first became aware of the entomophagous habit in insects. It is reasonable to surmise that he first observed predaceous insects and well understood the meaning of predation many centuries before any notion of parasitism was conceived. Certainly it seems likely that he did not relate the observed predatory habits of certain insects to the possible solution of his pest problems until agriculture became comparatively advanced in an area where some of the people had attained a degree of intellectual sophistication.

This is illustrated by a procedure, followed by Chinese citrus growers since ancient times, of purchasing and placing nests of the predaceous ant *Oecophylla smaragdina* F. in mandarin orange trees to reduce the numbers of foliage-feeding insects (McCook 1882). The farmers still assist the ants in travelling from tree to tree by installing interconnecting bamboo rods as bridges. Groff and Howard (1924) questioned the efficacy of this practice but the growers insisted that as long as they had strong colonies in their trees they were never troubled with *Tessaratoma papillosa* (Dru.), which is injurous to lichee and citrus fruits.

In a similar practice reported by Forskål (1775) and Botta (1841), the date growers of Yemen in south-western Arabia each year brought down from mountain colonies a beneficial species of ant which they placed in the palms to control harmful insects.

The beneficial work of the predaceous coccinellids has been common knowledge to mankind for centuries. Kirby and Spence (1815, 1856) praised the work of the ladybirds and other predators, as did Fitch (1856) in his writings, as follows: '. . . it is remarkable that long ago, in a superstitious age, and when the habits of this tribe of insects could have been but vaguely if at all known, they were regarded in this same light, and in different countries, and are supposed to have thus obtained in France the name of "God's cows" (Vaches à Dieu) and "The Virgin's cattle" (Bêtes de la Vierge) and in England "Our Lady's birds".' Kirby and Spence credit Dr. (Erasmus) Darwin with suggesting that hot houses could be cleared of aphids by the use of ladybirds.

A. Sidney Oliff, Entomologist of New South Wales, wrote in the *Agricultural Gazette* for 1890 (1(2): 63–6) that, 'In the hop-growing districts of the south of England these swarms (of ladybirds) occasionally occur, and I have myself seen them in such numbers that they had to be swept from the pathways about the houses. In seasons of scarcity, women and children collect the ladybirds in certain parts of Kent and Surrey and sell them to the hop grower, who afterwards sets them free, a practical application of one of nature's benefits, which, as far as I am aware, is almost unique in the history of economic entomology, but one, nevertheless, that has prevailed for many years, if not for centuries.'

DISCOVERY OF INSECT PARASITISM

So, while predaceous insects were known at an early date and came to be used in a practical way by agriculturalists in parts of Asia and Europe, a very long time passed before parasitism was recognized in insects. It is not at all surprising that a conspicuous and rather common case of insect parasitism should be the first one recorded in the literature. The common cabbage butterfly, *Pieris rapae* (L.), was attacked by a gregarious internal parasite *Apanteles glomeratus* (L.) which emerged to form conspicuous cocoons on the integument of its host. According to Silvestri (1909*a*) these pupae were noted by Aldrovandi in 1602, who thought they were insect eggs. Although Redi had made the same observation about 1668, apparently nearly a century passed before Vallisnieri correctly interpreted this phenomenon of insect parasitism in 1706. (However, this may not be the first true interpretation of insect parasitism, for the great microscopist Van Leuwenhoeck in 1701 discussed and illustrated a parasite of a sawfly on willows.)

Cestoni is said to have written a letter to Vallisnieri in which he discussed still other examples of parasitism of insects feeding on crucifers. Among these insects were aleyrodids and aphids which Cestoni in a picturesque way described as butterfly atoms and little cabbage sheep, and being consistent in the analogy he designated their parasites as wolf mosquitoes.

The literature of the eighteenth century shows an increasing number of references to entomophagous insects and some of the observations were remarkably perceptive. Especially is this true of the works of Réaumur who published about 1734 to 1742, and of the studies by DeGeer from 1752 to 1778. These two men were freely quoted by Kirby and Spence (1815) who also make the following interesting observation that certain predaceous Hemiptera feed upon bedbugs: '*Reduvius personatus*, which ought on that account to be encouraged, is particularly fond of the bedbug, as, according to Kuhn, is *Pentatoma bidens*, six or eight of which, shut up in a room swarming with the bedbug for several weeks, completely extirpated the latter.'

EARLY NINETEENTH CENTURY ORIGINS

Modern biological control is clearly based on interspecific population phenomena, and hinges on the fact that one species' population stands in an immediate and functional relationship to that of another species. Consequently, before biological control could be thought of it was necessary to recognize not only entomophagy, but also that entomophagous organisms through this habit suppressed populations of other species. About the end of the eighteenth ceutury the controversial publications of Malthus began to appear and they served to focus attention on population problems. Although Malthus has been much maligned and his idea that a population tends to increase until checked by the limits of its food supply is mostly erroneous, nevertheless he did create interest in the subject of populations. For example, Charles Darwin in 1838 started to read Malthus 'for amusement' but found himself tremendously impressed by the ideas presented. Later Darwin freely used the Malthusian expression, 'struggle for existence.' About 1838 the fine mathematical description of population growth following a sigmoid curve was formulated by Verhulst, but his work lay dormant and unrecognized until its discovery by Raymond Pearl in 1920. These were surface indications, however, of the growing idea that populations in nature were regulated by various factors which formed a balance of nature.

At the beginning of the nineteenth ceutury it was recognized that entomophagous insects tended to keep agricultural pests in check. Erasmus Darwin in 1800 wrote that, 'Cabbage caterpillars would increase in destructive numbers, but are half of them annually destroyed by a small ichneumon-fly which deposits its own eggs in their backs.' (Riley 1931). Similar references to the beneficial effect of entomophagous forms appeared with increasing frequency during the century.

This effect of entomophagous organisms in the economy of nature was very clearly seen by Vincent Kollär, a German naturalist. By the command of Emperor Francis I of Austria, Kollär's useful work was published in 1837 for the benefit of the farmers, foresters, and gardeners of that country.

Kollär in translation said that: 'The means of defence against noxious insects are twofold; first, those which nature employs to circumscribe the too great increase of certain insects; and secondly, those which human understanding can oppose to the evil arising from the superfluity of noxious insects.

'Beside mammalia, birds, and amphibious animals, nature, to restore the equilibrium among her creatures, and particularly to prevent the preponderance of some sorts of insects, makes use chiefly of insects themselves, namely those which feed upon others, and which by degrees obtain a superiority over those that are hurtful to us.

'Thus, many sorts of beetles, particularly of the family of ground beetles (Carabidae), destroy a multitude of the pupae of moths lying in the earth. Many flies, allied to our house fly, but much larger, lay their eggs in living caterpillars and destroy them. But the most useful are the Ichneumonidae. The females of this numerous family, 1300 species of which Professor Gravenhorst has described in Europe alone, lay their eggs entirely in the bodies of other insects.

'The manner in which the Ichneumonidae accomplish their work of destruction is highly curious and interesting. All the species are furnished at the end of the body with an ovipositor, composed of several bristles attached together, with which they pierce the larvae of other insects, and introduce their eggs into the flesh of the wounded animals. In some this sting is longer than the whole body, sometimes more than an inch long, namely, in those species which seek the object of their persecution in the interior of trees or wood that has been much and deeply perforated by the insects which reside therein. They perceive, either by their sense of smelling or by their antennae, that their prey is at hand, and introduce their eggs, not without difficulty, into the bodies of the larvae living in the wood. Some attack caterpillars feeding openly on plants, others perforate the various excrescences, or gall-nuts, which also contain larvae; there are even many species, scarcely visible to the naked eye, which lay their eggs in the eggs of other insects, such as butterflies, and thus anticipate their destruction.

'The eggs are hatched within the body of the living insect, and the young parasites, in the most literal sense, fatten on the entrails of their prey. At last the wounded caterpillar sinks, the enemies escape through the skin, and become pupae; or the caterpillar, notwithstanding its internal parasites, enters the pupa state, but instead of a butterfly, one or more Ichneumonidae appear. To these wonderful animals we often owe the preservation of our orchards, woods and grain.'

Kollär concluded that: 'We can only protect ourselves from the injurious influence of insects by an ample knowledge of the reciprocal relation in which one stands to another, and in order to obtain this, it is essentially necessary to acquire a knowledge of those kinds which are directly or indirectly injurious to man, their different stages of life, their nourishment, propagation, duration, and finally their natural enemies.'

From 1837 to 1852, Ratzeburg in Germany published on forest insects and their parasites. He recognized the importance of parasites and his *Ichneumon der Forst-Insekten*, published in 1844, was a reference consulted by the workers on the gypsy moth project in Massachusetts many years later. Ratzeburg held the erroneous belief, however, that entomophagous insects could be applied to the needs of agriculture by the beneficent hand of nature only, and that every effort to assist them would be in vain.

Trotter (1908) gives an account of two other Europeans who experimented with the application of predaceous insects in the control of pests. About 1840, Boisgiraud in France employed the predaceous carabid, *Calosoma sycophanta* (L.), in an attempt to destroy gypsy moth larvae infesting poplars in his village. At the same time he experimented with staphylinids to free his own garden of earwigs. He claimed to have had success with these predators in reports published in 1843.

This work of Boisgiraud caught the fancy of an Italian Society for the Encouragement of Arts and Crafts which offered in 1843 a gold medal to be awarded in 1845 to anyone who should in the meantime have successfully experimented with the artificial breeding of predaceous insects to be used in the destruction of agricultural pests.

Antonio Villa presented to the Society on December 26, 1844, a written account of such experiments carried on by him in the town of Desio, Province of Milan. After observing which pests were most troublesome in his garden, Villa decided: (1) to employ climbing carabids to hunt all the phytophagous insects hidden under the bark of posts and plants, in the crevices of walls, and under the bricks of the surrounding wall; (2) to employ staphylinids to destroy the insects which nest in flowers; and (3) to employ ground carabids for cutworms, root-feeding forms, and other herbivorous insects found on the ground.

Villa conducted these experiments for two seasons and claimed that the herbivorous insects and cutworms disappeared. He attributed their decline to the activities of the predators which, with the exception of two species, had multiplied. On the basis of his report, Villa was awarded the gold medal by the Society. His work was praised in principle and method by the various Italian and foreign periodicals which reviewed it. However, he received bitter criticism from Carlo Bassi, another Milanese naturalist, who was an acquaintance if not a friend. Bassi was influenced by the statement of Ratzeburg referred to above, and the exchange of scathing criticisms by Bassi and defensive replies by Villa and others went on for several years. Trotter (1908) thought that Bassi's views in this regard were often unfounded and puerile.

AMERICAN AGRICULTURE SETS THE STAGE

In the early nineteenth century America was still a pioneer country pushing its frontier westward. American agriculture was expanding rapidly, and the comparatively sudden appearance of a new continental agriculture in an increasingly enlightened world had much to do with the development of biological control. In this setting it was possible for a farmer in his lifetime to grow through successive seasons a series of pest-free crops and then helplessly witness the spectacularly destructive inroads of alien pests. This sequence of events was later particularly evident to agriculturalists in California. In that state, until after the gold rush, there had been no real agriculture other than superficial management of range cattle by the Spaniards. In the twenty years following 1850 there was an enormous planting of many kinds of crops throughout the state, and for years these grew free of the ravages of alien pests. Then in a short time the same growers who had started these farms witnessed plagues of pests that were obviously of foreign origin. Comparison of the damage done by such species in their native haunts with that being witnessed in America were inevitable, and there was conjecture as to the reasons for the obvious differences in destructive levels.

ASA FITCH

Asa Fitch, who was State Entomologist for New York, had watched closely the spread of the wheat midge *Sitodiplosis mosellana* (Gehin) (=*Contarinia tritici* (Kirby)), in America. He had early identified it correctly as the European species and asked (1856): 'Why is it so severe and unremitting a pest in our country when it is so slight and transitory in its native land? There must be a cause for this remarkable difference. What can that cause be? I can imput it to only one thing. We here are destitute of nature's appointed means for repressing and subduing this insect. Those other insects which have been created for the purpose of quelling this species and keeping it restrained within its appropriate sphere have never yet reached our shores. We have received the evil without the remedy. And thus the midge is able to multiply and flourish, to revel and riot, year after year, without let or hindrance. This certainly would seem to be the principal if not the sole cause why the career of this insect here is so very different from what it is in the old world.'

Although Riley (1893) thought C. J. S. Bethune of Canada was the first to suggest the importation of parasites of the wheat midge to America, certainly to Fitch must be attributed a very concrete suggestion to conduct conventional biological control, i.e., the purposeful importation of entomophagous organisms from a foreign country to suppress an immigrant pest. Fitch wrote (1856) as follows: 'It was after the disastrous results of the harvest of 1854, that, on giving this subject my most attentive consideration, and weighing all the facts bearing upon it, I became persuaded that we had not any parasites, or at least any genuine and efficient parasites of the midge in this country, and that our only effectual remedy for this insect was to import these, its natural destroyers, from Europe. I thereupon felt that the position I occupy, might be regarded as making it my duty to endeavor to obtain these insects. Accordingly, having previously had some correspondence with Mr. Curtis, I addressed a letter to him in May, 1855, chiefly on this subject, informing him of the immense amount of damage we were sustaining from the midge here in America, and that with us no parasites appeared to accompany this insect to give it any check in its destructive career. I suggested the manner in which I thought in any place where the midge was present, ichneumonized larvae of it might be obtained, and the mode in which they could probably be transmitted alive to this country, and requested if he knew of any person so situated that he could conveniently procure and forward to me such larvae, he would do me the favor of communicating to him my wishes to obtain them. When this letter reached him, Mr. Curtis was occupied in arranging for a tour upon the continent, with the hope of thereby recovering those faculties which had become impaired by protracted overexertion. Being President of the London Entomological Society, he laid this letter before the Society at its next meeting. I have not seen the published proceedings of that meeting, but was informed that the subject led to an interesting discussion, and the adoption of a resolution to the effect that if any member of the Society met with the parasite of the midge, under circumstances which would enable him to forward it to me, he would endeavor to do so. But I can readily conceive that this parasite may not be obtainable except upon particular exertions.' As might be expected under the circumstances nothing came of this suggestion. Fitch concluded that the loss from the midge 'will continue until by accident, or by the hand of man, the parasitic destroyers of this insect become introduced into this country, when it will disappear. . . .'

BENJAMIN WALSH

Benjamin Walsh was a contemporary of Fitch and the economic entomology of America owes a great debt to each of these remarkable men. A typical Walshian comment appeared in 1867 in the *Practical Entomologist* and its relevance to the history at this point justifies its reproduction in its entirety:

'IMPORTING EUROPEAN PARASITES'

'In the Compendium of the U.S. Census for 1860 (p. 82) the New York State Agricultural Society is complimented very highly for its "philanthropic spirit," in having "introduced into this country from abroad certain parasites, which Providence has created to counterwork the destructive powers of depredatory insects." In support of this assertion, a passage, occupying a page and a half of fine type, is quoted from a Report by Dr. Fitch, the Entomologist of that Society; but this passage says not a single word bearing upon the above subject, except that "we have no parasites in this country that destroy the Wheat Midge." The real truth of the matter is, that the New York State Agricultural Society has done nothing of the kind, which the U.S. Census asserts that it has done; though, like certain other Societies, it has got the credit of actually doing a thing, because it has simply talked about doing it. Unless my memory fails me, Dr. Fitch stated in one of his Reports that he had written to that distinguished English Entomologist, Mr. Curtis, to send him living specimens of the parasites that infest the Wheat Midge in Europe, but that, as might have been naturally expected, no practical results followed from that application. How could it be otherwise? Who, in this dirty, selfish, mean little planet of ours—which, as Sterne has suggested, seems to have been made out of the refuse clippings from larger and better worlds—ever gives something for nothing? To set the matter in its true light, we may suppose Dr. Fitch's application, and the answer thereto, to have run somewhat as follows:

Dr. Fitch to Mr. Curtis.—Imaginary letter

'My Dear Sir:—The State of New York is suffering an annual loss of many million dollars, by the fearful ravages of the Wheat Midge. Our State Agricultural Society is desirous of importing into the State some or all of the three parasites, which check and control that insect in your country, and prevent it from doing any material damage there. We wish for a very large number of living specimens of these parasites, so as to supply every one of the 59 counties in our State, and make it a moral certainty that the breed shall be permanently established in each. Of course, if the Society were to supply only one or two favored localities, it would give rise to a cry of partiality and favoritism, and would do us more harm than good.

'Will you be kind enough to meet our wishes in this respect? I am well aware that your time is very fully occupied by scientific investigations, which will shed lustre upon your name to the remotest generation, and that what we ask of you will take up many months of your valuable time, and add nothing to your scientific reputation. I am well aware, also, that what we ask of you will probably cost you a few thousand dollars, to be paid out of your own private pocket. For example, as the Wheat Midge is comparatively quite rare in England, it would be necessary for you to run all over the country, in order to find some particular locality where it can be met with abundantly in company with its parasites; and having found that locality, you would have to establish yourself there for a few months, and go hard to work at collecting specimens. But as the work to be done can only be done, properly and effectually, by a man of distinguished Entomological attainments like yourself, and cannot safely be entrusted to a mere tyro in Entomology, I hope you consent to assist us in the manner that we desire. Only conceive my mortification and disgust, if I were to be a party to the employment of some tyro for the object which we have in view, and that tyro, instead of sending us the parasites of the Wheat Midge, were to send us some new Noxious Insect, in addition to the hundred, which we have already imported accidentally from Europe, and which annually pick the pockets of our Farmers of hundreds of millions of dollars! Think, my dear sir, for one moment, of our Midge-ridden farmers in New York! Think that, by sacrificing a few months of your time, and a few thousand dollars out of your own private pockets, you will put millions of dollars into the pockets of our wealthy State, and, eventually, hundreds of millions into the pockets of the whole United States! With your well-known philanthropic sentiments, can you possibly, for one single moment, resist the temptation of making the American people more rich and more prosperous than they already are?

'You will please distinctly to understand, that neither the Congress of the United States, nor the Legislature of the State of New York, nor the New York State Agricultural Society, have appropriated one cent towards the furtherance of the above very important subject. It is possible, therefore, that, in addition to your own personal expenses, you may have to pay, out of your own pocket, the freight and express charges on the packages of living Parasites sent from time to time to us. But even if you have to do this, think of the glory you will acquire by annually, for all time, adding hundreds of millions of dollars to the profits of the great American nation!

Very respectfully, yours, &c., &c., &c.'

Mr. Curtis to Dr. Fitch.—Imaginary answer to the above

'My Dear Sir:—Very much obliged for your kind offer, but, as the old saying goes, "Charity begins at home." Please to accept the expression of my very distinguished consideration, &c., &c., &c.

Very respectfully, yours, &c., &c., &c.'

Walsh continued to criticize the inactivity of the government in regard to the wheat midge as is shown in a letter to a correspondent published in the June 1866 issue of the *Practical Entomologist* at page 101. 'The heads of wheat you send are infested—not very badly, however—with the orange colored larvae of the common Wheat-midge, an insect which was introduced into this country some twenty or thirty years ago from Europe, and which, according to returns from the different counties of the State of New York, which were thoroughly sifted and footed up by the Secretary of their State Agricultural Society, destroyed in one single year in that single State the enormous amount of *fifteen million dollars' worth of wheat*. In England the largest amount of wheat it was ever known to destroy in one single year was one-twentieth of the entire crop. Such a small percentage as that, American farmers would not think worth talking about; but here the Wheat-midge often takes over half of the entire crop. The reason is simple. In England there are no less than three parasitic insects preying upon the Wheat-midge; in this country there is not one, because it wisely emigrated here without its parasites. One would think that common sense would indicate to our Government the good policy, as a matter of dollars and cents, of importing the parasites, particularly as the whole operation need not cost more than a few thousand dollars. But no. Although the plan was long ago recommended by some of the best entomologists in the country, Dr. Fitch for example, it has never been adopted, and probably never will be. Why? Because our Legislatures think that insects are such very minute objects, that they are unworthy of their notice; forgetting that the plague of flies, the plague of lice and the plague of locusts were three of the worst plagues that God in his wrath sent to afflict the rebellious land of Egypt.'

In the September 29, 1866, issue of the *Practical Entomologist* an article by Walsh on 'Imported Insects' appeared in which he strongly advocated the method which we now call biological control. He pointed out that, 'It is a remarkable fact, that fully one-half of our worst Insect Foes are not native American citizens, but have been introduced here from Europe.' Walsh pointed out the extent of the damage that they caused annually and suggested that: 'The plain common-sense remedy for such a state of things is, by artificial means to import the European parasites, that in their own country prey upon the Wheat Midge, the Hessian Fly and the other imported insects that afflict the North American Farmer. Accident has furnished us with the bane; science must furnish us with the remedy.'

Walsh proceeded (page 119) with his typical biting criticism of legislators as follows: 'But the scientific mind is always ahead of the popular mind. Vaccination, Gas, the Steam-engine, the Steam-boat, the Railroad, the Electric-Telegraph, have all been successively the laughing-stock of the vulgar, and have all by slow degrees fought their way into general adoption. So will it be with the artificial importation of parasitic insects. Our grand-children will perhaps be the first to reap the benefit of a plan, which we ourselves might, just as well as not, adopt at the present day. The simplicity and comparative cheapness of the remedy, but more than anything else the ridicule which attaches, in the popular mind, to the very names of "Bugs" and "Bug-hunters", are the principal obstacles to its adoption. Let a man profess to have discovered some new Patent Powder Pimperlimpimp, a single pinch of which being thrown into each corner of a field will kill every bug throughout its whole extent, and people will listen to him with attention and respect. But tell them of any simple common-sense plan, based upon correct scientific principles, to check and keep within reasonable bounds the insect foes of the Farmer, and they will laugh you to scorn.'

The exceptional far-sightedness of Walsh and Fitch is best illustrated in the last paragraph of the article on page 124 of the above citation, and of especial significance is the suggestion for the biological control of weeds. 'Dr. Fitch has observed that no American plant-feeding insect attacks the toad-flax (*Linaria vulgaris*), a European weed, which, as it appears, terribly infests many pasture-fields in the State of New York; and has speculated on the propriety of importing some of the European insects that are known to feed on it in its native country. He has also advised the importation of some or all of the three parasitic insects that check and control the excessive multiplication of the Wheat Midge in Europe. But we should not stop here. The principle is of general application; and wherever a Noxious European Insect becomes accidentally domiciled among us, we should at once import the parasites and Cannibals that prey upon it at home.'

THE FIRST EXPERIMENTS BEGIN

Walsh had a very great influence on a young entomologist by the name of Charles Valentine Riley who was destined to direct the first great demonstration of biological control. In fact, Riley seems to have been the first to distribute *parasites* of an insect from one locality to another. He sent parasites of the weevil *Conotrachelus nenuphar* (Hbst.) from Kirkwood, Missouri, to other parts of the state in 1870. In the following year LeBaron transported apple branches infested with oyster-shell scale parasitized by *Aphytis mytilaspidis* (LeB.) between two towns (Galena to Geneva) in Illinois with allegedly good results.

In 1873, when all Europe and especially France sought for better means to destroy the phylloxera, they thought also of the enemies it might have in North America. Since Riley had just described a predaceous mite, *Tyroglyphus phylloxerae* Riley, which seemed active against phylloxera, he sent specimens to France in 1873 where the mite became acclimated but without the hoped for results.

In 1874 an effort was made to transport several enemies of aphids from England to New Zealand. *Coccinella undecimpunctata* L. became established but little is known about the results of this introduction. Possibly the first parasite introduction into Canada was made in 1882 by Saunders (1882), who imported *Trichogramma* sp. from the United States for the control of the gooseberry sawfly.

The first insect parasite known to man was also the first such species to be transported between continents for the biological control of an agricultural pest. In 1883 the United States Department of Agriculture succeeded in importing from England pupae of *Apanteles glomeratus*, the parasite of *Pieris rapae* which had been noted by Aldrovandi 281 years earlier. The parasites were distributed in the District of Columbia, Iowa, Nebraska, and Missouri, where they became established, and to this day form a useful part of our insect fauna (Riley 1893).

THE INTRODUCTION OF VEDALIA TO CALIFORNIA

Although the biological control method thus has a history antedating the introduction of the vedalia beetle, *Rodolia cardinalis* (Muls.), into California in 1888, it is everywhere agreed that this project against the cottony-cushion scale, *Icerya purchasi* Mask., established the procedure as a valid method of pest control. The event has been noted many times, and it is one of the most fascinating tales in entomological history. It contains much of human interest, and includes such surprisingly non-entomological items as an unhappy love affair, political intrigue, and a pair of diamond earrings (Doutt 1958).

In 1887 the infant citrus industry in California was threatened with destruction because a massive infestation of cottony-cushion scale (figure 1, facing p. 32) was forcing the farmers to abandon citrus growing as a commercial venture. The Convention of Fruit Growers meeting in Riverside, California, in April 1887, invited as their principal speaker Charles Valentine Riley, Chief of the Division of Entomology of the federal government, to whom the citrus growers looked to provide a remedy.

When Riley addressed the Fruit Growers Convention he had two field agents working in California. One was Albert Koebele, a naturalized German immigrant whom he had first met at a meeting of the Brooklyn Entomological Society. Riley had been impressed by the beautiful mounting of specimens that Koebele exhibited in a collection and invited Koebele to come to Washington, D.C., and work for Riley at the Division of Entomology. Koebele seems to have been so overwhelmed by this invitation that he immediately gave up his job and got ready to go to Washington. There appears to have been several agonizing months of waiting, and finally in October 1881 he received a letter from Riley saying: 'I have felt aggrieved at having been the unintentional instrument in causing you to give up your former position before I had secured one for you in Washington.' Riley then offered him a position as a temporary agent at $65 per month, and added: 'I hope you will bring along all the specimens possible.'

In 1885, after what is said to have been 'an unfortunate love affair' (Howard 1930), Koebele asked to be transferred to some distant place. At that time the most distant place was California, so Riley sent him there at a salary of $100 per month on a mission officially designated as 'Investigation of the history and habits of insects of California.'

The other agent in California was D. W. Coquillett, a native of Illinois. He was an entomologist by choice, had taught school in the middle west, but in 1882 after contracting tuberculosis had moved to Anaheim, California, to regain his health. His publications in entomology attracted the attention of Riley, who appointed him as field agent in 1885.

Coquillett was stationed most of the time around Los Angeles and was assigned to work on control of the cottony-cushion scale. Koebele, who had been stationed at Alameda in northern California, was sent down to work with Coquillett in February of 1886. Koebele's instructions were 'to assist Mr. Coquillett in every way that you can, not as his assistant, but as his associate. You both together will be able to do good work and you will have plenty of opportunity to collect as much as you wish.'

Koebele soon became critical of Coquillett and wrote his views to Riley. This may have influenced Riley to lay off Coquillett for about a year, although insufficient funds was the reason officially offered. Koebele's salary, however, was raised to $1,500 per year.

Coquillett was rehired in 1887 but, in the meantime, with Alexander Craw, foreman of the J. W. Wolfskill ranch at Los Angeles, he had conducted some private experiments on HCN fumigation for scale control.

FIGURE 1. Citrus twig with infestation of cottony-cushion scale, *Icerya purchasi* Maskell. Honeydew has accumulated on surface of adjacent leaf.

FIGURE 2. Adult Vedalia, *Rodolia cardinalis* (Mulsant), feeding on cottony-cushion scale.

Riley's Plan to Control Cottony-Cushion Scale

Riley's address to the Fruit Growers Convention contained the following major points:

1. The original home of *Icerya purchasi* was stated as Australasia, but he was not sure whether it was Australia or New Zealand.

2. He believed that the scale had been accidentally introduced to California at Menlo Park, on Acacia in 1868, but he was not certain of this as he had learned that all Acacias had been brought in as seed.

3. No parasites had hitherto been reported, but from specimens taken at Los Angeles he had reared two chalcids which L. O. Howard had named *Isodromus iceryae* How. This comment is particularly interesting for two reasons. We know now that *I. iceryae* is an encyrtid parasite of *Chrysopa*, not of cottony-cushion scale. Also an Australian, Frazer Crawford, had written Riley earlier in the year telling him that *Icerya* in Adelaide had been destroyed by a dipterous parasite. He enclosed drawings of the fly. Crawford wrote, '. . . this is the only instance I know of a true Dipteron being a coccid parasite.' Riley suggested that Crawford meant a predator when he said parasite, and Riley also remarked that this type of fly had its larval stage in the ground. Crawford's fly was the famous *Cryptochaetum iceryae* (Will.), a valuable parasite of *Icerya*!

4. Riley somewhat grudgingly admitted that HCN fumigation might have possibilities. However, he was rankled that this had not been developed under his supervision. He said, 'We cannot perhaps blame the gentlemen for endeavoring to realize something out of what they consider to be a valuable discovery that will compensate them for the time they have devoted to the purpose; but I am always suspicious of secret or patent insect remedies. My friend, Mr. Coquillett, perfected this gas after his employment by the Department of Agriculture ceased. But it is a general truth that the moment any person or persons become interested in a patent or in any remedy they desire to control from that moment their judgment can no longer be depended on as to value of other remedies.'

5. He indicated that Coquillett and Koebele had disagreed on the effectiveness of certain washes (sprays) they had experimented with. Coquillett believed in the efficacy of kerosene emulsions while Koebele believed in that of resin soaps.

6. Finally, Riley said: 'It had doubtless occurred to many of you that it would be very desirable to introduce from Australia such parasites as serve to keep this fluted scale in check in its native land. ... This State—yes, even Los Angeles County—could well afford to appropriate a couple of thousand dollars for no other purpose than the sending of an expert to Australia to devote some months to the study of these parasites there and to their artificial introduction here. But the agent must be an expert entomologist and his selection should be left to some competent authority.

'I would not hesitate, as United States Entomologist, to send some one there with the consent of the Commissioner of Agriculture were the means for the purpose at my command; but unfortunately, the mere suggestion that I wanted $1,500 or $2,000 for such a purpose would be more apt to cause laughter and ridicule on the part of the average committee in Congress than serious and earnest consideration, and the action of the last Congress has rendered such work impossible by limiting investigation to the United States.'

(This last comment referred to a rider put on the appropriation bill for the Department of Agriculture for that year. It prohibited foreign trips by employees and was purposely inserted in the bill to stop the frequent European junkets taken by Riley.)

As a result of Riley's address and persuasion the Convention adopted a resolution favouring the idea of sending someone to Australia to seek out natural foes of *Icerya* and to bring them to California if any were found (*Pacific Rural Press*, January 7, 1888).

Search for the Scale's Native Home

During this time Waldemar G. Klee, the State Inspector of Fruit Pests, had been corresponding with W. M. Maskell in New Zealand and Frazer Crawford in Australia about cottony-cushion scale. In the May 7, 1887, issue of the *Pacific Rural Press* a letter from Maskell to Klee was published in which Maskell stated positively that the *Icerya* was native to Australia. He pointed out that it had appeared at the Cape of Good Hope several years earlier and that the people there called it the 'Australian bug.' It was thought to have been carried there by people going to the diamond fields from Sydney or Melbourne.

On June 4, 1887, the *Pacific Rural Press* published an article by Riley noting the published correspondence between Maskell and Klee. In this article Riley pointed out that it was important to locate the native home of a pest, and proceeded to discard the idea that *Icerya* came from Australia. All the evidence, he said, pointed to the fact that *Icerya* was from the Island of Mauritius in the Indian Ocean.

Riley said that sugar was imported from Mauritius all over the world, and that it was customary to cover the top of every hogshead of sugar with pieces of cane. In this sugar there was an insect known to the trade as 'sugar louse' and Riley was sure that this was *Icerya*. Koebele was then directed by Riley to go to sugar refineries around San Francisco and collect some of the sugar lice to prove Riley's point. Koebele did make such a search and explained to Riley that the sugar people had pointed out that the sugar louse was actually a mite, an acarid.

However, by March 4, 1888, Riley had altered his position once more and wrote in the *Pacific Rural Press* that the view of *Icerya* as native to Australia was probably the correct one.

Koebele's Mission to Australia

Meanwhile the California growers had been putting pressure on their Washington representatives to get action. In a letter to Representative Felton (*Pacific Rural Press*, February 11, 1888) Norman J. Colman, Commissioner of Agriculture, pointed out that while travel by the Division of Entomology was restricted to travel in the United States, there was to be an International Exposition in Melbourne in which the United States Government was to take part. In a very pregnant statement Colman said: 'This exposition in many ways would further the investigation referred to in your memorial.' The opportunity to exploit the appropriation for the Melbourne Exposition was not overlooked. The Honourable Frank McCoppin of San Francisco was made United States Commissioner to the Exposition, and he arranged with other members of his Commission to set aside $2,000 to pay the expenses of an entomologist who was to accompany them, ostensibly to represent the State Department but actually to collect enemies of *Icerya*.

Riley selected Koebele to accompany the Commission, although the California people had suggested Coquillett. Koebele sailed for Australia on August 25, 1888.

Koebele had scarcely arrived in Australia when Riley became suspicious of the California people and began to guard jealously any loss of credit.

Jealousy of credit was not, however, limited to Riley. In 1887, Frazer Crawford, who had discovered the *Cryptochaetum* in 1886, sent some of these flies to Klee who liberated the material in San Mateo County in 1888, before Koebele sailed for Australia. (Today *Cryptochaetum* is a very effective enemy of *Icerya* in San Mateo and neighbouring counties around San Francisco Bay. It is also important in southern California.) A Los Angeles newspaperman became aware of the fact that three men (Coquillett; J. W. Wolfskill, owner of the Wolfskill ranch; and his foreman, Alexander Craw) were soon to be handling parasites of *Icerya* and wrote an article praising them and remarking that they would probably do more for southern California than had been accomplished in many years. This account came to the attention of Crawford in Australia and wounded his pride for he felt he was being denied the credit and recognition to which he was entitled. He wrote: 'All honor, then, be to this patriotic trio, and personally let me express my compliments to the writer of the article, because until I read it I labored under the delusion that I first discovered the Dipteron, that I first suggested its introduction into California and other countries afflicted by the *Icerya* scourge, and I have put myself to some little and my friends to much greater trouble in collecting and forwarding the coccid hosts of these parasite flies—all of which doubtless is a mistake.'

The Introduction of the Vedalia

In Australia, Koebele went to work. In October 1888 he wrote to Riley as follows: 'So far my work has been much more successful than I expected. I not only found the dipterous parasite within *Icerya* in large numbers, but also three predaceous larvae feeding upon the eggs of *Icerya*. One of these is a *Chrysopa* larva;—*the others are larvae of a small coccinella*.' (Italics Doutt's)

How perilous it is to make predictions about imported species before they are tested is illustrated in Riley's reply to Koebele's letter that: '. . . the sending of the coccinellids is of course desirable but I think we have much more to hope from the (*Cryptochaetum*).'

Through Koebele's efforts a total of approximately 12,000 individuals of

Cryptochaetum were sent to California, and relatively little attention was at first paid to his discovery of the vedalia feeding upon the *Icerya* in a north Adelaide garden on October 15, 1888. The actual introduction of the vedalia is best described in these words of Coquillett:

'The first consignment of these lady-birds reached me on the 30th of November (1888), and numbered 28 specimens; the second consignment of 44 specimens arrived December 29; and the third consignment of 57 specimens reached me on January 24, making 129 specimens in all. These, as received, were placed under a tent on an *Icerya*-infested orange tree, kindly placed at my disposal by J. W. Wolfskill, of this city (Los Angeles). Here they were allowed to breed unmolested, and early in April it was found that nearly all of the *Iceryas* on the enclosed tree had been destroyed by these voracious lady-birds (figure 2, facing p. 33). Accordingly, on the 12th of April, one side of the tent was removed, and the lady-birds were permitted to spread to the adjoining trees. At this date I began sending out colonies to various parts of the state, and in this work have been greatly aided by Wolfskill and his foreman, Alexander Craw, both of whom were well acquainted with the condition of the orchards in this part of the state. By the 12th of June we had thus sent out 10,555 of these lady-birds, distributing them to 228 different orchardists; and in nearly every instance the colonizing of these lady-birds on *Icerya*-infested trees in the open air proved successful. The orange and other trees—about 75 in number—and also the shrubs and plants growing in Wolfskill's yard, have been practically cleared of *Iceryas* by these lady-birds, and the latter have of their own accord spread to the adjoining trees to a distance of fully three-fourths of a mile from the original tree.'

Coquillett then continues to describe the distribution of the vedalia in California:

'Besides the three consignments of these lady-birds referred to above I also received two later consignments. The first of these reached me February 21, and numbered 35 specimens; these I colonized on an *Icerya*-infested orange tree in the large orange grove belonging to J. R. Dobbins, of San Gabriel. The last consignment of 350 specimens arrived March 20; one-third of these I left with Dobbins, while the remainder I colonized on orange trees in the extensive grove owned by Messrs. A. B. and A. Scott Chapman, in the San Gabriel Valley. All of these colonies have thrived exceedingly well. During a recent visit to each of these groves I found the lady-birds on trees fully one-eighth of a mile from those on which the original colonies were placed, having thus distributed themselves of their own accord. The trees I colonized them on in the grove of Dobbins were quite large and were thickly infested with the *Iceryas*, but at the time of my recent visit scarcely a living *Icerya* could be found on these and on several adjacent trees, while the dead and dry bodies of the *Iceryas* still clinging to the trees by their beaks, indicated how thickly the trees had been infested with these pests, and how thoroughly the industrious lady-birds had done their work.'

On July 2, 1889, citrus grower Dobbins had much to say about the work of the vedalia on his property: 'The vedalia has multiplied in numbers and spread so rapidly that every one of my 3,200 orchard trees is literally swarming with them. All of my ornamental trees, shrubs, and vines which were infested with white scale, are practically cleansed by this wonderful parasite. About one month since I made a public statement that my orchard would be free from *Icerya* by November 1, but the work has gone on with such amazing speed and thoroughness that I am today confident that the pest will have been exterminated from my trees by the middle of August. People are coming here daily, and by placing infested branches upon the ground beneath my trees for two hours, can secure colonies of thousands of the vedalia, which are there in countless numbers seeking food. Over 50,000 have been taken away to other orchards during the past week, and there are millions still remaining, and I have distributed a total of 63,000 since June 1. I have a list of 130 names of persons who have taken colonies, and as they have been placed in orchards extending from South Pasadena to Azusa, over a belt of country 10 miles long and six or seven in width, I feel positive from my own experience, that the entire valley will be practically free from *Icerya* before the advent of the New Year.'

On July 31, 1889, Dobbins' orchard was so completely clean of *Icerya* that he posted a notice saying that he had no more vedalias for distribution. The Los Angeles County Board of Horticultural Commissioners propagated the vedalia for distribution by caging five large orange trees heavily infested with *Icerya* and permitting the vedalia to increase within the enclosures. It is said that scores of people came each day, singly and in groups, with pill-boxes, spool-cotton boxes, or some sort of receptacle in which to place the beetles so that they could be carried home and placed in trees and on vines infested with the scale.

Mr. A. Scott Chapman, who a year earlier had stated that the *Icerya* was forcing him to abandon fruit growing, reported on October 18, 1889, that the vedalia had cleared the scale from 150 acres of his land. The shipments of oranges from Los Angeles County jumped in one year from 700 to 2,000 cars. The vedalia was hailed as a miracle of entomology. The cost of the project was about $1,500.

Koebele was skyrocketed to fame in California by his Australian trip. The Germans for a time called biological control the 'Koebele method.' The California fruit growers, stimulated by Lelong, then Secretary of the State Board of Horticulture, drafted resolutions thanking Koebele and McCoppin for their work. In appreciation a fund was started, and enough money was raised to present Koebele with a gold watch, and Mrs. Koebele with a pair of diamond earrings.

Dr. L. O. Howard later wrote (1925): 'I imagine that this presentation of diamond earrings to the wife of an entomologist as the result of his own work in entomology is probably unique. I happen to know of no other entomologist who has been able to see that his wife wears diamond earrings.'

In 1891 the California legislature appropriated $5,000 to send an entomologist on another expedition to Australia for other parasites of scale pests. Lelong wrote to the Secretary of Agriculture to make this a co-operative enterprise. He proposed that the United States Department of Agriculture pay the man's salary, thus the $5,000 would go much farther. Koebele's salary was then $1,500 per year. At first

Riley turned down this request. However, shortly afterwards, J. M. Rusk, the Secretary of Agriculture, was persuaded by California people to accept the proposition, Riley was forced to yield, and Koebele went on another expedition.

Riley became increasingly bitter toward the California situation and in September 1893 he recalled his agents from California. Coquillett returned to Washington, but Koebele had apparently seen the change coming and had corresponded with the Hawaiian government about employment. When Riley recalled him, he immediately resigned and went to work for Hawaii at a tremendous salary increase ($250 per month and expenses).

Since the suppression of *Icerya* in California, projects in biological control have been conducted all over the world, and many of these have been equally successful and effective. None, however, has equalled the drama of *Icerya*, or its appeal to the public's fancy. It has remained the outstanding project in biological control and an important milestone in applied entomology.

California Continues Biological Control

It is understandable that after the very impressive work of the vedalia some of the agriculturalists in California became very enthusiastic about the possibilities of biological control and gave it their continued and active support. One of the leading advocates in this was Ellwood Cooper, Chairman of the California State Board of Horticulture. He was instrumental in getting California to employ George Compere as a foreign collector of beneficial insects. The foreign exploration by George Compere began in 1899, and during the next decade he set an amazing record as a traveller and collector. The extent and character of these travels were so impressive that Paul Marchal wrote an article entitled 'L'incroyable Odyssée de Monsieur Compere.'

California built an insectary in the Ferry Building in San Francisco, and it was there that the shipments of beneficial insects were received and cultured. After the earthquake of 1906 destroyed the insectary, a new one was constructed in the Capitol Park in Sacramento in 1907.

Cooper's ideas of biological control appear in a report he made in 1907: 'California is to be congratulated upon the fact that she is the pioneer in the work of fighting insect pests with their natural enemies. For years we have stood alone in this work, but our example is now being followed by very many states and territories and by foreign nations, and this state is looked to as the great exemplar in this work. It is true that the good work done by predaceous and parasitic insects has been known for a great many years, but it remained for California to give a practical turn to this work, and introduce beneficial insects for work upon the destructive species.'

Criticism by L. O. Howard

L. O. Howard had been the loyal assistant to C. V. Riley in Washington during the vedalia project, and succeeded him as chief in 1894. It is therefore not surprising that he held the Riley viewpoint, and this may have early prejudiced his thinking about California. He apparently thought that California was a population of crackpots: 'There has been a tendency for many years for persons with strange beliefs to migrate to California, largely on account of the climate, and southern California today is known as the home of all of the heterodoxies.' (Howard 1930.) He was particularly annoyed by the enthusiasm of Cooper and other southern Californians about biological control, and the fact that these men were influential, articulate, and frankly critical of the policies of the entomological force in Washington did little to further good relations.

On several occasions Howard stated that the support of biological control in California, which was generated by the vedalia project, retarded the progress of economic entomology in that state by many years. For example, he wrote in 1930: 'So great an enthusiasm for natural control was aroused in California by the success of the Australian ladybird that the state made apparently no advances in her fight against insects for many years. Mechanical and chemical measures were abandoned. The subject of natural control held the floor. It is safe to say that a large share of the loss through insects suffered by California from 1888 until, let us say, 1898 was due to this prejudiced and badly based policy.'

When an eminent entomologist writes such a statement it is readily accepted as truth, and because the statement is today still capable of much mischief it deserves to be examined in the light of all known facts. For example in 1891, just two years after the vedalia project, Alexander Craw, then working for the State Board of Horticulture under Ellwood Cooper, wrote a paper in which he described *Aspidioti-phagus citrinus citrinus* (Craw). He pointed out that this internal parasite attacked the yellow but not the red scale of citrus, and said: 'So, our only protection against the true red scale is to fight it with hydrocyanic acid gas, or rosin wash.' Further on, in regard to fumigation, he wrote: 'This method is a California invention, and has proved the most successful of any remedy for destroying scale insects, especially upon citrus trees, as owing to their dense foliage and the difficulty of killing the insects located upon the fruit, spraying has not been altogether successful. With a tent covering the tree, and the proper amount of gas, portions of it are not missed, as is frequently the case in spraying.' In an article about the recent introductions by Koebele in 1892, Craw pointed out that the growers should not expect immediate results from the new importations, and added: 'For the present, orchardists having trees infested with red scale should not neglect spraying or fumigating this fall, so that their fruit will be bright and merchantable, and prevent injury to the trees for the present from the pernicious effects of the pest.' Howard's statement is also refuted by the fact that during this very period it was California that kept urging Congress to follow its lead and pass national quarantine legislation. Furthermore, the *Pacific Rural Press* and the technical agricultural publications in California of the time are filled with entomological material and with recommendations for both chemical and biological control. It was not, however, until 1905 (24 years after the California statute became law) that the federal government enacted quarantine legislation, and ironically it was this federal law that Howard threatened to use to put a stop to California's importation of beneficial insects.

Howard (1930) wrote that in hiring George Compere, California had employed a virtual tyro in entomology whose 'lack of entomological knowledge led him into many mistakes and demonstrated that work of this kind is extremely complicated and must be undertaken with the greatest care and only by the most skilled men. It is only by the barest chance that California escaped the introduction and establishment of more than one injurious insect and more than one secondary parasite through the wholesale sending of forms as carried on by Compere for some years. . . . Surely one very injurious hyperparasite was liberated during this period, and probably more than one.'

Howard was no more accurate in this statement than in some of his other statements about the California scene. In 1931 he was moved to publish this apologetic correction. 'It has come to my attention that I have, on the basis of insufficient information, done an injustice to the memory of George Compere in my recently published *History of Applied Entomology*. In that book I have indicated that George Compere was responsible for the introduction and establishment in California, under the impression that it was a primary enemy of the black scale, of a secondary parasite (now known as *Quaylea whittieri* (Grlt.)) which has destroyed very largely a very important primary parasite of the scale.

'Mr. Harold Compere, son of the late George Compere, himself an advanced student of parasites and a thoroughly sound scientific worker, has access to the correspondence of his late father and has found in this correspondence a distinct warning sent by George Compere to Alexander Craw (at that time in charge of the California state introductions of parasites) to the effect that this particular parasite might be a secondary and that he should be very careful about it.

'This particular parasite belongs to the subfamily Encyrtinae, and at that time I knew no hyperparasite belonging to that group. Mr. Craw sent specimens to Washington for naming and for advice. I sent him a manuscript name given to it by the late Dr. W. H. Ashmead and told him that I knew of no hyperparasites of this group. This would seem to place the onus on me, and would do so were it not for the fact that I was in the habit of visiting California each year and had repeatedly talked with Mr. Craw on the subject of these parasites, warning him again and again not to liberate anything without making careful life history studies in the little quasi laboratory that he had fitted up in his office near the ferry building in San Francisco.'

The Appointment of Harry Scott Smith

Howard (1930) wrote that the biological control work in California would have been stopped by the federal government had it not been for the fact that in 1912 they appointed Harry Scott Smith, a trained entomologist who had been working in the Parasite Laboratory of the United States Bureau of Entomology in Massachusetts, to take charge of the parasite work for the state.

'Mr. Smith, on taking this position, was made an official collaborator of the United States Department of Agriculture, and therefore in a way his subsequent efforts in this direction may be said to have been in cooperation with the Federal Government, or at least to have been tacitly authorized by the Federal Government.'

Professor Smith was able to establish and maintain friendly and co-operative relations with the federal agencies, and under his leadership the biological control work in California grew to maturity as one of the departments in the University of California. Professor Smith took justifiable pride in the accomplishments of the department in the control of insect pests; he became especially interested in and fostered the phases of biological control having to do with weed control and insect pathology.

MODERN EXPANSION OF BIOLOGICAL CONTROL

The value of biological control as a method of suppressing pests was strikingly demonstrated to the world by the control of *Icerya purchasi* by vedalia in 1889. It is of interest that after Koebele went to Hawaii he did some of the earliest practical work with an insect disease, the fungus *Metarrhizium*, in 1897, and possibly the first work in biological control of weeds when he sent, in 1902, insects that fed on *Lantana* from Mexico to Hawaii. After this early period many countries initiated biological control projects and achieved such satisfactory results as to encourage continuing support of this type of research. World-wide developments since 1900 have been too extensive for more than mention of a few here. These developments make up the body of this book. Outstanding work in biological control has been done in Australia, Canada, Chile, Fiji, Hawaii, Israel, Japan, New Zealand, the U.S.A., and the U.S.S.R., to name only a few. Outstanding successes have been obtained in over 60 countries in all parts of the world, and a list of over 200 successful cases of biological control is given in chapter 24. Modern biological control laboratories have been established in many countries (see chapter 13), and superb contributions, both theoretical and practical, are appearing each year from these centres.

The Commonwealth Institute of Biological Control with headquarters in Ottawa, Canada, is especially noteworthy for its contributions. From the Institute's beginning in 1927 until his retirement in 1958, Dr. W. R. Thompson, who has done much to put biological control on a truly scientific basis, was director. Perhaps indicative of modern trends towards international co-operation is the C.I.L.B. (Commission Internationale de lutte Biologique). This organization fosters biological control activities through promoting co-operation between workers and institutions in the various countries of Europe and to a certain extent elsewhere (see chapter 24).

The field of insect pathology has been expanding with remarkable rapidity in recent years and the historical development of this discipline has been thoroughly covered by Steinhaus (1956a) in his publication *Microbial Control—the Emergence of an Idea*, and in chapter 18 of the present volume. Historical aspects of the biological control of weeds are given in chapters 22 and 23.

As a final note on the history of biological control, it is very interesting that the expression 'biological control' is of comparatively recent vintage. It does not appear in the early writings of American and British authors; instead, one finds such expressions as 'the practical use of insect enemies of injurious insects,' 'nature's remedy,' 'parasitic control of injurious insects,' and 'bug vs. bug.' In 1916, Howard said it should be termed 'the biological method of fighting insects,' and Smith (1919) wrote on some phases of 'insect control by the biological method' and used the term 'biological control.' In the following year Smith and Armitage (1920) used the term in the title of a paper, *Biological Control of Mealybugs in California*. Even in this paper they had not completely adopted the term because they described the subjugation of mealybugs 'by the biological or "parasite" method.' Although this seems to be the first use of the expression 'biological control,' it did not gain immediate widespread acceptance. Three years later, when the work directed by H. S. Smith was transferred to the University of California, the newly created division there was called the Division of Beneficial Insect Investigations. The Index of American Economic Entomology does not list biological control until the 1925–29 edition published in 1930. However late it may have appeared, the expression 'biological control' is today widely accepted and is understood by laymen.

SECTION II

The Ecological Basis of Biological Control

CHAPTER 3

Population Ecology—Historical Development

C. B. HUFFAKER AND P. S. MESSENGER

INTRODUCTION

INSECTS are pests when they are sufficiently numerous to cause economic losses. Two species may be of equal noxiousness as individuals and yet, because of great differences in the densities attained by each, one is a pest and the other is not. Thus, in economic entomology our concern is with densities and how densities change. While the adaptations and behaviour of individuals in relation to their environments furnish us with clues to the problem of numbers, certain attributes of populations are distinct from those of the individuals. If we are to make the most of the trend in nature against excesses, we must study both individuals as such and groups of individuals, that is, *populations*. Individuals at different levels of abundance may behave differently or be affected differently by various natural forces. The term 'population dynamics' is applied to the forces affecting changes in population density. As a scientific discipline this subject has been termed 'demology.'

Entomologists with an interest in biological control made early significant contributions to this science (Howard and Fiske 1911; Thompson 1929a; Nicholson 1933; Smith 1935). Smith and Nicholson, in particular, emphasized the role of natural enemies and other biotic factors among the forces which control the abundance of organisms. This emphasis has aroused critical discussion of the relative importance of biotic factors in contrast to other factors of the environment which are conceived by some as deserving equal or greater weight in determining abundance (Bodenheimer 1928, 1930, 1938; Thompson 1929a, 1939, 1956; Uvarov 1931; Andrewartha and Birch 1954; Milne 1957b). Hence, there is need for integrating these roles, where such appears indicated, and for relating the status of natural enemies in the entire complex of forces involved in *determining* the abundance of populations in nature.

A history of population studies will thus aid in clarifying the role played by natural enemies as well as other forces. Such a review of concepts will set the foundation for our own view of natural control, to be described in the following chapter. This review will cover the history and development of concepts, the peculiar characteristics of populations, their growth in numbers, the resistance of the environment to growth, balance or equilibrium between population numbers

45

and the environment, the control or regulation of numbers, the contribution of the abiotic forces to regulation, and the role of natural enemies and other biotic factors in this environmental complex.

THE RISE OF POPULATION ECOLOGY

Here, we consider briefly the origin of certain general concepts of environment as well as more specific ideas on which our modern views of population dynamics are based. These include the concept of populations and communities of organisms as entities, the concept of the environment and its interacting elements, the tendency of populations to grow in number, the limited capacity of the environment for such growth, and the resultant struggle for existence. For more complete discussion of these origins the reader is referred to Bonar (1931), Allee et al. (1949), and Cole (1957).

Réaumur (1683–1757), who has a place near the beginning of modern natural history, made important contributions to our ecological concepts. He observed (1735) in detail some of the ways in which certain factors of the environment affect insects. Especially noteworthy in the field of biological control are his classics of early biological science on the phenomenon of insect parasitism, and the peculiar behaviour of parasitic Hymenoptera and certain social insects.

The concept of biotic communities as entities, with characteristics peculiar to themselves, evolved beyond the elementary views of the early Greeks and Romans through the work of Grisebach (1838), Forbes (1843), Kerner (1863), Möbius (1877), and Warming (1895). For an early statement of the idea that organisms interact with their environment, we may quote Forbes (1843) in reference to changes in animal life in the Aegean Sea: '. . . the multiplication of individuals dependent on the rapid reproduction of successive generations of Mollusca, etc., will of itself change the ground and render it unfit for the continuation of life in that locality until a new layer of sedimentary matter is deposited.'

The intricate and manifold relationships existing between coexisting organisms, and between groups of organisms and their environment—the 'web of life'—had an important role in Charles Darwin's (1859b) classic study on *The Origin of Species*.

The idea that groups of organisms interact with each other was given further stimulus by Semper (1881) with his appreciation of the role of monophagous predation, his development of the principle now known as 'the pyramid of numbers,' and the concept of 'key-industry' animals.

There followed a long period of significant observations and study of community origin and complexity, exemplified by V. E. Shelford's (1913) *Animal Communities in Temperate America*, H. C. Cowles' (1901) *The Physiographic Ecology of Chicago and Vicinity; A Study of the Origin, Development, and Classification of Plant Societies*, and W. M. Wheeler's (1923) *Social Life Among the Insects*. During this period qualitative relations were stressed. Although contributing to and being a necessary antecedent to quantitative studies, many of the tangled webs of food chains often seen in the literature fail to reveal any cause and effect relationship in the abundance of particular species. For, while several kinds of predators or a given number of one kind may feed on some prey species, this explains little about the numbers existing at any given time, or changes in numbers, unless we have quantitative data on the results from such feeding.

Limited Capacity of Environment; Struggle for Existence

The idea of overpopulation of organisms embodies the corollary concepts that populations tend to grow, that the environment can carry only certain numbers of the organism, and that such overpopulation then results in a struggle for survival among the individuals of the population. Hence we may justifiably lay the origin of these basic population concepts to such early forewarners of human over-population as Machiavelli (1521) and Botero (1588) in Italy, Hale (1677) in England, Franklin (1751) in America, and Buffon (1756) in France. However, it was only after the appearance of Malthus' (1803) *Essay on the Principles of Population*, which came at a particularly ripe time in England, that ideas involved in the phenomenon of overpopulation became subjects of general discussion and gave rise to scientific inquiry.

According to Cole (1957), the Italian, Giovanni Botero (1588), clearly enunciated, two centuries before Malthus, a concept of population regulation which has subsequently become known as the 'Malthusian Principle':

'Mankind, he concluded, was potentially as fertile in his day as in ancient times but populations did not grow because the resources of the environment were insufficient to support larger populations. He realized that one man and one woman could in 3,000 years have become the ancestors of more people than then existed and he considered that the human population of the world had rapidly grown (by "multiplicative growth") to a maximum and then ceased to grow despite the fact that generative powers had not decreased. Population growth was halted, sometimes by famine, sometimes by contagious diseases abetted by crowding, and sometimes by wars, earthquakes, floods, and other accidents, but generally, the basic limitation was that "the fruits of the earth do not suffice to feed a greater number." '

The ideas of Malthus have been criticized largely because he was considering man, which, alone among the animals, can drastically alter environments to favour his wholesale displacement of other species, and he alone may consciously control his own births. However, man cannot by such criticisms alter the concepts involved in Malthus' principle. The most valid criticism, as pointed out by Miner (1933), is on the other side of the ledger in Malthus' general assumption that the means of subsistence increase in arithmetic ratio; for if this were always so, populations would still increase without limit.

Doubleday (1841) criticized Malthus' views in a paper entitled *The True Law of Population Shewn to be Connected with the Food of the People*. In this peculiar view, derived from specific phenomena rather than more general ones, Doubleday stated the opposite of Malthus' principle: 'Overfeeding checks increase, whilst, on the other hand, a limited or deficient nutriment stimulates and adds to it. . . . Be the range of the natural power to increase in any species what it may, the plethoric state invariably checks it, and the deplethoric state invariably develops it; and this happens in the exact ratio of the intensity and completeness of each state. . . .'

The erudite Herbert Spencer (1852), who capably defended Malthus, held that if the amount of energy in a system is limited, the greater the amount used in non-reproductive aspects the less remains for reproduction. He further stated: 'Evidently, so long as the fertility of the race is more than sufficient to balance the diminution by deaths, population must continue to increase: so long as population continues to increase, there must be pressure on the means of subsistence: and so long as there is pressure on the means of subsistence, further mental development (perfections by selection of more mentally fit, or socially adjusted, for example) must go on and further diminution of fertility must result. Hence, the change can never cease until the rate of multiplication is just equal to the rate of mortality.'[1]

It is significant that Charles Darwin accepted Malthus' principle and his term 'struggle for existence' as a cornerstone of his essays on evolution. 'To eat' and 'to be eaten' were characteristic elements of his 'web of life.' He placed much stress on the *direct* action of biotic forces, which for lack of space we omit.

Darwin's observations led him to conclude that among the species there is no direct correlation between reproductive capacity and average population level; if any correlation exists it is an inverse one. He considered that most areas of the earth favourable to life are commonly already occupied by living things, and that the average means of subsistence remains unchanged, except in terms of gradual step by step processes of organic evolution or geologic change in climate or substrate. Competition by animals and plants for the things they need in environments of basically fixed average potentials, and the survival of the fittest, are concepts of Darwin.

Darwin not only argued the role of competition between different species, but he emphasized that the nearer alike are the needs of two species, the more intense will be the competition. He viewed intraspecific competition as more intense than interspecific competition. May it thus be assumed that he considered it the more important to natural selection?

Darwin commonly referred to competition for food, for places to live, for residences, for warmer or damper spots. He states (1859b, p. 95), 'Not until we reach the extreme confines of life, in the Arctic regions or on the borders of an utter desert, will competition cease. The land may be extremely cold or dry, yet there will be competition between some few species, or between the individuals of the same species, for the warmest or dampest spots.'

The distinct *roles* of climate and competition or biotic agents were maintained in Darwin's mind. He stated (1859b, p. 84), 'Climate plays an important part in determining the average number of a species, and periodical seasons of extreme cold or drought seem to be the most effective of all checks.' He accented the *indirect*

---

[1] In this connection, it is interesting to consider Lack's (1954) view that evolution has not produced in species a degree of balance between fertility and environmental pressures on survival. This view has not been accepted by other ecologists, such as Cloudsley-Thompson (1957) and Wynne-Edwards (1955).

actions of climate, since not only food but also suitable places to live, or residences, the objects of competition, are determined at least in part by climate.

Darwin also stated that climate acts in the main indirectly, 'by favouring other species' in determining the distribution of a species, for in the absence of competing species, most of our organisms would have wider range. A given distribution may thus be the result of varied interactions between the biotic and abiotic forces.

Lastly, Darwin also touched upon the density-dependent aspect of disease epidemics. Although he assumed that such diseases are largely not associated with the struggle for existence, he noted that with certain diseases the greater possibilities of diffusion of pathogens at high densities of the hosts may be involved.

Early Views on the Physical Factors

The striking variations in the form and abundance of animals in a given locality from season to season, year to year, or from place to place at a given time, early led students of natural history to consider the physical factors of their environment. Winter cold in contrast to summer heat, or humid regions contrasted with deserts stimulated interest in the influences of climate on the distribution and abundance of both plants and animals. However, it is significant that Hesse, Allee, and Schmidt (1937, p. 11) state that zoogeography as developed by Wallace and by Heilprin neglected physiological and ecological factors due perhaps to the fact that they were considering birds and mammals, '. . . these homoiothermal animals being largely independent on such an important factor as temperature, and hence the conclusion became widespread that climate is not clearly correlated with animal distribution.' They add that appreciation of such factors as relative humidity, rainfall, and sunlight lagged even after temperature began to be fully appreciated.

The development of ecological concepts pertaining to the physical environment and insects is perhaps best analysed by Uvarov (1931), and for much of the following we draw freely from his work.

Because temperature is perhaps the most apparent element of climate, it is only natural to find that the earliest contributions to the physical ecology of insects concerned thermal influences. Accordingly, we find in the works of Réaumur (1735) discussion of the lethal effects of cold on certain species of insects. Ross (1835) reported the effects of successive exposures to arctic frost on larvae of the lepidopteran *Laria rossii* Curtis. A very extensive study of cold resistance among certain beetles, bees, ants, moths, and flies was made by Rödel (1886).

At what may be termed optimal temperature conditions, early observations pointed to the quantitative influence between increase in temperature and duration of development (Réaumur 1735; Bonnet 1779). The concept of a thermal threshold, originating with the botanist de Candolle (1855), was early applied to insect development by Sanderson (1908). From these two concepts, a temperature threshold and a quantitative relation between temperature and development, the consequent idea of a thermal constant arose (Oettinger 1879; Sanderson 1908). It is upon this temperature-development relationship, termed thermal summation, that Merriam

(1894) based his life zone concept, and on which Hopkins (1918) based his relations of phenology.

With the early observations of an upper thermal limit to development and survival of insects, above which fatal effects occur (Nicolet 1841; Bütschli 1874; Graber 1887), a general summary of the influence of temperature, wherein various vital, limiting, and fatal zones and levels are depicted, was presented by Bachmetjew (1907). Similar relationships portraying the response of individual insects to different intensities of humidity, precipitation, wind, light, and various combinations of these climatic factors have been the consequence of the steady march of science.

It was upon this general background of the limiting and favourable levels of various factors of the physical environment acting upon individuals of an insect population, and upon the correlation between the seasonal rise and fall of the components of weather and the waxing and waning of insect abundance, that subsequent theories of the climatic control of populations were based.

Principle of Homeostasis; Homogeneous and Heterogeneous Systems

Herbert Spencer (1897a, 1897b) expounded the concept of stability of the heterogeneous state and, by implication, the instability of the homogeneous state. The tendency of living systems to maintain by their own regulatory devices an internal stability is known as *homeostasis*. This concept is a well-recognized principle of animal physiology. Its application to systems other than the individual animal is immediately suggested when the complex division of labour and organization of the social insects are considered. In fact, the expected pattern of evolution is a trending towards such homeostasis. For example, animal communities and the populations of which they are composed are considered to be more stable in environments where there is greater complexity of biotic elements—that is, kinds of organisms present—this tending also to greater complexity in the physical framework. This complexity provides a more adequate and reliable system of checks and balances against changes which occur. In the simple homogeneous communities, the contrasting condition, the tendency for excessive fluctuations in abundance is more pronounced, due to lack of the more reliable system of checks and balances.

More perfect adaptation of an organism to a physical stress, particularly if the latter varies in intensities with time, assures that organism a more secure position in the community (Allee *et al.* 1949, p. 6); hence, the interrelated species in that community and thus the total assemblage is made more stable. The same would apply to the origin of more secure interspecific relations between different species or organisms in the ecosystem. The concept of homeostasis thus applies to the individual, the population, and the biotic community or ecosystem (Allee *et al.* 1949, p. 695; Hutchinson 1954; Odum and Allee 1954).

The Spencerian view of greater stability of the more complex system is of great importance in biological control. MacArthur (1955) states it rather differently, that the number of paths which energy has in its course through a food web is a measure of the stability of the community. The heterogeneous state embodies greater compensation against disruption of control, particularly as arising from changed conditions (Solomon 1957), for all the organisms will not be equally tolerant or susceptible to changed conditions. Applying this idea some thirty years ago, Smith (1929a) forcefully argued that, when possible, the introduction of a complex of natural enemies (rather than a single species) should be employed. He held that the different kinds of natural enemies available vary as to the particular habitats where they excel, and that the biological control to be expected from their combined actions, as conditions vary from place to place and from time to time, would be greater than that to be expected from the action of any one of them alone.

For further consideration of the importance of biotic complexity to stability of populations and the relation to biological control, the reader is referred to chapters 4 and 5, and to Voûte (1946), Solomon (1949), and Elton (1958).

QUANTITATIVE POPULATION ECOLOGY

During the last century and the early part of the present one, detailed, quantitative studies in ecology pertaining to the influence of the environment on organisms were essentially of an autecological nature. Studies of groups of organisms, or even individual organisms, in relation to the interrelated factors of their environments, were understandably delayed, since group studies require a greater background of facts and concepts than was then available.

Gradually, however, during the early years of the present century, this concentration on the individual, in contrast to the group, gave way to an increasing number of quantitative investigations into the nature and properties of populations. Studies on ecological succession, the emergence of techniques in biometry, the initial understanding of the characteristics and attributes of groups, and the conception that populations of organisms are entities in their own right gave impetus to the development of quantitative population ecology (Pearl and Reed 1920; Pearl 1925, 1932). The nature of animal aggregations, and the concept of co-operation acting as a factor in the success of an organism and as a force in the evolution of such organisms, also took its place along with the concept of competition as points of departure for quantitative studies of interacting populations (Allee 1931).

Population Growth

If any one study can be pointed to as the initiation of quantitative population ecology, it is that of Pearl and Reed (1920) concerning the growth form of human populations. Their use (and independent development) of the logistic equation of Verhulst (1838) for analysing the growth of populations is a major stepping stone in our current concepts of natural populations (Lotka 1925; Pearl 1925).

The logistic equation of Verhulst and Pearl is essentially a mathematical representation of the Malthusian idea of population growth and environmental resistance. The logistic combines the tendency for populations of organisms to grow in numbers according to a geometric progression, and the tendency for the environment to inhibit the attainment of excessively high densities by such growing populations. Figure 3 shows the form of this equation. The shaded portion above the curve represents the 'still vacant places' available to the organisms, or the relative resistance of the environment at any given population density (Gause 1934).

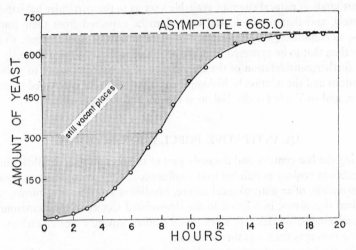

FIGURE 3. The logistic growth of a laboratory population of yeast cells.
(Redrawn from Pearl, after Allee *et al.* 1949, p. 307.)

The logistic growth relationship may be written:

$$dD/dt = nD(A-D)/A$$

where n is the potential reproductive rate of the organism (the maximum possible rate of reproduction under the conditions in existence); D is the density of the organisms at any given instant of time, t; A is the maximum density possible under the particular conditions; and the expression dD/dt refers to the rate of change in numbers with time. For the determination of density at any given instant of time after initiation of growth, we use the integral of this differential equation:

$$D = \frac{A}{1 + e^{a-bt}}$$

where the additional symbol, e, is the constant, $2{\cdot}718\ldots$, and a and b are empirical constants for the particular situation at hand.

The logistic relation may be expressed in words as follows: '... if, under physically constant conditions, a beginning of a population of an organism be introduced into a favourable environment, growth will start slowly and tend first towards a geometric increase; then the increase becomes more and more retarded until it reaches zero, at which point the population density is in equilibrium with its environment.' (Smith 1935.)

Environmental Resistance

The quantitative studies on the growth of populations of the flour beetle, *Tribolium confusum* Jaq. du Val, under the leadership and guidance of R. N. Chapman during the period 1920 to 1930, provided much information on the nature of population growth and the resistance of the environment to growth. These two basic premises of the logistic theory have thereby been explored and evaluated, and possible mechanisms as to how such premises may be accounted for have been acquired.

Chapman (1931) demonstrated that, starting with small numbers of flour beetles in vials containing suitable food media, the abundance of the resultant colonies of beetles increased, and eventually reached some maximum level at which the population remained, or from which it subsequently declined to lower levels. Chapman showed that, among other findings, adult *Tribolium* eat their own eggs and that as the densities of the beetles increase, eggs are eaten at an increasing rate. This factor thus serves as an internal check on the numbers of beetles that eventually can be maintained in such cultures. Chapman considered this intraspecific mortality factor a form of environmental resistance.

Such studies as these led Chapman (1931) to his concept of population determination as a balance between 'biotic potential' and 'environmental resistance.' In his rather ambiguous conception, the biotic potential of an organism is considered to be its maximum, inherent rate of reproduction, but only under any given set of conditions is it considered fixed. The environmental resistance is considered to be the totality of factors tending to limit the actual growth of populations. Since the biotic potential is considered fixed in value, the environmental resistance is considered as variable, depending upon the external conditions of the environment on the one hand, and on the density of organisms on the other. Chapman considered that, given an organism with a high biotic potential, the environmental resistance for this species must be high, and for a species with a low biotic potential, this resistance must be low.

Population Equilibrium or Balance

The events after a population has passed through its initial growth phases in new environments are most important to field ecologists. When projects in biological control of insects are initiated the pest species usually has reached this equilibrium position (Smith 1935). Studies by Gause and his associates, using populations of protozoa, yeasts, and mites, directed primarily at establishing the applicability of the logistic theory of Verhulst and Pearl, led him to the conclusion that the asymptotic level of the logistic equation was essentially the outcome of the concept of biotic potential and environmental resistance of Chapman (1928a, 1931). The work of Gause (1934) on the predator-prey relation indicated that the number of 'vacant places' (*vide supra*) in an environment may fluctuate rhythmically in a manner involving biotic interactions. Such fluctuations are then considered a modification in the equilibrium existing between biotic potential and environmental resistance.

The basic premises of the Verhulst–Pearl logistic theory and of Chapman's theory of biotic potential and environmental resistance introduce a concept of fundamental importance in population ecology, that of the equilibrium density or characteristic level of abundance of populations in nature. This is the basic idea of the balance of nature. Empirical studies, aimed at verification or evaluation of the logistic theory, indicate that under *given circumstances* organisms do in fact tend to reach, but not exceed, some maximum level of abundance. It has long been noted that the densities of natural populations, though tending to fluctuate in time, attain characteristic levels of abundance, rather than increasing without limit or decreasing to extinction. As Herbert Spencer put it:

'Every species of plant and animal is perpetually undergoing a rhythmical variation in number—now from abundance of food and absence of enemies rising above its average, and then by a consequent scarcity of food and abundance of enemies being depressed below its average . . . amid these oscillations produced by their conflict, lies that average number of the species at which its expansive tendency is in equilibrium with the surrounding repressive tendencies. Nor can it be questioned that this balancing of the preservative and destructive forces which we see going on in every race must necessarily go on. Since increase in numbers cannot but continue until increase of mortality stops it; and decrease of numbers cannot but continue until it is either arrested by fertility or extinguishes the race entirely.' (Quoted from Lotka 1925.)

Spencer here uses the term 'equilibrium' for the condition where the expansive tendencies of the population and the repressive forces of the environment are such as to produce the 'average' population density. This usage connotes 'balance' or dynamic equilibrium. On the other hand, Chapman (1931) considers biotic systems to be in equilibrium when populations remain more stable in numbers over a considerable period of time, and it is the attainment of this stability of density that is the basis for Chapman's theory of biotic potential and environmental resistance (*vide supra*).

In a subsequent section we shall consider again this concept of equilibrium, whether or not it is a dynamic state of balance, and what factors and mechanisms in nature produce this balance.

THE ORIGINS OF CONCEPTS OF NATURAL CONTROL

In this section, the origins of certain fundamental ideas concerning the different factors or processes of the environment that enter into, or may be presumed to enter into the determination of population abundance in nature are discussed. For this purpose natural control is defined as *the maintenance of a more or less fluctuating population density within certain definable upper and lower limits over a period of time by the combined actions of the whole environment* (see also Solomon 1949). Much of the discussion stems from theoretical treatment of the subject, while other insights are derived from empirical or experimental studies.

The various factors or influences making up the environment of an organism have long been divided into biotic factors, or those involving other organisms, or influences deriving from other organisms, and abiotic factors, such as those of climate, soil, air, space, and light. The question of whether biotic elements or abiotic factors are the more important in determining densities of populations has long been studied, and debated. Students of biological control are of necessity interested in this subject, because they work with biotic factors in the control of insect pests. Thus, they need to know how such factors influence abundance of pests and also how such influences are affected by, or may be confused with, other factors of the environment.

Influence of Biotic Factors

The importance of natural enemies, in particular entomophagous insects, in the control of insect pests has long been established both in theory and in practice (Darwin 1859*b*; Köllar 1837; Ratzeburg 1844; Fitch 1865; Walsh 1866) (see chapter 2). The relationship of disease and the abundance of insects have been understood more recently (see Steinhaus 1954, and chapter 19).

In commenting on the periodic rise and fall in the abundance of insect pests, Marchal (1908) observed, 'When an insect has been very injurious for two or three years, and has multiplied to the point of taking the proportions of a veritable plague, it disappears, usually in a sudden manner at the moment when the alarm which it has provoked has reached its highest degree. Experience has shown that it is almost always to the work of parasites that these rapid retrocessions of injurious species must be attributed.' He also considered the relationship of parasites to insect pests when the latter were customarily more stable in abundance. 'In other cases which more nearly approach the general and primitive law of nature the injurious species maintains always about the same rank, and the fluctuations which it presents are only of secondary importance. The parasites act as a moderating check to the continued increase and prevent the injurious species from multiplying in an excessive manner.' Howard (1897) drew similar conclusions regarding these phenomena.

Up to this time, conceptions regarding factors that control the abundance of insects considered such actions as mere contributants to total mortality. Mechanisms by which such mortality factors could control densities in any reliable manner were not considered. However, Howard and Fiske (1911) presented the first clear statement as to how such mortality factors must function in order to provide such control as they do. They proposed the idea that the intensity of action of certain factors of the environment must be related to the density of the population acted upon. Thus, they classified the natural causes of mortality into two groups, one destroying a constant proportion regardless of density, and the other destroying a percentage that increases as the density of the organisms increases. The former group of mortality factors was designated as 'catastrophic' and the latter, 'facultative.' Since the basis of such a classification was mortality in relation to density of the population, these two groups of factors have been much more descriptively designated as 'density-independent' and 'density-dependent' mortality factors (Smith 1935).

Howard and Fiske (1911) assign to the group of facultative or density-dependent factors the actions of parasites and predators, and, under certain circumstances, diseases. Smith (1935) assumed that, in general, the density-dependent factors are mostly biotic, while the density-independent group of mortality agents is mainly physical or abiotic, and principally climatic. However, Smith also recognized competition for food and other needs as density-dependent in nature. He argued that both sets of factors produce mortality and thus act to reduce populations, but that only density-dependent factors, by the very nature of their action, are able to govern the average population abundance or equilibrium level. He considered that the abiotic or density-independent factors cannot determine such population levels when acting alone. Smith also stated that climate so obviously affects average population levels that such action must be associated in a density-dependent manner, possibly involving protective shelters. Such interactions of the two groups of density-influencing factors will be considered again in this chapter and particularly in chapter 4.

Theoretical Models of Host–Parasite Interactions

By the end of the nineteenth century, while the practice of utilizing entomophagous insects in combating insect pests was coming into considerable use in many parts of the world (see chapter 2), very little was known of the precise, quantitative manner in which such biotic control might be effected, or what biological characteristics and habits make a parasite or predator an effective control agent. Thus, the empirical basis for biological control was becoming rather well understood, but a precise theoretical foundation for biological control or for the general relations existing between a host insect and its parasites and predators had not yet been developed.

The initial attempts at formulating quantitative relationships between coexisting animal species, such as a parasite and its insect host, mainly emphasized the character of fecundity. We may refer to the earliest treatment of host–parasite interaction we know of, that of Bellevoye and Laurent (1897, cited in Marchal 1908). These authors show that, given a fixed reproductive capacity of 100 eggs per female for the host, a similar fecundity for the parasite, sex ratios of 1 : 1 for both species, and with the parasite laying but one egg per host and multiplying thereby at the expense of the host, the host would be completely eliminated within four generations. Prior to this end result, the host would increase in numbers by a factor of 50. An almost identical, simple arithmetic model of host–parasite interaction was developed by Muir (1914).

Marchal (1908) pointed out that the theoretical result deduced from such a model, wherein a host species exhibits a threatening increase in numbers over a period of years subsequently only to disappear suddenly, finds many parallels in nature. He showed, however, that there also occur many cases in nature where a host species appears each year in more or less fixed numbers, with but minor fluctuations about some mean level. Marchal notes also that in nature we have all gradations between these extremes, and that these results are more theoretical than real since the factors involved in natural control are so much more complex and numerous than such a model suggests. According to Marchal, some of the factors appearing in nature but ignored by such a model are: (1) hyperparasites; (2) co-existing parasitic species; (3) coexisting host species; (4) general predators of both host and parasite; (5) differential climatic effects on host and parasite; and (6) asynchronous development of generations and hence asynchronous timing between host and parasite.

Muir (1914) considered that besides fecundity there is an additional factor involved in the interaction between host and parasite, and this factor is the ability of the parasite to discover its host. This concept is exceedingly important, for it implies that even though a female parasite possesses a certain fixed reproductive capacity, its more or less efficient searching capacity determines the degree to which these eggs shall be utilized. However, Muir did not incorporate this important original concept into his arithmetic model of host–parasite interaction.

Thompson (1922a, 1922b, 1922c, 1922d, 1930a, 1939), in an attempt to formulate a method for ascertaining the progress of introduced parasites in the field and for estimating the time at which complete control would occur, considered anew the mathematical basis for host–parasite interaction. He extended the above-described arithmetic models in several ways. Of major importance, he transformed the arithmetic model to an algebraic one, thus freeing it from the requirement of explicitly stated biological values, as, for example, fecundity levels.

By use of such equations, Thompson computed the number of generations at which the host density would be reduced to zero. Hence, when the reproductive rates of the host and parasite were equal, the host would be eliminated by the time (generation) t:

$$t = n/p$$

where n and p represent the initial density of host and parasite, respectively. Whenever the reproductive rate of the parasite is greater than that of the host, there is always some finite value of t, that is, some future generation, in which the host density becomes zero. Whenever the reproductive rate of the parasite, s, is less than that of the host, h, then for annihilation of the host in some finite generation, t, the ratio of initial densities, n and p, must be such that $p/n > (h-s)/s$. In the particular case where $p/n = (h-s)/s$, then the degree of parasitism remains fixed, and the two populations increase in the same proportion (see Bellevoye and Laurent, loc. cit.).

Thompson (1939) extended these rather simple, unrealistic models of host–parasite interaction to include the more complex but realistic cases of varying sex ratios of both host and parasite, varying destructive capacities of the latter (for example, the gregarious parasite, where more than one progeny issues from a single host, or the predator, where one individual destroys several host individuals), the case where parasite reproductive capacity varies with the density of the host and/or the parasite, and the influence of superparasitism on parasite reproductive capacity.

In the case where the parasite is found to lay more than one egg in a host, but only one is destined to produce a mature progeny, we have the phenomenon of superparasitism. If, as stated by Thompson (1930*a*), the proportion of parasites to hosts increases from generation to generation, the likelihood of superparasitism will increase. In the cases considered thus far, where but one parasite progeny is produced from each host individual, superparasitism tends to reduce the reproductive capacity of the parasite species. Hence, superparasitism leads to the result that as the relative density of the parasite increases, its reproductive efficiency tends to decrease. This is an example of a density-modified parasitic action.

The mathematical models of host-parasite systems developed thus far, having been based primarily on the mathematics of geometric progressions, have always led to the progressive increase in abundance of the parasite, and to either a similar increase, or an increase followed by the sudden extinction of the host. In none of these models is there any sort of cyclical or repetitive process.

Lotka (1923, 1925), in considering the theoretical work of Thompson (*vide supra*), was the first to devise a mathematical model of animal interaction that resulted in such a periodic relationship. The major departure of the Lotka model from that of Thompson lay in the premise that the destruction of host individuals by parasites was a function not only of parasite numbers but also of host numbers. By use of calculus, and assuming the overlapping of generations, Lotka arrived at the result that for each value of the host abundance there is a corresponding value for the parasite abundance, and that as the density of hosts rises, the density of parasites increases, which in turn leads to a fall in host numbers, followed by a fall in parasite numbers, and so on, for cycle after cycle. When carried further mathematically, the result, though still periodic, leads to a diminishing interaction which was considered by Lotka as a damped oscillation.

Under such an interaction the host species is not annihilated, but will always exist at some finite density between an upper and a lower limit, and similarly for the parasite. There is the implied premise of continuously periodic fluctuations. Here we see the implication of a stable, biological balance, such that in the event of a local upset in balance, the characteristic densities pertaining at the equilibrium condition are automatically restored by subsequent host–parasite interaction.

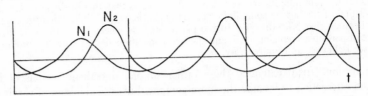

FIGURE 4. Variations, in time, of population densities of two species, one of which preys on the other. (From Volterra, after Chapman 1931, p. 421.)

A mathematical treatment of the interactions between coexisting animal species led Volterra (1926) (see Chapman 1931) to the formulation of a model of host–parasite interaction almost identical to that of Lotka (*vide supra*) (see figure 4). Again, based on the use of calculus, the fundamental premises of exponential growth in numbers, and modification of the coefficient of increase by the density of the coexisting species led to cyclic and continuously repeating fluctuations in numbers of both host and parasite. In addition, Volterra considered the influence of mortality factors common to both host and parasite, that is, the removal from the system of equal proportions of the two interacting species. From these considerations regarding the biological system of one animal feeding on another Volterra concluded (Chapman 1931):

1. Law of the Periodic Cycle.—The fluctuations of the two species are periodic and the period depends only on the coefficients of increase (of the host) and decrease (of the parasite) and the initial conditions of abundance.

2. Law of the Conservation of the Averages.—The averages of the numbers of individuals of the two species are constant whatever may be the initial values of the numbers of individuals of the two species just so long as the coefficients of increase and decrease of the two species and those of protection and of offence remain constant.

3. Law of the Disturbance of the Averages.—If an attempt is made to destroy the individuals of the two species uniformly and in proportion to their number, the average of the number of individuals of the species that is eaten increases and that of the individuals of the species feeding upon the other diminishes. Increasing the protection of the species fed upon increases, however, both the averages. If the individuals of the two species are destroyed, contemporaneously and uniformly, the ratio of the amplitude of the fluctuation of the species eaten to the amplitude of the fluctuation of the species feeding upon the other increases.

The Lotka–Volterra model of host–parasite interaction has been criticized on several rather fundamental points. One criticism stems from the use of infinitesimal calculus for the development of the model (Nicholson and Bailey 1935; Thompson 1939; Ullyett 1953). This usage presumes that interactions of host and parasite can be considered as continuous functions of both numbers of individuals and of time. It is stated that in reality animal abundance varies in discrete, finite increments, and at least for insects rarely if ever does the interaction between host and parasite proceed continuously in time. Insects must be born, grow to maturity, and then reproduce. Life cycles are finite, hence there exist periodic sequences of events we call generations. This imparts periodicity to reproduction and to mortality, and, in the case of two interacting animal species, makes synchronization of life cycles necessary.

A second criticism is directed at the presumption of random action in the relationships between host and parasite (Thompson 1939; Ullyett 1953; Andrewartha and Birch 1954). The Lotka–Volterra model does not postulate randomness in the sense criticized, but rather postulates that the frequency of encounters between host and parasite is a simple function of the product of their numbers.

Regarding randomness, Ullyett (1953) concluded that: (1) search for suitable environments or for the specific things required within the environments are the result of directed action; (2) the discriminating ability of the ovipositing female in the distribution of her eggs is not random; but (3) there is a degree of randomness in this chain of events apparently due to a modification of the more systematic actions of the animal by environmental factors which, in turn, produce aberrations of instinct on the part of the organism, and yet this modification is not sufficient to regard the behaviour of the animal as being random.

Other criticisms of the Lotka–Volterra model are: that it is based fundamentally on the logistic theory of population growth (*vide supra*), which, in turn, has been objected to as an unrealistic conception (Andrewartha and Birch 1954; Nicholson 1954*b*); that it implies completely discriminatory (though randomly acting) parasitic behaviour, with parasite females possessing unlimited egg-laying capacities, and that every encounter between parasite and host represents a 'capture,' or deposition of an egg, and that such encounters continue indefinitely, regardless of the densities of either parasite or host (Andrewartha and Birch, *loc. cit.*); that the reaction of the parasite encountering a host is instantaneous, and, hence, that there is no lag in time between such encounter and its eventual result, and that no allowance is made for the complex life cycles of the subject animals, which, in fact, require consideration of a lag effect due to growth and maturation (Nicholson and Bailey 1935; Nicholson 1954*b*); and, finally, that each individual in the respective populations cannot be considered equivalent to other individuals since different stages of development are involved (Nicholson and Bailey, *loc. cit.*). Watt (1962) also challenges the assumption in Volterra's model of birth rate as being density-independent, an assumption which may be most misleading.

The theoretical model of host-parasite interaction constructed and explored by Nicholson and Bailey (Bailey 1931; Nicholson 1933; Nicholson and Bailey 1935) is essentially an extension of the Lotka–Volterra model discussed above, with the elimination of many of the unrealistic premises implied in the latter model. Many aspects of this Nicholson–Bailey model underlie our own conception of the manner in which the abundance of animal populations is determined (see chapter 4).

The fundamental structure of the Nicholson–Bailey model rests on the basic postulates that in order to exist and perpetuate themselves, animals must obtain food, mates, and suitable places in which to live. Animals have the capability of self-reproduction and of increase in number when the conditions of the environment permit. Animals search for the things they need. Populations of animals search for such objectives at random even if the individuals do not. A summary of Nicholson's more complete view of natural control is presented in the last section of this chapter.

The hypothesis of random search, of fundamental importance to the Nicholson–Bailey theory, needs to be carefully defined and explained. It has been challenged by several authors (*vide supra*, Lotka–Volterra model). Nicholson and Bailey (1935) and Nicholson (1954*b*) carefully point out that it is the animal *population* that searches the environment for its requisites at random, not the *individual* animal. Systematic (directed) searching by each of a large number of independently searching individuals does not make the searching of the collective group systematic. So long as the search within a population is completely unorganized, it is random. Huffaker (1958a) also pointed out that even with the more directed behaviour of individuals, if they are ever situated beyond the zone of receipt of guiding stimuli or if barriers exist preventing the unerring result, randomness is involved. Actually, the descriptive term, 'random search,' expresses the previously stated fundamental premise of the Lotka–Volterra model that the success of a group of animals in finding a requisite, such as food, is a simple function of the product of the density of the animals and the density of the objects sought.

The Nicholson–Bailey theory of host–parasite interaction may be illustrated by the solitary, internal parasite. In this case there is a unique density of the parasite such that exactly the fraction of hosts that is surplus is destroyed, that is, will be found and parasitized, and also that there is a unique density of hosts such that this density of parasites is maintained. Thus the densities of host and parasite remain fixed. This situation is called the 'steady state' system, and the respective densities of the coexisting animals is called their 'steady densities' (Nicholson 1933).

Nicholson (1933) and Nicholson and Bailey (1935) explored this situation deductively and mathematically, and conclude that the steady densities of the host and parasite species are dependent only upon the reproductive capacity of the host, and the area of discovery of the parasite. Additionally, they explore other situations among which are the cases where the parasite lays more than one egg in a host, where more than one host is destroyed by each parasite, where the hosts are partially immune to attack, where a fixed fraction of the parasite offspring is destroyed by other environmental factors, such as weather, and where there is a lack of complete correspondence between the life-cycles of the host and parasite.

In addition to considerations of the steady state of the host–parasite system, Nicholson and Bailey also treat the case where, initially, the populations of the interacting animals are not at their steady state. This, of course, covers the much broader, and more realistic, situation of fluctuations in density. In the case of the specific parasite laying but one egg per host found, it can be shown that, if p_n and h_n are the densities of the parasite and host, respectively, during generation n, and a is the area of discovery (coefficient of encounters, or searching coefficient), and if F is the coefficient of reproduction (power of increase) of the host, then: The initial density of host offspring from h_n hosts is Fh_n:

The parasites, searching among these host offspring, cover an area equal to ap_n;

Because of the randomness of their search and the overlapping of their paths, the p_n parasites are not all able to encounter a host with the same probability of success. Hence, the most probable fraction of host offspring that escape parasitism is proportional to $1/e^{ap_n}$, or, as it is usually denoted, e^{-ap_n};

Hence, the final density of host offspring escaping parasitism, and thus constituting the next generation, $n+1$, is:

$$h_n+1 = Fh_ne^{-ap_n}$$

And, as the number of host offspring found by the parasites is equal to the initial number of offspring less those that escaped, the number of parasites in the next generation is:

$$p_n+1 = Fh_n-h_{n-1}$$

These recurrent equations, when explored over several generations, show that the host and parasite densities oscillate about their steady densities. Mathematical analysis shows that in the simple and restricted case under consideration, these oscillations continue indefinitely, but with increasing amplitudes (see figure 5).

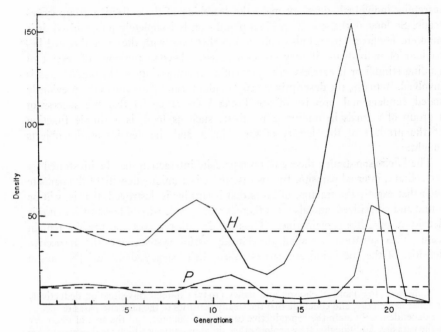

FIGURE 5. Interaction of a specific host species (H) and a specific parasite species (P). Power of increase of host 2. Area of discovery of parasite 0–035. Arbitrary initial displacement of host density from 40 to 44. H, host curve; P, parasite curve. The steady densities are represented by dotted lines. Parasite curve drawn to half the vertical scale of host curve. (After Nicholson 1933.)

The basic thesis of the Nicholson–Bailey theory of balance, as so described, is that it is the density of the animals themselves that governs the degree by which the inherent tendency to increase in number is greater than, equal to, or less than the repressive forces of the environment. In regard to these latter forces of environmental resistance, the simplest is the action of crowding by other individuals of the same species, i.e., intraspecific competition for space, shelters, food, or other requisites. Other agents of repression that may be brought into operation in similar manner are the actions of parasites, predators, and disease. This repression may act to reduce natality or to increase mortality.

These deduced results, that a parasite can act in such a manner as to hold its host, and hence itself, in a state of static balance (the steady state) or of dynamic balance (reciprocally related oscillation), are similar to the results deriving from the Lotka–Volterra model, except that the Nicholson–Bailey model incorporates the concept of lag effects. However, the essential mechanism in the Nicholson–Bailey model is also density-geared, although with a lag. As the number of hosts increase, their density supports an additional number of parasites. This increase in density of the parasites then causes a larger fraction of the hosts to become parasitized, leading to a subsequent decline in host numbers. The decrease in host density, in turn, reduces the fraction of parasites that is able to reproduce, hence subsequently reducing their numbers. These coupled interactions are thus the result of the density of one organism influencing the density of the second, and the modified density of the second in turn influencing the density of the first.

This idea of density-modified reproduction and mortality, and its particular application to the action of insect parasites, predators, and diseases, was developed independently by H. S. Smith (1929a, 1935). Smith (1935) based his reasoning essentially on the logistic theory of Verhulst and Pearl (*vide supra*), in particular as this theory was developed by Volterra.[1] The Verhulst–Pearl logistic theory is the first attempt to show quantitatively how the density of a population of organisms can influence their own growth in numbers. Now, from the Nicholson–Bailey theory, and from the deductions of Smith (1935), we also see how the density of a growing population of host organisms can eventually control its own ultimate abundance by operating through the mechanisms of natural enemies.

Influence of Abiotic Factors

Darwin's (1859b) emphasis on competition and on natural enemies in natural selection and in the determination of abundance of life seems to have stimulated great interest and study in the manner in which biotic factors act as controlling agents in the population dynamics of a species. However, with the rapid increase, during the last half of the nineteenth century, in knowledge of the precise and quantitative manner in which the physical factors of the environment, in particular, climate, influence the reproduction, development, and survival of animals, the role of abiotic factors in population phenomena has also become much better understood (*vide supra*, p. 8). More recently, it has been demonstrated that climatic factors have dominating influences on such aspects of an individual insect's life cycle as reproduction, development, fecundity, and longevity (Shelford 1929; Chapman 1931; Uvarov 1931; Birch 1945; Howe 1953).

Careful field observations on some insect pests indicate that, although pest densities fluctuate over a more or less characteristic range of values, suggesting that natural control of such species does occur, there are no obvious biotic factors, such as natural enemies, intraspecific or interspecific competition for food or space, or insect-induced lack of food supplies present in their environment to account for such natural control (Davidson and Andrewartha 1948a, 1948b; Andrewartha and Birch 1948, 1954). It was observed, however, that fluctuation in numbers was closely correlated with changes in weather. It was therefore concluded that population densities of these species were determined in the main by weather. In order to account for the characteristic population levels attained each year by the different species studied, it was postulated that such natural control derives from a balance

---

[1] Smith's graphic presentation of his concepts of density-dependent regulation of animal numbers was based on the linear relations inherent in the logistic curve. He presented a graph showing a linear relation between density-dependent mortality and density. Andrewartha and Birch (1954, p. 17) criticize this on the grounds that there is no empirical basis for such linearity (see discussion, chapter 4).

in the favourability and unfavourability of weather over periods of years (Andre-wartha and Birch 1954; Birch 1957). Hence, for part of each year, or for several years in a row, weather conditions were favourable for growth of populations of these species, and the populations therefore did increase in density. Subsequently, weather conditions became unfavourable, and, due to weather-induced depletion of food supplies and excessive drought conditions that caused high degrees of mortal-ity, the population densities declined. In chapter 4 we will discuss this concept of a balance in the favourability and unfavourability of environment.

Regarding proportionate mortality, if a study establishes the proportion of a population killed by various factors, it often happens that much of the total kill can be assigned to such factors as excessive temperature, humidity, rainfall, and the like. In some cases by far the greater part of total mortality can be assigned to such physical factors.

This has led some insect ecologists to conclude that the order of importance of factors determining the abundance of insects in a given area might well be depend-ent upon the amount of mortality caused by each factor (Bodenheimer 1928, 1930, 1931), or the degree of loss in vigour and fecundity (Janisch 1938, 1939). Hence, the relative importance of the various climatic factors coupled with the sometimes relatively small degree of mortality caused by parasites, predators, and diseases, have commonly been regarded as establishing the importance of the physical factors in determining the abundance of insects in a given population (Cook 1930; Uvarov 1931; Bodenheimer 1938).

The difficulty here is that percentage kill gives no indication of the number of insects surviving, and fails to answer the question of whether or not the surplus of insects produced by the previous generation was eliminated by such factors (Smith 1935). This aspect of mortality is quite important in population dynamics, since if the entire surplus produced in each generation is not accounted for by the various environmental mortality factors, the numbers in the area will increase year after year. Or, if the mortality factors kill more than the surplus produced each generation, the population will decrease year after year, eventually to become extinct. Neither of these results seems to be a common occurrence in nature.

For climate alone to control *through direct action* the density of an insect popula-tion, it must be of just sufficient intensity to kill exactly the surplus of progeny produced each generation, or else kill various proportions in successive years such that the mean mortality over this period of time has precisely eliminated the surplus of individuals produced.

While the direct action of climate could not act to achieve such a result, climate may nevertheless determine the conditions conducive to and restricting actions of a density-dependent nature which do so act (see chapter 4). Climate may often have important side effects. Bodenheimer (1938) and Clausen (1952*b*) state that in environ-ments of widely varying seasonal intensities (the authors would add ones having extremes to which neither host nor parasite is well adapted) the natural enemy, following adverse periods, starts again with a disadvantage, for if the mortality during the severe season were exactly equal on host and parasite species, the host would be favoured according to Volterra's 'law' (see also Nicholson 1933).

It is an important point that entomophagous insects are often more vulnerable to weather than are their insect hosts (Bodenheimer 1938; Bodenheimer and Schiffer 1952). This means that periodically the parasite population is reduced to a greater extent than the host and this serves to interrupt the parasite's action to a greater degree than the previous example. Such differential vulnerability is said to be due to two basic causes, a greater physiological sensitivity of the entomophagous species, if host specific, and a more vulnerable ecological susceptibility of such parasites by virtue of their particular habitat (in or on a host individual). The former type of vulnerability is due to a narrower tolerance to inhibitory weather conditions, or a more reduced performance. Examples of this are provided by Payne (1933, 1934a) and Burnett (1948). The latter type results because of the occurrence of otherwise tolerant parasite individuals in hosts that are killed. Assuming an equal suscepti-bility of host and parasite, a given weather catastrophe may directly kill 50 per cent of the hosts and 50 per cent of the parasites. Barring interactions, by mere chance half of the remaining tolerant parasites will be found in host individuals which were killed. They are therefore indirectly killed by the weather, and the total mortality of the parasites is 75 per cent.

As an additional point, Wellington (1957) states that development has had far more emphasis in bioclimatic studies than behaviour, although the latter may prove to be far more significant in population dynamics. Insects must *do* certain things to survive and to reproduce. They do these things according to prevailing conditions. Complex physiological and behavioural processes are involved and are of great importance (see Morris 1958b; and especially chapters 5 and 6).

It is thus obvious to any biologist that (as Thompson (1939, 1956) states) abiotic forces of environment react with biotic factors in an appalling complexity of ways, and that, directly or indirectly, climate may determine the abundance or scarcity of food and its quality, the nature and abundance of tolerable micro-habitats, or special abode requirements, the complex of, and efficiency of, species allied to a given form or inimical to it, or the thresholds at which crowding may become effective. We have omitted from this section discussion of any unified concept regarding the importance of the abiotic factors because we present Thompson's (1929a, 1939, 1956) views in the following section, and his views, although not confined to abiotic influences, contain the basic positions of those who stress the importance of the physical factors (see chapter 4).

OPPOSING VIEWS OF NATURAL CONTROL

There are many ramifications in the various views of the way in which natural control comes about. As a means of orienting some of the opposing viewpoints to our own as presented in the next chapter we discuss and appraise herein the two main contrasting views and bring in certain points of agreement or disagreement with other authors as the discussion progresses. We use the views of W. R. Thompson and A. J. Nicholson for this purpose, for we feel that important differences are found in these positions, and also because we have already considered some of the background of both views.

In addition to the early work of Thompson (1929a, 1939), Smith (1929, 1935), Uvarov (1931), Nicholson (1933), and Nicholson and Bailey (1935), the reader is referred to various other authors who have presented more recently their views on this important subject (Schwerdtfeger 1941; Solomon 1957; Nicholson 1954b, 1958; Andrewartha and Birch 1954; Lack 1954; Smith 1955; Thompson 1956; Milne 1957b; Huffaker 1957, 1958a; Cole 1957; Cloudsley–Thompson 1957; and Debach 1958b).

In his review of this subject, Solomon (1949) classifies the various concepts as: (1) early 'biotic'; (2) competition; (3) physical; (4) periodic fluctuation; and (5) comprehensive theories.

The views of Nicholson and of Thompson represent divergent positions regarding whether or not internal self-governing aspects are important. Thompson holds that the primary factors controlling the abundance of animals are extrinsic, that is, primarily climatic and edaphic in nature and that populations are not self-governed. Nicholson stresses the biotic elements of the environment, and the self-governing aspect of populations in relation to *given* environmental conditions.

Thompson (1929a, 1939, 1956) considers that the 'balance of nature' is only the fact of natural control, that is, numbers simply do not increase indefinitely (see chapter 4). A species is limited in its abundance simply by its own intrinsic limitations, that is, it can eat only certain things and can thrive only under certain conditions. With the properties of species thus limited, the primary extrinsic factor of natural control is the climatic and edaphic conditions which are the basis of the tremendous complexity and diversity of environmental conditions in time and space, and which produce not only a fragmentation of habitats but a constant change in their character and location. A cogent argument is that while the changes in the fortunes of organisms are dependent upon the pervading physical conditions, the latter are not dependent on the organisms. Limitation is thus related to the fact that the range of changes towards increased favourability or toward decreased favourability is very restricted by the fundamental nature of geographic position relative to the basic climates of the earth, thus populations would not continue to increase indefinitely nor decrease to zero.

The 'balance' of Thompson is a balance in the environment. Conditions simply do not remain favourable long enough for a species to overwhelm its environment nor do they remain unfavourable long enough for it to dwindle to extinction— except in places which are in any case unsuitable.

Thompson thus does not see any necessity for invoking density-geared or self-governing mechanisms. Thus he maintains that populations are not self-governed, they merely vary. In fact, he holds that populations are not entities, that they have no special properties distinct from those of the individuals making up the population. Thompson also states that as an organism increases in abundance 'the action it exerts upon its environment, both directly and indirectly, increases in intensity, producing changes which are on the whole, insofar as they depend purely and simply on the numerical increase, disadvantageous, since they consist to a great extent in the progressive exhaustion of the nutritive power of the environment. . . .' While he recognizes that density-dependent stresses may be among the environmental forces which cause conditions to become unfavourable, he considers the operation of such factors the exception rather than the rule, though he states (1929a) that they may be the rule in calm, favourable environments in contrast to the status in widely fluctuating environments.

Thompson (1948, 1956) uses his basic position to argue against the uses that have been made of mathematics in attempts at telling us what is actually happening in nature. He states that if mathematics cannot be used to predict the climatic conditions and reduce their fluctuations to mathematical terms, then the primary force behind changes in populations is thus beyond such description. Regarding this question Watt (1961, 1962) considered that the utility of mathematical models depends upon what is expected of them. He feels that if better interpretation, if not prediction, is achieved through use of models, in terms of such variables as are present and have been accurately recorded, then the model approach is useful. It may give many leads to better research along the way (of value in itself), and promote the development of more generally useful integrated concepts. Watt also considers that, even if a given biological characteristic taken as a constant in a model, is in fact quite variable, it is nevertheless admissible under certain circumstances to take the average value of such variables as constants.

Lastly, Thompson (1928b, 1955) (followed with reservations by Morris 1957), holds a view of the way an entomophagous parasite usually operates in natural control, which is the inverse of the view of Nicholson (1933) and Smith (1935) (see discussion, chapter 4). Nicholson's view is summarized by him (1954b, p. 59), as follows:

(1) All animals have an innate ability to reproduce and to multiply under favourable conditions.

(2) The favourability or otherwise of the environment for a given species determines whether its population is permitted to grow or is caused to decrease.

(3) As every animal born must die, and can die only once, a population cannot persist for long periods in any given environment unless the birthrate and deathrate are virtually equal (when each is averaged over a representative period); for if numbers of births and of deaths remained appreciably different the population would decrease or increase geometrically, so either directly falling to extinction, or causing its own extinction by overwhelming its environment, in a comparatively short time.

(4) As populations grow, the constituent animals use up more and more of the limited available quantities of depletable requisites (such as food and favourable space), and increasing density often intensifies the action of inimical factors (for example, by increasing the densities of any natural enemies dependent upon the animals concerned, or by increasing the concentration of harmful metabolities).

(5) Because animals produce such effects upon their environments, growing populations progressively reduce the favourability of some factors, whereas decreasing populations permit favourability to recover. Such compensatory reaction inevitably governs population densities at levels related to the properties of the animals and those of their environments.

(6) Consequently, when operating in association with density governing factors, non-reactive factors (such as climate) may have a profound influence upon density, for many non-reactive factors influence either the properties of animals or environmental favourability.

(7) Operating by themselves, however, non-reactive factors cannot determine population densities for, if sufficiently favourable, they permit indefinite multiplication or, if not, they cause populations to dwindle to extinction. On the other hand, they inevitably limit distribution to those areas within which they are favourable.

Nicholson recognizes that in nature the host-parasite oscillations predicted by the Nicholson–Bailey model (*vide supra*) could not continue indefinitely to increase in amplitude. He recognizes two possibilities. First, the increasing amplitude proceeds to the point of causing local annihilation of the host species and hence the parasite, and this creates a pattern of fragmented distributions in nature, with migrants then moving back into the depopulated areas from time to time to reinitiate the process. Secondly, the tendency towards increasing amplitude of the oscillations is in nature damped by the actions of other factors. For example, utilization of food to the limit of supply in localized places by the phytophagous prey would serve to prevent the still greater increase of prey, and consequently their predators, which would otherwise cause increasing amplitude and a more severe crash effect subsequently (Huffaker 1958*b*). Klomp (1958*a*) discusses the action of a number of such damping mechanisms. Holling (1961) pointed out that not only may the fragmentation phenomenon of Nicholson prevent the annihilative increase in amplitude, but that other damping mechanisms intrinsic to the predator–prey relation itself may be involved. Firstly, with the special type of functional response wherein percentage-take increases (within a given range) with prey density, there is an immediate relaxation in effect with decline in prey density. Secondly, the interference component (not considered in Nicholson's formula) is related to predator density and this provides another intrinsic damping mechanism.

Although Nicholson and Bailey refer mainly to fragmentation resulting from parasite–host interaction, this could occur due to other governing agencies, such as infectious diseases, in which there is a lag between the intensity of the action of the agency as triggered by host density, and the time such pressure is exerted effectively against the host population. Smith (1955) and Huffaker (1958*b*) pointed out that this fragmentation phenomenon, which results in a lower average density of a pest than that predicted by the 'steady density,' serves to greatly increase the degree of control by natural enemies.

Cockerell (1934) recorded ideas, which, historically, might antedate Nicholson's fragmentation concept had they been published at the time:

'I recall some observations on Coccidae made in New Mexico many years ago. Certain species occur on the mesquite and other shrubs which exist in great abundance . . . yet the coccids are only found in isolated patches here and there. They are destroyed by their natural enemies, but the young larvae can be blown by the wind or carried on the feet of birds, and so start new colonies which flourish until discovered by predators and parasites. This game of hide and seek doubtless results in frequent local extermination, but the species are sufficiently widespread to survive in parts of this range, and so continue indefinitely.'

By way of defining the area of agreement and contrasting the positions of Nicholson and Thompson, we present the following discussion. Thompson himself (1956) states that he agrees with Nicholson's points 1 to 4 and the first sentence of point 5 (*vide supra*).

Thompson also states 'It will now be amply clear that the argument in which we are engaged turns to an important extent on the meaning of the word "control". By control Nicholson means regulation or government, whereas control in my view simply refers to the fact that no organism increases without limit.' To this Nicholson (1954*b*) has replied that the discontinuity and variability of habitats does not inconvenience organisms to any extent; 'most species', he says, 'are well adapted to cope with such fragmentation'. These adaptations, in his view, enable animals to occupy fully all favorable sites and in these sites the populations are governed by density reactions.

We feel that Nicholson's view on this oversimplifies the case. However, for a density-governing mechanism to be a key feature of natural control, thus giving realism to the concept even in variable environments, it is not necessary that conditions be constant. It is only necessary that the conditions do not vary so often and so widely as to disengage or preclude specific regulation at a characteristic level. Thus, vedalia controls cottony-cushion scale in diverse climates throughout the world, as does *Cactoblastis* control several species of *Opuntia* in areas similarly diverse and widespread.

The Thompson–Nicholson argument revolves about the ability of a species to thrive under different degrees of fluctuating physical conditions of the environment. The ability to thrive involves the specific properties of the species, properties not only of the individual, but also of the group or population. To the degree that changes in the environmental conditions are sufficiently limited that the population is capable of fully compensating for changes in the stresses encountered, such change is unimportant to balance. With somewhat more violent change in the physical conditions of the environment, there will commonly occur a shift from the one balancing mechanism, with its characteristic equilibrium position, to other distinct mechanisms acting at either higher or lower equilibrium densities. Finally, the extrinsic environment may fluctuate so greatly that the ability of the population to compensate for varying stresses is no longer effective in maintaining any characteristic equilibria. At this time, states of balance or trends towards balance occur only momentarily, and imbalance is the rule.

It must be remembered also that, for simplicity, Nicholson assumes given genetic properties. There is evidence that gene flow may result in populations of quite different behaviour and physiology at different times and under different stresses (see Dobzhansky 1951; Franz 1952; Andrewartha and Birch 1954; and chapter 4).

Thompson argues that 'balance' is an improper concept for employment as Nicholson uses it, since populations do not exist in such balance—they merely vary (a view shared by Uvarov 1931).

Nicholson recognizes diversity and fluctuation in the environmental setting, but, in explaining his concept of natural control of an animal organism, he necessarily emphasizes the isolated, interacting biotic elements, while other factors of the environment are presumed to be relatively calm, or at least not disturbing. He also assumes that populations of animals possess powers of compensation for the effects of such mortality stresses as are encountered in the real situation, such compensation deriving from their ability to adapt to environmental stresses and from their high reproductive capacities. Hence, regardless of the diversity and fluctuations of the environment Nicholson feels that balance, in Nicholson's sense, is usually more characteristic than the perpetual disturbance of balance.

Nicholson maintains that as density increases, density-induced reactions are invoked that check increase; that resultant populations thereafter cannot be said to be determined (with respect to density) solely by other factors of the environment acting on the population independently of density. Admittedly, such subsequent actions may cause more or less sharp increases or decreases in abundance for longer or shorter periods of time, but to ascribe the determination of density to these density-independent factors ignores the fact that the density levels acted upon have already been determined, and repeatedly so in past history.

Holling (1961) has recently presented a thought-provoking analysis of predator performance, the term 'predator' correctly including entomophagous parasites. Comparing Nicholson and Bailey's (1935) and Watt's (1959) treatments relating to predator response to predator density, he commented that although the exploitation component is more reasonably handled by Nicholson and Bailey, Watt's treatment includes interference which is not included in the Nicholson formula, and, furthermore, that the area of discovery, required by the Nicholson formula to be a constant, clearly is not a constant. Varley and Edwards (1957) and Huffaker (1958b) had previously discussed the inapplicability of a constant area of discovery, the former authors presenting analytical evidence. Watt's formula was found by Miller (1959, 1960) and Watt (1959) adequately to describe a wide variety of situations. Although admitting the utility of Watt's model, Holling pointed out that it includes an unreasonable treatment of the exploitation component, and that simple descriptive utility of a model does not necessarily imply a meaningful relation.

Probably the most cogent argument against the general concept of Nicholson is that it loses some of its significance in widely fluctuating environments, as our previous analysis shows (see also Watt 1959). Under such conditions, a given governing mechanism may be short-circuited almost before it begins to act and another mechanism, operating at quite different levels of abundance, may assume the governing role. This in turn may then be circumvented by still further violent change in the framework of requisites provided by the environment (Huffaker 1958a). Indications that such may happen in nature to the degree that population changes can be correlated well with changes in weather, but not with action of governing agencies, have led Thompson (1939, 1956), Andrewartha and Birch (1954), Milne (1957), Reynoldson (1957), Cloudsley–Thompson (1957), and others to suggest that populations may be controlled for very long periods without density-dependent mechanisms becoming involved (see further chapter 4).

Most of these authors recognize density-geared actions to a degree but some of them do not think it realistic to apply such a conception, or at least not universally so, to natural populations. L. C. Birch has said, in private conversation, that even if the population base on which such density-independent mortality factors act has at some time been determined by governing mechanisms, the ecologist studying a population is interested in interpreting the changes in density that he observes during a given period. Birch's objective is specific; it does not refute the special role of the density-geared mechanism. Therefore, the results obtained during such a period of limited study cannot properly be used to reject the concept. (See chapter 4 regarding the criticisms of Andrewartha and Birch, 1954, of the concept of density-dependence.)

The only explanation seemingly alternative to the concept of density-dependence is based on the idea that in natural environments change in the favourability of conditions is incessant and of marked complexity in time and place. Thus, favourability may change to unfavourability before populations are checked by reactions induced by their own densities, and, likewise, unfavourability may change to favourability before populations are annihilated, whether or not there is a lessening of density-dependent stresses as density falls. Thompson (1939, 1956), Andrewartha and Birch (1954), and, to a degree Reynoldson (1957) and Schwerdtfeger (1958), among others, think that this 'balance in the environment' makes it superfluous to postulate that density-dependent actions must be invoked.

Against this view, Nicholson (1958) presented logical argument with which we agree, and Solomon (1957) has commented that no one has shown just how such an explanation could conceivably function to *regulate* densities. If, on the average, in any general areas presumed to be exactly balanced as to periods of favourability and unfavourability, there is any change in the environment or in the adaptive properties of the animal rendering the environment even slightly more favourable than otherwise, the population would gradually increase to infinitely high levels even if along a tortuous and vacillating path. If more often unfavourable, the trend would be to annihilation. For conditions to be so exactly balanced while undergoing perhaps even violent fluctuations, requires from us a viewpoint of climate or of edaphic factors, or of the invariability of the organism, contrary to experience. In such a conception, species are truly balanced on a knife edge.

This idea is perhaps derived from the notion that a species' capacity for reproduction is, through evolution, exactly fitted to just equal these violently fluctuating stresses of the physical environment. A little reflection will show that no such species would ever have evolved. A form which had no plasticity, no very great reserve in reproductive capacity against these purely density-independent stresses, with their intensities varying in time and in space, would be lost if it ever faced any degree of density-induced pressure, and this of course includes the action of most natural enemies and shortage of shelter or food occasioned by super-abundance.

Concerning this balance of the environment, which is essentially equivalent to the random or heterogeneity hypothesis, Cole (1957) stated that a population would very quickly 'random walk itself to exhaustion.' Cole adds, 'Whatever view we may hold regarding the terminology of regulating factors, it is clear that in a given environment of constant carrying capacity the governing factors must, at some level, exert greater restraint on a denser population than is exerted on some less dense population which is still able to grow.' Cole then suggested that an auto-regulatory mechanism, inhibitive in nature, is required and that this governing factor is a function of density plus the other conditions of the environment—a view in sharp contrast with his earlier criticism (1955) of the reality of auto-regulatory mechanisms of Smith (1935) and Nicholson (1933, 1954b). Cole's statements are the very essence of the density-dependent philosophy, as is the statement of Milne (1957) that intraspecific competition is the only factor assured of producing ultimate regulation. Yet, intraspecific 'inhibition' (to use a more inclusive term than 'competition') can come about in more ways than Milne recognizes as such. His contention that the ultimate factor is seldom evoked is but a relative guess. However, even if, as he implies, it is rarely evoked, it still performs a governing role.

In the presentation which follows in chapter 4 there is considerable agreement with the views of Nicholson (1933, 1954b), Smith (1935), and Solomon (1957), but there are also incorporated certain concepts of Thompson (1929a, 1939, 1956), Andrewartha and Birch (1954), and others. With Nicholson and Smith, we contend that density-dependent actions are commonly very real, the tendency always present, and that they have a very special importance, if no more nor less so than density-unrelated forces. We recognize that chance factors may have very significant and prolonged effects, but we believe that for most natural populations thorough study would reveal that density-dependent mechanisms are involved in association with the variations in density, or the magnitude of the mean about which the variations occur.

RECENT EMPHASIS OF EXPERIMENTAL STUDIES

During the past twenty-five years there has been an encouraging combination of the theoretical, mathematical approach with empirical studies, and, as well, a greatly improved approach to experimental analysis of natural populations.

Regarding the former, the work of Gause (1934) and Gause, Smaragdova, and Witt (1936) is outstanding in integrating the mathematical approach with controlled experimentation. The works of Stanley (1953), Park (1955), Neyman, Park, and Scott (1956), and Watt (1955) on *Tribolium*, Utida (1953a, 1955, 1957) on *Callosobruchus*, Nicholson (1957) on *Lucilia*, and Slobodkin and Richman (1956) on *Daphnia*, are also important. The work of Watt, Nicholson, and Slobodkin coincided in showing the existence of internal compensatory and self-regulatory reactions to destruction by external forces.

Perhaps the most promising path out of the labyrinth of discussion and debate on population dynamics is to be found in studies of actual populations under laboratory and field conditions. Since it has been proposed by some that populations may be regulated simply by the heterogeneity of the environment and by others that density-dependent mechanisms are invoked, it is important that means are available for testing such views. Since, for instance, it is in varying environments, or in ones of 'marginal occupancy' that the 'heterogeneity' hypothesis is said especially to apply (Reynoldson 1957), study can be concentrated in marginal environments as suggested by Reynoldson (*loc. cit.*) and by Smith (1935). The technique used by Nicholson (1954*a*) and Hairston (1957) is to depress one population by application of external force and to observe whether the reduced population then exhibits a compensatory rise in density above that experienced by the control population during the same period of time, or remains indefinitely at correspondingly lower densities than the control population. By this method, or by adding large numbers *to* a population, it is easy to tell whether some density-dependent factor is in operation, but this alone may not reveal what that factor is. In fact, the compensatory resurgence of insect pest populations following applications of insecticides is so universal that the technique is hardly required except in marginal situations where existence of density-dependent factors is presumed to be absent.

Huffaker (1958*b*), Burnett (1958*a*, 1958*b*) and Pimentel (1961) have also experimentally considered the role of dispersion of hosts as a parameter in host–parasite and predator–prey relations. The results suggest that such differences in dispersion may account for significant differences in population dynamics.

The method of controlled field experimentation has been developed in recent years by entomologists. The results have not only been a clear proof of the efficacy of natural enemies in population regulation of insect pests, but, as well, the roles of quality of food and certain weather factors have become more clear (see chapter 14, section on 'Evaluation of Effectiveness of Natural Enemies'). Smith and DeBach (1942) point to the necessity for experimental field studies in an evaluation of the forces of natural control, suggest certain techniques to be used, and present examples. Additional 'check methods' have been developed since and the fact established that certain natural enemies do regulate their hosts at low densities, examples being various pests of citrus, strawberries, avocados, and apples (DeBach 1951, 1958*b*; Dowden, Jaynes, and Carolin 1953; Huffaker and Kennett 1956; Fleschner, Hall, and Ricker 1955; Lord 1956). These studies involved the use of chemical, mechanical, or biological removal, inhibition, or exclusion of parasites or predators from certain portions of the habitat, and a comparison of population trends in the natural-enemy-free portions with trends in the natural-enemy-present portions (for details see chapter 14).

An additional important method of analysis has been extensively employed by Canadian forest entomologists in recent years. This can only be touched upon here, but the method basically is the recording of causes of mortality by age classes, and the use of such data over several generations in time and from many sites. The object is not only to reveal the factors accounting for specific portions of total mortality at given times and places and thus affecting *changes* in density, but, as well, to learn if the intensity of specific mortality factors varies with population density, and how it varies. Thus, Smith's (1935) dictum that only by showing such relationships can we uncover the factors regulating population densities is a primary object of this method. Using such methods, Morris (1959) reported the uncovering of a single, key predictive factor for populations of the black-headed budworm, *Acleris variana* (Fern.) (see also Holling 1959).

CHAPTER 4

The Concept and Significance of Natural Control

C. B. HUFFAKER AND P. S. MESSENGER

INTRODUCTION

THE OBSERVED FACT that species of organisms do not increase indefinitely in abundance or in range has its roots in both abiotic and biotic causes. Biological control of insects as a practice arose from observations that biotic factors, principally entomophagous parasites, predators, and pathogens, are capable of suppressing many pests and thus preventing serious damage to our crops and products. In recent years it has been strikingly demonstrated that the use of various agricultural chemicals may cause many previously innocuous insects and mites to become serious pests. This is usually found to be due to the curtailment of the enemies of such pests (see chapter 17).

To understand the limitations and potentialities of natural enemies that affect the biological control of insect pests we must relate their action to all forces of environment affecting either their own success or that of the species they attack. Thus, it is necessary to consider all factors which contribute to the abundance of organisms. This chapter is devoted to our views on the integration of these forces in natural control.

Natural control, as defined in chapter 3, involves the combined actions of the whole environment in the maintenance of characteristic population densities. Various authors have referred to the existence of these characteristic densities by use of the term 'balance,' 'balance of nature,' or 'balance of animal populations.' But the 'balance' referred to by these authors seems to involve different ideas, different mechanisms, and different characteristics. Some refer mainly to the limitations on densities of natural populations, some refer to results of density regulatory mechanisms, while others include factors in the environment that tend to disturb population densities. Hence, we first explain the kinds of 'balance,' then discuss the roles and interactions of the various factors of environment, and we use four illustrations (see figures 6, 7, 8, and 9) of our view of the integration of such a complex of forces. We then elaborate on the roles of both density-dependent factors and abiotic conditions, presenting some examples of the way in which

74

natural control has come about. Lastly, we discuss the total environment and the role of natural enemies, the importance of dispersal, and genetic aspects of natural control.

THE KINDS OF 'BALANCE'

Since the numbers and kinds of animals and plants are dependent upon the evolutionary past, natural control rests on a base of evolution. If there are many kinds utilizing a resource there must be fewer individuals of a given kind. As the pattern of evolution has unfolded there has been seen to exist a balance between the many forms of opposing elements in nature. Evolution leads to the origin of new forms to fill new roles or to fill old ones more efficiently. Thus, there is a tendency towards increasing biotic complexity of communities as new resources, and thus new potential roles and interactions are added.

The characteristics of a species originate in adjustment to the total environment. There arise interdependencies between different kinds of organisms, such that certain species exist in numbers related to those of others in the ecosystem. We define 'ecosystem' as *the interacting system composed of all the living organisms and their non-living environment, in an area sufficiently large to permit the characteristic exchanges of energy and perpetuation of the component organisms.*

To carry the concept of stability or homeostasis a little further than was done in chapter 3, organisms whose interrelations are such that their contribution to the ecosystem is one of marked instability would tend to be replaced by other species which utilize the resources in a more stable, efficient manner and which disrupt the community and thus the habitat less. We must also remember that evolution is a continuing thing and what we see is not a final result.

Herbert Spencer's concept of greater *stability of heterogeneous* systems is generally subscribed to by modern ecologists (Voûte 1946; Solomon 1949; Odum 1953; Richards 1955; Huffaker and Kennett 1956; MacArthur 1955; Klomp 1958a; Elton 1958; Holling 1959). The greater complex of checks and balances existing in complex biotic communities makes for greater stability within the species population and the ecosystem itself. Since the various species of allied forms, competitors, and natural enemies associated with a given species population are differentially affected by changed conditions, existence of a complex of natural enemies, for example, is increasing assurance against complete numerical escape by a species from its enemies, particularly with a change in conditions.

Assuming a given genetic composition,[1] the broad general 'balance of nature' results from the interaction of two basic parameters: (1) the supplying of a limited amount of the requisites for life by the environment, and (2) the utilization of those requisites. A species' competitors, its natural enemies, and those forms necessary to its success and abundance either retard or enhance the utilization of those requisites. These living things can only exist in the biotic community if the abiotic environment is on the average favourable.

---

[1] Regarding the suggested role in population dynamics of variations in genetic composition of a population, see later section.

It is thus obvious that one aspect of restrictiveness in the numbers of organisms involves only the first of the two parameters. The earth and living things being what they are, there occur natural limitations in the range of climatic and edaphic conditions available to the organism. The organism, in turn, is intrinsically limited in capacity to exist in these varied conditions and to utilize the various resources (Thompson 1929a, 1939 ,1956). If a population always utilized some particular type of requisite limiting it, such as nesting sites, without interference in this usage by the abundance of its own kind, i.e., without any density-induced suppression of either the quantity of the requisite or the efficiency in which utilization is effected, then the abundance of organisms would be simply limited by this fixed environmental capacity. In such case, 'balance' would appear to depend solely on the level of the requisite. In such a balance, the concept of density-dependence as a necessary element in the production of such balance is superfluous (Nicholson 1958; Huffaker 1958a).

If limiting resources were not themselves bound within limits but progressively increased indefinitely, then, so far as those resources alone were concerned, the population would progressively increase indefinitely at a rate commensurate with the increase in the limiting resource. There would be no determinateness except at a given time, even though the population could be said to be continuously maintained in balance in relation to the conditions. Thus, it is not density-dependence which prevents indeterminateness on an *a priori* basis. It is the limited capacity of environment which does so. With natural populations, however, we cannot visualize a situation in which density-governing reaction does not have a meaningful role of modifying or adjusting density in time to the conditions prevailing, and which is involved in the mortality of surpluses. Thus, Thompson's (1929a, 1939) concept of balance is an essential element of natural control. Yet, Nicholson's (1933, 1954b) view on balance concerns a more precise relationship of a different nature, involving the mechanisms governing the balance of populations in relation to given environmental conditions.

Within the broad concept of balance of Thompson, which we view not as balance but as natural control, there are possibilities of both stable and unstable states. Weather variations, for example, may be very great in some regions and narrowly circumscribed in others. In the former case the environment is unstable and a greater number of species populations will experience imbalance or instability due to disturbances by weather. Contrariwise, if the abiotic forces are more constantly favourable or stable, there is nothing to check indefinite increase except some eventual form of action related to densities. The engagement of such mechanisms would not be short-circuited or changed in kind by change in the environmental conditions or capacity. The population would exist at a characteristic equilibrium of abundance of realistic nature—a true balance as Nicholson (1954b) uses the term, that is, *the tendency of corrective return to an equilibrium position upon displacement.* The inherent biotic interactions, even in a constant physical environment, may, and usually do, cause population fluctuations about the equilibrium position. This is the form of balance which we view as the result of specific mechanisms.

Intracommunity Balance and Intraspecific Balance

'Balance' in the broad sense is a relative thing. It implies that forces or things exist at characteristic levels—in the absolute sense or in relation to other forces or things. The magnitudes of levels of abundance are not today almost zero and to-morrow infinitely great, nor is absolute stability probable. Environments change, as do the animals themselves, and hence the balance of favourability and un-favourability is altered. It is, however, surprising that some argue that the word 'balance' has no meaning because the biota of an area has varied markedly from one geologic period to another.

Intracommunity balance is very complex, particularly in very heterogeneous communities, but, by the same token, there is greater stability in the complex communities (*vide supra*). Insect pests are often more severe on crops or in pure-stand timber than on host plants in complex stands of natural vegetation. However, in the more simple communities, single environmental factors that dominate changes in density or can be used to predict future densities can often be demon-strated (DeBach 1958*b*), although the key factor may vary in time and place. In the complex communities more controlling factors are present and more potentialities for compensating actions. If one enemy fails, another may take its place, even if at a somewhat higher level of prey density. Yet, even in a rather complex situation, Morris (1959) has shown by means of single-factor analysis that single environ-mental elements may also dominate changes in density.

The hypothetical situation described on pages 90–91 relative to the strawberry plant, the cyclamen mite, and the cyclamen mite predator is only suggestive of the high degree of integration in complex communities. The interrelations of insects and their plant hosts in this respect are further discussed in chapter 22.

In economic entomology the researcher necessarily concentrates on a single pest species (Andrewartha and Birch 1954). We are thus interested in intraspecific balance, although we recognize that this may be affected by the general balance or imbalance of the community of which a given population is a part. However, by use of the 'check method' of analysis we are able to establish the effect a natural enemy has on a given population, even if the other conditions are composed of unknown quantities (see chapter 14).

Thus, we are concerned with the mechanics of natural control of single species populations in nature. We consider a 'natural population' as *a group of interbreeding individuals of the same species that occupies a natural area of sufficient size for the population to reproduce, maintain continuity in time, and display such characteristics as growth, dispersion, fluctuation and turnover, dispersal, and genetic variability.*

THE MECHANICS OF NATURAL CONTROL

The environment acts as a totality, and the elements of this whole are in im-portant, sometimes delicate, interaction. In classifying roles or factors we tend to break apart the inseparableness of the environment which lies at the core of natural control. Yet, we need to differentiate between those forces and occurrences which are delicately geared to density and those which are not, in order to understand the essential nature of their roles.

Natural control has two checking components. First, there is the limit to the general degree of favourability and to variations in favourability, depending upon the basic climatic and edaphic elements of a region or, more particularly, for specific locales. This is coupled with the fact that species have intrinsic limitations (*vide supra*). Secondly, for any given level of conditions as ultimately set by the environment, governing mechanisms check populations within such a framework. The levels of needed resources, for example, do not determine densities in simple fashion; if so, there would be no need to conceive of 'governing mechanisms.' Rather, for most populations, if not all, density-induced reaction, or inhibition, greatly modifies or reduces the population densities from the maximal levels potentially permitted (see section on examples, page 98). The facts of biology strongly support the view that: (1) there are forces in nature limiting population potentials which, considered alone, occur largely independent of the density of a population concerned; (2) there are other forces affecting populations, the intensities of which bear progressive relationships with density; (3) the forces of (1) do not limit numbers in simple fashion, although they may directly alter concurrent densities; and (4) the forces of (2) govern densities in relation to the framework set by the former.

The Basic Mechanisms and Elements of Balance

To attain and maintain balance there exist in nature two powerful resilient forces, which are, in a sense, aligned in opposition. These are high inherent procreative ability and density-dependent actions restricting procreation, the latter most characteristically being represented by interspecific and intraspecific competition. The repressive agencies of any given environment are made up of many forces opposing population growth, but those repressive forces which act independently of density have no qualities in the sense of sensitive resilience paralleling the great resilience in procreative ability, i.e., they have no special role as a mechanism of balance.

These two resilient forces, then, come into play as the conditions of the environment, including the densities of populations, vary, with high reproduction usually being more powerful at positions of low density and with high mortality or low natality from density-induced causes being of increasing significance as densities increase and approach their actual or potential maxima. At full saturation of a given environmental capacity, the total resistance to population growth would automatically be sufficient to balance deaths with births. Since we consider the pattern of utilization of available places, and the elimination of surplus numbers, (see figure 3, chapter 3), as some function of density, there must be at least one component of environmental repressive forces which is geared to density. All the resistant or repressive factors of the environment need not act in such a way for populations to be maintained in such balance. It is only necessary that at least one factor act in this way. We may call such actions density-dependent action (Smith 1935), density-induced reaction (Nicholson 1933, 1954*b*), or density-induced inhibition (Huffaker 1958*a*). We define this element, the 'governing mechanism' or 'density-dependent action,' as *the actions of repressive environmental factors, collectively or singly, which intensify as the population density increases and relax as this density falls.* The population acted upon is the focal point.

To clarify our terminology, in addition to classifying mortality factors, or other direct repressive factors of the environment, according to whether their action or occurrence is related to the density of the population acted upon, as did Smith (1935), we also classify the actions of occurrences of a general nature according to their relation to density. The category of general forces which occur and act without regard to density we term 'conditioning forces' defined as, *environmental factors or agents which, uninfluenced by density, contribute to the setting or fixing of a framework of potential environmental capacity or affect interim population realization when capacity is not attained.* Thus, conditioning forces include not only the *direct* density-independent repressive actions but, as well, the *indirect* ways in which such density-uninfluenced forces operate in natural control, that is, indirect in that the action is not direct on the individuals of a population. We restrict our usage of 'density-independent actions' to the direct, repressive aspect in order not to confuse this terminology with past usage. However, we wish to point out that the role of the physical environment, for example, as it waxes and wanes entirely uninfluenced by density, sets the framework of potentialities, and this is distinct from the usage of density-independent mortality factors of Smith (1935). Obviously, climatic difference can be the reason why regulation occurs at much lower levels in one environment than in another (see figure 6).

However, of the two types of rather *direct* repressive forces, density-independent factors and density-dependent factors, only the latter can govern densities in any real sense of the word, for the former occur in a manner unrelated to the density of the populations on which they act.

Of course weather may kill individuals which have not reached a tolerant stage of development, and in dense populations a higher proportion of such susceptible stages may be present. Yet weather has not acted in a density-dependent manner. It has not and never does, in itself, act as a density-dependent mechanism. For example, competition for food may be the reason for the high proportion of retarded individuals which weather kills. It should now be clear that, although the role of density-dependent action is the governing of population densities within the potential environmental capacity, such density-dependent actions do not determine that potential. Furthermore, the direct density-independent actions may be important in determining average densities during a given period of time, particularly for species which spend much time recovering from catastrophe, or they may be involved in interactions, but such actions do not determine the equilibrium position associated with a given governing mechanism.[1]

[1] Average density may be closely correlated with the equilibrium position, or only slightly so.

'Environmental capacity' is *the level of population for a species which an environment can sustain without permanent change.* We do not view this concept as having a restricted meaning. Maximal capacity would be dependent upon the food and space present, but the actual capacity of an environment may be decidedly different. For example, the actual capacity for a species where a very effective predator exists may be determined by the interactions between the physical conditions, cover, and the qualities of the predator and the prey in relation to the whole environment, and not simply by the level of food or necessary space. Thus, environmental capacity may be determined rather simply or it may arise from the most complex biotic and abiotic relations.

The conditioning (density-uninfluenced) forces of environment are ultimate in nature and predominantly abiotic, although biotic factors, such as host resistance, or quantity and quality of food, may be involved, and also there may be important biotic interactions with the abiotic forces. There may be a general waxing and waning of potential capacity and a direct variation in population size with variations in the conditioning forces.

Schematic Representation and Discussion of Natural Control

The present view of natural control does not minimize the importance of forces which are conducive to changes in density in a manner independent of that density. Rather, density-uninfluenced changes in abundance, due to conditioning forces, the density-governed tendency towards re-establishment of characteristic abundances following the effects of such density-uninfluenced changes, or the tendency towards the maintenance of characteristic abundance in the absence of influences unrelated to density are all common elements in natural control. The importance of each element in the practical view depends on the circumstances.

The genetic properties of a species are an intrinsic parameter of population dynamics. For simplicity, the average qualities may be taken as relatively fixed. These genetic properties are a part of the compensatory potential of a population to varying kinds and levels of stress. (Regarding changes in genetic composition, see later section.) Although a population may possess remarkable powers of adapting to or compensating for stresses encountered and may thus maintain a characteristic density in relation to the conditions prevailing, this self-determining action is necessarily restricted—the limits to its influence being determined by the conditioning forces.

Competition between different species (at the same trophic level) is, or may be, very important either in determining a species' distribution or its abundance at particular times and places (see later discussion), but for simplicity, there is assumed some characteristic dominance or relative sharing of a common requisite by each such species, and discussions generally are concerned with the utilization of whatever amount a given species characteristically has available to it. This, of course, is not altogether satisfactory, for there may be important density interactions between two species. Competition with another species for the same food, for example, may be an important variable and, obviously, prior use of the food by a competitor would preclude another's use of it and *vice versa* (Nicholson 1954*b*).

A clarification of the superimposed positions of *direct* and *indirect* causes of population restriction is important. Nicholson (1954*b*) referred to the action of climatic and edaphic factors as the 'ultimate' determinant and governing mechanisms as the 'immediate' factor. Huffaker (1958*a*) used the terms 'ultimate' and 'proximate' in this sense in order to stress, as did Solomon (1949) and Nicholson (1958), that the importance of the forces, which determine the pervading conditions of environments or which set potentials, is in no sense subordinated to the importance of governing mechanisms. It is the distinct *roles* of these forces which are emphasized. Thus, the conditions which set the potential levels of resources (and other conditions) and the mechanisms which govern their use are mutually compatible, not contrary, explanations. The word 'potential' is used since the actual (original) level of a resource (food, for example) governing the abundance of a predator may later be determined by that predator as a marked modification (reduction) from the potential level. Each of these roles forms a part of natural control, our understanding of which is based in part on the ideas of Friederichs (1927) and Schwerdtfeger (1941) who regard the whole ecosystem as *determining*.

Regarding the direct and indirect actions, Huffaker (1958*a*) stressed, for example, that during a cold period an individual may die as the direct result of cold and at the same time as a result of competition for favourable places to live. It is not easy to disassociate the direct and indirect aspects. There is much evidence that deaths due to cold at a particular time may be largely unassociated with an *immediate* prehistory of density effects. Some of the individuals, at least, are killed because of genetic variability in tolerance, or because they just happen to be situated in unfavourable places, or just happen to be in a stage of development or physiology more susceptible at the time. Chance factors must be involved to some extent. On the other hand, organisms have adaptive behavioural patterns presumably beneficial to them in concentrating somewhat in places offering better shelter, and perhaps more decidedly in these places this has resulted in greater density-induced pressures from simple crowding, food shortage, etc., causing population decline or emigration. Furthermore, past cold periods have tended to emphasize this concentration at the favourable places (by killing those in other places). Thus, the past history of density-induced pressures is a parameter of the base level of population on which the direct action of the cold acts at a given time. There is here an interaction between the instrument of death (cold) and a density-influenced seeking of shelters.

In natural control both balance and the disturbance of balance are involved. The abiotic environment has a very important role in either condition. If an environment is sufficiently stable that a given density-governing mechanism is the dominant cause of the changes in density, then the conditioning forces act mainly in an indirect way. These forces determine or greatly influence the potentials in the environment and the properties of the organisms, and thus influence the levels at which the density-dependent mechanism governs. It is assumed in this example that the direct influences of changes in weather are not sufficient to alter population size significantly. Under the more variable conditions, weather may alter the specific kind of density-governing mechanism, or the degree of its operation in time, or it may significantly alter population size directly.

In all environments there must eventually come a time when the limitations to density are imposed automatically as density increases and as numbers approach the limiting capacity of some material resource or the point of density-induction of some other controlling stress. However, this need not occur continuously, or at every generation, or within any other specified period of time. Although we believe that most populations are under more or less continuous pressure of varying degree from density-dependent forces, we recognize that the direct density-independent actions may greatly alter population size (see later discussion) and, in addition, that, in a multitude of ways, weather, for example, may indirectly alter populations (see section on abiotic conditions, page 104). It is understood that, acting entirely independently of density, weather, for example, may directly destroy individuals or contribute to greater or lesser rates of natality, and that these actions are exceedingly important in determining average population size, particularly during interim periods following or prior to highly significant density-induced actions. As Solomon (1955) stated, some species spend most of their time recovering from catastrophe, and hence the direct actions of weather would be of great importance relative to the changes in population size. But the fact is inescapable that the base level from which such changes depart has been set by a prehistory of repeated curtailment from density-dependent causes.

To represent our view of the way the complex of forces operates in natural control we present four illustrations (figures 6, 7, 8, and 9). Figure 6 is taken from Smith (1955) and shows schematically and hypothetically how the rate at which density-dependent mortality increases with density determines the final density level of such a population at equilibrium. It shows also that the level of density at which the population is governed is also a function of the environment (compare environments A and B). Regardless of differences in environments or differences in the rate at which mortality increases with density, the final level of population density is a function of the density-dependent governing action *in relation to environmental potential*. This graph deals with the magnitude of equilibria positions and not with fluctuations in density. Indeed, Smith (1935, 1955) made it clear that he was considering only average densities and not fluctuations in density, which later, he stated, would have to be considered as a separate topic.

Our use of the linear relationship between increase in mortality and density in figure 6, as mentioned in a footnote, chapter 3, is subject to the criticism (e.g., Andrewartha and Birch 1954) that the linear relation is not proved, and may not properly represent the growth of real populations. Smith's usage of this linear relationship was based on the Verhulst–Pearl logistic formula. It is true that in specific cases neither natality nor mortality could be expected to vary with density in an exact linear manner. Yet, the linear relation as used in figure 6 is the simplest symbolic assumption as a generalized representation for all possible cases. Smith's

1935, 1955) text definitions of the variation in mortality with increase in density expressed no such linear relation, nor were his fundamental positions dependent upon it.

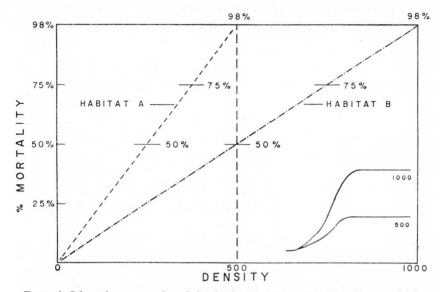

FIGURE 6. Schematic representation relating density-dependent and density-independent mortality factors of natural control to the magnitude of population density in two different environments. Actually, a density-independent component of mortality should cut across the base of this illustration between zero and, say, the 25 per cent mortality level. (After Smith 1955.)

Smith (1955) theorized that the rate at which the *probability* of premature mortality increases with density determines the density of the population at equilibrium. If the probability increases rapidly as in habitat A, figure 6, the population density will be low (i.e., 500); if it increases slowly, the density at the equilibrium position will be high (i.e., 1,000). This explains in terms of total mortality why this hypothetical, generalized species is abundant in some habitats and rare in others. According to this theory, the introduction of an effective parasite or predator increases the rate at which mortality increases with density and, hence, the equilibrium position is therefore lower. This graph also indicates why the percent mortality is not an index of the importance of a mortality factory. It is seen that any given percentage mortality occurs at a lower density in habitat A than in habitat B.

While this graph presents the role of *mortality* in relation to density under different environmental conditions, there may also be a relation between both *natality* and *emigration* and density. If we ignore emigration, we may say that in total the relation of density to the checking of population increase involves the influence of density on natality/mortality ratios. With some mammalian populations, natality may be a very important parameter (Errington 1954), whereas mortality carries the greatest share in this role, perhaps, with most insect populations (Huffaker and Kennett 1956).

The purpose of figures 7 and 8, on the other hand, is to depict for various types of environments the causes of *changes* in density, rather than the magnitude of equilibrium densities, and to relate these changes in density to both the governing

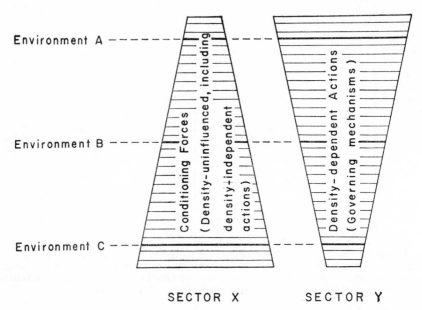

SECTOR X   SECTOR Y

FIGURE 7. Schematic representation relating the density-dependent and density-uninfluenced environmental forces of natural control to changes in population density under different types of environments.

Relative widths of sector lines indicate relative correlation of corresponding forces with changes in population densities in time or in space. Sectors X and Y are considered together as parallel parameters.

Environment A: Physical factors continuously favourable; heterogeneous plant life; biotic factors predominate; natural enemies, food, suitable habitats numerous. Microhabitats spatially contiguous.

Environment B: Intermediate between A and C.

Environment C: Physical factors fluctuate excessively; intermittently favourable; plant life tends towards less complex stands, biotic factors, natural enemies, food, suitable habitats fewer, or not continuously present. Microhabitats more scattered, non-contiguous.

Sector X—Conditioning forces (density-uninfluenced, including density-independent repressive actions): climatic and edaphic conditions, light, protective places, quality and potential levels of food, conditions for existence of allies, direct competitors, parasites, predators, pathogens.

Sector Y—Density-dependent (governing) actions: competition for food, shelter, breeding places, density-induced inhibitive reactions.

mechanisms and the conditioning forces, which latter includes the density-independent repressive actions. Again, these illustrations are symbolic. The truncated triangles of figure 7 and the straight lines of figure 8 depicting the degree of cause and effect correlation between the type of the environmental forces and the fluctuations in density are the simplest approximations representative of all possible cases. The geometric form representing specific cases would vary greatly (see later discussion).

Since the direct repressive actions of a given environmental framework tending to preclude population growth, either through natality or mortality, may be factored into the two kinds of actions, density-dependent and density-independent, each of these kinds of actions influence the density of the populations. Hence, *changes* in density may be significantly correlated with changes in these various factors. Within any given environmental capacity the density-dependent (governing) actions and the density-independent actions may affect population numbers simultaneously, or continuously, or at different and distinct times and places. In either case, either kind of density-influencing action will possess some degree of correlation with the concurrent density of the population. In addition, there may be a significant waxing and waning of the given environmental capacity, potential, or framework by the conditioning forces, entirely independent of densities.

In figure 7, the relative degree of this correlation for each kind of density-influencing action is given for generalized types of environments by the relative lengths of the horizontal lines. It is not expected that all the conditions detailed as conducive to maximal correlation (environment A for density-dependent actions and environment C for the conditioning forces) would in fact be satisfied or required in a single case. In some environments, typified by environment A, physical conditions of weather, climate, and soil are equable, the quantity and quality of the potential levels of food and shelter are optimal and ever-present, plant life is potentially abundant and heterogeneous, and natural enemies are numerous in variety. In such environments, therefore, biotic factors predominate and there will be a high degree of correlation between the intensity of action of these biotic factors and changes in population density. The correlation with temperature, humidity, rainfall, light, total potential quantity of food (but not the modified levels in event the level of plant food is reciprocally controlled by a user), and so on, will be low.

On the other hand, in environments such as C, physical factors fluctuate widely between favourability and unfavourability, plant life is less complex and characterized by fewer kinds of plants, food supplies (exclusive of use), are seasonal and limited in variety, and biotic factors are relatively few in kind. In such environments natural enemies are also few in kind, alternative foods for predators and parasites are less abundant, and habitats and shelters are scattered and less contiguous. In such conditions, insect species tend to be univoltine, and variations in population densities are commonly highly correlated with changes in weather, plant phenology, and seasonal abundance of food or adequate places to live. In such environments the changes in weather, for example, tend to dominate the situation in repeatedly short-circuiting or obscuring the tendency of density-dependent mechanisms to maintain any characteristic balance. Such changes may be so great as to alter the efficiency of specific governing mechanisms or to disengage a given mechanism entirely. This situation is characterized as disrupted balance, although the tendency for other mechanisms to assume governing roles at different thresholds of effectiveness is still present.

Other environments will be intermediate in this degree of relative correlation of population densities and the two general kinds of environmental factors. Such an intermediate environment is represented by B.

It is emphasized that in any environment there will be some influences on the populations by both types of environmental factors, hence, some degree of correlation of changes in abundance with both. As shown in figure 7, there is no environment where influences of either density-dependent or conditioning (density-uninfluenced) forces are completely lacking; hence, the truncation of both triangles.

It is imperative to keep in mind that what we here show schematically is correlation with *changes* in density. This sketch gives no explanation of average densities or equilibria positions from which the populations vary. Viewed in combination with figure 6, it does indicate the distinct roles of the density-dependent, governing mechanisms and the conditioning (density-uninfluenced) forces, which latter, in addition to altering population size directly, fix the potentials of capacity and thus influence the levels at which the density-dependent actions govern.

Where changes in density are highly correlated with changes in weather, it is probable that, perhaps correlated with each critical season, some governing mechanism is brought into play which, in conjunction with other factors of the environment, determines the characteristic density levels known to exist year after year. Hence, weather phenomena may determine population abundance directly through considerable portions of each year, but periodically or occasionally some regulatory (density-induced) process must be invoked to restore the 'feedback' connection between density and the repressive factors of the environment.

Figure 7 shows that formulae such as those of Lotka, Volterra, Nicholson, and Bailey, etc. (see chapter 3), applying to the governing actions under constant conditions, have particular significance under continuously favourable climatic conditions and less significance in environments varying markedly from favourability to unfavourability (Watt 1959). As is true in figure 6, in figure 7 also the conditioning force (left sector) and the governing mechanisms (right sector) are always considered as parallel parameters, taken together, although their *roles* are distinct. The density-modifying or conditioning forces, involving for example climatic and edaphic factors, affect the potentialities for existence of the organisms in the ecosystem. The conditions of general favourability as to temperature, humidity, terrain, light, pressure, protective features, and places for nests, etc., are examples. Also, the potential level of resources such as food, its quality, and resistance to attack are a part of this framework, although these are biotic features of the environment. Also included is the action of such forces in setting conditions of favourability to growth, reproduction, and longevity, independent of density effects, and the possibilities for existence of significant allies, direct competitors, predators, parasites, and pathogens.

The density-governing mechanisms include, separately or collectively (*vide supra*), all actions which increase in severity as the population acted upon increase in density: competition for food, shelter, or breeding places, density-induced inhibitions such as non-infectious disease syndromes, intraspecific strife, or the generation of heat or waste products which may contaminate or make the food or habitat unsuitable, and, indirectly, most actions of predators, parasites, and pathogens (see examples).

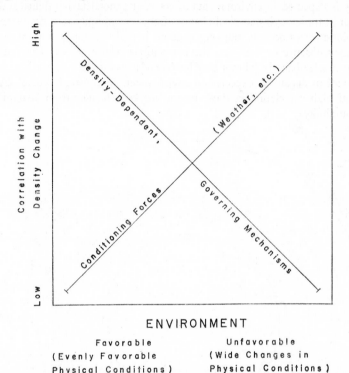

FIGURE 8. Conventional schematic representation showing the relation of density-dependent and the density-uninfluenced, conditioning forces of natural control to changes in population density under constantly favourable and widely fluctuating environments.

Considering the truncated triangles of figure 7, actual cases would not necessarily be represented by such figures. For example, constant conditions are not necessary for an effective natural enemy to exert essentially continuous effective control of a host species. Thus, a high degree of correlation of the action of vedalia with changes in density of its host holds over a very wide range in environments in time and place. This relation might be disrupted only by a very great variation in climatic conditions, for example. The appropriate geometric figures illustrating the concomitant roles of the conditioning forces and the density-dependent mechanisms regarding changes in density of the cottony-cushion scale would, in the case of the conditioning (density-uninfluenced) forces, be a long-necked figure with a more or less abrupt enlargement to a broad base. The converse of a long, broad-bodied figure tapering only near the base to a narrow but truncated base would represent the relative influences of the governing mechanism. All variations of such converse pairs of figures would be represented in depicting all populations.

Figure 8 illustrates more conventionally, but less completely, the relation shown in figure 7. In general, high correlation of the governing mechanisms with changes in density is expected in environments of constant general favourability and low correlation in those having marked changes from favourability to unfavourability. As the abiotic forces become more conspicuous in their waxing and waning, these changes may obscure or dominate the correlations relative to any characteristic governing mechanism. It follows that low correlation of the conditioning forces with changes in density is expected in environments of constant general favourability and high correlation in those having marked changes from favourability to unfavourability.

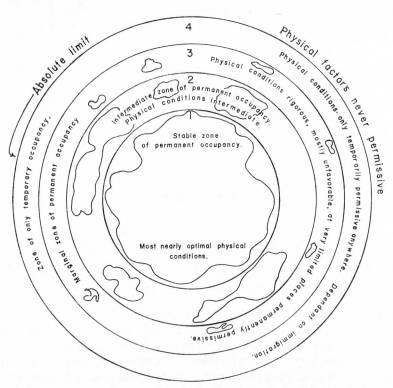

FIGURE 9. The geographic distribution of a species population and the interrelation of conditioning and regulating forces. Zones 1, 2, and 3 are comparable with environments A, B, and C, respectively, in figure 2. Irregular patches in each zone represent localized areas of relatively permanent favourability and the interspaces indicate room for waxing and waning of such areas in time.

Figure 9 illustrates schematically the relationship between the geographic distribution of a species population and the interrelatedness of conditioning and regulating factors. Each circle (zone) of the concentric series represents a type of environment, and the zones 1, 2, and 3 are comparable with environments A, B, C, respectively, of figure 2. The irregular patches in each zone represent localized areas of relatively permanent favourability as to physical conditions, and the interspaces represent the degree of waxing and waning of such areas in time. The relative sizes of these zones as shown here have no significance. One population may be characterized by existence mostly in areas like zone 1, while others may be limited largely to areas like zone 3.

The environment of zone 1 has nearly optimal climatic conditions, or at least conditions rather permitting increase in numbers generation after generation in the absence of density-induced stresses. In the environment of zone 4, at the other extreme, only hazardous temporary existence is possible.

In the environment of zone 1 essentially the total area is represented by maximum favourability in the conditioning framework of the environment; hence, there is little room for waxing and waning of the physical conditions to alter the population potentials. It follows that density-induced pressures constitute not only the regulating agency as to magnitude, but, as well, interactions resulting from such pressures are the main source of *changes* in density.

In the environment of zone 3, on the other hand, *permanently* favourable localized habitats are greatly reduced quantitatively, but the general unfavourability often is shifted to general temporary favourability. Thus, the waxing and waning of population potentials (conditioning aspects) is a dominant feature relative to population *change* in this zone, just as density-induced forces are dominant in the environment of zone 1. However, the *roles* of conditioning forces and density-induced regulating agencies in determining magnitudes in the permanently favourable areas of this zone are still the same as in the environments of zones 1 and 2. The two types of forces still act as inseparable twin parameters in determining population size. Also, the direct impact of climatic changes on existing populations for the marginal environment of zone 3 or intermediate environment of zone 2, although causing changes in density which may be largely independent of density, cannot be said to operate independent of the source of migrants from the favourable permanent habitats where density-induced regulation is quite pertinent. It is also true that in the environment of zone 4 where permanent existence is not possible, the waxing and waning of potentials may be such as to dwarf the impact of density-induced regulation with regard to *changes* in density. In this zone such regulation would come into play only temporarily and would not furnish any fixed characteristic lower limit—the lowest level being zero. In this zone density-induced regulation cannot serve one of its usual functions—that of tending to keep the population in being. However, this zone is not pertinent to regulation since permanent existence is not possible, and migrants from the more favourable areas are necessary to populate the area when favourability is temporarily permitted. For this reason we omitted this zone from figure 2.

HYPOTHETICAL EXAMPLE OF COMPLEXITY OF NATURAL CONTROL. The concept of natural control adopted here may be clarified if we assume known relations of cultivated conditions transposed to a hypothetical natural scene, for example, where wild strawberry plants are present under conditions relatively conducive to the cyclamen mite, *Steneotarsonemus pallidus* (Banks), and its predators, *Typhlodromus reticulatus* Oud. and *T. bellinus* Womer. The microenvironment required by the cyclamen mite relative to temperature and humidity, and the continuous maintenance of vigorous new shoot growth by the plants, would be only delicately maintained in natural situations. The strawberry plants would be subjected to competition by other plants. In the absence of *Typhlodromus*, the cyclamen mite may severely injure strawberry plants and this would influence the success of the strawberry in the habitat. Hence, in the absence of the predator, the abundance of the cyclamen mite is determined (partly self-determined) by a complex involving physical habitat favourability (the physical microenvironment of which is delicately affected by biotic actions), the competitive position of the strawberry in the plant community, and the role of cyclamen-mite feeding on this relation (Huffaker and Kennett 1956).

The *potential* level for strawberry plants in the absence of cyclamen mites would be different from that when cyclamen mites are present. That potential level would be altered by the cyclamen mite/strawberry interaction, and the cyclamen mite's abundance would also be determined by this ecosystem interaction. The level for cyclamen mites as so determined by the complex, and also the level of strawberry plants, would be affected if we introduce the predator element. We may say that all is restricted within a framework ultimately made possible by the abiotic environment, but what happens specifically may bear little relation to the maximal potentials thus permitted if the predator were not present. The more proximate factor, the predator, may dominate in determining the specific levels and the patterns of change within such exceedingly broad potentials. It would lower the stress of the cyclamen mite upon the strawberry plant and thus the latter would not be hindered in its competition with other plants. This results in increasing the density of strawberry plants per unit of area and therefore in tending to increase the cyclamen mites per unit of area except as this is offset by a great reduction by the predators of cyclamen mites per host plant within the area.

Within an environmental framework generally favourable to both, the predator governs the density of its host and, by feed-back mechanics, in turn is governed by that host density—a typical reciprocal, density-dependent relation. Thus, the predators determine the level of the requisite (the prey) for which they compete with others of their kind, and this relation is reciprocally geared to the inhibition resulting from the cyclamen mite's own increase in numbers which causes the build-up of predators and thus lessens the cyclamen mite's own chances of survival.

It would be tidy if we could say simply that the actual governing levels of all needs are supplied directly by the abiotic environment, but such is far from true; hence, we must be content with viewing self-inhibitive reactions in the utilization of requisites as the basic governing (adjusting) mechanism, but recognize that the level at which numbers are governed is very complex, indeed, and is a product of the ecosystem of which the populations are a part—with this including the parallel parameters of density-uninfluenced conditioning forces and the density-dependent mechanisms which govern in relation to those conditions.

Elaboration of the Role of Density-dependent Action

Because in biological control we are concerned with the prevention of high densities, our definition of a density-dependent or governing action (*vide supra*) includes only the direct, as opposed to the inverse, form of such relations. Yet we realize that many populations may be adversely affected by low densities such that below some level the disadvantages of low density outweigh the advantages per individual (Allee *et al.* 1949; Solomon 1953; Andrewartha and Birch 1954, pp. 334–37; Huffaker 1958a). Allee *et al.* (*loc. cit.*) termed this relation 'undercrowding.' It is a very important aspect of natural control (see definition, chapter 3) that, in general, with a total stress of a given level, the automatic lowering of the density-dependent part of that total stress (*vide supra*), lessens the probability that a population or species will reach such low levels that either undercrowding phenomena or catastrophe unrelated to density will endanger its existence. Thus, the criticism of Andrewartha and Birch (1954) of the density-dependent concept, because it does not assure against extinction, is improper (Huffaker 1958a). The idea of a 'guaranteed floor to decrease' is a misinterpretation of the role of density-dependent action.

Here, we discuss certain other criticisms made against Smith's (1935) classification of mortality factors as 'density-dependent' and 'density-independent,' and consequently against any concept which stresses density-induced effects. We point out, however, that our usage of density-dependent actions and density-independent actions may apply to natality and population movements as well.

It is very significant that Thompson's basic view (1928b, 1955) of the way in which an entomophagous parasite's capability of destroying a host population is *ordinarily* determined is just the opposite of that of Smith (1935) or Nicholson (1933). While Thompson (1955, p. 265) equates his usage with Smith's and recognizes '. . . the probability that the effective parasite reproductive rate will rise when hosts are abundant and fall when hosts are scarce . . .,' he nevertheless emphasizes and illustrates his contention that a parasite will usually, because of limited egg capacity, take only a constant number of hosts whether host density is high or low. This is clearly an inverse density-dependent action (Solomon 1958a), and operating in this manner, the parasite could not possibly serve as an effective control (see also chapter 14). Morris (1957) follows Thompson's reasoning, adopts much of the consequences of this conception, but covers himself somewhat by stating that the assumption that the number of hosts destroyed by parasites will be constant regardless of preceding mortality in the same generation is not realistic. To us it is *most* unrealistic, although we recognize that various factors, including satiated appetites or egg capacity, etc., may place a limit to the effective response of a natural enemy population to increase in density of the hosts or prey (see later section).

A seemingly attractive but misleading argument of Andrewartha and Birch (1954) against the use of these terms is that no factors of the environment act entirely independent of density. Here is a large element of truth, but when this is so there is interaction with density-dependent mechanisms. Milne (1957*b*) rebuts this contention of Andrewartha and Birch with several examples of environmental factors that act entirely independently of density. However, both Andrewartha and Birch (1954) and Milne (1957*b*) misinterpret the reference made by Howard and Fiske (1911) and Smith (1935) to the *constant* mortality from 'catastrophic' and 'density-independent' factors, respectively. Clearly, Howard and Fiske and Smith meant only that at a specific time at a specific place one particular occurrence of weather, for example, acting on two populations exactly equivalent in every respect except density, would kill the same percentage of a high population as a low one. To illustrate, we may use one of Milne's examples, with elaboration. If 10 cows on one grazing strip ate 10 per cent of the host plants in the strip, containing all the 1,000 insects on them, and if on the adjacent strip 10 cows ate 10 per cent of the host plants containing all the 100,000 insects on them, the cows took the same (constant) percentage of the insects under the two different densities of the adjacent strips. The factor would not have to take the same percentage when acting at some other time or place under other conditions, or at a different intensity of action, in order to satisfy the meaning originally stated.

The idea that the actions of all mortality factors of the environment are related to density is to us a misunderstanding of this type of phenomenon; the misunderstanding in part may stem from an erroneous idea of population density, on the one hand, and population size or population variability on the other (Andrewartha 1957; Solomon 1959). *The great logic of the density-dependent concept is that it focuses adequate attention on the part that its own density plays in the sequence of subsequent events relative to a given population. This role is distinct from, and equally important with, the role of those forces which basically change in ways very significant for the population, but which changes are themselves in no way dependent upon its density.*

Andrewartha and Birch (1954) correctly state that the assumption is wrong that climate controls populations near the limits of distributions, while density-dependent actions control events near the centres. As Huffaker (1958*a*) points out, in the practical view regarding *changes* in density, there is a greater dominance of climatic forces near margins of distributions and, on the contrary, a greater dominance of density-dependent forces near the centres or optimal areas of the range (*vide supra*, figure 9, and related discussion). Significant forces may vary greatly in kind, in intensity, in time, and in place. There is no imaginary line beyond which climate alone determines densities and within which density-dependent actions do so. This is a facet of the consideration of stable and unstable conditions with peripheral areas representing unstable environments (figures 7, 8, and 9; Glen 1954*a*).

The view is also commonly encountered that the abiotic environment alone determines distributions, but there is abundant evidence that the restrictive nature of the environment is made up of significant biotic as well as abiotic elements. For example, many species of insects, birds, and other animals are known to be restricted from occupying much more extensive habitats simply by the occupation of those habitats by other more efficient competitors (Brian 1958; Andrewartha and Birch 1954, p. 457; Lack 1944; Elton 1958). Ultimate prohibition by the physical environment is obvious.

Obviously, tenuous existence in areas not permanently habitable would depend upon the fluctuating conditions and immigration from permanently habitable places. Some form of density-dependent action serves as the governing mechanism throughout the permanent areas of distribution, but this action is always confined within the levels of the framework set by the environments—being perhaps competitition for, or in, the ever-more-limited suitable abodes or habitats near the periphery, and, perhaps, for other needs near the centre. The influence of climatic factors on the population is important at both the centres and at the limits to occurrence, and, of course, may ultimately prohibit existence at these distributional limits. Such factors as weather or edaphic conditions are vastly more critical, and, in the practical sense, may be said to dominate fluctuations in numbers by causing waxing and waning of favourability, continuity, or abundance of suitable microhabitats near the periphery. Near the centre, or more optimal area, the requisites are more continuously ample in time and in space, and the population tends to be more obviously determined by density-dependent actions, with relatively more importance on mortality and less on natality; the degree of mortality will appear more closely correlated with density.

Cloudsley-Thompson (1957) suggests that climatic forces control the normal fluctuations of populations at low densities, while the action of natural enemies, or competition for space and food is characteristically invoked only at times of high density—i.e., during or following outbreaks. Thus, in this view density-dependent mechanisms become significant *only* after drastic economic loss has resulted. This means that such losses are usually prevented only by climatic factors. This view seems to be an unfortunate result of seeing only the conspicuous consequences of a breakdown in the more usual natural-enemy controls at a time when observation is intensely concentrated on an economic problem. Close study at the low, pre-outbreak densities of many insects over extended periods of time has revealed significant action of natural enemies in checking increase at low densities. While the fluctuations may be caused by changes in climatic factors in certain types of environments, the observed fluctuations in other, more constant environments are a function of interactions inherent to the governing mechanism. Furthermore, the density-uninfluenced fluctuations due to climate depart from some base level which is not independent of a prehistory of density-dependent action (see figures 6 and 7).

Andrewartha and Birch (1954) also say that the density-dependent view is unrealistic because it ignores the fluctuation of r, the population growth rate parameter, with time (which may be induced by seasonal and other periodic fluctuations in the environment), and also because this view is believed to ignore the heterogeneity of the places where animals may live. Our understanding of natural control includes both the influence of nonbiotic factors on the power of increase of a species, and the variability of environments.

As Nicholson (1958) states, 'It is clear from these equations (equations of Lotka, Volterra, Nicholson, and Bailey) that if the value of r varies in space or in time this will vary the levels which the animals attain, or oscillate about. Thus, these equations and analogous discussions indicate what would happen when r is influenced by the heterogeneity of the places where animals may live.' Furthermore, Solomon (1955) and Huffaker (1958a) state that many populations spend much of their time recovering from catastrophe such that the value of r following such periods of seasonal or less frequent stress would be an important aspect of average densities under such fluctuating conditions. Nevertheless, this involves a waxing and waning of favourability—the conditioning aspect, not the governing aspect.

A point of importance regarding natural enemies as governing agents is the relation of superimposed exploitation. On largely theoretical grounds, it is felt that the more steps removed from the basic requisites (the lowest trophic level), the greater the complexity of adaptations, and the greater the number of times such adaptations (e.g., synchronizations) are required, the less likely that a biotic relation will have evolved wherein the exploiter acts as a dominant control of the exploited (Huffaker 1957). Although direct evidence is largely lacking, the consensus seems to be that more effective governing action is likely from primary parasitism of a phytophagous host insect than will result from parasitism of the parasitic host insect—that is, a secondary parasite, on the average, is less likely to control *its* host, the primary parasite. A tertiary is still less likely to control *its* host, and, on the other end of the food chain, there should be greater chance that a phytophagous insect will control its plant host than that it will be checked from doing so by its own enemy. However, this last comparison is not necessarily sound because the plant's fortunes are affected in rather different ways—it is probably more directly influenced by the physical environment and by interspecific competition.

Another question of some general importance, and related to the complexity of governing mechanisms, is 'population dispersion' which we define as *the pattern of spacing shown by members of a population within its occupied habitat and within the total area over which the given population may be spread*. The relation of this parameter in natural control is somewhat illustrated by Andrewartha and Birch (1954, pp. 490-504), Burnett (1958a), Huffaker (1958b), and Pimentel (1961), but it is still little understood. Different patterns of dispersion of a given supply of a requisite may result in quite different adjustments in the governing mechanisms. This may be an important reason for variable effects from the same natural enemy of a given insect or weed, for example, in one environment compared with that in another.

The governing mechanisms and instruments; degree of density-dependence.—A source of misunderstanding is the word 'factor.' To speak of density-dependent or governing 'factors,' if *activity* is not implied, is confusing. A factor which has potential density-dependent action may not become involved in such an action. A predator may cause deaths and yet not act as a governing agent. Food, as such, is not a density-dependent factor. Shelter, food, predators, parasites, and pathogenic organisms are not in themselves density-dependent factors, but they may *become* agents of density-dependent actions. Such *combined* action as is induced with greater intensity as the population acted upon increases, is density-dependent, or governing, action (see definition, *vide supra*). It may be simple, or collective and of variable composition. Specific forces brought into play are the instruments or agents of the mechanism, and any one alone may or may not have a key role. The combined action, however, is no different as to role or importance than food shortage, for example, as visualized by Milne (1957*a*) and this combined action is similarly of density-induced intraspecific origin. Food shortage is, in fact, the governing requisite for many predatory species, and both their populations and those of their prey are thus reciprocally governed (Huffaker 1958*a*, 1958*b*).

Smith (1935) intended as a most important part of his density-dependent category the regulating action of parasites, predators, and diseases, but he neither restricted the category to these natural enemies nor implied that they as a group, or any particular species member of the group, are to be so considered at all times and places. In fact, he said that shortage of food and suitable places to live also fall in this category.

Since density-dependence is properly looked at from the focal point of the population acted upon—not specifically with respect to the instruments or agents brought into play which cause the repression—the view taken here is consistent with Smith's usage and with his well-known appreciation that a parasite or predator does not always act in a density-dependent way, to say nothing of doing so in an exact linear manner, with never any lag in response and efficacy. Regarding 'exact,' 'linear,' or 'perfect' density-dependence, see also previous discussion and Varley (1958), Solomon (1958*a*, 1958*b*), and Milne (1958).

Although of variable composition, density-governance always arises as some form of intraspecific inhibition or competition (Huffaker 1958*a*). Because of this, Milne's (1957*a*) distinction between 'perfect' and 'imperfect' density-dependence[1] seems unnecessary. This view also integrates Varley's contention that only the simple 'non-lag' factors conforming to the Verhulst-Pearl type of governing mechanism properly come within the concept of density-dependence, with Solomon's view that we cannot exclude the parasites, predators, and natural enemies from the density-dependent category when they were considered by the originator of the term among the principal examples of such factors, simply because they do not continuously and immediately exhibit response to increase in density of the prey in an exact, linear manner.

It is doubtful whether any single agent in nature, taken alone, would satisfy such

---

[1] Milne's 'imperfect' density-dependent category cannot possibly perform the role he assigns it unless it does, in fact, act as a true density-dependent governor, whether it is termed 'perfect' or not (Nicholson, 1958).

an exacting requirement. In this connection Holling (1959) called attention to the fact that certain natural enemies (in this case three species of small mammals) may tend to govern their prey within certain ranges of density and fail to do so if the prey population 'escapes' to densities beyond the capacity of the predators to respond further, either *functionally*, by eating more prey per individual, or *numerically*, by increasing in numbers. He argues that this is nonetheless governing action at the time and place that it occurs. He also stresses that the functional response is immediate, and is an intrinsic mechanism which tends to damp oscillations. Entomophagous parasites which as adults also feed on their hosts as predators exemplify this functional response, and such action would tend to offset a lag in numerical response. Many general entomophagous predators may act in a similar manner (see chapter 5).

Holling (1961) further developed his concepts on predation. Although he has fully recognized that the predator performance he discusses is only part of the complex of regulation of numbers, the specific data he presents may be misinterpreted and erroneous inferences drawn. Holling deals essentially with inherent performance of specific predators. For example, he shows that the attacks per predator for most predatory or parasitic insects rises with prey density, most rapidly at first and levelling off gradually with further increase in prey density (appetite satiation). There is no increase in *percentage* take per predator as prey density increases. Only the more rare special kind of example shows an increase in percentage take as prey density increases, and even then this relation applies only within a limited range in prey density.

A perhaps more fundamental part of his views as bearing on regulation of numbers has to do with the numerical response, but this cannot be separated from the functional response since the increase in numbers is to some extent derivative of the functional response mechanism.

However, if in fact the total effect from predation by a given species (from both functional and numerical aspects) were that as prey density increases the total take by the predatory species also increases, but with a decreasing percentage take, then the predator would not act as a density-dependent or governing instrument. The total effect must be one of increasing percentage take as prey density increases. The many proved examples of striking biological control of pests species could not occur in the absence of an increase in percentage take, at least within some range of prey density not automatically surpassed during a lag period.

In a parasitic insect which has a greater potential of reproduction than its host, each successful contact of the parasite with its host not only results in death of the host (normal to predation in general) but also in a new parasite (predator) subsequently. Since many parasites have two or more generations within the generation time of the host this numerical increase may be very substantial. Although a single parasite does not take an increasing percentage as prey density rises, the total effect from the population of parasites (if the parasite is a good one under the conditions prevailing) is one of increasing *percentage* take as host density increases. In those cases where the numerical response is direct a limit to such a response is at least very uncommon in host specific entomophagous parasites. Hence, there is no ceiling to the phenomenon of increasing percentage take by the parasite *population* as the host population increases, even if there is a ceiling to the performance efficiency of individuals.

Another factor which Holling only touched upon but was not dealing with, and which may readily be overlooked by those who become engrossed with the performances of given predators, is the multiple nature of the density-dependent mechanism of population regulation.

Our conception of true density-dependence derives only from the relation that as organisms increase in numbers they necessarily use up things they need, defile the place in which they live, and attract or generate, as a result of their own increase in density, elements in the environment inimical to them. Elements that are so attracted or generated include not only parasites, predators, and pathogens, but also physical changes such as excess heat or harmful waste products.

As a population increases in density the intensity of reaction induced in various instruments or agents would not usually follow a straight-line relation, because, for most such factors capable of density-dependent action, there is some characteristic threshold of density at which this action is significantly initiated. Even above this threshold, the relation would more probably be on the order of a curvilinear relation than a linear one. As Holling (1959) showed, there may also be a high-density maximum above which the agent is ineffective, due in this case to factors other than food which limited the predators.

Lag in response of parasite density to increase in host density, for example, is relative, and, if it is sufficiently long, the density of the host may increase to the point where the threshold for induction of some other governing action (e.g., defoliation of the plant) is reached before subsequent parasite action is felt. In such event the parasite did not act as a density-dependent agent (Huffaker 1958a). However, if the plant fed on were very tolerant to the phytophagous insect, the parasite might then act as a governing agent in spite of a prolonged lag in response (there is always some lag) and even if the density at which it governs is above the economic injury level. If the parasite's action is only partially effective it may share with food shortage or other instruments the role of density-governance.

If the average result over a period of time for given conditions is such that a population is maintained under natural control primarily by a given natural enemy, even if other forces contribute (Huffaker 1957), the natural enemy acts as the governing agent. It cannot be a requirement that it *alone* (Milne 1957a) causes all variations in density and is the sole cause of the level of which it is the main instrument (DeBach 1958; Holling 1959b).

If the general equilibrium position of a pest insect, prior to introduction of a parasite, was consistently very high, and subsequent to such introduction its density dropped quickly and assumed a consistent but much lower level, all other conditions assumed unchanged, the parasite has acted as a governing instrument. Yet there is some lag in response of the parasite to changes in host abundance, and the relation to absolute host density is not necessarily continuously held, either for area as a whole, or at the many small locales where the phases of interaction may be quite unsynchronized in time (Huffaker 1958*b*).

It is thus misleading to attempt to classify types of environmental factors in general categories (Varley 1958; Milne 1958; Solomon 1958*a*, 1958*b*) based on degree of density-dependence, for the density-dependence stems only from specific action in the particular case in time and place.

Examples of Density-Dependent Actions

The density-dependent factors may operate in either a reciprocal or nonreciprocal way.

NONRECIPROCATING DENSITY-DEPENDENT ACTIONS. In some instances the rate of supply of a requisite governing for a population is entirely determined by forces independent of the population's density. In its simplest form, approach of density to the level set by this type of limiting requisite induces more intense competition which eventually completely eliminates surpluses. If the requisite is not changed by use and if there is no wasteful, scramble type of competition (Nicholson 1954), there is a theoretical point where all of the requisite, for example certain nesting sites (Andrewartha and Birch 1954, p. 23), could be utilized, and the population surviving is the same whether the numbers searching are high or low. Yet, the destruction of the surpluses is clearly related to intensity of competition. Thus, it is important whether we stress the survivors or the mortality. Density-dependent stress or competition in such simple, hypothetical cases does not determine the level of density, but rather is caused by the fixed capacity to become progressively severe as capacity is approached (Huffaker 1958*a*). Thus, in such situations, or those closely resembling this status, the concept of density-dependence is of negligible impact.

However, only at this theoretical extreme, and pertaining only to requisites the governing levels of which are in no way significantly influenced or modified by the population itself, is the concept of density-dependence superfluous as is sometimes maintained (e.g., Andrewartha and Birch 1954; Cole 1955). In complex environments with requisites variously dispersed, it is most unlikely that the whole supply of such a requisite will be utilized equally by a low density of searchers as by a high density. Thus, the degree of utilization of limited numbers of auger holes in fence posts, which serve as nesting sites for solitary bees (Andrewartha and Birch 1954, p. 23), is also probably dependent on the density of the searching bees, even when the supply of such a requisite is set entirely by forces independent of the population. For this reason we hold that positions based on the density-induced relations in the destruction of surpluses are valid.

Insects which feed on non-vital parts of a plant, in no way affecting the density of the plants, exemplify the non-reciprocal relation. An insect which destroys an annual plant too late in its growth to affect its seed production would illustrate this. Thus, the subsequent density of the plant in the environment would be unaffected and no reciprocal relation is involved. Nevertheless, there would be a one-way density-geared pattern of utilization by the insect.

Another example which does not represent a marked modification from the potential limiting capacity due to density relations is illustrated by animals which defend large territories. Crowding relative to the animals' instincts, socio-psychological states, previous history, etc., is involved. Such evolved behaviour precludes the more violent biotic interactions which would be likely to arise if the population were governed directly by shortage of food, for example, particularly if utilization of the food by high densities would prevent a sustained rate of supply of the food subsequently. Such adaptations may also avoid the violent interactions associated with some disease epizootics. The territory defended, although com-pressible, is relatively fixed and sufficient to maintain the individual 'proprietors,' and thus the population, in a relatively *secure* position.

However, it must be remembered that, even with the non-reciprocal relations, very marked fluctuations in density may result from density-induced interaction in the use of food or space even under a constant supply or rate of supply. This we believe is a common occurrence. Nicholson (1957) reports studies with *Lucilia cuprina* Wied. which illustrate that even when the rate of supply of food is held constant, regardless of the numbers of insects using it, the patterns of changes in density in tests utilizing two levels of liver showed violent and similar oscillations, though at different average densities (see figure 10).

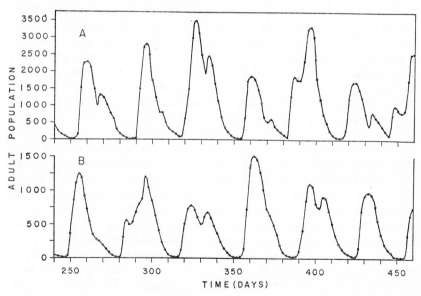

FIGURE 10. Adult populations of *Lucilia cuprina* governed by the supply of meat for the larvae—excess ground liver, water, and sugar being supplied for the adults. In A, 50 g of larval food were supplied and in B, only 25 g. Note that the vertical scale in A is only half that in B. (After Nicholson 1954.)

A population may also be held at a density much below its potential by natural enemies which are not wholly dependent upon, and therefore not keenly sensitive to, increase in its numbers, at least throughout all usual ranges of prey density. The action and numbers of such natural enemies are thus not governed, or are only partially governed, by the density of the particular species of prey. The action of a complex of such predators may be a partial explanation of the control of some pests of forest and orchards at low levels over a period of years (Schwerdtfeger 1941; Pickett 1959). Such actions *per se* are not necessarily density-dependent, but if heavier action is induced through functional or numerical increase by higher prey densities, which probably often occurs, the action becomes density-dependent (Holling 1959).

RECIPROCATING DENSITY-DEPENDENT ACTIONS. Many populations are governed by reciprocal biotic interactions, albeit always in relation to the conditions of the environment. A monophagous parasite which controls its host at a low level is in turn reciprocally controlled at its own characteristic level by the shortage of its hosts. Such biotic interactions may produce oscillations of wide amplitude, though these oscillations may be damped by other factors (Nicholson 1933, 1958; Klomp 1958a; Huffaker 1958b; Holling 1959).

Such examples show that the actual average level of a resource which is governing for a population may be a great modification from the potential level of that resource otherwise, such modification being effected by the population using it.

Figure 11 (from Huffaker and Kennett 1956) shows two types of such biotic interactions involving the same species of mite. Two groups of strawberry plants invested with the cyclamen mite, *Steneotarsonemus pallidus*, were maintained in a greenhouse. The predator was present in one group but excluded in the other. The cyclamen mite on the strawberry plants, in the absence of predatory *Typhlodromus* (see figure 11, 1C), periodically built up to high densities, which then so retarded the growth of the plants and altered the microenvironment that the high densities crashed. Such fluctuations in density recurred several times. Each successive wave was of decreasing amplitude due to progressive loss in vigour of the strawberry plants. In the group containing the predator of the cyclamen mite (see figure 11, 1A), the predator controlled the mite at a very low level, and this prevented the drastic interaction between the cyclamen mites and the strawberry plants. Instead, the predator itself was limited by the scarcity of cyclamen mites caused by its own feeding. The fluctuations were very low in magnitude, the prey being protected against severe overexploitation by the occurrence of a limited number of protective micro-areas. The predators were also able to utilize alternative food for survival. This aspect means that there was not total reciprocity in the relation.

Huffaker and Kennett (1959) published a ten-year study of the control of Klamath weed in northern California by *Chrysolina quadrigemina* (Suffr.). Prior to the introduction of this beetle, beginning in the early years of the century, this weed steadily increased its occupancy of range lands (Sampson and Parker 1930), some 2⅓ million acres being infested by 1950. While climatic and edaphic factors influenced the rate of increase and the relative or maximal densities of stands from one place to another, the final attainment of the characteristic maximal densities was not prevented by either the fluctuations or the heterogeneity of the climatic and edaphic conditions. During the early years of beetle activity, after introduction of *C. quadrigemina*, the patterns of change in densities of the weed and the beetle larvae were compatible with an explanation of reciprocal density-dependence. In the study areas, the weed was reduced to a level less than 1 per cent of its former densities and the beetles dropped synchronously to a low level commensurate with their much reduced food supply.

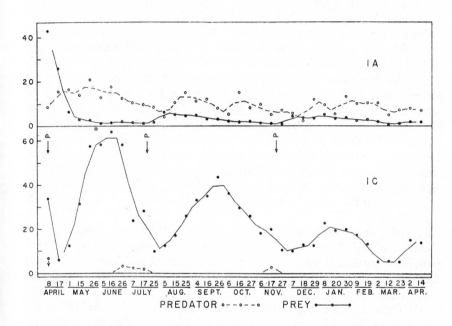

FIGURE 11. Greenhouse plots: Changes in densities of *Steneotarsonemus pallidus* (=prey) in predator-present and predator-free plots, and *Typhlodromus* (=predator) frequencies. One plot (1A) with predators, the other kept predator-free (plot 1C). The *S. pallidus* in the two plots are plotted on a per-leaflet basis. The predator frequencies express the number of leaflets among 36 which had one or more *Typhlodromus*. 'P's by arrows indicate dates of parathion treatment. (After Huffaker and Kennett 1956.)

It is significant that the temporal fortunes of the weed at this new, low density are not *now* so immediately determined by beetle action at specific times and places, for a great variety of other forces such as rainfall, temperature, sunlight, fire, soil disturbances, litter accumulations, etc., may account for erratic germination of seeds, or reduced establishment or destruction of stands. These physical factors have now a relatively greater importance as influences on *changes* in the fortunes of the weed than they did during the precontrol years when weed densities were maintained at near maxima regardless of variations in such factors. However, the

beetle still holds the key role whether it is now responsible for the major destruction of weeds or not. Its action alone is so geared to increase of the weed as to
preclude the weed's return to its former status. This is the clearest kind of answer
to the claims of Uvarov (1931), Bodenheimer (1938) and others that climate rather
than density-dependent factors determines the abundance of animals because the
former causes the greatest mortality or is omnipresent while the biotic elements are
not (Morris 1959). In fact, by the very nature of the action, the balance is struck at
a density position where the key governing agent *appears* to be of low importance.
Certainly, the beetles' action is the reason Klamath weed is no longer a problem in
California, whereas formerly it threatened a major industry.

DeBach (1958*b*) presented a number of examples wherein the effectiveness of
many biological control agents had been demonstrated by various researchers. The
method of demonstration is the removal of natural enemies or the interference with
their action in plots otherwise the exact counterpart of other plots used for comparison. Since, in the particular crops and environments involved the control of
pest species was mainly by natural enemies possessing a rather high degree of host
specificity, these are examples of the reciprocal relation. DeBach illustrated red
scale control in detail. He showed that the California red scale in a climatically
favourable area: (1) may be held under excellent natural control by normal natural
enemy effectiveness; (2) may be held under fair natural control by natural enemies
even when the latter are retarded by ant interference; and (3) will increase to a
serious status if the natural enemies are more seriously inhibited by use of DDT
applications.

Regarding other examples, DeBach (1958*b*) states: 'Similar experimental *proof*
of cases of biological or natural control also has been developed with several other
pests, including the following: on citrus: the yellow scale (*Aonidiella citrina* (Coq.))
(DeBach 1955), citrus mealybugs (DeBach, Dietrick, and Fleschner 1953, p. 247;
DeBach 1946, p. 696), soft scale (*Coccus hesperidum* L.) (DeBach 1951, p. 765),
aphids (DeBach 1951, p. 764), citrus red mite (*Panonychus citri* (McG.)) (DeBach,
Fleschner, and Dietrick 1950, p. 810; Debach 1951, p. 765; Fleschner 1952), and
the cottony-cushion scale (*Icerya purchasi* Mask.) (DeBach 1946, p. 696; DeBach
and Bartlett 1951, p. 375); on avocados: the omnivorous looper, the six-spotted mite
(*Eotetranychus sexmaculatus* (Riley)), the long-tailed mealybug (*Pseudococcus
adonidum* (L)), the avocado brown mite and the latania scale (Fleschner, Hall, and
Ricker 1955); and on apple trees: phytophagous mites (Lord 1956)' (see chapter 14,
'Evaluation of effectiveness of natural enemies').

Schwerdtfeger (1958) cited a rather different type of example of the role of
population density in determining the rate of supply of requisites governing the
population:

'Still more clearly and impressively the action of mechanisms is seen in rhythmical
fluctuations which are less characteristic for insects than for certain rodents, especially
for species of the Leporidae and Microtinae. Owing to a fast succession of litters and
to an early beginning of maturity, these species have a high fertility which causes a
rapid increase in abundance. After it has reached a certain level, a conspicuous breakdown of the population takes place, the causes of which have been disclosed to a certain

degree by the work of Green, Larsson, Chitty, Frank, and other authors. The population that has increased to high abundance begins to suffer from shortage of food which first causes a decrease in weight and draws on the reserves of the body; secondly, requires increased expense of energy to get food and room; and, lastly, intensifies the intra-population competition. For the individual, this means increased activity and psychic excitements which influence the endocrine system; by way of the hypothysis the adrenal gland is caused to produce more adrenalin which leads to reduction of the glycogen reserves, and finally to the lethal hypoglycemic shock (Frank 1954, pp. 346–47). The interaction of high fertility and of this physiological–pathological process, called "shock-disease" may be considered as a classical example of the regulation of abundance by means of mechanisms.'[1]

As an example of control by a complex of enemies, Holling (1959) shows the role of three small mammals, *Blarina brevicauda talpoides* Gapper, *Sorex cinereus cinereus* Kerr, and *Peromyscus maniculatus bairdii* Hoy and Kennicott in the control of the pine sawfly *Neodiprion sertifer* (Geoff.) at low densities in Canadian forests. His studies considered the action on the sawfly cocoon stage only. These predators have peaked curves of predation response to increase in density of sawfly cocoons. There are two types of response, as mentioned previously, a functional response (numbers of prey consumed per predator), which is immediate, and a numerical response (increase in abundance of predators), which is not long delayed because of high rates of reproduction of these predator species. The form of the response curve of prey eaten with change in prey density, for each species, is different, such that when these response curves are combined, effective control is illustrated throughout a greater range of densities than would be true if only one of the species alone were considered. Therefore, in certain instances, at a given place, several enemies together may be better than the best one alone.

This limited response curve is contrary to common conception and most experiences in the biological control of insect pests by more specific entomophagous parasites or predators. The difference lies in the fact that entomophagous parasites and predators at least do not usually have a peaked curve. Their action is progressively more intense as the density of the host increases; there is no finite host-density level above which the intensity of the response again declines, except, perhaps, as the parasites themselves induce heavier attack by their own natural enemies (that is, secondary enemies) as their own density reaches higher levels.

The type of control exhibited by the small mammals (*vide supra*—a peaked response of predation to increase in prey density) was such that at high densities the prey may 'escape' from predator regulation so that other enemies, food shortage, or other catastrophe may be presumed to be necessary to reduce the sawflies to a low level again. Since entomophagous parasites do not appear to have the limitations exhibited by the small mammals, the parasite species acts effectively at a very low host density and does so even more quickly and effectively at still higher host densities. Thus, it is doubtful that the addition of other host-specific entomophagous enemies showing slower response to increase in host density would add

---

[1] For a contrary view relative to the causal mechanism of this crowding effect—that is, not hypoglycemia but rather hemolytic anaemia—see Chitty (1957).

to the control at the *given* place unless changes in weather or cultural aspects, for example, are such as to occasionally, or periodically, alter the status of efficiency of the two species of enemies. Obviously, with variations in the conditions in time and place, two such enemies may be superior to either one alone (Smith 1929*a* and chapter 5). Other examples are discussed in later chapters.

Elaboration of the Role of Abiotic Conditions

The abiotic, or physical factors of the environment, which commonly include the elements of weather and climate, light, type and conditions of soil, slope and exposure, influence population densities of insects in several different and important ways. As previously stated, these conditions act either directly on the individuals of a population, alter the basic capacity of the environment, or act in a number of very indirect ways. Important in the field of biological control of insect pests, such factors of the environment may act upon coexisting populations (host and parasite, predator and prey) in different ways or in different degrees.

While other environmental factors must also be permissive, the physical factors are perhaps basic in determining whether or not a species can exist in a given habitat. Hence, the latter factors are of predominant importance in determining the actual or potential geographic distribution of a species (*vide supra*) (Cook 1931; Messenger 1959).

DIRECT ACTIONS OF ABIOTIC FACTORS. Physical factors exert direct actions upon the population, such as by modifying the timing of events in the life cycles, controlling rates of growth, reproduction, and longevity, and by causing the premature death of various proportions of the individuals in the population (Shelford 1929; Chapman 1931; Uvarov 1931; Messenger and Flitters 1954, 1957). Thus, the physical factors may at any time directly modify population natality, i.e. power of increase, or population mortality, i.e. survival to fulfilment, or both. They may also cause dispersal. Hence, if density-induced actions do not intervene, physical factors may determine whether or not a population shall increase or decrease from one generation to the next, or the rates at which such shall occur, or the duration of time intervals over which such rises and declines of the population density shall extend (Birch 1957).

In more complicated cases often found in natural situations, the physical factors act as contributors towards population mortality in conjunction with other environmental factors. Besides a mere contribution to total mortality occurring each generation due to physical, density-independent factors, the timing or sequence of action of such factors relative to other mortality factors may be important. Hence, the relative influence of a parasite or predator may be affected by the degree of mortality inflicted upon the population by weather prior to the time of action of that factor. Bess (1945) and Morris (1957) consider that variations in mortality due to factors acting early in the life cycle of the insect are relatively less important, with respect to the elimination of the surplus individuals, than are similar variations due to late-acting factors, and that this is true regardless of whether or not such variations are invoked by changes in density of the population acted upon (see discussion of Morris' views in chapter 14, 'Evaluation of effectiveness of natural enemies').

Density-independent mortality factors, if acting equally severely on a host and parasite population, would act differentially in favour of the host over the parasite (see chapter 3). Furthermore, such physical forces may act severely on an early-stage phase of a generation of hosts, almost annihilating a population of parasites dependent upon them. On the other hand, if not nearly annihilated, the progeny of such parasites may again act on that stage, and their progeny on later stages as well. Therefore, variations in early-stage mortality (if by natural enemies) may be of very great significance relative to later-stage mortality; in fact, such may be the precursor or antecedent to more extensive and significant later mortality. Also, the generalized statements referred to do not take into account the density of the population acted upon in a sequence of abundance in time or the consequences of compensating mortality. If early-stage mortality from a given natural enemy is density-dependent in action while the late-stage mortality agent is not, or is less density-geared, then the early-stage acting mortality factor is more important than the late-stage acting factor in maintaining natural control of the given population.

The evaluation of mortality according to the timing of occurrence thus involves the concept of compensatory or dispensable mortality. This concept follows from the philosophy of density-dependence (see discussion *vide supra* relative to views of Thompson (1955) and Morris (1957)). The density at which a species is regulated by a given natural enemy is characteristic for the given conditions of terrain, temperature, properties of the organisms, etc. Since there is often a marked resilience in the action of the natural enemy, and since its increase in efficiency is geared with increase in host density, the absence of mortality at one point in time during host population increase often assures a greater mortality by that natural enemy or some other natural enemy at a later time. Hence, early occurring mortality by some density-independent action would be merely compensatory or dispensable to the final result, i.e., to the degree that such would be replaced by natural enemy action in any event (Errington 1946). This is the reason why we feel that factual records of mortality do not necessarily carry importance commensurate with the magnitude of observed data, and it is also precisely why we emphasize the use of 'check methods' of analysis where possible (see chapter 14).

Furthermore, from the standpoint of economic control, early-stage mortality often prevents serious destruction of the crop which would not be achieved by equivalent late-stage mortality.

Therefore, only careful study of each case can reveal the importance of variations in mortality from various sources, whether they are advantageous or disadvantageous from man's economic point of view, whether they are ecologically compensated (meaningless) or non-compensated (meaningful). Under some circumstances, if an effective predator or parasite increases sufficiently to bring a high pest population down, even though the pest population had suffered substantial destruction by some other previous factor, then obviously the predator or parasite may have acted even more quickly or effectively if the previous destructive factor had not acted. On the other hand, mortality of hosts from other causes may serve to bring about a balance between the host species and its natural enemies which is more favourable to control (Stern *et al.* 1959).

This general discussion shows that mortality from physical factors, dependent merely on when they act and how they vary, can influence radically the effects on population abundance of other mortality factors, including such governing factors as competition for space or food, disease, parasitism, or predation.

INDIRECT ACTIONS OF ABIOTIC FACTORS. Finally, besides such direct or inter-acting effects as above described, the abiotic factors of the environment influence and modify the actions of other factors, the latter in turn acting directly on the population (DeBach, Fisher, and Landi 1955; Huffaker 1958*a*; Stern *et al.* 1959). Such indirect conditioning action may operate by modifying the quantity or quality of various requirements for the survival of the individuals in the population, or by altering, stimulating, or inhibiting the actions of other forces acting on the population. Involving some overlap with previously discussed interactions, this may occur: (1) as an effect on the food supply or suitable places to live; (2) by short-circuiting the effectiveness of a natural enemy by reducing its host to a level inimical to its own survival or efficiency; (3) by reduction of the host species and thereby serving to increase the effectiveness of a natural enemy by bringing about a more favourable ratio of enemies to hosts and/or at a density of hosts more con-ducive to effective control by the natural enemy; (4) by direct action differentially affecting the host species and a given natural enemy; (5) by similar differential action on other kinds of enemies among a complex which results in altering the relative roles of certain species (both primary and secondary forms) and hence the population considered; (6) by changing the status of existence of allies, essential alternative hosts or alternative food sources of either the host species, its primary enemies, or secondaries; and (7) among other possibilities, by changing the relative tolerance to crowding, of territorial animals for example, and thus the triggering level for intraspecific regulatory actions.

EXAMPLES OF INFLUENCE OF ABIOTIC FACTORS. Nicholson (1933) and Nicholson and Bailey (1935) have shown by theoretical considerations how the control of a host population by a parasite can be influenced by climatic factors. On the one hand, climate may act as a mortality factor on the parasite while exerting no deleterious effect on the host. Thus, the equilibrium position of the host species will increase, while that of the parasite will remain the same (e.g., DeBach, Fisher, and Landi 1955). On the other hand, climate may contribute to the mortality of the host but not of the parasite; in such event the equilibrium position of the parasite will decrease (less is needed to eliminate the surplus of hosts produced each generation). The effect of such a situation on the host density depends upon the timing of the mortality factor, whether the mortality due to climate occurs before or after mortality due to the parasite.

Nicholson (1933) has also shown deductively how climate may also change the equilibrium position of a host insect that is normally kept in balance by a parasite by acting upon or modifying the host's reproductive capacity or power of increase; the power of increase being one of the factors determining the level at which the equilibrium of the host is maintained by the parasite. When climate causes host females to lay more eggs, this in turn will require a greater number of parasites to maintain control. Hence, the equilibrium position of the parasite must increase; that of the host varies only slightly. If climatic conditions reduce the relative searching ability of the parasite, the densities at which host and parasite are in balance are both raised (Holling 1959). Thus, especially fluctuating temperatures, merely by periodically altering the searching efficiency of a natural enemy, can cause periodic fluctuations in host and parasite densities. The above conclusions of Nicholson are essentially deductions from simple theoretical host-parasite models.

The manner in which physical factors may influence the natural control of an insect species in the field has also been investigated. Ullyett (1947) illustrates many of the ways in which weather influences the actions of certain natural enemies of the diamondback moth, *Plutella maculipennis* (Curtis). As a direct influence on populations of the moth, weather itself is of little importance. But, acting with greater severity on parasites and predators than on the moth, it interferes with the control they exert. Weather also influences moth populations by reducing the primary host plant abundance during certain periods of the year, forcing the populations to shift to alternative food sources that are located in other environments. Moist weather also promotes fungus infections in populations of the diamondback moth, which in turn drastically reduce the populations.

Burnett (1956) has demonstrated how temperatures can enhance the capacity of a given number of parasites to parasitize their hosts. With higher temperatures greater numbers of hosts were stung and greater numbers of parasite eggs were laid.

Birch (1948) has shown that temperature can vary the intrinsic rate of increase of an insect population, and that when two coexisting species are actively competing for a given source of food which is in limited supply, the species with the higher rate of increase will most probably be the successful competitor (Birch 1954). Hence, temperature may determine the outcome of competing populations.

With regard to inherent reproductive capacity, attempts to ascertain the value of a given natural enemy simply by use of comparisons of its inherent fecundity and generation time with that of the host or prey species has been overstressed. A parasite may have a lower inherent reproductive capacity than its host and yet serve as an effective natural control.

If a large part of the total fecundity of the host is negated by mortality factors, while this is not so with respect to the parasite, a sufficient fecundity in the parasite is exhibited if it is just enough to take care of the excess host individuals which do not die of other causes. If a given host rather characteristically suffers, say, fifty per cent mortality from other causes, the parasite's fecundity can be correspondingly less and yet sufficient to serve as a dependable and resilient regulating factor. C. P. Clausen (personal communication) considers that in general entomophagous parasites which have relatively low powers of reproduction have proved to be better control agents than those with very high powers of reproduction, for example, those exhibiting polyembryony. This may mean only that such a habit arose as an adaptation against rather hazardous circumstances requiring a high reproduction for mere survival, a condition which at the same time would seem to preclude the parasite's action as a reliable control factor.

At this point we discuss two examples which have been cited as control of populations by weather, entirely independent of density.

Allee *et al.* (1949, p. 308) refer to the 'regulation' of populations by physical factors as revealed by the work of Terao and Tanaka (1928). The latter authors found that populations of water fleas, provided with a superabundance of food, grew in essentially a logistic fashion to asymptotes of 199 at 19·8° C, 429 at 24·8° C, and 271 at 33·6° C. Clearly, 24·8° C gave the highest asymptote or level of abundance, but this is irrelevant. What stopped each population from going still higher if temperature regulated the populations independent of density? Since in these studies constant temperatures were used, the same thermal conditions existed at the beginning of growth as at the end. This surely means that as the asymptote was approached for each group there was a curtailment of reproduction and/or an increase in mortality associated with some shortage or defiling of the environment, or mere interference between individuals. The quantitative way in which these latter factors made their effects felt was most probably influenced by temperature, but certainly this is not 'regulation' by temperature. This example illustrates our present concept which envisages a clearer distinction between the roles of physical conditions which may set the levels at which densities are governed, and governing or regulating mechanisms which actually *do* the regulating.

Andrewartha and Birch (1954) and Andrewartha (1957) used the population dynamics of *Thrips imaginis* Bagnall (Davidson and Andrewartha 1948*a*) as evidence that meteorological factors may wholly determine the abundance of a population without density-dependent factors becoming involved. Regarding this, Nicholson (1957) commented as follows: 'It is not true, however, that meteorological factors were wholly responsible for determining the abundance of thrips, for the equation derived from the statistical analysis by Davidson and Andrewartha of the data referred to contained a constant upon which the close association between the calculated and observed number of thrips each year was basically dependent. The only possible interpretation of the biological meaning of this constant is that at the beginning of multiplication each year the population reached approximately the same level; although this was influenced somewhat by the temperature during the preceding active season. This strongly suggests that a density-dependent factor must have operated to bring this about.' (Solomon 1957; Nicholson 1958.)

Smith (1961) analysed these data on *Thrips imaginis* and concluded that, far from indicating that no density-dependent factor was operating, as claimed by Andrewartha and Birch, the data strongly suggested that the population was in fact regulated by some density-dependent factor. There is another very significant point which seems to have been missed in the various discussions of this question. Since their sampling of rose populations can serve only as an *index* of the *Thrips imaginis* population in the general environment, and since only the adult thrips constituted the sample and were taken in roses, and no effort was made to study the immature populations, mainly produced on other plants, then it is obvious that a source of density-dependence would not necessarily be revealed by the study. J. Evans (1933) stated that very few immature thrips are found in roses ' . . . as roses are evidently not favorable breeding sites.' Thus, the total brood relations were not covered. Food for adult thrips in the form of rose blossoms may well have been relatively abundant, but was nymphal food always abundant, for one thing?

The Total Environment and the Role of Natural Enemies

The over-all complexity of environments, both as to climatic variations and biotic constitution, may greatly influence the roles of natural enemies and the nature of the natural control experienced.

Modern agriculture and silviculture is departing steadily from the more natural status of mixed vegetation. Even though single crops are grown on respective pieces of land, small-scale farming represents a closely mixed mosaic of small habitats. Interchange of faunal elements is readily accomplished. However, with increasing use of extensive plantings of single crops or trees, the tendency for extremes to be damped by the opposing actions of complex systems is lessened. In biological control, this also means that the advantages formerly to be had from the actions of a vast array of more polyphagous predatory and parasitic species will be lessened in these faunistically impoverished environments. The relative inefficiency of natural control factors in large plantings of single crops, i.e., monocultures, may also be due to reduction in environmental suitability. Such may come about by change in the micro-climate, or in food supplies, or in shelter, in the monoculture that in turn interferes with normal activities of natural enemies (see chapter 16).[1] Natural control in such situations will normally rest on the actions of the more specialized natural enemies—ones capable of controlling their hosts at non-economic levels largely without assistance by other species. Many of the best examples of biological control fall into this category.

Chapman (1928b) and Dobzhansky (1950) point out that where many unfavourable climatic periods of different nature alternate, fewer species can have met the challenges to evolution, whereas in mild, constantly favourable environments many species have evolved on the basis of complex challenges of biotic nature. Hesse, Allee, and Schmidt (1937) state that the closer even a single factor approaches a limiting value the fewer will be the number of species. Thus, the physical environment is a basic factor in the biotic complexity. Not surprisingly, it is from a comparison of equable tropical environments with the more rigorous, arctic or continental environments that we have our best indications supporting the view that in more complex biotic assemblages there is greater stability, and fewer phytophagous species become pests (Voûte 1946; Solomon 1949; Elton 1958).

---

[1] The authors express acknowledgment to F. R. Lawson (private communication) concerning this point.

The calm or salubrity of environments is an important factor in the control by entomophagous parasites of their hosts. Insect pests having homodynamic life cycles are better subjects for biological control because the effectiveness of the natural enemies is not so likely to be intercepted by adverse physical conditions or absence of hosts in the proper stages for attack. The point here is that the type of life cycle is an evolutionary result of the type of climate. (For full discussion, see chapter 5.)

It is commonly stated that alien pests are more troublesome than native species because of the absence of effective natural enemies of the former in the new environment. Generally, this is undoubtedly true. Yet, we must emphasize that, considering specific examples, there are other reasons why an alien pest may be more troublesome in a new area than in the region where it is endemic (Wilson 1950; Huffaker 1957; and others). We must consider the total environments involved, as these bear on the potentialities and limitations of both the alien pests and the prospective introductions. Wilson (1950) summarized some important points: Soil and climate could be more suitable. Competition from other species could be less intense. Agricultural practices in the new country could favour it and, perhaps most important, the absence in the new environment of its normal natural enemies may greatly enhance the pest's opportunities therein. It does not necessarily follow that natural enemies in their native habitats play as important a part in control of their hosts or prey there, as may prove to be the case when they are introduced to control the same species in environments new to both. Furthermore, as stated or implied by Lack (1954), Elton (1958), and others, we are very far indeed from being able to predict in advance which alien species will thrive, whether pests or beneficial forms, the remarkable results of Taylor (1937) in a specific instance notwithstanding.

The point of origin of a species does not necessarily represent its most favourable possibilities. Gleason (1939) emphasized that the dominant plants of an area are only those which, among the *existing* flora, win out in the environment. If other species from a different part of the world were present, the dominants would not necessarily be those same species. The presence of different kinds of animals may also affect the situation for plants, and the general concept applies as well to animal populations. The physical conditions in some other part of the world may be at least as suitable qualitatively, and more extensive or more favourably dispersed quantitatively. It is important to stress, as did Smith (1954) that the microenvironment may be a key to understanding here. Suitable microenvironments, as these represent a modification from the general environment, may be very abundant in the new region and yet restricted to very limited parts of trees, for example, in very restricted areas in the original home area.

However, we emphasize that the previously mentioned factors may *augment* the chances of control by the importation of natural enemies, contrasted to the control exercised by the same agents in the native region, just as readily as these environmental factors may increase the potentials of the pest in the new region. Not only has an introduced enemy greater chance of controlling an alien pest because of the absence of its own natural enemies in the new region, but the new total environment may be inherently more conducive to the beneficial species than was the original one. Also, in general, the greater the abundance of the pest the greater the chances of finding an enemy capable of bringing it under some degree of control.

Wilson (1949) states that when an introduced beneficial insect has been of value in one country, an attempt is often made to establish it in another country having the same pest. More often than not favourable results occur, but this practice is no guarantee of success, for the insect may have less effect in the second country than would another species which was ineffective in the first. Also a natural enemy which is less effective than another in its native home may prove more useful in a foreign invaded region (Cameron 1935).

DISPERSAL AND NATURAL CONTROL

Many pests of our crops do not move readily or over great distances. Scale insects exemplify this relation. Population analysis in such situations is comparatively simple. On the other hand, analysis is complicated if movements of insects into or out of study areas are substantial. A meaningful study must include the gains or losses in density from immigration and emigration. Movements into an area may greatly alter the course of events in natural control, and if the movements are from great distances the analysis may be quite formidable. Also, differential patterns of movement of both host and parasitic species, for example, have an important bearing upon whether such a parasite is precluded from effective control of its host. We can only touch upon the complexity introduced by movement phenomena and this can best be done by giving examples.

Migratory locusts exhibit striking examples of movements, and it is undoubtedly due to the migratory habits of representatives of this group that their population dynamics are so complicated. Basically, movements of populations of locusts involve search for places having food and ovipositional sites. Such movements may consist of less extensive, nomadic-type swarming or dispersal wherein new food habitats are sought as current ones are either used up or disappear due to weather, or these movements may consist of outbreak-type swarming and flight over long distances. In either case, dispersal may be considered a response to lack of food or breeding sites or, in some cases, to spatial crowding. Swarm migration is commonly considered a response to overcrowding, leading to physiological and morphological changes in the individuals, resulting in the more or less permanent removal of the majority of individuals to areas outside the normal breeding centres (Pepper 1955; Williams 1957). In many cases, such migrations lead to eventual extermination of the migrating population (Uvarov 1957). In other cases, migration is essentially a movement from one breeding ground to another. Sometimes this migratory dispersal may involve a circular movement from one breeding area to another and then back to the first.

Hence, migratory locusts may be considered to have a 'normal ecology' in their normal breeding grounds during non-outbreak years, and within which areas 'characteristic' density levels may be ascertained. Such densities might then be considered as base levels from which may be measured density effects leading to nomadic or solitary-phase dispersal (solitary population dynamics), and density effects leading to phase change, swarming, and outbreak migrations (gregarious population dynamics). Considerations of the ephemeral nature of many of the breeding or feeding habitats of locusts, based mainly on weather phenomena rather than on feeding activities, and active dispersal inherent in individuals regardless of density, will require careful evaluation.

The beet leafhopper, *Circulifer tenellus* (Baker), undergoes a significant dispersal in western United States. This insect breeds in late winter and spring in the coastal foothills adjacent to the San Joaquin Valley of California where the vegetation contains an abundance of suitable host plants. The extensive winter annuals dry in early summer and millions of immature leafhoppers starve, while other millions of adults disperse under characteristic meteorological conditions (Lawson, Chamberlain, and York 1951). There is an element of sudden waning of the food resources due to climatic conditions and, as well, some further diminution of food by the leafhoppers. Yet, a very limited residual population is left in the foothill areas on the few summer annuals which occur there in the most favourable spots. For the most part, the population perishes in spite of the fact that extensive emigrations to sugar beets and other row crops some 20 to 40 miles distant may occur. From these migrants extensive reproduction occurs in the summer breeding areas. In late autumn there is movement back into the foothills, usually before the winter annuals have germinated, and the population is again drastically reduced.

This pattern of population changes does not contribute to an expectation of effective action by natural enemies. For example, in the arid microenvironments of the foothill breeding areas there are numerous predators such as *Geocoris pallens* Stål and *G. punctipes* Say, and one very common egg parasite, *Aphelinoidea plutella* Grlt. These enemies are drastically limited in their survival during the summer period when the beet leafhopper and other hosts are absent. It is known that *A. plutella* can survive only to a very limited extent within the host eggs in dried plant tissues for several months. This is a hazard which appears to be far greater than that faced by the host species. Consequently, this parasite must start at a very low level each year when the leafhoppers return and have begun oviposition. By April or May the parasites have reached parasitization levels around 10 to 30 per cent. If there were continuity in favourability and presence of hosts they would then be in a position, theoretically, to reduce the host population, but just at this point the host moves out of the area. The predators, too, are dependent upon continuity of hosts in this environment unless they too disperse and return later, in which event the level of food in the alternative environment (not necessarily inhabited by beet leafhoppers) would determine the number successfully returning. This apparent preclusion of effective natural-enemy control due to asynchronous life histories, in this case involving dispersal habits, is comparable to the preclusion of natural control involving asynchronies of life histories in time, as discussed in relation to homodynamic and heterodynamic life cycles (chapter 5).

The complexity of natural control of such forest pests as the spruce budworm involves, in part, extensive movements from outbreak areas into non-outbreak areas (Morris 1958a). This movement may upset the local balance existing between the natural control forces and budworm numbers, thus suddenly permitting the development of an abundance of budworms greater than can be handled by the local natural enemies and hence starting the area on an outbreak phase. Fleschner (1958) has obtained related results recording movement of orchard mites from tree to tree.

Movements of natural enemies may be of importance comparable with the movements of the pest species. Thus, Huffaker and Kennett (1956) found that the lag in time of appearance of cyclamen mites, *Steneotarsonemus pallidus*, and that of the effective predators, *Typhlodromus* spp., accounted for the fact that the cyclamen mite is customarily a serious pest in young strawberry fields, if not controlled by acaricides. On the other hand, cyclamen mite populations are held at non-economic levels by these predators in older fields after the predators have attained general distribution. Smith and Hagen (1956) discuss the role of migratory movements of *Hippodamia convergens* Guér. in the control of aphids in lowland areas in California.

GENETIC FACTORS AND NATURAL CONTROL

The various factors of natural control of insect populations have thus far been considered only as affecting population abundance, by providing checks to unlimited multiplication of organisms, by setting environmental limits and modifications to population growth, and by controlling or governing densities within the framework of these limits. But natural-control factors, of both density-dependent and density-independent nature, can also act as agents of natural selection (Huxley 1943; Dobzhansky 1951). That is, by their very action natural-control factors tend to alter gradually but progressively the properties of the individuals of a population in time. Our concern here is to consider just how such selective change in a population affects the natural control of abundance of such an adapting group of organisms, and what may be the influences of such adaptive change on the population dynamics of the species.

Individual members of a given sample of a species are commonly found to vary among themselves in greater or less degree in size, structure, physiology, behaviour, fecundity, rapidity of development, and other such properties. In particular, variations will most commonly be noted in their genetic constitutions. Hence, these individuals will exhibit variations in many of their ecologically important properties (Dobzhansky 1951; Andrewartha and Birch 1954; Birch 1957). When these variations are genetically induced, any action by environmental factors on survival, natality, or mortality will tend to be selective. Such differential effects of these environmental factors of natural control will tend to lead gradually to adaptation of the population to these environmental stresses. When such adaptive variation eventually occurs in such properties of the individuals as fecundity, viability, longevity, speed of development, dispersability, or the like, there will obviously result an alteration in the quantitative way in which the population interacts with, and in, its environment.

By the same token, natural selection will tend to alter the relationship between insect pests and their more or less closely associated parasites, predators, and diseases. This can come about by gradual, progressive adaptation in the ability of the host species to evade or defend itself against such enemies, or in the adaptive alterations in the abilities of enemies to attack the host. Other ways in which the characteristic relationship between enemies and hosts can become altered are in changing the ability of the host to disperse more or less swiftly than its parasites or predators, in the tolerance of hosts relative to parasitism or disease, and in the development of differential responses of enemies and host to environmental factors, such as climate or soil or food, that limit the spread of these organisms geographically.

Indications that insects are selected adaptively by cyclical changes in the intensity of various climatic factors, that is, seasonal weather changes, are provided by the seasonal variations occurring in the genetic constitution of certain species of *Drosophila* in California (Dobzhansky 1943, 1948). Here, selection is indicated by the varying proportions of certain characteristic genetic patterns occurring regularly and seasonally among individuals in wild populations of *Drosophila pseudoobscura* Fro. and *D. persimilis* Dobz. Evidence that this seasonal alteration in these genetic 'weather patterns' is caused by natural selection by weather factors comes from corresponding results derived from laboratory experiments (Wright and Dobzhansky 1946).

Based on similar phenomena, long-term adaptations in populations of these *Drosophila* species, as indicated again by these same 'weather patterns' in the genetic constitutions of individuals in the samples, appear to occur in association with long-term trends in climate in the localities concerned (Dobzhansky 1956).

Such temporal, cyclical or long-term trends in chromosomal patterns, as the above, may bear no direct relation to the actual properties of the individuals in a way which influences population abundance, though they do indicate that such may be possible (Birch 1957). Nor do such variations point out the actual selecting agent operating. Indeed, intraspecific competition has been shown to select certain chromosomal types by the mechanism of differential mortality occurring in the life histories of individuals somewhere between the egg stage and adulthood (Dobzhansky 1947). And, in the experimental verification of the selective influence of temperature in the development of chromosomal 'weather patterns' in *Drosophila* species (see above), the technique was to rear individuals in large 'competition cages,' where it appears that the selection was brought about by intraspecific competition under given temperatures, rather than by direct, differential mortality due to temperature as the selecting agent (Wright and Dobzhansky 1946; Birch 1955).

There have been other demonstrations of temporal changes in population qualities, either genetic or physiological, suggesting consequent influences on population properties that are involved in population abundance. The greater abundance of the European corn borer, *Ostrinia nubilalis* (Hbn.), in North America, relative to abundance in comparable habitats in Europe, and its occurrence in many more diverse environments in North America has been explained as a sort of 'physiological reconstruction' or adaptive alteration in the species involving increases in polyphagy and ecological plasticity relative to the older stock in Europe (Bodenheimer 1938).

From earlier discussion in this and the previous chapter, we see that the population dynamics of a species may be influenced considerably by permanent alterations in such individual characteristics as the level of fecundity, duration of longevity, or speed of development, which in turn are components of the important population property of rate of increase in density (natural or intrinsic rate of increase, Lotka 1925; power of increase, Nicholson 1933; coefficient of increase, Smith 1935). For example, in the case of *Drosophila funebris* Fabr. that type of individual found in greater abundance during and just after the winter period is that having a higher fecundity relative to other population types (Dubinin and Tiniakov 1945). Strains of *D. pseudoobscura* have been selected artificially for increased viability, faster developmental rates, and higher fertility (Dobzhansky and Spassky 1947). A related species has been artificially selected for larval developmental time, both fast and slow, by Sang and Clayton (1957). An inherited genetic alteration in the rate of increase of natural populations of the fruit fly *Dacus tryoni* (Frog.), presumably as a consequence of strain isolation followed by natural selection, has been shown to occur in eastern Australia (Birch 1957).

Hence, we have a considerable amount of evidence that environmental factors can select populations of insects for properties quite important in population regulation. Students of animal ecology who have been concerned with the causes of natural control of animal abundance have commonly felt that this characteristic of adaptiveness, more or less general in extent among species, provides a mechanism whereby any balance or equilibrium existing between a population of individuals and its environment thus tends continuously to become upset (Uvarov 1931; Nicholson 1933; Thompson 1939). Adaptations in response to selective pressures of the various natural-control factors tend to alter in one way or another the quantitative relation that exists between the multiplicative properties of animals and the repressive forces in their environments. Because of this ever-present tendency, any theory of natural control must include some mechanism or mechanisms whereby this tendency toward 'escape' by adaptation, especially when such adaptation results in a potential increase in numbers, may be compensated by an automatic readjustment in the environmental checks.

Intense competition, a very potent natural-control factor in itself, may be an instrument of natural selection. Laboratory populations of the blowfly, *Lucilia cuprina* (Wied.), in which competition among adults for limited food is the major factor controlling the abundance of flies, have been shown to change slowly but progressively in certain populational characteristics, the result of which leads to a similar, slow but progressive change in the density of the populations and the nature of their intraspecific oscillations (Nicholson 1957). The particular property of the blowfly that apparently was selected here was an increased fecundity relative to the limited amount of food provided the adults.

Such effects as these caused by the various elements of natural control of insect populations may influence radically the dynamic fluctuations that occur in population densities, in particular the ability of numbers to increase in unit time. On the other hand, genetic or physiological changes of a contrary nature, that is, leading to weakness or greater sensitivity towards environmental-control factors, may presumably occur relative to the natural control of insect populations. Franz' (1949) theory, based on genetic 'degeneration,' holds that a reason for mass outbreaks and subsequent mass declines of insect populations is the accumulation at certain locales[1] during periods of environmental favourability of less fit genotypes due to the greater chances for recombination during such relaxed environmental conditions. Such accumulations of increasing proportions of less viable, less fecund, or less vigorous individuals in the population then leads to the like accumulation of deleterious homozygotes in the population. With the restoration of normal environmental conditions (intergradation conditions) these individuals are no longer able to survive, and the population density therefore crashes. Solomon (1957) has qualified this theory as less one of genetic control of outbreaks than as one resulting from environmental variations (intergradation *versus* outbreak conditions).

In those theories of natural control wherein control is presumed accomplished by 'balances' between favourability and unfavourability of the environment in time (Andrewartha and Birch 1954; Birch 1957), or in place, or both (Thompson 1929a, 1939), with density-dependent mechanisms not involved, adaptations would seem to tend to overcome such balance. Thus, it is difficult to see how such alteration in the properties of the organism, caused by such adaptations, can elicit a corresponding reaction in the controlling agents which would be required by these theories of 'balance' between favourability and unfavourability, involving temporal and spatial heterogeneity of the environment. But, without such readjustment by these 'balanced environments,' if this alone is presumed adequate, the changed organism would appear able to increase, albeit in an irregular and fluctuating manner, without limit. For example, relative to the theory of weather control of animal abundance of Birch (1957), populations of organisms that gradually adapted to the stresses of those particular weather elements involved—say cold temperatures—would presumably develop higher capacities for increase at moderate temperatures, and less negative values for increase at low temperatures. If the relation between increase and higher temperatures remained the same, the over-all effect would obviously be an imbalance in 'r,' leading to a greater average capacity for increase and hence an increase without limit, relative to control by this factor of weather.

Hence, it appears to us mandatory that a suitable theory of natural control of animal abundance should include some provision whereby the tendency of the

---

[1] The accumulation of better adapted individuals would be expected at other locales.

animals to adapt to, and hence in numbers to overcome, stresses from the environment, in particular the physical factors in the environment, be met by reaction of some sort or other. To us, again, the mechanism of reactive change in the intensity of action of a given controlling factor elicited by change in abundance, i.e., density-dependent control factors, provides the simplest and most elegant explanation of how such adaptational possibilities are counterbalanced.

CHAPTER 5

Some Biological Control Concepts and Questions

RICHARD L. DOUTT AND PAUL DeBACH

THE SPECIAL NATURE of biological control work has enabled those engaged in it to contemplate many natural phenomena, often from a somewhat novel viewpoint. This in turn has led to the development of concepts peculiar to biological control, which now form a philosophical background to the field and at the same time are useful in a practical way as guiding principles. While there is general agreement on certain of these concepts, there is a marked divergence of opinion on others. New ideas are evolving. Some older ideas have been so greatly changed by time or shaped by newer information that their once sharp edges are now blunted and incapable of causing cries of anguish from opposing minds. These somewhat controversial opinions merit special treatment and this chapter has been set aside for that purpose.

BIOLOGICAL CONTROL AS APPLIED ECOLOGY

It is almost axiomatic that to reduce a pest population one must increase the unfavourability of its environment. Aside from the use of chemical pesticides, various possibilities exist for modifying the environment; therefore, it is imperative that any agricultural entomologist engaged in field research be familiar with ecological principles and use them whenever possible.

Biological control of pests is so obviously based on the utilization of ecological principles that it is quite frequently, and correctly, considered to be applied ecology. Not only does the applied biological method bring about control by manipulating the biotic factors to create an environment less suitable for the pest species, but its major advantage lies in its characteristic of prolonging this situation. Biological control is essentially permanent and this is one of its most important aspects. To understand how this permanency is possible, it is necessary to recall several important concepts, particularly those relating to population phenomena. These have been treated in a definitive fashion in chapters 3 and 4. They are condensed and discussed here to give a 'bird's-eye view' of the place of biological control in population regulation.

Balance of Nature

Every student of biology is aware that in any given locality certain species are more or less consistently abundant, others are less common, and, finally, some species are so rarely encountered that they become collectors' items. This condition among the resident species tends to exist year after year, albeit relative and absolute numbers vary somewhat, but on the average really substantial changes rarely occur in the numerical relationship between the several species inhabiting a given, more or less stable, environment. This quantitative relationship between the populations of the different species has been termed the 'balance of nature,' and it can be defined as 'the tendency of the population densities of all species in the same general area to maintain a more or less consistent numerical relation to each other, due to interactions between each other and between the physical environment.' The term 'balance of nature' is an important concept but an unfortunate choice of words, for while the term implies a stability of numbers, nevertheless it is obvious to everyone that population densities are continually undergoing change. For example, insects may be far more abundant in one year than in another, in one season than in another, or they may be far more numerous immediately following a restricted reproductive period than immediately preceding it. Seemingly, then, there is a paradox in which insect populations are characterized by their inherent stability on the one hand and by their recurrent fluctuations on the other. Smith (1935) pointed out that, however strange the statement may sound, it is not contradictory that populations can at the same time exhibit both static and dynamic qualities. It merely depends on one's point of view. According to Smith (1935) we would be presenting a fairly true picture of the quantitative characteristics of population densities if we could express the idea that population densities of organisms are continually changing, but that their values tend to oscillate about a mean which is relatively stable, though itself subject to change. In other words, there is no balance in the strictest sense of the word, but the numerical variations fall within certain typical limits.

Population Equilibrium and Equilibrium Position

From the foregoing it is evident that a single species population tends to fluctuate both positively and negatively with varying intensity and that an 'average' density can be derived from the observed numerical fluctuations. Although occasional fluctuations may be rather extreme, the population thus moves about an average level for its particular environment. This phenomenon is known as 'population equilibrium.'

Logical reasoning alone seems to support the fact that a population equilibrium of this sort exists; it is easily observable in the field; otherwise, of course, a species would either increase to infinity or would decrease to the point of extinction. According to Smith (1935), population equilibrium is one of the most important of all biological phenomena.

If one accepts the idea of population equilibrium (i.e., environmentally limited density fluctuations), then one can conceive that for each species in each habitat there is a theoretical average population level about which the normal fluctuations take place. This is termed 'the equilibrium position' by Smith (1935) and 'the steady density' by Nicholson (1933).

Different Equilibrium Positions for the Same Species

It is commonly recognized that a single species may have different average population densities, i.e., equilibrium positions, in different habitats. In one habitat it may be abundant, in another, scarce. Such differences in the equilibrium position of a species in different environments are of very great practical interest and may result from one of several types of causes. Differences in food, shelter, natural enemies, or physical factors are frequently involved. Smith (1935) has shown that the great entomological problems of the world are largely those in which the value of the equilibrium position has been more or less permanently increased.

Permanent displacements of the equilibrium position of a species are caused by disturbances which usually fall in one of two groups. First are those disturbances resulting from a major change in the habitat, and this can result either in lowering the equilibrium position or in raising it to a much higher level. For instance, if a swamp is drained there will be a marked decrease in the population levels of many of the species. On the other hand, the population levels of phytophagous species are often raised by introducing into their habitat a favourable food plant or by increasing through extensive cultivation their native food plant. Second are those disturbances which result from transferring an insect from its native home into a new habitat where natural checks are absent or ineffective. In the case of phytophagous forms the introduced species may become enormously abundant and its equilibrium position much higher than in its native habitat. Elton (1958) has covered this general subject in his book *The Ecology of Invasions by Animals and Plants*.

Pests of Foreign Origin

Since most pest species are immigrants, it is easy to classify them in the second category. In fact, the introduced pest species usually are of little consequence in their native home where their equilibrium position is kept at a low value by effective natural enemies. Applied biological control attempts to restore the natural balance by duplicating the conditions in the pest's native home through the importation of natural checks, for by introducing effective natural enemies the pest population often may be reduced to the low status that it formerly held in its endemic area. This successful restoration of the natural balance exemplifies the ecological basis for biological control.

Pests of Domestic Origin

It has been thought in the past that the possibilities of biological control are largely limited in each country to those pests which are of foreign origin. There is a growing realization, however, that biological control may be effectively applied to pests of domestic origin. The possibilities in this respect for the biological control of weeds appear to be as good as or even better than those for domestic pest insects.

There is good biological evidence to suggest that native weeds might be suppressed by the introduction of biotic mortality factors from foreign sources. This reasoning is based on the reports of the terrible destruction of the native Bermuda cedars by the accidentally imported diaspine scales *Carulaspis visci* (Schrank) and *Lepidosaphes newsteadi* (Sulc). Thompson (1954) reported that both scales were lethal to the trees, and that *Lepidosaphes* was lethal at a very low density. It is an exciting idea to contemplate the possibility that some noxious native plant, such as poison ivy, might be destroyed through the importation of some alien biotic agent. This agent need not necessarily be an insect, but could well be a plant pathogen. The destruction of the chestnuts in the United States by the chestnut blight, *Endothia parasitica* (Murr.) And. and And., from oriental sources shows the possibilities of such organisms.

There is a growing list of examples of the successful introduction of exotic natural enemies against indigenous insect pests. The most logical approach is to introduce natural enemies of species closely related to the indigenous pest. The successful biological control of the coconut leafmining beetle, *Promecotheca reichei* Baly, in Fiji, furnishes the most outstanding example of work against an indigenous pest. *Pleurotropis parvulus* Ferr., a parasite of the larval and pupal stages, was introduced from Java where it parasitized other species of *Promecotheca*. Complete control occurred within one year (Taylor 1937).

ATTRIBUTES OF AN EFFECTIVE NATURAL ENEMY

Experienced workers in biological control have learned that it is not yet possible to make an entirely reliable prediction on how effective a given exotic entomophagous species will be following its importation and establishment. This is something that at the present time is determined empirically in the field. Neither the behaviour of the introduced species in the laboratory nor its role in its native home is an entirely reliable index of its effectiveness in the new environment. However, certain promising characteristics are often evident prior to introduction. For example, there is the distinction which can be drawn in the native home between natural enemies which are intrinsically capable of maintaining the host at low population levels (i.e., enemies with high searching capacities) and those enemies whose searching ability is such that they can exist only at high host population levels. Thus, the most easily found or most common natural enemy is not necessarily the best. It may be common because the host population is upset for some reason. Indeed, it might often be said that a good natural enemy is a scarce natural enemy.

In spite of the difficulties in their application, repeated efforts have been made to describe the attributes of an effective natural enemy. The prime requisite would seem to be a high searching capacity, that is, the ability to find its host when the host is scarce. This is probably more important than a high fecundity in the natural enemy. In fact, the existence of a somewhat inverse relationship between searching ability and fecundity has been suggested.

Another attribute often considered important is for the beneficial species to be fairly host-specific in its feeding rather than to be polyphagous. At least most successes have resulted from the introduction of rather host-specific entomophagous species. A high degree of host-specificity indicates good bio-physiological adaptation to the host and a fairly direct dependence on changes in the host's population. However, polyphagous species also may have certain advantages which are discussed later under the heading, 'Specific Versus General Predators or Parasites.'

A third attribute—potential rate of increase—is also recognized as being very important, especially in variable environments. This would include a short developmental period and a relatively high fecundity. Thus, several generations of the natural enemy can be produced to one generation of its host, and the natural enemy can overtake its host quickly whenever the host begins to increase in numbers, as, for instance, usually occurs following inclement winters or other adverse climatic conditions.

A fourth characteristic that is also important is the ability of the natural enemy to occupy all the host-inhabited niches and to survive well. Ideally, the host and parasite would have absolutely equivalent distributions. This also means that the natural enemy is well adapted to a broad range of climatic conditions.

Flanders (1947) suggests other attributes which are highly desirable in any entomophagous species, and which often determine its effectiveness because they influence its ability to discover or utilize the host. Essentially, these characteristics merely mean that the natural enemy is well adapted biologically, physiologically, and ecologically to the host.

One practical consideration which might be added to the above list is the fact that the species should be amenable to culture in the insectary. This facilitates the breeding of material for colonization and distribution, and thus makes the early control of the pest more probable.

THE ROLE OF SUPERPARASITISM

One of the attributes of the effective parasite mentioned by Flanders (1947) is the ability to restrict oviposition to hosts suitable for development of the progeny. This includes the ability of the female to distinguish between healthy hosts and those already parasitized, and to avoid ovipositing in the latter. If oviposition takes place in an already parasitized host, it results in either the phenomenon of superparasitism or that of multiple parasitism, depending on whether the parasites are of the same or of different species. Smith (1916) called attention to the importance of distinguishing superparasitism from multiple parasitism with which it has frequently been confused. Whereas superparasitism is the parasitization of an individual host by more larvae of a single parasitic species than can mature in that host, multiple parasitism is the simultaneous parasitization of a host individual by two or more different species of primary parasites. When an individual host is parasitized by more than one larva of a single parasitic species, but all survive, this is either gregarious or polyembryonic parasitism.

Although Fiske (1910) was the first to recognize that superparasitism and multiple parasitism were of more than academic interest, he did not distinguish between them but lumped them together as does Sweetman (1958). Although superficially similar, the two phenomena are actually quite different, especially in their importance to biological control.

When a parasite superparasitizes a host, it usually condemns its own progeny, or at least individuals of its own species, to death, and, although superparasitism thus results in a wastage of progeny and has side effects in that the survivors of such intraspecific competition for a host may be dwarfed and somewhat weakened individuals, it undoubtedly occurs in nature in nearly all parasitic species, particularly when the need to oviposit is great and hosts are scarce. Thus, while this phenomenon is of interest to students of population dynamics and insect behaviour, its occurrence is no reason to bar the introduction of any species. Multiple parasitism has been subjected to the much more serious indictment of causing reduced effectiveness of a promising species through interspecific competition with other primary parasites. This problem is treated fully in the next section (*infra*).

Fiske (1910) believed that generally the female parasite could not distinguish between healthy and parasitized hosts and tended to oviposit indiscriminately in both types. Hence, as the percent parasitization of a host population increased, the female parasite would oviposit in more and more hosts which already had been parasitized. Fiske treated this problem arithmetically and calculated that in a given host population of 100 individuals, about 60 parasite eggs would have to be laid to produce 50 per cent parasitization, about 100 eggs to produce 64 per cent parasitization, and about 450 eggs to produce 99 per cent parasitization.

Salt (1934) noted that theory had far out-stripped experiment, stating that, '... the assumption that parasitism is distributed by chance has not been experimentally examined, and the end result, the superparasitism occurring in nature, has been merely observed and not adequately measured.'

As a result of very ingenious experiments with *Trichogramma evanescens* Westw., Salt (1934) concluded that *Trichogramma* is able to distinguish between healthy hosts and those already parasitized and that it tends to avoid attacking the latter. However, when hosts are few or when the parasite fails to find unparasitized hosts, superparasitism does occur. This, he says, complicates any analysis of the interaction of parasite and host populations for when a number of parasites oviposit among an equal number of hosts, neither the 100 per cent parasitism to be expected from a perfect distribution, nor the 63 per cent parasitism to be expected from entirely random distribution results, but something between them. The fact that some discrimination and some superparasitism occur prevents an easy arithmetical solution of the problem.

Lloyd (1938) suggested that the incidence of superparasitism in the field cannot be referred to any single constant cause. If only parasitized hosts are accessible, the female tends to retain her eggs rather than deposit them. The exercise of this restraint in the case of *Ooencyrtus kuwanai* (How.) is shown to be related to the developmental stage of the parasite in the parasitized host; the age and condition of the ovary of the female; and the number and nature of the hosts available.

Lloyd (1940) says that the question of the relative mortalities in superparasitism and multiple parasitism in any two or more species is one which appears to have been overlooked, although it is an important consideration in gauging the alleged deleterious effects of multiple parasitism. Lloyd (1940) suggests the possibility that the oviposition responses of the parasites are such as to result in more superparasitism than multiple parasitism.

MULTIPLE PARASITISM AND THE QUESTION OF MULTIPLE IMPORTATIONS

The questions brought up by a consideration of multiple parasitism and other forms of competition between parasites, pathogens, or predators are perhaps the most important in applied biological control because they bear directly on importation policies.

Multiple parasitism occurs when two or more primary species attack the same host individual at the same time. This results in direct competition for food between the parasitic larvae so that usually one fails to mature. Typically, nearly all individuals of one species eliminate those of the less aggressive species. The occurrence of such a phenomenon with the Mediterranean fruit fly and two introduced parasites in Hawaii led Pemberton and Willard (1918) to develop the hypothesis that multiple parasitism was detrimental because the supposed inherently better parasite was greatly decimated when competing as larvae with the other species. Hence, they believed it would have been better to have introduced only one. Thus, regardless of the validity of their hypothesis, the problem is posed as to whether in foreign importation of parasites it is better to seek out the one 'best' parasite (the authors know of no really reliable means of determining this) for importation or to import as many as possible and take a chance on multiple parasitism occurring between two or more species. An alternative choice would be to screen each new import and reject those which exhibit multiple parasitism and are intrinsically superior (see Smith 1929, for terms). A similar problem occurs when a fairly good parasite already is established and the decision must be made whether or not to import additional species. However, if more than one species is imported, and even if multiple parasitism does not occur, types of competition other than multiple parasitism can be expected to occur and presumably be detrimental to one or the other species. Thus our problem is really much broader than that posed by multiple parasitism alone, and it becomes one of whether multiple importations and the resulting competition which occurs between all species preying on the host produces a greater total mortality of the host, i.e., better control, than would the best one or possibly two or three natural enemies acting alone. This broader problem is not restricted to parasites, but includes predators and pathogens as well. The question is, will the introduction of new natural enemies be likely to reduce the average total host mortality which already occurs, and cause a rise in the equilibrium position?

Smith (1929a) analysed the problem of multiple parasitism as presented by Pemberton and Willard (1918) and largely refuted their claims. Briefly, they concluded that *Opius humilis* Silv. acting alone would have caused greater mortality of the host, the Mediterranean fruit fly *Ceratitis capitata* (Wied.), than the mortality actually occurring from all the introduced fruit fly parasites. This was ascribed largely to the fact that larvae of the other parasites, and in particular those of *Opius tryoni* (Cam.), always eliminated the larvae of *O. humilis* when they occurred together in the same host. On the basis of results secured just after the introduction of *O. humilis*, Pemberton and Willard were led to believe that *O. humilis* had the best potential. One reason for that was that *O. humilis* had the higher reproductive capacity. Smith (1929a) points out that inherent reproductive capacity alone is rarely if ever an indication of the success of a parasite in the control of its host, hence the higher prolificacy of *O. humilis* meant little. Then, through the use of very convincing logic, Smith concludes that multiple parasitism will never result in a lesser total mortality of the host than would have occurred if one or the other parasitic species had been acting alone. Conversely he says that in many cases a greater total host mortality will result. He uses the data of Pemberton and Willard (1918) and Willard and Bissel (1926) to show that even though the per cent parasitization by *O. humilis* decreased from 1915 to 1921, the total parasitization by *O. humilis*, *O. tryoni*, etc., was greater than that caused originally by *O. humilis* alone.

Willard and Mason (1937), continuing the work begun by Pemberton and Willard, present parasitization data for the period 1914 to 1933 which show that total parasitization in all fruits in 1915 when *O. humilis* was acting virtually alone was less than in subsequent years when *O. tryoni* and others were well established even though *O. humilis* was reduced in effectiveness by competition with the others.

The most significant data bearing on this problem relate to parasitization by three species of *Opius* on coffee berries in the Kona district of Hawaii for the twenty-year period, 1914 to 1933. The striking part of this case is that coffee is the only crop of several attacked by the Mediterranean fruit fly where completely satisfactory biological control occurred, and it is also the one where the most intensive multiple parasitism and competition occurred. That this intense competition between these three species was not detrimental to over-all biological control is shown by the degree of infestation of coffee berries by the fruit fly before (1916–24) and after (1925–33) the time when *O. humilis* was virtually completely eliminated. During the early period there was a good degree of biological control with an average of 0·4 larva per coffee berry. After the disappearance of *humilis* from the complex due to multiple parasitism, the degree of control became even better and there was an average of only 0·1 larva per coffee berry. Thus we must conclude that in the case of the Mediterranean fruit fly and its parasites, multiple-species introductions were advantageous regardless of the occurrence of multiple parasitism between the species.

Inasmuch as, in most other biological control projects involving multiple-species introductions, data have not been published regarding the actual occurrence of multiple parasitism, we will review some of these projects from the broader viewpoint of the effect of interspecific competition on total parasitization or on the total degree of biological control.

Pemberton (1948a) shows that a succession of introductions of six species of egg parasites of the sugar-cane leafhopper between 1905 and 1916, plus the introduction of an egg predator in 1920, added to the total degree of control. *Paranagrus optabilis* Perk., introduced from Australia in 1905, more or less greatly reduced leafhopper populations by 1907; other species apparently added little until the introduction of *Ootetrastichus formosanus* Timb. from Formosa in 1916 proved additionally helpful to the other parasites. Finally, the introduction of an egg predator, *Cyrtorhinus mundulus* (Bredd.), from Australia in 1920 resulted in a much improved and very excellent degree of biological control. Competition from the well-established and rather effective egg parasites did not prevent this.

Van den Bosch and Haramoto (1953) in a study of the effectiveness of introduced parasites of the oriental fruit fly, *Dacus dorsalis* Hend., in Hawaii showed that *Opius longicaudatus* (Ashm.) increased rapidly following its release on Oahu in 1948, but suddenly lost its dominant position during the latter half of 1949 to *Opius vandenboschi* Full. which had been released initially about the same time. In turn, *O. vandenboschi* was replaced during 1950 by *Opius oophilus* Full. which had become established in 1949. Each of these replacements was accompanied by a higher total parasitization and a greater reduction in fruit fly infestation. By late 1951 both *O. longicaudatus* and *O. vandenboschi* had nearly disappeared from the complex. Laboratory studies of multiple parasitism showed *O. longicaudatus* to be intrinsically inferior to *O. vandenboschi*, and *O. vandenboschi* to be intrinsically inferior to *O. oophilus*. According to Clausen (1956a) and Bess and Haramoto (1958b), *O. oophilus* has maintained its dominance and the same high degree of parasitization (about 70 per cent) since 1950, with the other two species contributing little.

In Mexico the establishment of five competing oriental species of parasites of the citrus blackfly, *Aleurocanthus woglumi* Ashby, has resulted in an excellent degree of biological control in nearly all areas with, however, different species producing control in different ecological areas (Paul Oman 1959 personal communication). Thus *Eretmocerus serius* Silv., which gave excellent control in Cuba and other countries (Clausen 1958b) was largely a failure in Mexico because of adverse climatic conditions, but between *Amitus hesperidum* Silv., *Prospaltella clypealis* Silv., *P. opulenta* Silv., and *P. smithi* Silv., complete biological control was produced. In general, *Amitus hesperidum* is the dominant parasite throughout Mexico but in the dry areas of the north-west *P. opulenta* is most important. *P. clypealis* is also widely effective and as a whole is more important than *P. opulenta*. *P. smithi* and

Eretmocerus are of only local or occasional importance (Paul Oman 1959 personal communication).

Many other cases of a similar nature could be cited. Multiple introductions, whether simultaneous or spread over a period of time, have apparently nearly always added something to the effectiveness of host population regulation, either in time or space, regardless of the intense competition which occurs between the parasitic and/or predatory species for the hosts.

Utida (1953*b*) studied experimental laboratory populations where two parasite species competed for a single host species, and compared the results with those obtained when each species of parasite operated singly. It should be noted that his results and conclusions are based on the relative percent parasitization obtained in a single generation, and do not represent populations in equilibrium, hence have little application to field conditions. Nevertheless he found that the better parasite produced a higher parasitization (in one generation) acting alone, than it and a second parasite species did when acting together, and he concluded that Smith's (1929*a*) theory on multiple parasitism is not always valid. On the other hand, in similar experimental tests using two species of *Aphytis* and their host, *Aonidiella aurantii* (Mask.), we found that the two species of parasites acting together in a single generation produced a higher total parasitization than the better one acting alone.

Aside from theoretical considerations, some biological information would indicate that situations could occur where the introduction of additional parasites might be deterimental. There seems to be little indication that an additional newly introduced species would do other than produce better biological control of the host, if it is more efficient than the already established species. However, if it became superior only during certain annual periodic increases of the host and during this period so modified the host population by attacking certain stages that the host changed from an uneven-brooded to an even-brooded condition, then the other natural enemies might be adversely affected to the extent that the host population would be higher on the average. Ullyett (1947) has called such factors 'catastrophic' and has shown that an epizootic occurring in an insect population can result in subsequent higher pest populations than occurred before the epizootic. It is even possible that the introduction of a single parasite or predator species in the absence of any other established natural enemies could result in a higher average host-population density. This could occur only with an inefficient parasite which, for example, might destroy just enough larvae to reduce competition between larvae for food and hence result in a greater total surviving into the pupal and adult stages. Utida (1950) has postulated such an occurrence on the basis of limited laboratory studies. As yet, nothing of this sort has been reported in nature.

On the positive side of the ledger, biological observations indicate that various advantages usually accrue from multiple introductions. First, a series of parasites which live in the same habitat but attack a sequence of host stages is advantageous because environmental variations which adversely affect one species may favour another, so that the second will tend to compensate for the first (see following discussion on the sequence theory, this chapter), and even under more uniform conditions total host mortality should be greater. Second, when several parasite species are established on a common host, they are more likely to inhabit the total geographical range of the host than would one alone, i.e., there will usually be a broader habitat coverage. Third, past records of field projects demonstrate that improved results frequently accrue from multiple-species introduction and that detrimental effects rarely occur. Fourth, multiple introductions increase the chances of obtaining a given species which will attack more than one host in the new environment. This enables the natural enemy to overcome difficulties of even-broodedness or host scarcity which might occur if only one host were involved.

In the light of all available evidence, we must concur with Smith (1929) who stated that, 'On theoretical grounds as well as on the data so far available, the policy of entomologists in introducing all available primary parasites of an injurious species is justified, and . . . this policy should be continued.' Balch, Clark, and Brown (1958, p. 810) agree that, 'There would seem to be little likelihood of prejudicing the success of biological control by the introduction of a number of species. . . . The larger the number of species in the complex the greater the chances that it will regulate the population of the prey with some degree of constancy in a varied and changing environment. . . . The probable compensating effects of a large complex of predators seem to justify the introduction of all available species.'

If multiple introduction of new natural enemies is accepted as a policy and undertaken, the effect of competition between the established and the newly imported natural enemies again assumes importance. Not in this case because of any detrimental effects which might upset the host-population balance, but rather because a new introduction, even though intrinsically more effective, may conceivably be overwhelmed by the numerical superiority of the already established species unless it is colonized under conditions which enable it to attain a good start. Principally, this would include selecting sites which momentarily, at least, had a minimum of established natural enemies, selecting sites in varying habitats, and colonizing as large numbers as possible.

THE SEQUENCE THEORY

This constitutes a special phase of the problem discussed in the section on multiple parasitism. It is here treated separately because of the controversial nature of the sequence theory. In 1910, Fiske put forth the belief that in the control of an insect like the gypsy moth it would be inexpedient to depend upon the parasites which confine their attack to any one stage of the host. This was more fully developed into the sequence theory by Howard and Fiske (1911) in which they concluded that with the gypsy moth or the brown-tail moth, parasitic control must come about through a variety of parasites, working together harmoniously, rather than through one specific parasite. They believed that the successful biological control of the gypsy moth depended upon whether or not they would be able to import and establish in America each of the component parts of an effective sequence of parasites.

The sequence theory was very effectively criticized by Thompson (1923a), and it is generally believed now that while a sequence of parasites may sometimes be desirable, nevertheless a single effective parasite on one stage of the host may well bring about control. This has proved to be true in the majority of highly successful projects. A recent striking case of this was reported by Tooke (1955) on the control of the eucalyptus snout beetle, *Gonipterus scutellatus* Gyll., in southern Africa by an egg parasite *Patasson nitens* (Grlt.). As a result of his experience, Tooke was not convinced that the use of several enemy species is always the better course, and in the campaign against *Gonipterus* it is difficult to see how the introduction of additional parasitic species could have helped materially.

Not only did this project show that a single parasite could be effective in the control of a holometabolous host on a subcontinental area, but it also demonstrated that the belief that egg parasites are relatively unimportant is fallacious.

Tooke (1955) remarked, 'The control of *Gonipterus* by the mymarid egg-parasite may be the exception which proves the rule, but it does show that an egg-parasite can be as efficient as a larval parasite in this work. The success of the mymarid is no doubt due to the fact that it is a specific parasite of the eggs of *Gonipterus* and its energies are thus not dissipated over a number of hosts. It would seem that the efficiency of a parasite depends entirely upon the role it plays in the biotic complex of its host in the country of origin. In some cases, as in this, egg parasites play the major role in keeping the host in check; in other cases larval or pupal parasites may be the most important.'

We conclude that a sequence of parasites may not always be necessary to achieve a satisfactory degree of biological control, but if the degree of control is not sufficient, a more complete sequence of natural enemies may make it so.

RELATIVE VALUE OF PARASITES AND PREDATORS IN BIOLOGICAL CONTROL

It is usually possible to distinguish predators as being those organisms that must consume more than one individual host (prey) in order to reach maturity. On the other hand, parasites develop to the adult stage on a single host individual. Both categories possess a general similarity as a parameter in population dynamics for they are lethal and tend to be density-dependent mortality factors.

Since a larval predator consumes many individuals of the pest during its life, while a larval parasite consumes only one, it might appear that a predator has greater destructive power than a parasite and would consequently be more important as a controlling agent. However, our empirical knowledge tends to indicate that this is not the case, for Clausen (1956a) reports that of 95 species of entomophagous insects imported and established in continental United States, 81 are parasites and 14 are predators and the data in chapter 24 show that about two-thirds of the successes in biological control have resulted from parasites. It has been suggested that the frequent superior performance of parasites is due to the fact that their food requirements permit them to maintain a balance with their hosts at lower host population densities than is inherently possible in a predator-prey relationship. The fact that a larval predator must consume several prey individuals in order to develop to maturity may necessitate a greater supply of food in a given area. Furthermore, it has been noted that the host finding is done by the highly motile winged female parasite, and while adult predators may locate host areas, the larval stage of the predator must still find hosts and is therefore relatively handicapped if they are scarce. However, this argument is somewhat weakened by the studies of Fleschner (1950) on the searching capacity of certain predators. He found, for example, that the distance travelled by a newly hatched larva of *Chrysopa plorabunda* Fitch (= *californica* Coq.) from the time it hatched until it died from not having food or water was 702 feet. Thus, a predator with a high searching ability could be superior to a parasite with a poor one.

Because there are many data more favourable to parasites than to predators, there has been a tendency to discount somewhat the role of predators in the control of agricultural pests. This view has also been encouraged by the analysis of the action of vertebrate predators. However, as the techniques employed in measuring the effectiveness of natural enemies in the field have become more refined, there has been an increasing awareness of the importance of the predatory species. It is worth noting that this view has been accelerated in recent years by the outbreaks of formerly secondary pests following the application of certain insecticides. In certain cases these chemicals had a particularly selective effect on certain predators, and consequently put into sharp focus the value of these species which previously had not been fully appreciated.

Some of the most spectacularly successful examples of biological control have been achieved by the use of predacious species. In this regard there immediately springs to mind the control of cottony-cushion scale by the vedalia beetle in California, the reduction of the coconut scale by *Cryptognatha nodiceps* Mshll. in Fiji, and the suppression of the sugar-cane leafhopper by *Cyrtorhinus mundulus* in Hawaii. This has been explained, at times, on the grounds that these particular predators were almost specific in their feeding habits and consequently quickly responsive to changes in host density. There has been a belief that most predators by contrast are somewhat general feeders and accordingly their numbers from year to year are not strongly influenced by the abundance or scarcity of any particular species of insect among the many upon which they prey. Thompson (1929b, 1951a) has pointed out that, in spite of the rather common belief and the indications given by the literature, the coccinellids are remarkably specific in their habits. This probably also applies to many other predators that may not be absolutely restricted in feeding habits but are very limited in their choice of habitat.

The predators which tend to inhabit a rather restricted niche and yet may be somewhat general feeders can be very important in the suppression of agricultural pests. DeBach (1951) considers them as a sort of balance wheel in the pest–natural enemy complex. He stated . . . 'Although in themselves perhaps incapable of causing natural control below economic levels, they slow down the rate of increase of potential pests or reduce peak infestations when specific natural enemies have perhaps been reduced by other factors.'

Thompson (1929b) noted that the relative importance of parasites and predators as controlling agents could be decided only by careful investigations in the field. He concluded, 'The part played by predaceous insects has been underestimated; that they are worthy of more careful attention than they have generally received, and that the possibility of their utilization in practical work is considerable.' The vital role of predation was clearly demonstrated by Huffaker and Kennett (1956) in field experiments with the predatory mites, *Typhlodromus* spp. in the control of the cyclamen mite, *Steneotarsonemus pallidus* (Banks), on strawberries. The authors point out, 'Broad statements minimizing the role of predators in regulating the numbers of their prey are invalid. In this example, predators controlled the fortunes of the prey; other causes of mortality appeared to be only a substitute for death by predation.' In summing up their five-year study they conclude, 'The results have significance in relation to theories of population dynamics, a field in which there have been few controlled experiments. Some recent work on vertebrate predation has been interpreted as more generally applicable to all predation than is justified. Conclusions minimizing the role of such predation in the regulation of prey populations is not transferable to the field of biological control of insects, for example.'

The role of vertebrate predators in the control of insects is not completely clear, and there are differences of opinion on it. Howard and Fiske (1911) pointed out that such predators are not affected by the abundance or scarcity of any single item in their varied menu. Since their numbers from year to year are '. . . not influenced by the abundance or scarcity of any particular species among the many upon which they prey they cannot be ranked as elements in the facultative control of such species.'

Smith (1935) agreed with this view in his discussion of density-independent and density-dependent mortality factors. He said, 'There is still another category which destroys a percentage that decreases as the density increases. This type of factor is well illustrated by many insectivorous birds and mammals, the numbers of which are not strongly influenced by the numbers of any particular species of insect and which for this reason can have no important effect on its average density.'

While this analysis seems generally true, there are special situations where the vertebrate predators form an important component of the natural-enemy complex (see chapter 4). For example, MacLellan (1958) found that the eastern hairy woodpecker and the northern downy woodpecker are both important in control of the codling moth in Nova Scotia.

In summarizing the comparative roles of parasites and predators, it appears that while practical work has more frequently demonstrated the importance of parasites, there is an increasing appreciation of the effectiveness of predators. Certainly in some enemy complexes the predators are clearly dominant. In recent years, both the repercussions from the use of selective and powerful insecticides and the results of carefully conducted ecological studies have focused attention on the importance of the general predators in nature. In the past their effectiveness has often been either disregarded or dismissed as minimal, but now there is an awareness of the stabilizing influence of this massive reservoir of naturally occurring predators. It is apparent that each case is *sui generis* and the comparative roles of parasites or predators in a given instance cannot be foretold. This can be ascertained only by field evaluations after their establishment, and it is clear that either predators or parasites are fully capable of effecting complete commercial control of pests.

SPECIFIC VERSUS GENERAL PREDATORS OR PARASITES

Although the value of the general predators has been mentioned, there is a belief among biological workers that the best possibilities of achieving the greatest degree of control are by using monophagous (specific) parasites or predators. This belief is borne out by the most notable successes in biological control where the controlling species was one tending to be specific to the host. However, if the host population is periodically depressed by other factors, a specific natural enemy will suffer most, whereas a more general feeder will maintain itself on other hosts during adverse periods. The utilization of specific plant feeders in biological control of weeds obviously is necessary because of the risks of more general phytophagous insects doing damage to commercial crops.

The operative steps by which a parasite or predator becomes restricted in its feeding habits are outlined in chapter 6. It is clearly evident that a natural enemy which tends to be specific on a given host is inherently closely attuned to the host species and responsive to changes only in its density. While in actuality very few natural enemies are strictly monophagous, many are definitely oligophagous and are sufficiently restricted to a particular host to be considered as offering the greatest promise for initial trials in biological control projects. These are the species most often deliberately sought out and imported. However, this should not lead to the exclusion of more general feeders. Success must still be found by empirical trials.

A host of widespread distribution that feeds on a number of plants and lives in many ecological situations will have a complex of natural enemies that varies qualitatively and quantitatively in these different situations. It is obvious to field workers in an area of great ecological diversity and steep climatic gradients, such as California, that a given parasite species may not be equally effective throughout the range of its host. This shows not only a high degree of specificity in host relations, but, as Thompson (1951a) points out, a very high degree of specificity in the selection of, or adaptation to, an environment. Hence, a high degree of specificity may be correlated with less adaptability to environmental spread or change. This needs more study and certainly more general recognition by workers in biological control. It is quite probable that importations which did not succeed in establishing themselves in one locality may be very successful in a different ecological situation. In fact, the reasons for failure of establishment have seldom been ascertained, and yet it is from an explanation of these failures that biological control might gain much valuable knowledge.

IMPORTANCE OF RACES OR STRAINS OF NATURAL ENEMIES

Associated with the diversity of habitats with which an imported parasite may have to cope is the matter of races or strains of the particular species. As Smith (1941) pointed out, there are races of insects which are not, so far as we know, visibly distinguishable from each other. They differ in habitat, in physiological or psychological characters rather than in structure or colour. With increasing experience in biological control it becomes more evident that many so-called species are often composed of races, strains, or sibling species which are morphologically indistinguishable but are very distinct biologically. Thus, any given parasitic species may have forms which are adapted to different host species or to different habitats. Such forms may or may not interbreed one with the other, and usually their exact taxonomic status will be difficult to determine. The important thing is to recognize that such forms exist and that from the viewpoint of practical biological control these forms may be just as important as distinct species.

In biological control it is the behaviour of the entomophagous individual that determines its usefulness. For example, those that can find hosts at low densities, those that have aggressive tendencies, and those that can withstand adverse periods are the ones that will be most effective as control agents. Accordingly, if any species has within it a strain or race which exhibits advantageous characters, it should be introduced. The problem is to distinguish such forms. Clausen (1936) pointed out, 'At one time it was assumed that a given species had a definite and fixed capacity in relation to its host and that this applied throughout its range of distribution. Recent work has demonstrated that this is not the case. . . . Heretofore we have obtained our supply [of parasites] for importation from localities where large numbers could be more easily and cheaply secured. It now appears, however, that to secure the maximum results, each species must be studied throughout its range, and importations made from different regions, if there is reason to believe that a difference in habit or quality exists.' We would go a little further than this and simply say that importations definitely should be made from different regions throughout the range of the parasite or predator.

Sometimes these biological entities are actually entitled to the rank of a species and are entirely distinguishable from a known species in every way except on a morphological basis, the conventional taxonomic criterion. Biological control workers have learned to be alert for such cryptic, sibling species and therefore no longer discard a parasite merely because it appears morphologically identical to a species already introduced (Hafez and Doutt 1954; DeBach 1960).

Cases in point include two strains of *Comperiella bifasciata* How., one of which attacks the yellow scale, *Aonidiella citrina* (Coq.), and the other the California red scale, *A. aurantii*. Similarly, a strain of *Prospaltella perniciosi* Tower from Georgia was found to attack successfully the San Jose scale in California but not the California red scale, whereas a strain of *P. perniciosi* obtained later from Formosa successfully attacks the California red scale (DeBach 1958a). At the present time we are working with several strains or sibling species of *Aphytis*, all of which attack the

California red scale and are indistinguishable from sister strains except for biological differences and failure to interbreed. A few years ago these would have been passed over as already established in California (DeBach 1960). Clausen (1936) states that two forms of *Tiphia popilliavora* Roh. are known and that there is a distinct difference in reproductive capacity and time of emergence between stocks from Korea and those from Japan. He felt that the stock exhibiting later seasonal emergence should have a distinct advantage in the eastern United States because more host grubs are suitable for parasitism at that time.

Aside from the consideration of rather discrete biological strains which may be reproductively isolated, the disturbing possibility exists that in the introduction of exotic species we are not actually acquiring a true genetic representation of the species. Not infrequently the initial stock culture of a beneficial species may be started with the progeny from a single fertilized female. It is not unusual in the quarantine handling of the imported material to obtain only three or four females from a shipment, and from them, or only one of them, the insectary production begins which ultimately may yield the thousands that are colonized in the field. By beginning with such a small stock, we may be establishing a parasite that only partially resembles the parental species in the native home. As Zimmerman (1948) has stated, 'The impregnated female carries only the genotype of herself and her mate, not the genetic make-up of an inbreeding species population. She does not represent an average of her population. The implications and potentialities of such action are great.' In part, this means that the possibilities of adaptation to the new environment may be greatly reduced.

It would appear that the application of genetics to biological control has distinct possibilities, and this has been treated by DeBach (1958a). According to him, it is only when naturally occurring races are unknown, or show no advantages, that a programme for artificial development of an adaptive race should logically be undertaken. Possibilities along this line are explored in chapter 14.

THE EFFECT OF HYPERPARASITES

Hyperparasitism occurs when a parasite attacks and develops on another parasite. There are several degrees of hyperparasitism and this can be illustrated in the following example. If a parasite attacks a host which is phytophagous, then the entomophagous species is termed a primary parasite. If, in turn, this primary parasite is itself parasitized, then its enemy is called a secondary parasite. The food chain would thus be host, primary parasite, secondary parasite, tertiary parasite, and so on. Degrees of parasitism beyond secondary are reported but are not very common, and this discussion restricts itself to a consideration of the hyperparasites that are termed secondary.

It is the policy in biological control to prevent the introduction of secondary parasites. For this reason, carefully conducted studies are made of parasitic propensities of the introduced material in the quarantine laboratory before releases are made. This policy of exclusion of hyperparasites is based on the notion that the secondaries may seriously impair the functioning of a primary parasite in the control of its host. While this seems to be a logical idea, it has never been subjected to rigorous experimental or field analysis as far as the authors are aware. Flanders (1943*a*) states, 'The influence of hyperparasitism on the effectiveness of parasites used in biological control is difficult if not impossible to evaluate. In the laboratory, hyperparasitism may completely eliminate a primary parasite. Only by establishing a hyperparasite in a region where primary parasites are responsible for keeping a pest under control can the influence of hyperparasitism be tested.' Obviously, this would never be done deliberately, but there are alternative methods. One is to eliminate or retard the hyperparasite by the use of a differential insecticide. This possibility was demonstrated by DeBach (1949) with the mealybug parasite *Anarhopus sydneyensis* (Timb.) and the hyperparasite *Lygocerus* sp. where DDT had little effect on the primary parasite but greatly retarded the secondary. This study strongly indicated that the hyperparasite sufficiently depressed the efficacy of the primary parasite during the summer months that the host mealybug population increased considerably.

On the basis of theoretical studies, Nicholson (1933) concluded that the adverse influence of hyperparasites on the control of pests has been overemphasized, and that the lack of success which has been attributed to the presence of hyperparasites has probably been due to some other cause.

According to Muesebeck and Dohanian (1927) a primary parasite may be overwhelmed by hyperparasites before it can succeed in firmly establishing itself in the region to which it has been transported.

While it is possible that hyperparasites already present in a region may have in some cases prevented, or at least delayed, the establishment of introduced primary parasites, there are no known data available to show that this has actually ever occurred. It is perhaps significant that the introduced primary parasites that have brought about control of a pest are species that are equally successful in their native habitat, in spite of attack by their natural enemies. In any event, it is doubtful that the initial population density of a newly colonized parasite would be great enough to furnish an ample host base for secondaries.

There is a belief that hyperparasites are usually less discriminating than primary parasites in their selection of hosts, but this perhaps should be carefully examined. According to Flanders (1943*a*), 'The generally indiscriminate host relations of hyperparasites seem to indicate that only rarely will an introduced species do more than replace a native species through competition . . . the introduced hyperparasite is likely to find all suitable niches occupied.'

Muesebeck and Dohanian (1927) state that hyperparasitism is a most interesting field of insect behaviour that has been only superficially investigated, but which is intimately related to problems in economic entomology. They reason that hyperparasites play an important part in the maintenance of the balance between insect species in nature. The phenomenon needs very careful study from the aspects of population dynamics. There is some evidence that the secondaries may not be as serious as formerly supposed, but in spite of the fact that the relative importance of hyperparasitism seems diminished rather than increased as a result of a better understanding of the subject, this affects the matter scarcely at all. In biological control work the greatest care is still exercised to eliminate hyperparasites.

The cautions which apply to the introduction of hyperparasites carry over to parasites which attack predators or weed-feeding insects. Technically these latter are primary parasites, but from a practical viewpoint they fall in the same category as hyperparasites. Certain ones are known to become very common and there is no reason to believe that at times they do not seriously depress their host populations.

THE ISLAND THEORY IN BIOLOGICAL CONTROL

Some of the most striking successes of biological control have occurred in insular areas such as Hawaii and Fiji, whereas, particularly in earlier times, a rather high proportion of projects in the continental areas have failed to control the pests as hoped. Accordingly, some doubt has been expressed concerning the utility of biological control in continental areas, and it has been theorized that the method might be limited to insular areas. Where spectacular results were obtained on parts of continents, such as in California, the proponents of the island theory have said that these did not vitiate their theory but, in fact, confirmed it, as these particular areas were 'ecological islands' (Imms 1931).

The importance of such a theory to the underlying policies in biological control prompted Thompson (1928*b*) to make a study of biological control and parasite introduction in continental areas. He noted that three objections could be raised to use of biological control in continental areas. First, he compared the continents of Europe and North America and called attention to the similarity between the biota of the two continents. The indigenous insect faunas of both these continents have in common many of the principal genera of injurious insects, and what is true of these pests is also true of their parasites.

The second objection, therefore, springs from the view that the transfer of a phytophagous insect from the Palaearctic to the Nearctic region and *vice versa*, should not produce any marked change in its economic status, in so far as this is regulated by its natural enemies, since there exists in both regions a variety of similar parasitic species of polyphagous but similar habit, apparently sufficient to replace automatically those by which the introduced insect was controlled in its native home. This view was actually taken by the well-known American ento-mologist, Fernald, in 1896, when the importation into America of the parasites of gypsy moth was first being considered. His attitude was probably responsible, at least in part, for the delay in the inauguration of the work of importation (Thompson 1928*b*).

The third argument considered by Thompson was found in the behaviour of certain hyperparasites as described by Howard and Fiske (1911). They found that the cocoons of *Apanteles fulvipes* (Hal.) were attacked by some 25 species of secondary parasites in Europe and Japan. Naturally, great care was taken to prevent the escape of these secondary forms, and as a result the rapid multiplication of the braconid was expected in America. However, after the establishment of the species it was found that the cocoons of *fulvipes* were attacked to practically the same extent as in its native home by an almost equally great variety of hyper-parasites.

Thompson (1928*b*) then carefully analysed these objections and showed that the parasites of insects inhabiting continental areas play a real part in the natural control of their hosts and that the increase and spread of the latter when transported to new areas are due to their escape from these parasitic and predaceous enemies, which are not replaced by any effective agencies of this type in the new environment.

The probability, therefore, is that the absence of parasitic or predaceous enemies is the real cause of the increase of the imported species and thus there is a good *prima facie* case for the introduction of parasites in continental areas.

Thompson concluded that although few unqualified successes on continents from parasite introduction could be reported in 1928 the results even then tended in general to support the theoretical arguments in favour of the employment of the natural enemies of introduced insects in continental areas.

There is now a growing list of successful examples of biological control in continental areas (see chapter 24, table 12). A splendid recent example of control on a continental area (South Africa) is described by Tooke (1955) in the suppression of the eucalyptus snout-beetle, *Gonipterus scutellatus*, by the egg parasite, *Patasson nitens*. Tooke noted that when biological control is applied to imported pests menacing crops widely distributed over vast continental areas manifold difficulties are encountered, and he was cognizant of the serious doubts expressed as to whether such a method is likely ever to prove really efficient under such conditions. Accordingly he wrote that it is not only surprising that so large a measure of success has been obtained, but it is a strong indication that the potentialities and mechanics of biological control are not yet fully understood.

While it could be argued that the southern and south-western Cape is ecologically an island, the argument certainly cannot apply to the summer rainfall area, or eastern half of South Africa where the parasite is also the controlling factor on *Gonipterus*.

Although the arguments against introducing parasites into continental areas must now be rejected, it was nevertheless true, a few years ago, that by far the greatest proportion of successful control had been obtained in insular areas and in only certain parts of the continents. A principal reason for this—one that should be obvious but never has been pointed out—is that biological control was stressed in islands such as Hawaii and Fiji from the earliest days. For the size of these islands more research was carried out and more importations made than for any other comparable area, except perhaps southern California. The remainder of the explanation of this is to be found in a consideration of the broadest possible relationship between the climate and the role of biotic factors in the regulation of population densities. More discussion of this subject will be found in the first portion of chapter 24.

SALUBRIOUS AND RIGOROUS ENVIRONMENTS AND NATURAL ENEMIES

If we analyse the climatic areas in which biological control has been most successful, it becomes obvious that they are most frequently areas of warm or at least mild climates (see chapter 24, table 12 and discussion). The oceanic islands thus fall in this category, but not particularly because they are islands. In a sense, then, the successes in biological control are to some extent products of latitude. As one goes from tropical latitudes to more rigorous climates we might expect the environment to become somewhat less favourable for many parasites and predators, thus perhaps making a good, regular, and undisturbed natural balance less likely. There would seem to be two major explanations for this: (1) excessive natural-enemy mortality due to climatic extremes, and (2) the more discrete annual cycles of the insect species in temperate climates which require more precise synchronization of host–natural enemy voltinism or diapause.

The adverse effect of climate in negating successful biological control can be illustrated by the reports of Lord and MacPhee (1953), DeBach, Fisher, and Landi (1955), and Burnett (1949). Others are reviewed by DeBach (1958a). In brief, these authors showed that certain parasites may produce good biological control in one area but may fail to do so in another area which is climatically different. The areas need neither be distant geographically nor the climates very distinct. In fact, they may be very close together with climates very similar. One set of conditions may favour the host over the natural enemy and the other may produce the reverse effects. Both differential mortality and differential fecundity of host and natural enemies caused by varying weather conditions are used to explain the results obtained.

On the other hand, it must be remembered that natural enemies, like their hosts, may have become highly adapted to rigorous climatic environments. Attention is directed to the now large numbers of successes in Canada (especially British Columbia), the United States (aside from California and Hawaii), Australia (especially Tasmania) and New Zealand (see chapter 24).

Annual seasonally induced physiological cycles may also tend to upset the host–natural enemy balance. As pointed out by Wigglesworth (1939, p. 67), there exist among insects fairly well-marked physiological types, termed 'heterodynamous' and 'homodynamous.' Certain species are able, under favourable conditions, to reproduce for an indefinite period, generation after generation. Low temperatures will slow down their development, but it is immediately resumed with the return to normal temperatures. Such insects are homodynamous in their annual cycle and in general are the most favourable subjects for biological control.

On the other hand, there are insects which are unable to reproduce continuously throughout the year. After one or more generations in which the individuals develop rapidly, there follows a period of obligatory diapause. During this period there is no further development even if external conditions are favourable to it. Such insects are heterodynamous in their annual life cycles and are generally the most difficult species to suppress by the use of parasites and predators. Therefore, if one looks at the most spectacular examples of biological control one will in most instances find that the pest has a homodynamous annual cycle, which in turn is most likely to occur in a warm climate (see chapter 24).

Generations of insects with the homodynamous pattern tend to overlap and lose their discreteness. Under such a situation all stages of the insect host are present at any one time. This is often important for the effective functioning of certain parasites. For example, *Metaphycus helvolus* (Comp.) succeeds in achieving commercial control of *Saissetia oleae* (Bern.) when all stages of the host scale are present, but is much less effective when the black scale is in an even-brooded condition.

Taylor (1937) emphasized the importance of appreciating the significance, from an economic point of view, of this one-stage condition. '... There is little doubt that many insects, known to be pests in the tropics, are pests simply because they are caused to occur in the one-stage condition by abnormal factors. A few are known, but the effect of this condition in rendering useless the indigenous, and ordinarily efficient, parasites is not generally appreciated. In most of these cases, control by biological means would probably prove practicable, provided only that the parasites introduced for the purpose were selected especially with a view to combating the pests in the one-stage condition; and in tropical countries this applies to any large continental area having a large insect fauna as well as to an island group with a small fauna. It is certain that the great majority of parasites which would ordinarily be effective would be useless in one-stage conditions, but it is nevertheless probable that at least one suitable parasite could be found in nearly all cases, and one is sufficient. The only respect in which these special cases, like that of *P.* [*Promecotheca*] *reichei*, differ from others is in the greater degree of care with which the selection of parasites must be made.'

THE TIME FACTOR AND THE VALUE OF PARTIAL ECONOMIC SUCCESSES IN BIOLOGICAL CONTROL

A number of early workers attempted to calculate mathematically the amount of time required for an introduced parasite to overtake its host. This gave rise to the term 'time factor in biological control.' In 1951, Clausen analysed results from the most successful biological control projects in the world and measured the period of time it had required to achieve full commercial control. From this he derived his three-generation, three-year theory, which states, '... An *effective* parasite or predator might be expected to show evidence of control *at the point of release* within a period of three host generations or three years.'

From his review of the successful examples of biological control, Clausen said, 'We are justified in concluding that natural enemies that are capable of exercising effective control of their hosts will reveal their capacity in this respect very quickly after colonization. In the greater majority of past instances of full commercial control, where the detailed history of the project is available, definite control was achieved, *in the vicinity of the colonization points*, within three host generations after release, and in no instance was the time interval longer than three years, even with hosts having an annual cycle. This is equally true of both parasites and predators. Not a single instance is known of an introduced parasite adapting itself to a new environment to the extent of becoming fully and consistently effective after a period of years of comparative ineffectiveness immediately following establishment. No general statement can be made regarding the time required for partially effective species to attain their maximum control status, as this is governed by changing environmental conditions.

'The attainment of full control in the minimum period after colonization is no assurance that such effectiveness will be permanent, whereas ineffectiveness during the same period constitutes definite evidence that the species will never consistently control its host.

'If the above conclusions regarding fully effective introduced parasites and predators are accepted, it follows that certain other related conclusions may be drawn, and these have a direct bearing on the conduct of current and future projects.

'1. A *fully effective* parasite or predator is always easily and quickly established. In many instances there is an excellent chance of establishment from the release of a single pair.

'2. Failure of a parasite or predator to become established easily and quickly is an indication that it will not be fully effective after establishment is achieved.

'3. The colonization of an imported parasite or predator may well be discontinued after three years if there is still no evidence of establishment. This is on the assumption that the following requirements have been met; (a) that colonization has been effected in each distinct climatic zone occupied by the host; (b) that the colonies were adequate in size and number; (c) that releases were synchronized with the time of abundance of the preferred host stages; (d) that recovery collections were adequate; and (e) that no biological factor directly affecting continued reproduction is involved (i.e., sex differentiation in host relationships, as in *Coccophagus*). This does not imply that establishment might not be attained by further perseverance, but a parasite that requires such efforts will be of little real value and mere establishment will not compensate for the additional cost and labor that are involved.

'It is felt that much time and money have been fruitlessly expended in the past in prolonged efforts to establish many parasites and predators. If a species has not become established after the trial period mentioned, there should be no hesitation in discarding it and concentrating upon another of possibly greater value. Similarly, if a species is established but some evidence of control is not forthcoming within that period, it probably never will be attained and colonization aiming at direct control should therefore be discontinued and the program rearranged on a reduced basis, with greater allowance for natural spread to cover the infested area.'

These views of Clausen's elicited the following response by Thompson (1951b), who did not think the arguments were completely convincing.

'Dr. Clausen's theory may perhaps be criticised as one-sided. His practical objective is the discovery of a species of parasite or predator capable by itself of effecting complete commercial control within a short period of time. The idea that by the accumulation of a number of species attacking different stages or attacking the same stage in different micro-environments, a controlling complex might eventually be built up, is not clearly envisaged by him. Yet when we consider the natural control of an organism in the native environment, we are almost always forced to ascribe the limitation of their numbers to a combination of factors, biotic and physical, varying from time to time, and from point to point. Rarely do we find cases in which a species is held down to a low numerical level by a single parasite or predator.'

A critique of the time factor was published by Sellers in 1953. He cautioned that an enemy that is to become useful but not completely effective does not show its value within three years; '. . . consequently the adoption of Clausen's conclusions involves a danger of discontinuing programmes prematurely.'

The work of Tooke (1955) suggests merit in the views of each of the above authors. Tooke found that in a twenty-five-year study of the control of the eucalyptus snout-beetle by the mymarid egg parasite there was a difference in the time required to effect degrees of control. The following statement would tend to support Clausen's thesis, for Tooke says, '. . . Within three years after the introduction of the Mymarid egg parasite into the south-western Cape, not only was the increase of *Gonipterus* checked, but its population density so greatly reduced that damage to all species of eucalyptus became negligible. In other words, a very effective control was exercised by the parasite in a matter of three seasons.'

The views of Thompson (1951*b*) and Sellers (1953) would seem to have support in Tooke's findings that in some areas of high altitude, an economic control on all species of eucalyptus was obtained in five to fifteen years. The parasite was introduced in 1926 and in 1933 the general position was described as having achieved control in the majority of eucalyptus plantations in the coastal belt but in the high-veld areas no appreciable control had been obtained. 'Since 1933 there has been a steady improvement in the condition of plantations in the highveld. . . .' In 1955, Tooke reported economic control in these areas of high altitude on 62 of a total of 65 species of eucalyptus originally attacked, and a definite but not an economic control on the remaining three species.

Nevertheless, as Thompson (1951*b*) points out, the views advanced by Clausen are a challenge to all workers in the field of biological control: '. . . a working hypothesis which it is imperative to test, since it may eventually form the basis of a drastic and thorough-going revision of our practical programmes and our plans for research.'

We would emphasize the fact that Clausen purposely restricts his discussion to cases of fully effective biological control. He neither infers nor states that cases of partially effective biological control are being considered nor that such cases are unimportant. Unfortunately, some students of the subject seem to have acquired such an inference. Naturally, if newly introduced entomophagous species are somewhat poorly adapted to the host or to the environment, a longer period of time will elapse before their maximum effect is reached. Even though this effect may not result in completely satisfactory biological control, such cases—and they are numerous—may well reduce the frequency or degree of outbreaks and, as a result, the amount of chemical treatment necessary. A case in point has been reported recently by DeBach and Landi (1959*b*) who showed that the partial degree of biological control exerted by *Aphytis lepidosaphes* Comp. against the purple scale, *Lepidosaphes beckii* (Newm.), on citrus, enabled an integration of chemical with biological control which, in test plots, reduced pest control costs by at least 50 per cent of the total required before introduction of the parasite.

SECTION III

Biology and Systematics

CHAPTER 6

Biological Characteristics of Entomophagous Adults

RICHARD L. DOUTT

INTRODUCTION

Parasites and Predators

ENTOMOPHAGOUS SPECIES are frequently classified on the basis of certain functional relationships with their food supply, and an initial and major dichotomy is the distinction between parasites and predators. The test here is whether in their development they consume merely a single individual or must devour several in order to reach maturity. Larval predators require the consumption of more than one individual in order to reach the adult stage, and as a consequence there is developed a predator–prey relationship. On the other hand, parasites are distinguished on the basis that the immature stages develop at the expense of a single individual which is termed the host.

Host–Parasite Relationships

The species with the parasitic habit are subject to further classification into many subcategories, depending upon the mode of attack and the type of host. Accordingly, if the parasite develops within the host's body it is an internal or endoparasite, whereas if it feeds from an external position it is called an external or ectoparasite. A parasite is termed solitary if only one individual develops per host, but many species habitually develop several progeny on a single host and are therefore said to be gregarious. These simple categories are often combined so that there are solitary internal parasites as well as solitary external ones, and of course the gregarious species, too, may be either internal or external feeders.

Classification does not stop here. Since all stages of insect hosts are subject to attack we find there are species which are egg parasites, others are larval parasites some attack pupae, and a few parasitize adults. There may be intermediate categories, such as is seen in certain braconid genera like *Chelonus*, in which the host egg stage is attacked and yet the parasite continues to develop within the host larva. These are appropriately termed egg-larval parasites because their development extends through the two stages of the host.

It has been noted that although entomophagous insects may have a parasitic habit, they differ from true parasites in ways sufficient to set them apart and to justify the use of the distinguishing term *parasitoid*. They are recognized as being different because: (1) the development of an individual destroys its host; (2) the host is usually of the same taxonomic class; (3) in comparison with their hosts they are of relatively large size; (4) they are parasitic as larvae only, the adults being free-living forms; (5) they do not exhibit heteroecism; and (6) as a parameter in population dynamics their action resembles that of predators more than that of true parasites.

There is a system for classifying entomophagous insects based primarily on their host relationships in any particular food chain. For example, if a parasite attacks a host which is phytophagous, then the entomophagous species is termed a primary parasite. If in turn the primary parasite is itself attacked, then its enemies are called secondary parasites. Degrees of parasitism beyond the secondary level are not common. Any degree of parasitism beyond primary is termed hyperparasitism, so this would include those parasites that are secondary, tertiary, and so on.

A very special case of hyperparasitism is found in certain species of Aphelinidae, where the male develops as a hyperparasite but the female develops as a primary parasite. In some species the male develops as a secondary parasite on the young females of its own species. This peculiar habit was discovered by Flanders (1937*a*) and has been termed autoparasitism.

Finally there are two categories of parasitism which are very distinct and should be kept as separate concepts. Unfortunately the literature is contradictory regarding these two different categories of superparasitism and multiple parasitism. Superparasitism is the parasitization of an individual host by more larvae of a *single* parasitic species than can mature in that host. Multiple parasitism on the other hand is the simultaneous parasitization of a single individual host by *two or more different* species of primary parasites. For a definitive treatment of this subject see chapter 5.

BIOLOGICAL CHARACTERISTICS OF ADULT PARASITES

The adult stage of entomophagous insects would be of considerable importance if it merely furnished the morphological basis for the taxonomy of the various groups. But the adult stage does much more than this, for the behaviour of the mature female is commonly the major determinant of the efficiency of the species as a controlling agent of its host. This is so because it is the adult female which finds and selects the host on which, or in which, her progeny will develop. She not only exhibits discrimination in her choice of hosts but, if efficient, she has the ability to find such hosts when they are scarce. These two characteristics of the adult female are tremendously important in biological control.

Thus, as an initial basis for biological control we start with something more than the fact that some arthropods are obligatorily entomophagous, for we note that they are restricted in this feeding habit to a relatively few species. This tendency toward specificity, which implies a high degree of adaptation, is very important in biological control work for if it did not exist, entomophagous forms would act indiscriminately and would not be adapted to or synchronized with the great variety of host types and habits; hence, the introduction of parasites from the country of origin would be a method of very doubtful utility (Thompson and Parker 1927).

While the restricted feeding habit and discrimination among host species are basically important, they alone are not sufficient to make an entomophagous species an effective agent in biological control. An efficient natural enemy must have the ability to find hosts when they are at low population densities. The measure of this ability is termed the 'searching capacity' of the entomophagous species and its importance has been stressed by Muir (1931, p. 25) and by Smith (1939), who concluded that the parasite's capacity to discover hosts in relation to host density more than any other quality determines its effectiveness as a control agency.

The searching ability of a parasite is a composite of several qualities, both physical and psychological, which at best are elusive and difficult to measure. Important among these are: (1) its power of locomotion; (2) its power of perception (of its host); (3) its power of survival; and (4) its aggressiveness and persistence. It is to these and related qualities that we must look for an explanation of a parasite's effectiveness rather than primarily to its potential reproductive capacity. As pointed out elsewhere, reproductive capacity may influence rates of increase but not primarily the average host density or equilibrium position. Relative reproductive capacity of a natural enemy assumes added importance, of course, following periods adverse to the enemy. Then a high reproductive capacity may determine how rapidly it is able to overtake the host. In view of all this, it is obvious that the biological and behaviouristic characteristics of the adult stage merit a thorough discussion, which is the purpose of this chapter. Doutt (1959) has reviewed this general subject.

Premating Period

A premating period after emerging from the pupal stage is generally not a necessary characteristic of the parasitic life. If the opposite sex is present then, in most Hymenoptera, mating will take place immediately after emergence.

Simmonds (1952) found that the males of the pteromalid *Cyrtogaster* sp. show interest in host puparia from which females are about to emerge. In Diptera the tachinids also mate soon after emergence and it seems that an obligatorily prolonged mating period is not ordinarily encountered in parasitic forms. In fact, Simmonds (1948c) found in the ichneumonid *Trachysphyrus inornatus* (Pratt) that mating did not occur if the females were several days old. Similarly, Crandell (1939) found that if mating is delayed for several days the females of *Pachycrepoideus vindemmiae* (Rondani) (= *dubius* Ashm.) do not respond to mating stimuli. However, there are distinct exceptions to this rule, as there are to most rules in biology, and Rosenberg (1934) noted that the ichneumonid *Trichomma enecator* Rossi mated ten days after emergence and that *Ephialtes extensor* Tasch. had a premating period of three weeks. Hagen (1953) found that unlike other members of the braconid genus *Opius* there are two species (*O. oophilus* Full. and *O. vandenboschi* Full.) in which the males exhibit a marked prepaternal period. No sexual behaviour was observed in these males until the spermatozoa migrated to the vesicula seminalis, which required a period of five or six days at 80° F. Temperatures are also important in the case of the miscogasterid *Callitula bicolor* Spin. where Simmonds (1952) found that a low temperature during the pupal period may necessitate a preoviposition period following emergence for the complete maturation of the eggs. Similarly he noted in breeding *Cremnops vulgaris* (Cress.) that adult females emerging from cocoons kept at 83° F commenced oviposition on the day of emergence, but those emerging from cocoons kept at 75° F required a preoviposition period of seven to ten days.

Actually, there is relatively little information on this premating aspect of adult life, but from logical reasoning one would tend to conclude that at least in arrhenotokous Hymenoptera a satisfactory sex ratio could best be maintained by habits which favour mating soon after emergence. This is aided in nature by the fact that the males of most parasitic Hymenoptera have a shorter developmental period than the females, and precede them to the adult stage by one or two days.

Mating Habits

Some attention has been paid to the mating habits of entomophagous Hymenoptera because a form of courtship is seen in the behaviour of the males of many species. Swarming of males in the braconid genus *Blacus* has been observed on warm evenings over a limited area while the females remain on the vegetation beneath until ready to mate (Benson 1944; Donisthorpe 1944; Stelfox 1944). The thynnids have a mating flight in which the apterous females are picked up by the winged males and carried some distance. After copulation the females are returned to the sites where they were captured (Lloyd 1952). This mating habit is far more elaborate than that exhibited by most Hymenoptera which follow a pattern basically similar to that described by Simmonds (1952) for *Spalangia drosophilae* Ashm., where the male becomes excited in the presence of the female and walks towards her with wings alternately vibrating and motionless, approximately in alternate seconds. The vibration takes place with the wings half extended from the body and gives the appearance of a half-flying motion. The male mounts on the female's back and strokes the latter's antennae with its own, meanwhile maintaining the periodic vibrating movement of the wings. After about half a minute of this, the male slips back and turns the tip of its abdomen under that of the female, and copulation rapidly occurs.

In the Hymenoptera it is not uncommon to find that when a female is once fertilized she will resist any further attentions of the males. However, Simmonds (1953) found that a single mating is insufficient to enable a female *Spalangia drosophilae* to produce fertilized eggs throughout her life. Simmond's experiments showed that a male is capable of fertilizing several females in succession. Under field conditions, therefore, both males and females probably mate more than once.

Jackson (1958a) found that a single mating is sufficient to allow fertilized eggs to be laid throughout the life of the mymarid *Caraphractus cinctus* Hal. This tiny wasp, which attacks the eggs of *Dytiscus*, normally mates under water—as the males emerge first and mate with the females as they come out of the host eggs—but mating may also occur out of the water.

Effect of Mating on Female Behaviour

Flanders (1946a) believes that the act of mating or the presence of sperms in the spermatheca has a marked effect on the psychology of the female. In certain Aphelinidae, mating certainly has a remarkable effect in that it causes a significant behaviouristic change in the type of host selected and the manner of oviposition. Extreme examples occur in the genera *Aneristus*, *Casca*, *Coccophagus*, *Euxanthellus*, and *Physcus*. When unmated, the females of certain species in these genera oviposit only hyperparasitically in an insect already parasitized by the same or similar species. Consequently, the male develops only as a secondary parasite of the immature instars of its own or similar species, and the host of the male is never the host of the female. Tropism may be changed by mating. *Nasonia* is negatively phototropic before mating, positively phototropic after.

Flanders (1946a) indicates that the females of certain species are normally multinuptial, mating several times; those of other species are uninuptial and refuse the subsequent males.

Preoviposition Period

The interval between emergence as an adult female and the deposition of the first egg is termed the preoviposition period. No general rule can be stated about this particular interval in the adult life of entomophagous insects, for while it does not occur in some species, in others it is facultative, and in some it is obligatory. The occurrence and duration of a preoviposition period are usually determined by complex physiological processes normally associated with the nutritional requirements of the adults.

Some groups of parasitic Hymenoptera reach the adult stage with a complete complement of ripe eggs, deposit them in a brief period, and develop no other eggs during their life. Such females are termed 'proovigenic' (Flanders 1950), and the production of the eggs in these species is entirely from stored nutrients carried over from the larval stage. Examples of this are perhaps best illustrated by the eucharid parasites of ants which in a short time deposit thousands of eggs in the buds of plants.

Most parasitic Hymenoptera continue to produce eggs throughout the adult stage and these are termed 'synovigenic' by Flanders (1950a). In such cases the production of eggs is dependent on the nutrition of the adult female rather than on the metabolites retained from the immature stages, and as a consequence the nutritional requirements of the adults assume considerable importance in biological control.

Adult Nutrition

The female parasites that are synovigenic require a source of protein for the continuous production of eggs throughout their effective adult life. The protein needs in some species may be supplied by feeding on honeydew or plant nectaries, both of which have been shown to contain free amino acids. There is a growing awareness of the essential role of honeydew in the longevity and fecundity of insect species, and in recent years its importance to entomophagous forms has been clearly indicated by the work of Hagen (1950, 1953).

In a number of species it is quite evident that the location of the food sources of the adults has a strong influence on the distribution and effectiveness of these parasites. Clausen, Jaynes, and Gardner (1933) found that *Tiphia matura* Allen and Jaynes lacks effectiveness as a parasite of the Japanese beetle because it is limited by its adult food habits to areas smaller than that occupied by its host. Detailed information is given by Gardner (1938) on *Tiphia vernalis* Roh., another parasite of the grubs of the Japanese beetle, which feeds almost exclusively on aphid honeydew and tends to congregate where the honeydew is available. Wolcott (1942) notes that tiphiids in Haiti depend on the flowers of wild parsley, *Pastinaca sativa* L., which is prevalent throughout the year. He also shows that *Larra americana* Sauss. has a distribution in Puerto Rico which is determined by the availability of the nectar from two weeds. Allen and Smith (1958), studying *Apanteles medicaginis* Mues., found that certain areas contain many sources of food for adult *Apanteles* and thus favour increased longevity and fecundity. They found that in these areas there is generally a higher degree of parasitism of the lepidopterous host *Colias philodice eurytheme* Bdvl. than in localities where there is not an abundant source of plant nectaries and aphid honeydew. Townes (1958) emphasizes the great importance of direct moisture sources to species of Ichneumonidae, and notes that the great majority of species and individuals occur only where and when rain or dew are regularly available.

While actual parasitism is a function of the immature stages of parasites, nevertheless the adult females of some parasitic Hymenoptera also feed on the hosts. This host feeding and host mutilation on the part of the female constitutes a form of predation (DeBach 1943b; Flanders 1953c). It is well established that this feeding on the body fluids of the host is necessary to obtain protein needed for ovigenesis.

The manner by which the female parasites feed on the host body fluids is of considerable interest. Marchal (1905) reported that *Tetrastichus* fed on the host fluid which exuded from the oviposition wound. This habit was also noted in other species by Howard (1910) and beautifully photographed by Doten (1911) (see figure 12, f. p. 160). These, however, were cases of feeding on exposed hosts, and host-feeding under such circumstances is relatively simple, but a remarkable adaptation for feeding on hosts that are in cells, cocoons, or puparia, and accordingly cannot be reached directly by the female's mouthparts, was discovered by Lichtenstein in 1921. He found that a feeding tube was constructed from a puncture in the host body to the outside of the wall of the cell or other space occupied by the host. The fluids rise to the top of this tube and are there fed upon by the female parasite. A very complete account of the construction of the feeding tube by *Habrocytus cerealellae* (Ashm.) was given by Fulton (1933). He found that after this parasite had stung its host, the Angoumois grain moth, *Sitotroga cerealella* (Oliv.), it withdrew its ovipositor until only the tip penetrated through the wall of the cell which the host larva occupied. Then a viscid fluid was oozed from the ovipositor tip. The ovipositor was used as a spatula, and by twisting and vertical movement the material was worked gradually downward until the host was reached. The ovipositor was then reinserted into the oviposition puncture and the tube completed. After this the ovipositor was withdrawn slowly and carefully, then the female turned about and fed on the fluids from the tube.

While the general view is that the feeding tube is constructed of material produced by the alkaline or Dufour's gland (Flanders 1950a) it has been suggested by Simmonds (1956a) that when *Spalangia drosophilae* feeds on its host the feeding tube is formed by the coagulation around the ovipositor of host-body fluids seeping from the puncture in the pupa.

Flanders (1951, 1953c) has associated the habit of using the ovipositor as a trophic mechanism with the habit of using it to mutilate the host. Flanders (1953c) suggests that the mutilation habit may have been the first step in the evolutionary development of the habit of host-feeding by the parasite adult, since it is usually a prerequisite for such feeding. In such parasites as *Spalangia* and *Nasonia* both feeding and oviposition may occur on the same host individual (Simmonds 1953; Varley and Edwards 1957), while in other species such as *Metaphycus helvolus* (Comp.) the act of feeding renders the host unsuitable as an oviposition site. In this case the host-feeding by the adult parasite is of considerable economic importance (DeBach 1943b).

Ovisorption

If the synovigenic female does not obtain proteinaceous food or is unable to find hosts for an extended period of time, then the ripe eggs in the ovarioles are not deposited but are absorbed (Flanders 1942a, 1945b). Consequently, the sequence of egg production may follow either of two courses: (1) cyclic (ovigenesis-ovisorption-ovigenesis), or (2) linear (ovigenesis-ovulation-oviposition).

A good demonstration of this has been made by Edwards (1954) in his studies on *Nasonia vitripennis* (Wlkr.). He compared the ovarian condition of starved females with ovaries of females fed on honey and with those of females fed on the host blood. When the females were starved, rapid ovisorption occurred and at death (which occurred in five days) there were only three eggs in the ovaries. By comparison, when females fed on honey the ovaries contained 22 eggs after two days and then ovisorption began on the third day and continued indefinitely. Edwards states that in these honey-fed females, eggs continue to mature at a low rate and there appears to be a slow cycle of maturation and resorption, the two processes just keeping pace with each other for the first 16 days so that the condition of the ovaries remains more or less constant. After 16 days, ovisorption is more rapid and by 28 days there are only one or two mature eggs. By contrast with these conditions the effect of feeding on host blood is dramatically reflected in the ovarian condition. The eggs mature rapidly in a female feeding on the host fluids and after five days the ovaries contain 40 mature eggs even though 260 have been deposited.

Edwards (1954) found that an egg which has been resorbed leaves no trace in the ovariole, so that the number of eggs being resorbed at any one time bears no relation to the number of eggs already resorbed. Flanders (1942a) on the other hand found that in *Encyrtus fuliginosus* Comp. the complete exochorion is extruded through the wall of the ovariole and into the body cavity. He wrote that the collapsed shells of the absorbed eggs accumulate in the body cavity, having apparently been forced by the pressure of ovigenesis through the ovariole sheath. This penetration of the sheath can occur readily because the aeroscopic plate of the egg, when the shell is collapsed, forms a sharp, spinelike process.

The phenomenon of ovisorption emphasizes the economy of parasitism, and this conservation of reproductive material is correlated with a high searching capacity. Those species of parasites with long-lived females in which both the cyclic or linear courses of egg disposal occur with equal facility are generally the most effective agents in biological control. This is because they are able to search in low host densities and yet conserve their eggs and restrict oviposition to sites suitable for the development of their progeny (Flanders 1947).

Behaviour in Host Selection

The manner by which hosts are actually found, and the many factors that determine the existence and maintenance of a particular host–parasite relationship are among the most challenging and fascinating research problems in the biology of parasites. It is obvious that to achieve a host–parasite relationship the two species must meet the initial requisites of being seasonally, geographically, and ecologically coincident. But even when these requirements are met, the parasitic relationship may still not be established if there are physical, psychological, physiological, or nutritional barriers.

In the artificial environment of a laboratory it is possible to remove the barriers of time and space which separate potential hosts and parasites in nature, and under these insectary conditions the parasite may breed readily on 'unnatural' or 'factitious' host species. From this and other evidence, the fact emerges that a parasite in nature limits its attack to a fraction of the suitable host species that may be available to it (Salt 1937). This interesting fact and its great importance to biological control have stimulated investigations of the searching behaviour of the adult parasites and the criteria used by the females in selecting their hosts. With entomophagous insects, as Thompson (1951a) has pointed out, behaviour, just like their morphological characteristics, is specific and adaptive, but the adaptive action is based on a foundation of specificity. The understanding of what we call specificity is one of the most important problems involved in the scientific investigation of biological control.

From the investigations which have thus far been carried out it appears that several distinct and consecutive processes of host selection occur (Salt 1935, 1937; Flanders 1953*d*), and through their operation the host list of a parasite becomes restricted to fewer host species than are potentially available to it in nature. There is considerable merit in Salt's analysis of these processes (Salt 1934, 1935, 1937). He classifies them into three broad categories which follow in proper sequence. These are first, *ecological selection* (host finding), then *psychological selection* (host selection), and finally *physiological selection* (host suitability). Another way of considering these eliminative steps is to think of the host selection being achieved through four phases: (1) host habitat finding; (2) host finding; (3) host acceptance; and (4) host suitability. Actually the first two are divisions of Salt's 'ecological selection,' and steps 3 and 4 are equivalent respectively to Salt's 'psychological selection' and 'physiological selection.' A description of the operation of each of these four eliminative steps is as follows:

HOST HABITAT FINDING. The first factor which eliminates many species from the potential host list of a parasite is the failure of the habitats of the two species to coincide. A parasite initially and fundamentally seeks a certain environment, and it does this irrespective of the presence of hosts. Laing (1937) showed that some parasites, when ready to oviposit, do not immediately seek the host itself but first search for a special kind of situation. Thus *Alysia manducator* (Panz.) is a parasite of maggots which live in decomposing carcasses, but it is attracted to meat whether or not the latter contains, or has ever contained, host larvae. However, this is not in agreement with the view expressed by Jacobi (1939), Edwards (1954), and Wylie (1958*a*), who concluded that only meat that had been infested with the host influenced the movement of female *Nasonia vitripennis*.

In species with a preoviposition period the attraction to a particular habitat is associated with the ovarian development. Nishida (1956) found that *Opius fletcheri* Silv. was attracted to a medium irrespective of the presence of larvae of its host, the melon fly, but because there was a preoviposition period of three days, only those female *Opius* that were four to five days old responded to the attraction. A most striking case is described by Thorpe and Caudle (1938) for *Pimpla ruficollis* Grav., a parasite of the pine shoot moth, *Rhyacionia buoliana* Schiff. It appears that during the life of the female *Pimpla* a marked change takes place in its olfactory response to the odour of oil of the host pine tree, and that this change is correlated with the degree of development of the ovaries.

A particular plant species may exert a strong attraction for a parasitic species even though suitable hosts are not present on it. Conversely, the parasite may ignore suitable hosts growing on plants to which it is not attracted.

Muir (1931, p. 22) describes a classical case as follows: 'Phytotropism of phytophagous insects was recognized in the early stages of entomology and has been studied and commented upon by many, especially the fact that the mother insect is attracted to plants on which to lay her eggs, which she never herself uses as food. But the fact that certain predacious and parasitic insects may be attracted to certain plants, apart from the presence of the insects they prey upon, has not received much attention. For this reason the case of *Cyrtorhinus mundulus* is of interest.

'In captivity, *Cyrtorhinus mundulus* will live and breed upon maize, and feed upon the eggs of the corn leafhopper, *Peregrinus maidis* (Ashm.), equally as well as on sugar cane and Perkinsiella eggs. It was, therefore, a great surprise to me when first studying it in Queensland to find few or no *Cyrtorhinus mundulus* on maize even when it was growing among sugar cane and was heavily infested with corn leafhopper, while the surrounding sugar cane contained very few sugar cane leafhoppers. The same thing has been observed on many occasions in Hawaii where maize containing great quantities of corn leafhoppers would be free of Cyrtorhinus, whereas adjacent sugar cane containing hardly any Perkinsiella would harbor comparatively large numbers of Cyrtorhinus.'

This phenomenon of insect parasites sometimes being more strongly attracted by the food plant of the host than by the host itself has been discussed by several authors (Cushman 1926a; Laing 1937; Picard and Rabaud 1914; Salt 1935; Monteith 1958).

In a recent experiment Zwölfer and Kraus (1957) placed pupae of the fir bud-worm, *Choristoneura murinana* Hb., in artificially formed leaf rolls of oaks resembling those made by the oak tortricids, *Tortrix viridana* (L.) and *Archips xylosteana* L. In this situation the *C. murinana* pupae were readily attacked by the ichneumonid *Apechthis rufata* Gmel., but 5,000 naturally occurring pupae of *C. murinana* on firs growing side by side with the same oaks were not attacked. The authors state, 'From these findings one may draw the conclusion that *A. rufata* belongs to that type of insect parasite which is attracted primarily by the food plant of the host (in this case oak), and only secondarily by the host itself, attacking then the fir budworm pupae transferred into artificial oak leaf rolls, as well as the pupae of the true oak tortricids. On the other hand, because of this behaviour (seeking first the food plant, and then the host itself), the *A. rufata* population of the observation area completely failed to parasitize the *C. murinana* population, the density of which was ten times higher on firs, just in the neighborhood.'

The host finding by *Eurytoma curta* Wlkr. under natural conditions was studied by Varley (1941). He noted that the females fly slowly and when they reach a flower head of knapweed they hover around it and either pass on or settle on it and with their antennae explore bracts for their host, the knapweed gall fly. Varley concluded that the female parasites recognized the flower heads as objects of especial significance.

Closely related species of parasites may exhibit very marked differences in their behaviour on various plants which harbour their common host species. For example, Smith (1957) reported that two species of *Aphytis* liberated in a small greenhouse showed differential responses to their host, *Aonidiella aurantii* (Mask.), growing on different plant species. Smith reared a ratio of *Aphytis chrysomphali* (Mercet) to *Aphytis lingnanensis* Comp. of 1:3 from hosts growing on *Yucca*, whereas on sago palm the ratio was 1:81.

HOST FINDING. Once the parasite is in the habitat of the host, it still must be able to locate a host individual, and this is thought to be the second in the series of four steps which tend to limit the host list of an entomophagous species.

There have been a number of studies on the behaviour of searching females and the resulting distribution of their progeny. Most of these investigations have been prompted by the desire to determine whether searching of individuals is random or directed. It would appear that most of the results of the behaviouristic studies indicate something of a compromise between random and non-random searching (Salt 1934). For example, the searching of the natural environment by *Angitia* sp., a parasite of *Plutella maculipennis* (Curtis), has been shown to give results midway between what would be expected from a random search and what would accrue from a systematic one (Ullyett 1943, 1947).

Of the senses used by the parasite in detecting the presence of hosts, the ones most commonly reported are tactile and olfactory. Ullyett (1953) witnessed the remarkable swarming habits of the ichneumonid *Pimpla bicolor* Bouché, a pupal parasite of the moth *Euproctis terminalia* Wlkr., on pines in South Africa. If a cocoon of the moth is broken open in the forest, both the pupa from the cocoon and hands and arms of the observer are covered by a swarm of the parasite females within a few minutes, although few or no parasites may have been observed in the vicinity previously. The normal attraction of the pupa within the cocoon is no doubt intensified by breaking open the latter.

It is sometimes difficult to separate the two steps of host habitat finding and host finding within the host-containing area and, as noted above, these are really a sub-division of Salt's category of 'ecological selection.' Wylie (1958a) concluded that the great variation in physical characteristics of the host environments located by females of *Nasonia vitripennis* ruled out any possibility that they recognized them by sight, and therefore he thought the females perceived the host habitat by odour. However, both Edwards (1954) and Wylie (1958a) found that the females were not attracted to any distinctive odour of the puparia from which the source of the host environment had been removed. (This result disagrees with Jacobi (1939) who concluded that the odour of the puparium is attractive to the parasites.) The host puparium is usually not perceived until the female's antennae touch it, although Edwards (1954, 1955) noted that optical stimulation plays a role in host finding, although a minor one, for the parasites only turn aside to investigate a puparium when at a distance of 2 to 3 mm from it. They will similarly turn aside to make a preliminary investigation of any small object such as wheat grains, but in all instances the response disappears in a dim red light.

Wylie (1958a) notes that the ability of *Nasonia vitripennis* to find puparia of a host is closely related to the pupation habits of the host species. In a humidity gradient the *Nasonia* females prefer the drier side and this avoidance of damp habitats is important in the ability to locate hosts because the puparia of many host species are in a drier habitat than that in which they developed as larvae.

Ullyett (1953) noted that a parasite tends to search in the parts of its environment most likely to contain its host and that this is caused by a combination of preadaptation in habits and a specific attraction exerted by the portion of the environment concerned.

Sharp turning movements are sometimes made by entomophagous species in the vicinity of their hosts. Wylie (1958a) found that *Nasonia* tends, by walking or flying, to travel upwind in a fairly straight line if there is no odour of infested carrion, but if this odour is present *Nasonia* makes many sharp turns and these frequent turns keep the females in a favourable zone for finding hosts. Laing (1937) showed that females of *Trichogramma evanescens* Westw., travelling in fairly straight lines before they found hosts, made many short radius turns immediately after leaving hosts. Similarly Fleschner (1950) showed that predacious species from several families followed unusually twisting paths after feeding. Because of this changed behaviour after an initial contact with a host is made, the area near the host is thoroughly investigated. If the host is one which tends to be sessile and closely grouped, such as a cluster of eggs, then the turning movements tend to increase the chances of the entomophagous species finding all the host individuals in the area.

Many parasites find their hosts by first locating traces or host indicators in the vicinity. For example, *Macrocentrus ancylivorus* Roh. probes into piles of frass which indicate the opening of burrows of the potato tuber worm; *Apanteles aristoteliae* Vier. can quickly follow the trail made by its host, the orange tortrix; and when the female of *Solenotus begini* (Ashm.) walks across a leaf she is quickly responsive to the presence of a serpentine leaf mine made by her host, *Phytomyza atricornis* Meig. Once the serpentine mine is detected the female parasite progresses along its length, and as she does so she continually swings her body from side to side in order that her sensitive antennae can trace the margins of the mine. This reaction is displayed irrespective of the presence of a host susceptible to attack (Doutt 1957).

HOST ACCEPTANCE. Even though a parasite actually finds or contacts a suitable host, it still may not attack if the proper stimuli are lacking. This acceptance of the host by the parasite is the third step in the process of determining the host specificity of the parasite. This step is truly host selection and is clearly a matter of innate behaviour of the parasitic species. It encompasses the category designated by Salt (1935) as the psychological selection of hosts, and it remains as a fertile field of research.

The marked change in behaviour which characterizes this step can be seen in a description by Edwards (1954) of the activities of a female *Nasonia* when placed in a petri dish with puparia of *Musca domestica* L. He found initially that there is an aimless wandering, and a fly puparium has no marked attraction until it is within 2 to 3 mm. The parasite then turns, walks straight toward the puparium, stops, and touches it with the antennae. After an investigation lasting five to ten seconds she climbs on to it.

As soon as the parasite mounts a puparium there is a marked change in behaviour. She moves forward slowly with the flagella of the antennae held vertically and moving rapidly up and down as if tapping the surface of the puparium with the tips. This process has been called drumming (fig. 13).

The change to the next stage of the behaviour pattern occurs suddenly. The parasite stops drumming, flexes the body, and begins tapping with the tip of the abdomen on a restricted area of the surface of the puparium. Tapping apparently places the tip of the ovipositor in position for drilling.

Once the tip of the ovipositor is in position the body is partly straightened, the full length of the ovipositor is exposed and the female starts to drill through the puparium. When the wall of the puparium has been pierced and the hole is large enough, the entire length of the ovipositor is inserted.

If the host is suitable, eggs are laid and a feeding tube is formed. The female, on removing the ovipositor seeks for the end of the tube with the antennae and sucks up the host's blood.

Edwards (1954) makes a general analysis of this behaviour pattern and shows that although the female may follow alternative paths at some points, there are other parts where the behaviour is invariable. 'Thus, if a parasite touches a puparium she may stop and mount, or she may continue walking; but if she stops and mounts she invariably drums. Drumming is not always followed by tapping with the tip of the abdomen but tapping with the abdomen is always followed by drilling, though this may be a short duration. Tapping is always preceded by drumming, and drilling is always preceded by tapping. Drilling is followed by insertion whenever the puparium has been pierced. A parasite may stop drilling after a few seconds and return to drumming in a different part of the puparium. This may be repeated two to three times before the ovipositor is inserted, and often occurs when the tip of the ovipositor is not located at an intersegmental notch. Insertion of the ovipositor is followed by oviposition and feeding-tube formation, or by immediate withdrawal and abandonment of the puparium. Feeding-tube formation without oviposition occurs when a female has no eggs in the ovaries.'

Edwards concludes that there are therefore four distinct phases of behaviour: (1) finding the host area; (2) finding a fly puparium; (3) drumming and drilling response; and (4) oviposition and feeding response.

These are not arbitrary divisions of the behaviour pattern, but clearly recognizable stages. The drumming and drilling, though separate actions, are considered together, for the presence or absence of stimuli during both these stages leads to the acceptance or rejection of the fly puparium. Clearly the first two phases designated by Edwards correspond to the categories of host habitat finding and host finding. The third and fourth phases of behaviour are parts of the process designated herein as host acceptance.

Although *Anagasta kühniella* (Zell.) is the normal host of *Exidechthis canescens* (Grav.) it has been found that preimaginal olfactory conditioning of the parasite can alter its ovipositional pattern. Thorpe and Jones (1937) experimented with *Exidechthis* and concluded that it had an inherited ovipositional response to larvae of *Anagasta*, but that an additional ovipositional response, which is entirely lacking in the normal insect, can be induced by contact with the new host. It was first found that oviposition in the larvae of the small wax moth, *Meliphora grisella* (F.), would occur if the wax moth larvae were in close contact with *Anagasta* larvae and thoroughly contaminated with the smell of the normal hosts. Once the *Exidechthis* eggs are inserted in the body cavity of *Meliphora* they develop normally and adults are eventually produced. Thorpe and Jones (1937) then used an olfactometer to compare the behaviour of the *Exidechthis* from *Anagasta* with those reared on

Meliphora. The experiments indicated that there is a strong germinally fixed tendency to follow up the odour of *Anagasta*. Insects which have been reared on *Anagasta* show little or no reaction to the smell of *Meliphora*, but those reared from *Meliphora* while still preferring *Anagasta* show a significant attraction to *Meliphora* such that when given the alternative of the two hosts in the olfactometer the proportion choosing *Anagasta* is reduced from 85 to 66 per cent.

At this point when the host is found it is apparent that certain criteria are used by the female to determine whether the host is acceptable. For example, while dead or etherized larvae are stabbed by *Exidechthis*, oviposition may not take place unless the host moves. When a normal caterpillar is pricked, it rapidly recoils and in doing so greatly excites the parasite, which pursues its victim, stabbing vigorously until a succesful thrust is achieved. Williams (1951*a*) tied a thread to an etherized larva and jerked it when the ovipositor touched the host thereby simulating the normal host reaction; he found that the parasite reacted as it does to a normal host, and oviposition quickly resulted.

Motion of the host has been reported as a necessary stimulus for oviposition in other parasites also. Lathrop and Newton (1933) found that the stimulus to oviposition of *Opius melleus* Gah., a parasite of the blueberry maggot, is the vibration produced by the movements of the host larvae within the plant tissue. They induced the act of oviposition of *O. melleus* by making simulated larval movements under the skin of the blueberry by means of a needle or a pair of forceps. Smith (1952) found that *Microctonus vittatae* Mues. is stimulated to oviposition principally by the motion of its host, *Phyllotreta*. Motionless beetles were palpitated by wasp's antennae and caused to move before the wasps would attack. Bryden and Bishop (1945) reported the same phenomenon in a study of *Perilitus coccinellae* (Schrank). Visual stimuli produced by movement of exposed hosts or prey are important in their selection by a number of entomophagous species. According to Tinbergen (1951) it is the principal stimulus by which the bee-hunting digger wasp, *Philanthus triangulum* (F.), locates its host. It is well known that dragonflies and preying mantids also rely on visual stimuli. Monteith (1956) showed experimentally that the stimulus provided by movements of the sawfly host is effective only if the olfactory senses of the tachinid *Drino bohemica* (Mesn.) are already stimulated.

It was suggested by Ullyett (1936) that the heartbeat of the larva of *Diprion* is of importance in releasing the oviposition response in *Microplectron*. Edwards (1954) attempted to test this experimentally with *Nasonia vitripennis* but the understandable difficulties gave only inconclusive results, and he decided that *N. vitripennis* can distinguish between a live and a dead host and will oviposit only on the former.

Obviously host movement is not always a stimulus for attack since many hosts are sessile, and the criteria for accepting a host in such cases include host odour, size, location, and shape. The pioneering experimental work in this field was that of Salt (1934, 1935) on the hosts of *Trichogramma*. A more recent study of such criteria has been made by Edwards (1955) in his studies of *Nasonia*. He found that the host's shape, size, physiological condition, and its production of a vaguely defined but necessary chemical contact stimulus (termed the 'puparium factor') were requisites for attack.

An experimental analysis of the factors involved in superparasitism led Salt (1934, 1935) to the discovery that female *Trichogramma* would tend to reject otherwise suitable hosts on which other females had walked. This avoidance was caused by an odour left on the host by the parasite which first contacted it, and Flanders (1951) called this the spoor effect. It is also well known now that many parasites have the ability to discriminate between parasitized and healthy hosts and thus avoid superparasitism by not ovipositing in the former. It has been suggested by Simmonds (1943) that by means of chemoreceptors on the ovipositor the female was able to discriminate between such hosts. This was later demonstrated to be the case by Dethier (1947*b*) who, in using a technique similar to that employed in testing tarsal chemoreceptors, showed that *Exidechthis canescens* responds to chemical stimulation of the ex-sheathed ovipositor. There is considerable evidence to show that it is through such receptors that parasites are able to determine the condition of their host even though they are otherwise separated from it by physical barriers. For example, *Stenobracon deesae* (Cam.) attacks *Chilo* larvae which are stem borers in graminaceous crops and thus, according to Narayanan and Chaudhuri (1954), the only possible way *S. deesae* can judge the quality of the host seems to be by means of its ovipositor. Beard (1952) found that usually acceptable *Galleria* larvae were avoided by *Bracon* females when the *Galleria* had been poisoned by DDT. Lloyd (1956) suggests that the neuromuscular upset caused by the injection of DDT approximates conditions of paralysis under which the discriminatory mechanism is brought into function.

It should be noted that if only parasitized hosts are accessible to the discriminating female she will tend to retain her eggs rather than deposit them. Thus the females, in avoiding superparasitism, exhibit both discrimination and restraint (Lloyd 1938; Salt 1934, 1935).

HOST SUITABILITY. Even though a hymenopterous parasite has found the potential host in its habitat and selected it for attack, the host–parasite relationship may still not succeed if the potential host individual is immune or otherwise unsuitable. This matter of host suitability is, then, the fourth and final step in the process by which the host list of a parasite species becomes restricted. Bess (1939) has recognized this and accordingly has said that oviposition by a parasite is not necessarily an index to host suitability, the attractiveness of the host being often independent of its suitability for parasitic development. The suggestion that a once susceptible host population may become resistant to parasitic attack is to be found in the work of Muldrew (1953). In Canada the larch sawfly, *Pristiphora erichsonii* (Htg.), was for years heavily parasitized by *Mesoleius tenthredinis* Morley, but it later became apparent that in Manitoba and Saskatchewan the efficiency of the parasite had greatly decreased. Muldrew's studies showed that the hosts in the provinces of Manitoba and Saskatchewan were inhibiting the parasites' embryonic development.

It should also be mentioned that in some cases an otherwise normal host can be rendered unsuitable by the host plant on which it grows (Flanders 1953*d*; Smith 1957). An outline of the factors which may cause a host to be unsuitable is given by Salt (1938), and in this paper he points out that the relative importance of the eliminative steps described above seems to differ in the two principal taxonomic groups of parasites. The parasitic Hymenoptera are, on the whole, more discriminating than the Diptera in their selection of hosts. It appears that in the Hymenoptera, selection plays the leading role, whereas in the Diptera, host suitability is the important phase.

Manner and Place of Oviposition

The reason for the differences in the relative importance of the steps leading to host specificity among the various groups of parasites can be associated with the manner and place of oviposition. Obviously those species which oviposit merely in the vicinity of a host or in its habitat are not exercising much discrimination in the choice of any particular host, while on the other hand the steps of host finding and host selection are developed to a very high degree in some species, even to the extent of ovipositing in a specific organ of the host. For clarity in the discussion it seems advisable to place the oviposition habits into three categories: (1) oviposition *apart from* the host; (2) oviposition *on* the host; and (3) oviposition *in* the host.

The Diptera have many species which habitually oviposit in the habitat frequented by a host, and there are a few parasitic Hymenoptera of similar habits. There are tachinids and acrocerids which oviposit more or less randomly on foliage or other plant parts. The eggs may be microtype which are ingested by host caterpillars, or they may be normally sized eggs which hatch into planidium-type larvae that actively attach themselves to a passing host individual. The Nemestrinidae often deposit such eggs in crevices in tree trunks. In the Hymenoptera the females of Perilampidae oviposit on the leaves and the planidia from these eggs invade caterpillars to feed as hyperparasites. The Eucharidae deposit hundreds of eggs in buds or leaves of plants or at random on the foliage and the active larvae attach themselves to worker ants in order to be transported to the ant colony where they attack the immature stages of the ant species. In some Diptera there is uterine incubation of the eggs and the females thus larviposit rather than oviposit. Some Diptera have the fascinating habit of ejecting their progeny while in flight; this has been reported in the bombyliids, dexiids, and acrocerids.

The eggs of many species of both parasitic Diptera and Hymenoptera are deposited on the host, and the resulting larvae may feed from this external position or they may enter the host and develop as internal parasites. The eggs may be attached to the host by some mucilaginous material or by some structural modification of the chorion, such as a stalk or pedicel which is inserted through the host's integument. Some species of tiphiids habitually oviposit on specific locations on the host body, and the pattern of arrangement of the eggs is so constant as to be a useful criterion in distinguishing species. It is said that when a tiphiid female locates a previously parasitized host she will remove the eggs deposited by the prior female before she deposits her own. Similarly, the female *Euplectrus* which

A

FIGURE 12. Female of *Pteromalus puparum* feeding at puncture wound made by her ovipositor on a pupa of *Pieris rapae*. As she becomes engorged her abdomen swells in size.

(Photographs by S. B. Doten, from F. E. Skinner collection.)

B

C

D

A

B

C

D

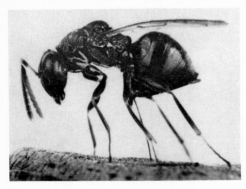

E

FIGURE 13. Ovipositional behaviour exhibited by *Pteromalus puparum* on pupa of *Pieris rapae*.

A. Drumming   B. Tapping
C. Drilling   D. Oviposing
     E. Withdrawing

(Photographs by S. B. Doten, from F. E. Skinner collection.)

finds a host bearing an egg cluster of another *Euplectrus* female will often destroy the existing eggs before depositing her own clutch.

It is a general rule that hosts living in exposed situations tend to be attacked by parasites which develop internally, whereas hosts that are in some protected situation are parasitized by external feeders. Examples of hosts in protected situations are those in burrows, leaf mines, leaf rolls, puparia, or cocoons. Accordingly, the parasites of free-living or exposed hosts, such as caterpillars or insect eggs, generally possess the habit of ovipositing in the host. Most commonly the internally placed eggs are free-floating in the body cavity, but sometimes they are placed in specific host organs. Baltensweiler (1958) gives an example of this in the ichneumonid *Triclistus* which places the egg in the ganglion of the larch bud moth, *Zeiraphera griseana* (Hbn.). The female of *Caraphractus cinctus* not only goes under water to oviposit in the eggs of dytiscids, but this mymarid directs her ovipositor deep into the egg so that it penetrates the midgut of the embryo where the parasite larva develops (Jackson 1958a).

Utilization of the Ovipositor

The power of the parasite to utilize its ovipositor is one of the attributes of an effective parasite according to the interesting analysis by Flanders (1947). This power is measured by such factors as the strength of the ovipositor, its length and flexibility, and the time required for insertion.

Oviposition can be very rapid if the eggs are very small, but many eggs are larger than the lumen of the ovipositor and undergo considerable compression and distortion during the passage down the ovipositor. Fulton (1933) describes the passage of the egg down the ovipositor in *Habrocytus cerealellae* as being like sand through an hour glass.

Paralysation of the Host

In many parasitic Hymenoptera the injection of venom to paralyse the host and the act of oviposition are two distinct operations. According to Ullyett (1945), *Bracon hebetor* Say first paralyses all the host individuals in the immediate environment before it begins to lay eggs on any of them. However, not all parasitic Hymenoptera paralyse or kill their hosts prior to oviposition. Some species apparently never inject venom into the host; and in other species it is obviously essential that the host be killed or paralysed before it is suitable for the development of the immature wasps. The host reaction to the venom may be immediate, as in *Perisierola emigrata* Roh. when it paralyses a lepidopterous host, or the reaction may be delayed with no symptoms evident for several minutes, as in *Phytomyza atricornis* when it is stung by *Solenotus begini*. In some parasites the paralysis of the hosts is permanent, in others the effect is merely temporary and the host soon recovers and resumes its normal activities.

Very little is known about the venom of parasitic Hymenoptera, and the work of Beard (1952) on the venom of *Bracon hebetor* is the first serious investigation of the subject. He calculated that as little as one part of venom in 200 million parts of host blood was sufficient to cause permanent paralysis. The venom is transported by the host's blood to the site of action. Since paralysis results from impairment of the excitatory processes of the body wall musculature, the site of action is considered to be the neuromuscular junction.

Mechanisms of Fertilization, Sex Determination, and the Regulation of Sex Ratio

The females of most species of Hymenoptera possess a spermatheca that functions as a storage organ for the spermatozoa which were received in the act of mating. In such individuals the spermatheca becomes a sex-changing mechanism, according to Flanders (1939), for the sex of the egg in these species is normally determined during oviposition. As the egg passes down the oviduct, if the proper stimulus is present, the spermatheca will discharge sperm on to the egg. These spermatozoa enter the egg where one of them will unite with the egg nucleus. The egg is then changed from the haploid condition (in which it would have developed parthenogenetically into a male) to the diploid condition which develops into a female.

Because most Hymenoptera produce both sexes—and yet there are other species that habitually produce only the female sex—it is worth while to discuss the phenomenon of sex determination in these parasites.

Whereas the eggs of most insects undergo meiosis and normally develop no further unless activated by fertilization, this is not the case with ants, bees, and wasps, for the entire order Hymenoptera is characterized by parthenogenesis. Among the parasitic Hymenoptera this development by parthenogenesis can be subdivided into three categories: thelyotoky, deuterotoky, and arrhenotoky.

THELYOTOKY. Some species, such as *Exidechthis canescens*, are obligatorily parthenogenetic and each generation consists entirely of females. Such a species in which males are virtually unknown is thelyotokous in the strictest sense, and all individuals are termed 'impaternate' or 'uniparental.'

DEUTEROTOKY. There are other species, such as *Habrolepis rouxi* Comp. and *Tropidophryne melvillei* Comp., which normally exhibit thelyotoky, but also produce a few males. The occurrence of these exceptional males would classify such species as being deuterotokous or ampherotokous. Here again the individuals are all uniparental.

ARRHENOTOKY. Most species of parasitic Hymenoptera exhibit facultative parthenogenesis, i.e., the eggs may develop either parthenogenetically or zygogenetically, depending upon the occurrence of fertilization. In these cases the fertilized eggs are diploid and give rise to females, whereas the azygotes from the unfertilized eggs are haploid and are males. This type of parthenogenesis is termed 'arrhenotoky.' In an arrhenotokous species the females are normally biparental and the males are termed uniparental or impaternate.

This type of genetic system, variously referred to as 'haplodiploidy,' 'haploid parthenogenesis,' or 'arrhenotoky,' is common among the parasitic Hymenoptera, and the rule that applies to such species is often termed Dzierzon's Law. It is so named because in 1845 Johannes Dzierzon, a keen student of honey bees, put forth the theory that drones develop from unfertilized eggs while the female workers and queens come from fertilized eggs. Dzierzon's theory stemmed from the observations that unmated and old queens produce drone broods and that in race crossing the drones are matroclinous while the daughters are hybrid. It is perhaps of more than passing interest to biologists that Dzierzon was aware of segregating heredity at least 12 years before the publication of Mendel's classic paper on peas (Whiting 1935). Furthermore, it is evident that Dzierzon glimpsed the fundamental gametic ratio when in an 1854 paper he stated that the drones of the second generation of a cross resemble either the paternal or maternal race and that these two types occur in equal numbers.

Thus, in accordance with Dzierzon's Law, the usual pattern in parasitic Hymenoptera is that the eggs undergo reduction in chromosome number and thus become haploid as if in preparation for fertilization. If fertilization does not occur, then these eggs develop by parthenogenesis into haploid individuals of the male sex.

The maintenance of haploid arrhenotoky requires a combination of at least three conditions not generally found in animals: (1) survival of the azygote with reduced chromosome number; (2) a regulation of spermatogenesis so that the sperms of the haploid male retain the full haploid set of chromosomes; and (3) a rather special system of sex determination, i.e., one which may be different from that based on the idea of genic balance (Whiting 1945).

The viability of the haploid male is an exception to the general rule among animals. Greenshields (1936) suggests that the males are viable because the apparent or presumed haploid set of chromosomes is fundamentally diploid. Since females have been shown to possess twice the male chromosome number, in certain tissues at least, it follows that the females would be tetraploid. It was reported by Speicher and Speicher (1938) that the occasional uniparental females appearing in *Bracon hebetor* originated from patches of tetraploid tissue in an ovary which was otherwise diploid, and the idea has been extended by Flanders (1945) who believes that the occurrence of males in *Prospaltella perniciosi* Tower is the result of the existence of patches of diploid tissue in ovaries that otherwise are tetraploid. Whiting (1945) prefers to speak of the males of the Hymenoptera as 'impaternate' (fatherless) rather than 'haploid' in view of the presumed endopolyploidy of most of their somatic tissue.

Another requirement for haploid arrhenotoky is that spermatogenesis be regulated so that the sperm cells will have the full haploid set. Since male Hymenoptera are haploid, it is clear that their spermatogenesis will be unlike the normal meiotic divisions in most other animals. Cytologists believe that there is a failure of nuclear division in the first spermatocyte and instead of any splitting of chromosomes there is only the pinching off of a small cytoplasmic bud. The second division is equal, involving simple mitosis which results in the formation of two equivalent spermatids, each of which develops into a functional sperm.

Whiting (1945) stated that sex determination in *Bracon* has been shown to depend upon a series of multiple alleles, of which nine have thus far been identified. These are designated *xa*, *xb*, *xc* to *xi*. Any heterozygote (diploid) *xa/xb*, *xa/xc*, *xc/xd*, etc., is female; any azygote (haploid), *xa*, *xb*, *xc*, etc., or any homozygote (diploid), *xa/xa*, *xb/xb*, etc., is male.

In haplodiploid species multiple-sex allelism may be the more primitive and general method of reproductive economy, for closely inbred species apparently have adopted some other method. Schmeider and Whiting (1947) studied *Melittobia*, where close inbreeding is the natural habit. Here there were no diploid males even in the backcrossing of sons to mothers.

Most of the hypotheses on sex determination in the parasitic Hymenoptera need more experimental support, and there are many problems to be solved. One is how the diploid condition is maintained in thelyotokous species (Smith 1955), and another is how intersexes originate in such insects (Doutt and Smith 1950).

SEX RATIO. Obviously there is no problem of sex ratio in the obligatorily thelyotokous species, and neither is there in practical work any concern expressed over the appearance of the males in deuterotokous species. However, the widely variable and often greatly fluctuating sex ratios of arrhenotokous species may cause difficulty in biological control projects both in the insectary culture and in the colonization of such parasites. Thus it may be that in biological control the concern over the sex ratio of the species being considered is something that arises from the artificiality of the laboratory. Arrhenotoky, to a species in nature, may have great survival value, as indicated by White (1954) when he points out that this is a method of sex determination as well as a form of reproduction, the frequency of the males in the population being determined by the frequency with which unfertilized eggs are laid. Forms in which sex determination depends on male haploidy will likewise be free to develop, through natural selection, whatever sex ratio is best adapted to their reproductive economy. Variable and fluctuating sex ratios are particularly characteristic of haplodiploid groups.

There are many factors, both intrinsic and extrinsic, which influence the sex ratio of arrhenotokous species. Flanders (1946*b*) found that when the females of *Macrocentrus ancylivorus* were subjected to repeated matings under insectary conditions a great preponderance of males occurred in their progeny. He reports: 'The *Macrocentrus* female, at each mating, receives a spermatophore from the male. After the spermatophore is adjusted so that it makes contact with the opening of the spermatheca and sperms have begun to move into the sperm capsule, a second mating rarely if ever takes place. Females that mate before this adjustment is completed will mate many times. They receive so many spermatophores that none become adjusted and all are discarded before the female becomes impregnated. Multiple mating prolongs the preoviposition period and results in the production of progeny predominantly male.'

In summary Flanders (1946*b*) states, 'Sex ratios are determined *extrinsically* by the effect of the density of oviposition sites (hosts) on: (a) differential mortality during development; (b) the premating interval after emergence, which determines the proportion of eggs deposited before mating and the inhibition of mating;

(c) excessive mating; (d) the difference in oviposition response before and after mating; (e) the occurrence of preferred oviposition sites; and (f) the rate of oviposition.' He also points out that sex ratios may be 'determined *intrinsically* by (a) the number of eggs deposited at one insertion of the ovipositor, (b) the number of ovarian eggs ready for deposition, and (c) the differential in the polyembryonic proclivity of the sexes.'

Jackson (1958) found that the sex ratio in *Caraphractus cinctus* usually varied according to the rate of egg laying. Thus, when a single host egg is offered to a female *Caraphractus* at intervals of three hours or more, she usually lays at a single thrust of the ovipositor two female and one male egg. If, however, hosts were supplied to the female in rapid succession, the number of eggs at each thrust is reduced and a much higher proportion of female eggs is laid. Jackson believes that when a female lays in one host directly after another the flow of spermatozoa will be stimulated, so that a higher proportion of the eggs passing into the ovipositor will have been fertilized. She thinks that this is contrary to the view expressed by Flanders (1939) that an increase in the rate of oviposition probably increases the number of eggs escaping fertilization.

Simmonds (1947*a*) found that in breeding *Mastrus carpocapsae* (Cush.) a higher percentage of females was obtained by breeding from males and females selected from 'high sex ratio families,' and he suggests that the sex ratio in this case is genetically determined. Jackson (1958) discovered a strain of the mymarid *Caraphractus cinctus*, bred from a single female, which produced almost entirely female eggs and whose daughters, when unmated, rarely produced healthy males. Miss Jackson consulted Professor Whiting about this abnormal strain and his words give a very appropriate note on which to end this section: 'The problem of sex determination is fundamental to sex ratio and this is not as yet explained for the chalcidoids.'

CHARACTERISTICS OF ADULT PREDATORS

Predators have been defined in this chapter as those entomophagous species whose larvae develop by consuming more than one individual of the prey. As might be expected, the line of demarcation between predators and parasites is not always clear cut. There are, for example, species of Hymenoptera whose larvae develop in a host egg mass and accordingly these technically might be called egg predators. On the other hand, there are coccinellids which seem to be able to develop at the expense of one large coccid individual, and in this respect would tend to met the definition of a parasite. These exceptions, however, are not sufficiently numerous or important as a distinct group in biological control to offset the usefulness of the general terms. Many of the adult characteristics previously described for parasites apply in a general way to predators, hence this section is restricted.

In the predaceous species, unlike the parasites, the larval stage is forced to find several prey individuals and accordingly the searching behaviour of the larva as well as that of the adult is important in any analysis of predator–prey population dynamics. Prey selection by the adult stage of the predator ranges from highly selective to comparatively minimal. The vedalia beetle, *Rodolia cardinalis* (Muls.), commonly deposits its egg on the egg sac of a mature cottony-cushion scale. The diaspine scale predator, *Lindorus lophanthae* (Blaisd.), deposits its egg under the old scale coverings of dead prey individuals but in the vicinity of live prey. Most coccinellids place their eggs near the prey. Another type of predaceous adult which finds food for its young is a digger wasp in the genus *Bembex*. According to Ullyett and DeVries (1940) this wasp provisions its nest with dipterous insects which the female encounters on her foraging flights. While these *Bembex* wasps are restricted in their choice of prey to dipterous insects, they are able to make use of a wide range of species belonging to several different genera and families.

Baerends (1950, 1959) has reported some fascinating observations on the behaviour of digger wasps in the genus *Ammophila*. These wasps demonstrate the idea of Tinbergen (1950, 1951) that instinctive activities are grouped into physiological systems, each of which is characterized by the fact that all behavioural elements belonging to it share common causal factors. Each of these systems may be composed of a chain of subsystems under Tinbergen's concept of a hierarchy of instinctive behaviour. A system is generally activated by a special stimulus situation which may be inside the animal or may be in its environment. A good example of the role of autonomous impulse production in insect behaviour is given by Baerends (1959) in his analysis of the significance of the inspection visit by *Ammophila campestris* Jur. to its nest while it is in the phase of progressive provisioning. In this species an inspection visit is made to the nest without the insect bringing a caterpillar. Provisioning follows only if an enclosed wasp larva is present, and the number of caterpillars is determined by the size of the larva and by the amount of food present in the nest at the inspection visit. 'This means that during the inspection visit a system comprising and controlling the entire provisioning behaviour of a phase is activated.'

Baerends (1950) writes that every releasing mechanism has its own sign stimuli. 'For example, the digger wasp, *Ammophila adriaansei* Wilcke, that catches caterpillars and drags them to its nest as food for its larva, may respond to the perception of a caterpillar in different ways, all depending on which instinct is activated. When it is hunting, a caterpillar is caught and stung; when it is found near the nest opening, just after the wasp has opened the nest, it is drawn in; but when it lies close to the nest when the wasp is filling the nest entrance, it may be used as filling material. Finally, when we put it into the nest shaft when the wasp is digging out the nest, then it brings the caterpillar away, exactly as she would deal with another obstacle, for instance, a piece of plant root. It is therefore, the same object, that with different conditions of the animal releases different responses. Still, in every situation the caterpillar is always sending visual as well as chemical stimuli to the sense organs of the wasp where they will be always transformed into impulses.'

The hunting behaviour of the water bug, *Notonecta glauca* L., is also described by Baerends (1950). This insect makes use of waves that spread over the water surface when some insect falls on the water. It is able to perceive these waves and directs itself towards the vibrating source. *Notonecta* can perceive the source from a distance of 20 cm and after having arrived within about 5 cm of the vibrating object the behaviour changes. *Notonecta* swings the third pair of legs powerfully backwards and falls upon the prey. This sudden leap is not released by the vibrations, but by visual perception of the moving object. When the object is seized the mouthparts may be inserted if the object is not too hard. If the proper chemical stimuli are present then sucking will take place.

Quite often the adult predators feed on the same prey as their progeny. This is especially true of the coccinellids. However, many other predators, such as the Neuroptera and predacious Diptera, may have adult food sources different from those of their immature forms. Honeydew is important as a source of protein for these adults and it can affect their longevity, fecundity, and distribution (Hagen 1950).

A premating period after emergence from the pupal stage is frequently seen in predaceous species, although it may be relatively brief (two to six days) as in certain species of *Hippodamia*. On the other hand, there are coccinellids which are active adults for a long period prior to mating, and an example is *Pullus impexus* (Muls.) which emerges in May or June but does not copulate until August (Delucchi 1954). This species copulates again in the spring after a hibernation period of six months.

There does not appear to be any particular courtship on the part of male coccinellids nor most other entomophagous Coleoptera prior to mating. However, certain male flies, such as the tiny empidids, offer prey to the female prior to mating. Courtship is carried out by males of several species of *Dolichopus* and these males may have the foretarsi or antennae developed ornamentally for use in display. Smith and Empson (1955) describe the courtship of the dolichopodid *Poecilobothrus nobilitatus* (L.) in which the males with conspicuous white wing tips make short display flights and wing movements. Mating in the *Bembex* spp. occurs on the wing during sunny weather and has been observed principally over the nesting sites (Ullyett and Devries 1940).

Sex ratios tend to be more even with the predator species than with the hymenopterous parasites because the mechanism of sex determination is different. Some insight into this subject in the Coccinellidae is given by Smith (1959). Parthenogenesis in most predacious species is rare, and unmated females usually deposit no eggs, but if they do, then the infertile eggs do not hatch.

One notable difference between parasites and predators is seen in their diurnal activities. Few parasites are active at night, whereas many of the predacious species are crepuscular or nocturnal. Predatism is thought by some to be a more primitive mode of life than parasitism, but there are differences of opinion on this as well as on the relative importance of the two groups.

CHAPTER 7

Developmental Stages of Parasites[1]

K. S. HAGEN

INTRODUCTION

PARASITIC INSECTS, like other animal parasites, evolved from free-living forms. The diverse preimaginal forms found among the endoparasitic insects reflect remarkable adaptive characteristics in both form and ontogeny.

The entomophagous parasites, or parasitoids,[2] have sprung from the orders that make up the Endopterygota or Holometabola, i.e., insects with a complete metamorphosis, including a pupal stage, and having wings that develop internally. The immature stages—eggs, larvae, and pupae—differ markedly from adults in structure, behaviour, food needs, and habitat.

The holometabolous orders, as recognized by Imms (1957), that contain some parasitic species are Neuroptera, Lepidoptera, Coleoptera, Strepsiptera, Diptera, and Hymenoptera. The parasitic habit apparently has not been found in the remaining endopterous orders, Mecoptera, Trichoptera, or Siphonaptera.

It appears then that the genetic plasticity that has permitted insects to adopt the parasitic habit resides entirely in those having a larval form rather than a nymphal stage in their development. Not only are there many larval types found among the entomophagous parasites, but, intraspecifically, there are usually different larval types manifested; thus, in these species hypermetamorphosis, to some degree, is the rule rather than the exception. These different larval forms within a species reveal obvious adaptive structures which are correlated with changes in their microhabitat, again accenting the plasticity of Endopterygota.

The rise of the pupal stage in the developmental cycle permitted these insects to invade successfully a great many more habitats than insects lacking this extra stage. The form of the larva could depart radically from the adult, enabling each stage to occupy completely different environments. It is the pupal stage that permits the transition between these great changes in form. The magnitude of the changes at this point in endopterygote metamorphosis is so great that Lower (1954) proposed the term mettalaxis to denote that period in metamorphosis which marks the end

---

[1] This chapter was intensively cut and modified by the editors during Dr. Hagen's absence abroad.

[2] A parasitic insect as defined herein is one which develops in or on a single host or on the eggs of one host. Some authors have proposed the term 'parasitoid' for a parasitic insect.

168

of the larval and the beginning of the pupal stages. The development or completion of imaginal muscles, for one thing, apparently cannot occur in a larval instar (Poyarkoff 1914; Hinton 1948). Other organ systems are also replaced or transformed to a high degree in the pupa (Tiegs 1922; Henson 1946; Hinton 1948; Lower 1954; Snodgrass 1954).

It is probable that the pupal stage arose after there was considerable specialization in the larval form but this was not before the larvae became specialized for internal feeding in environments in which there is a heavy selective pressure against the possession of external larval wings (Hinton 1948), and, to a certain extent, legs.

The complexity of life histories traced in representatives of parasitic protozoans and helminths show diversity and modification which are apparently adaptations to different and changing environments in which survival has been the determining factor (Stunkard 1940). The life cycles of some parasitic cestodes are most elaborate but some parasitic Hymenoptera exhibit a number of different stages in the course of their development that are no less remarkable. Instead of presenting examples of typical life histories on a phylogenetic or taxonomic basis as did Clausen (1940a) and Sweetman (1958), the biologies herein are more or less host-oriented in relation to where the egg or larva is placed.

The most important general account of the immature stages is found in Clausen's book on entomophagous insects (1940a) which has been reprinted (1962). An attempt is made here to follow the categories of immatures that he described. The theme of this chapter is the diversity of form and function found among the entomophagous parasites.

The types of immature stages of parasites and their habits are stressed in this chapter. The activities of the adult entomophagous insects are discussed in chapter 6.

EGG TYPES

The egg form of entomophagous parasites is by no means uniform. Obvious adaptive modifications, which are common, are superimposed on those differences with which phylogeny may have endowed the egg facies. Often parasitic species of Hymenoptera that belong to the same genus exhibit differences in their eggs that would ordinarily seem to be restricted to different families, and some hymenopterous groups display egg forms similar to those of certain Diptera. These parallel modifications are obviously products of selection towards occupancy of similar environments.

The size of eggs is not necessarily proportional to the size of the female of the parasite producing them. Iwata (1960) has found among the ichneumonoids that the egg is generally large in the majority of species of Ichneumoninae, Cryptinae (= Gelinae), Ephialtinae, Xoridinae, and Acaenitinae. The three latter subfamilies were once under the taxon Pimplinae (Townes and Townes 1960). The larger eggs in certain species of these subfamilies are correlated with a smaller number of short or moderate ovarioles with fewer mature oocytes present. By comparision, many of the Ophioninae (except the Ophion group), Tryphoninae (except the Xletelia group), and Banchinae produce relatively small eggs and the ovarioles are usually long and numerous. In these latter groups the ovaries retain a large number of mature eggs (Iwata 1960).

A similar correlation of small eggs with a large number of ovarioles is found in Trigonalidae, Perilampidae, some Braconidae, and in those Tachinidae that deposit microtype eggs (Clausen 1940a). Small egg size in comparison to adult size has been associated with species that are egg-larval parasites (Clausen 1954b).

The eggs of a single female can vary somewhat in size and shape, as was observed by Proper (1931), in a pteromalid, and by Rosenberg (1934) and Iwata (1958) in some ichneumonids.

It is possible to associate newly deposited eggs with ovarian eggs in many parasites. However, size and shape may be considerably altered after deposition. The eggs in the braconid subfamily Euphorinae increase about 1,000 times over their original volume after deposition in the host (Ogloblin 1924; Jackson 1928; O. J. Smith 1952). Schlinger and Hall (1960) noted the eggs of an aphidiine wasp to increase in volume after deposition by 634 times. There are other examples of some egg expansion in the host (Simmonds 1947a).

The shape of the ovarian eggs of Encyrtidae, Miscogasteridae, and some Aphelinidae are double-bodied and dumbbell-shaped, but during oviposition one of these bodies collapses. The contents of the proximal or cephalad body (that part which is oriented cephalically in the ovary and is the last to pass down the ovipositor) are forced into the distal body which travels down the ovipositor first and contains the embryo after deposition. The proximal body remains as a collapsed bulb at the end of the stalk or neck (Compere 1925; Flanders 1937a; Maple 1947). Some cynipid ovarian eggs are also double-bodied (Frühaufie 1924). Orientation of mature ovarian eggs in polytrophic ovarioles usually follow 'Hallez's law' (1886) in that the anterior pole of the egg is directed cephalad within the mother and the posterior pole lies caudad.

The narrower extended end of most stalked or acuminate ovarian eggs is directed distally and is the first part to move down the ovipositor (Pampel 1914; Bronskill 1959; Iwata 1959, 1960), but in some ichneumonids and platygasterids the stalk or narrower end of the egg lies proximal or cephalad in the ovary and the larger end is distally oriented before deposition (Marchal 1906; Crawford 1933). The embryo in the egg may lie cephalocaudal in the mother and following deposition may remain in this position or, in some cases, it may rotate so that the embryo becomes turned in the opposite direction after deposition. This rotation of the embryo leads to confusion in describing the end from which a stalk or pedicel may arise in a deposited egg unless the embryology is known. Among the sarcophagids where uterine incubation occurs the larva may be deposited head first, but in some species in which the larvae have setae directed anteriorly they are apparently deposited tail first (Knipling 1936). The larviparous tachinids usually deposit larvae, with choria, tail first.

Modifications, departing from the oval- or sausage-shaped egg (hymenopteriform), may include extensions from one or both poles. There are some eggs which bear processes that arise from the chorion of the egg body between the poles. Egg processes at times are not extensions of the chorion but originate from accessory glands in the female.

The functions of extensions are obvious in some eggs particularly where the eggs are external and the pedicels are used for attaching the egg to the host. In some Encyrtidae that deposit the eggs internally in their hosts the stalk protrudes to the outside of the host body and the portion that bears the aeroscopic plate has been shown to be respiratory in function. In many hymenopterous eggs the stalks or extensions reveal no obvious function. They are often associated with first-instar larvae that possess long tails. The stalk conforms to the larval shape; however, the tail of the caudate-larva is usually curled underneath the body. The stalk may, in some cases, allow greater area for egg expansion while in the host prior to eclosion; however, there are eggs in which the shell expands but not the stalk. Haviland (1921b) reviews the suggested functions of the stalk and surmises that the increase of the egg surface, in proportion to its mass, may bear some relation to oxygen absorption; thus, in some cases the shell has a respiratory function and in others it is used for attachment. Grandori (1911) suggested that the projection of the egg of *Apanteles glomeratus* (L.) serves as a hook to attach it to the host's viscera which thereby prevents the egg from being swept about by circulating fluids. Smith O. J. (1952) agrees with this view in regard to the egg of *Microctonus vittatae* Mues. The eggs that are elongate, acuminate, or stalked are often associated with Hymenoptera that have long ovipositors thus indicating conformity to the structure of the ovipositor, the extension permitting the egg to be compressed and stretched while passing down the ovipositor. Fulton (1933) believes such eggs pass through the ovipositor in the manner of sand passing through an hour-glass, only a small portion of its bulk being in the ovipositor at one time.

The minute microtype eggs that are deposited apart from the host, and which must be ingested before the larva will hatch, clearly show their adaptive nature in being tiny and having a thick dorsal cover of chorion which offers protection during periods of indefinite exposure.

Usually the chorion is more or less transparent and unsculptured. This is true in the majority of endoparasitic Hymenoptera but among the external hymenopterous parasites the eggs are often tuberculate, reticulate, and may even be spined (figure 14d). In many Tachinidae and some Hymenoptera, the chorion is thickened dorsally and may be sculptured; at times in profile the egg is conical and asymmetrical. The usual colour of a parasite's eggs is milky white or pale yellow but some are deep yellow, orange, or occasionally black.

Striking differences occur in the deposited eggs of some aphelinid species. The male egg of some *Coccophagus* spp. that are direct, secondary ectoparasites is attached to the host externally by means of a pedicel; however, the female egg of such species is deposited internally and the stalk is apparently non-functional since the egg floats free (Flanders 1937a). Also, in some *Coccophagus*, the fertilized egg (female) possesses a trophic membrane while the unfertilized male egg does not (Flanders 1942*d*).

The following descriptions of eggs and their general types largely follow Clausen (1940*a*). Parker's paper (1924) is a valuable reference to various chalcidoid egg forms. The interesting eggs of some Ichneumonidae are discussed by Cushman (1926*b*), and Iwata (1958, 1960) has illustrated hundreds of eggs from different ichneumonid species. Iwata (1959) also discusses the ovarian eggs of some Proctotrupoidea and Agriotypidae. Pantel (1910), Baer (1920), Townsend (1908, 1934), Thompson (1924), Clausen (1940*a*), and Biliotti (1958) discuss the various types of tachinid eggs. Mesnil (1953, 1955) in his systematic coverage of Palaearctic Tachinidae mentions the egg type of many species.

The main egg types of parasitic Hymenoptera and Diptera are shown in figure 14. The main recognized types are hymenopteriform membranous, stalked, acuminate, pedicellate, encyrtiform, macrotype, and microtype. In addition to these we recognize the acroceriform egg as a distinct type. Certain eggs are intermediate in shape and fall between the designated types.

Hymenopteriform eggs (figure 14*a*, *b*) are of general occurrence in most hymenopterous families. This is especially true in Ichneumonidae (Iwata 1958, 1960). They also occur in some Diptera–Nemestrinidae, Bomblyiidae—and in some Cecidomyiidae (Clausen 1940*a*).

Membranous-type eggs (figure 14*l*) are commonly found in Tachinidae and Sarcophagidae (Pantel 1910; Townsend 1934; Clausen 1940*a*). Such eggs when ejected externally contain a maggot which immediately casts off the chorion and either leaves the shell completely or uses the crumpled chorion as a base of attachment to a surface which is apart from the host. In some tachinids this type of egg may be deposited internally in a host, in which case it is incubated.

Acuminate-type eggs (figure 14*c*) are associated with ichneumonids, braconids, and some chalcidoids which possess long ovipositors and usually oviposit in or on or near hosts that inhabit galls, galleries, tunnels, or mines. In the Ichneumonidae this type is mainly found in Ephialtinae, Xoridinae, Acaenitinae, and in some Cryptinae (Iwata 1958, 1960).

Stalked-type eggs (figure 14*e*; Clausen 1940*a*) are of common occurrence in the parasitic Hymenoptera including the Ichneumonoidea, Chalcidoidea, Proctotrupoidea, and Cynipoidea. A few dipterous parasites also exhibit this type of egg. Among the Braconidae the egg stalk is often short and inconspicuous as in many *Apanteles* and Euphorinae; in *Coeloides subconcolor* Russo the extension is segmented (Russo 1938). In the Ichneumonidae: Ephialtinae, the genera *Megarhyssa*, *Rhyssa*, and *Epirhyssa* have eggs with extremely elongate stalks arising from one pole (Iwata 1958). In these eggs the stalks are at least three times longer than the egg body. Such eggs should, perhaps, be considered as the acuminate-type since the stalks probably permit deposition through extremely long ovipositors. However, since the eggs are constricted, being more oar-shaped, they fall under the stalked type. The ichneumonid *Euceros frigidus* Cress. deposits stalked eggs which resemble those of *Chrysopa* (Tripp 1961); however, these parasite eggs are easily separated from neuropterous eggs since they do not possess a conspicuous micropyle. Among the Chalcidoidea, stalked eggs are common in the Mymaridae, infrequent in Trichogrammatidae and most Pteromalidae, but common in the Cleonymini. They occur in the following genera in the Aphelinidae: *Aphytis*, *Centrodora*, *Aspidiotiphagus*, and *Marietta*. The stalks of Tetrastichinae, if present, vary in length, the maximum attaining the length of

PARASITE EGG TYPES

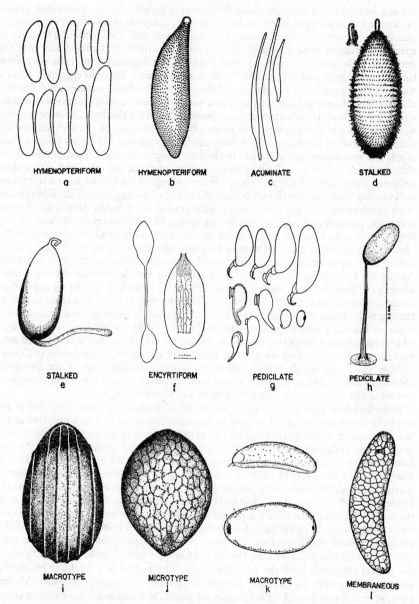

FIGURE 14. Parasitic egg types: (*a*) ovarian eggs of Ichneumoninae, from Iwata (1960); (*b*) *Monodontomerus dentipes* (Dal.), from Morris, Cameron, and Jepson (1937); (*c*) Ephialtinae, Xoridinae, from Iwata (1958); (*d*) *Eurytoma tylodermatis* Ashm., from Pierce and Holloway (1912); (*e*) *Eupelmella vesicularis* (Ret.), from Morris (1938); (*f*) *Microterys flavus* (How.), from Maple (1947); (*g*) Tryphoninae, Ophioninae, from Iwata (1958); (*h*) *Euceros frigidus* Cress., from Tripp (1961); (*i*) *Poecilogonalos thwaitesii* Westw., from Clausen (1929); (*j*) *Zenillia libatrix* Panz., from Dowden (1934); (*k*) *Phorocera* sp., from Prell (1915); (*l*) *Bonnetia comta* Fall. (Strickland 1923.)

the egg body. Among the Encyrtidae the following genera contain species that display unbanded (no aeroscopic plate) stalked eggs: *Aphidencyrtus*, *Cerapterocerus*, *Eusemion*, *Anarhopus*, *Comperiella*, *Cheiloneurus*, *Chrysopophagus*, and *Tetracnemus*. The stalk in species observed in these genera by Maple (1947) is twisted and doubled back over the neck and can become melanized. In many Eupelmidae a flagellum or tubercle arises from the 'posterior' pole, and the 'anterior' stalk is often twisted. Torymid eggs have either a stalk or a short rounded protuberance, and the chorion often bears minute rounded tubercles; the eggs of some are distinctly bent near one end. Some Leucospidae possess, besides a thick stalk, a small protuberance at the opposite pole and the chorion is variously covered with tubercles and short spines. The externally deposited eggs of the Eurytomidae are similar to those of the leucospids. Miscogasterid eggs possess extensions ranging from nipple-like and minute protuberances to elongate conspicuous stalks. Perilampid eggs are subcylindrical, arched on one side with one end pointed and the other end with a short peduncle; the surface is finely reticulate. The minute eggs of Eucharidae possess an anterior stalk ranging from one-fourth to two times the length of the egg body. Chalcidid eggs are often hymenopteriform but some are elongate bearing short stalks. Among the Proctotrupoidea, platygasterid eggs are usually lemon-shaped with 'anterior' stalks of varying length. Some genera contain species whose eggs have flagella or small protuberances at the 'posterior' pole. Most scelionid species have stalked eggs, some of which have a small pedicel at the opposite end. Ceraphronid eggs have minute extensions at one or both ends. Among the Cynipoidea some *Charips* have stalks that are shorter than the egg bodies, while in the Figitidae some species possess stalks about equal in length to the egg bodies. In certain *Eucoila* and in *Ibalia leucospoides* Hoch. the stalk is about four times as long as the egg body. Some Evaniidae have cylindrical eggs which terminate in a broad conical structure bearing a minute pedicel. Among the Chrysidoidea some Cleptidae have eggs which bear minute micropylar projections. Among the Diptera evidently very few parasite eggs possess extensions that are non-functional after deposition. Some species of *Cryptochaetum* have eggs which exhibit micropylar projections. The egg of the pyrogotid *Adapsilia flaviseta* Ald. is extended at one pole and bears a small projecting micropylar process at the opposite pole (Clausen, Jaynes, and Gardner 1933).

Pedicellate-type eggs (figure 14g, h) are usually deposited externally. One end of the egg body is variously modified to form an anchor which is inserted in a puncture in the host integument, or the anterior end may be twisted or knotted during deposition to serve as an anchor. If deposited internally, the ventral surface of the egg is attached to the host integument by an elevated structure (Clausen 1940a). Some ophionine eggs (e.g., those of *Therion morio* Fabr. (Tothill 1922), *Exochilum*, *Heteropelma*, *Schizoloma*, and *Trichomma* ovarian eggs) exhibit cushion-like pedicels (Iwata 1958) which are evidently attached to the inside body wall of caterpillars. Most pedicellate eggs are at least partially visible on or in the host's integument. In some the pedicel originates from the side of the egg and is not stalked, e.g., some Tryphoninae, *Anisoclerion alacer* Grav. (Clausen 1932b); some Eulophidae (Elachertinae), *Euplectrus*, *Elachertus* (Clausen 1940a); some Aphelinidae, male eggs of *Euxanthellus philippae* Silv. (Smith and Compere 1928; Flanders 1937a). In others the pedicel originates from the end of the egg. The pedicel is a modified micropylar structure arising from the 'anterior' (cephalic) end of the egg in some Conopidae (Meijere 1904, 1912; Clausen 1940a). In other cases the pedicel is not a modified micropylar structure but usually arises from the 'posterior' end (end that enters ovipositor first) and usually takes the form of an elongate filament-like pedicel which may bear at its distal end a long, heavily pigmented bar attached at the middle and serving as an anchor deep within the host tissues. Included in the group of parasites having this type of egg are some Tryphoninae (Clausen 1932b, 1940a; Morris 1937; Barclay 1938; Simmonds 1947d; Iwata 1958) and some Agriotypidae in which the 'anterior' end of the egg bears a pedicel that is of glandular origin (Clausen 1931*b*) and is not present on the ovarian egg (Iwata 1959). Male eggs of certain *Coccophagus* spp. (Aphelinidae) which are direct secondary ectoparasites (Flanders 1937*a*) are of this type. In the Diptera the tachinid genus *Carcelia* exhibits eggs with slender cylindrical pedicels which expand distally into adhesive knobs; these eggs are attached to the integument or hair of the host caterpillars (Pantel 1910). The egg of the phasiine *Helomyia lateralis* (Meig.) has a similar appearance (Dupuis 1949*b*). In the Cecidomyiid *Endopsylla endogena* Kieff. the minute egg pedicel is embedded in the wing of a psyllid host (Lal 1934).

The encyrtiform-type egg is deposited internally but the anterior egg stalk protrudes through the host integument. The stalk and a portion of the egg body exhibits a longitudinal stripe or bank down one side—the aeroscopic plate—which is utilized by the larva or embryo for respiration (figure 14*f*). Such eggs occur in many genera of the Encyrtidae including *Acerophagus*, *Anagyrus*, *Blastothrix*, *Encyrtus*, *Metaphycus*, *Microterys*, and *Ooencyrtus* (Clausen 1940*a*; Maple 1947). Not all species in some genera produce eggs with aeroscopic plates; for instance, *Isodromus niger* Ashm. (Clancy 1946) and *I. perpunctatus* Masi (Principi 1947) exhibit a plate but *I. iceryae* How. does not (Clancy 1946). The eggs in this latter species, as well as the eggs of *Apoanagyrus* spp., *Melanaphycus fumipennis* (Timb.), and some others, have stalks that penetrate the host integument but do not show a typical aeroscopic plate.

Macrotype eggs (figure 14*i*) are found only in the Tachinidae. Eggs of this type are large (0·4 to 0·9 mm in length), oblong in outline when viewed from above, and semicircular in lateral view; the micropylar area is usually dorsal and somewhat pigmented; the surface is usually smooth but minute reticulations occur on eggs of some species. Uterine incubation rarely occurs with such eggs which are deposited externally on hosts (Pantel 1910; Townsend 1934; Clausen 1940*a*). Pantel (1910) further divides this type of egg into two groups: the dehiscent type with a fracture line across the anterior end and the indehiscent type with no fracture line. The larva in the latter type hatches through the thin flattened ventral surface of the egg directly into the host body. Townsend (1934) includes the membranous-type egg under the macrotype egg category using size alone as a criterion.

Microtype eggs (figure 14*i*) are minute (0·2 to 0·44 mm in length) and hardly perceptible to the unaided eye. When viewed from above, they are oval or circular with the anterior ends narrower. In lateral view these eggs are semicircular but can have asymmetric chorionic protuberances. The micropyle usually is visible at the narrower anterior end. Surface sculpturing and colour are diverse. Microtype eggs are deposited on foliage apart from the host and are ingested by the host or by a caterpillar harbouring a host. Such eggs are commonly found in the Tachinidae; they usually undergo complete uterine incubation (Townsend 1908, 1934; Pantel 1910; Thompson 1924; Clausen 1940*a*; Mesnil 1953, 1955). A remarkable similarity is founded between the tachinid microtype egg and the eggs of the hymenopterous family Trigonalidae (Clausen 1929, 1931*a*, 1940*a*; Raff 1934; Cooper 1954).

Acroceriform eggs are pear-shaped in outline and brown to dull black in colour. A well-defined circular cap occurs at the small anterior end and is forced off upon hatching (Schlinger 1960*b, c*).

EMBRYOLOGY

Usually the parasite deposits partially or completely incubated eggs in, on, or apart from the host and the larvae upon hatching commence to feed. Eggs of this type are monoembryonic for only a single larva is produced from an individual egg.

The type of embryogenesis in which more than one individual is produced from a single egg is called polyembryony. Parthenogenesis occurs in both monoembryonic and polyembryonic Hymenoptera.

In monoembryony, the usual method of reproduction for parasites, the embryology does not depart essentially from that in non-parasitic groups. There are some eggs of endoparasitic Hymenoptera that completely lack yolk and the type of cleavage that occurs in such eggs is total resembling a similar cleavage found in the Collembola. The lack of yolk is apparently compensated for by the rich medium in which the embryo resides in the body cavity of a host.

The embryology of a monoembryonic ichneumonid is covered in detail by Bronskill (1959). She related her findings with other embryological studies in the Hymenoptera and found that the embryogenesis of *Coccygomimus turionellae* (L.) is more similar to that of *Apis mellifera* L. and *Eurytoma aciculata* Ratz. as described by Ivanova-Kazas (1958) than that of other parasites including another ichneumonid, *Banchus femoralis* (Thoms.). Thus, Bronskill concluded that embryogenesis is not necessarily influenced by a parasitic existence. However, she points out that in some other parasitic insects embryonic development has been simplified and the embryo hatches before histogenesis of its larval tissues is completed. Examples of this latter type of development have been shown in a series of papers by Ivanova-Kazas (1948 to 1958). Included are descriptions of embryological development of a mymarid, a trichogrammatid, a chalcidid, a eurytomid, and two aphidiine braconids.

The incubation and hatching period is extremely variable among parasites. Complete incubation can occur in the uterus and among some tachinids and sarcophagids either larviposition occurs or hatching takes place at the time of egg placement. Some eggs, though completely incubated, do not hatch immediately. The microtype eggs deposited by the Trigonalidae and Tachinidae may contain larvae that will live for months within eggs awaiting ingestion by caterpillars. Some eucharitid eggs that are placed in plant buds overwinter in a completely incubated condition.

Polyembryony occurs among some endoparasitic Hymenoptera and few Strepsiptera. Since polyembryony is such an unusual biological phenomenon it has received attention from many workers. Marchal (1898) first described the phenomenon in insects in the encyrtid *Ageniaspis fuscicollis* (Dalm.). The embryology of this species was further investigated by Marchal (1904) and Martin (1914).

Polyembryony as a mode of reproduction has arisen independently in at least three other hymenopterous superfamilies that include parasites but occurs only in scattered genera in three families. Other encyrtids that exhibit polyembryony are *Litomastix* (Silvestri 1906; Patterson 1917) and *Copidosoma* (Patterson 1915; Leiby 1922; Silvestri 1923; Doutt 1947, 1952b). These are egg-larval parasites of Lepidoptera. Although not all species of the following genera are polyembryonic, some do possess this mode of development. The braconid genus *Macrocentrus* (Parker 1931b; Daniel 1932; Paillot 1937) develop polyembryonically in lepidopterous larvae. Similarly, certain species of *Platygaster* (Marchal 1906; Leiby and Hill

1923, 1924) that are egg-larval parasites of Cecidomyiidae show polyembryonic development. The dryinid *Aphelopus* (Kornhauser 1919) which attacks leafhoppers is also polyembryonic. Leiby (1929), Imms (1931), Silvestri (1937), Clausen (1940a), and Doutt (1947) have reviewed or discussed this intriguing phenomenon.

In polyembryonic species the time required for a generation ranges from several weeks to nearly a year. The development of a polyembryonic species begins exactly as does that of a monoembryonic egg parasite which also has poorly yolked eggs. However, instead of the embryonic nuclei or polar bodies entering directly into the blastula stage and developing into a larva in a few days, the polar nuclei in the polyembryonic species give rise to an embryonic membrane—the 'trophamnion.' This membrane surrounds the embryonic area of the egg and functions in a nutritive fashion extracting and concentrating nutrients from the host haemolymph to the embryonic area. Polyembryony begins to become apparent when the embryonic area divides into small groups of cells or polygerm (morulae) within the 'trophamnion.' The 'trophamnion' then lengthens into a chain-like structure with the morulae arranged in a row or branching cluster. Later this breaks up and separate embryos are formed. In *Litomastix* as many as 1,500 embryos may be produced in a single lepidopterous larva (Silvestri 1906). The number of progeny produced seems limited only by the volume of the host since they completely occupy the host skin. Doutt (1947) suggests that polyembryony may result from the change in cytoplasmic-nuclear balance when the formation of the polar region removes about half the cytoplasm of the egg and that nuclear material from the sperm nucleus evidently also increases polyembryonic division.

Among the hundreds of hymenopteriform larvae that may be produced from a single egg by polyembryony there often occurs a caudate-type larva. This 'precocious' larva resembles an endoparasitic ichneumonid type and has been called an 'asexual' larva. Doutt (1952b) found this peculiar larval type to be correlated only with the progeny of fertilized females. Thus, this dimorphism resulted only from polygerms of the female sex. Such an individual has been termed a teratoid larva by Doutt. This interesting larva never matures but dies when other larvae develop toward maturity.

The occurrence of embryonic membranes surrounding the embryos of endoparasitic Hymenoptera is common. Their main function is considered to be both protective and nutritive for they are correlated with eggs that have little or no yolk. Usually such eggs are minute when deposited into the host; then, presumably by osmosis or active absorption of fluid through the egg membranes, they gradually become larger (Imms 1931; Simmonds 1947b). Flanders (1942a) terms these eggs that expand in the host hydropic eggs. Flanders (1942d) found that in *Coccophagus capensis* Comp. only the fertilized egg produced a trophic membrane; this suggests that polyembryony possibly arose from monoembryonic methods.

The embryonic membranes are known by several names such as trophamnion, trophic membrane, amnion, serosa, pseudoserosa, or trophserosa. The problem of determining the origin of the membrane has led to this synonymy. The number of membranes and their origin vary between species. Basically there appear to be two sites of the membrane formation. Johannsen and Butt (1941) describe the membrane origins as being derived partly from polar bodies that are not thrown off during maturation and partly from a 'differentiated part of the egg.'

Imms (1931), reviewing the subject of embryonic membranes, mentions that one membrane may arise from the division of the polar nuclei of the egg, as in polyembryonic forms, or a membrane may be formed from the delamination of the blastoderm; in some eggs both types of membranes may occur. Imms suggests that the term trophamnion be confined to a membrane derived from the polar bodies of the egg while that formed from blastoderm delamination or by cellular extrusion should be termed a pseudoserosa. Caltagirone (1959) believes, however, that since the membrane originating from the polar region in polyembryonic species is not homologous with the amnion, the term trophamnion should not be applied to this particular membrane; he terms the cellular trophic membrane that surrounds the embryo of the ichneumonid *Lathrostizus euurae* (Ashm.) the trophserosa, for in this embryo the serosa originates from the undifferentiated blastoderm.

Bronskill (1959) considers the two embryonic membranes that commonly envelop insect embryos as a serosa and an amnion, and points out that both membranes appear to be absent in some chalcidoids as well as in the few ichneumonids that have been studied embryonically. In the chalcidoids, the encyrtid *Pseudaphycus* sp. and the eurytomid *Eurytoma aciculata* were found by Ivanova-Kazas to have one embryonic envelope according to Bronskill.

The ichneumonid *Coccygomimus turionellae* has a serosa which entirely surrounds the developing embryo and exhibits a rudimentary amnion (Bronskill 1959). The euphorine braconids have a particularly interesting embryonic membrane and its trophic function is clear and further specialized. *Perilitus coccinellae* Schrank (Ogloblin 1924), *P. rutilus* Nees (Jackson 1928), and *Microctonus vittatae* (O. J. Smith 1952) produce eggs that swell enormously, some as much as 1,000 times.

During eclosion when the embryonic membrane (trophamnion) is broken and cells of the membrane float free in the host's haemolymph, these cells increase in size proportional to the growth of the larval parasite; they become tremendously enlarged while retaining their trophic function inasmuch as the larva feeds upon these cells.

The nutrition of the host influences the development of these cells and in turn influences the parasitic larva. Experiments by the author (unpublished) indicate that if *Hippodamia convergens* Guer. adults were fed only carbohydrate solutions the parasitic larvae of *Perilitus coccinellae* would not develop beyond the first instar and the trophamnion cells would remain proportionally small. When either aphids or a complex diet including an enzymatic protein hydrolysate of yeast plus a carbohydrate solution were fed to parasitized beetles, the parasitic larvae and the trophamnion cells grew normally.

Some embryonic membranes persist and surround the larva as in *Apanteles glomeratus* (Grandori 1911) or localize around the anterior end as in some *Opius*.

NUMBER OF LARVAL INSTARS

Most dipterous larvae cast their skins three times during growth; however, in the Nematocera there are mostly four larval instars while in the Brachycera between three and eight are known. The last larval skin is normally shed at pupation. In the Cyclorrhapha, as a rule, there are three apparent instars; the pupa is coarctate with the third-instar larval skin hardening and forming the outer shell or puparium which encloses the pupa. Another moult, the fourth, may occur within the puparium and surround the pupa. Possibly in *Cryptochaetum iceryae* (Will.) four instars may occur; the primary larva being an 'embryo larva' (Thorpe 1930*a*).

The number of larval instars among the hymenopterous parasites is variable. Five seems to be the more common number and probably represents the primitive condition for in the Symphyta there are five instars. A lesser number is perhaps the result of specialization. Morris (1937) suggests that an instar is lost in the development of the Ichneumonidae but the prepupal phase represents a lost instar which occurs in the more primitive Tenthredinidae. There also appears to be a tendency for ectoparasitic larvae to have five instars and endoparasitic forms fewer than five. However, there are many exceptions to this, for even in a single genus the number of instars can vary. As more biological studies are conducted and the numbers of larval instars in the various species carefully noted, perhaps useful criteria will be obtained that will help explain the interspecific variations in moults.

It is difficult to determine the actual number of instars in many parasite groups because the mandibles of some groups are only faintly sclerotized. The number of different sets of mandibles found in the host upon completion of the parasite larval development usually offers the best evidence as to the number of instars. At times the larvae of certain ectoparasites will eat their cast skins. In other groups the cast skins may slip and collect posteriorly on the developing larva. At least the primary and final larval instars should be described in any biological study of parasites for these two stages generally offer the best clues to the nature and kind of parasite the investigator has found.

The following examples offer an idea of the variability of the number of larval instars found in the entomophagous Hymenoptera.

In the Ichneumonoidea, the majority of the Ichneumonidae have five instars although four occur in some genera. However, some *Hyposoter* spp. seem to have only three while other species in the same genus have been clearly demonstrated to have five (Muesebeck and Parker 1933). In the Braconidae, similar variability occurs within the genus *Bracon* but in *Apanteles* all the species that have been studied have had only three instars. Other well-known genera in which some of the species appear to have only three instars are *Meteorus*, *Rogas*, and *Chelonus*. *Opius*, *Ascogaster*, and *Macrocentrus* possess four larval instars while in *Phanomeris*, *Chremylus*, *Colastes*, and *Microctonus* there are five. Variable numbers of instars have been reported for species in the Aphidiinae; however, Schlinger and Hall (1960, 1961) claim only three instars for species of *Praon* and *Trioxys* and suggest that three may be correct for all known species.

The Chalcidoidea exhibit an even greater variability in the number of larval instars but it is more difficult to detect the transition between instars in these smaller species. The

Mymaridae apparently have two or three, rarely four instars. In the Trichogrammatidae the number of instars apparently ranges from one to five. *Trichogramma* has three according to Flanders (1937b). The Torymidae, Eurytomidae, Eupelmidae, and many Pteromalidae normally have five instars. The number of larval instars in the Encyrtidae has been poorly investigated but seems to range from three to five. The Perilampidae and Eucharitadae generally have three larval instars although one species of the former family possesses four. The Aphelinidae seem to have three instars and the Leucospidae probably have four.

The families of Proctotrupoidea appear to have less than five larval instars. Species of *Platygaster* have either one, two, or three and only one instar has been recorded for *Allotropa*. Scelionidae usually have three, rarely two. The Evaniidae, Heloridae, Diapriidae, and Proctotrupidae evidently have three, and Ceraphronidae exhibit either three or four larval instars.

Among the parasitic cynipoids, the Figitidae and the subfamilies Eucoilinae and Charipinae seem to have three or four larval instars. At least one species in the Ibaliidae shows four.

A few species studied in the Trigonalidae, Dryinidae, Chrysididae, Rhopalosomatidae, Thynnidae, and Tiphiidae have been found to have five larval instars. It may seem that the smaller the parasitic species the lesser the number of larval instars but some Scoliidae have been found to have four larval instars and these are among the largest parasites.

LARVAL DIMORPHISM

Dimorphism may occur in the same larval stage of certain parasites. One type is clearly sexual dimorphism and another type is associated with polyembryonic Encyrtidae.

Sexual dimorphism may occur with no obvious difference in the biology between the two sexes. In addition, there are some groups of chalcidoids in which the early instars of the sexes will be both biologically and morphologically distinguishable.

Larvae of the mymarid *Anaphoidea nitens* Grlt. exemplify the morphological type of sexual dimorphism. Both the first and second instars exhibit differences correlated with their ultimate sex yet they are both endoparasitic in the eggs of the Eucalyptus snout-beetle (Tooke 1955). The first-instar larva of *A. nitens* is mymariform (figure 17e) but two distinctive types occur. In the female, the thorax and abdomen are composed of five segments bearing numerous heavy spines while in the male there are six segments and the spines are restricted to the thorax and first abdominal segment. The tail of the female larva is abruptly bent while the male larval tail is curved. Sexual dimorphism persists into the second instar but disappears in the third and final instars (Tooke 1955).

Sexual dimorphism is even more striking in certain aphelinid larvae. Not only do the sexes differ morphologically but also habitudinally. The female larvae of *Coccophagus* are primary parasites of coccids or pseudococcids and may be either ecto- or endoparasitic. The male larvae in some species resemble the females and develop similarly. In other species, eggs and first-stage larvae are morphologically dissimilar and this is correlated with endoparasitic development of the females and ectoparasitic development of the males (Zinna 1961). In yet other species the male larvae may be either indirect or direct secondary parasites, often on their own species (Flanders 1937a; Zinna 1961).

Coccophagus gurneyi Comp. is an example of an indirect secondary parasite. An unmated female deposits its male egg into a mealybug. The larva does not hatch until the body fluids of the mealybug have been consumed by a primary parasite. The male larva appears planidium-like, for it is heavily sclerotized, and plate-like structures occur on nearly all body segments. After the mealybug body fluids are consumed by the primary larva, the male larva attacks the primary parasite (which may be its own species), at first externally but eventually internally (Flanders 1937a). The female larva, which is a primary parasite, hatches from the egg soon after deposition in the mealybug. It is a typical caudate-type and its integument is not sclerotized (Cendaña 1937).

Coccophagus capensis is an example of a direct secondary parasite. Larval sexual dimorphism is well-marked in this species. The unmated female usually oviposits into the prepupa or pupa of its own species but it may also deposit eggs in other species of *Coccophagus*. The male larva appears mymariform (figure 17e) and is very hairy (Flanders 1937a), but the female larva is typically of caudate-form (Cendaña 1937).

The polyembryonic Encyrtidae exhibit another type of larval dimorphism. In these encyrtids the teratoid larva (Doutt 1952b) differs greatly from the mass of hymenopteriform larvae arising from the polygerm. For further discussion see polyembryony under the embryology section of this chapter.

FIRST-INSTAR LARVAE

The most distinctive parasitic stage in the life cycle is the primary or first-instar larva. Subsequent larval stages are usually grub-like without any conspicuous structures. Forms of first-instar larvae range from the unsegmented sac-like type of some species to the elongated and segmented type with a distinct head capsule often bearing large mandibles. Various 'appendages' may occur but these are unsegmented except in the triungulin-type larva which bears true legs.

Some authors, following Berlese (1913), categorize larvae into protopod, polypod, oligopod, and apodous types. Imms (1925, 1931) adopted these terms since they provided a useful descriptive system. Thus, under protopod larvae he used the primary larvae of Platygasteridae, Scelionidae, and Dryinidae as examples. These relatively unsegmented larvae with apparently rudimentary cephalic and thoracic segments were suspected to emerge from the egg in an early embryonic phase, and, since they were parasitic, survived by being immersed in a nutritive medium. Under the polypod larvae, which include the eruciform larvae, Imms places certain parasitic Cynipoidea and Proctotrupidae, since their larvae possess abdominal limbs either in the first or second instar. Oligopod larvae have well-developed thoracic legs and no abdominal appendages except, perhaps, cerci-like processes. The Meloidae, Stylopidae, and Ripiphoridae are placed in this group. And finally, under apodous larvae, which have no trunk appendages, many aculeate hymenopterous larvae are placed.

This concept is not followed here. It has been evaluated morphologically by Snodgrass (1954) and physiologically by Wigglesworth (1954) who found that structures or lack of structures and certain functions which appear to be embryonic are, in reality, often specialized adaptations. Snodgrass (1954) states: '. . . the specialized structure of the larva has been forced back on the embryo until the embryo becomes a preliminary larva.' Keilin and Baume–Pluvinel(1913)considered pseudopods to be entirely adaptive and, even though Eastham (1929) employed the term polypod for the first-instar *Phaenoserphus*, he acknowledged that the larva exhibited a morphological gradient from head to tail with only the middle proleg-bearing region being comparable to Berlese's (1913) polypod stage. One structure or another of these so–called 'embryonic larvae' is usually specialized beyond what would be expected in the embryo. Thorpe (1930a) called attention to this fact but was convinced that the primary larva of *Cryptochaetum* and some other parasites could be described as embryonic. Chen (1946) was also impressed by the resemblance of many first-instar larvae to embryonic developmental phases and believed them to be precocious larval types, but he rejected Berlese's 'hatched embryo' concept as occurring in other insects.

The principal hymenopterous larval types stressed herein are those recognized by Richardson (1913), E. W. Wheeler (1923), Imms (1931), and summarized by Clausen (1940a). These descriptive first-instar larval types often connote form or function but do not necessarily indicate phylogenetic relationships. Some larval types include larvae of several orders. The primary larval types or groups of Diptera stressed herein are largely based on the works of Townsend (1908, 1934 to 1942), Pantel(1910), Thompson (1915b, 1921, 1922e, 1923c, 1926), Clausen (1940a), and Hennig (1952).

The main types of first-instar larvae recognized among the parasites or egg predators are: triungulin, planidium, sacciform, teleaform, mymariform, cyclopiform, eucoiliform, mandibulate, microtype, muscoidiform, encyrtiform, hymenopteriform, chrysidiform, agriotypiform, vesiculate, and caudate. Many first-instar types are shown in figures 15, 16, 17, 18, and 19.

There are endoparasitic hymenopterous primary larvae that often possess a combination of larval characteristics. Some are both mandibulate and caudate, and others may be mandibulate, caudate, and vesiculate. The forms of these various larvae are products of adaptation to special environments and the obvious unique structures often offer a clue as to their function.

The functions that are expressed by morphological characteristics in the larvae include locomotion, protection, ingestion, and respiration. The ectophagous forms are usually more complex than the specialized endophagous feeders.

LOCOMOTION. The parasites or egg predators that deposit their eggs apart from the host require an ability in the egg or early larval stages to seek out or be carried to the host (phoresy). Triungulins use their segmented legs while the planidium type larvae use elongated setae which arise from the thoracic region or caudal regions or both. If 'walking setae' are absent, as in some Tachinidae, the larva may move by jumping or looping or may whirl around with its base attached to its

TRIUNGULIN TYPE

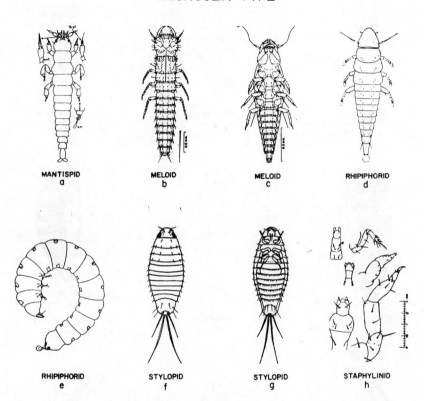

MANTISPID
a

MELOID
b

MELOID
c

RHIPIPHORID
d

RHIPIPHORID
e

STYLOPID
f

STYLOPID
g

STAPHYLINID
h

FIGURE 15. Triungulin type first-instar larvae: (*a*) *Mantispa interrupta* Say, from Peterson (1951*b*); (*b*) *Epicauta pardalis* (LeConte), from MacSwain (1956); (*c*) ventral view *Zonitis bilineatus* Say, from MacSwain (1956); (*d*) *Rhipiphorus smithi* Linsley and MacSwain, from Linsley, Mac-Swain, and Smith (1952*b*); (*e*) *R. smithi* first-instar endoparasitic phase, from Linsley, MacSwain, and Smith (1952*b*); (*f*) *Eoxenos laboulbenei* Peyer. dorsal view, from Bohart (1941); (*g*) *E. laboulbenei* ventral view, from Bohart (1941); (*h*) *Aleochara sparsa* Heer. labium and leg of first, second, and third instar, from Wright, Geering, and Ashby (1947).

PLANIDIUM TYPE

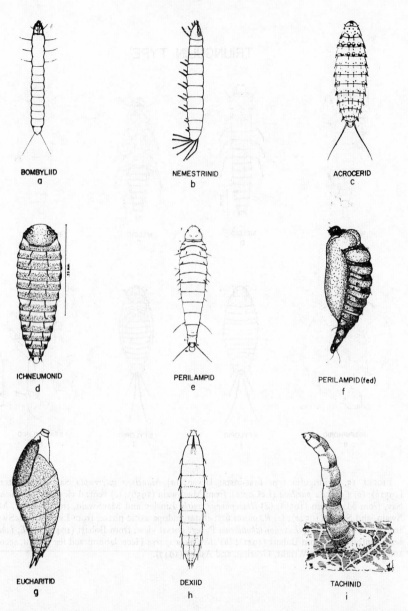

FIGURE 16. Planidium type first-instar larvae: (a) *Hyperalonia oenomaus* Rond., from Clausen (1928); (b) *Trichopsidea clausa* (O.S.) lateral view, from Prescott (1955); (c) *Pterodontia flavipes* Gray, dorsal view, from King (1916); (d) *Euceros frigidus* Cress., dorsal view, from Tripp (1961); (e) *Perilampus laevifrons* Dalm., dorsal view from Principi (1947); (f) *Perilampus chrysopae* Cwfd. engorged planidium, lateral view, from Clancy (1946); (g) *Schizaspidia tenuicornis* Ashm., lateral view, from Clausen (1923); (h) *Callirrhoe siberita* (F.), from Clausen, King, and Teranishi (1927); (i) *Tachina magnicornis* Zett., showing the egg chorion serving as an attachment 'cup' to leaf, from Townsend (1908).

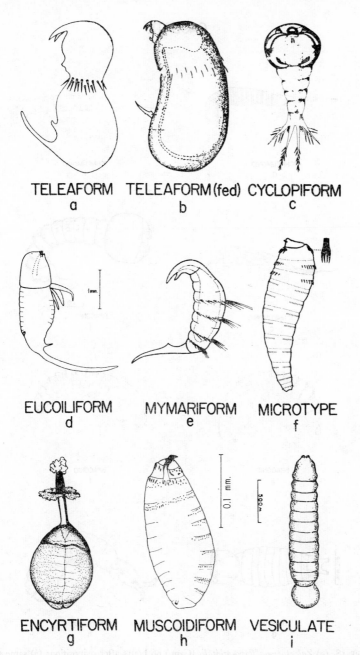

TELEAFORM   TELEAFORM(fed)   CYCLOPIFORM
a   b   c

EUCOILIFORM   MYMARIFORM   MICROTYPE
d   e   f

ENCYRTIFORM   MUSCOIDIFORM   VESICULATE
g   h   i

FIGURE 17. Various types of parasitoid first-instar larvae: (*a*) *Telenomus gifuensis* Ashm., from Hidaka (1958); (*b*) engorged *Hadronotus ajax* Grlt., from Schell(1943); (*c*) Platygasterid, from Ganin (1869); (*d*) *Hexacola sp.*, from Simmonds (1952); (*e*) *Polynema striaticorne* Grlt., from Balduf (1928); (*f*) *Orthogonalos debilis* Teranishi, from Clausen (1931*a*); (*g*) *Isodromus niger* Ashm., from Clancy (1946); (*h*) *Phorocera incrassata* Smith, from Coppel (1958); (*i*) second stage of *Apanteles medicaginis* Mues., from Allen (1958).

CAUDATE

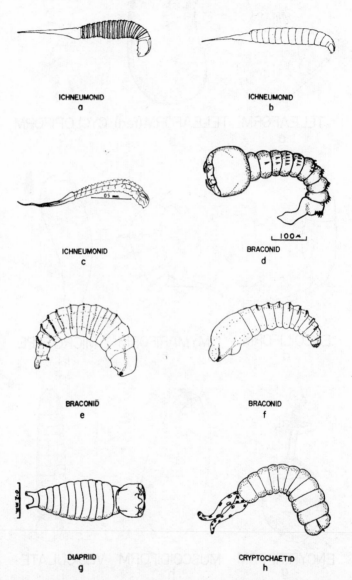

FIGURE 18. (a) *Zaleptopygus flavo-orbitalis* (Cam.) 96 hours after oviposition; (b) same species after 240 hours, from Bradley and Burgess (1934); (c) *Cremastus interruptor* Grav. early first-instar, from Thorpe (1932a); (d) *Apanteles medicaginis* Mues. first-instar larva (Allen 1958); (e) *Praon palitans* Mues. first-instar larva (Schlinger and Hall 1960); (f) *Trioxys utilis* Mues., first-instar larva (Schlinger and Hall 1961); (g) *Loxotropa tritoma* Thoms. first-instar larva, from Wright, Geering, and Ashby (1947); (h) *Cryptochaetum grandicorne* Rond. late first-instar larva, from Thorpe (1934).

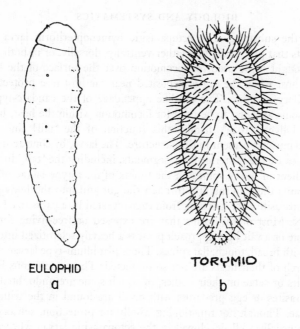

EULOPHID
a

TORYMID
b

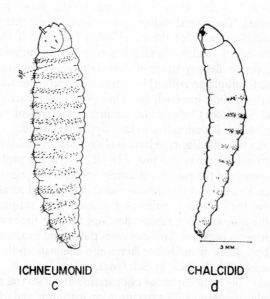

ICHNEUMONID
c

CHALCIDID
d

.3 MM

FIGURE 19. Hymenopteriform first-instar larvae: (*a*) *Sympiesis* sp., from Dowden (1941); (*b*) *Monodontomerus dentipes* (Dal.), from Morris, Cameron, and Jepson (1937); (*c*) *Phanomeris phyllotomae* Mues., from Dowden (1941); (*d*) *Spilochalcis side* (Wlk.), from Arthur (1958).

egg shell or the substrate. The ectoparasitic hymenopteriform larva may have body segments that project slightly either ventrally, dorsally, or in both directions. These are thought to be used for locomotion over the surface of the host or for reaching the host when the egg is deposited near the host in a protected habitat such as a gallery or mine. The tail-like appendage of the caudate-type larva is thought, by some authors, to be used for locomotion within the host, but Thorpe (1930a) and Ullyett (1944) dismiss this function of the 'tail' since there are apparently no muscles present in this structure. The larva, by contracting its body, however, can cause the posterior body segments, including the 'tail,' to arc widely. The arrangement of heavy spines on the thorax of microtype larvae of secondary parasites permits them to migrate through the gut and into the body cavity of a primary endoparasite after hatching from eggs ingested by a parasitized caterpillar.

PROTECTION. Most of the forms that are exposed or free-living for indefinite periods of time or await host approach possess a heavily sclerotized integument or are covered with broad, tough, flat spines. Those planidium-type larvae that burrow in soil in search of their hosts are not so protected. The ectophagous larvae often bear long hairs or setae on their bodies, of which some are undoubtedly sensory. The only parasites or egg predators with ocelli are found in the triungulin-type primary larvae. Though not functioning wholly for protection, sensory hairs and antennae are usually well developed in the ectoparasitic larvae whereas they are minute in most endoparasitic types.

Aggressive action between larvae is reflected in the possession of strong mandibles (Salt 1961). The typical endophagous solitary larvae that display large sickle-shaped mandibles are called the mandibulate-type, and if they possess a caudal process are called caudate-mandibulate-type. Many authors report that these larvae quite readily destroy larvae of their own species (superparasitism) or of different species (multiple parasitism) by biting the supernumeraries. However, this is not the only method involved, for Thompson and Parker (1930), O. J. Smith (1952), and Salt (1961) believe that the first larvae present may give off a 'cytolytic enzyme' which is destructive to later-appearing larvae.

It appears that the mandibulate-type larva is always solitary and is the stage that is usually found to overwinter in the host. Also, if there is any prolonged period during the development of the parasite, it usually involves the primary larva with its large mandibles. Examples of this sort are found in egg-larval parasites or in the *Opius* species where the parasite remains as a primary larva throughout various larval instars of the host and then rapidly develops through the rest of its larval instars as the host nears pupation. In some cases the second instar, as well as the first, is mandibulate. These mandibulate larvae also eliminate rivals by mangling them. This was reported in *Collyria* by Salt (1931, 1932).

FEEDING. Larvae of the hymenopterous egg parasites are of several types, usually being greatly simplified creatures. The sacciform, mymariform, and teleaform types appear virtually unsegmented and apparently absorb much of their food through the skin. The polyembryonic teratoid larva (Doutt 1952b) also obtains its food in this manner and the polyembryonic hymenopteriform types with their invisible mandibles may do the same thing. Doutt (1947) suggests that the 'feeding embryos' of polyembronic species ingest food through the trophamnion.

Among the Diptera, *Cryptochaetum* is perhaps the most simplified or specialized for an endoparasitic existence. It lacks mouth-parts, nervous system, sense organs, tracheal system, spiracles, salivary glands, muscles, and heart, and it absorbs food through its cuticle (Thorpe 1931*a*, 1934). Other dipterous parasites are more differentiated but some take food through their skin, as a few tachinids do. The coleopterous parasites or egg predators consume eggs or ingest host tissues via the mouth. The stylopids evidently feed cutaneously.

The expansion of eggs after deposition in the host is a result of host fluids passing through embryonic membranes. The larva also increases in size in these cases. The braconid caudate-mandibulate larva often has this type of development (Simmonds 1947*b*, *c*). The cells of the surrounding membrane increase in size and retain their trophic function after the membrane dissociates into free cells. The larva then eats these giant cells (Jackson 1928; O. J. Smith 1952).

The most striking change between subsequent larval stages occurs in the structure of the mandibles in Hymenoptera and in the buccopharyngeal apparatus in the Diptera. The buccopharyngeal apparatus changes from a single anterior hook in the primary larval stage to a pair of hooks in later instars; in Hymenoptera the mandibles often become more triangular in shape as contrasted to the sickle-shape of the first-instar larval mandibles (figures 21*a*, 25*a*).

RESPIRATION. First-instar larvae exhibit the greatest diversity in methods of exchanging gases for the respiratory structures and methods differ in later instars. Reviews on insect respiration including that in parasites have been made by: Seurat (1899) mainly on Hymenoptera; Wigglesworth (1931, 1939); Edwards (1953); Chauvin (1956) on insects in general; Thorpe (1930*b*, 1932*b*, 1934) on certain Diptera and Hymenoptera; Keilin (1944) on Diptera; and Krogh (1941) on various animals including some insects. Clausen (1950) reviews respiration of immature parasitic insects. (Also see section on mature larvae in this chapter.)

If the first-instar larva is endophagous, it is immersed in fluids and either obtains oxygen from surrounding host fluids or possesses a mechanism for obtaining air from outside of its host. Many authors visualize a parallel in respiratory methods between parasites and aquatic insects.

Many endoparasitic larvae exchange gases through the integument. This cutaneous respiration method occurs whether a tracheal system is present or not. In the Hymenoptera, the tracheae are filled with fluid during the first instar and are non-functional (Seurat 1899). There are usually no open spiracles (apneustic) in the larvae that respire cutaneously. Clausen (1950) points out that there are some endophagous larvae with open spiracles which are apparently non-functional and Parker and Thompson (1925) appear to have found a transitional form, the eupelmid *Anastatus* sp., which has four pairs of open spiracles and yet is endoparasitic.

Cutaneous respiration occurs among the parasites having larvae which pass part of their development in various organs of the host, as in some Tachinidae,

Encyrtidae, and Platygasteridae. The egg parasites (Mymaridae, Trichogrammatidae, and Scelionidae) are all apneustic in the primary stage. The oxygen requirements of *Trichogramma* larvae are apparently extremely low as indicated by Flanders' (1930*a*) experiment of placing the parasitized host (*Ephestia*) eggs in water for a week. The parasites developed as far as the late pupal stage before they died.

Most other parasites that are endoparasitic and respire cutaneously have larvae either of the vesiculate (figure 17*i*) or caudate types (figure 18). These larvae are often tracheate but have no open spiracles. The vesiculate type larvae are commonly found in the Braconidae and are not necessarily limited to the primary larval stage (Muesebeck 1918; Gatenby 1919; Tothill 1922). This type is also found in a few ichneumonids and encyrtids (Clausen 1940*a*). The vesicle is a caudal projection of the proctodaeum. This everted proctodaeum becomes gradually withdrawn into the body during later growth and forms the hindmost region of the intestine (Grandori 1911). In the Diptera the bilobed anal vesicles which appear in endoparasitic larvae of the Pipunculidae and Conopidae may have the same function as in the Hymenoptera (Clausen 1940*a*, 1950). In the Hymenoptera tested by Thorpe (1932*b*) the vesicle was shown to be the site of respiratory activity. The studies of Narayanan, Rao, and Gangrade (1956) with *Apanteles* seem to confirm this since the caudal vesicle was shown to be intimately associated with the circulatory system, thus resembling a blood gill.

The caudate type larva has been a subject of much discussion and many different functions have been attributed to the long tail-like process. This larva is commonly found in the endophagous Ichneumonidae, is often present in the Braconidae and Encyrtidae, and is occasionally seen in other hymenopterous families but rarely occurs in the Diptera. In the Hymenoptera the 'tail' diminishes in size as the larva develops. As far as respiration is concerned, Timberlake (1910) thought the 'tail' to be a blood gill; Tothill (1922) sectioned the caudal process and thought it to be so full of tracheae that it would not permit ample blood exchange; he, therefore, considered it to be a tracheal gill. However, Thompson and Parker (1930) found the 'tail' to be filled primarily with fat body and carrying two tracheal trunks. The function of the tail, however, does not seem to be respiratory, for Thorpe (1932*b*), using flagellate protozoans to determine where oxygen is absorbed by some caudate ichneumonid larvae, concluded that the 'tail' is of no importance for respiration in this type of larva.

Ullyett (1944) reviewed the theories which have been attributed to the function of the 'tail' and suggests, first, that the primary function is to serve as an egg burster based on his own observations with *Horogenes* sp.; secondly, that it serves for absorption of food substances from the host haemolymph; and thirdly, it may be a balancing organ as proposed by Cameron (1938) to compensate for the massive head that occurs in this type of larva. All three functions may occur in the same larva.

Another form of larva falls under the caudate-type (figure 18*h*). In this form the long, paired caudal tubules, which increase in length as the larva develops, are important to respiration. Thorpe (1931*a*, 1934), again using flagellate protozoans as indicators, definitely showed that the caudal filaments of the dipterous *Crypto-*

chaetum larva serve to increase the area of surface through which gaseous exchange may take place and thus acts as a kind of tracheal gill. The same structure is also used for absorption of food in early instars.

The encyrtiform primary larvae are among the few metapneustic larvae that occur in the Hymenoptera. There is but a single pair of spiracles upon one of the posterior segments. Since this type of larva is endoparasitic in various coccids or in insect eggs, it must have some method of conveying oxygen to its open spiracles. Unlike the Tachinidae that induce a funnel formation by the host, the encyrtiform larva uses its egg-stalk, which protrudes through the host wall, for respiration. The egg is not simply the common stalked-type, for it bears a dark longitudinal band, the aeroscopic plate, which extends the full length of the stalk and partly into the egg body (Maple 1947).

The encyrtiform larva orients its posterior spiracles inside the stalk and it was thought by Imms (1918), Silvestri (1919), and Thorpe (1936) that this permitted free gas exchange through the lumen to the larva. Flanders (1937a), however, observed that in *Leptomastix*, a parasite of mealybugs, the spiracles were always associated with the aeroscopic plate on the egg chorion. A detailed study of another encyrtid, *Ooencyrtus johnsoni* (How.), by Maple (1937) revealed that the embryo revolves before hatching, which brings the spiracles into position with the stalk end of the egg. However, apparently no free air passes directly down the stalk since its lumen is closed. In a later study, Maple (1947) concluded from various correlations that air is directly conveyed to the larva down the band on the egg. Clausen (1950) discusses various ways in which the aeroscopic plate may function. Maple's (1947) studies of the eggs and first-instar larvae of a number of Encyrtidae involve many species that are metapneustic, some of which have tracheal trunks extended into long tubular stalks with spiracles at their apices. Within the genus *Isodromus*, *I. niger* (Clancy 1946) and *I. perpunctatus* (Principi 1947), parasitic in *Chrysopa* larvae, have typical encyrtiform eggs and larvae; but *I. iceryae*, also a parasite of *Chrysopa* larvae, manifests stalked eggs which are extruded through the host derm. However, the stalk does not possess an aeroscopic plate typical of the encyrtiform egg and the larva is apneustic (Clancy 1946).

The intermediate instars of encyrtiform larvae retain their connection with the egg but the final stage larva usually becomes peripneustic and reflects the normal chalcidoid spiracle arrangement.

There is one interesting way in which the chalcidoid ectoparasitic first-instar larvae differ from similar larvae in the Ichneumonoidea. The chalcidoids commonly show only four or five pairs of spiracles in the primary stage and in later instars exhibit the normal nine pairs. But in the Ichneumonoidea the number of spiracles in the first stage is similar to the subsequent instars which usually have nine.

The internal anatomy of most primary larvae of parasites is similar to that found in later stages except for the tracheal systems in endoparasites. A discussion of the internal anatomy of parasitic larvae will be found under the section on mature larvae. Formation of the respiratory funnel in Diptera, as well as the spiracle arrangement that commonly occurs, are discussed under the section on mature larvae.

INTERMEDIATE AND MATURE LARVAE

The larva usually exhibits a change of form other than size as it develops through its various instars. The form change may be subtle but, since hypermetamorphosis is the rule rather than the exception among endoparasitic larvae, there usually are conspicuous modifications between certain instars. Generally the larva loses any bizarre first-instar characteristics as it develops towards maturity and, although the subsequent larval stages become morphologically simplified, they still reveal recognizable structures.

In the insect families where parasitism is relatively rare, as for example in certain carabids and staphylinids of the Coleoptera, the first-instar or primary larva as well as the adults resemble morphologically their non-parasitic relatives. However, in these groups the intermediate or mature larvae depart so radically from the normal (usually through degeneration of certain structures) that they cannot be identified by characters used to classify the larvae of free-living species in the same families (Boving and Craighead 1931; van Emden 1942).

Endoparasitic first-instar larvae and the same stage of those parasites that deposit their eggs or larvae apart from their hosts display far more diversity in form than do the subsequent larval stages. The appearance of similar structures in phylogenetically unrelated groups is common in the first-instar stage and it is difficult to assemble them into natural groups. However, certain characteristics appear in the mature larvae which often permit separating them into taxa which are comparable to those proposed by systematists for the adult parasites.

The intermediate- and final-stage larvae of most ectoparasitic species of Hymenoptera do not differ in any essential character from their first-instar larvae. In some groups, however, more open spiracles appear in later stages. The endoparasites undergo greater changes as they develop through the various instars.

Intermediate Larval Instars

The intermediate stages of both dipterous and hymenopterous parasites usually resemble the form of the final larval stage. The large head and falcate mandibles are lost after the first moult. In caudate type larvae the 'tail' is either lost or reduced in the later instars but in the vesiculate type the vesicle becomes more pronounced until the final stage where it is retracted. In the Hymenoptera there are some groups, however, that display unique intermediate instars. These have received special names.

The second-stage larva of the cynipoid groups Ibaliidae, Eucoilinae, and some Figitidae is the so-called 'polypodeiform type.' In this type the larval body is segmented and bears paired fleshy processes ventrally (figure 20a). The Proctotrupidae and Heloridae of the Proctotrupoidea have a similar stage. As already discussed, some authors consider such a type an ontogenetic stage of a hatched embryo but now it is believed to be an adaptive form and does not reflect recapitulation.

In the Chalcidoidea, the mymarid egg parasites that possess the sacciform, primary larval form (*Anagrus*), moult into a so-called 'histriobdellid' second-instar larva (figure 20*b*). This larva is described by Clausen (1940*a*) as being cylindrical with six body constrictions, of which the first and last are larger. The head bears a pair of large, conical or cylindrical, fleshy, lateroventral appendages and a pair of extruded, slender, curved mandibles which lie parallel to each other. The caudal body segment bears a pair of large, ear-like lateroventral organs. The first-instar microtype larva of the Trigonalidae develops into a mandibulate second stage and then changes into hymenopteriform larva in later stages (Clausen 1940*a*).

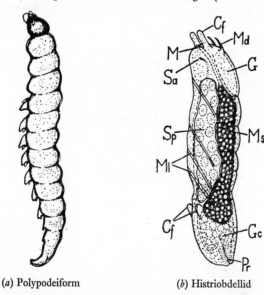

(*a*) Polypodeiform   (*b*) Histriobdellid

FIGURE 20. (*a*) 'Polypodeiform' first-instar larva of *Helorus paradoxus* Prov., from Clancy (1946); (*b*) 'Histriobdellid' intermediate larval stage of *Anagrus incarnatus* Hal., from Bakkendorf (1934).

The intermediate larval stages of many Meloidae also exhibit different forms from both the primary and mature stages. The succession of these types is discussed under the section concerning parasites that deposit eggs or larvae apart from their hosts.

Last Instar Larvae

In general, the entomophagous cyclorrhaphous dipterous larva is more or less muscoidiform (maggot-like), and the entomophagous hymenopterous larva is hymenopteriform (grub-like) upon attaining the final instar (figure 21). Superficially, one maggot looks like another and one grub-like larva appears inseparable from another. In recent years more intensive morphological studies on the parasitic larvae have uncovered structures that permit the determination of various taxa including that of species in some groups. The head structures and the anatomy of

7—I.P.W.

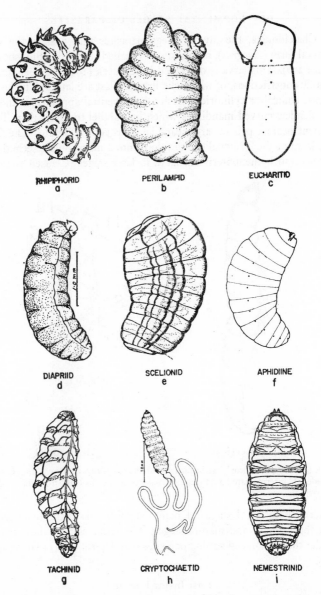

RHIPIPHORID
a

PERILAMPID
b

EUCHARITID
c

DIAPRIID
d

SCELIONID
e

APHIDIINE
f

TACHINID
g

CRYPTOCHAETID
h

NEMESTRINID
i

FIGURE 21. Mature larvae of various parasites: (a) *Rhipiphorus smithi* Linsley and MacSwain fully fed sixth instar, from Linsley, MacSwain, and Smith (1952*b*); (*b*) *Perilampus chrysopae* Cwf., mature third instar, from Clancy (1946); (*c*) *Stilbula tenuicornis* (Ashm.) third instar, from Clausen (1940*b*); (*d*) *Loxotropa tritoma* Thoms. third instar fully grown, from Wright, Geering, and Ashby (1947); (*e*) *Hadronotus ajax* Grlt. third-instar larva, from Schell (1943); (*f*) *Trioxys utilis* Mues. third instar, from Schlinger and Hall (1961); (*g*) *Sturmia harrisinae* Coq. third-instar larva, from Smith, Diboll, and Rosenberger (1955); (*h*) *Cryptochaetum grandicorne* Rond. young third-instar larva, from Thorpe (1934); (*i*) *Trichopsidea clausa* (O.S.) prepupal-larva dorsal aspect, from Spencer (1958).

the spiracles have been used most extensively. Spiracle arrangement is used to distinguish higher taxonomic categories of Diptera.

The remains of a parasitic larva within its cocoon can lead to the identification of the parasite particularly in the Ichneumonoidea. Beirne (1941) and Short (1959) principally used this type of material for study. The parasite cocoon is opened by means of a longitudinal cut which reveals the cast larval skin, the cast pupal skin, and dried meconium. The larval skin is extracted and placed overnight in a five or ten per cent KOH solution or it may be boiled for a few minutes in this solution. After clearing, the skin may be placed in acetic acid and then mounted in Faure's or Berlese medium or it may be washed in distilled water, stretched, dehydrated, and mounted in Canada balsam. A modification in technique is to place the skin, after the acetic acid bath, in clove oil and then into the balsam. Fresh larvae, after being opened by a mid-ventral cut, can be boiled for five minutes in five per cent KOH solution, washed, dehydrated, and mounted.

The contents of fly puparia from which a parasite has emerged should be carefully removed and placed into cedar oil or alcohol on a microscope slide and covered with a coverslip. Thus, any magnification can be used in studying the material. Hill and Pickney (1940) used this technique to determine parasites that attacked the Hessian fly.

Finlayson (1960) determined the parasites of *Neodiprion sertifer* (Geoff.) from cocoons and puparia associated with this diprionid. She softened the cast larva skins in 10 per cent KOH solution, washed them in water, and then immersed the skins for 30 seconds in a weak solution of carbol fuchsin, washed them again in water, and then mounted them on a slide in Faure's solution.

Maple (1947) found that he could study and draw the eggs and larvae of the Encyrtidae by placing a specimen in a drop of normal salt solution on a slide. In order to orient a specimen in a desired position he placed small bits of modelling clay at four or more equidistant places on the circumference of the cover glass which was then lowered directly over the egg or larva floating in the drop. By carefully pressing the sides of the cover glass the material could be rotated on a longitudinal axis with little danger of rupture. As the water or salt solution evaporated distilled water was added.

HYMENOPTERA. *Body form.* Though mainly hymenopteriform, there are a few groups whose larvae differ conspicuously from the grub-like form. In general, the caudal modifications found in some primary larvae are lost or greatly reduced in the last instar, but the agriotypid larva bears a pair of heavy opposed hook-like caudal appendages when mature.

Body segmentation is usually evident with 13 postcephalic segments being the usual number. Although certain cynipoid parasitic groups (Ibaliidae, Anacharitinae, and evidently *Charips*) possess the normal 13 segments, *Kleidotoma*, *Figites*, and *Eucoila* exhibit only 12 segments (Huzimatsu 1940). The larvae in all eucharid genera except *Eucharis* are devoid of external segmentation except for constrictions between the three principal parts of the body (figure 21c). Segmentation in mymarid larvae is often indistinct.

The number of integumental folds in the body segments varies between groups as does the arrangement of some fleshy tubercles that protrude from various segments at different locations. Some eulophids and pteromalids that are ecto-parasitic on concealed hosts often possess either dorsal or ventral tubercles, or both, and these arise at the intersegmental zones. These ridge-like tubercles are suspected of being used for locomotion. Paired, dorsal, conical tubercles arise from the cynipoid Anacharitinae larvae which are parasitic in and on neuropterous immatures in cocoons. These larvae emerge from the host in its last larval stage and complete their feeding externally. In the diapriid *Loxotropa tritoma* Thoms., the mature larva possesses a single, dorsal median 'papilla' which projects from the mesothorax (Wright, Geering, and Ashby 1947), but in another species of *Loxotropa* this process is not present (Simmonds 1952). Ichneumonid larvae that are ectoparasitic on spiders (mainly Polysphinctini) or are spider egg predators have either dorsal tubercles adorned with hooks or ventral fleshy processes for attach-ment to the spider or the web.

Conspicuous setae are often present on the bodies of ectoparasitic larvae and are very much reduced or absent in the endoparasites. The integument is often sha-greened, however, in the endophagous forms.

Head structures. The heads of parasitic larvae, though often simplified, display differentiated structures which can be recognized. Often the parts are pigmented and the mandibles at least are somewhat sclerotized in most species (figure 22). The head structures usually offer the best characters for separating taxonomic groups.

The trend towards specialization of the larval head is very apparent among the parasitic forms (Snodgrass 1935). Short (1952) compared the larval head morpho-logy, including muscle arrangement, between certain Symphyta, proctotrupoids, cynipoids, chalcidoids, some aculeates, and ichneumonoids. From these studies Short showed that the head structure of *Gasteruption* was strikingly different from that of the Ichneumonidae, Braconidae, and Agriotypidae and was much closer to the aculeate and evaniid type heads with their small sclerotic bands and large mandibles. Today *Gasteruption* is placed in family Gasteruptiidae under the Procto-trupoidea by most authors. Michener (1953a) compared larval morphology of certain Symphyta with various aculeates, stressing the morphology and evolution of bee larvae. The galeae of the Apoidea are like those of the Evaniidae and Gasteruptiinae in which there is only one papilla (palpus) on each maxilla but these groups differ from wasps and ants by lacking the maxillary cardines as distinct sclerites. Among the Apocrita, the vespoids, sphecoids, scoliids, and related wasps display the greatest differentiation in the head. All main structures are recognizable. The bee groups, including some ectoparasitic forms, show some specialization perhaps followed, in this regard, by the cynipoids and proctotrupoids which are mainly endoparasitic. The ichneumonoids, though rather specialized, have pigmented rods or bands which permit recognition of most parts but the palpi are reduced to disc-like structures. The chalcidoids appear to be the least differentiated, the maxillae being fused with the labium and the palpi usually being unrecogniz-able. The mandibles are often the only parts discernible.

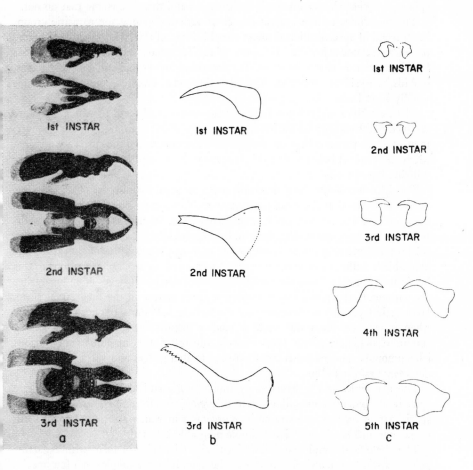

FIGURE 22. Changes in mouth structures of parasitic larvae through larval instars: (a) *Bessa selecta* (Meig.), from Hawboldt (1947); (b) *Apanteles solitarius* (Ratz.), from Parker (1935); (c) *Phobocampe disparis* Vier., from Musebeck and Parker (1933).

The antennae in the parasitic Hymenoptera are evidently one-segmented. This segment may be horn-like and quite conspicuous in ectoparasites but in most endoparasities it is often reduced to a disc-like structure in the middle of a large, circular outlined, antennal socket. Michener (1953a) points out that bee larvae which spin cocoons have larger antennal papillae and palpi than bee larvae that do not.

The mandibles exhibit a great degree of variation among the parasitic groups but a trend of specialization through simplification of the larval mandible is more or less correlated with the phylogeny of the Hymenoptera as a whole and to a lesser extent to food relationships. The mandibles of vespoid and sphecoid wasps, scoliids, chrysidids, mutilids, tiphiids, thynnids, evaniids, and gasteruptiids usually have large, apical, tridentate teeth.

The mandibles of bees generally possess many small teeth of which some are grouped to form a cusp on the inner surface some distance from the apex; however, in most of the parasitic bees the mandibles are attenuate and the cusps are missing. Michener (1953a) believes that this latter condition may be correlated with bees utilizing liquid foods.

The ichneumonoids show much diversity in larval mandibular structure. The mandible is broad at the base, tapering sharply to form a pointed apex. Rarely is the apex bifid and trifurcation is apparently absent. In most ectoparasites, mandibular teeth are present on the blade and are apparently necessary for holding on to the host and piercing the host skin, while in most endoparasites of this group the mandible is without teeth (Beirne 1941; Short 1959). There are exceptions to this but in many of these cases the mandibles of the early larval stages of endoparasites are without teeth on the blade. However, teeth appear in the final larval stage. Here again teeth may be necessary for the larva to hold on to the host or substrate when it emerges from the host. A similar mandibular change occurs among certain chalcidoids. Gerig (1960) nicely illustrates the mandibles of various ichneumonids showing differences between related genera and species that attack *Zeiraphera griseana* Hbn.

The mandibles of the parasitic cynipoids *Ibalia* and *Anacharis* are tridentate apically but bidentate mandibles occur in *Figites, Charips,* and *Hexacola.* Cynipoid specialization reaches its extreme in *Kleidotoma* in which a series of small teeth occurs and in *Eucoila* in which a simple mandible is found.

The chalcidoid larval mandible is generally triangular in form with a narrow pointed apex. In the majority of species the mandibles are simple. In a few species a row of fine teeth occurs on each edge of the blade. It appears that mandibles with two large teeth, one near the middle and one apical, are associated with species that are phytophagous. Parasitic species in families otherwise mainly phytophagous may show a bidentate mandible as in *Eurytoma.* According to Parker (1924), bifid mandibles are rare in the Chalcidoidea.

The maxillae, perhaps, portray most strikingly the evolutionary trends of hymenopterous larvae. Michener (1953a) traces the specialization of maxillae from the primitive well-developed maxillae of the tenthredinids through the wasps to the bees showing the reduction and fusion of parts that have occurred. The palpus and galea show particularly important manifestations of specialization. Forms having two pairs of projecting processes grade into those in which the galea is lost or is represented by a papilla. The palpus follows the same trend until it cannot be recognized in some species. The various degrees of this specialization were used by Michener (1953a) as key characters in separating the mature larvae into major categories. A key to the mature parasitic hymenopterous larvae would be based largely on the same framework stressing the maxillae. Detailed studies on the morphology of the head are lacking for many of the parasitic proctotrupoids, cynipoids, and chalcidoids. Such studies would contribute significantly to the classification of the larvae of these parasitic groups.

It appears that the ichneumonoids, cynipoids, and proctotrupoids follow the bees with respect to specialization (reduction) of the maxillae. The greatest reduction in maxillary structure occurs in the Chalcidoidea. In the latter group, the maxillae are fused with the labium and the palpi are unrecognizable.

The labium and its palpi follow a similar trend of specialization through reduction as was just pointed out for the evolution of the maxillae. From groups having distinct projecting lobes with short palpi, progressive reduction occurs to groups in which the labium becomes flattened, less distinct, and the palpi become flattened disc-like structures. Finally, in the Chalcidoidea the labium is ill-defined without a labial sclerite and often apparently without recognizable palpi. Short (1952, 1959) divides the labium into the prelabium and postlabium while Snodgrass (1935), Beirne (1941), Alam (1952), and Michener (1953a) use the terms prementum and postmentum. Apical tubercles on the prementum may represent labial palpi. The prelabial sclerite evidently appears among the Campoplegini of the Ichneumonidae (Short 1959). The orifice of the silk press (spinneret) is found on the prelabium. The silk press does not occur in all hymenopterous larvae but some form of an orifice to the salivary or silk glands is usually present.

The cephalic skeleton does not necessarily involve only the tentorium but may include sclerotized rods or bands. However, Vance and Smith (1933) and Beirne (1941) restrict the term tentorium to the internal skeleton and do not include the sclerotized rods that appear to be external. These rods or bands are most conspicuous in the Ichneumonoidea.

A terminology for the cephalic skeleton is given by Short (1959) (figure 23). Several sets of terms have been proposed for the skeletal rods or bands found in the larval heads of parasitic Hymenoptera. Attempts have been made to homologize the structures but different opinions are found in recent literature.

Stuart (1957) concluded from his studies of certain ichneumonids that Salt's (1931) observations were valid in that the sclerotized rods of the larval head could not be homologized with the skeleton of the adult head. Thus, Thorpe (1930b), Salt (1931), and Cameron (1938) were justified in using terms based on the probable function of the larval cephalic structures and did not imply homology with adult structures. However, Vance and Smith (1933), Beirne (1941), and Short (1952, 1959), according to Stuart (1957), attempted to homologize the adult tentorial structures with the sclerotic rods of the larva. Short (1952) compares his

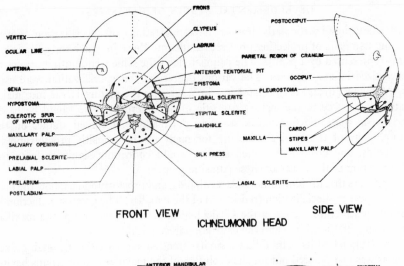

FRONT VIEW   SIDE VIEW

ICHNEUMONID HEAD

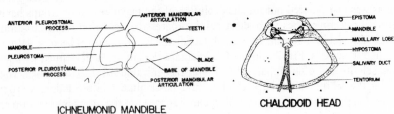

ICHNEUMONID MANDIBLE   CHALCIDOID HEAD

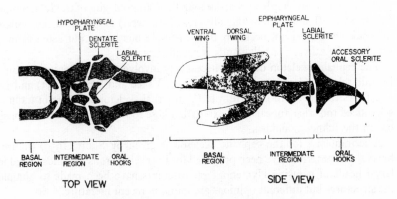

TOP VIEW   SIDE VIEW

CYCLORRHAPHOUS BUCCOPHARYNGEAL APPARATUS

FIGURE 23. Head structures of various mature larval parasites. Ichneumonid head and mandible adapted from Short (1959). Chalcidoid head, *Sphegigaster flavicornis* Wlk. redrawn from Cameron (1939). Cyclorrhaphous buccopharyngeal apparatus top view adapted from Hennig (1952); side view from various authors drawn by K. Shea.

interpretations and terminology with those of Vance and Smith (1933) and Beirne (1941). Stuart (1957) lists his terms in relation to those used by Beirne and Short. Gerig (1960) compares some 50 terms proposed for the larval head parts of parasitic Hymenoptera and mainly employs Beirne's and Short's terminology but also outlines the terms used by Alam (1952), Snodgrass (1935), and Thorpe (1930a).

The tentorium is never visible in preparations made from cast skins of parasites taken from cocoons or host remains (Beirne 1941). In whole mounts or heads taken from whole larvae, the tentorial structures can be observed. Larval head structures of various representative groups are shown in figure 24. Short (1952, 1959) based his keys to the ichneumonoids upon larval remains instead of whole larval mounts.

Internal anatomy. The internal anatomy of parasitic hymenopterous larvae is relatively simple. All normal organ systems of a generalized insect are usually present but specialization or degeneration is common, which accounts for the considerable variability that is found between groups. Full-grown larvae of endoparasites are less specialized internally than the first-instar larvae, for in the latter complete organ systems are often lacking. As the larvae of diverse groups progress through the instars, there is convergence towards similarity of form. Such convergence is reflected also in the external anatomy.

Ratzeburg (1844), Seurat (1899), Grandori (1911), Timberlake (1912), Tothill (1922), and Bischoff (1927) are some early investigators who made comparative studies of internal structures and the unique external processes of the first-instar larvae of endoparasites. Subsequent to these early works, there have been numerous studies of larvae of individual species of parasitic hymenoptera in which the internal anatomy either has been described or illustrated. However, there remains considerable need for such comparative studies. A good example is Maxwell's (1955) study of larval internal anatomy of sawflies. Following are some references that include discussions and/or illustrations of internal structures.

Ichneumonoidea: Keilin and Picado (1913); Tower (1915); Haviland (1922); E. Wheeler (1923); Genieys (1925); Spencer (1926); Thompson and Parker (1930); Parker (1931a, 1931b); Hill and Smith (1931); Vance (1931, 1932); H. D. Smith (1932); Dowden (1938, 1941); Kamal (1939); Fallis (1942); Vevai (1942); Given (1944); Simmonds (1947d); Hafez (1947); Alam (1952); Moutia and Courtois (1952); O. J. Smith (1952); Ivanova-Kazas (1956); Bronskill (1959, 1960); Osborne (1960); and Schlinger and Hall (1960, 1961).

Chalcidoidea: Parker (1924) summarizes many larval characteristics of this group. Tiegs (1922) not only traced the changes that occur during the metamorphosis of a pteromalid but treated in detail the anatomy of *Nasonia*. Some other papers that refer to the internal anatomy of immature chalcidoids are: Ayers (1884); Silvestri (1906, 1916); Richardson (1913); Martin (1914); Imms (1916, 1918); Leiby (1922); Noble (1932, 1937, 1938c); Parker and Smith (1933); Bakkendorf (1934); Dowden (1935, 1941); Crandell (1939); Flanders (1944a); Ivanova-Kazas (1958); and Zinna (1959). The latter paper is an outstanding example of detailed research on all stages of a single species of encyrtid.

Proctotrupoidea: The Platygasteridae has received the most attention in this superfamily. Ganin (1869), Marchal (1904, 1906), Silvestri (1921), Hill (1923, 1926), and Hill and Emery (1937) have considered the internal anatomy of platygasterid larvae. The following authors have at least illustrated internal organs of species belonging to other

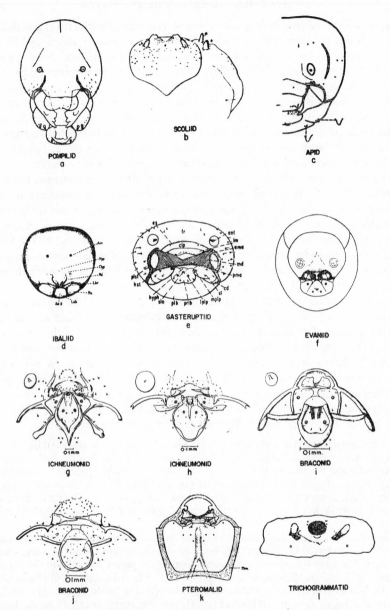

FIGURE 24. Head characteristics of mature hymenopterous larvae: (a) *Pepsis thisbe* Lucas, from Evans (1959); (b) *Scolia* (*Scoliodes*) *hirta* Schrk., from Grandi (1954); (c) *Triepeolus* sp., from Michener (1953); (d) *Ibalia leucospoides* Hoch., from Chrystal (1930); (e) *Gasteruption assectator* (L.), from Short (1952); (f) *Evania appendigaster* (L.), from Cameron (1957); (g) *Rhyssa* sp., from Short (1959); (h) *Horogenes comptoniellae* (Vier.), from Short (1959); (i) *Dendroster middendorffii* (Ratz.), from Short (1952); (j) *Apanteles compressiventris* Mues., from Short (1952); (k) *Sphegigaster flavicornis* Wlk., from Cameron (1939); (l) *Trichogramma semblidis* (Aur.), from Parker (1924).

families: Haviland (1921*a*); Kamal (1939); Schell (1943); Clancy (1946); Simmonds (1952); and Pschorn-Walcher (1956).

Cynipoidea: The internal anatomy of the larvae of parasitic cynipoids is poorly known. The following authors have treated some species: Haviland (1921*b*); Chrystal (1930); Huzimatsu (1940); Wright, Geering, and Ashby (1947); Jenni (1951); and Moutia and Courtois (1952).

The digestive system (figure 25) usually includes a foregut, midgut, and hind gut. The foregut is a straight tube extending from the buccal cavity into the prothorax. Often two parts can be distinguished, the pharynx and oesophagus. The former is usually thicker and has a chitinous lining on its floor. Alam (1952) proposed naming two portions of the pharynx since the anterior part is a sucking region. The oesophagus leads into the midgut usually in the prothoracic region. In some species there is a valve present at this junction.

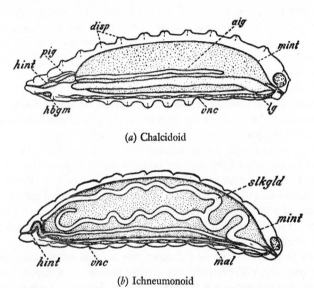

(*a*) Chalcidoid

(*b*) Ichneumonoid

FIGURE 25. Internal anatomy of hymenopterous parasitic larvae: *lg*, labial gland; *mint*, midgut; *vnc*, ventral nerve cord; *aig, pig, mal*, Malpighian tubules; *hbgm*, histoblasts of male genitalia; *hint*, hind gut; *slkgld*, silk gland; *disp*, dorsal intersegmental tubercles. (*a*) *Sympiesis* sp. fully grown larva, from Dowden (1941); (*b*) *Phanomeris phyllotomae* Mues. fully grown larva, from Dowden (1941).

The midgut is a large simple sac which until the time of prepupal ecdysis is without a posterior opening. It occupies most of the body cavity and is usually more or less straight in the normal hymenopteriform larva. It functions as a storage organ (Seurat 1899) as well as for digestion. Often the full amount of food required for development of each instar is ingested before much of it is digested. The volume of the midgut can increase as much as 80 per cent in some species of *Bracon* (Grosch 1948).

The midgut is usually lined with a peritrophic membrane. This membrane is closed posteriorly to form a complete sac (Parker 1931*b*, Clancy 1944). Clancy (1946) found five distinct sacs in the midgut of *Helorus*. Each sac was within the next larger one and this structure was considered homologous with the peritrophic membrane.

The hind gut is usually a short tube located in the area of the last few body segments and ends with an anal opening. In some species in which the hind gut is enlarged it may comprise two enlarged portions ending in a narrow rectum. The hind gut becomes excretory in function only when the final prepupal ecdysis is about to take place. At this time, or later, all fecal material (meconium) accumulated and stored in the midgut during larval feeding is excreted.

In certain cynipoid parasites of aphidiines, the anal opening is an unusually large dorsocaudal process. In these species, the proctodaeum is an enlarged chamber which Haviland (1921*a*) suggests may be respiratory in function inasmuch as the body of the first-instar larva is covered with sclerotized plates which would permit little gas exchange in an apneustic system. The anal opening and the proctodaeal cavity decrease in size as the larva matures, loses its sclerotized plates, and develops a tracheal system.

The Malphighian tubes, if present, arise at the fore part of the hind gut and are closed but the apices are free. The number of tubes is variable but at least one pair is usually present (figure 25). In the pteromalid *Nasonia*, Tiegs (1922) found none and in larvae of the predacious mud dauber *Sceliphron*, Shafer (1949) found no trace of tubes. Vance (1932) was convinced that no Malpighian tubes occurred in *Chelonus* but he considered the number of short outgrowths on the upper part of the hind gut to be the rudiments of Malpighian tubes which develop later in the adult. The paired short papillae located at the base of the hind gut in *Diadromus* were determined as Malpighian tubes by Given (1944). In *Encyrtus* the tubules begin to appear in the next to last larval instar and in *Mesopeltis* and *Scutellista* they appear during the prepupal period (Flanders 1938*b*).

Most often there are two or four distinct tubules that extend anteriorly. Many chalcidoids, however, differ in that they usually possess three tubes. Two of these tubes are long and run anteriorly. The third tube is shorter and extends posteriorly (figure 25). Some species of *Platygaster* and *Helorus* possess three tubules which extend anteriorly. In most 'parasitica' the Malpighian tubes are narrow elongate tubes but Noble (1938*b*) describes a unique modification of the tubes in *Euplectrus*. There are three voluminous tubes, two long and one short, which function to produce silk used for cocoon building. These eulophids are among the few species of Chalcidoidea that spin silken cocoons. In the Ichneumonoidea the silk is produced by labial glands.

The salivary glands or silk glands are evidently homologous and also are known as labial glands (figure 25). The Chalcidoidea, Proctotrupoidea, and Cynipoidea rarely spin silken cocoons but the labial glands in some Chalcidoidea exist in conjunction with ileac glands which are believed by Flanders (1938*b*) to secrete cocoon (sheath) forming substances. The glands that are attached posteriorly to the walls of the ileum and anteriorly combine with ducts which open on the labium are called ileo-labial glands by Zinna (1959) in *Leptomastix dactylopii* (How.) They correspond to the ileac glands found by Flanders (1938*b*) and are believed to result from fusion and anastomosis between the labial glands and the Malphigian tubes during embryonic development (Zinna 1959). The labial glands are evidently also salivary in function. The glands occur as two broad tubes. A common short duct which usually opens into the floor of the mouth bifurcates and each gland extends posteriorly into the body cavity on each side for varying distances. In most Ichneumonoidea, the glands primarily serve for silk production and open upon the labial sclerite. From this opening the short common duct bifurcates into one tube on each side and in most ichneumonids these, in turn, bifurcate again. Thus, commonly these are paired narrow tubes extending posteriorly nearly the entire length of the body on each side. In some ichneumonids each of the two lateral tubes bifurcates again so that posteriorly in the body there may be four tubes on each side (Given 1944). Histologically, the glands of *Apanteles* are similar to those found in Lepidoptera and Trichoptera. They are similar, as well, in the production of a double thread (Matheson and Ruggles 1907) and chemically the silk is similar to that of *Bombyx* (Baccetti 1958).

In some braconids, e.g. Opiinae and Aphidiinae, where the parasite pupates within the host, the labial glands appear like the salivary glands found in species occurring in the other superfamilies mentioned above, since there is only one large elongate gland present on each side of the body. *Heterospilus cephi* Roh., which spins its cocoon within the plant stalk which supported its host, also has but a single stout gland on each side. Baccetti (1958) not only discusses the morphology and physiology of the secreting organs but compares several typical silk producers with a species of *Diplazon*, a non-cocoon maker.

Alam (1952) describes an accessory silk gland in *Stenobracon*. It is a convoluted glandular tube lying below the first thoracic ganglion. A small duct passes below the suboesophageal ganglion which empties into the common duct of the main silk glands.

The silk glands in some braconids apparently become reduced to small glandular structures after cocoon spinning has occurred (Hill and Smith 1931).

The nervous system in parasitic hymenopterous larvae is usually a very primitive type consisting of a brain, suboesophageal ganglion, and a comparatively unspecialized double chain of ganglia connected by longitudinal and transverse commissures. In many chalcidoids the ventral cord exhibits no obvious differentiation into ganglia and connectives. In other chalcidoids the ventral nerve cord in the thoracic region is separated but is then united in the rest of the body (Parker 1924). The opposite is found in some *Apanteles* in which the cords are apparently united in the thoracic region but are separate in the abdominal region (Hafez 1947).

Larvae of certain species of *Opius* that parasitize dipterous immatures are unique in that the general aspect of the body is opposite the normal condition. In these larvae the concave side which is normally the ventral surface of larval parasitic hymenoptera is reversed. Keilin and Picado (1913) found that in *Opius crawfordi* the ventral surface is actually the dorsal one, for the nervous system occurs dorsally. Cameron (1941) also found this to be true in *O. ilicis*. What appear to be antennal lobes on the head are actually maxillary or labial lobes.

The respiratory system in later instars is peripneustic or holopneustic (figure 26) and usually is throughout the entire larval period. In endoparasitic species, however, the first-instar larva is generally apneustic. Later a tracheal system develops and, finally, in the last stage spiracles become functional. When the parasitic larva approaches maturity, so much of the host has been consumed that it no longer represents a 'haemolymph bath.' The parasite may then abandon the host and feed upon it externally. In any event, such parasite larvae are exposed to free air. Even among ectoparasitic chalcidoids there is a change in the number of functional spiracles as the larva matures. Usually there are four or five functional spiracles in the first-instar stage and when full-grown the same larva normally exhibits nine pairs. Larvae of the Mymaridae and Trichogrammatidae apparently never develop tracheal systems.

The tracheal system is usually made up of two longitudinal trunks which extend along each side of the body from the first thoracic to the ninth abdominal segment. These trunks are joined anteriorly by a transverse commissure which passes above the digestive tract in the prothoracic segment. Posteriorly they are connected by a ventral commissure in the vicinity of the ninth abdominal segment. Thus, the main tracheal system is usually a ring with short trunks extending laterally ending in spiracles in nearly all body segments. There are, of course, numerous branching tracheae leading from the main ring (figure 26) that penetrate all areas. The first two instars of the pteromalid *Stenomalus micans* Ol. possess two supplementary, longitudinal, visceral tracheal trunks which extend from the anterior commissure along the dorsum to the eighth abdominal segment (Kearns 1931).

The mature larvae of most Ichneumonoidea, Chalcidoidea, and Cynipoidea usually have nine open spiracles. It is mainly in the Ichneumonidae and in the ectoparasitic Braconinae that the first pair of spiracles occur on the prothoracic segment and usually there are no functional spiracles appearing on the meso- or metathoracic somites. The remaining spiracles are on abdominal segments one to eight. The presence of the accessory longitudinal tracheal commissure of the thorax perhaps accounts for the lack of spiracles on the two thoracic segments. In the majority of other 'parasitica' the first pair of spiracles occurs on segments posterior to the prothorax. However, many of the Braconinae that are ectoparasitic on concealed hosts have the first pair of spiracles on the prothorax.

Seurat (1899) made one of the first detailed comparative studies of the tracheal systems of an ichneumonid, braconid, and chalcidoid. He attached much significance to the difference in the tracheal system of the Ichneumonidae and Braconidae. Today the presence of the accessory longitudinal tracheal commissure is still the only known character that permits separation of the larvae of these families. There are some exceptions, such as in the *Collyria*, where the accessory system is lacking (Salt 1931).

Most aculeate hymenopterous larvae have ten pairs of open spiracles (Michener

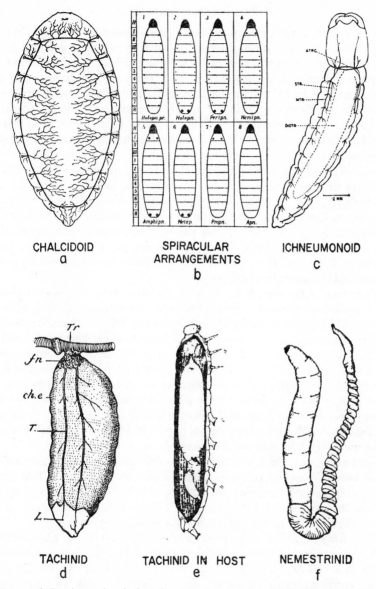

CHALCIDOID
a

SPIRACULAR
ARRANGEMENTS
b

ICHNEUMONOID
c

TACHINID
d

TACHINID IN HOST
e

NEMESTRINID
f

FIGURE 26. Respiratory larval adaptations of various parasites: (a) *Sphegigaster flavicornis* Wlk. mature larva showing tracheal system, from Cameron (1939); (b) Schematic representation of respiratory systems in dipterous larvae showing only functional spiracles ranging from holopneustic (1,2) to apneustic (8), from Keilin (1944); (c) *Melanichneumon rubicundus* (Cress.) first-instar larva showing tracheal system, from Wishart (1948); (d)*Hygria tibialis* (L.) larva surrounded by host-produced envelope originating from host trachea, from Pantel (1910); (e) *Panolis* larva parasitized by two first instar, one second instar, and one full-grown larva of *Ernestia rudis* (Fall.) showing tachinid larvae and associated respiratory funnels, after Prell (1915); (f) *Trichopsidea clausa* (O.S.) half-grown larva with respiratory tube, from Spencer (1958).

1953*a*, Grandi 1954, 1958, and 1959). The Pompilidae also have ten pairs but the second thoracic pair is vestigial (Evans 1959). It is interesting to note that Imms (1918) also found ten pairs of spiracles in some large ichneumonid larvae but the pair on the mesothoracic segment was vestigial. Thorpe (1930*b*) believes that this condition may be general for the Ichneumonidae with the second thoracic pair being overlooked. Some tryphonine larvae only have one pair of thoracic spiracles.

Larvae of the Proctotrupoidea and Cynipoidea tend to have fewer than nine or ten pairs of spiracles. In certain genera, however, the number is variable depending upon the species.

The number and position of the spiracles in the Encyrtidae varies greatly. The encyrtiform first-instar larvae that have a single pair of spiracles on the last apparent abdominal segment exhibit a variable number of spiracles in the third and fourth instars. Usually nine pairs appear but in some species of *Encyrtus* three pairs occur in the fourth instar with one pair on the prothorax and the remaining two at the caudal end of the abdomen. A posterior pair is lost when the larva moults to the fifth stage (Thorpe 1936). This spiracle arrangement is similar to the common amphipneustic one of Diptera.

The structure of the spiracle itself (figure 27) varies between groups. Spiracle structure is used as a taxonomic character for separating various taxa. The atrium is usually spherical but in many chalcidoids it is more funnel-shaped and is variously sculptured. Also, length and shape of the annular stalk often show specific differences. Thorpe (1930*b*) used the structure of the spiracles to separate three common ichneumonid species that parasitized one host species. Morris, Cameron, and Jepson (1937), Beirne (1941), and Short (1952, 1959) used the spiracles in keys to separate mature larvae of the Ichneumonoidea. Michener (1953*a*) illustrates the spiracles of bee larvae in great detail showing interspecific variability. Finlayson (1960) found spiracles within the contents of parasitized sawfly immatures which could be used to identify parasites that were present.

An outstanding example of a distinct respiratory adaptation in an ectoparasitic hymenopteron is found in the Agriotypidae. These agriotypid larvae feed upon caddis fly prepupae and pupae in cases under water. From the anterior end of the case when the parasitic larva matures there appears a floating air-filled silken ribbon. If the ribbon is broken the parasite dies (Clausen 1950).

DIPTERA. *Body form.* The majority of parasitic dipterous larvae when mature are muscoidiform or maggot-like, being devoid of legs. Often the larva is somewhat crescentic in lateral view and the abdominal region is the broadest. The Cryptochaetidae, coccid endoparasites, depart the most from this form. They are easily recognized by having paired elongate caudal tubes. Body segmentation in most parasitic dipterous larvae includes 11 or 12 segments and a head. However, among the Cecidomyiidae the prothorax appears subdivided into two parts; thus, 13 segments plus the head can be counted. The head is usually not well developed in most species.

Head structures. The Cecidomyiidae and Chironomidae are the only families in the Nematocera that contain parasites. The mouth parts are indistinct in this group but short antennae are usually present. In the Brachycera, parasites or egg-predators occur in the Bomblyiidae, Nemestrinidae, and Acroceridae. The head is somewhat distinct and visible although much reduced, being incomplete posteriorly, and can be found retracted into the thorax in some species (Paoli 1937; Crouzel and Salavin 1943; Berg 1940; Brooks 1952; Spencer 1958). The brachycerous mouth parts are intermediate between those of the well-differentiated heads of primitive Nematocera and the greatly simplified head of Cyclorrhapha. The head in the latter group represents an 'acephalous' condition since it is vestigial and without much indication of external mouth parts.

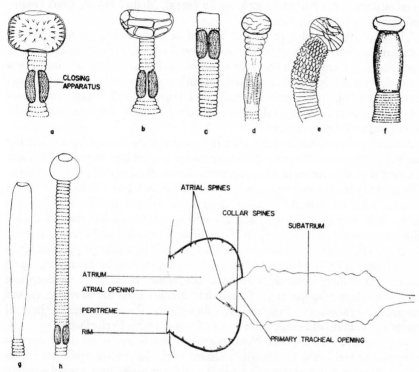

FIGURE 27. Spiracles of various mature hymenopterous parasitic larvae: (*a*) Ephialtinae, (*b*) Metopiinae, (*c*) Anomalinae, from Beirne (1941); (*d*) Pteromalid, *Sphegigaster flavicornis* Wlk., from Cameron (1939); (*e*) Pompilid, *Dipogon sayi sayi* Banks, from Evans (1959); (*f*) *Evania appendigaster* (L.), from Cameron (1957); (*g*) *Aphidius* sp., from Short (1952); (*h*) Dacnusinae, *Polemochartus liparae* (Gir.), from Short (1952); (*i*) Longitudinal section of spiracle of *Anthophora stanfordiana* Ckll., from Michener (1953*a*). All figures redrawn from original authors by K. Shea.

The mouth parts of the Cyclorrhapha reveal scarcely any trace of maxillae or labium for only papillae remain to indicate their presence. The complex set of dark sclerites found internally in the head and thoracic region are variable in structure between different families and become more complex in each instar (figure 22a). This framework of sclerities is called the buccopharyngeal apparatus (figure 23) or cephalopharyngeal skeleton in the Cyclorrhapha and is composed of the following principal sclerites. The most anterior are the oral hooks, mouth hooks, or mandibular sclerites. Following is an H-shaped sclerite which is called the intermediate region or hypostomal sclerite by some authors. Posterior to this sclerite is the basal region or pharyngeal sclerite which has several 'wings' upon which muscles are attached. Accessory hooks are found at times beneath the oral hooks and a structure, the epipharyngeal plate, sometimes occurs above the intermediate region. For discussion on homologies and terminology for dipterous larval structures see Nielsen (1909), Keilin (1915), Meijere (1916), Cook (1949), and Hennig (1948, 1950, 1952).

The buccopharyngeal apparatus of Tachinidae tends to become fused so that oral hooks appear directly connected to the basal region. This condition leads to confusion and there is an assortment of terms applied to various sclerites. For a discussion on tachinid and sarcophagid mouth part terminology consult Pantel (1910), Prell (1915), Thompson (1920), Baer (1921), Bissell (1945), and James (1947). Thorpe (1930a, 1934) should be consulted for information concerning the mouth parts of *Cryptochaetum*.

Internal anatomy. The internal anatomy of parasitic dipterous larvae does not seem to differ essentially from the non-parasitic groups but, in general, is more complex than that found in hymenopterous larvae. Sasaki (1886) was one of the first to study the internal organs of a tachinid. Evidently he was inspired by the classical work on muscoid anatomy done by Weismann (1864). Pantel (1898) exhaustively treated the biology and anatomy of a tachinid, *Thrixion*, which led him into several huge works on the Tachinidae. The calliphorid *Melinda cognata* Meig., an endoparasite of snails, was studied in detail by Keilin (1919). The larval anatomy of many sarcophagids was comprehensively covered by Thompson (1920) and in 1923 he investigated the anatomy of the primary larvae of the echinomyiine tachinids. Thorpe (1931a, 1934) found after detailed study of larvae of various species of *Cryptochaetum* that, although these larvae were parasitic, the internal organs did not differ basically from larvae of non-parasitic Cyclorrhapha.

The digestive system in the Nematocera and Brachycera is relatively short as compared to that in the Cyclorrhapha (Imms 1957). In the latter group the larva has an elongate, coiled alimentary canal. The foregut passes back from the mouth along the floor of the trough formed by the basal region of the buccopharyngeal apparatus. Posterior to this structure the oesophagus passes between the circum-oesophageal connectives and joins the midgut via an oesophageal valve.

The midgut usually bears gastric caecae near the anterior end and extends posteriorly in the form of an elongate convoluted sac which is closed posteriorly where it narrows. When the larva matures the midgut forms an opening with the hind gut.

The hind gut is usually a narrow tube supporting the Malpighian tubules anteriorly and ends as the anus. Its length differs between groups.

The four Malpighian tubes are composed of two pairs, each with a short common duct. They are blind apically and loosely attached to the body wall. One pair extends anteriorly and the other posteriorly.

There are two salivary glands. They extend from the region of the oesophageal commissure posteriorly to the region of the ventral nerve mass. Anteriorly, these hollow tubes join into a short common duct which empties into the floor of the pharynx usually immediately behind the hypopharyngeal plate. The glands are relatively large in the first instar of Nemestrinidae but in older larvae they are much smaller. Spencer (1958) suggests that the small larvae require secretions for penetration of the host integument.

The circulatory system consists of a heart which is closed posteriorly in the area of the tenth body segment and extends anteriorly to the eighth segment. It appears generally to have three chambers located in the posterior segments. The aorta extends from the heart through the thorax and into the head.

The nervous system is of phylogenetic significance. In the Nematocera the larval nervous system usually comprises a brain, a suboesophageal ganglion and three thoracic and eight abdominal ganglia. In some families of Brachycera, a similar system exists but in other families the system is intermediate, approaching that of the Cyclorrhapha. In this latter suborder there are but one thoracic and five abdominal ganglia. Sasaki (1886) describes and illustrates the system in a tachinid as an oblong ventral mass formed by condensation of the ventral chain of ganglia which lies in the fifth body segment of the maggot. On its anterior end, which is in the fourth segment, it is attached to the bilobed supraoesophageal ganglion. Sasaki could not make out the intra- or suboesophageal ganglion. From the ventral nerve mass twelve pairs of nerve trunks radiate respectively to each of the twelve segments of the maggot.

The respiratory systems of dipterous larvae have been reviewed by Keilin (1944) and the respiratory adaptations of the parasitic species were reviewed by Imms (1931) and Clausen (1950). Keilin's classification as to the placement of spiracles is summarized in figure 25b.

Unlike most Hymenoptera, the dipterous parasitic larvae are nearly always provided with at least a metapneustic tracheal system. Therefore, in the endoparasites of this order some connection with the outside air must be made during their development. Later stages often become amphipneustic. However, in the Pipunculidae, a few Tachinidae, and in Cryptochaetum there may be a lack of typical open spiracles. The egg is deposited into the host in these cases.

The following discussion covers Keilin's (1944) four categories of dipterous respiratory systems based on associations of the larvae with the host:

Category 1. Larvae with spiracles attached to a respiratory aperture by means of a funnel-like structure which is produced by the host but induced by the parasite. This occurs among the Tachinidae, Nemestrinidae, Acroceridae, and a few sarcophagid parasites in isopods. The species that provoke the 'funnel' formation are mainly those that enter the host from the outside. The larvae may originate from eggs placed on the host or apart from the host.

When the larva enters the host it may live for a few days without any direct contact with the air. Usually the perforation which the maggot utilizes for the respiratory connection is the initial entrance hole but an additional or secondary perforation may be made from the inside through either the integument, a tracheal trunk, or a spiracular trunk. At the site of connection a sheath begins to surround the posterior end of the larva which is now oriented to the perforation. The sheath is thickest at its base and may envelop nearly the entire larva (figure 26e).

The 'funnel' is considered by Beard (1942) to be wound tissue. Its formation is determined by the parasite *Trichopoda pennipes* Fabr., and it acts as a mechanical barrier to the normal healing of the injured tracheal trunk.

The most spectacular respiratory tubes or funnels are associated with Nemestrinidae that parasitize grasshoppers (figure 26f). The planidium of *Neorhynchocephalus sackeni* (Will.) penetrates a grasshopper through unsclerotized tissue. It then punctures and enters a main tracheal trunk and feeds in the trunk for a short time. The larva punctures the trachea again and, with its posterior end remaining in the trachea, it cuts a respiratory pore through the host's integument to which it orients by bringing its metapneustic spiracles to the opening. A respiratory funnel or tube begins to develop at this point. Instead of the funnel developing over the body of the parasite it maintains close contact only with the posterior extremity of the larva. Therefore, as the larva penetrates deeper into the host the longer the respiratory tube becomes. The tube differs in appearance from those of the tachinids in being a spiral, rope-like tube and in some nemestrinids may become twice as long as the parasite larva (Prescott 1961).

Category 2. Larvae that attach to the tracheae of the host but are devoid of an induced funnel or tube. This occurs in some Tachinidae, in the Conopidae, in some Acroceridae (Millot 1938), and possibly in the Pyrgotidae. These parasites mainly deposit their eggs into the host. The Acroceridae differ in that their eggs are deposited apart from the host. In any event, the larvae have morphological structures which permit tapping into the tracheal system of the host. The first-instar larvae may respire cutaneously so that only the two subsequent instars make a connection. In some tachinids the later instars may only sporadically tap into the trachea or air sacs of the host (Clausen 1950).

Category 3. Larvae with spiracles that perforate the integument of the host but which are devoid of an induced respiratory funnel or tube. This occurs in the genus *Cryptochaetum*. Thorpe (1930a, 1931a, 1934) has contributed most to the knowledge of these interesting endoparasites of monophlebine scales. The eggs are deposited into the scale insect body and, as already mentioned, the first- and second-instar larvae respire cutaneously. The third-stage larvae, besides having longer caudal tubes, possess two pairs of well-developed spiracles, thus becoming amphipneustic. The older third-instar larvae were found with their caudal spiracles penetrating the wall between the visceral chamber and the egg chamber of the scale.

Category 4. Larvae which exhibit no definite respiratory relationship with hosts. Included here are some Tachinidae (Thompson 1915b), Pipunculidae (Keilin and Thompson 1915), and some Sarcophaginae and Miltograminae which are parasitic in Orthoptera (Pantel 1910). Larvae of this type live free within the body cavity of the host and possess posterior spiracles in the form of dark tubercles bearing numerous spiracular papillae. By means of their hardened spiracles these larvae may damage the small tracheae or intersegmental membranes of their hosts, thus permitting air bubbles to appear in the body cavity of the host with which they establish intermittent contact (Keilin 1944).

Some Diptera that parasitize aquatic insects have evolved special respiratory adaptations to obtain air. This parallels similar developments in the hymenopterous family Agriotypidae. Keilin (1944) summarizes Lloyd's (1919) study of *Ginglymia acrirostris* (Towns.), a tachinid that attacks an aquatic lepidopterous larva. The host larva has gills and lives under a thin web of silk in running water until it is ready for pupation. Just before pupation a silken tent is constructed which covers the larva and which contains free air in contact with its spiracles. The full-grown tachinid larva thrusts its unique strong post-abdominal spiracles (which are on a large dorsally projecting V-shaped siphon) through the suture separating the fourth and fifth abdominal segments of the host larva and thus pupates with its spiracles in free air under the silken tent of the host. The respiratory process of the tachinid persists in the puparium.

Some major references dealing with last-instar larvae of parasites and egg predators are: Hymenoptera (Parker 1924), Diptera (Hennig 1948 to 1952), Coleoptera (Boving and Craighead 1931), and general groups (Thompson 1930*b*; Chu 1949; Peterson 1951*a*, *b*).

Of all the hymenopterous parasitic larvae, perhaps those of the Ichneumonidae are best known, for Beirne (1941) and Short (1959) have written keys to various taxon levels of this order. Short (1959), in his classification of the last instars of the Ichneumonidae included keys to genera. The nomenclature of Townes and Townes (1960) is different from Short and may be preferred by some. The mature larvae of the main subfamilies of the Braconidae have been studied and classified by Short (1952) and keys to the groups were presented.

In many families of the Chalcidoidea and the Proctotrupoidea, the morphology of the mature larva is so poorly known that little in the way of keys has been published. There is need for a great deal of study in these groups before a sound classification of these larvae can be made. Parker (1924) and Parker and Thompson (1925) treat mainly the first-instar larvae of many families of Chalcidoidea. The former paper is still one of the best general reviews of the immature Chalcidoidea. Clausen's book (1940*a*) is also a valuable source of information.

Hennig's (1948, 1950, 1952) comprehensive classification of dipterous larvae is a key reference for the student of Diptera. Besides keys to many groups, this work includes an exhaustive bibliography to Diptera.

PREPUPAE

When the last larval instar ceases to feed prior to pupation and shows scarcely any external movement, it has entered a prepupal state. However, within the body certain rapid developmental changes take place. In the parasitic groups this stage is not marked by ecdysis as in certain phytophagous Hymenoptera.

The period of metabolic reorganization in the metamorphosis of a hymenopterous parasite is essentially the same as in any holometabolous insect but certain internal changes occur which are different from those found in other holometabolous groups. The principal difference between the parasitic Hymenoptera and other groups is the linking of the proctodaeum (hind gut) with the midgut which up to this time have been separated. This permits excretion of the fecal material accumulated in the midgut during the larval feeding period. The connection usually begins to develop at the time of the last larval ecdysis. The blind end of the proctodaeum touches or nearly touches the posterior blind end of the midgut. Here the living cells in the walls of the blind ends proliferate rapidly until they meet and connect so that the living wall of the digestive canal becomes continuous from mouth to anus (Seurat 1899; Grandori 1911; Tower 1915; Tothill 1922; Shafer 1949). A full account of the many changes that take place during metamorphosis in the chalcidoid *Nasonia* is given by Tiegs (1922).

The prepupal stage of many Hymenoptera has two distinctive forms—the 'eonymphal' and 'pronymphal' phases. These phases are discussed by Morris (1937) in regard to several ichneumonids and the following descriptions are based on his observations. In certain *Exenterus* the forms (figure 28) are quite distinct

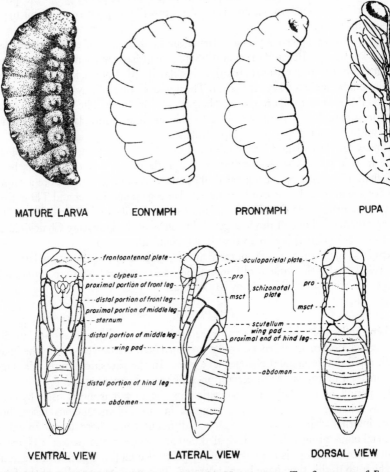

FIGURE 28. Prepupal and pupal stages of parasitic Hymenoptera. Top figures are of *Exenterus abruptorius* Thb., from Morris (1937). Lower figures are various aspects of *Eupelmus allynii* (French), from Hill and Pinckney (1940).

but in other ichneumonids, including various cryptines, the differences are less apparent and this variability may have phylogenetic significance (Morris 1937).

The eonymphal phase resembles the mature larva but the various lobes, swellings, or proturberances of the mature larva are less prominent than in the pronymphal stage and often the larval colour changes from yellowish-white to opaque white. In some species hibernation occurs in this stage. The pronymphal stage is indicated by the appearance of faintly developed imaginal eyes and by a lengthening of the body. The most distinctive characteristic exhibited by this stage is a narrowing of the thoracic section in relation to the swollen abdomen. A constriction between the fourth and fifth larval segments produces this appearance. This phase is usually motionless.

PUPAE

Most parasitic larvae pupate within the host remains. Often they pupate within the host cocoon or puparium or in a mine or tunnel produced by a host where they are protected. Many parasites which pupate in such places do not form cocoons. Other species pupate in the open usually attached to, or near by, the dead host. This occurs where mature full-fed larvae have emerged from the host or where feeding has been completed externally. With some species the larvae drop to the soil and pupate.

The dipterous pupa is either free as in the Nematocera and most Brachycera (figure 29) or is enclosed in a puparium as in the Cyclorrhapha. A cocoon is formed in some Cecidomyiidae and a few Diptera pupate in the host.

In the Brachycera, the Acroceridae usually pupate near the dead spider host and inside a protective web spun by the spider just prior to death (Schlinger 1952). The Nemestrinidae pupate in the soil while the Bombyliidae pupate in various sites. Those bombyliids that are egg predators in acridid egg pods form pupal cells in the soil. Those that are ectoparasitic on bees pupate in the host cells (Bohart, Stephen, and Eppley 1960). Endoparasitic species pupate within the host's pupa. However, prior to adult emergence the bombyliid pupa moves and ruptures the enclosing host or host-associated structure which permits easy exit for the adult parasite.

Among the cyclorrhaphous groups that pupate within the host remains or within the host cocoon are the Conopidae, Pyrgotidae, Cryptochaetidae, and many Tachinidae. Pupation in the soil is also common among the Tachinidae, Sarcophagidae, Pipunculidae, and some Anthomyidae. Some Chamaemyiidae pupate in the open near their hosts.

The tachinid larvae that enter the soil to pupate reverse their position and orient head upwards (Thompson 1910; Landis and Howard 1940). Some tachinids that are gregarious as larvae and pupate in soil form clusters of puparia that are cemented together (Greene 1921).

Since the adult cyclorrhaphous fly must escape through its puparium and at times through the host cocoon by means of the ptilinum, there must be weak points in these containing structures to permit escape. The puparia have lines of fracture which form a kind of operculum for easy exit. The neat circular opening found in some host cocoons is evidently prepared by the tachinid larva before it pupates. Baldwin and Coppel (1947) believe that the adult of the tachinid *Phorocera*

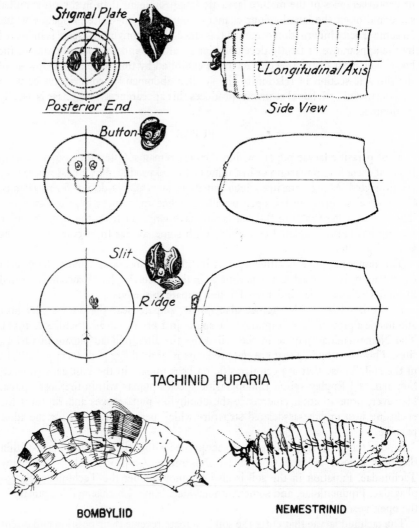

FIGURE 29. Tachinid puparia: top, *Sturmia sociabilis* Greene; centre, *S. distincta* Wied.; bottom, *Phorocera meracanthae* Greene, from Greene (1921). Bombyliid pupa: *Villa* sp., from Brooks (1952). Nemestrinid pupa: *Neorhynchocephalus sulphureus* (Wied.), from Crouzel and Salavin (1943).

hamata A. and W. emerges from sawfly cocoons through a circular opening which was scored by its larva before pupation. This was demonstrated when a mature larva placed within a gelatine capsule made, through a continuous rasping action with its mouth hooks, a circular groove corresponding to the outline of the typical emergence holes found in parasitized cocoons.

Since the spiracle arrangement on the spiracle plate of cyclorrhaphous puparia is similar to that of the third-instar larvae (figure 26*b*) a puparium can often be identified as to species. Greene (1921, 1925*a*, 1925*b*) and Ross (1952) have described the puparia of many tachinids and sarcophagids using the spiracular plate and slits as well as their relation to the longitudinal axis of the puparium as diagnostic criteria.

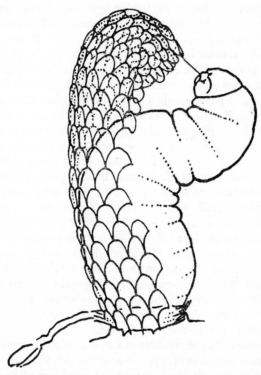

FIGURE 30. *Apanteles congregatus* (Say) mature larva spinning a cocoon on its host, from Fulton (1940).

The hymenopterous pupa is exarate and it may or may not be surrounded by a cocoon. Most larvae of the Ichneumonoidea spin cocoons. These are of variable shapes, sizes, and colours and often are banded or white, speckled with black. Baccetti (1958) discusses many aspects of cocoon formation and the lack of cocoons in some ichneumonids. Fulton (1940) illustrates the looping action used in the construction of a cocoon by *Apanteles congregatus* (Say) (figure 30). He purposely destroyed half of a cocoon and cut the silk strand while the *Apanteles* was forming it. The larva, instead of going back and beginning again, continued at the same level, going through the motions of completing the series of loops without drawing any silk until it reached the end of the row. Then it attached the silk to its body at that point and continued building the frame normally but with the bottom half missing.

Very few chalcidoids construct silken cocoons. Their exarate pupae are naked but usually occur in some concealed habitat. However, species of *Euplectrus* do construct cocoons (R. C. Smith 1927; Noble 1938*b*), but cocoon formation does not occur in species in the related genera *Neoplectrus*, *Platyplectrus*, or *Autoplectrus* which pupate beneath the host larval remains (Gadd and Fonseka 1945; Gadd, Fonseka, and Ranaweeva 1946). The species in these genera are external parasites of exposed lepidopterous larvae. In *Euplectrus* the silk is not produced by the labial glands but by the enlarged Malpighian tubules and is extruded from the anus (Thomsen 1927; Noble 1938*b*). In *Scutellista cyanea* Motsch., whose larvae are egg predators beneath the body of egg-laying soft scales, the pupa is attached to the substrate by strands of silk. A similar egg predator *Enargopelte* was observed by Ishii (1928) to construct a complete cocoon beneath the body of the host.

Often the gregarious pupae within a host seem to be isolated from one another in cells or by surrounding sheaths. Such separation often occurs among the polyembryonic encyrtids and platygasterids. The sheath is thought to be made up of the cast larval cuticula which, instead of becoming crumpled and forced to the rear of the body as are most larval exuviae, remains over the larva and hardens to form the wall of the pupation chamber just as occurs in the Diptera. There is no evidence that these pupal chambers are lined with silk (Marchal 1904; Leiby 1929).

Thorpe (1936) did not believe that the sheaths surrounding the pupae of certain encyrtids were composed of cast skins for he found the cast skins to be discarded within the sheaths. Thorpe suggested that the sheath is a product of the host being formed mainly from phagocytic blood cells which surround the parasite.

Flanders (1938*b*), in reviewing cocoon formation in the chalcidoids, evalutates the various theories concerning the formation of the pupal chambers or sheaths and discusses the function and origin of the cocoon. He concludes that many chalcidoid larvae secrete cocoon-forming substances. The secretions are from three ileac glands which usually occur in conjunction with the labial glands.

The cocoons produced by individuals of a hymenopterous species may vary in colour and thickness. Schmieder (1939*a*, *b*) observed thin white cocoons and thick brownish cocoons among individuals of the same population of *Sphecophaga*. The brownish cocoons were correlated with larvae that entered diapause. Schlinger and Hall (1959, 1960) observed similar colour differences in cocoons of *Praon palitans* Mues. The cocoons containing diapause larvae were usually brown and were constructed with extra layers of silk while those with non-diapause larvae were thin and usually white. However, cocoon colour was often reversed and this indicated a condition of partial diapause.

In the cocoons of certain sphecoid wasp larvae there is a constriction near one end which partitions the cocoon into the unequal chambers. The larger of these becomes the living chamber and the smaller becomes a 'chuck' chamber where the meconium is discharged within a peritrophic membranous sac (Shafer 1949). Cleptids partition off the host remains within the cocoon (Clausen 1940*a*). The endoparasite *Pelecystoma* shows further specialization (Smith, Diboll, and Rosenberger 1955). This species pupates within the host cuticle inside a thin transparent double casement which is made from fine silk threads held together with a clear plastic substance. The larval meconium is excreted so that it occurs between the capsules. Parasite larvae may also void their meconia in a peritrophic sac within a one-celled cocoon but often the meconium is a solid, pellet-like material which is not enclosed in a sac. Certain eulophids that parasitize leaf-mining larvae void their solid meconial pellets in an orderly fashion. Two straight rows of vertical meconial pellets are placed on each side of the larva forming rows of pillars which prevent the collapse of the mine on to the naked pupa (Doutt 1957). Meconial pellets may vary in size and shape between parasite species and they have been used to identify some groups of parasites (Flanders 1942e).

OVIPOSITIONAL SITES AND DEVELOPMENTAL CHARACTERISTICS

Parasitic insects may be grouped according to the egg or larval deposition site and the larval feeding site. Townsend (1908) placed the tachinids in five groups based upon placement of eggs or larvae with respect to the host. Pantel (1910) on a biological basis classified the parasitic Diptera, mainly tachinids, into 10 groups using the type of reproductive systems of the females, the type of egg deposited, and the incubation period. Imms (1931) divided the life cycles of parasitic Diptera and Hymenoptera into four groups somewhat similar to Townsend's groups of tachinids. Clausen (1940a, pp. 3, 4) outlined three major groups for the parasitic Hymenoptera with numerous subcategories based on exact placement of the egg. Biliotti (1958) recognized three main groups of tachinids in respect to placement of eggs or larvae in relation to the host. Sweetman (1958) distinguished five major types of life cycles in entomophagous parasites.

The above-mentioned classifications, except for Pantel's, are based on the placement of eggs, or, more rarely, of larvae in relation to the host. They distinguish between the egg being deposited apart from the host, upon the host, or within the host, and whether or not the larvae feed externally or internally. Cushman (1926b) discusses the life cycles of ichneumonids and divides the ectoparasitic and endoparasitic groups into smaller categories. The following classification is largely taken from the above-mentioned systems.

A. Eggs or larvae deposited apart from host.
   1. Eggs hatch or larvae deposited before host contact.
   2. Eggs hatch after ingestion by host.

B. Eggs or larvae deposited on or near host.
   1. Larvae develop externally on host.
      (a) Among eggs (egg predators).
      (b) On hosts concealed in cocoons, puparia, mines, galleries, galls, etc., or under scale coverings.
      (c) On exposed hosts.
   2. Larvae develop internally in host.

C. Eggs, or more rarely larvae, deposited in host.
  1. Deposited in host egg.
    (a) Development completed in host egg.
    (b) Development completed on other eggs as egg predator.
    (c) Development completed in larva, prepupa, or pupa of host.
  2. Deposited in host larva or hemimetabolous insects.
    (a) Development completed in host larva or in nymphs.
    (b) Development completed in host pupa.
    (c) Development completed in homopterous nymphs or adults.
  3. Deposited in host pupa.
  4. Deposited in host adult.

D. Oviposition site correlated with the sex of the egg.

Eggs or Larvae Deposited Apart from the Host

Parasites that oviposit or larviposit apart from their hosts display the most complex type of life cycle for their larvae must have some mechanism for reaching the host. The primary (first-instar) larva either searches actively, is carried to, or waits for the host in order to make contact. Those that wait often do so within their eggs only to be freed on ingestion by the host. In nearly all cases the primary larva reflects in its morphology and physiology special features that give it mobility as well as enable it to resist desiccation and to maintain energy during the indefinite periods of exposure. Within the host the larva loses its specialized adaptive characters after the first moult and usually a quite different larval form appears.

Thus, larval hypermetamorphosis occurs in the majority of species that oviposit apart from their hosts. The primary larva is either triungulin, planidium, or microtype in form. Following the first moult, which occurs after the larva reaches a suitable feeding site, it transforms into a simplified parasitic form in which there is diminution or loss of legs or locomotory projections and loss of sclerotization. The larva becomes a more general hymenopteriform type at this time or a muscoidiform type. Even further larval forms may appear in species that require subsequent movement to reach pupation or overwintering sites. Snodgrass (1954) discusses larval hypermetamorphosis among the parasites and calls particular attention to the succession of adaptive forms which demonstrate the plasticity of larval tissues. These tissues seemingly can be moulded and remoulded yet maintain juvenile status through suspected hormonal control. Wigglesworth (1954) also suggests that hormones are concerned in hypermetamorphic species for the larval transformations in some Meloidae, at least, are regressive in nature and parallel the experimental reversal of metamorphosis where hormones are involved.

The different types of immature stages found in parasitic trematodes resemble the hypermetamorphosis found in insects, for the eggs are deposited apart from intermediate hosts and the first stage (the miracidium, a counterpart of the insect planidium) is motile and searches out the host. The trematodes transform into strikingly different forms in the course of their development. Perhaps the physiological mechanisms involved in the metamorphosis of helminths are similar to those in insects. The ability of the planidial larva to find its host compensates for the inability of the adult to oviposit directly upon its host. This precarious method of locating the host is compensated for by a high reproductive capacity. This also occurs in the parasitic helminths.

All the insect orders which contain parasitic species have representatives that deposit either eggs or, more rarely, larvae apart from their hosts. It is thought-provoking to speculate upon the reasons why the few parasitic species that are found among the Neuroptera, Lepidoptera, and most parasitic Coleoptera exhibit this ovipositional habit. Could it be that limited genetic plasticity of the adults in these orders precludes the ability of their either perceiving the host or ovipositing directly in or upon it? Or is it the remoteness of the host, in either space or time, that blocks direct contact by the parasite adult? Perhaps both of these 'pressures' have been involved. In any event, larval plasticity, as indicated by the diversity of larval stages in certain species, permitted natural selection of planidial forms which are able to contact the host. The scarcity of parasitic species in the Neuroptera, Lepidoptera, and Coleoptera that oviposit directly in or on hosts indicates a common lack of adaptability on the part of the adults in spite of a vast number of potential host insects. These potential niches were mostly filled by Hymenoptera and some Diptera which have evolved structures and synchrony of habit for direct oviposition and subsequent parasitism. Even in the Tachinidae, which embraces the bulk of parasitic Diptera, there are relatively few species that oviposit internally, indicating, perhaps, the recent development of an adult form possessing an ovipositor that can penetrate the insect integument.

EGGS HATCH OR LARVAE DEPOSITED BEFORE HOST CONTACT. In the Neuroptera, the mantispid larvae have departed from the wandering predacious habit characteristic of most species in this order. Mantispids prey only upon spider eggs in a single mass or parasitize wasp larvae. The triungulin-type primary larvae of mantispids are not unlike most neuropterous immatures but the mature mantispid larvae are grub-like, small headed, and bear rudimentary legs.

The interesting lepidopterous families Epipyropidae and Cyclotornidae comprise species which parasitize leafhoppers. A species of the latter family has one of the most complex life cycles found in insects. A leafhopper acts as an intermediate host while ant larvae are the final hosts of subsequent larval stages. After parasitizing a leafhopper the first-stage larva moults within a 'cocoon' giving rise to a larva which upon leaving the cocoon doubles up to form a circle with its ends nearly meeting over its dorsum. Ants seize these waiting larvae and transport them to their nests (Dodd 1912).

The Coleoptera manifests all degress of entomophagy from general predation to true parasitism. However, nearly all of the species oviposit apart from their insect hosts. The few species that do place their eggs upon the host do so by placing the egg in or on the host's egg mass. Species of the anthribid genus *Brachytarsus* break the hardened integuments of lecaniine scales and feed at the wounds. After feeding, the female reverses her position and thrusts the ovipositor into the wound, placing the egg within the egg chamber (Silvestri 1919; Clausen 1940a). The coccinellid genus *Rodolia* contains species that may oviposit directly on or beneath margarodid coccids, particularly on the egg mass. An individual larva can complete its development on a single host female bearing an egg mass. In such species, larval hypermetamorphosis is not expressed for here no planidial form is necessary to reach the host. The clerids *Trichodes ammios* (Fabr.) and *T. flavacintas* Spinola—solitary egg predators in locust egg pods—are suspected of laying their eggs directly on the egg pod and have a normal metamorphosis (Canizo 1957). It should be pointed out, however, that not all species which oviposit apart from their hosts or prey necessarily require hypermetamorphic larval development. For example, *Trichodes ornatus* Say lays its orange-coloured eggs in flowers and the first-instar larva, which does not differ radically from the later instars, is suspected of being carried to a bee or wasp nest where it eats the immature hymenopterous stages or stored pollen (Linsley and MacSwain 1943). It is interesting that certain meloids occupy a similar niche and exhibit similar life histories but undergo distinct larval hypermetamorphosis.

The Coleoptera that oviposit or place their progeny apart from their hosts or prey and display larval hypermetamorphosis occur in the families Carabidae, Staphylinidae, Rhipiceridae, Meloidae, and Rhipiphoridae. At least two distinct larval forms occur in the development of each species in these groups but in certain Meloidae there may be as many as five different forms. The triungulin, carabiform, and scarabaeiform larval types appear successively during the period that feeding occurs upon locust eggs in a pod. These forms bring the larva through four or five instars after which it leaves the egg pod and burrows down a short distance into the ground. The next stage, usually the fifth or sixth instar, does not feed but transforms into a thick, rigid, dark-coloured form with much reduced mandibles and legs. This is an overwintering form which has been referred to by different authors as a pseudo-chrysalis, coarctate larva, ipnotica, pseudonymph, pseudolarva, or pseudopupa. The ensuing larval instar reverts somewhat to a scarabaeiform type which is active and burrows upward close to the surface of the ground where it transforms into a pupa.

The Strepsiptera are among the few insect groups that are entirely parasitic on other insect groups. The strepsipterous females usually do not leave their hosts and the triungulins and adult males are the only free-living stages. The triungulins may wait for and attach to the host or may be carried by an adult to the immature host in its nest. Linsley and MacSwain (1952) found that some triungulins are carried to the site of the host after being ingested by the bee and then regurgitated in the bee's nest.

The parasitic Diptera that oviposit or larviposit apart from their hosts that display larval hypermetamorphosis and that rely on the larva to reach the host occur in the brachycerous families Nemestrinidae, Acroceridae, and Bombyliidae. Also, some species of the cyclorrhaphous families Tachinidae and Sarcophagidae reach their hosts through the action of their larvae.

The primary larvae of the brachycerous families mentioned above are of the planidium type (figure 16). They possess setae which are often modified for locomotion in the search for their hosts. Evidently few of these planidia are carried to their hosts.

The tachinid planidia are either larviposited on vegetation as are those of the Sarcophaginae or are deposited as membranous-type eggs which hatch immediately on the vegetation, often near the host. Many of the first-instar tachinid planidia have been described by Thompson (1923c). The eggs of some species are deposited vertically so that upon hatching the chorion slips down and forms a cup in which the larva 'stands' (figure 16). In this vertical position the larva rotates in response to moving objects and attaches to the host as it passes. In other tachinids, the larvae following deposition or hatching begin actively searching for their hosts. The primary larvae differ in some respects from the planidium type found in the Brachycera. Those of the tachinids are more maggot-like and are clothed with pigmented plates or heavy spines and usually do not possess long caudal setae.

The habit of some Hymenoptera in ovipositing apart from the host is a specialization correlated with planidial larvae which hatch apart from the host. This habit occurs in the parasitic Perilampidae, all known Eucharitidae, and a species of Tryphoninae of the Ichneumonidae.

A perilampid was the first hymenopterous parasite found to oviposit on leaves. After finding the planidial larva of *Perilampus hyalinus* Say and never observing the adult to oviposit on or in its host (a primary parasite of the fall web worm), H. S. Smith (1912) speculated that oviposition might occur upon the food plant in the vicinity of a colony of the caterpillars. It was not until 1917 that Smith had an opportunity to corroborate his view on perilampid oviposition. He observed leaf oviposition in another species, *P. chrysopae* Cwfd. Since Smith's discovery, several perilampid species have been studied in detail. The first-instar larva is the planidium type (figure 16e, f) and awaits the host. In some species the planidium attaches to the host and develops as an ectoparasite. In others, the planidium enters a caterpillar and attacks a primary parasite, if present. The mature larva is somewhat hymenopteriform (figure 21b).

All the known Eucharitidae deposit stalked-type eggs apart from their hosts which are larvae and prepupae of ants. The eggs are deposited in great numbers, often in leaf buds. However, the ovipositional site differs according to the species (Clausen 1940b).

The planidium-type larva (figure 16) normally attaches itself to a worker ant and is carried to the ant nest. The larvae of most species develop as external parasites but a few are endoparasitic in mature larvae or prepupae of ants. The mature larva (figure 21) is not typically hymenopteriform. Pupation occurs in the host cocoon or at times in the open in the ant nest.

A recent study by Tripp (1961) describes the biology of a curious ichneumonid, *Euceros frigidus* Cress. It departs from the normal habits of ichneumonids in several ways. It deposits a stalked egg (figure 14h) on foliage near colonies of young sawfly larvae. A planidium-type larva (figure 16d) hatches and remains upon its empty chorion until contact is made with a sawfly larva which acts as a carrier. The planidium comes to rest in a pocket-like depression between the integumental folds of the sawfly larva near the thoracic legs and is not shed when the carrier moults. It hibernates upon the sawfly prepupa within the latter's cocoon. If the carrier is not parasitized by a primary parasite the planidium transfers to the pupa and to the adult sawfly. If the sawfly is parasitized by a primary parasite the planidium apparently enters and develops endoparasitically. Its biology in many respects resembles that of some Perilampidae. The planidium, and the second, third, and fourth larval instars develop as endoparasites while the fourth moult occurs externally, and the fifth to seventh or eighth instars are ectoparasitic and hymenopteriform.

Further references to entomophagous species whose eggs hatch prior to host contact follow:

Neuroptera—Mantispidae (Balduf 1939a; Linsley and MacSwain 1955; McKeown and Mincham 1948).

Lepidoptera—Epipyropidae (Balduf 1939a; Mukerji and Venkatraman 1948; Kirkpatrick 1947).

Coleoptera—Carabidae (Clausen 1940a). Staphylinidae (Calhoun 1953; Wright, Geering, and Ashby 1947). Rhipiceridae (Dodge 1941). Meloidae (MacSwain 1956). Rhipiphoridae (Linsley, MacSwain, and Smith 1952b; Grandi 1951).

Strepsiptera (Linsley and MacSwain 1957; Bohart 1941; Oglobin 1939; Esaki and Miyamoto 1958; Silvestri 1941b, 1943).

Diptera—Nemestrinidae (Spencer 1958; York and Prescott 1952; Crouzel and Salavin 1943; Prescott 1955). Acroceridae (Plomley 1947; Lamore 1960; Schlinger 1952, 1957, 1960b, c). Bombyliidae (Brooks 1952; Linsley, MacSwain, and Smith 1952a; Bohart, Stephen, and Eppley 1960; Painter and Hall 1960). Tachinidae (Ramachandran 1950; Mesnil 1939, 1955; Hennig 1952; Baker, Bradley, and Clark 1949; van Emden 1950; Parker 1959; Bissell 1945; Walker 1943). Sarcophagidae (Cumber 1949).

Hymenoptera—Perilampidae (Principi 1947; Clancy 1946). Eucharitidae (Clausen 1940a, b, c, 1941; Boucek 1956).

EGGS HATCH AFTER INGESTION BY HOST. In these cases a microtype egg (figure 14i, j) is deposited on foliage and it must be ingested by a host caterpillar or larva before the first-instar larva is freed. Once hatched from the egg, the microtype larva bores through the gut of the host and enters the body cavity. The subsequent activity of the larva depends upon the family and the species to which it belongs.

Two families of different orders, the Trigonalidae:Hymenoptera and some species of Tachinidae:Diptera, have independently evolved this most interesting method of host contact. The remarkable parallelism of adaptations between unrelated insects is excellently illustrated by the similarity between the microtype eggs of these two families.

Sasaki (1886) first discovered this type of life cycle while studying the so-called 'Uji' disease of silkworms which was caused by a tachinid. The mature tachinid larva upon leaving its host ate through the silken cocoons, thus destroying the value of the latter for the production of silk. The tachinid *Blepharipoda zebina*

Walk. (= *Ugimya sericaria* Rond.) was observed by Sasaki's father to deposit minute eggs on mulberry leaves. This gentleman believed that the tachinid larva penetrated the silkworm through the spiracles. But the son carefully followed the complete life cycle of the tachinid and found that the eggs were ingested and subsequently hatched in the digestive tract. After about eight hours the larva passed through the gut wall and entered a ganglion beneath the midgut.

The larvae of the different tachinid species that develop from microtype eggs select different organs in the body cavity after penetrating the gut wall. The maggot may remain in a ganglion for about a week and then leave the enlarged ganglion and move to the integument where, for respiratory purposes, it perforates a main tracheal trunk at the base of a spiracle. In a species studied by Coppel (1958), the first-instar larva remained in the host muscle until the host pupated, then moved.

Sasaki (1886) observed the respiratory funnel that was formed around the posterior end of the maggot and the host-trachea but thought that the parasite constructed it with bits of fat and muscle cementing it together with its saliva. As discussed under the section 'Last-Instar Larvae: Diptera' (p. 208), the funnel is a host response to the wounding by the parasite. Upon completing larval development the tachinid was seen to bore out of the silkworm through the cocoon and drop to the soil for pupation. In Sasaki's detailed study of this tachinid it was noted that the pupa was not only surrounded by the last larval skin (puparium) but that two other membranes surrounded the pupa.

Pantel (1910) placed the tachinids that deposit microtype eggs into his Group II. This group includes various genera which are not necessarily phylogenetically related on the basis of adult classification. Thompson (1924) described many larvae of this group and made keys to the primary larvae.

There have been several opinions expressed concerning the hatching mechanism of the ingested egg. The egg upon deposition is fully incubated and the larva is ready to hatch when swallowed by the host. The upper surface of the egg has a thick chorion while the ventral surface is thin. Townsend (1908) believed that the host digestive juices caused a weakening of the egg shell, thus releasing the larva. Swezey (1909) thought the mandibles of the host cracked the egg shell allowing the maggot to escape. Severin, Severin, and Hartung (1915) experimented by placing the microtype eggs in various solutions and found that the eggs hatched the fastest in the salivary juices from the mouth of the host. They concluded that the larva responded to the juices through the micropyle of the egg and was immediately activated to free itself from the egg.

According to Clausen (1940a), Nishikawa confirmed the latter observations and also found that the larva hatched by breaking through the ventral chorion. In *Zenillia libatrix* (Panz.), Dowden (1934) found that the microtype egg did not hatch from the effect of the digestive juices alone but the juice caused a swelling of the egg ventrally and allowed the larva to rupture the ventral chorion.

Both the cracking of the egg by the host mandibles during ingestion and the influence of the pH in the gut of the host were involved in the hatching of eggs of

8—I.P.W.

the *Aplomya* studied by Wishart (1956). The range of pH of 11·75 to 12·50 was found optimum for rapid hatching and larval survival. A higher pH caused death to the larvae following hatching. A lower pH slowed the hatching period. Wishart concluded that the pH of the fore part of the midgut sets limits to host specificity since most lepidopterous larvae studied usually have lower pH values in the gut than the few hosts that are susceptible to *Aplomya*.

Most trigonalids have a more complex biology than the tachinids. The eggs of these Hymenoptera are deposited upon leaves and either a sawfly or lepidopterous caterpillar ingests them along with the leaf tissue. If the egg remains on the foliage it fails to hatch, yet the larva will remain alive, *en ovo*, for several months (Clausen 1940a).

If the chorion is ruptured, then a weak alkaline solution will induce the larva to hatch (Clausen 1940a). Upon hatching in the gut the microtype larva makes its way into the body cavity of the caterpillar. The larva, depending upon the species, will either continue its development in the host that ingested the egg, in which case it acts as a primary parasite, or some species may require the presence of a primary parasite before further development will occur. Since development does not occur beyond the first instar in the latter case, the ingesting caterpillar cannot be considered an intermediate host in the parasitological sense but simply a carrier for the trigonalid larva which either immediately attacks or waits for a primary endoparasitic larva to be introduced into the carrier.

It appears that certain hunting wasp species which provision their larvae with trigonalid infested caterpillars may serve as hosts for the trigonalids (Cooper 1954).

If a primary larva (other than a trigonalid) is present or becomes available in the carrier host, the trigonalid larva invades it and moults into a hymenopteriform second instar. The third instar resembles a mandibulate larva and in this stage destroys any other trigonalid larvae present. It then moults twice into a modified hymenopteriform larva and finally spins a cocoon within the host.

Further references to entomophagous species whose eggs hatch only after ingestion by the host follow:

Diptera—Tachinidae (Mellini 1956; Mesnil 1950 and 1956; Wishart 1945 and 1946; Thompson 1953; Maw and Coppel 1954).

Hymenoptera—Trigonalidae (Cooper 1954; Townes 1956).

Eggs or Larvae Deposited On or Near Host

In the majority of the families of Hymenoptera and Diptera that contain parasites, there are some species that deposit their eggs or larvae upon the hosts. The larva which hatches on the host or is deposited upon or near the host may either be ectoparasitic or endoparasitic.

EXTERNAL PARASITES. These include species either predacious on host eggs (egg predators), parasitic on concealed hosts, or parasitic on exposed hosts.

Egg predators. The species that lay their eggs among deposited host eggs occur in many families of Hymenoptera and Diptera. Hymenopterous families containing

representatives of this type are Ichneumonidae, Evaniidae, Eulophidae, Eupelmidae, Encyrtidae, Eurytomidae, and Pteromalidae, while the dipterous families
include the Anthomyiidae, Calliphoridae, Chloropidae, Drosophilidae, and
Otitidae. The parasite deposits its eggs usually among host eggs which are in a
mass. In the sense that an egg mass represents an individual host, such larvae
are parasitic rather than predatory. Frequently the host eggs are in capsules or
cocoons. A few species deposit their eggs in plant tissue next to host eggs that
have been inserted in a leaf or stem.

Larvae that feed in an egg mass but which did not originate from eggs placed
directly in the mass have planidial larvae. Such larvae are either carried phoretically
to the egg-pod or cluster or search out the egg mass. A few Hymenoptera oviposit
in one egg and the larva develops as an egg predator of other eggs. Hypermetamorphosis occurs among these types.

The larva that hatches from an egg placed in a host egg mass is normally hymenopteriform in the case of the Hymenoptera or muscoidiform if a Diptera is involved. The mature larvae are usually similar in form to the first-instar larvae for
no hypermetamorphosis occurs among these species. Pupation commonly occurs
in the host egg capsule or mass; however, some Diptera pupate adjacent to the
egg 'pod' if it is in the soil.

Ectoparasites on concealed hosts. The ectoparasites of concealed larvae or pupae
are many but are confined mainly to Hymenoptera. No hypermetamorphosis
occurs, for the egg is placed either on or near the host. With most species of
'Parasitica,' the host is hidden from the adult parasite when it oviposits, whereas
with most 'Aculeata' that attack hidden hosts the adult penetrates the concealment
and oviposits directly on the host.

Representative families of 'Parasitica' that have species which parasitize concealed hosts are: Braconidae, Ichneumonidae, Eulophidae, Pteromalidae, Aphelinidae, Signiphoridae, Eupelmidae, Torymidae, and Eurytomidae (figure 31).

Aculeate parasites that enter cells or cocoons (often in the soil) permanently
paralyse the host and then oviposit directly on its body. Such parasites occur in the
following families: Chrysididae, Bethylidae, Tiphiidae, Scoliidae, and Thynnidae.
However, a few aculeates, such as some Mutillidae, burrow in the soil and oviposit
through the cell walls of bee nests. The females of the Cleptidae, parasitic on sawflies in cocoons (Clausen 1940a), and some Chrysididae, parasitic on mature
lepidopterous larvae in cocoons (D. E. Parker 1936), gnaw a hole in the host cocoon
through which they employ their ovipositor to paralyse the host and oviposit. Some
Multillidae gnaw a hole in fly puparia and oviposit (Lamborn 1915), and these
usually seal the hole with mouth secretions. The egg-placement site is rather
constant in a given species but differs between species. Figure 32 shows the egg-
placement sites on a scarab grub of several species of tiphiids and scoliids. The
necessity of direct contact with the host among the aculeate wasps perhaps relates
to where the egg issues from the ovipositor. Since in the aculeates the egg issues at
the base of the ovipositor, it is probably necessary for the adult to come in close
contact with the host.

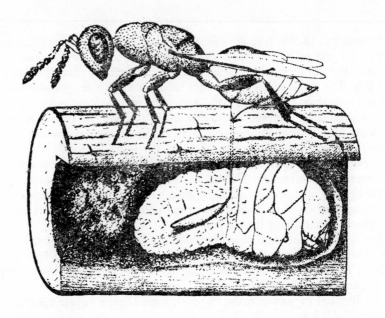

FIGURE 31. *Eurytoma masii* Russo ovipositing externally on *Phloeotribus scarabaeoides* (Bern.) in woody branch, from Russo (1938).

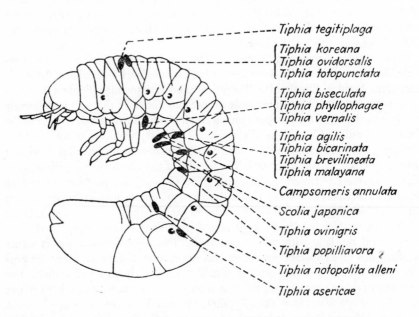

Tiphia tegitiplaga

Tiphia koreana
Tiphia ovidorsalis
Tiphia totopunctata

Tiphia biseculata
Tiphia phyllophagae
Tiphia vernalis

Tiphia agilis
Tiphia bicarinata
Tiphia brevilineata
Tiphia malayana

Campsomeris annulata

Scolia japonica

Tiphia ovinigris

Tiphia popilliavora

Tiphia notopolita alleni

Tiphia asericae

FIGURE 32. Egg positions of a series of Tiphiidae and Scoliidae on a scarab grub, from Clausen and Berry (1932).

On the other hand, females of 'Parasitica' that parasitize concealed hosts do so only by penetrating the cocoon, puparium, scale, cell, or plant tissue with the ovipositor.

The host is either permanently paralysed or killed outright by the sting of the adult parasite before oviposition occurs or it may not be 'stung' at all. Subsequently, one or more eggs may be deposited depending upon the species. *Eurytoma pini* Bugbee oviposits on a stem-boring lepidopterous larva only after the host had been paralysed by another parasite, and Arthur (1961) termed such a natural enemy a cleptoparasite. The eggs are either elongate hymenopteriform, acuminate, or stalked. The latter two types of eggs are usual for adults equipped with a very long ovipositor. Apparently no pedicellate egg is known to be deposited on concealed hosts. Among the chalcidoids, the egg usually exhibits some sculpturing and often is spined or hairy.

The first-instar larva is usually a simple hymenopteriform type and may possess a pair of short projecting antennae. The spiracles are usually open, with four or five pairs being present in the chalcidoids and usually nine pairs in the ichneumonoids. The chalcidoid larvae may bear long body hairs.

The larva develops rapidly and generally there are five instars. Often the ectoparasite completely consumes the host, which is most frequently a larva though pupae are also attacked. Pupation occurs at the feeding site and if the parasite is an ichneumonoid or an aculeate a cocoon is usually formed.

Many hymenopterous species that are ectoparasitic on concealed hosts are hyperparasitic. Some Ceraphronidae are hyperparasitic on aphids through Aphidiinae or on lepidopterous larvae through *Apanteles*. The biology of *Lygocerus testaceimanus* Kieff. is an example of the former (Haviland 1921a; Spencer 1926) and an example of the latter is *Ceraphron* (= *Calliceras*) on *Apanteles* (Moutia and Courtois 1952). Some Ceraphronidae (e.g. *Conostigmus* spp.) are primary ectoparasites on syrphid pupae within the puparia (Kamal 1939). Not all Ceraphronidae are external parasites, however, for Pschorn-Walcher (1956) described a new species, *Aphanogmus nigrofornicatus*, which he found to be an endoparasite of a cecidomyiid aphid predator, *Aphidoletes*.

Ectoparasites on exposed hosts. The parasites that attack exposed hosts are probably more specialized than those that attack hidden hosts. Certainly they are less common, possibly because mechanisms had to evolve which would permit the secure attachment of eggs to the hosts. The Pompilidae and Ampulicidae appear to be more primitive than the few Ichneumonidae, Braconidae, and Eulophidae that oviposit on exposed hosts. For example, the aculeates permanently paralyse the host and often drag it to some protected place where oviposition and larval development occur. Some Larrinae, parasitic on mole crickets, temporarily paralyse their host, then oviposit. The mole cricket regains activity only to be killed later by the feeding of the larrine larvae. In these cases, neither the egg nor the larva exhibits special structures for clinging to the host.

The ichneumonids (Polysphinctini) that parasitize spiders have larvae whose posterior body segments are firmly attached to the egg shell which, in turn, is fastened tightly to the spider by a secretion applied by the adult. The egg is placed where it will not be dislodged easily. The spider host, only temporarily paralysed by the parasite's sting but bearing the wasp egg, resumes its activities. The hymenopteriform larva often bears special ventral processes on the fifth and sixth abdominal segments. The egg shell is used as a base to anchor the larva to the host. These are telescoped into the corresponding structures of the previous instar's exuvium. The cast larval skins accumulate on the top of the egg shell at the caudal end of the parasite larva. Paired rounded tubercles with minute hooks occur. These are attached to the spider web while the larva spins its cocoon in the web.

The tryphonine ichneumonids attack lepidopterous or sawfly larvae. The Phytodietini and Eclytini usually parasitize lepidopterous larvae whereas the rest of the tryphonine tribes parasitize sawfly larvae (Muesebeck, Krombein, and Townes 1951). The adults temporarily paralyse their hosts, then oviposit. The host larva subsequently regains activity, feeds, and forms a cocoon or pupal cell. The ectoparasitic larva then develops on the host, which is now concealed. It is important in some parasite species that the egg does not hatch until the host cocoon is spun because the host larval movements during the spinning process might dislodge the parasitic larva (Morris, Cameron, and Jepson 1937).

A most interesting adaptation among these insects is the pedicellate egg (figure 14g, h). This type of egg is either partly embedded in an integumental puncture in the host larva or possesses a posterior chorionic extension which forms an anchor when it is deeply embedded in the host. The egg body is usually black or brown and very conspicuous. Some adult tryphonines carry exposed fully incubated eggs near the tip of the ovipositor. At the time of oviposition only the stalk of the egg remains within the channel of the ovipositor (Kerrich 1936; Clausen 1940a).

The pedicellate egg serves at least two purposes. It is not shed if or when the host moults, and the egg shell serves as a base with which the posterior end of the larva retains connection during the first instar and often during subsequent instars. The tryphonine larvae are hymenopteriform. The first instar often has only one open pair of spiracles on the thorax. Numerous spines may occur on the last abdominal segment. These apparently serve to anchor the larva to the egg shell. Some tryphonine primary larvae have tufts of hair projecting from the body segments that appear to be utilized for larval movement. When mature, the larva has nine pairs of spiracles and spins a papery cocoon. The host remains are sealed off within the host cell or cocoon.

The Elachertinae apparently include the only chalcidoids that attack exposed hosts. The adult temporarily paralyses the lepidopterous host and deposits from one to several eggs. In some species the egg is fastened securely to the host and can be considered pedicellate although the pedicel in some species is formed during oviposition. The host caterpillar, after having been temporarily paralysed and oviposited upon, again becomes active and feeds. The parasite eggs hatch and, if gregarious, the larvae remain at the egg-site with their posterior ends within the egg shells. As moults occur the larval exuviae slip down and collect at the base of the larva on top of the egg shell. When mature, the larvae change position and usually spin cocoons between the host larval remains and the leaf surface.

Gadd and Fonseka (1945) and Gadd, Fonseka, and Ranaweeva (1946) studied three elachertine species in three different genera. All three species were solitary. During oviposition by these species the ovipositor is inserted fairly deeply into a temporarily paralysed caterpillar and during the same time a flowable substance streams down the ovipositor into the host forming a pedicel. The egg, which is too large to pass through the ovipositor, issues at the base of the ovipositor and is attached to the pedicel. The egg rests in an indentation in the host skin made by the adult parasite. The anchoring pedicel prevents the egg from being lost during the moulting of the host. Upon hatching, the larva moves to the venter of the caterpillar and begins to feed, quickly killing the host. The larvae of these species do not spin cocoons but rather lie free beneath the host remains.

Further references to external parasitic species that deposit eggs or larvae on or near the host follow:

Hymenoptera—Ichneumonidae (Townes and Townes 1960; Short 1959; Stuart 1957; Nickels, Pierce, and Pinkney 1950; Dowden 1941; Clancy 1946; Blunck 1951, 1952a; Silvestri 1941a; A. Monteith 1956; Simmonds 1944a, 1947d, Iwata 1942a; Gerig 1960; and Mason 1956). Braconidae (Ryan 1961; Nickels, Pierce, and Pinkney 1950; Bennett 1960; Somsen and Luginbill 1956; Nelson and Farstad 1953; Ayyar 1940; and Dowden 1941). Evaniidae (Edmunds 1952, 1954; Roth and Willis 1960; and Cameron 1957). Eulophidae (Baker, Bradley, and Clark 1949; Dowden 1941; Doutt 1957; Narayanan, Rao, and Gangrade 1956; Walz 1957; Lucchese 1941; Telford 1961; Saunders 1960; Van Lith 1955; Silvestri 1941a; and Gadd, Fonseka, and Ranaweeva 1946). Pteromalidae (Beacher 1947; Simmonds 1952; Clancy 1946; Doutt and Finney 1947; v.d. Merwe 1943; Schneiderman and Horowitz 1958; Woglum, La Follette, Landon, and Lewis 1947; and Fulton 1940). Aphelinidae (DeBach and White 1960; DeBach and Sizojevic 1960; and Hafez and Doutt 1954). Signiphoridae (DeBach, Kennett, and Pence 1958). Eurytomidae (Pemberton and Rosa 1946). Eupelmidae (Roth and Willis 1954, 1960; Flock 1941; Clancy 1946; Flanders 1942e, 1944a; and Hill and Pinckney 1940). Torymidae (Moser 1956).

INTERNAL PARASITES. External egg deposition or larviposition and subsequent internal development of the larvae is the general habit among the parasitic Diptera but is rare in the Hymenoptera. The inability of most dipterous parasites to oviposit within the host is compensated for by the larvae being able to penetrate the host's integument.

The main dipterous groups that utilize this type of host invasion are the Tachinidae and Sarcophaginae. However, several other groups of flies are known to have this habit. The cecidomyiid *Endaphis perfidus* Kieff. deposits an egg on the dorsum of a winged aphid and the hatching larva bores into the host body cavity. After maturing, the larva escapes through the anus and pupates in the soil (Barnes 1929, 1930). *Endopsylla* sp. attaches its stalked egg to the wing of a psyllid. The larva upon hatching feeds externally for a few days then penetrates the host body cavity to complete its feeding. The mature larva leaves the host and pupates in the soil (Lal 1934). Some phorid species develop in a similar way. *Megaselia fasciata* Fall., a gregarious endoparasite of coccinellid pupae, invades the host after external oviposition (Lichtenstein 1920; Menozzi 1927). More recently another phorid, *Phalacrotophora berolinensis* Schmitz, with a similar biology has been studied by Colyer (1952), Delucchi (1953), and Wylie (1958*b*). This species oviposits beneath the wing pads of coccinellid pupae.

The Sarcophaginae are mainly viviparous and most parasitic species larviposit on or near the host. Some representative species place their progeny apart from the host while others oviposit directly into the host. The latter type is discussed under the section dealing with internal oviposition.

The host range for the subfamily Sarcophaginae, and even for several individual species, is wide. Included are Orthoptera, Heteroptera, Neuroptera, Lepidoptera, Diptera, and Hymenoptera. For general papers on sarcophagine habits see Thompson (1920) and Clausen (1940*a*). Sarcophagine associations with grasshoppers are discussed by Smith and Finlayson (1960) and R. W. Smith (1958), and the structural characteristics of puparia are covered by Greene (1925*b*). The biologies of the following species more or less represent the habits of the group.

Kellymyia kellyi (Ald.) parasitizes grasshoppers. The females of this species can larviposit on a grasshopper in flight. The maggot usually enters the body through the thin membrane at the base of the wing (Kelly 1914). This species, however, will also larviposit on non-flying, inactive, or even dead hosts (Smith 1958).

Agria affinis (Fall.) parasitizes lepidopterous larvae. The first-instar larva is deposited on or near the host larva and it then penetrates the host integument, completing its development as an endoparasite. The mature larva emerges and drops to the soil to pupate (Coppel, House, and Maw 1959).

Very few sarcophagine larvae are associated with respiratory funnels. The first instar is metapneustic, the second and third are amphipneustic. Crouzel (1944) noted the presence of a pair of claw-like organs near the posterior spiracles of the first-instar larva of a sarcophagine parasite of a grasshopper. She suggests these structures may be used by the larva to grasp and rupture the host trachea in order to obtain air for respiration.

Tachinids attack their hosts in various ways. Pantel (1910) defines ten types of tachinid oviposition and Baer (1920) names most of these types after genera which were known to exhibit each type to which Pantel had assigned a number. Some types of oviposition have already been discussed where the egg or larva is placed apart from the host. Like the sarcophagines, some tachinids larviposit on or, more rarely, in the host. However, many species either place a membranous egg (figure 14*l*) or a macrotype egg (figure 14*k*) upon their hosts. The larvae hatching from macrotype eggs may enter the host in two ways depending upon whether the eggs are dehiscent or nondehiscent. The larva normally hatches from dehiscent eggs by splitting the chorion fracture and then enters the host near the egg shell. The larva often uses the egg as a fulcrum by keeping its posterior segments pressed against the broken chorion while boring into the host integument with its mouth hooks. The larva hatching from a nondehiscent egg usually bores directly beneath the egg, through the thin chorion of the venter, and then through the host integument. These latter larvae often perforate the integument again from within, forming a secondary opening for the formation of an integumental respiratory tunnel.

Some tachinids deposit pedicellate membranous eggs. *Carcelia* fastens the expandable apex of the stalk to a hair or to the integument of a caterpillar and the hatched larva penetrates the host (Pantel 1910; Klomp 1958*b*). The phasiine *Helomyia lateralis* (Meig.) has a macrotype egg with a pedicel-type structure (Dupuis 1949*b*).

Most tachinid species parasitize a wide range of host species within the same order but there is a fair number of species that attack hosts in several orders. Lepidopterous and sawfly larvae are the usual hosts for a great majority of tachinid genera. The Dexiinae are regularly parasites of larval Coleoptera (van Emden 1950) and in the Phasiinae, the Leucostomatini, Ocypterini, and Phasiini are exclusively parasitic on species of Hemiptera. The Dufourini generally are parasites of adult Coleoptera (van Emden 1950, 1954). Dupuis (1949*a*) observed that among most Phasiinae the eggs are deposited on almost any hemipteran regardless of stage, sex, or species. The bugs most numerous in a given locality were the most highly parasitized and those already parasitized by euphorine braconids were more susceptible to phasiine attack because of their slower movements.

The tachinid first-instar larva is metapneustic and the second and third instars are amphipneustic. Most species develop respiratory connections with the host trachea or integument and usually a respiratory funnel is formed. Pupation may occur in the host or in the soil. The puparia of tachinids are often of value in identifying the species (Greene 1921, 1925*a*; Bissert 1938; Gardner 1940; Lloyd 1951; and Finlayson 1960). For a general account of tachinid biologies the reader is referred to Nielsen (1909 to 1918), Pantel (1910), Prell (1915), Baer (1920, 1921), Thompson (1923*b*, *c*, 1926, 1928), Clausen (1940*a*), DuPuis (1947, 1948, 1949*a*, *b*), Hawboldt (1947), Hennig (1952), and van Emden (1954).

The few species of Hymenoptera that deposit eggs externally and develop internally in a host occur in the aphelinid genus *Coccophagus*. In some *Coccophagus* the male egg may be placed on the female larva of the same species which is itself a primary parasite of a coccid or mealybug or the egg may be placed on a host which harbours a female parasite (Flanders 1937*a*).

Further references to internal parasites which deposit either macrotype or membranous eggs or larvae upon their hosts follow:

Diptera—Tachinidae (Hafez 1953; Coppel and Maw 1954*a*; Lucchese 1941; Coppel and Smith 1957; Iwata and Nagatomi 1954; Maw and Coppel 1953; Vodjdani 1954; Dietrick and van den Bosch 1957; Mellini 1957, 1959; and Smith, Dunn, and Rosenberger 1955).

Eggs, or More Rarely Larvae, Deposited in Host

Almost all of the parasites that oviposit directly into their hosts and develop internally undergo some degree of hypermetamorphosis. That is, the first-instar larva differs in form from the mature larva. Thus, hypermetamorphosis is common and most striking in the parasites that place their eggs or larvae apart from the host, is rare in those that oviposit or larviposit on the host, but is the rule again in groups that oviposit internally.

The reason for the evolution of hypermetamorphic larvae and their subsequent survival in an environment of darkness and blood (as internal parasites) is not clear. One reason for hypermetamorphic development is perhaps the necessity of the larva to move from one part of the host to another. These movements may have facilitated structural changes in the larval stages. This question is an important one and offers good research potentialities.

Endoparasitism resulting from an egg placed in the host occurs mainly in the 'Parasitica' of the Hymenoptera. Eggs, larvae, pupae, or adults serve as hosts of various species that deposit eggs internally. There are very few endoparasitic aculeates, and in the Diptera this habit is confined to a few cyclorrhaphous families of which only the family Cryptochaetidae is composed entirely of species that deposit their eggs internally.

DEPOSITED IN HOST EGG. There are three developmental paths that may occur after a parasite egg is deposited into a host egg, namely: (1) the development of the parasite may occur completely in the host egg and give rise to an adult, or (2) after destroying the host egg the parasite larva completes its development by feeding externally upon other host eggs, hence is an egg-predator, or (3) in a more advanced host relationship an egg is placed in a host egg but the parasitic larva only completes its development when the host larva nears pupation. These are known as egg-larval parasites.

Develop in host egg. These are true egg parasites. In the Insecta only Hymenoptera contains species that are endoparasitic in insect eggs. There apparently are no Ichneumonoidea that are true egg parasites but in the Chalcidoidea there are several families limited to such a host relationship. The Myrmaridae and the Trichogrammatidae are exclusively endoparasitic in eggs. A few eulophids (*Tetrastichus* sp., *Tetracampe* sp., *Achrysocharis* sp.), encyrtids (*Ooencyrtus* spp., *Comperia*), eupelmids (*Anastatus*), and the cleptid *Mesitiopterus kahlii* Ashm., develop in eggs.

In the Proctotrupoidea, all species of Sceliondae are evidently true egg parasites. All parasitize insect eggs except the Baeinae which attack spider eggs.

Girault (1907) lists the hosts of the egg parasites known from North and South America. He mentions the eurytomids *Macrorileya* and *Neorileya* as true egg parasites but these actually are egg predators. *Eupelmus coccidis* Grlt. and *Podagrion mantis* Ashm. are unique in a way for they develop on single mantid eggs but do so external to the egg although they are within the oöthecal cell (Breland 1941).

The primary larva of most true eggs parasites differs from the hymenopteriform type in the early stages but begins to resemble that type when mature. Some of these larvae are shown in figures 17*a*, *b*, and *e*.

Further references to internal parasites which deposit their eggs and complete their development in host eggs follow:

Hymenoptera—Mymaridae (Tooke 1955; and Romney and Cassidy 1945). Trichogrammatidae (Henderson 1941; Ivanova-Kazas 1952*b*; and Jackson 1956). Eulophidae (Niklas 1956*b*; and Jackson 1958*b*). Encyrtidae (Maple 1947; Lawson 1954; and Huffaker 1941). Eupelmidae (Breland 1941). Podagrionidae (Breland 1941). Cleptidae (Milliron 1950). Scelionidae (Moutia and Courtois 1952; Hidaka 1958; Boldaruev 1956; Liu Chung-Lo 1959; Pemberton and Rosa 1940; Vachon 1955; and Mills 1942).

Develop as egg-predators. Some few hymenopterous species deposit an egg within a host egg but once this host egg has been consumed the parasite larva searches for additional eggs; thus, it is an egg predator since many eggs are required for its development. Species exhibiting this behaviour include the evaniid *Zeuxevania splendidula* Costa (Roth and Willis 1960), and the eulophids *Anellaria conomeli* Bakk. (Bakkendorf 1934), *Ootetrastichus beatus* (Perk.) (Perkins 1907), and *Tetrastichus hagenowii* (Ratz.) (Roth and Willis 1960).

Develop as egg-larval parasites. The parasite that oviposits into an egg of a host and finally emerges from the last or penultimate larval stage or from the pupal stage is called an egg-larval parasite. This type of host relationship has been observed only in hymenopterous parasites and has recently been reviewed by Clausen (1954).

There appears to be a greater degree of host specificity exhibited by egg-larval parasites than by many other Hymenoptera or Diptera. Synchronization with the host's life cycle must be close since the development of the parasite nearly spans the period of immature development of the host. Many of the hosts are borers in plant stems or are gall makers. This may account for the evolution towards oviposition into host eggs, for subsequent stages would be out of reach of the adult parasites.

Egg-larval parasites are represented in several superfamilies. In the Ichneumonoidea, the braconid subfamily Cheloninae has several genera with several species each which are limited to oviposition into host eggs. There are several species in the Dacnusinae that are known to oviposit in eggs of mining Diptera. Other braconids such as species of *Apanteles* and *Opius* which display the egg-larval habit are exceptional for most of the members of these genera oviposit into larval stages.

The Diplazoninae is the only group in the Ichneumonidae which contains several genera whose members oviposit into eggs; however, most of these species also oviposit into first-instar larvae. Their hosts are aphidophagous Syrphidae from whose puparia they emerge. Other egg-larval ichneumonids are represented by single species in five or six genera.

In the Chalcidoidea, the polyembryonic Encyrtidae deposit eggs into developing embryos of lepidopterous hosts. The numerous parasite adults later emerge from the mature host larva. The Eulophidae and Torymidae each have only one known species with the egg-larval habit.

The Cynipoidea is represented only by *Ibalia leucospoides* which oviposits into the egg or young larva of *Sirex*. The Proctotrupoidea, on the other hand, has many members that place their eggs into host eggs and develop later. The hosts are mainly cecidomyiids. Many *Platygaster* species are polyembryonic and oviposit into cecidomyiid eggs while other species of this genus oviposit into young larvae.

Clausen (1954*b*) calls attention to the correlation between the size of the parasite egg and the stage of the host that is attacked. Most egg-larval parasites have relatively small eggs in relation to the size of the adult.

The eggs of egg-larval parasites are inserted either into the embryo or cytoplasm of the egg. The primary larvae are variable in form depending upon the group. The mature larvae are more or less hymenopteriform and in the monoembryonic species the final-instar often emerges from the host and feeds externally. The egg-larval parasites often strikingly influence the size of the host. A parasitized lepidopterous larva may be half the size of a non-parasitized larva in the same population. Pupation occurs within the host or in close proximity to the site where the larval feeding was completed. This may occur in the host's cocoon or puparium.

Further references to parasites which develop as egg-larval parasites follow:

Hymenoptera—Braconidae (Bennett 1960; Tadic 1958; van den Bosch and Haramoto 1951; and Martin 1956). Ichneumonidae (Schneider 1950; and Osborne 1960). Encyrtidae (Doutt 1947).

DEPOSITED IN HOST LARVA OR NYMPH OR IN HOMOPTEROUS NYMPHS OR ADULTS. In some ways the endoparasites of larvae resemble the internal parasites of hemi-metabolous insects. However, phylogenetically large groups of parasites—even families—are restricted to holometabolous insect hosts whereas other parasite groups are limited to hemimetabolous hosts, particularly Homoptera. Therefore, the parasites of homopterous nymphs or adults are considered separately herein. Other reasons for doing this include the many specializations shown by parasites of Homoptera, their considerable host specificity, and their great value in many successful biological control projects.

Development completed in host larva or nymph. Many parasite species oviposit or larviposit into host larvae and complete development before the host pupates. Most of these parasites are hymenopterous species but a few dipterous species also have this type of life cycle. Also, some Diptera develop in orthopterous nymphs.

The Braconidae commonly display this type of host relationship. Many parasites that are important to biological control are included in this family. At least nine braconid subfamilies contain species that are larval parasites. Nearly all *Apanteles* oviposit in larvae and emerge as larvae from the host. Most of the braconids are solitary and many emerge from the host larva after the host has spun its cocoon. However, some *Apanteles*, particularly the solitary species, emerge from medium-size host larvae. In *Apanteles* there are some gregarious species but the primary larvae in these species are not mandibulate and often are not caudate but are a vesiculate type. Evidently the Rogadinae is the only braconid subfamily that has species with the hymenopteriform first-instar larva. A polypodeiform primary larva occurs in several braconid subfamilies. Generally the 'polypod' is caudate and occasionally mandibulate. Most species pupate outside of the host but often within the host's cocoon. The Rogadinae pupate within the host's skin.

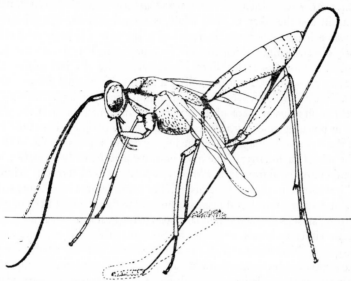

FIGURE 33. *Macrocentrus ancylivorus* Roh. ovipositing into Oriental fruit moth larva, from Garman and Brigham (1933).

Some of the Ichneumonidae most important in biological control are larval parasites. The majority of Ophioninae fall under this category. Among the three subfamilies which include larval parasites nearly all the members have caudate primary larvae and are solitary. Pupation occurs outside the host body but the parasite may pupate within the cocoon of the host. The parasite cocoon is often banded or speckled.

A few parasites of Cynipoidea develop on larvae. In this group there are three subfamilies represented with a varied host range.

A few Proctotrupoidea like *Helorus paradoxus* Prov. oviposit into *Chrysopa* larvae and emerge from their hosts after the latter have cocooned (Clancy 1946). Some Proctotrupidae, i.e. *Phaenoserphus viator* Hal. (Eastham 1929), *Codrus* (Williams 1932), and *Cryptoserphus parvulus* (Nees) (Osborne 1960), are parasites of coleopterous larvae and pupate with the host larva. The young larvae are usually of a mandibulate-polypodeiform-caudate combination and in some species the final instar is sacciform.

Evidently the Chalcidoidea embrace only a few groups that oviposit internally in larvae and complete their development before the host pupates. The Eulophidae contains species with diverse habits; among them are a few species that oviposit into larvae. Their hosts are mainly leaf miners. *Chrysocharis laricinellae* (Ratz.) deposits its egg internally in a sawfly larva, *Phyllotoma*, in its mine. A posteriorly-truncated hymenopteriform primary larva hatches and develops through four instars, then breaks through the host skin to pupate, or hibernates as a prepupa in the leaf mine (Dowden 1941). Cameron's (1939) study of the parasites of the leaf-miner *Phytomyza ilicis* discussed two *Chrysocharis* sp. One, *C. gemma* Walk., is a larval parasite and the other, *C. syma* Walk., is a pupal parasite. The primary larva of *C. gemma* is hymenopteriform, is truncated posteriorly, and bears rows of short, posteriorly directed spines which are used for propulsion. This species also pupates in the mine. *Tetrastichus taylori* Ferr. is a hyperparasite of a leaf mining hispid, *Promecotheca reichei* Baly, for it normally parasitizes the external primary parasite *Elasmus hispardarum* Ferr. by ovipositing into the later larval stages of the primary. The first-instar larva of *T. taylori* is hymenopteriform. If the *Elasmus* succeeds in pupating, the *Tetrastichus* pupates within the pupa but if the host is killed in the larval or prepupal stage, the hyperparasite pupates outside of the host but in the mine (Taylor 1937). The most effective parasite of *Promecotheca* in Fiji is a eulophid introduced from Java, *Pleurotropis parvulus* Ferr. It readily oviposits in all larval instars and in pupae of the hispid. The primary larva is hymenopteriform and after undergoing four larval instars it pupates within the host (Taylor 1937).

Dipterous parasites that oviposit or larviposit in the host larval stage are relatively few and are either tachinids or species of Sarcophaginae. The European species *Blondelia* (= *Lydella*) *nigripes* (Fall.) is a polyphagous parasite which commonly parasitize gypsy and browntail moth larvae. Dowden (1933) studied the biology of *Blondelia* and a close relative. The adult female genital apparatus is armed with a piercing organ which is used to break the skin of the host larva and enables the larvipositor to enter and deposit the small parasitic maggot posterior-end first. After larviposition, the maggot bores into the midgut of the caterpillar and attaches to the gut wall by means of its posterior stimatic hooks. In this way, the anal spiracles lie against one of the host's tracheae. The third-instar larva develops outside of the gut feeding on organs of the body cavity. Usually the mature larva leaves the host and pupates.

The tachinid *Spathimeigenia spinigera* Tns. oviposits directly into the body cavity of *Neodiprion* larvae of any stage. The maggot becomes attached to a tracheal trunk with its spiracular hooks holding it in place. The second instar is associated with a respiratory funnel which the third instar abandons following the breakdown of the tissues of the host. Pupation occurs within the host cocoon (Tripp 1960).

Some tachinids inject eggs into hemipterous hosts. Dupuis (1953) reviews the host range of the Leucostomatina group of the Phasiinae which includes species that inject unincubated eggs into hemipterous nymphs.

The Sarcophaginae contain species that are able to penetrate the host integument for larviposition or that introduce the egg into the host via the mouth. *Servaisia* (*Protodexia*) *arteagai* (Blanch.) inserts its ovipositor between the mandibles of *Dichroplus* and deposits a living larva; however, Salavin (1958) also notes that the same species places the larva externally on *Schistocerca*. The larva, in this case, enters the host through the cervical membrane. *Sarcophaga falciformis* (Ald.) is able to insert a larva with its strong larvipositor through the cuticle and into the muscles of the hind femur of *Melanoplus* and *Oedaleonotus*. The larva migrates into the grasshopper's thoracic cavity where it matures and the host dies when the mature maggots emerge (Middlekauf 1959).

Further references to parasites whose development is completed in the host larva or nymph follow:

Hymenoptera—Braconidae (Simmonds 1947*b*; Finney, Flanders, and Smith 1947; Osborne 1960; Beirne 1946; Nickels, Pierce, and Pinkney 1950; Dondale 1954; Hafez 1951; Boldaruev 1958; Narayanan, Rao, and Kauv 1956; Johansson 1951; Brown 1946*a*; Dowden, Carolin, and Dirks 1950; MacDonald 1959; Moutia and Courtois 1952; Bennett 1960; Davis 1944; Fallis 1942; Short 1953; De Saeger 1942; Allen 1958; and Hafez 1947). Ichneumonidae (Brown 1946*b*; Muldrew 1953; Dowden, Carolin, and Dirks 1950; MacDonald 1959; Bronskill 1960; Baker, Bradley, and Clark 1949; Fisher 1959; Michelbacher 1940; Gerig 1960; and Puttler 1961).

DEVELOPMENT COMPLETED IN HOST PUPA. In parasites that oviposit in host larvae of various stages the first-instar larva may remain unchanged until the host larva pupates. Then the parasitic larva quickly develops through its remaining larval stages and pupates. These are termed larval-pupal parasites. Various authors have suggested that the larval host's hormonal systems inhibit further development of the first-instar larva. The first-stage parasitic larva may also have a physiological effect on the host. The larva of *Eurytoma curta* Wlk. causes premature pupation of its host *Euribia* (Varley 1937), and, according to Clausen (1940*a*) early pupation occurs in dipterous hosts parasitized by *Eurytoma* spp., *Brachymeria*, and *Alysia*.

Certain entire subfamilies in the Ichneumonoidea reveal the larval-pupal type host relationship. In the Braconidae, species with this type of development are mostly parasites of Diptera. Alysiine species oviposit into maggots which are usually associated with carrion and then emerge from puparia, e.g. *Aphaereta* (Evans 1933; Salkeld 1959) and *Alysia* (Roberts 1935). The genus *Opius* includes important larval-pupal parasites of fruit flies. The host larval stages attacked by the species of *Opius* vary but all of these parasites emerge from tephritid puparia. There are a few *Opius* species that also parasitize leaf miners. The primary larvae are typically mandibulate and often exhibit thoracic processes. The mature larva are hymenopteriform and pupate within the fly puparium, generally in the soil.

The Ichneumoninae are parasites of larvae or pupae of Lepidoptera but all species emerge from the host pupa. Heinrich (1960) points out the rather constant relationship between whole phylogenetic groups of Ichneumoninae and corresponding phylogenetic groups of host species. The Trogini of the Callojoppa group are parasites of sphingids and the Trogus group parasitizes species of *Papilio*. The tribe Listrodromini is associated with lycaenids. With one exception, the tribe Platylabini parasitizes geometrids. Certain parasite genera are specific on particular groups. Some species are monophagous and others are restricted to closely related hosts.

The females of ichneumonine species in which the hypopygium is prolonged and covers all or most of the slit for the ovipositor are called amblypygous; those without the prolonged hypopygium are designated oxypygous (Heinrich 1960). This author correlates amblypygous females with the habit of ovipositing into larvae and the oxypygous females with the habit of ovipositing into the pupa of the host. In both groups, however, development is completed in the pupa.

Detailed biological studies in the Ichneumoninae are few. Some ichneumonines deposit eggs into internal organs. *Pseudamblyteles subfuscus* (Cress.) places eggs into salivary glands of cutworms. The caudate primary larva is also found in this organ, then later breaks out and feeds in the body cavity (Strickland 1923). Cameron (1950, 1951) describes the immature stages of *Ichneumon suspicious* Wesm. which parasitize *Hepialis*. The first-instar larva resembles the mandibulate type and is not caudate; the mature larva is hymenopteriform and the prepupa is a pronymph type.

Only a few biologies of the species belonging to the ichneumonid subfamily Metopiinae are known. Townes and Townes (1959) report the species to be solitary parasites of Lepidoptera. Oviposition is in the host larva but emergence is always from the pupa. A flimsy cocoon is spun within the host's pupa. The metopiines locate their hosts by smell (Townes and Townes 1959). *Triclistus* spp. have been found by Gerig (1960) to oviposit into the supraoesophageal ganglion of large larvae of *Zeiraphera*. The first-instar larva is caudate; the 'tail' is short, conical, and broadly rounded apically. The head is rather distinct, being elongate, narrowing anteriorly, and has a constriction near its base.

The ichneumonid subfamily Ophioninae contains a few species with interesting biologies in connection with the larval-pupal host relationship. *Therion morio*, according to Tothill (1922), probably inserts its ovipositor deep into the larva of *Hyphantria* placing a pedicellate egg on the body wall opposite the point of penetration of the host. The egg is fastened to the wall and the young larva receives nourishment through its embryonic membrane which swells. The larva remains within the membrane until the caterpillar pupates. Shortly thereafter, the mandibulate-caudate primary larva moults and the second-instar larva breaks through the membranous sac and transforms into a hymenopteriform larva. Pupation occurs within the host pupa.

Several families of Chalcidoidea include species that are larval-pupal parasites. In the Chalcididae, *Brachymeria compsilurae* (Cwfd.) and *B. fonscolombei* (Dufour) oviposit in dipterous maggots and emerge from the puparia. The former is hyperparasitic on lepidopterous caterpillars parasitized by tachinids (Dowden 1935), and the latter attacks blowfly larvae (Parker 1923; Roberts 1933). Both chalcidids are solitary and have caudate primary larvae. The larval-pupal habit is represented in the Eulophidae by *Pleurotropis amyntas* Walk. which attacks *Phytomyza* (Cameron 1939). *Tetrastichus*, an extremely diverse genus, has some species such as *T. giffardianus* Silv. that oviposit in nearly mature fruit fly maggots and emerge from the puparia (Pemberton and Willard 1918). *T. giffardianus* is gregarious. A few Pteromalidae, such as *Stenomalus micans* Ol. which parasitizes *Chlorops*, kill the maggots as they are pupating (Kearns 1931). The mature larvae of *Stenomalus* possess unique conspicuous spines on their heads (Short 1952). Eurytomids normally are ectoparasites but some species of *Eurytoma* are larval-pupal endoparasites in gall-making tephritids.

The cynipoid family Figitidae and the subfamily Eucoilinae include larval-pupal parasites and here again they are parasitic on Diptera. The figitid *Hexacola* sp. showed no interest in eggs or puparia of *Drosophila* in the laboratory but Simmonds (1952) believes that it oviposits in the larval stage, since the typical eucoiliform larva was found in *Oscinella* larvae. After maggot pupation, the parasite larva grows quickly and pupates in the fly puparium. The intermediate stage is not polypodeiform in *Hexacola*, but rather indistinctly segmented, and of caudate form with a pair of short, ventral, thoracic processes. The mature larva is hymenopteriform.

Larval-pupal parasitism by proctotrupoids is apparently rare and this host relationship does not appear in the Diptera.

Further references to parasites whose development is completed in host pupa follow:

Hymenoptera—Braconidae (Biliotti and Delanoue 1959; Cameron 1941; Busse 1953; and van den Bosch and Haramoto 1951). Cynipoidea (Huzimatsu 1940; and Jenni 1951).

DEVELOPMENT COMPLETED IN HOMOPTEROUS NYMPHS OR ADULTS. Some of the most important natural enemies used in applied biological control are parasites of Homoptera. Entomophagus species attacking aphids, scale insects, and mealybugs have received much attention by biological control workers throughout the world. The scale insects, with their sessile habits and often homodynamic generations, seem to be ideal targets for applied biological control. (See discussion in chapter 24.)

Only a few of the numerous studied species of parasites that attack homopterous pests can be mentioned here. Parasites of aphids occur in the chalcidoid family Aphelinidae and the braconid subfamily Aphidiinae. Parasites of soft scales, diaspine scales, and mealybugs mainly belong to the Encyrtidae and Aphelinidae. Other homopterous pests, such as psyllids and aleyrodids, also are parasitized by species of encyrtids and aphelinids.

Some key references (since Clausen 1940a) to biological characteristics of immature endoparasites according to host groups follow:

Aphids

Aphelinidae—*Aphelinus* (Evenhuis 1958; and Schlinger and Hall 1959). Braconidae: Aphidiinae—*Praon* (Beirne 1942a; Sekhar 1957; and Schlinger and Hall 1960); *Aphidius* (Hafez 1961; and Vevai 1942); *Trioxys* (Beirne 1942b; and Schlinger and Hall 1961).

Mealybugs

Encyrtidae—*Acerophagus* (Maple 1947); *Anagyrus* (Maple 1947; and Moursi 1948a); *Leptomastidea* (Maple 1947); *Leptomastix* (Lloyd 1958; Moursi 1948b; and Zinna 1959).

Soft scales

Encyrtidae—*Encyrtus* (Compere 1940; and Maple 1947); *Metaphycus* (Alam 1957; and Clausen 1956a); *Anagyrus* (Riherd 1950); *Euaphycus* (Alam 1959). Aphelinidae—*Coccophagus* (Flanders, Bartlett, and Fisher 1961; and Zinna 1961).

Diaspine scales

Encyrtidae—*Comperiella* (Flanders 1944a).   Aphelinidae—*Aspidiotiphagus* (Benassy 1958a); *Prospaltella* (Benassy 1958a, b).

Psyllids

Encyrtidae—*Prionomitus* and *Psyllaephagus* (Jensen 1957).

Aleurodids

Aphelinidae—*Prospaltella* (Novoa-Zanartu 1956); *Encarsia* and *Euderomphale* (Bagley 1953).

Eggs of the endoparasitic species are generally placed in the host body cavity, but a few encyrtids place their eggs in certain organs. If the eggs have a stalk bearing an aeroscopic plate (encyrtiform egg), the species involved is an encyrtid. There are other encyrtids having stalked eggs in which the stalks do not project through the derm of the host. The primary larvae of many parasites of homopterous species are hymenopteriform or caudate and apneustic. Those of some Encyrtidae which are metapneustic are associated with the encyrtiform eggs. Usually the parasite pupates within the host and mummifies the host skin. The adult parasites usually emerge by cutting a circular hole in the skin of the host. Gregarious development is common.

DEPOSITED IN HOST PUPA. Several superfamilies of Hymenoptera have representative species that oviposit in pupae and complete their development in this host stage. There are also apparently some Diptera that only attack pupae.

It is interesting that there are no known pupal parasites in the Braconidae. However, certain groups of the Ichneumonidae are well known as pupal parasites. They are among the commonest ichneumonids and belong to the tribe Ephialtini (in the sense of Townes and Townes 1960).

The host range of individual species of the Ephialtini is usually very wide. A single species may attack exposed or semi-exposed pupae of various species of Lepidoptera (Townes 1958). As a result, there may be great intraspecific size differences in the parasitic individuals because of the different sizes of host attacked. Normally the parasites from smaller host pupae tend towards a higher male sex ratio. Oviposition occurs in prepupae and pupae and larval development is solitary. The parasite overwinters within the host pupa. The Ephialtini includes *Itoplectis*, *Ephialtes*, and *Coccygomimus*. Various authors consider species in the latter two genera as belonging to the genus *Pimpla*.

The adults of the Ephialtini have stout ovipositors whose apices are hooked in some species (*Apechthis*). Cole (1959) interprets the hooked tip as an adaptation facilitating the insertion of the ovipositor between overlapping sclerites of the host. Tests involving species with straight ovipositors showed that the hardened pupae could not be penetrated when the ovipositor was directed at right angles to the host body surface. Hardness and smoothness of the cuticle, as well as movement, were found to be important defences of naked pupae of butterflies against parasite attack. Some newly formed pupae of Lepidoptera exposed to various ichneumonids were vulnerable to attack for a few hours, but not after becoming hardened (Cole 1959).

The oxypygous females of Ichneumoninae are rather specific to certain lepidopterous groups (Heinrich 1960) as was previously discussed in the section on larval-pupal parasites.

The primary larvae of the pupal ichneumonids parasitic in pupae are mandibulate and noncaudate. This is interesting because the caudate type is by far the commonest form of the endoparasitic larva of the family.

There are few chalcidoids which are endoparasitic in insect pupae though species from several families exhibit this habit. In these species the primary larvae are hymenopteriform and usually apneustic but in *Brachymeria femorata* Panz. the spiracles are open in the primary larva (Kamal 1938). The chalcidids seem to be solitary but the common pteromalid *Pteromalus puparum* L. is gregarious. Included in the Torymidae which are normally ectoparasitic on concealed hosts are some species which are pupal parasites. The Eulophidae that are pupal parasites occur in genera which are diverse in their habits.

Even though cynipoids may emerge from puparia they oviposit in the larval stages of the hosts. There seem to be no species in this super-family which are strictly pupal parasites. However, in the Proctotrupoidea the Diapriidae are all pupal parasites. The solitary species have mandibulate primary larvae with bilobed caudal processes.

In the Diptera some Phoridae are pupal parasites. Diptera that emerge from coccinellid pupae are probably phorids. *Megaselia fasciata* is a gregarious internal parasite of coccinellid pupae in Europe (Lichtenstein 1920; Menozzi 1927). The Coccenellid *Aphidecta* which feeds on aphids that infest conifers suffers attack from the gregarious pupal parasite *Phalacrotophora berolinensis* (Colyer 1952; Delucchi 1953; Wylie 1958*b*). However, these authors found that the eggs are actually deposited externally beneath the pupal wing pads and the larvae on hatching penetrate the host.

Further references to parasitic Hymenoptera which oviposit in host pupae and emerge from host pupae follow:

Ichneumonidae (Aubert 1959; Gerig 1960; Silvestri 1941*a*; Townes and Townes 1960; and Wishart 1948). Chalcididae (Arthur 1958). Eulophidae (Juillet 1959). Diapriidae (Simmonds 1952; and Wright, Geering, and Ashby 1947).

DEPOSITED IN HOST ADULT. Although the braconids are not represented among the pupal parasites, one subfamily, Euphorinae, includes many parasites that attack adult insects, mainly species of Coleoptera and Hemiptera. The genera *Perilitus* and *Microctonus* contain well-known parasites of adult insects. Occasionally, *Perilitus coccinellae* oviposits in pupae of coccinellids and emerges from the adults.

The biology of *Perilitus coccinellae*, a common parasite of adults of many coccinellid species, has been treated by several authors (Ogloblin 1913, 1924; Balduf 1926a). *P. rutilus* (Nees) which parasitizes *Sitona* weevils has a biology similar to that of *P. coccinellae*. *Microtonus vittatae*, a parasite of chrysomelid adults, also has a biology that does not differ essentially from *P. coccinellae* (O. J. Smith 1952). The adult *Microctonus* is attracted to the moving beetle and inserts its ovipositor through the soft membranes near the anal opening. The internal stalked egg swells enormously, increasing to over 1,000 times the size of the ovarian egg. During eclosion the surrounding chorion and embryonic membrane (trophamnion) is ruptured, the cells from the embryonic membrane are freed into the body cavity and then they begin to grow proportionately with the parasite larval growth. These 'trophamnion' cells are apparently consumed by the larva. The adult female beetle host does not die as an immediate result of larval feeding but does become reproductively sterile.

The primary larva is mandibulate and caudate with only one individual per host completing its development. The mature hymenopteriform larva breaks through the dorsum of the host's abdomen and spins a cocoon beneath the beetle. The moribund beetle seemingly has an affinity for perching on the cocoon.

Other genera of Euphorinae that parasitize adult insects are *Aridelus* and *Euphorus* which parasitize Hemiptera. *Meteorus* and *Euphoriella* are exceptions to the usual euphorine habit of parasitizing adults, for the former is mainly endoparasitic in lepidopterous larvae and the latter has been reared from a psocid (Muesebeck 1956).

Species of Neoneurinae, another braconid subfamily, oviposit into ant adults. The Blacinae includes a few parasites that attack adult insects such as *Syrrhizus* in chrysomelids (Muesebeck, Krombein, and Townes 1951) and *Centistes scymni* Ferr. in coccinellids. Delucchi (1954) observed *Centistes* attacking adults of *Pullus impexes* (Muls.). It inserted its stalked egg laterally through the pleura into the abdomen. The larval parasite's presence inhibits ovarian development. The mature larva leaves the beetle and spins a cocoon.

The Ichneumonidae, Chalcidoidea, Proctotrupoidea, and Cynipoidea apparently do not contain species which attack adult holometabolous insects.

There are species in several families of Diptera, however, that parasitize adults. The diverse Phoridae are at times pests since they will commonly attack adult bees in the vicinity of apiaries. The female of *Melaloncha ronnai* Borgm. oviposits in the abdomen of a bee and the larva finally destroys muscles in the thorax and pupates in the host (Ronna 1936, 1937). Several genera of phorids include species that attack adult ants. Species of Conopidae attack adults of larger aculeata such as *Vespa*. de Meijere (1904, 1912) observed oviposition in flight. The parasite larva is endoparasitic, normally solitary, and usually pupates in the host remains. The

Pyrgotidae are interesting flies that attack scarab adults through the dorsum of the abdomen while the beetle is flying. *Adapsilia flaviseta* Ald. is a solitary endoparasite of *Popillia* (Clausen, Jaynes, and Gardner 1933).

Specialized structures have evolved in the Tachinidae which are employed during oviposition or larviposition into adult hosts. The hosts are mainly species of Coleoptera. *Chaetophleps setosa* Coq. larviposits into an *Acalymma* adult while the beetle is in flight attacking it dorsally on the abdomen. The first-instar larva moves about for a time in the body cavity, then attaches itself to the host integument where a respiratory funnel is formed. The third instar abandons the beetle remains and pupates in the soil (Bussart 1937).

Oviposition Site Correlated with the Sex of the Egg

In certain sections of this chapter, especially the one pertaining to larval dimorphism, there has been repeated reference to the unusual phenomenon in certain species of the Aphelinidae of the obligatory development of the male as a hyperparasite. This habit has been studied most in the genera *Coccophagus* and *Physcus*. Diverse illustration of the male developing as a hyperparasite in species of *Aneristus*, *Casca*, *Coccophagoides*, *Coccophagus*, *Encarsia*, *Euxanthellus*, *Physcus*, and *Prospaltella* has been summarized by Flanders (1959*b*, p. 127). Subsequent studies which extend such information are those of Flanders, Bartlett, and Fisher (1961) on *Coccophagus basalis* Comp., of Fisher (1961) on *Physcus* sp. (since described as *Physcus debachi* Comp. and Ann.), and of Zinna (1961) on *Coccophagus bivittatus* Comp.

In this group of aphelinids according to Flanders (1959*b*) ovipositional behaviour, i.e. the ovipositional sites chosen, is determined by whether or not the female is mated. If unmated, the egg to be laid is always haploid (male producing) and a particular kind of host or site is chosen. However, it appears that following mating the female usually prefers to lay female-producing eggs and since such eggs develop on or in a different kind of host or in a different place on the host, mating is considered to change the ovipositional behaviour of the female. On occasion mated females may lay either haploid or diploid (female-producing) eggs during a single oviposition. In this event, however, due to differences in environmental requirements of male and female larvae, apparently only the latter complete their development.

The following outline gives a single example for each category of ovipositional behaviour as influenced by the mated status of the female:

Ovipositional Behaviour Unchanged by Mating

Males and females normally primary parasites

Male-producing eggs deposited ectoparasitically; female-producing eggs deposited endoparasitically. Males develop ectoparasitically; females develop endoparasitically (*Coccophagus ochraceus* How.).

Males hyperparasites; females primary parasites

Male- and female-producing eggs deposited endoparasitically in a healthy coccid host. Male-producing eggs not deposited directly on or in the primary parasite (*Coccophagus basalis*).

Ovipositional Behaviour Changed by Mating

Males and females normally primary parasites

Male-producing eggs deposited endoparasitically in lepidopterous eggs; female-producing eggs deposited endoparasitically in homopterous hosts (*Encarsia* spp.).

Males hyperparasites; females primary parasites

Only parasitized hosts selected for deposition of male-producing eggs which are deposited directly on or in the primary parasite; female-producing eggs deposited endoparasitically and females develop endoparasitically; male-producing eggs deposited ectoparasitically on an immature primary endoparasite (*Physcus debachi*).

Male-producing eggs deposited endoparasitically and within an immature primary endoparasite (*Coccophagus scutellaris* (Dalm.)).

Marked sexual dimorphism is apparent in the first-larval instar and it clearly reflects morphological adaptation to the different media in which the respective sexes develop in that the male larvae possess spiracles and the female larvae do not have spiracles. Female aphelinids of the genera named above always develop as endoparasites but the males develop either as primary or secondary endo- or ectoparasites depending on the species. Additional discussion of the hyperparasitic male habit will be found in chapters 6, 10, and 11.

CHAPTER 8

Systematics in Relation to Biological Control

EVERT I. SCHLINGER AND RICHARD L. DOUTT

INTRODUCTION

WITHOUT SOME SYSTEM of classification, scientific knowledge of organisms would be in a chaotic state. Therefore, it has been essential in all fields of biology to develop a science of classification termed 'taxonomy' or 'systematics.' Two things are essential to a classification of organisms: (1) a sound and logical basis for establishing and ranking taxonomic units, and (2) a system of nomenclature by which these units can be appropriately designated. The Linnaean system of binomial nomenclature has world-wide acceptance and species of organisms have conventionally been distinguished on the basis of morphological differences. However, as the general biological knowledge has become more sophisticated there has developed the modern science of biosystematics which denotes the study of living functions in relation to classification of organisms.

Classical taxonomy is usually considered an empirical science which simply involves naming and describing species and arranging taxonomic categories. The new systematics as brought out by Huxley (1940) and many subsequent authors such as Mayr (1942), Mayr, Linsley, and Usinger (1953), and Ross (1954) involves much more than naming and describing species. In the modern approach to taxonomy there are included, whenever possible, data from such fields of study as ecology, cytology, chorology (biogeography), biometry, selection theory and evolution, genetics, palaeontology, development physiology, anatomy, climatology, geology, and geography, as well as data on morphology. The trend and basis of systematic investigations, together with the philosophy of its foundations, have been so thoroughly discussed in informative articles by Gahan (1923), Ferris (1928, 1942), Brues (1929), Silvestri (1929), Horn (1929a, 1929b), Simpson (1945), Gilmour (1940), Myers (1952), Blackwelder and Boyden (1952), Thompson (1952), Mayr, Linsley, and Usinger (1953), E. Ross (1954), Schenk and McMasters (1956), Michener (1957), and H. Ross (1958a) that no further treatment is necessary here.

Systematics is without question the most important fundament to biological control. It is the key to all fields of research related to any biological control problem and when properly undertaken can supply such basic information as

247

where to undertake projects of foreign exploration, what host specificities are involved, what major biological and ecological references are available for life history and mass-production studies, and to what extent biological races, subspecies, sibling species, and strains are involved with any 'species.' Gahan (1923) summarized this view on a larger scale when he said, '. . . without the fundamental work of the taxonomist the great mine of entomological literature would not exist, and the accumulation of knowledge would be largely limited to what one could personally observe and remember.'

It has often been stated that it is the principles and methods and not so much the direct findings of systematics that need to be taught and appreciated. By way of pointing out the importance of biosystematic studies to the field of biological control and of introducing the subject matter contained in this chapter, we quote the following statement from the preface of *Methods and Principles of Systematic Zoology* by Mayr, Linsley, and Usinger (1953): 'An understanding of taxonomic theory and practice is essential not only to the beginning and the practising taxonomist but to all those who draw upon the results of his studies. This is true to a greater or lesser extent for all biological sciences, but in particular for such fields as ecology, population genetics, comparative morphology, anthropology, comparative physiology, and applied biology. Sound taxonomy is a prerequisite to intelligent conclusions in all these fields.'

MATERIALS AND METHODS FOR BIOSYSTEMATIC STUDIES

Materials

COLLECTIONS. Indispensable to the systematist are adequate series of museum specimens of the group under study. Far too often the worker finds his problems insoluble because there is a shortage of specimens or the specimens are improperly preserved. Large series are necessary to determine the geographic range and sex ratios of the species and it is desirable that with the adult series there should be associated the immature stages, hosts, and bioecological data. Otherwise, few satisfactory conclusions can be drawn from the material at hand. The lack of adequate material often results in eventual publication of data under such headings as 'Species A,' 'Species Inquirenda,' or 'Species near *californicus*,' which result, in turn, invariably compounds the problems of future systematists working on the group. It is therefore the responsibility of the collector to gather and preserve as many specimens and as much bioecological data on the group throughout as wide a range as possible. It is the responsibility of the curatorial staff to label, mount, prepare, and preserve this material in such a manner that it will be available to other workers at a later date in a satisfactory condition and catalogued in such a way as to be easily referable.

PRESERVATION OF IMPORTED AND NEWLY RECOVERED SPECIMENTS. In the case of species sent from one country to another for biological control purposes, it is imperative that all the parent stock and as many as possible of the reared F_1 generation of the species be retained for the museum collection after oviposition is completed. It is further desirable to collect specimens from the new habitat after one or more generations have passed so that the systematist may be able to compare the 'new' population with the imported specimens and the 'old' or native population (if present) at a later date. Since in many instances a mass-production programme is undertaken for the newly introduced biological control agent, one or more samples of specimens taken from the colony being produced would be an additional asset. The systematist would then be able to compare the native population with the reared and introduced populations. The imported population may be somewhat different from either the native or the reared ones, and may offer the systematist data from which to form a better concept of the variation within the species as well as to furnish a more positive check on establishment, especially where similar species or subspecies were already established.

IMPORTANCE OF HOST DATA. The host of a parasite may have a marked influence on the morphological and physiological characteristics of its parasitic species. As a general rule, the larger hosts produce larger parasites and, therefore, a somewhat polyphagous parasite may have a different size range for each of its host species.

Not only may adult parasites vary in size as a result of the amount of food available to their immature stages but the host may influence the size and proportion of parts. For example, the length of wings, the number of macrotrichia on the wings, and the number of antennal bristles on males can often be correlated with the size of the individual. Also, the presence or absence of wings in the adult wasps can be determined by the condition of the host and it is not uncommon to find apterous or brachypterous male *Trichogramma* if they have developed in small or partially unsuitable hosts.

Therefore, it follows that the host is one of the important factors that must be considered and controlled in any critical, and especially any quantitative, study of insect parasites. Accounts of behaviour, data on rate of reproduction and longevity, measurements of length, even descriptions of structure—none of these has any absolute validity for the species, none can be considered biological constants of a parasite unless the host is known and recorded (Salt 1941). It goes without saying that it is virtually as important to identify the host correctly as it is the natural enemy.

SYSTEMATIST'S TOOLS. The systematist whose study of a group of insects involves essentially a morphological analysis does not require many tools beyond microscopes, reagents, and materials for making slide mounts, insect pins and boxes, labelling materials, and perhaps some simple dissecting equipment. Other more special types of systematic analyses require particular types of apparatus, and many of these are discussed by Oldroyd (1958) in his recent thorough treatment of *Collecting, Preserving and Studying Insects*. Ross (1953) has published an excellent, well-illustrated treatise on how to photograph insects and anyone interested in using the photographic medium for systematics is urged to consult this work. The recent work by White (1954) on animal cytology should be consulted by anyone whose systematic endeavours involve cytology and cytogenetics. Other recent works concerning tools and entomological techniques useful to the systematist are those of Oman and Cushman (1946), Peterson (1953), and Beirne (1955).

In regard to microscopes, it should be mentioned that the microscopic examination of insects is the most common and practical way to detect the morphological differences between species and for many years will remain the basis of all taxonomy. The use of a microscope is actually only an extension of the scientist's sense of sight and this is the most important taxonomic tool which he possesses. Even though the new systematics utilizes more than anatomical differences as a basis for species differentiation, some of these approaches, e.g., cytology, are nevertheless dependent on good microscopic equipment and techniques. It is unfortunately true that many, if not most, taxonomists are not well trained in microscopy. Furthermore, there is microscopic equipment on the market which can do much to extend the vision of taxonomic workers. Many cryptic characters become clear and evident by the use of such instruments as a phase microscope or an 'Ultrapak'. The authors, therefore, suggest that better microscopic techniques and the use of instruments that are now available are a part of the new systematics and open up entirely new vistas for the taxonomic worker who must still basically rely on the morphological examination of his material.

Often special equipment is required for collecting different kinds of insects. Some of this equipment, such as insect nets, Berlese funnels, beating sheets, and various kinds of light traps, are reviewed in the above-cited works and others are discussed in chapters 10 and 14 of this book. One device which is particularly useful in collecting an entire insect, mite, and spider fauna in field crops is a suction collecting machine recently described by Dietrick, Schlinger, and van den Bosch (1959) and Dietrick, Schlinger, and Garber (1960). A discussion of this subject can be found also in the various chapters of Mayr, Linsley, and Usinger (1953).

Working in conjunction with the reference collection of speciments and techniques employed to collect and study living and dead specimens is the systematist's all-important reference library. Indispensable for taxonomic references and abstracts are the *Zoological Record* (1864 to date), *Biological Abstracts* (1926 to date), and the *Review of Applied Entomology* (1913 to date). Prior to 1864, the *Catalogue of Scientific Papers* published by the Royal Society and covering the years 1800 to 1863 is an important reference. In 1942, R. C. Smith published his *Guide to the Literature in the Zoological Sciences* and it remains today an excellent starting point for any systematist. Certainly one of the more important recent journals that should be consulted for articles dealing with all phases of systematics is *Systematic Zoology* (1952 to date).

Methods

With the advent of the *New Systematics* (Huxley 1940) the old, narrow, morphological concept of taxonomy began to change. There were, however, some workers in the field (mostly biologists and bacteriologists) who previously had endeavoured to study taxonomic problems by other than morphological means. For example, Howard (1893) showed correlations of structure with host relations among some encyrtids; Cobb (1904) mentioned that the physiological requirements of parasitic worms would give valuable clues to the taxonomic relationships of the group; Brues (1908, 1921) attempted to correlate feeding habits of parasitic Hymonoptera with their taxonomic affinities; and Metcalf (1929) pointed out how a study of parasite–host relationships furthered the study of taxonomy, geographical distribution, and palaeogeography. As a rule, however, since the days of Linnaeus the insect taxonomist has been content to describe the differences between species only on a morphological basis. Taxonomic problems are now being studied and solved by a variety of different methods and, by joining these new methods with the morphological one, a new taxonomic product is appearing on the scene. A brief discussion of the various methods now used in systematics follows.

MORPHOLOGY AND ANATOMY. Since all articles concerning new species usually contain a morphological description of at least the type adult specimen, this method of distinguishing species is obviously of primary importance from the comparative standpoint. That species 'A' may differ from species 'B' due to an antenna with 13 segments vs. an antenna with 15 segments or a clypeus that is bidentate vs. a clypeus that is tridentate are common ways of separating species. Since the main studies concerning species identification have been morphological, a need was seen by taxonomists and others to define accurately the different structures of insects. In 1935, Snodgrass published his book on the *Principles of Insect Morphology* and to help clarify the many definitions used for entomological structures and functions Torre-Bueno (1937) published *A Glossary of Entomology* and Kenneth (1953) published *A Dictionary of Scientific Terms*. Due to a recent publication (Tuxen 1956) on insect genitalia, some degree of uniformity may now be found concerning the names and theories applied to these structures and Michener (1958) has discussed the great need for more conformity of morphological terminology, particularly in regard to homologous structures throughout all systematic groups. That immature stages of insects offer good morphological characteristics of taxonomic significance is shown by the excellent work of van Emden (1957).

Descriptions of species by external morphological means are now being complemented to a certain degree by anatomical or internal morphological studies. Two recent books by Snodgrass (1952, 1956) on arthropod and bee anatomy will be extremely useful to anyone studying organisms from an anatomical point of view. Although anatomy appears to offer as many important phylogenetic characteristics as does morphology, the taxonomist is often handicapped by not having live or properly preserved material available for his study. Persons working in biosystematics have this opportunity and should make complete use of it. Recently the senior author had occasion to study the female reproductive organs of representative species of most of the North American genera of the Aphidiinae (Braconidae). Not only were the structures different in shape, size, number, and in presence or absence, but the types of ovaries and ovarioles and degree of ovigenesis were found to be quite distinct between the different genera. Whether these features will later be found to be specific, superspecific, or generic, remains to be seen but the general phylogenetic significance of these structures was obvious and compared quite favourably with the external morphological characters of the group now in use to distinguish and relate the genera. Embryological features can also be of great help in taxonomic problems and de Beer (1940) has given an excellent summary of this subject. Even spermatozoa may be used as indicators of taxonomic differences according to Doutt (1952c). Other more common morphological and anatomical taxonomic characters that are used in present-day systematics are given by Mayr, Linsley, and Usinger (1953).

BIOLOGY, ECOLOGY, AND ETHOLOGY. There is increasing evidence that many so-called 'morphological species' are actually made up of several 'biological' or sibling species. Systematics studied by the biological method is, because of the very nature of the study, more time-consuming and difficult than is the morphological one but the results are nonetheless rewarding. It is really not practical to attempt separation of certain biological, ecological, and ethological traits in this discussion, although specialized studies have been made which have been categorized under one or the other of these subscience headings.

Many of the features used by taxonomists to elucidate sibling species are cited in subheading form in chapter 6. Those that seem to offer greater possibility in these methods of study are host–parasite relationships, mating habits, preoviposition period, adult and larval nutrition, behaviour in host selection, host suitability, and type of sex determination. An excellent summary of various bioecological examples of systematic studies was given by Thorpe (1940). Thorpe also gave detailed accounts of his work on 'biological races' in two earlier publications (1930a, 1931b). Other general reviews of this subject were given by Robson (1928), Mayr (1947, 1957c), and Cain (1953), and still other examples are cited by Clausen (1942), Flanders (1953b), and Sabrosky (1950, 1955), while Michener (1953b) gave an interesting account of how life-history studies can be used in systematics.

Within the last ten years or so, considerable work has been done on ethology or the behavioural characteristics of insects. Most of these studies were involved only with the aculeate Hymenoptera, primarily because of the high degree of behavioural development exhibited by this group of insects. Two important works (von Frisch 1950; Ribbands 1953) on the honey bee have now been completed and Evans (1953, 1957) has made important contributions on the comparative ethology of certain spider and digger wasps. The works of Adriaanse (1947) on *Ammophila* and Barber (1951) on *Photuris* led to complete separation of certain species on behaviour alone. Interesting and important reviews of ethology are found in the works of Tinbergen (1951), Roe and Simpson (1958), Mayr (1958), and Spieth (1958), and for a recent review of the entire field the work of Baerends (1959) should be consulted.

GENETICS, CYTOLOGY, SEROLOGY, AND PHYSIOLOGY. That systematic and evolutionary studies of *Drosophila* have been furthered rapidly by genetical studies is attested by the voluminous references to these flies (Patterson and Stone 1952). Some other groups are also receiving similar attention (White 1957). The main complication of working along these lines is that one must have living and cultured individuals available for study. If living cultures are available, crossing experiments can be undertaken that may result in important data to support or reject the separation of the two species in question. The recent works that should be consulted on genetic problems and methods of study in relation to systematics are those of Muller (1940), Darlington (1940), Hogben (1940), Timofeeff-Ressovsky (1940), Mayr (1948, 1954), and Patterson and Stone (1952).

Cytogenetics is now being intensively studied by a few workers and the recent work of S. G. Smith (1959) on the cytogenetics of *Chilocorus* species is an outstanding example of what can be accomplished. Smith concludes his work by stating '... the chromosomes thus provide us with an indelible picture of the sort that the theory of evolution envisages but which the taxonomist has been consistently unable to provide.' Similarly the work of White (1949) on Diptera has been most revealing. White's book on *Animal Cytology and Evolution* (1954) and his recent summary of the subject (1957) should certainly be referred to by the interested student.

Some species have been found to differ in their reactions to antigens or antibodies and serological investigations are now under way for several groups of arthropods. Boyden (1943) has summarized work in this field in an excellent manner. Other taxonomic studies along biochemical lines which have been shown to be quite useful are those of microbiological assay, microelectrophoresis, and paper chromatography. Paper chromatography has recently been shown by Ball and Clark (1953) to be an effective method of differentiating species of *Culex*, and Stephen (1958) has shown how hemolymph proteins might be used in taxonomic studies. Micks (1956) and Micks and Gibson (1957) have also done considerable work on distinguishing various insects and ticks by their free amino acid contents and the latter authors concluded, '... in most instances, different strains of the same species presented considerably different amino acid patterns.'

One study which has not been thoroughly investigated concerns the specificity problem in the symbiotic relationships of insects. Some evidence that certain species which are closely related have distinct symbionts present was noted by Richards and Brooks (1958) and this discovery, together with the background of Wallin's (1927) work on the general subject, might be extremely helpful to anyone interested in carrying out this type of investigation.

BIOGEOGRAPHY, PALAEONTOLOGY, CLIMATOLOGY, GEOLOGY, AND PHYLOGENY. All of these sciences offer good aids for determining taxonomic affinities. The science of the distribution of animals (zoogeography or chorology) has finally begun to take its significant place in systematics. Two books on zoogeography, one by Darlington (1957) and the other by Lindroth (1957), are the first really important large works of this kind dealing with insects since the famous works of Wallace (1876, 1880). For specific reviews, ideas, and patterns of insect distribution and methods of study, the reader should consult Hubbs (1958), Ross (1958*b*), Rehn (1958), Linsley (1958), and Hovanitz (1958), and the recent general review on the zoogeography of insects by Gressitt (1958*a*). Other articles, such as those by Simpson (1953), Schmidt (1954), and the revised edition of *Ecological Animal Geography* by Allee and Schmidt (1951) are equally important. Certainly, palaeontological evidence is most helpful to any systematic study and Arkell and Moy-Thomas (1940) have given a summary of this in their article, *Paleontology and the Taxonomic Problem*. The effect of climate and weather on insects is likewise an important study which may throw considerable light on a particular systematic investigation. Uvarov's work on *Insects and Climate* (1931) is outstanding and should be thoroughly digested by any student of this science. Recently DeBach (1958*b*) discussed the role of weather and entomophagous insects in the natural control of insect populations. Certainly the limits of a species' distribution and its effectiveness in nature become a part of its complete systematic description and placement.

A knowledge of insect migration (Williams 1958) which involves zoogeography and climate may also be quite useful to the taxonomist, since often the different 'phases' of a migratory species are morphologically distinct. This has frequently led to many problems in the naming of migrant species. An understanding of the ecology, geology, and climate of the past, such as that reviewed recently for western North America by Martin (1958), P. King (1958), and MacGinitie (1958), might prove extremely useful to a taxonomist who is confronted with problems of present-day geographic isolation, discontinuous distributions, or geographic races. Of course, phylogenetic studies, if analysed properly and thoroughly, can be quite useful to everyone concerned with a given group of insects. If proper phylogenies were complete for different groups of insects, the job of a biological control entomologist who is looking for a particular type of beneficial insect to introduce from a foreign country would be made much easier. He would be able to realize the pertinent facts on relationship, distribution, extent of host–parasite specificity, and degree of commonness merely by examining an adequately prepared article treating the phylogenetic analysis of the group.

BIOMETRY. Quantification of systematic investigations has become more popular in recent years and this method of study and evaluation should now be applied whenever possible. Often, simple statistics (such as the use of the mean, standard deviation of the mean, range and type of distribution) are helpful in determining taxonomic affinities and degree of speciation. Wright (1940) gave an excellent discussion on 'the statistical consequences of Mendelian heredity in relation to speciation,' and Cazier and Bacon (1949) published a good article on how to apply quantification to systematics. This subject is also nicely reviewed by Mayr, Linsley, and Usinger (1953) and several recent articles by Dice (1952), Sokal (1958), Coppel and Leius (1958), and McGuire and Wirth (1958) show how these methods may be applied to systematic investigations.

CONCLUSIONS. The authors do not mean to imply that each systematist studying each group of insects needs to apply all of the above methods to his investigations even though this might give the ideal result. In certain cases, one method or another will be found to suffice for any particular group; however, all methods should be considered and perhaps many should be tested to determine which one(s) applies best to the situation. In any case, no matter what alternative methods are used, a description should always be given based on morphological features in order that comparisons with previously described species may be facilitated.

SYSTEMATIC UNITS IN BIOLOGICAL CONTROL

As with any systematic study, an understanding of the concepts and definitions of the terms 'genus,' 'species,' and 'subspecies' are all-important to the biological control worker. Equally important is a knowledge of the terms 'sibling species,' 'strains,' 'races,' and 'forms.' Work in biological control often progresses at a greater speed than does the systematics of the populations being dealt with. Hence, it is not uncommon to find in the literature species being referred to as '*Aphytis A*,' '*Coccophagus* sp. ?,' '*Aphytis maculicornis* (Masi)—the Persian race,' or at times such unnameable entities as 'Ichneumonid A' when even the correct generic assignment is in doubt. Often, the problem lies not only with the systematist being unable to name correctly the desired population but also with the fact that systematic studies in many parasitic groups have not been fully supported (financially and academically) and are, therefore, not available. The following discussion was prepared to show how and, in many cases, why the various systematic units have been and should be applied in biological control work. To aid the reader in characterizing particular systematic units, the taxonomic discrimination grid of Mayr, Linsley, and Usinger (1953) is given in table 2.

TABLE 2

Taxonomic discrimination grid (Mayr, Linsley and Usinger 1953)

Item	Not reproductively isolated	Reproductively isolated
Morphologically identical:		
Sympatric	(1) Same population	(5) Sibling species
Allopatric	(2) Same subspecies	(6) Sibling species
Morphologically different:		
Sympatric	(3) Individual variants of the same population	(7) Different species
Allopatric	(4) Different subspecies	(8) Different species

The Species

The question 'What is a species?' cannot be analysed here but we believe certain important references should be given in order that the student may better acquaint himself with the various concepts involved. Most of the works referred to have, in turn, cited many references so that altogether a rather complete picture of the species problem can be acquired through these sources. Specific references include those of Robson (1928), Diver (1940), Simpson (1943, 1951), Dobzhansky (1951), Mayr (1942, 1957*b*), Mayr, Linsley, and Usinger (1953), and Brown (1959), while more general discussions on the species and evolutionary thought are given by Huxley (1940, 1943), Jepson, Mayr, and Simpson (1949), Huxley, Hardy, and Ford (1954), Dobzhansky (1955), Bates and Humphrey (1956), and Mayr (1957*a*).

The definition of a species as given in Mayr, Linsley, and Usinger (1953) seems to the authors to be quite acceptable, i.e., species are '. . . groups of actually (or potentially) interbreeding natural populations which are reproductively isolated from other such groups.' The morphological concept of a species is well understood and need not be elaborated here in any detail but the biological concept is of such great importance to the biological control worker, as well as to the general systematist, that it will be covered here in some detail.

Before discussing this subject, it appears as though a distinction should be made between a 'biological race' and a 'biological species.' In many cases, the 'biological species' is a true, though often cryptic, entity called a 'sibling species.' Mayr, Linsley, and Usinger (1953) define sibling species as '. . . pairs or groups of closely related species which are reproductively isolated but morphologically identical or nearly so . . .' and further state that '. . . sibling species are not a different type of species; they are merely those species that are near the invisible end of the spectrum of morphological species differences. They grade imperceptibly into species that are morphologically more and more distinct from one another. Morphological differences are often eventually found after a particularly painstaking scouting of previously unstudied structures.' These authors further note that sibling species are often quite inconvenient to the museum taxonomist. Nevertheless, they do exist and it is the belief of the authors that species which can be separated on ecological or behavioural features need to be studied and described just as much as do species which differ morphologically. This is particularly true in biological control work. Too often the biosystematist has been content to note the biological features which separate two or more sibling species without formally describing them as discrete entities. This results in calling these undescribed entities strains or races, which, in fact, they are not; for a strain, race, variety, variation or form should be considered simply as a population or part of a population of a subspecies or species. Terms of this nature do not imply reproductive isolation.

Soon after Darwin published his *Origin of Species*, Walsh (1864, 1865) published accounts of races of some phytophagous insects in the United States. These important works, for the most part, have been overlooked. One of the more important findings by Walsh was the fact that presumably individuals of populations of the same species (biological races?) had different colour patterns when reared on different plant species. Thorpe's works (1929, 1930a, 1931b, and 1940) on biological races brought to light many new findings and methods of research on races of insects and he summarized the work in his 1931 paper. Thompson and Parker (1927) were among the first to recognize distinct races in entomophagous species (tachinids). For an excellent review of racial segregation in insect populations consult the work published by H. S. Smith (1941).

In recent years workers in biological control have uncovered many interesting cases of sibling species in insects and no doubt as time goes on much work along this line will be carried out. In 1954, Hafez and Doutt published an article on the biological evidence of sibling species in *Aphytis maculicornis* (Masi), a parasite of the olive scale, *Parlatoria oleae* (Colv.). Detailed studies on sex ratios, developmental periods, emergence patterns, and number of progeny per female disclosed that at least three distinct sibling species were involved. The three species were inseparable morphologically and were designated the Persian-Indian, the Spanish, and the Californian forms. They noted that it seemed impractical at that time to assign names to these biological entities and such may have been the case; however, the quantitative data expressed in their report were highly significant, much more so than is often the case of the qualitative date given for descriptions of morphological species.

DeBach (1959), working with morphologically similar species of *Aphytis* attacking the California red scale, *Aonidiella aurantii* (Mask.), found two new species of *Aphytis* principally based on biological data. Although adult differences between the new species, *A. fisheri* DeB. and *A. melinus* DeB., were very slight, distinct pupal differences were found and crossing did not occur. He also observed evidence of biological forms (sibling species) in *A. lingnanensis* Comp. and noted the reproductive isolation of some of these forms.

Hall, Schlinger, and van den Bosch (1962) using differences in host specificity, cross mating, and progeny production between a walnut aphid parasite *Trioxys pallidus* Hal. and a spotted alfalfa aphid parasite *T. utilis* Mues. demonstrated that both of the morphologically similar and recently synonymized species are distinct sibling species.

It is of interest to note that investigations of various parasites carried on by biological control workers have turned up evidence for sibling species in some of the host species such as oleander scale, *Aspidiotus hederae* (Vall.) (DeBach and Fisher 1956), and Baker's mealybug, *Pseudococcus maritimus* (Ehrh.), according to unpublished data of A. J. Basinger, and Flanders (1944*b*).

A somewhat different study was undertaken by Emerson (1935) when he found two 'physiologically distinctive' forms of the termite *Nasutitermes quayanae* (Holm.) in British Guiana. These forms were morphologically similar and ecologically equivalent but the termitophilous Staphylinidae occupying the nests of these forms were composed of distinctly different species. He found four genera and four species in the nests of *N. quayanae* and two other species of two of the same genera in the nests of his new species *N. similis* Emer. He applied quantification features to separate his termite species after noticing that the termitophilous species were different for each species of termite involved.

Van den Bosch and Dietrick (1959) published a very interesting account of the relationships of the Egyptian alfalfa weevil, *Hypera brunneipennis* (Boh.), and the ichneumonid parasite *Bathyplectes curculionis* (Thom.). This parasite was originally imported from Europe to attempt biological control of the alfalfa weevil *Hypera postica* (Gyll.). The two species of weevils are almost identical morphologically (almost sibling species), and each occupies distinct geographical areas in California and, hence, they are allopatric. The parasite occurs within the range of both species of weevils but the parasite's eggs in *H. brunneipennis* undergo phagocytosis while *H. postica* '... has essentially no humoral defense mechanism to resist attack by *Bathyplectes curculionis*' (van den Bosch and Dietrick 1959).

9—I.P.W.

Superparasitism is essential to a maximum attack by this parasite on *H. brunnei-pennis*; thus, by biological features reacting on the parasite one is able to distinguish between its host species. The discussion which occurs in an article by Puttler and van den Bosch (1959) gives evidence how phagocytosis might be utilized by the systematist as a criterion for sibling species.

Another example of 'sibling species' involves the case of *Prospaltella perniciosi* (Tow.), a parasite of several diaspine scales as noted by Flanders (1950*b*, 1953*b*). He stated (1953) that there are three 'geographical species' of this parasite. These are '. . . a biparental species in the North Atlantic states and a uniparental species in the South Atlantic states, both of which are parasites of San Jose scale, and a uniparental species in East Asia, which is a parasite of the California red scale.' He further stated that '. . . the red scale-feeding species does not attack the San Jose scale, nor does the San Jose scale-feeding species attack the California red scale. Both uniparental species are now established in California and are perfectly isolated although morphologically alike. When the biparental and uniparental Atlantic states species are cultured together in the laboratory the uniparental species becomes dominant and eliminates the biparental species, in spite of the fact that the males of this latter species are hyperparasitic.' Thus, here we are involved not simply with forms which are morphologically alike but forms that differ in their sex regulation mechanisms. Also, one might ask, are uniparentalism and biparentalism good specific criteria or can one form change back and forth under different environmental conditions? Also, in the case of *P. perniciosi* we find the biologist discussing the different forms as species without names since the taxonomists have been unable to find distinct morphological characters to differentiate them. This appears to be another case of sibling species.

Concerning use of the features of uniparental and biparental reproduction as specific criteria (which no doubt is the case in some species), mention can be made concerning the Israel form of *Aphelinus semiflavus* How., a parasite of the spotted alfalfa aphid *Therioaphis maculata* (Buck.). Schlinger and Hall (1959) found that the sex ratio of the supposed uniparental strain was apparently determined by environmental conditions. In another experiment (unpublished data) several females were selected from a uniparental stock of the parasite which were being reared at 70° F and 50 per cent R.H. and placed with aphid hosts in 85° F and 30 per cent R.H. The next generation consisted of nearly 90 per cent males and thus a biparental stock was obtained simply by altering the temperature and humidity.

Behavioural characteristics of insects have recently been studied by several persons and an authoritative summary of behaviour and systematics is given by Mayr (1958). Adriaanse (1947) found that nest construction, host specificity, sequence of egg laying and provisioning, and breeding season were different in certain populations of the digger wasp *Ammophila campestris* Adria. This study revealed that two sibling species were involved and the new sibling species *A. adriaansei* Wil. was described primarily on the basis of behavioural features. Barber (1951), working with fireflies of the genus *Photuris*, found that several sibling species were involved in the genus. These sibling species were separated from one another mainly on the basis of frequency and colouration of the fireflies' lighting signals. Evans (1953) also found sibling species in his study on the comparative ethology of the spider wasps.

There are many more references to sibling species in the literature but those cited above show some types of physiological, ecological, and ethological differences that might be expected and looked for by future systematists working with 'similar' species which are often called races, strains, or forms. That the discovery of sibling species in biological control work should be carefully investigated and terminated with a full, formal description of the species seems both practical and desirable to the authors. In this way only the confusion of 'similar' species will be made clear at least to those people involved with the problem of making determinations and evaluations of sibling species in the future.

The Subspecies and Other Infraspecific Categories

Many definitions of subspecies have been formulated by enthusiastic systematists. Mayr, Linsley, and Usinger (1953) have given the following simple, useful subspecies definition: 'A geographically defined aggregate of local populations which differs taxonomically from other such subdivisions of the species.' Since 1940 there has been considerable discussion on the subspecies concept and selected important references on this subject which should be consulted by the student are those of Mayr (1942), Mayr, Linsley, and Usinger (1953), Wilson and Brown (1953), J. Edwards (1954), Hubbell (1954), Pimentel (1958), and Starrett (1958).

Actually, very few species utilized in biological control work have had subspecies assigned to them. Clausen (1956a) lists 95 species of satisfactorily established entomophagous species in the United States, only one of which (*Leis dimidiata* 15-*spilota* (Hope)) is given subspecific rank. This is highly significant since many of the 95 species are known to consist of one or more 'races,' yet past taxonomic investigations have failed to reveal these 'races' as subspecies. The terms 'race,' 'strain,' and 'form,' in the authors' opinion, are poor catch-all terms, and it is believed that further research will show that many species containing so-called races, forms, and strains will actually consist of sibling species or subspecies. We consider the terms 'race,' 'strain,' and 'form' to be virtually synonymous in that all apply to genetic variant portions of a population below the subspecific category. We, therefore, propose that the term 'biological race' be reserved and used for the ecological or geographical population which is not deemed to constitute a subspecies.

The subspecies is the lowest taxonomically nameable entity. Recently Wilson and Brown (1953) have proposed the abolition of trinomials but we believe, with Borgmeier (1957) and others, that there is a definite place for the taxon subspecies if properly diagnosed and studied. It is well known by anyone who has attempted studies of species with variant populations (possibly subspecies) that the work involved in delimiting these populations is much more difficult than simply including the variants in with the discussion of the species. Hence, one arrives at the feeling that the term 'subspecies' is not more in vogue because of: (1) a lack of adequate specimens which are representative of the entire range of species; (2) an absence of bioecological data; and (3) the extra amount of work involved in arriving at what constitutes the subspecific population(s).

Although such infraspecific terms as 'subspecies,' 'microsubspecies,' 'races' (ecological, physiological, geographical, biological, etc.), 'forms,' 'strains,' 'variations,' etc., have been utilized in systematics, only the subspecies should receive a latinized scientific name. Such terms as 'physiological' and 'host races,' 'forms,' and 'variations,' have been considered as including important infra-subspecific categories, but populations having these features should not be formally named. Much controversy over the terminology and separation of the terms 'geographical,' 'biological,' and 'ecological' races has been summed up by Mayr, Linsley, and Usinger (1953), who state, 'It must be emphasized that there is no geographical race that is not also an ecological race, nor an ecological race that is not also a geographical, or at least a microgeographical race. The geographical and the ecological aspects are two facets of the same phenomenon, the subspecies.' The works of Thorpe (1940), Hubell (1954, 1956), Ford (1954), and Mayr (1954) on geographic races all give important summaries of this subject and should be consulted for further reading. Before leaving this point, it seems proper to discuss the use of the 'cline' concept in taxonomy. Huxley (1939) coined the term 'cline' to apply to a series of adjacent populations in which the gradual and nearly continuous change of a character occurs. Differences in adjacent populations in clines may be ecological, morphological, physiological, etc., and they may be smooth or quite stepped. Although clines do not receive scientific names, often the populations which terminate one or both ends of a cline may be specific or subspecific and thus nameable. Recognition and analysis of clines by the systematist may be very useful in biological control but to our knowledge they have not yet been applied.

For more information on infraspecific categories and a method of treating different types of variations the reader is urged to consult the work of Linsley (1944) on the naming of infraspecific categories.

In summary, we may say that the systematic units most applicable to biological control workers are species, sibling species, subspecies, clines, and biological races. The terms 'host race,' 'physiological race,' 'form,' and 'strain' may be used providing no trinomial is implied; however, we prefer to use the term 'biological race' for all of these.

THE INTERRELATIONS OF
SYSTEMATICS AND BIOLOGICAL CONTROL

Of all the various fields of entomology, probably no two need the degree of association and teamwork quite as much as do biological control and systematics. Usually the co-operation between specialists in these two fields has been excellent and the results of their co-operative studies have led to better understanding of both the taxonomic and the biological problems involved. In 1955, Sabrosky discussed and summarized the problem as follows:

'Biological-control workers are dealing with complex biological problems, with the interactions of populations of one to many parasites, with one to many species of hosts, and with each other, and with hyperparasites, and all with populations of predators, and all in turn with climatic and other environmental factors. Likewise, the taxonomy in biological-control problems can be a complex matter, involving the identification and classification of species of all those categories. All in all, the problems pose a real challenge to both taxonomists and biological-control workers, a challenge that can best be met by the fullest teamwork possible.'

The Importance of Biological Control to Systematics

As early as 1929, M. M. Metcalf realized how important parasites were as aids to taxonomy and other problems. In the same year Silvestri briefly noted the relationship of taxonomy to the different branches of entomology. Brues (1939) noted how the addition of genetical, biological, and ecological knowledge would likely change the approach to taxonomy and in 1940, Huxley edited a book on *The New Systematics* which analysed all fields closely related to taxonomy. In 1942, Clausen gave an interesting account of the relationships of taxonomy to biological control and cited instances where taxonomic studies were utilized by the biologist to help solve the problem at hand and vice versa.

Another important paper on this subject was that by Flanders (1953*b*) on the biology of certain aphelinids with respect to their applications to taxonomy. He studied the biologies of about 45 aphelinid species representing 12 genera and summarized the biological characteristics in such a manner as to develop a composite (biological and morphological) key to the genera of the Aphelinidae (Aphelininae of authors). Ideally, though, his key would have been more applicable if the composite characters had been given for each couplet of the key rather than given as biological characters for one couplet and morphological characters for another. This work was the culmination of many years of work on the biological control of scale pests in California and it is the writers' opinion that similar works, if integrated with morphological characters, would be most helpful to the taxonomist and the biological control entomologist as well as to the general field of biosystematics.

Sabrosky (1955) discussed some of the more important points that biological control workers could do for taxonomists. Among these were: (1) the furnishing of important data on 'host-parasite lists, reared material, series for analysis of variation, associated immature stages, and distribution data,' as well as all other bioecological features that may be observed; (2) techniques, such as those used in genetics, cytogenetics, serology, and paper chromatography, may be utilized by the biologist, the results of which will certainly complement a taxonomist's study of dead museum specimens; and (3) 'the furnishing of clues to possible differences in populations' and subspecies, sibling species, and morphological species. He cites several cases where such data were helplul, one of which was that of the spruce sawfly. This species was later found by biologists to consist of two species, *Diprion hercyniae* Hart. and *D. polytomum* Hart., which differed in chromosome numbers, type of parthenogenesis, and diapause tendency.

Another example discussed by Sabrosky (1955) and elaborated upon by Dietrick and van den Bosch (1957) is that of the tachinid fly, *Trichopoda pennipes* Fabr., a parasite of several species of Hemiptera representing the families Coreidae, Pyrrhocoridae, and Pentatomidae. The fly occurs in both western and eastern North America but appears to exist in at least three host-determined 'strains.' One 'strain' is eastern and attacks the squash bug, *Anasa tristis* (DeG.); one 'strain' is south-eastern and attacks pentatomids, chiefly *Nezara viridula* (L.); while another 'strain' is western and attacks the bordered plant bug, *Euryopthalmus cinctus californicus* Van D. Since the squash bug is a pest in south-western United States, it was felt that the introduction of the eastern 'squash bug strain' of *T. pennipes* into California might aid this problem. Unfortunately, this 'strain' apparently did not become established; however, it was found readily to attack the western squash bug population in the California laboratory but would not inter-breed with the native western strain of *T. pennipes*. Also, it would not attack the bordered plant bug in the laboratory. Although sibling species have been found most often to be sympatric, the evidence presented by the biological control workers might indicate that the 'strains' of *T. pennipes* are in reality sibling species as evidenced also by the fact that morphological characters are not available to separate the three strains. Other important cases like this were cited previously under the section in this chapter on systematic units in biological control.

The Importance of Systematics to Biological Control

Both Clausen (1942) and Sabrosky (1955) have discussed this subject at some length. As an introduction, the classic example reported on by Pemberton, as quoted by Clausen (1942), on the discovery of the native home of the fern weevil is given as follows: 'Some 20 years ago [from year 1942] the fern weevil, *Syagrius fulvitarsis* Pasc., became very destructive to Sadleria ferns in a forest reserve on the island of Hawaii, and control measures became necessary. Entomological literature failed to reveal its occurrence anywhere outside Hawaii except in greenhouses in Australia and Ireland. These records, of course, gave no clue as to the country of origin. However, while engaged on other problems in Australia in 1921, Pemberton had the opportunity of examining an old private insect collection at Sydney, and among the beetle specimens was a single *Syagrius fulvitarsis* bearing the date of collection, 1857, and the name of the locality in Australia from which it was obtained. This provided the key to the solution of the problem, for a search of the forest areas indicated on the label revealed a small population of the beetles and, better still, a braconid parasite attacking the larvae. Collections were made im-mediately for shipment to Hawaii, and the establishment of the parasite was quickly followed by satisfactory control of the pest. The data borne on a label attached to a single insect specimen in 1857, in Australia, thus contributed directly to the successful biological control of the pest in Hawaii 65 years later.'

This case shows the importance of having taxonomic collections of specimens available for reference by biological control workers. Had that specimen not been collected in 1857, there is no way of knowing how long the successful biological control of the fern weevil would have been delayed.

Sabrosky (1955) discussed 'what taxonomists can do for biological control workers' somewhat as follows: (1) They will furnish the basic information concerning the identification of the various species involved. This may be easy and definite or it may take considerable research and time, particuarly if the question 'Where is its native home?' arises, as it always does in biological control problems. The proper identification of the pest and its natural enemies is obviously fundamental since without a scientific name previous references to the species could not be adequately examined. The taxonomist is aware that an improper identification could send a biological control man on foreign exploration to Europe instead of South America looking for natural enemies and actually this has happened on at least one occasion. It is also important to mention that failure to recognize differences between similar cryptic species of *Aphytis* by taxonomists led to the failure of importing new ones into California for many years (DeBach 1959). (2) The job of 'cataloguing and assimilation of knowledge about species is accepted by modern taxonomists as their responsiblity.' The complex problem of host–parasite and predator relationships, alternative hosts, and hyperparasites must be organized by the taxonomist. (3) The gathering together of fundamental information on the classification and phylogeny of a group of insects may not be directly appreciated by the biological control worker; however, it might be just this sort of information which would actually turn out to be the most applicable. He cites the work by P. W. Oman and others on the sugar beet leafhopper as an example and, here briefly summarized, stated that the early surveys for the native home of this leafhopper, *Eutettix tenellus* Bak., were carried out in South America. Later, Oman found that this species actually belonged in an entirely different group of leafhoppers and to the genus *Circulifer* and that its native home would be in arid regions around the Mediterranean. Biological control workers then searched in that area and succeeded in finding several natural enemies.

BIOLOGICAL CONTROL SYSTEMATICS IN THE FUTURE

Problems to be Overcome

Different aspects of what kinds of systematic investigations will be needed in this day of new systematics have been noted by several authors in Huxley's book (1940), and enlarged upon by Mayr (1942) and Mayr, Linsley, and Usinger (1953). The particular needs and uses of systematics in applied entomology have been pointed out by Smart (1940), Thorpe (1940), Clausen (1942), Essig (1942b),

Ferris (1942, 1954), Frison (1942), Muesebeck (1942), Keifer (1944), Ross (1954), and Sabrosky (1955), and need not be rediscussed at this time.

Certainly, one of the most important problems in the field of systematics is finding financial support for many more trained systematists. Instead of progressing steadily in systematic research concurrent with the discovery of thousands of new species of insects each year, we find we are falling hopelessly behind. For example, in 1923 Gahan made the following observation on the systematics of the Chalcidoidea: '. . . The tremendous world-wide interest in economic entomology has resulted in swelling the number of economic workers to a veritable army, while the number of systematists has apparently not kept pace. As a concrete example, I may state that in the whole world today there are probably not over a dozen individuals actively engaged in the taxonomic study of chalcid-flies, notwithstanding the fact that the interest in parasitic insects is greater than ever before, and this group is probably the most numerous of all the parasitic forms.' This statement might be repeated verbatim at this time—some forty or so years later—except that the dozen or so taxonomists now working actively on the chalcidoids are confronted with many hundreds of more species and Gahan's 'veritable army' of economic workers has nearly doubled. Is it any wonder that a large percentage of determinations are of necessity given only provisionally, hesitantly, and with qualifications?

One possible answer to this problem at the present time is for all interested and properly equipped persons who are working with species problems in biological control work to undertake a systematic investigation on the particular group with which they are concerned. Such was the case recently with DeBach (1959). For many years he was working with the biology and use of *Aphytis* species in the biological control of red scale in California. He summarized the biological and morphological features of several closely related species and was able to describe new species which otherwise would probably have been masked and confused for an indefinite period of time.

Another important obstacle which must be overcome if we are to enjoy the values of good systematic work is that of making it easier to publish large, well-illustrated revisions and monographs. Ferris (1942) and others have noted that there is no longer any incentive for the enthusiastic worker to plan, develop, and complete important monographs (often on obscure groups of organisms), since he has little or no place to publish his work, or, if it can be published, it often takes several years to be processed and funded by the organization involved. This problem often results in the publication of short, detached systematic studies. At times, short studies may be desired, such as when a concurrent biological study has been made involving a species new to science which necessitates a description of the species. However, instead of increasing the number of newly described species, priority should be given to the publication of revisions of existing genera and families. One of the paramount problems involved with producing larger revisions is that of being unable to examine type specimens. Most museums have a policy which precludes their men sending type specimens away from the museum. Some revisors have an opportunity to examine types in a few of the major museum collections but very few are able to study types that are now placed in many collections throughout the world. It seems to us that in order to facilitate the production of important revisions, type specimens should be made available for study in one of two ways: (1) all holotypes should be deposited in a single large museum, or (2) museum personnel should be allowed to send type material to a qualified revisor.

In order to expedite the development of biosystematics, adequate training in the biological sciences, especially in the fields of bioecology and genetics as well as morphology and the principles of classification, is absolutely necessary for future systematists. Only in this way can we be assured of closer contact between the fields of biology and taxonomy.

The field of ethics and co-operation between systematists likewise can be improved considerably. Ethics for systematists to remember, such as proper credit, acknowledgment of loaned material, and the renaming of homonyms, are fully discussed by Mayr, Linsley and Usinger (1953) and need not be reiterated here. However, several points concerning closer co-operation of systematists should be emphasized at this time. In this day of rapid transit, there can be no excuse whatsoever for one not being in close contact with other people working in the same or closely related field of systematics. It seems bad enough to find homologous structures with different names in different orders but to find this true for genera or even species in the same family seems rather inexcusable and yet such is the case in numerous instances. This fact, for example, prompted Tuxen (1956) to systematize the definitions of all the parts of insect genitalia. Ideally, more of this type of work should be completed but in the meantime it is up to the individual systematist to contact and discuss with his fellow workers various problems on the naming of structures, questions about synonymy, status of generic concepts, and, above all, to let each other know precisely what their range of studies includes. The recent publication *Directory of the Zoological Taxonomists of the World* by Blackwelder and Blackwelder (1961) certainly should help to strengthen some of these desires.

The Desired End-Product

In order to achieve desirable works on biosystematics of entomophagous species, it seems almost imperative that the biologist and museum taxonomist be in close contact with each other. It is highly desirable that the biologist should do a certain amount of biosystematics on his own and that the museum systematist should orient his work to include biological data. Many ideas come to mind concerning the necessary requirements for adequate biosystematic studies but, for the most part, these have already been cited by various authors. Thorpe (1940) listed six requirements which certainly apply today and which we quote in full as follows:

'1. All specialists should have facilities for studying their group in the field. Only with the aid of long experience in the field as well as in the museum can a really first-class systematist be developed.

'2. Properly equipped biological laboratories should be attached to each museum department so that material of certain particularly plastic and difficult groups can be reared under properly controlled conditions.

'3. Where this is impossible, as in certain types of marine and fresh-water biology especially, the museum should work in as close association as possible with a laboratory where the necessary facilities can be obtained, and provision should be made for interchange of staff.

'4. Facilities for the adequate preservation of the early stages of animals should be made. This is particularly urgent in the case of insects and is perhaps the first need of present-day entomological museums.

'5. Facilities should be provided for securing and recording exact measurements of the structure of a large series in the case of difficult species, and it should be possible to have these adequately treated by modern statistical methods.

'6. Finally, secretarial and other help should be available for the preservation of the fullest and most exact data for all specimens in a convenient form.'

The desired end-product in this field of research should be systematic revisions or monographs and, whether concerning an order, family, subfamily, tribe, or even a single genus, the author should strive to include as much about each of the following subjects as possible: history of the group, keys to all taxonomic categories, a complete list of synonymy, descriptions of all life stages, life histories or complete biologies, lists of hosts and hyperparasites, a synopsis of geographical distribution together with specific distributional data, an analysis of the phylogenetic relationships of the group, and a complete bibliography.

It seems to the authors that only by aiming at this type of study will one begin to mould the field of systematics in relation to biological control into something more than a detached science which so often leaves the present problems unsolved and the work of the future almost untouchable.

KEYS TO IMPORTANT FAMILIES OF
ENTOMOPHAGOUS INSECTS

Lack of specialized keys to the major entomophagous groups has been a real drawback to those interested in biological control. Although Clausen (1940a) treats entomophagous insects in 224 families representing 15 orders, many of these families are of limited practical importance. The specialized keys which follow include the larger and more important families using as a guide the principal ones discussed by Clausen.

The purpose of these keys is to allow a person who has reared or is studying the biology of a given entomophagous species to quickly and simply place a species in its proper family. Once the correct family is known, the person may then acquire pertinent biological information from Clausen's book on *Entomophagous Insects* (1940a) and he may also send material to the proper specialist for species determination. In many cases it is difficult for a worker to know whether he is dealing with an encyrtid or an eulophid, a tachinid or a sarcophagid, and it is hoped that the simple keys supplied here will be useful to the biological control worker who may himself not be a taxonomist or who may not happen to be near one who can determine his specimens for him. These keys may also help to supplement the biological information given in chapters 6 and 7 of this book.

It is important to note that these keys include only those families which are well represented by entomophagous species and, unless the specimens concerned are known to have an entomophagous habit, other more inclusive keys should be sought and utilized.

In preparing these keys, the authors have made considerable use of the broader ones published by Comstock (1940), Essig (1942a), Imms (1948), Brues, Melander, and Carpenter (1954), and Borror and Delong (1954). Other references to particular orders are cited under the appropriate order.

DIPTERA

Of the approximately 125 families of flies, 39 contain many entomophagous species and are listed in the following key form. Several other families contain entomophagous species but in rather insignificant numbers. Aside from the general references cited in the proceding paragraph, keys given by Curran (1934) were consulted. Figure 34 shows three general types of dipterous wing venation, characters of which are utilized in the key to families which follow.

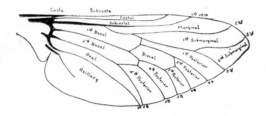

A. TABANIDAE

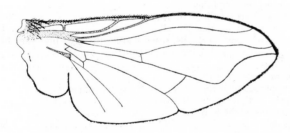

B. MUSCIDAE

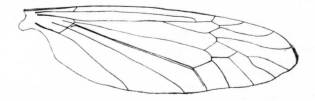

C. TIPULOIDEA

FIGURE 34. Wing venation of three groups of Diptera.

Keys to Adults of the More Important Families of Entomophagous Diptera

1. Antennae usually longer than thorax; flagellum consisting of 6 to 39 similar free segments in addition to the 2 basal joints; anal cell usually open; palpi elongate and usually comprising 4 or 5 segments; body usually aseptate (Suborder *Nematocera*)........................2
   Antennae shorter than thorax, usually with 3 segments, but terminal segment may be distinctly annulated, or bearing a distinct style or arista; anal cell distinctly narrowed or closed, or absent; palpi short, usually with 1 or 2 segments, body often with setae, bristles or spines (Suborder *Brachycera*) 9
2. Wings without network of fine folds or creases....................................3
   Wings with network of fine folds or creases ....Blephariceridae
3. Costa extending around entire wing, occasionally weakened behind 4
   Costa extending to or nearly to wing tip 6
4. Mesonotal suture transverse, not V-shaped.......................................5
   Mesonotum with an entire, V-shaped suture ....Tipulidae
5. Ocelli present and/or venation quite reduced ....Cecidomyiidae
   Ocelli absent; venation strong.....................................Culicidae
6. Ocelli present...7
   Ocelli absent..8
7. Antennae inserted below compound eyes close to oral margin.................Bibionidae
   Antennae inserted at middle of head, well above oral margin.............Mycetophilidae
8. Mesonotum short, without longitudinal groove ....Ceratopogonidae
   Mesonotum long, with median longitudinal groove ....Chironomidae
9. Empodium pulvilliform, the three pads nearly equal 10
   Empodium hairlike or absent..14
10. Third antennal segment compound, composed of annuli 11
    Third antennal segment simple, often bearing an elongated style or arista..............12
11. Squamae large and conspicuous ....Tabanidae
    Squamae small or vestigial ....Stratiomyiidae
12. Squamae small or vestigial...13
    Squamae very large, covering halters ....Acroceridae
13. Tibiae without spurs; venation intricate ....Nemestrinidae
    Middle tibiae with spurs; venation normal ....Rhagionidae
14. Wing with 2 or more submarginal cells; anal cell distinctly longer than second basal cell..15
    Wing with 1 or no submarginal cell; anal cell shorter 21
15. Front hollowed between eyes..16
    Front not hollowed between eyes 17
16. Three ocelli; palpi usually prominent; proboscis adapted for piercing ....Asilidae
    One ocellus; palpi vestigial; proboscis with fleshy tip.........................Mydaidae
17. Costa continuing around the wing 18
    Costa reaching only to apex of wing ....Scenopinidae
18. Wing with 5 posterior cells 19
    Wing with at most 4 posterior cells 20
19. Fourth vein ending beyond apex of wing ....Therevidae
    Fourth vein ending before apex of wing ....Apioceridae
20. Sixth vein does not reach wing margin; body usually rather apilose ....Empididae
    Sixth vein reaching wing margin; body often extremely pilose ....Bombyliidae
21. Wing normal, not rounded apically; venation normal 22
    Wing rounded apically; veins strong anteriorly ....Phoridae
22. Spurious vein absent; anal cell short, ends much before margin of wing................23
    Spurious vein present, anal cell closed close to wing margin..................Syrphidae
23. Frontal lunule entirely absent 24
    Frontal lunule present 25
24. Head extremely large, hemispherical; front and face very narrow ....Pipunculidae
    Head not unusually large; front and face usually wide ....Dolichopodidae
25. Coxae close together at base 26
    Coxae widely separated at base ....Braulidae

HYMENOPTERA

The order Hymenoptera is especially rich in families exhibiting the entomophagous habit and most of the parasitic species utilized in biological control belong to this order. Accordingly, it is desirable for all workers in biological control to have some familiarity with the biology and taxonomy of the parasitic wasps. One is often a clue to the other and such knowledge is essential to efficient work in the foreign exploration and quarantine phases of biological control.

The following keys are to the groups of parasitic Hymenoptera which are most commonly encountered in biological control work. For this reason, not all the families of Hymenoptera have been included and those in the Tenthredinoidea and Apoidea have been entirely omitted. For additional information the keys given by Borror and Delong (1954), Brues, Melander, and Carpenter (1954), and Comstock (1940) are highly recommended. Figure 35 shows the more important morphological features of a chalcid wasp used in connection with the following key to the families.

Keys to the Adults of the More Important Families of Entomophagous Hymenoptera

(Based primarily on winged females)

1. Hind wing with less than 3 basal cells; abdomen petiolate or subpetiolate. Ants, bees, wasps, chalcid flies 2
Hind wing with 3 basal cells; abdomen broadly sessile, attached over a large area. (*Caveat*: this character should not be used solely by itself as some of the minute Chalcidoidea exhibit a similar character.) Saw flies, horntails........................... (Tenthredinoidea)

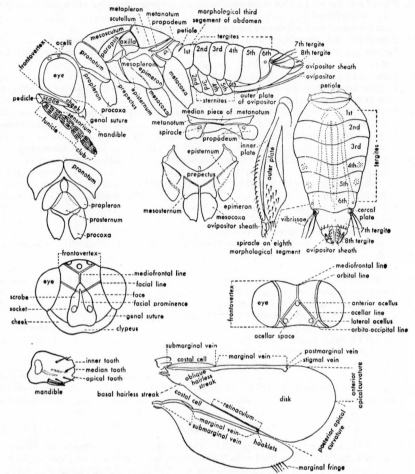

FIGURE 35. Morphological details of the hymenopterous parasite, *Coccophagus malthusi* Grlt. (Adapted from Compere 1931.)

2. Last abdominal sternite of female divided longitudinally, the ovipositor issuing from anterior to tip of abdomen and provided with a pair of narrow exserted sheaths as long as the ovipositor; hind wing usually without an anal lobe; trochanters 1- or 2-segmented..............3

    Last abdominal sternite of female not divided longitudinally, the ovipositor issuing from tip of abdomen (usually as a true sting) and without a pair of exserted sheaths; trochanters of 1 segment; costal cell often present; hind wing often with anal lobe..................5

3. Venation well developed in both fore- and hind wings; forewings with well-developed stigma; abdomen with ventral surface usually soft; antennae not elbowed and usually with 16 or more segments. Trochanters 2-segmented (Ichneumonoidea)..............................9

    Venation of forewings reduced and usually without a stigma; antennae are filiform or elbowed and are usually with less than 14 segments......................................4

4. Pronotum extending laterally back to tegulae; antennae not elbowed; prepectus absent; trochanters usually 1-segmented. Body often compressed (Cynipoidea)..............35

Pronotum not reaching tegulae; prepectus usually present; antennae usually elbowed; trochanters usually 2-segmented; venation of wings much reduced (Chalcidoidea)........16

5. Pronotum extending laterally back to or nearly to the tegulae 6

Pronotum short, not extending back to tegulae and with a rounded lobe on each side posteriorly...8

6. Wing venation well developed; hind wing with several veins, if veinless then having a basal lobe 7

Wing venation more or less reduced; hind wings nearly veinless, not lobed (Proctotrupoidea) 37

7. Hind wing with venation reduced and without closed cells (Bethyloidea) 42

Hind wing with normal venation and at least 1 closed cell (Vespoidea) 45

8. First segment of hind tarsi slender, not broadened or thickened, and usually bare; all body hairs simple, unbranched; abdomen often petiolate (Sphecoidea)....................51

First segment of hind tarsi elongate, usually thickened or flattened, and often hairy; some body hairs branched or plumose; abdomen not petiolate. Bees....................(Apoidea)

9. Costal cell absent 10

Costal cell present, may be narrow...12

10. Ventral abdominal segments soft and membranous, with a median fold 11

Ventral abdominal segments hard, heavily sclerotized; scutellum armed with a sharp spiniform process ....Agriotypidae

11. Two recurrent veins, or if only 1 then with abdomen three times as long as rest of body; size variable, length (excluding ovipositor) ranging from a few millimetres to more than 40 mm (figure 36-A)...Ichneumonidae

One recurrent vein or none; abdomen not greatly elongate; propodeum not prolonged beyond hind coxae; mostly small insects, rarely over 12 mm in length (figure 36-B)   Braconidae

12. Abdomen inserted on propodeum of thorax far above hind coxal bases, sometimes on nipplelike protuberance, antennae with 13 or 14 segments 14

Abdomen inserted normally, close to bases of hind coxae, between or slightly above them, antennae with 18 or more segments 13

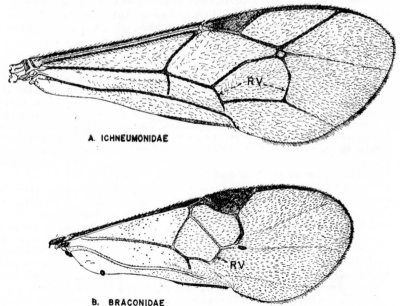

FIGURE 36. Wing venation of an ichneumonid and a braconid wasp (Hymenoptera).

13. Forewing with 2 or 3 closed submarginal cells, antennae with 18 or more segments, head large, quadrate; mandibles with 4 teeth; hind wing with 2 large closed cells; moderate-sized, often brilliantly coloured species ....**Trigonalidae**

Forewing with only 1 closed submarginal cell or none; antennae setaceous, with 30 segments or more; abdomen long and slender; ovipositor long; hind femora swollen and toothed before apex; head tuberculate above ....**Stephanidae**

14. Prothorax long and necklike; abdomen long and slender 15

Prothorax short, not necklike; abdomen short, oval, and flaglike, borne on a cylindrical petiole; marginal cell broad apically..**Evaniidae**

15. Hind tibia strongly swollen towards the tip; forewing can be folded lengthwise **Gasteruptiidae**

Hind tibia not swollen towards the tip; forewing cannot be folded ....**Aulacidae**

16. Front basitarsus more or less distinctly modified to form a strigil, the spur of front tibiae long, curved, and sometimes bifid at apex; posterior margin of mesoscutum usually transverse, the axillae usually not much produced forward beyond a line connecting the tegulae; tarsi usually 5-segmented; antennae most often with more than 10 segments 17

Front basitarsus simple, the spur of front tibiae short and straight; posterior margin of mesoscutum usually more or less excised, with the axillae usually produced forward beyond a line connecting the tegulae; tarsi usually with 3 or 4 segments; antennae usually with less than 10 segments 33

17. Forewings with normal chalcidoid venation (figure 35), the marginal and stigmal veins both usually well developed 18

Forewings nearly veinless, the marginal vein usually extremely short and terminating about one-fourth to one-third of the length of the wing from the base, the stigmal vein much reduced or absent; wings usually with a long marginal fringe, the hind pair very narrow; tarsi with 4 or 5 segments; minute wasps, egg parasites ....**Mymaridae**

18. Mesopleura never convex, but more or less furrowed to receive the middle femora; spur of middle tibiae never saltatorial 19

Mesopleura convex or at most weakly furrowed, spur of middle tibiae large and saltatorial. .30

19. Gaster of abdomen more or less pyramidal or bipyramidal, thickest near the middle, the first segment as large as the remaining segments combined, or the first 2 subequal and the following segments retracted in the second.....................................20

Gaster of abdomen not pyramidal in shape..21

20. Pronotum hardly or not at all visible from above; abdomen petiolate; first segment of gaster much larger than any of the following segments, which are more or less retracted within it; mandibles slender and falcate; axillae more or less connate, usually entirely fused (except in the more generalized forms such as *Orasema*) and forming a transverse segment between the mesoscutum and scutellum ....**Eucharidae**

Pronotum with a distinct collar, its anterior face either concave or conically produced; abdomen either sessile or petiolate; first 2 segments of gaster subequal and enclosing the following segments; mandibles stout and not at all falcate; axillae usually widely separated ....**Perilampidae**

21. Hind coxae more or less greatly enlarged 22

Hind coxae not enlarged..26

22. Propleura not separated from the mesopleura by a prepectal plate 23

Propleura separated from the mesopleura by a linear or triangular prepectal plate........24

23. Hind femora greatly enlarged, toothed or minutely denticulate beneath; pronotum with a well-developed collar; abdomen without a peculiar sculpture, globose, ovate, or conic-ovate, often with a well-developed petiole; hind coxae subfusiform to conical, and frequently elongate, never sharply angled above..**Chalcididae**

Hind femora and tibiae slender and unmodified; hind coxae compressed and rather sharply angled above; pronotum with a well-developed transverse collar; mesoscutum without parapsidal sutures; abdomen sessile, conic ovate, usually with a peculiar scalloped sculpture on the intermediate tergites, often preceded by coarse punctures............**Ormyridae**

24. Prepectal plates triangular; wings not folded longitudinally 25

Prepectal plates linear; wings folded lengthwise; pronotum very large and quadrate; abdomen fusiform, with the tergite beyond the first fused (males), or clavate-fusiform, with the ovipositor curved forward over the tergum (females); hind coxae compressed and somewhat angled above, the hind femora greatly enlarged and toothed beneath ....Leucospidae

25. Hind femora somewhat swollen and simple, or greatly enlarged and toothed beneath, the hind coxae compressed and more or less sharply angled above; first femora somewhat swollen and thicker than the middle pair; abdomen sessile, conic ovate to conical, the ovipositor not or hardly protruded; stigmal vein usually well developed....................Cleonymidae

Hind femora usually slender, or only slightly swollen, but sometimes enlarged and toothed beneath (*Podagrion*), front femora only slightly thicker than middle pair; hind coxae compressed and sharply angled above, or compressed-ovate and rounded on dorsal margin (*Podagrion*); ovipositor always prominently produced and often very long; stigmal vein usually very short, but sometimes ending in large circular knob (*Megastigmus*) Torymidae

26. Pronotum with a large quadrate collar...27
    Pronotum short, not prominent, the collar transverse 28

27. Collar quite or almost as broad as mesoscutum; mesoscutum with parapsidal sutures but the parapsides not prominent; antennae inserted high on the face; abdomen usually more or less compressed ....Eurytomidae

    Collar about as wide as the middle lobe of the mesoscutum and more or less conically produced forward; parapsides very prominent; antennae inserted at the oral margin; abdomen more or less depressed ....Spalangiidae

28. Axillae not or barely produced forward beyond a line tangent with hind margin of tegulae 29
    Axillae very large, placed in front of the scutellum, produced far forward beyond a line tangent with the hind margin of tegulae and separated by the middle lobe of the mesoscutum; the parapsides smaller than the axillae and crowded far forward; prepectal plates obscure or absent ....Eutrichosomatidae

29. Parapsidal sutures complete, usually distinct and more or less deeply furrowed; hind tibiae usually with 2 apical spurs; prepectal plates distinct..................Miscogasteridae
    Parapsidal sutures incomplete, usually distinct only anteriorly; hind tibiae usually with 1 apical spur; axillae well separated; prepectal plates small, or rather small, and not very distinct ....Pteromalidae

30. Axillae usually distinct; spur of middle tibiae without spines on inner margin 31
    Axillae absent, the dorsum of thorax composed of 5 more or less transverse sclerites (pronotum, mesoscutum, scutellum, metanotum, and propodeum); mesopleura hardly convex and slightly furrowed; antennae at most 7-segmented, the funicle segments all very short, the club elongate and cylindrical; middle tibiae armed with strong spines; the apical spur with a fringe of long stout spines on the inner margin ....Signiphoridae

31. Mesopleura evenly convex (except in some males), axillae not produced forward.........32
    Mesopleura somewhat depressed and often with a slightly impressed furrow; axillae widely separated, often fused posteriorly with the scutellum and frequently produced forward into the basal region of the mesoscutum; parapsidal sutures of mesoscutum distinct; antennae rarely with more than 8 segments ....Aphelinidae

32. Mesosternum short, the middle coxae approximated to the anterior pair, mesoscutum more or less convex, rarely with parapsidal sutures, which curve outward anteriorly; antennae normally with 11 segments in female, 9 in male ....Encyrtidae
    Mesosternum elongate, the middle coxae widely separated from the anterior pair; mesoscutum usually longitudinally impressed in the middle, the parapsidal sutures absent or incomplete; mesoscutum and scutellum usually movable at the mesoscuto-scutellar suture and upon the underlying pleural parts; males usually with the mesopleura furrowed, the mesoscutum not impressed but with more or less complete parapsidal sutures; antennae usually with 13 segments ....Eupelmidae

33. Hind coxae normal 34
    Hind coxae very large, and almost laminately compressed; middle and hind femora broad and compressed; tarsi 4-segmented, the middle and hind pairs elongate; mesoscutum without parapsidal sutures; axillae small and produced forward into the base of the mesoscutum; marginal vein very long, the stigmal vein very short ....Elasmidae

34. Tarsi usually 4-segmented, or rarely heteromerous; marginal vein long, the stigmal vein well developed, the postmarginal sometimes absent; parapsidal sutures of mesoscutum complete or sometimes poorly developed; prepectal plates usually large and triangular. . **Eulophidae**
Tarsi 3-segmented; marginal vein short, the stigmal vein short or sometimes absent, the postmarginal always absent; venation seldom reaching beyond the middle of wing and frequently ending at the basal third; pubescence of forewing often arranged in lines . . . . **Trichogrammatidae**

35. Largest segment of abdomen (in side view) tergite IV, V, or VI with at least 2 short tergites behind the petiole preceding the large tergite. Radial cell closed. Mostly large, heavy-bodied forms . . . . **Ibaliidae**
Largest segment of abdomen (in side view) tergites II or III, and never more than 1 short tergite preceding the large tergite. Mostly smaller species 36

36. Tergite II not forming one-half the abdomen . . . . **Figitidae**
Tergite II (or II and III fused) the largest and usually forming at least one-half the abdomen . . . . **Cynipidae**

37. Antennae inserted close to clypeus 38
Antennae inserted on middle of face 40

38. Abdomen acutely margined at sides 39
Abdomen rounded at sides; marginal vein usually stigmated . . . . **Ceraphronidae**

39. Forewings with marginal and stigmal veins . . . . **Scelionidae**
Forewings at most with an incomplete submarginal vein . . . . **Platygasteridae**

40. Forewings with a stigma 41
Forewings without a stigma . . . . **Diapriidae**

41. Mandibles without teeth; claws simple, antennae 13-segmented . . . . **Proctotrupidae**
Mandibles dentate, antennae 15-segmented, claws pectinate . . . . **Heloridae**

42. Antennae 10-segmented, inserted close to clypeus; front tarsi of female often pincers-like (chelate); parasites of leafhoppers . . . . **Dryinidae**
Antennae 12- or 13-segmented; front tarsi not pincers-like 43

43. Abdomen with 3 or fewer (4 in males of *Parnopes*) visible tergites, the last often dentate apically; venter of abdomen concave; body metallic blue or green and with coarse sculpturing . . . . **Chrysididae**
Abdomen with 4 to 7 visible tergites; venter of abdomen convex 44

44. Abdomen with 6 (females) or 7 (males) visible tergites; head usually oblong and elongate; ovipositor a true sting . . . . **Bethylidae**
Abdomen with 4 (females) or 5 (males) visible abdominal tergites . . . . **Cleptidae**

45. First abdominal segment forming a scale or node, or the first 2 abdominal segments nodiform and strongly differentiated from the rest of the abdomen. Ants . . . . **Formicidae**
First abdominal segment not scale-like 46

46. First discoidal cell shorter than the submedian cell (usually very much so); forewings very rarely folded; solitary species, never living in colonies 47
First discoidal cell very long, as a rule much longer than the submedian cell; forewing almost always folded longitudinally when in repose; frequently social species, living in colonies. Hornets, yellow jackets . . . . **Vespidae**

47. Mesopleura divided by an oblique suture into a lower and upper part; legs, including the coxae, very long; hind femora unusually long; middle tibiae with 2 spurs. Spider-hunting wasps, Tarantula hawks . . . . **Pompilidae**
Mesopleura not thus divided; legs shorter, the hind femora not usually extending to the apex of the abdomen 48

48. Meso- and metasternum together forming a flat plate which is divided by a transverse, more or less sinuous suture, and overlies the bases of the 4 posterior coxae; wing membrane, beyond the closed cells, finely longitudinally wrinkled. Large, often brightly coloured wasps . . . . **Scoliidae**
Meso- and metasternum not forming such a plate overlying all 4 posterior coxae; sometimes provided with a pair of thin backwardly directed plates or laminae which overlie the bases of the middle coxae 49

49. Mesosternum with 2 laminae that overlie or project between the bases of the middle coxae and usually extend to the midline where they are separated by a median suture; ocelli small .... Tiphiidae
   Mesosternum simple, without appendages behind, or with the laminae reduced to a pair of minute teeth-like projections 50
50. Hind wing with a prominent separated lobe at the anal angle; body bare ....Sapygidae
   Hind wing without a lobe at the anal angle, at most with an obtuse emargination at the posterior basal angle; body almost always conspicuously pilose. Velvet ants............Mutilidae
51. Metasternum produced into a forked process posteriorly; parapsidal sutures distinct and complete; pronotum long, conically produced anteriorly, usually with a median groove; abdomen of male with 4 to 6 exposed tergites ....Ampulicidae
   Metasternum not so produced; parapsidal sutures indistinct or absent; abdomen of male usually with 7 exposed tergites..Sphecidae

COLEOPTERA

Representative species of about 40 of the approximately 150 families of Coleoptera exhibit the entomophagous trait. Due to the apparent confusion in the literature on the characteristics forming the various coleopterous superfamilies, this taxonomic category could not be utilized in the key to families except in two instances. This key is essentially a modification of Brues, Melander, and Carpenter (1954).

Key to the Adults of the More Important Families of Entomophagous Coleoptera

1. Head not prolonged into a beak; gular sutures double, at least anteriorly and posteriorly...2
   Head usually beak-like; gular sutures fused or lacking (Rhynchophora) ....Anthribidae
2. First visible abdominal sternite divided by hind coxal cavities; outer lobe or galea of maxillae palpiform (Adephaga) 3
   First visible abdominal sternite not normally interrupted by the hind coxal cavities; outer lobe or galea of maxillae not palpiform (Polyphaga)....................................7
3. Abdomen with 6 or more visible sternites; antennae filiform..........................4
   Abdomen with 4 visible sternites; antennae greatly thickened apically, clavate or broadly laminate (Paussoidea)..Paussidae
4. Eyes entire, not divided; antennae elongate, slender (Caraboidea)......................5
   Eyes divided, appearing as 2 pairs; antennae short (Gyrinoidea) ....Gyrinidae
5. Metasternum with a distinct transverse suture demarking a triangular antecoxal sclerite....6
   Metasternum without a transverse suture or antecoxal sclerite ....Dytiscidae
6. Antennae inserted on the front above the base of the mandibles; clypeus extending on each side beyond base of antennae..Cicindelidae
   Antennae inserted on the sides of head between the base of mandibles and eyes; clypeus not extending beyond base of antennae ....Carabidae
7. Antennae usually not clubbed, but if so, then club joints are not lamellate 8
   Antennae with the last 3 to 7 joints enlarged, club-like ....Scarabaeidae
8. Hind tarsi with 4 joints, front and middle tarsi with 5 joints 9
   Hind tarsi with at least as many joints as front and middle tarsi.....................15
9. Front coxal cavities closed behind 10
   Front coxal cavities open behind..11
10. Abdominal sternites freely movable (males only) (see also couplet 32) ......Rhizophagidae
   First 2 to 4 abdominal sternites more or less fused or immovable.........Tenebrionidae
11. Head strongly and suddenly constricted behind eyes 12
   Head not strongly or suddenly constricted behind eyes ....Pythidae
12. Prothorax usually rounded on sides, without sharp lateral margin....................13
   Prothorax with sharp lateral margin ....Mordellidae
13. Base of prothorax narrow than elytra 14
   Base of prothorax as wide as elytra ....Rhipiphoridae
14. Hind coxae large and prominent ....Meloidae
   Hind coxae transverse, not prominent.....................................Anthicidae

15. Maxillary palpi much shorter than antennae...................................16
    Maxillary palpi as long or longer than antennae ....Hydrophilidae
16. Elytra short, exposing much of abdomen ....Staphylinidae
    Elytra covering most of abdomen, not shortened 17
17. Tarsi 5-jointed on at least 1 pair of legs, usually on all legs 18
    All tarsi with less than 5 joints 41
18. Abdomen with at least 6 sternites...19
    Abdomen with 5 sternites or less 27
19. Front coxae conical, large and prominent 20
    Front coxae globular, small and not prominent ....Leptinidae
20. Abdomen with 6 sternites 21
    Abdomen with 7 or 8 sternites 24
21. Hind coxae not grooved 22
    Hind coxae grooved for reception of femora (see also couplet 39) ....Rhipiceridae
22. Hind coxae prominent, at least internally 23
    Hind coxae flat, not prominent (see also couplet 38) ....Cleridae
23. Tibial spurs large ....Silphidae
    Tibial spurs small, indistinct ....Malachiidae
24. Middle coxae in contact 25
    Middle coxae distant ....Lycidae
25. Antennae inserted on the upper part of the front or at the base of its anterior lobe........26
    Antennae inserted at the sides of the front, before the eyes ....Drilidae
26. Head more or less completely covered by prothorax ....Lampyridae
    Head not at all covered by prothorax ....Phengodidae and Cantharidae
27. Front coxae globular or transverse 28
    Front coxae more or less conical and prominent 38
28. Front coxae transverse, more or less cylindrical 29
    Front coxae globular...33
29. Hind coxae grooved to receive the femora 30
    Hind coxae flat, not grooved 31
30. Front coxae without a distinctly separated side piece (trochantin) ....Helodidae
    Front coxae with trochantin ....Dascillidae
31. Tarsi more or less dilated, first joint not shortened 32
    Tarsi slender, the metatarsus very short ....Ostomatidae
32. Maxillae with only a single lobe ....Nitidulidae
    Maxillae with both inner and outer lobe (see also couplet 10) ....Rhizophagidae
33. Prosternum without median process 34
    Prosternum prolonged behind into a median process which is received in the mesosternum
    ....Elateridae
34. Hind coxae not in contact although close together in some species 35
    Hind coxae in contact ....Phalacridae
35. Elytra entire, covering the pygidium 36
    Elytra short, leaving 2 segments of abdomen exposed ....Histeridae
36. Antennae consisting of 10 or 11 segments 37
    Antennae consisting of only 2 apparent segments ....Ectrephidae
37. Maxillae covered by corneous plates ....Passandridae
    Maxillae exposed ....Cucujidae
38. Hind coxae dilated into plates which are grooved to receive the femora 39
    Hind coxae not grooved (see also couplet 22)...............................Cleridae
39. Antennae with last 3 joints much enlarged forming a strong club ....Dermestidae
    Antennae not capitate (see also couplet 21) ....Rhipiceridae
40. Tarsi with 3 joints 41
    Tarsi with 4 joints 42
41. Second joint of tarsi dilated...Coccinellidae
    Second joint of tarsi not dilated ....Lathridiidae
42. Abdominal sternites all free and movable ....Myceptophagidae
    Abdominal sternites 1 to 4 firmly united...............................Colydiidae

HEMIPTERA

Of the approximately 60 families of Hemiptera (Heteroptera), 18 have species which are entomophagous. This key has been adapted mostly from Brues, Melander, and Carpenter (1954).

Key to the Adults of the More Important Families of Entomophagous Hemiptera

1. Antennae as long or longer than head, if not then eyes and ocelli absent.................2
   Antennae shorter than head, usually hidden in cavities beneath the eyes 13
2. Eyes, and often ocelli, present...3
   Both eyes and ocelli absent ....Termitaphididae
3. Claws apical, last tarsal joint with entire tip 4
   Claws of at least front tarsi distinctly anteapical, the apex of last tarsal joint more or less cleft 12
4. Antennae 4-jointed, not counting minute intermediate ring joints or antenniferous tubercles
   on the head if present...5
   Antennae 5-jointed ....Pentatomidae
5. Tarsal claws devoid of basal pads (arolia), if present then meso- and metasternum are composite
   or front legs are raptorial...6
   Tarsal claws provided with arolia 11
6. Meso- and metasternum composite, formed of more than 1 piece 7
   Meso- and metasternum simple, formed of a single piece 8
7. Proboscis 3-jointed ....Anthocoridae
   Proboscis 4-jointed ....Miridae
8. Pronotum simple, often large and broad, or long and narrow; head not constricted at base
   behind eyes...9
   Pronotum divided into 3 lobes; head constricted at base behind eyes .....Enicocephalidae
9. Antennae elbowed, slender filiform or often thin apically 10
   Antennae short, with last joint swollen or enlarged.......................Phymatidae
10. Prosternum with a cross-striated median stridulation groove; proboscis 3-jointed Reduviidae
    Prosternum without a stridulation groove; proboscis usually 4-jointed ....Nabidae
11. Antennae not elbowed; head not constricted in front of eyes ....Lygaeidae
    Antennae elbowed; head constricted in front of eyes ....Neididae
12. Hind femora extending much beyond apex of abdomen; proboscis 4-jointed......Gerridae
    Hind femora not extending much beyond apex of abdomen; proboscis 3-jointed....Veliidae
13. Ocelli present..14
    Ocelli absent...15
14. Antennae exposed; front legs formed for running ....Ochteridae
    Antennae hidden; front legs raptorial ....Nerthridae
15. Front coxae inserted at or near front margin of prosternum; hind tarsi with distinct claws..16
    Front coxae inserted at hind margin of short prosternum, hind tarsi without claws.........
    .... Notonectidae
16. Upper wings with membrane reticulately veined 17
    Upper wings without veins ....Naucoridae
17. Hind coxae hinged; hind legs fitted for swimming ....Belostomatidae
    Hind coxae globular, rotating; hind legs formed for walking, not flattened ....Nepidae

NEUROPTERA

Because certain stages of nearly all the neuropterous families have entomophagous habits, the key that follows includes all families of this order. This key has been adapted from Essig (1942a) and Brues, Melander, and Carpenter (1954).

Key to Adult Neuroptera

1. Head hypognathous; hind wing not folded fan-like when at rest 2
   Head prognathous; hind wing folded fan-like when not in use (Sialodea) 3

2. Antennae usually filiform; ovipositor not exserted (Planipennia) 4
   Antennae setiform; ovipositor exserted (Raphidiodea) 23
3. Ocelli absent; fourth joint of tarsi bilobed ....**Sialidae**
   Three ocelli present; fourth joint of tarsi not bilobed ....**Corydalidae**
4. Veins and usually cross veins abundant; wings without whitish powder 5
   Veins and crossveins less in number; wings covered with whitish powder.**Coniopterigidae**
5. Large moth-like species; costal area of forewing not broad; head small and closely set on
   prothorax; antennae long, filiform, 40 to 50 segmented ....**Ithonidae**
   Not as above 6
6. Antennae never enlarged apically, moniliform, filiform, or rarely pectinate..............7
   Antennae at least thickly cylindrical, usually enlarged towards apex 19
7. Hind wings not longer than forewings, the 2 pairs similar in form and venation...........8
   Hind wings greatly elongate and ribbon-like, often with widened, spoon-like ends..........
   .... **Nemopteridae**
8. Front legs not raptorial...9
   Front legs raptorial ....**Mantispidae**
9. Forewing with 2 or more branches of R_s arising from the apparently fused stems of R_1 and
   R_s...10
   Forewing with all branches of R_s arising from a single sector 12
10. Antennae moniliform in both sexes; ocelli absent; ovipositor not exserted..............11
    Antennae pectinate in male; ocellus-like tubercle present; ovipositor exserted.....**Dilaridae**
11. Forewing with 3 or more branches of R_s present, veins R_4 and R_5 arising separately ....
    .... **Hemerobiidae**
    Forewing with apparently 2 radial sectors (R_s), one of which is R_2+3 and the other R_4+5..
    .... **Sympherobiidae**
12. Large moth-like species; costal area of forewing very broad; the S_c, R_1, and R_s are closely
    parallel ....**Psychopsidae**
    Not as above 13
13. Ocelli absent...14
    Ocelli present ....**Osmylidae**
14. Humeral cross vein forming a recurrent vein; discal area of wings distinct from costal and
    marginal areas by series of cross veins; S_c and R_1 fused apically ......**Polystoechotidae**
    Humeral cross vein not forming a recurrent vein; discal area of wings not differentiated from
    marginal area 15
15. Vertex flattened 16
    Vertex convex ....**Sisyridae**
16. Costal cross veins not forked 17
    Costal cross veins forked 18
17. Wings of nearly equal width ....**Chrysopidae**
    Forewing distinctly wider than hind wing.................................**Apochrysidae**
18. Forewing with S_c and R fused before wing tip; seed-like scales often present on wings........
    .... **Berothidae**
    Forewing with S_c and R not fused apically; hairs of body and wing conspicuously long......
    .... **Trichomatidae**
19. Wings about one-third as wide as long; costal area wide ....**Myiodactylidae**
    Wings much narrower 20
20. Antennae more or less distinctly clavate or flattened, subcostal cell without cross veins....21
    Antennae elongate cylindrical; subcostal area with many cross veins ....**Nymphidae**
21. Antennae about as long as head and thorax.....................................22
    Antennae longer, slender and strongly clavate............................**Ascalaphidae**
22. Antennae weakly clubbed, or flattened apically; body and wings pubescent ....
    .... **Myrmeleontidae**
    Antennae strongly clubbed; abdomen and wings shining ....**Stilbopterygidae**
23. Ocelli present ....**Raphidiidae**
    Ocelli absent ....**Inocellidae**

LEPIDOPTERA

Twelve of the approximately 160 lepidopterous families have species which exhibit entomophagous habits. The following key is adapted primarily from Brues, Melander, and Carpenter (1954).

Key to the Adults of Known Families of Entomophagous Lepidoptera

1. Antennae simple or modified, but usually not swollen apically; hind wing with frenulum; ocelli often present (Heterocera) 2
   Antennae knobbed at tip; hind wing without a frenulum; ocelli absent (Rhopalocera).......
   ....Lycaenidae
2. Wings absent or greatly reduced in size 3
   Wings normally developed...5
3. Moth not developing in a sac constructed by the larva 4
   Moth developing in and often never leaving sac constructed by larva (see also couplets 7, 9, and 10) ....Psychidae
4. Proboscis absent or vestigial (see also couplet 12) ....Pyralididae
   Proboscis present (see also couplets 11 and 12) ....Noctuidae
5. Hind wing with 3 anal veins; forewing usually with first anal vein reaching wing margin...6
   Hind wing with 2 anal veins, rarely with 1 10
6. Hind wing with veins $S_c + R_1$ and R_s widely separate beyond discal cell 7
   Hind wing with veins $S_c + R_1$ and R_s fused or closely parallel between discal cell and wing tip 12
7. Forewing with radial (accessory) cell 8
   Forewing without radial cell (see also couplets 3, 9, and 10)..................Psychidae
8. Proboscis vestigial 9
   Mouth parts usually developed, with scaled proboscis...............................13
9. Tibial spurs short or absent...Epipyropidae
   Hind tibia with 2 pairs of spurs (see also couplets 3, 7, and 10)...............Psychidae
10. Forewing with single complete anal vein...11
    Forewing with anal veins more or less fused or connected by a crossvein so as to end as a single vein (see also couplets 3, 7, and 9)......................................Psychidae
11. Shaft of antennae tapering evenly from base to tip 12
    Antennae thickened before tip, usually ending in a recurved hook (see also couplets 4 and 12) ....Noctuidae
12. Hind wing with S_c usually free from R_s along the cell, though sometimes approaching it (see also couplet 4) (Chrysauginae, Phycitinae, Pyraustinae)...............Pyralididae
    Hind wing with S_c fused with R_s for short distance before the middle of cell (see also couplets 4 and 11)..Noctuidae
13. Maxillary palpi straight and porrect, or vestigial 14
    Maxillary palpi conspicuous, folded in resting position ....Oenophilidae
14. Basal joint of antenna simple, though often with scales, hairs, or bristles...............15
    Basal joint of antenna enlarged and concave beneath, forming an eyecap (see also couplet 21)...Blastobasidae
15. Hind wing with well-developed anal region; venation more or less complete 16
    Hind wing narrow-lanceolate or linear; venation often reduced 18
16. Hind wing with anal vein not distally forked 17
    Hind wing with third anal vein distally forked ....Cyclotornidae
17. Upper side of hind wing with fringe of long hairs on basal part of C_u ......Olethreutidae
    Hind wing without fringe of long hairs on basal part of C_u ....Tortricidae
18. Forewing with discal cell formed 19
    Forewing without closed cell (see also couplet 19) ....Heliodinidae
19. Hind tarsi without evident groups of bristles 20
    Hind tarsi with more or less distinct groups of bristles near the ends of the several joints (see also couplet 18) ....Heliodinidae

20. Forewing with discal cell set obliquely, the end distinctly closer to the hind margin than to costa; vein Cu$_2$ very short and usually extending directly back to wing margin..........21
    Forewing with discal cell axial and central; vein Cu$_2$ normally long and continuing parallel with median veins (see also couplet 21) (**Lavernidae**) ....**Cosmopterygidae**
21. Forewing with blunt discal cell; veins R$_2$ and Cu arising from the end of discal cell (see also couplet 14)...**Blastobasidae**
    Forewing without stigma; vein R$_2$ arising distinctly before end of discal cell (see also couplet 20) ....**Cosmopterygidae**

Since all known species of this order are parasitic, a key to all families is given (adapted from Bohart 1941). It should be noted that males are unknown for Stichotrematidae and females are unknown for Myrmecolacidae.

Key to Adults of the Families of Strepsiptera

(Males)

1. Tarsi with fewer than 5 segments and clawless..2
   Tarsi 5-segmented and clawed ....**Mengeidae**
2. Tarsi 4-segmented 3
   Tarsi 3- or 2-segmented...5
3. Antennae with less than 7 segments...4
   Antennae with 7 segments ....**Myrmecolacidae**
4. Third and fourth antennal segments laterally flabellate ....**Callipharixenidae**
   Only third antennal segment laterally flabellate ....**Stylopidae**
5. Tarsi 2-segmented; antennae 4-segmented.................................**Elenchidae**
   Tarsi 3-segmented; antennae 7-segmented..........................**Halictophagidae**

(Females)

1. Adult stage partially endoparasitic, without legs, antennae or eyes 2
   Adult stage free living, with legs, antennae and eyes........................**Mengeidae**
2. Cephalothorax without hook-like projections behind spiracles 3
   Cephalothorax with hook-like projections behind spiracles ....**Stichotrematidae**
3. Cephalothorax with single pair of spiracles; thoracic segments not well defined............4
   Cephalothorax greatly elongate, with 2 pairs of spiracles, or with head and thoracic segments distinct ....**Callipharixenidae**
4. Parasites of Homoptera or Gryllidae 5
   Parasites of Hymenoptera ....**Stylopidae**
5. Brood-passage opening a narrow, linear or obling slit; thorax prominent   **Halictophagidae**
   Brood-passage opening broad and semicircular; thorax reduced and ringlike in back of brood-passage opening ....**Elenchidae**

SECTION IV

The Introduction, Culture, and Establishment Programme

CHAPTER 9

Foreign Exploration for Beneficial Organisms

B. R. BARTLETT AND R. VAN DEN BOSCH

INTRODUCTION

PLANTS AND ANIMALS transplanted to a new land may flourish in their new location and become pests primarily because the natural enemies preying upon them in their native habitat are left behind. By introducing the natural enemies, the abundance of the pest in the new environment may be lowered. This is the basic principle of the biological control of immigrant pests—a concept which emerged logically and independently wherever naturalists studied outbreaks of exotic pest species.

The application of this concept to particular pest problems and the successes attained with the method are presented in other chapters. Many of the earlier accomplishments in this field were achieved under very difficult circumstances and with handicaps which to a large extent no longer exist. Today, with greatly improved transport facilities and increased information on host and natural-enemy distribution, the expectation of success in foreign exploration and importation is much greater than it used to be.

Many of the biological control projects of the past have merely been concerned with the redistribution of efficient natural enemies successfully used in previous campaigns in other areas. Such programmes are usually conducted without elaborate preparation, facilities, and specially trained personnel. On the other hand, pioneer foreign exploration programmes for new parasites and predators are comparatively complex operations requiring close teamwork among well-trained personnel, and unique facilities which are ordinarily available only to organizations especially equipped for this type of work. The concern of this chapter is principally with the pioneer type of programme, including the planning for exploration and the techniques of search, collection, and shipment of beneficial species with special reference to entomophagous insects. Programmes involving introduction of insect pathogens and of plant-feeding insects for weed control present some specialized problems which are discussed in chapters 18 to 24.

The first section of this chapter is devoted to consideration of certain general concepts and rules which guide the development of the project, the collection, and the importation of exotic beneficial organisms. These basic concepts are treated

283

separately from techniques and procedures in order to present a more orderly and informative background for effective exploration. A full appreciation of these principles is essential if the obstacles to project initiation are to be overcome and adequate support is to be received for the programme. This is often the most difficult part of the campaign.

IMPORTANT CONCEPTS RELEVANT TO THE SEARCH FOR EXOTIC BENEFICIAL ARTHROPODS

Amenability of Pests to Biological Control

The first consideration in the initiation of a foreign introduction programme is a realistic appraisal of the characteristics of the pest problem as they affect the probability of successful biological control. The experience in Hawaii that every pest as it developed upon sugar cane proved amenable to complete biological control is admittedly not reproducible everywhere with every agricultural crop. However, there have been few complete failures with the method where an intensive, well-supported campaign was followed.

One of the primary concepts in considering the amenability of a particular pest to biological control is that, as a general rule, immigrant pests offer much better prospects for success than do indigenous pest species. Although some native pest species have been controlled by purposefully introduced natural enemies in past campaigns, the number of successes have been few in comparison with those obtained against immigrant pest species. This is true for the obvious reason that native pests are usually already attacked by a complex of natural enemies which have evolved with them. Sometimes existing biological control of native species is upset by some new cultural or agricultural practice and these species then arise to pest status (see chapters 16 and 17). The probability is low that biological control of such pests may be re-established through introduction of exotic natural enemies.

Often proposed exploration for natural enemies of pests fails to gain support unless there have been some convincing examples of success with comparable pests in other campaigns. For this reason, many of the introduction programmes have followed previous models directed against relatively few types of agricultural pests. Where there have been no previous patterns from which we can judge the chances of attaining biological control of a pest, the possibilities of success must be inferred to a large extent from naturally occurring cases of biological control. Many striking cases of biological control of this type are only now being brought to light through upsets caused by the new powerful insecticides or by improved natural-enemy evaluation techniques. This increased appreciation of naturally existing biological control is forcing us to revise our previous ideas of the limitations of the biological control method. In considering these cases it becomes increasingly apparent that, on a theoretical basis at least, there are no special pest habits or habitats which should arbitrarily preclude the possibility of any insect's control by entomophagous species. Some pest habits, habitats, or some climatic deterrents to the survival of a pest's natural enemies may reduce the probability of complete biological control but none can arbitrarily be said to exclude the possibility of success. Parasites and predators have developed specialized adaptations to overcome almost every handicap imposed upon them in nature. Explosive host reproductive capacities, univoltinism, hibernation, all types of diapause, and protective development, such as with fruit fly and borer larvae within plant tissue and scarabaeids within the soil or eggs in plant tissue, have not discouraged host discovery and attack in nature.

The frequency of success attained in past campaigns against white-flies, mealybugs, and scale insects has, in some cases, prompted the view that only these types of pests lend themselves well to biological control. Aside from the highly significant fact that more intensive efforts have been directed against these pests, which in the past have been difficult to control with chemicals, it is believed that biological control of such insects has been favoured because they are, in general, immigrant species usually occurring in areas of mild climate and they are relatively exposed, sessile, and colonial in habit and have overlapping life cycles.

Arboreal pests have, in general, received the greatest attention and perhaps because of this have appeared to be most amenable to biological control. This is presumably because with orchard-tree pests, as well as those of forest and rangelands, the possibilities for successful biological control are definitely enhanced by the relatively stable nature of such environments.

The prospects for biological control of pests upon annual crops with host–plant-free periods have, in general, been viewed in a comparatively unfavourable light despite the fact that many potential pests on native annuals are apparently restrained by natural enemies. There have been, however, some impressive introduction programmes involving pests of vegetable and field crops and a greater number of successes against cereal and forage pests where more extensive campaigns have been conducted (Clausen 1956).

Biological control of relatively few of the pests of medical and veterinary importance has been attempted. Exceptional opportunities unquestionably exist in this field (Pemberton 1948a; Laird 1959) but most prospective programmes have been too extensive to be undertaken by existing organizations.

There does not appear to be any scientific support for the opinion sometimes expressed that the biological control method could not be expected to supply a satisfactory answer to problems involving plant or animal diseases carried by insect vectors. This supposition is based on the erroneous theory that natural enemies can never continuously maintain their hosts at exceedingly low population densities. This theory is effectively refuted by a number of cases where pests have been reduced to extremely low population levels through biological control. These cases include, among others, control of cottony-cushion scale (*Icerya purchasi* Mask.) in California and elsewhere, citrophilus mealybug (*Pseudococcus gahani* Green) in southern California, the alfalfa weevil (*Hypera postica* (Gyll.)) in lowland middle California, and the Florida red scale (*Chrysomphalus aonidum* (L.)) in Israel.

Pest and Natural-Enemy Associations in Their
Native Home as a Basis for Search

A basic tenet of biological control is that natural enemies capable of attacking and destroying the pest species in its new home are best sought in the land of pest origin. A close adaptation of a natural enemy to its host, presumably arising from the long-standing association of the two in their native home, is reflected in greater efficiency of the natural enemy in finding its host and holding it at low densities. This concept is a good rule for emphasis of effort in natural-enemy search, but some misleading suppositions have stemmed from its strict interpretation. For instance, in the early developmental years of biological control there was a widely held belief that no plant-feeding insect was a serious problem in its land of origin since there must have originated enemies there to restrain it (Compere 1961). Today we know this to be an over-optimistic view. Not only are indigenous species sometimes serious problems in their land of origin, but also the rarity of a pest in its native habitat is not irrefutable evidence of restraint by natural enemies alone.

Another common early assumption stemming from the above precept was that the native home of the pest species offered the only reasonable area of search for efficient natural enemies. Today the exclusion of areas other than the native habitat of the pest species cannot be categorically accepted. It is not at all uncommon for pests, in the course of their peregrinations, to acquire effective natural enemies from allied native insect hosts. A well-recognized instance of this sort occurred when *Macrocentrus ancylivorus* Roh. found the introduced oriental fruit moth, *Grapholitha molesta* (Busck), as much to its liking as its native host, the strawberry leaf roller, *Ancylis comptana fragariae* (W. and R.) (Daniel 1932). Haeussler (1930) recorded 56 species of parasites capable of attacking *G. molesta* in the United States in his survey preliminary to the undertaking of a foreign introduction programme against this pest. The tachinid *Compsilura concinnata* Meig. has found approximately 100 satisfactory hosts in the United States since its introduction in 1906 from Europe (Webber and Schaffner 1926). *Aphytis chrysomphali* (Mercet) in California and *Habrolepis rouxi* Comp. in South Africa, two of the most important parasites of California red scale, *Aonidiella aurantii* (Mask.), have most assuredly originated on their imported host in this fashion because these parasites are unknown in the Orient where the pest is indigenous. Again in this connection, it is significant that in the campaign against the oriental fruit moth 25 parasite species were discovered attacking this pest in France and Italy, although the pest was a relative newcomer to the area, while 10 species were found in Australia which is also an invaded area (Allen, Holloway, and Haeussler 1940).

With predatory species where host specificity is less pronounced than in parasites, acceptance of new species of prey is common; and with hyperparasites, transfer to many newly encountered hosts is generally expected.

From the above examples it is logical to deduce that not only can the search for natural enemies be profitably extended to areas other than the native home of a pest species, but also that indigenous pest species may be amenable to control by introduced parasites and predators. The success attending the importation of *Ptychomyia remota* Ald., the tachinid parasite of another moth species, *Artona catoxantha* (Hamps.), to control the coconut moth, *Levuana iridescens* B.-B., in Fiji (Tothill, Taylor, and Paine 1930) presented such an example, as did the utilization of the eulophid parasite *Pleurotropis parvulus* Ferrière to control the coconut leaf-mining beetle, *Promecotheca reichei* Baly, in Fiji (Taylor 1937). The use of the wasp *Campsomeris marginella modesta* Sm., native to the Philippines, to control grubs of the anomala beetle, *Anomala orientalis* (Waterh.), attacking sugar cane in Hawaii (Pemberton 1948a), presents a somewhat comparable example wherein the pest which was indigenous to Korea and Japan was controlled by a parasite obtained from another host in another area. Also, *Opius tryoni* Cam., the most effective parasite on the Mediterranean fruit fly, *Ceratitis capitata* (Wied.), in Hawaii was introduced from Australia where it parasitized *Dacus tryoni* (Froggatt) (Silvestri 1914). Actually, there is often considerable doubt as to the native home of a pest species. Presumptions are frequently based upon host-plant origins which are themselves often subject to question, or upon the immediate source of the pest introduction without regard to the possibility that the pest entered the country by a circuitous route.

In foreign collection programmes it is taken as a general rule that the predominant natural enemy occurring at relatively low host densities in the native home of a pest offers the greatest promise for introduction to a new environment. The rule is substantially valid but it can be misleading. The unpredictable effects of climate and other ecological factors in the new home of the imported parasites and predators very often overshadow other characteristics which lead to efficiency of a species in its native habitat. Furthermore, the fact that a particular natural enemy may not predominate at all times and places often makes it difficult to determine which species actually dominates in the native area. Accidental attack at low host densities by parasite species primarily adapted to other hosts also makes this precept difficult to use as anything more than a guide for emphasis of effort in collection and colonization. As an illustration, *Metaphycus helvolus* (Comp.), which is the most efficient parasite of black scale in California, was overshadowed in abundance in its native African environment by at least three other parasite species (*Coccophagus rusti* Comp., *C. ochraceus* How., and *C. capensis* Comp.), none of which has provided efficient control in the new locality despite permanent establishment (Bartlett, personal observation).

Climatic Similarities Between Areas of Origin and Destination as a Basis for Search

In the importation of exotic beneficial arthropods it is generally felt that the more nearly similar the climate of the native home and that of the land of introduction, the greater the probability for natural-enemy establishment and success. However, it is almost impossible to predict exactly how an imported species will respond to a new climatic environment. In California, extremes of cold and to some extent of heat and aridity, have in general, appeared to be the greatest factors limiting adaptation and establishment of natural enemies introduced for scale insect and mealybug control.

As a rule, it appears that the prospects for successful natural-enemy establishment are in many respects comparable with those encountered in plant introduction, viz., that it is more common to find successful adaptation going from colder to warmer areas than vice versa. There are some exceptions to this rule. *Comperiella bifasciata* How. and *Prospaltella perniciosi* Tower are important parasites of California red scale in regions of California where the climate is less equable than it is in the tropical areas where the parasites originated. A similar exception was observed in South Africa by Tooke (1955) for the egg parasite of *Gonipterus scutellatus* Gyll. which was obtained from a subtropical area of Australia and spread from areas of a similar climate to more temperate parts of South Africa.

The relatively high degree of early successes in biological control in insular as compared with continental areas is now considered to be related in part to the generally subtropical or tropical climates of such areas and the normally homodynamic development of host species on these islands but not to the mere fact that they were islands. This subject is discussed in more detail in chapters 5 and 24.

Very few entomophagous species are likely to be uniformly active throughout the entire range of their host. Different natural-enemy species frequently show distinctive distributional patterns within the region occupied by the host (Thompson and Parker 1928; Clark 1934). These may be largely climatic adaptations and can, of course, overlap to varying degrees. These relationships clearly emphasize the importance for search and collection of natural enemies over as wide an area of the host distribution as can reasonably be accomplished. Usually more than one species of imported natural enemy will be necessary to obtain coverage of all the diverse habitats of the host. The more entomophagous species imported and the greater their range of climatic adaptation, the greater will be the expected geographical extent of biological control in the land of destination. Marked differences in climatic extremes due to geographical elevation and other climatic determinants occur in most regions. Efforts should be made to collect in areas of diverse climate, not only to determine the possible ranges of natural-enemy species but also because these areas may be inhabited by especially adapted forms which should be incorporated in rearing stocks for the sake of increased genetic diversity.

The Importance of Host-Specificity and Interspecific Competition in Natural-Enemy Introduction

A highly developed host-specificity (narrow host range) has been emphasized as an attribute closely allied with the efficiency of parasitic species (Howard and Fiske 1911), while the polyphagous habit (capacity to reproduce on more than one host) is often associated with the high host-density attack characteristic of many general predators. Furthermore, it has frequently been noted that in successful cases of biological control a single entomophagous species has been a key to success, and that such species are frequently highly specific in their host relationships. From these often-repeated generalizations and from the obvious needs of some parasites for special adaptations to synchronize their life histories with those of their hosts, it might be assumed that there could be no completely effective biological control without highly developed host specificity. On the contrary, a wide host range may, on occasion, permit natural enemy development on alternative hosts to substitute for single host synchronization requirements and may permit natural enemies to bridge over periods of host scarcity which would otherwise be fatal.

The discovery of host-specific natural enemies in foreign exploration is always stimulating since, like uniquely specific biological and physiological adaptations between the host and natural enemy, it indicates the long standing coexistence of the two, but it does not necessarily ensure superior efficiency in control of the host.

Many natural-enemy species eventually prove to be much less specific than originally believed, and the concentration of effort in foreign collection is, in general, placed more justifiably upon natural-enemy species which have a high degree of preference for the host. Varying proportions of the parasites obtained in any extensive biological control campaign will probably consist of accidental or casual species which have developed to high levels on their preferred hosts and have over-flowed to other hosts upon which they are less well adapted. To some extent this characteristic can be assessed by the collector on the basis of the natural enemies' distribution and upon other observed host relationships. Apparently, failure to recognize this relationship has repeatedly led to disappointment in introduction programmes.

Some workers have attached great significance to the advantages of parasite specialization and their theories have furnished the basis for a controversy in connection with natural-enemy introduction that has had far-reaching effects upon foreign exploration policies. One school of thought has maintained that where several natural-enemy species attacking the same host were considered for import, only one species having the best predetermined attributes should be introduced, while the opposing view holds that all natural-enemy species should be imported and colonized.

The evidence and arguments relative to this problem have been discussed in detail under the subjects of multiple parasitism and specific versus general parasites or predators in chapter 5. Although there are rare instances where competitive species have worked to the over-all detriment of a pest's subjugation, these cases are probably no more serious than are the cases where a single species has tended to reduce its own potential maximum efficiency through the evening of host stages, superparasitism, cannibalism, etc. The view has been widely accepted that where competitive species are involved, ordinarily those with the greatest adaptability to the new environment will eventually replace the less efficient species without over-all detriment to control. Where a number of species are introduced which have slightly different ecological niches in the host's habitat, greater total host mortality usually will result.

Inasmuch as results cannot be adequately predicted prior to trial in the new

10—I.P.W.

environment, emphasis should be placed upon importation of all natural-enemy species which will provide a sequence of attack against all host stages in time and space. The probable capacities of the various species can and should be estimated by the collector from studies on abundance and distribution, but these observations should not be used as anything more than indications for emphasis on collection and guidance of colonization policies.

Importance of Genetic Races in Foreign Collection

The questions concerning morphologically indistinguishable races of natural enemies and their complex interrelationships are covered in chapters 5 and 8. To the foreign collector, however, these phenomena sometimes present puzzling problems concerning their recognition and the weighing of their importance. The decision to import a suspected biological or ecological strain of an entomophagous insect may at times rest largely upon the collector's identification and determination of its significance. Adequate time or facilities for complete assessment of the value of such suspected forms are not always available to a foreign collector. However, where geographical isolation or biological evidence indicates that a genetic race may exist, the general policy should be to assure that it is imported and incorporated into the rearing stock. Presumably the genetic characteristics of such a race will remain in the stock and will be available for adaptive segregation when selective forces are again encountered in the new environment.

Some speculation has arisen concerning the possibile limitation of genetic variability by the introduction of only a very narrow segment of a given natural-enemy population. In a few cases, the entire release stocks of some natural enemies have developed from the progeny of single mated females, resulting in what are presumably highly isogenetic strains. To assure genetic variability, shipment stocks should be as large as practicable, and should include collections from areas as widely different as possible. From such genetically diverse stocks the possibility of a species' adaptation to a new environment should be enhanced. Also, such diverse shipments actually may include sibling species or very closely related ones whose morphological differences may not have been recognized.

Host-Plant Preference of Natural Enemies

In their search for hosts, natural enemies are often first attracted to particular habitats, the primary attractant usually being certain plant species upon which the host feeds (Cushman 1926a). As a result, there is frequently an avoidance of some plants by natural enemies and a marked preference for other plants (Williams 1931; Ullyett 1947). Thus, to be successful on an agricultural crop the natural-enemy adult should habitually frequent that host plant. These complex responses of entomophagous insects are analysed in greater detail in chapter 5 and are considered here only in so far as they relate to foreign collection procedures.

One might assume that search for natural enemies in the land of pest origin should be concentrated upon the pest as it occurs upon native plants which, presumably representing a long-standing host relationship, would harbour the most perfectly adapted natural-enemy species or strains. This type of search is sometimes pursued, but, because of the variable host-plant affinities of pests in different lands and for other practical reasons, the search is frequently concentrated upon the plant species which are affected by the pest in the land of destination. It is not uncommon for the foreign collector to find significantly different natural-enemy complexes upon the different plant species inhabited by the host. The same host-plant preferences by natural-enemy species logically might be expected to follow transfer to a new environment. In the absence of reliable evidence concerning possible natural-enemy preferences, it is considered desirable to collect material from as wide a variety of host plants as is possible, with emphasis upon collections from the host plant with which the pest is associated at home.

PLANNING AND PREPARATION
FOR NATURAL ENEMY INTRODUCTION

Taxonomic Identification and Origin of the Pest Species

In the planning of a programme for the introduction of new natural enemies, great reliance is ordinarily placed upon help and suggestions from many sources. This co-operative effort starts with the proper determination and taxonomic affinities of the pest species. Authoritative answers as to the identity, host-plant relationships, and geographic distribution of new pests are often difficult to obtain. Frequently this information must be sought from museums and specialists in foreign countries.

Occasionally, when the pest is undescribed it is impossible to obtain conclusive evidence as to its native home, and the only evidence of its origin may lie in the information afforded by the geographical distribution of closely allied species, or in the distribution of its host plants. Sometimes shipments of infested plant material may be traced to their point of origin. Quarantine officers at the major ports of entry can frequently be of service in this connection. Even conjecture based upon principal trade routes has provided clues to the probable origin of certain pests (Compere and Smith 1932).

Literature references to the pest species receive detailed attention when they are available. However, the greatest amount of information on both the pest and its natural enemies is commonly obtained through personal inquiry or correspondence with entomologists working on the pest group in foreign countries. Their familiarity with more obscure published and unpublished records on the fauna of the region can be most helpful. It was in this manner, for instance, that parasites of *Therioaphis maculata* (Buckton) were first recognized as occurring in the Middle East (van den Bosch *et al.* 1959*a*, p. 136). Prior knowledge of a pest's natural enemies is, of course, always an aid to the collector in centring and timing his search and to the receiver in preparing for insectary propagation. It commonly happens, however, that comparatively little information is available on natural enemies. The parasite catalogue (Thompson 1943 to 1955) is very useful as a check list of recorded natural enemies. Aside from this source of information, major bio-ecological works on the pest species and taxonomic studies on entomophagous groups can be consulted. However, many of the parasite records should be accepted with reservation unless they are based upon rearings from properly isolated and identified host material. Furthermore, even when extensive records have been obtained from the literature, experience has shown that the recorded natural enemies of a pest will often comprise only a small proportion of those subsequently taken by a foreign collector.

A taxonomic background is of advantage to a foreign collector, but lack of specialization should not be much of a handicap to a well-trained entomologist. The collector should have as much knowledge as possible of the species closely allied to the pest of interest and the characters used in their separation. Recognition specimens of the known, closely related species and notes and drawings of critical characters will prove invaluable.

Finally, the explorer should be widely familiar with the general arthropod pest problems in his home area so that in his foreign activities he will be able to recognize these pests and their natural enemies and collect them or note their existence for future reference.

The Timing and Organization of a Foreign Exploration Programme

After the area of search has been determined, the most opportune period for foreign collection must be fixed. Here, consideration must be given to the synchronization of the foreign collecting and domestic culture and colonization programmes. The seasonal abundance or availability of host material, both at the place of origin and the place of destination, has great influence upon the final decision. The greatest latitude in synchronizing suitable collection periods with desired insectary rearing and colonization programmes is provided by the development of good laboratory host-production techniques at the receiving station. The culture methods and techniques which may be used here are discussed in chapters 10 and 11. Until adequate handling procedures have been developed at the point of receipt, a thorough and intensive exploration and introduction programme should not be undertaken.

The seasonal availability of natural enemies at the point of origin often cannot be fully anticipated. Therefore, although establishment of temporary laboratory quarters for the first part of the collection effort may be previously arranged for, the decision to maintain operations at a predetermined station should be left to the discretion of the collector.

It is often necessary to be prepared for at least some propagation of natural enemies in the area of collection. The greatest possible degree of flexibility must be maintained by the collector with respect to decisions as to where and to what extent these programmes should be pursued. The amount of rearing to be done will depend largely upon developments in the over-all programme. However, in light of modern air-transport facilities, extensive rearing on the collector's part will not usually be necessary. The seasonal availability of suitable host stages in the home area may limit the period during which the natural enemies can be received and cultured. This often occurs where seasons are reversed, as between the northern and southern hemispheres (Jaynes 1933).

When exploration for natural enemies of a pest is being undertaken for the first time, it must be anticipated that the search will extend over at least one full season of pest activity and will cover the widest possible range of habitats occupied by the pest. Of course, where the pest is extremely widespread and is attacked by a large complex of natural enemies, all of the necessary survey and collection activities cannot always be done in a single season.

Where an organization is constantly at work seeking natural enemies of a wide variety of pest species, semipermanent laboratories are often established at strategic points in foreign countries. The United States Department of Agriculture has maintained a laboratory in France for nearly thirty years, and the Commonwealth Institute of Biological Control has likewise maintained laboratories in the United States, Switzerland, and Trinidad, and has recently established stations in India and Pakistan.

Semipermanent laboratories in foreign countries offer many advantages. From them, timing of shipments can be synchronized with needs in the domestic area and shipments can be maintained on regular schedules. Furthermore, with adequate laboratory facilities, pure cultures of the natural enemies may be maintained so that they can be shipped free of host material and with perfect exclusion of hyperparasites. Direct liberation of such previously screened natural-enemy species can be made under certain circumstances following very careful re-examination of the stocks prior to direct colonization. This procedure has been employed by most biological control organizations at one time or another. When circumstances permit and the procedure can be carried out by highly competent personnel, the policy of sending adult stages only of the beneficial species almost completely eliminates the possibility of accidental importation of pests or of secondary parasites. In fact, wherever quarantine facilities are not available at the point of destination, this is the only means by which exotic material can be received. However, it must be recognized that some risk is still involved, and that strict quarantine processing at destination is to be preferred. Where the policy of laboratory rearing and shipment for direct release is pursued, the foreign collector's laboratory need not necessarily be elaborately equipped, but the collector himself must be a highly responsible and well-trained specialist familiar with the identities and biologies of the entomophagous insects and pests involved. With foreign-laboratory arrangements, additional help usually is required to permit the unencumbered pursuance of a collector's programme. Some biological control organizations, which have established semipermanent foreign laboratories to facilitate direct natural-enemy release at destination, have assigned teams of their most highly qualified men to handle the propagation and exportation work in the foreign field.

Preparation for Transport and Receipt of Exotic Natural Enemies

The facilities, preparations, and planning required for receipt of shipments of exotic natural enemies are covered in detail in chapters 10, 11, and 13. However, it is the responsibility of the foreign collector to see that all arrangements function without serious conflict, particularly where transport and entry of the natural-enemy shipments are concerned.

Federal permission is required by most national governments whenever living organisms are to be brought into a country. These permits ordinarily are issued to qualified officials of a biological control organization through the federal quarantine agencies following consultation with other interested governmental regulatory and research groups. In the United States, introduction permits for beneficial organisms are issued to an individual official in charge of the import programme, who is then responsible for the activities of those to whom he designates collecting and receiving responsibilities. Permits are granted only upon satisfactory evidence of adequate facilities for reception and screening and of strict adherence to precautionary quarantine regulations. The permits, affixed to each parcel shipped, designate the nature of the contents as parasites or predators of a specific host insect, and exempt the parcels from opening and inspection by federal quarantine or customs officers at the port of entry. Special state or provincial permits are likewise sometimes required for entry of parcels exempt from inspection. These, too, are affixed to the parcel upon shipment.

After approval is obtained for a specific import programme from quarantine regulatory agencies, it may be desirable for the collector to acquaint the customs and quarantine officers at the port of entry with the nature of the programme and the type of parcels that will be entering, and to enlist their aid in seeing that foreign shipments are not subject to unnecessary delay or adverse physical conditions while passing through their jurisdiction. This is particularly advisable when air-freight transport is to be used. When air mail is used, the postal authority at the point of destination is called upon to hasten dispatch of the shipment by telephoning the recipient on arrival of a parcel. A sticker requesting the local postmaster to telephone the receiver's number is ordinarily attached to the parcel. With air-freighted parcels, arrangements are often made for special care in handling and dispatch of the packages. It has been possible at times to secure special treatment for the parcels, as, for instance, their removal from the cargo spaces if an aeroplane is to be treated with an insecticide. Co-operation of airline officials has, on occasion, been extended to the placing of packages in the cabin compartments of the plane when extreme temperatures were anticipated in flight or during cargo transfers.

The co-operation of customs brokers is sometimes needed in the export of parcels by air freight from a foreign country. However, receipt and clearance of the shipment without opening for inspection can usually be expedited by prior arrangements with customs and quarantine officials rather than through a broker.

Special arrangements at a high level of authority may be necessary for clearance of an exploration programme with the agricultural agencies of a country where the exploratory work is to be done. It is desirable that the agricultural attaché of the country, or other appropriate governmental representative, be requested to inform his agricultural ministry of the impending project, giving full credentials of the director of the biological programme and those of the designated collector. This should be followed by correspondence from the director of the import programme to the foreign agricultural ministry requesting acceptance of the mission and setting forth the qualifications of the personnel involved, the area to be visited, the duration of the project, and the personal contacts desired. These channels usually provide the best avenues through which arrangements for laboratory quarters can be made in locations near transport facilities and in close association with local entomological institutions. Also, through these official sources it is easier to make further contact with foreign customs and quarantine authorities so that parcels for export will not be subject to opening for inspection when shipped.

It is usually advantageous for the collector to acquaint local specialists with the technical details of the mission, and to enlist their aid in locating possible sources of host and natural-enemy material.

Aside from the required passport, visas, and health inoculation certificates, the following simple preparations for the foreign collector are suggested. Personal identification cards are desirable and an international driving permit should be obtained. Serial or model numbers for all optical and other valued research equipment should be available for registry with customs officials.

THE COLLECTION OF NATURAL ENEMIES

Before the days of rapid air transport there were many problems in the work of a foreign collector, which now are only of historical interest. Many interesting and informative published accounts of the travels of the early explorers for beneficial insects illustrate the difficulties encountered. Those described by Perkins (1906), Silvestri (1914), and Muir and Swezey (1916), offer especially interesting reading. The task of introducing exotic beneficial insects was an art which was entrusted only to specialists with extensive knowledge and experience in the field of entomophagous insect culture. The discovery and collection of natural enemies often constituted a relatively small part of their labours. Maintaining culture stocks and getting them safely to their destination required the greatest of care and ingenuity and frequently the bulk of the explorer's effort. The odysseys of certain of the famous early explorers who sometimes encircled the globe seem incredible when it is realized that host and parasite stocks were maintained for extensive periods on voyages under every conceivable condition of transport. Losses of stocks were calamities, but often unavoidable. Adverse weather conditions, scarcity of host material, hyperparasitism, failure of reproduction in the culture stocks, and loss through the domination of competitive species made the odds against successful importation fantastically high. With exasperating frequency the foreign collector arrived at his destination with alluring tales of the natural enemies he might have introduced had fortune favoured their transport.

Though air transport has taken much of the glamour from foreign exploration, it certainly has added to the fruitfulness of the explorer's efforts. The problems of the culture of host and natural enemies under difficult circumstances are no longer to be contended with. A foreign collector can now concentrate his efforts upon the search for new and efficient species so that there is very little excuse for missing any desirable natural enemies present in the area. With the modern network of air transport, the collector can quickly cover a much greater area than previously. Above all, he can safely and rapidly transship adequate numbers of almost any stage of an entomophagous species from the most remote areas.

Present-day collecting policies and procedures have changed drastically as a result of the relative ease of transport and the consequent change of emphasis of natural-enemy culture from the area of exploration to the land of destination. A collector has always relied heavily upon the aid and advice of foreign associates in his field of interest. Now it is common for a collector to make arrangements with foreign workers for future shipment of natural enemies and then for him to return home where he can supervise the domestic aspects of the import programme. By properly acquainting a foreign associate with the location and desirable seasonal sequence for shipment of entomophagous material, and by supplying the requisite shipping instructions and approved permits, it is often possible to have continued shipments of material sent by air with only moderate inconvenience to the collaborator. In this way it is possible to receive all the available natural enemies in a sequence such that proper care and attention can be given to each species.

Host scarcity is one of the greatest problems confronting the collector. Where effective biological control exists, it is often difficult to find satisfactory host infestations and to obtain sufficient numbers of the entomophagous species.

A colonial type of pest distribution is commonly associated with a high degree of natural-enemy efficiency (Nicholson 1933). These localized host infestations very often shift in status, both numerically and spatially, flourishing prior to discovery by natural enemies, then waning to complete or near-complete extinction as they are attacked by the beneficial species. The number and size of pest loci will vary with many environmental factors and with the habits of the entomophagous species; however, from a practical standpoint, infestations of the host will be most prevalent in locations not readily discovered by the natural enemies or at places where, for other reasons, the normal activity of beneficial species is at times inhibited. A collector's efforts, then, if efficient biological control exists, will ordinarily be concentrated in locations characterized by such conditions.

Localized outbreaks of the pest in commercial plantings often constitute a favourable source of collection for exotic natural enemies, but such sources of collection, too, have their disadvantages. There is, of course, a higher expectation for adaptability of the natural enemy in the home area, providing it is taken on the same agricultural crop in a foreign land. However, following insecticide-induced pest outbreaks, the dominant natural enemies may not necessarily be the species usually responsible for control at low host density. The collector should be cognizant of such possibilities and be on guard against overenthusiasm for temporarily dominant forms.

In a foreign country the search for a pest and its natural enemies need not be conducted upon native vegetation in relatively inaccessible areas. Experience has shown that botanical gardens, parks, experimental plantings, domestic gardens, national forests, ornamental vegetation along walkways and roads, and similar accessible plantings or non-cultivated vegetation will generally support populations of the insects being sought. This practical emphasis by foreign collectors upon dooryard and comparable search areas has been aptly referred to as 'sidewalk exploring.' Plants growing under such conditions are often isolated one from the other and tend to become infested at different times. This frequently results in the pest temporarily evading discovery by natural enemies and thus producing localized outbreaks which ultimately, however, come under heavy attack by parasites or predators.

Dusty conditions, which inhibit natural enemy activity, also often contribute to pest increase and ultimately, as the dusty condition ameliorates, to substantial natural-enemy populations. Ant activity may at times encourage localized pest outbreaks. Collectors, by eliminating the ants and awaiting subsequent build-up of parasite or predator populations, can at times obtain natural enemies in large numbers. It should be noted that under the 'abnormal' conditions just discussed, the relative abundance of the various parasite species may also be affected, and the most common species may not be the one which is dominant under normal conditions. Since the assessment of efficiency of the natural enemies by the collector in a foreign country weighs strongly in the choice of species to be cultured and colonized at home, it is most important that the collector analyse carefully the circumstances which contribute to local outbreaks of the pest.

When the host is scarce in an area, a technique commonly referred to as the 'host-exposure method' is often found useful for the collection of entomophagous species. It involves the exposure of colonies of the host species in the field to attract natural enemies. Sometimes the host is propagated on a plant in the field under a cloth sleeve or cage so that it is protected from its natural enemies; then, at the appropriate time, the colony is exposed to attack by natural enemies. The same purpose is accomplished by placing laboratory-infested host plants in a habitat where natural enemies will be able to discover the 'trap' host material. In both types of exposure the material is then returned to the laboratory where the progeny of the attacking natural enemies are reared (Haeussler 1940). Another modification of this type of collection involves confining field-gathered host specimens so that the mesh of the cage will permit ingress of natural enemies but prevent the host from escaping. The host-exposure technique is also effective as a means of capturing mated adult female parasites or predators for direct shipment to the homeland, since even those species incapable of attacking or successfully developing on the particular host stages exposed may be attracted to, and remain with, the host. The procedure has a particularly interesting application in that it is possible to place a host-infested potted plant near or within the foliage of plants rarely attacked in the foreign land but on which biological control is desired at home. In the host-exposure collecting method, care should be taken to prevent contamination of the stocks by other pest species, since natural enemies attacking these forms may be mistakenly considered as enemies of the pest of interest. Ordinarily the 'trap' material is suspended by a wire or otherwise kept away from direct contact with contamination sources. With this technique, it is also sometimes necessary to remove general predators at frequent intervals in order to avoid extermination of the host material. Examples of the host-exposure method are shown in figure 37, facing p. 304.

The techniques for capturing and retaining natural-enemy specimens alive and in robust condition differ considerably from ordinary museum collecting procedures. For instance, the search for exotic natural enemies is quite often limited to the preferred host plants of the pest of concern and does not embrace the full range of host plants. Once the host habitats and the collecting sites have been established, activity involves finding the host species in all of its stages of development and in quantities which will supply adequate numbers of natural enemies. This frequently requires repeated visits to the same area.

The mechanics of collecting are ordinarily simple but frequently time-consuming, since manual collection is often necessary, particularly where living insects are to be captured without injury. When the host is discovered, it is a normal procedure first to examine carefully the immediate surrounding area for the presence of adult parasites or predators and to determine quickly, if possible, the stages of the host which these entomophagous species attack. When adult parasites or predators are desired for biological observation, they can be captured alive by netting, by collection with a mouth-suction aspirator, or by placing vials down over them. On occasion, a beating sheet with a soft nap which impedes rapid flight of parasite and predator adults can be used to advantage. Immediately after the capture of such forms they should be fed. Usually honey applied as thin strips to the inner sides of the vial containing the adults will suffice as nutriment.

Where parasitism is involved or suspected, the host specimens are examined for any evidence of attack of this type. Host relationships of parasites can be accurately determined by isolating parasitized specimens in separately labelled containers until emergence has occurred.

From this point on, the task is one of collecting as much host material as possible to hold for parasite emergence. Parasitized hosts sometimes act differently from unparasitized individuals by seeking shelter in protected places or by moving to distinct locations on the plant such as upper or lower leaf surfaces, growing tips, leaf axils, etc. In searching for parasitized hosts, attention should be directed to such places.

It is normal procedure to hold field-collected host material in cages or containers for parasite pupation or emergence. Usually the bulk of the parasite pupae or adults obtained in this manner is transshipped to the home quarantine laboratory. However, where adequate laboratory facilities are available, adult parasites can be retained and used to initiate stock cultures. These cultures can then provide material for large-scale shipments to the home laboratory and also will provide material for more intensive biological studies on the parasites of interest.

Sometimes it is found convenient to send large shipments of field-collected material to the home quarantine laboratory without discrimination as to presence or absence of parasitism. This procedure, however, is unusual. Whenever possible, only adult parasites, parasite cocoons or pupae, or parasitized host material should be shipped. At times, sufficient natural-enemy material may be taken by direct field collection to supply the demands for culture at home. When the host is rare, the host-exposure techniques previously described may be used to advantage in obtaining greater numbers of the natural enemies. At other times, temporary field helpers are employed to gather large amounts of host material for examination and holding for future parasite emergence.

Collecting equipment required in a programme depends to a great extent upon the type of organisms sought and no definite list of articles covering all possible contingencies can be prescribed. However, the itinerant collector is limited in the amount of baggage that can accompany him, hence simplicity of equipment is often an important consideration. A typical collecting kit with a mounting for the inclusion of a dissecting microscope is illustrated in figure 38, following p. 304. The contents of this kit are fully described in the legend accompanying the figure.

Three different types of mouth-suction aspirators are commonly used in parasite collection. The ordinary two-hole type fitted with large-bore copper tubing is used for wide-mouth vials in the collection of large parasites or predators. The single-hole type is used for direct aspiration of small specimens into small vials. The straight glass-tube type aspirator with a meshed-screen plug is most useful in field examination and sorting of adult parasites and predators. Living specimens collected into the tube are restricted in movement and can be observed readily with a hand lens.

A rubber syringe bulb fitted with a hypodermic needle, used to dispense thin stripes of honey to glass surfaces for natural-enemy food, is another useful piece of equipment. A horse-hair attached to a dissecting needle, when dipped in honey, is useful to place honey stripes in deep vials.

Glass fruit jars or lamp chimneys are frequently used as cages for confining and rearing parasitized host material. These are purchased as needed. Some auxiliary supplies, such as cellulose acetate sheets and fine-mesh wire screening for preparing specialized insect cages, are often included for emergency use in temporary laboratory quarters. A battery-serviced light source for microscope field illumination is desirable in many areas where electricity is unavailable or electrical circuits will not accommodate illuminators with special voltage requirements.

THE SHIPPING OF EXOTIC NATURAL ENEMIES

Natural-enemy shipments from foreign sources ordinarily consist of cocoons or pupae, mated adult stages of the entomophagous species, or parasitized host material from which parasites will emerge. Both the type of shipment containers and the modes of air transport used depend upon which type of material is being sent. Ordinarily some trials will be desirable to establish the most successful manner of transport, especially if adult natural enemies are being shipped. Air freight may be advisable for the larger and heavier parcels. Air-freighting agencies are accustomed to handling perishables, and agreements for special handling are most easily arranged with this method of transport. Where it can be used, ordinary air mail is advantageous since parcels are not so liable to transfer delays. On the other hand, mail-bags frequently are exposed to excessive heat or cold while awaiting transfer at airline junctions. Where such exposure seems a critical hazard to successful shipping of parcels, they should be sent by air freight and arrangements made for special handling. Past experience indicates that the greatest hazards in the transport of living entomophagous insects have existed during air-cargo transfers rather than in transit. Results of a recent inquiry into the matter by the senior author would indicate that there is little danger of exposure of air-mail parcels to extremely cold temperatures in jet or other high-altitude air-liners during flight.

Basically, the shipping containers, whether used for the transportation of adult or of immature entomophagous forms, should be strongly constructed, escape-proof, and crush-resistant. Containers of light metal, plastic, wood, or rigid pressed paper have been used. When it is possible to do so, as an additional safeguard against escape, the living material is enclosed in an insect-tight cloth bag before being wrapped.

In the shipment of immature stages of natural enemies, where no emergence is expected en route, the simplest types of containers suffice. Screw-top mailing tubes, with the parasite or predator material in a cloth sack within the container, are easily sealed and require no wrapping. With this type of carton there is no moisture accumulation as occurs in those of non-porous metal or plastic. If additional humidity is desired, it can be supplied by adding moistened cellulose sponge, or sometimes even succulent plant leaves, to the container. Paper, wooden, or plastic pill-boxes can often be used in transporting the natural-enemy stages desired, and they can be conveniently handled. A number of these containers, enclosed in cloth sacks, may be taped inside cloth-reinforced manila envelopes. This method has proved ideal for the transportation of parasitized homopterous insects and egg parasites when a number of different types of host material are being sent in a single shipment (figure 39 B, following p. 304).

The scattering and possible injury of cocooned larval or pupal stages of parasites or predators, or even of parasitized host material, can be prevented either by affixing the material to cards with shellac or by including loose sphagnum moss or paper strips in the container.

Where the isolation of different types of immature stages of natural enemies is desired in shipment, this is ordinarily accomplished by placing them in separate plastic vials with wire or cloth tops, or in wooden or plastic pill-boxes.

When some emergence of parasites is expected during transport, the parasite pupae or parasitized hosts are often confined in small separate containers covered with screen or mesh netting to preclude scattering. After emergence the adult parasites escape through the screen to the larger confines of the container where food, moisture, and resting sites are provided (figure 40, following p. 304).

Opinions differ widely on the most desirable types of containers for use in transporting adult entomophagous insects. Since the advent of air transport there has been little investigation of the relative merits of different insect shipping containers. There still is, in fact, considerable use of containers designed decades ago for sea-going transport.

Some controversy exists over the merits of ventilation in shipping containers. The desirability of ventilation to retard mould where plant material is included is unquestionable, and it may well be that certain entomophagous insect species require air circulation as well as the moderate light source provided by a screened opening in the container (Parker 1949). The disadvantage of ventilation is that it reduces the insulation qualities of the container and also may necessitate additional humidification. The complete darkness of the non-ventilated container may be advantageous because it reduces excessive movement and agitation of most natural enemies but still ordinarily permits some feeding. For these reasons, dark, well-insulated containers are most frequently used in shipping adult specimens. Mailing tubes and other pressed-paper containers, very loosely packed with excelsior (wood wool), have proved very satisfactory for the shipment of adults of a variety of species of beneficial insects. The excelsior provides resting sites, and a few strands rubbed with honey supply adequate food during transport (figure 42, following p. 304).

Various groups of natural-enemy adults require different degrees of freedom of movement in containers. Some coccinellids held in darkened containers have been transported over long distances under closely packed conditions. On the other hand, the restlessness of adult dipterous parasites, especially tachinids, is well recognized, and containers affording ample room for movement are sometimes considered necessary if injury to the flies is to be avoided. Many of the predatory Hemiptera and Coleoptera, as well as species in other groups in which the adults or larvae are cannibalistic, must be isolated in shipments.

Feeding of adult parasites or predators before shipment should be a standard practice. Prefeeding with honey is usually sufficient for trips of a very few days' duration. The provision of food and water for adult natural enemies during transit at times poses a problem. Honey, caramel candy, moistened raisins, or sugar water are usually used as food sources, with honey probably being the best all-purpose food. A semi-solid agar-base mixture of honey and water is frequently used for both parasite and predator food in long-distance shipping of adult entomophagous forms. For use in ventilated containers the medium can be prepared for different anticipated atmospheric humidities by adding to 50 ml of a 1 per cent agar solution 25 ml of honey for up to 40 per cent R.H., and an additional 10 g sugar for 40 to 70 per cent R.H., or 25 g sugar for 50 to 90 per cent R.H. (Holloway 1939). In non-vented containers pure honey is usually supplied in thin stripes on celluloid acetate or wax paper sheets or rubbed on a few strands of excelsior.

The practice of supplying living host material as a food source for adult predatory forms is useful or necessary at times but may be undesirable from a quarantine standpoint. Since periods of one week or less now represent the maximum time required for air transport of natural-enemy material from the most remote parts of the world, problems of food and water for natural-enemy transport are less critical than formerly but nonetheless highly important. Water is frequently supplied to adult parasites from wet pieces of sponge or from wick-fed vials placed in the cages (figure 43). A high humidity in the container minimizes dehydration of natural enemies and may avoid the necessity for adding drinking water. A base pad of sphagnum moss or of cellulose sponge moistened before shipment is a common addition to most adult shipping cages which are well ventilated. Sometimes plant leaves are used to maintain humidities in well-sealed shipment containers (figure 39 B).

Many of the old-type shipping containers were designed for transport under ship-stores' refrigeration. No methods of refrigeration or anaesthetization of natural enemies during air transport have so far been developed. Precooling the packaged container before shipment is commonly used to avoid temporary local heat conditions while awaiting air loading.

Suggestions for the wrapping of parcels include the liberal use of a heavy paper covering for insulation purposes. An inner cloth covering is ordinarily provided to prevent insect escape in case of breakage. Generous use of printed caution labels showing the perishable nature of the contents is desirable since considerable importance is attached to such labels in certain areas. With air-mail service, registry of parcels in some countries may cause delays in delivery and is ordinarily unnecessary unless required by postal authorities at the point of origin. The ordinary packaging supplies used for a foreign collector are shown in figure 44, facing p. 305.

PRECAUTIONS AGAINST INTRODUCTION OF INJURIOUS ORGANISMS

The absolute exclusion of potentially injurious insects and plant pathogens in foreign exploration programmes requires exacting care and a sound knowledge of the habits and biologies of parasitic and predacious insects by everyone connected with the importation programme. In special cases where quarantine facilities are not available at the receiving station and are not legally required, only well-studied species should ever be considered for introduction. These should be sent preferably as adults reared from pure host cultures under laboratory conditions. When material is shipped to a quarantine laboratory, as it should be, the foreign collector is relieved of much of the responsibility for excluding dangerous plant material or animal species. Under many circumstances, however, the foreign collector is considered the first line of defence against the introduction of detrimental organisms. In certain cases it is recognized that he will have to complete all the biological studies necessary for assurance that the species to be shipped are entirely beneficial.

One of the most dangerous errors that can be made in foreign collection work is that of introducing secondary parasites (hyperparasites) on the assumption that they are primary beneficial species. Hyperparasites generally show a low host specificity as compared with primary parasites (Muesebeck and Dohanian 1927). Once established, a hyperparasite may adapt itself to a wide variety of naturally occurring parasitic species, and conceivably prevent both existing primary parasites and certain species that might be introduced later from realizing their full capacity as control agents. Practically no primary parasites, except perhaps the diminutive species which parasitize insect eggs, escape attack by at least some species of hyperparasites. A more complete discussion of the effects of hyperparasitism is presented in chapter 5.

Because of the great danger of secondary parasites and the seemingly great complexities of their biologies, there sometimes is an unreasonable fear that the habit may pass unrecognized. If the biologies and life histories of the species are well established by both culture and dissection of immature parasite stages, there is virtually no chance of overlooking the existence of the secondary habit in a species. The detailed techniques used in these procedures are discussed in chapter 10.

A number of simple observations, aside from complete life history and biology studies, may provide a basis for suspicion of the hyperparasitic habit to a collector. The discovery of distinctive pupal remains of secondary parasites, or even sometimes those of both the secondary and primary species together inside a host from which the suspected hyperparasite has emerged, may, on occasion, serve to identify the secondary habit in a species. The existence of two distinctive types of meconia (fecal pellets) in the old host body may likewise show that hyperparasitism was involved. In addition to the above-mentioned evidence, the taxonomic affinity of the species to known hyperparasitic groups may be cause for suspicion (see chapters 8 and 10), as may size or abundance of a species relative to other species occurring on the same host. However, laboratory trial rearing upon both unparasitized and parasitized hosts accompanied by dissection and examination provides the final answer. Where the secondary habit is obligatory, as is frequently the case, there can be no reproduction upon hosts free of primary parasites. When reproduction in the host proceeds only in the presence of other parasites, the obligatory hyperparasitic role is established.

The fact that attack and development proceed upon hosts known to be parasite-free does not always provide positive proof that the secondary habit does not also occur. The fairly common existence of facultative hyperparasitism, such that the same species may be a primary parasite under one set of circumstances and a hyperparasite under others, complicates detection procedures in these cases. The dual role of primary and secondary parasitism can be established only by carefully testing the suspected species on associated parasitic forms where development can be followed through dissection.

The problem of hyperparasitism is further complicated in certain genera of the Aphelinidae, which include some of the most effective parasites of mealybugs and scale insects, by the fact that although females always are primary parasites, the males may develop hyperparasitically on females of their own or related species.

Since this is the only method by which necessary males may be produced for perpetuation of the species, this type of hyperparasitic behaviour is normal and not detrimental. Inasmuch as a major function of the quarantine laboratory is to screen out hyperparasites, the reader is referred to chapter 10 for discussion of techniques used to this end, as well as for a list of the main groups of hyperparasites.

Closely allied with the problem of hyperparasitism is the danger of importing and establishing parasites which attack beneficial predators. Predatory species which are being considered for importation should either be known to be free of parasites or they must be reared for at least one complete generation under quarantine at the receiving station to assure their freedom from detrimental parasitic forms. Certain parasitic species of the encyrtid genera *Homalotylus* and *Isodromus* attacking coccinellid and neuropterous larvae, respectively, may be very dangerous because of the wide range of host species attacked. Certain braconid species of the genus *Perilitus* (= spp. of *Dinocampus* and *Centistes* of authors) are particularly likely to be overlooked because they emerge from adult coccinellids. Caution should be exercised with some predatory Hemiptera and Diptera, and certain predatory vespoid wasps whose feeding may extend in some degree to other entomophagous insects. The decision to import such species must be based upon a careful balancing of their value against phytophagous arthropods as compared with their detrimental effect on beneficial forms. The precaution must also be observed that no entomophagous species be imported which might attack useful insects such as bees or silkworms.

Fortunately, parasitic insects do not extend their feeding to include plants or plant products. Rare exceptions to this relationship have been recorded in the Eurytomidae where the phytophagous habit is restricted to feeding upon lacerated plant tissue within the galls formed by the primary host (Phillips 1927, Varley 1937), and in one instance in the Eupelmidae (Woodruff 1929) where animal and plant food are indiscriminately taken. This dual role, however, is not uncommon with some species of hemipterous predators and with certain predatory mites. A number of Hemiptera which are efficient predators are not viewed as favourable subjects for importation into other countries because they occasionally feed on plant tissue and therefore might conceivably serve as vectors of plant diseases.

The indiscriminate transport of living host material from one country to another regardless of its occurrence in both areas should be avoided, since unrecognizable strains of such hosts with different adaptations may be involved.

The introduction of exotic natural enemies should always proceed on a cautious basis; however, in general, all precautions necessary for a well-conducted programme are simply and easily applied if responsible and competent personnel are entrusted with the project.

A

B

FIGURE 37. Variations of the host-exposure technique for obtaining natural enemies in the field when the host is rare:

A. Mealybugs and scale insects propagated in the laboratory being exposed in the field on potato tubers and potted oleander plants for the attraction of natural enemies.

B. Exposure of potato tubers (above men's heads) infested with California red scale at Lingnan University, Canton, China, in 1949 for attack by parasites emerging from scales on the potted pummelo plants below. Young scale insects dropping from the tubers above supported a continuous population of parasites (after Flanders, Gressitt, and Fisher).

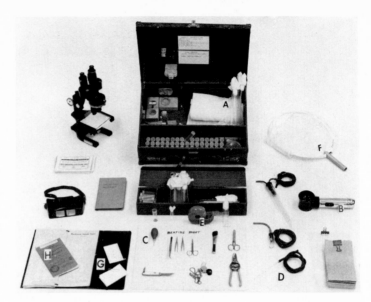

FIGURE 38. A collecting kit used in foreign exploration for beneficial insects.

A. Gauze and plastic bags for evaporative cooling of living insect material in test tubes. B. Battery-lighted magnifying lens for field examination of specimens. C. Syringe fitted with hypodermic needle to supply honey in thin stripes as food for adult entomophagous insects. D. Three types of mouth suction aspirators. E. Translucent plastic mending tape (inscribable) for labelling specimen vials. F. Collapsible insect net. G. Collector's personal cards with reverse side printed in the language of the country being visited. H. International driving permit and identification papers.

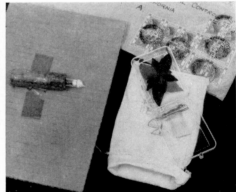

A   B

FIGURE 39. Old and new methods of transporting insects.

A. Caged cycads infested with California red scale, *Aonidiella aurantii* Mask., used in the transport of scale parasites from the Orient to California in 1932.

B. Two methods used in the shipping of California red scale material from the Orient to California in 1957.

FIGURE 40. Container used by the parasite introduction laboratory of the U.S. Department of Agriculture for the transport either of adult dipterous and hymenopterous parasites or for immature forms which are expected to emerge en route. Moisture is supplied by a wetted sponge under bottom cloth covering and food from agar-honey mixture on cards attached to the side of the cage. The cloth bands serve as resting sites for adults. The screen-covered boxes attached to the sides hold the immature parasite stages until upon emerging as adults they escape to the larger confines of the container.

FIGURE 41. A shipping cage designed by the Commonwealth Institute of Biological Control for the shipment of adult natural enemies.

FIGURE 42. Coccinellids being released inside a laboratory sleeve cage after transport in a pressed paper mailing tube containing loose strands of excelsior.

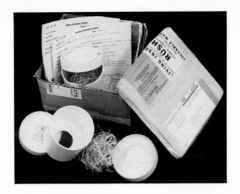

FIGURE 43. Waxed paper cartons fitted with screen bottoms which can be pressed tightly down against a piece of moistened sponge for use in the transport of adult parasites or predators.

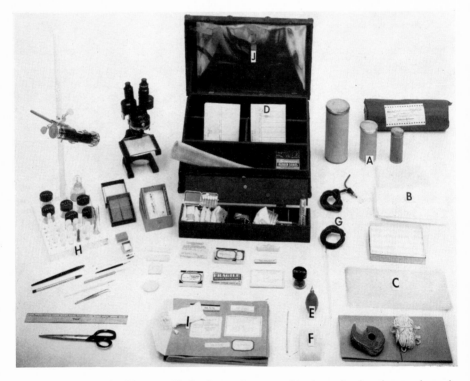

FIGURE 44. A travelling laboratory kit showing equipment used in the study of exotic natural enemies and in the preparation for their shipment.

A. Three sizes of pressed paper mailing tubes with screw-type caps. B. Bleached muslin and organdie cloth for rearing jar covers. C. Plastic bags for wrapping to maintain high humidity in shipping parcels. D. Shipping cards for sender's collection data on one side and receiver's report on reverse side. E. Syringe fitted with hypodermic needle, and horse-hair applicator for supplying thin stripes of honey as food for entomophagous insects. F. Cellulose sponge for supplying moisture during shipment of natural enemies. G. Two types of mouth suction aspirators used in the examination and transfer of living specimens. H. Supplies for sorting and preserving specimens and demountable battery light illuminator. I. Plastic cases for protection of vials containing parasite material to be placed in cloth bags and taped inside cloth-reinforced envelopes for shipment. J. Cellulose acetate sheets for laboratory cages.

CHAPTER 10

Quarantine Handling of Entomophagous Insects

T. W. FISHER

INTRODUCTION

THE PURPOSE of handling intentionally imported entomophagous insects under quarantine conditions is to prevent any concurrent introduction of undesirable species of phytophagous insects, hyperparasites, weed pests, or plant diseases. In order to confirm the habits of newly introduced species, it should be propagated for at least one generation in quarantine.

In order to implement this objective in California, an agreement among authorities of the United States Department of Agriculture, California State Department of Agriculture, and the University of California was reached (Swain 1952) wherein the quarantine personnel of the Department of Biological Control of the University of California is charged with the safe handling of such material. Under the provisions of this agreement, shipments from foreign collecting areas which display the proper federal permits (United States Department of Agriculture, Agricultural Research Service, Plant Quarantine Branch, form PQ-21) normally proceed undisturbed through customs and quarantine inspections at the port of entry to the biological control quarantine laboratory. This results in receipt of imported material with minimal delay. For example, average travelling time for shipments sent air mail from Tokyo, Japan to California is three days; from New Delhi, India and Capetown, South Africa six days.

For a summary of current quarantine regulations and their history, particularly in California, the reader is referred to the recently published book by Ebeling (1959, pp. 1 to 24).

Importance of the quarantine facility and procedures to biological control projects can be appreciated when it is realized that proper handling of imported material is essential in order to obtain the beneficial insects with which biological control entomologists must work. This is the essence of comments made by others familiar with importation problems. For example, Burgess and Crossman (1929), reporting on the twenty-four years of work involved in the introduction of 47 species of insect enemies of gypsy and brown-tail moths, state (p. 16), '... the actual gathering of suitable material in foreign countries, and landing it at our shores, are only a small [but obviously essential] part of the procedure necessary

305

for the establishment and dispersal of the beneficial insects in this country.' In the chain of events which make up a biological control programme, quarantine handling is actually the link between foreign collecting and the insectary production programme which permits dispersal.

It is no understatement to say that the success or failure of importation programmes depends in large measure on the degree of training, resourcefulness, and dedication of quarantine personnel. Thus, it follows that personnel who will perform this vital function should possess certain basic qualifications, namely: (1) the attitude that each imported species or strain of primary parasite or predator may contribute significantly to control of a pest species; (2) profound interest in insect biologies; (3) a general taxonomic knowledge within major entomophagous groups; and (4) a knowledge of disease symptoms. Paramount to the foregoing qualifications is complete acceptance of rigid discipline regarding personal habits and handling procedures in order to eliminate any possibility of dangerous organisms escaping to the local environment. Of obvious benefit to this type of work is the ingenuity to devise new rearing methods, to make innovations on cages, and to use imagination and willingness in trying new approaches.

Biological control has been concerned mainly with insect pests, and as a consequence much of the information in this chapter relates to the handling of insect parasites and predators. Accordingly specialized quarantine practices required for the introduction and study of insect pathogens and of phytophagous insects for the control of introduced noxious plants will not be discussed in this chapter. For such information the reader is referred to chapters 21 and 22.

THE QUARANTINE LABORATORY

The basic function of a quarantine laboratory is to provide facilities which will permit the handling of imported material in a manner that precludes escape of potentially dangerous organisms. Ideally, it is a completely equipped self-contained, insect-tight, highly functional laboratory (Doutt 1951a)—literally an insectary within an insectary.

This is not to imply that less elaborate facilities are necessarily inadequate. Some of the finest importation programmes had very simple but highly efficient quarantine facilities, the effectiveness of which was made possible only by the highest devotion to duty of the personnel in charge. An excellent example is the quarantine insectary utilized during the introduction of entomophagous insects into Fiji for control of the coconut moth (Tothill, Taylor, and Paine 1930, p. 21, plate 14). Similar quarantine field insectaries are currently used in Australia and Mauritius.

A satisfactory location of the quarantine facility is in a relatively isolated portion of the insectary, and access should be restricted to a minimum number of authorized personnel. Certain Commonwealth Institute of Biological Control stations utilize a separate building for quarantine use. At the end of chapter 13 is a list of some of the insectaries throughout the world. Those which include quarantine facilities are marked with an asterisk (*).

Since chapter 13 deals with insectary facilities and equipment, these aspects will be considered here only in a general way with emphasis on features of particular importance to proper quarantine procedure.

The minimum quarantine facility properly consists of at least two separate rooms: (1) an anteroom which contains a continuously operating light trap between the insectary area and the quarantine room; and (2) the quarantine room itself where shipments are opened and initial studies begun. If floor space can be planned to accommodate one or more additional small rooms for isolation of various cultures, so much the better. Diagrams of quarantine facilities at Moorestown, New Jersey (U.S.D.A.), and at Albany, California, are shown in figure 45.

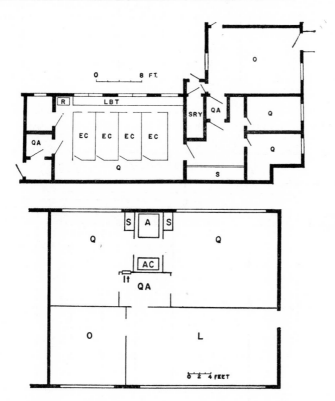

FIGURE 45. Floor plan of biological control quarantine facilities. Portions of existing buildings were remodelled to provide these laboratories.

A. Moorestown, New Jersey (U.S.D.A.).

B. Albany, California (University of California).

A autoclave. AC air conditioner. EC emergence chambers. L laboratory. LBT laboratory table. lt light trap. O office. Q quarantine. QA quarantine anteroom. R refrigerator. S sink. SRY stairway.

Dept. of Biol. Control, Univ. of California Exploration for entomophagous insects, etc. SENDER'S REPORT				S & R No._____ Shipper's No._____		
Country_____ Shipping point_____ Date of shipment_____ Transport_____ Packaging_____			Shipper_____ Shipped to_____ Remarks_____			
Vial or packet #	Host Insect	Entomophagous Species	Host Plant	Collection locality	Date coll.	Collector

RECEIVER'S REPORT								
Date received_____ Examined by_____			Condition of shipment_____					
Vial or packet #	Host insect	Entomophagous species	Number received		Total emergence		Propa- gated	Consign- ment
			Alive	Dead	Fem.	Male		

FIGURE 47. Sender's and Receiver's Report. This is the original record of material received. The sender's report appears on one side of the 5 × 8-inch card, and the receiver's report on the reverse side.

Natural lighting for reasons of uniform intensity should, for the most part, enter from the north in the northern hemisphere and from the south in the southern hemisphere. Windows should consist of large double panes. The inner pane is fixed and, since it is one continuous piece, collection of insects from it is unrestricted. The outer pane is removable to facilitate cleaning the enclosed surfaces of the two panes. It is made of wire-reinforced glass as added protection against breakage. The outer pane and its weather-tight gaskets are held in place by appropriate clamps. Electric lighting and convenience outlets will be much the same as in the insectary proper; that is, two or more electrical circuits for outlets and lighting per room should be provided and fluorescent lights and receptacles should be flush with wall and ceiling.

Minimum plumbing facilities should include a sink equipped with hot and cold water. Desirable additional facilities are distilled water, gas, air vacuum, air pressure, and carbon dioxide gas in both the anteroom and quarantine room. If possible, toilet and washroom which contains a light trap, should be provided for use of quarantine personnel only.

If the insectary is equipped with a central air-conditioning system, and if the quarantine facility is included in the same building, recirculation within the quarantine area should be independent of the main insectary and exhaust-air should pass through a filter. If rooms are individually air conditioned, i.e., by conventional window-mounted household-type machines, it must be ascertained that insects cannot pass either way through the damper systems of the machines. This can be achieved by taping or bolting the dampers at the desired position. As an independent unit, it is conceivable that a heat-pump could provide the necessary heating, cooling, recirculation, humidifying, and filtering for the entire quarantine facility (see chapter 13 for further details).

Equipment for the handling of insects will be much the same as used elsewhere in the insectary with the proviso that it be restricted to the quarantine rooms. Because of the independent nature of the quarantine facility, it is necessary to provide adequate internal storage for glassware, cages, cloth, and miscellaneous supplies for the manufacture of propagation equipment.

In the event that large quantities of hibernating parasitized host material must be held in quarantine in order to synchronize the life cycles of the expected parasites with their locally established hosts, it will be necessary to obtain adequate refrigeration within the quarantine laboratory. In order to satisfy diapause requirements of European corn borer larvae, large amounts of hibernating material were held in refrigerated rooms at $34°$ to $36°$ F for about three months (Baker, Bradley, and Clark 1949, p. 48) (figure 46, facing p. 320). Household refrigerators will adequately store considerable amounts of hibernating material but when refrigerated cooling is used it is very important to keep a close check on the relative humidity as it may become dangerously low.

Desiccation will be minimized if the refrigerant in the cooling coils is approximately $5°$ below the desired temperature of the cold room or refrigerator.

A univoltine pest species held at normal temperatures until issue of its parasite complement may create a space problem in the quarantine laboratory. For the purpose of holding numerous grubs of *Popillia japonica* Newm. pending emergence of *Prosena siberita* Fabr., King and Hallock (1925) used a cage of 22 ft × 7 ft × 6 ft dimensions. These are two situations which required special techniques and they clearly indicate the need of strictest quarantine precautions when considerable quantities of imported living host species must be held for an extended period.

In order to dispose safely of shipping containers and shipment residues, an autoclave or incinerator should be located preferably within the quarantine laboratory. A small and fairly inexpensive portable autoclave with a capacity of approximately 800 cubic inches will suffice for sterilization of material normally received via air mail. Unwanted shipping materials ultimately should be burned. If it is physically impossible or impractical to build an incinerator into the quarantine area, it should be located near by for use by insectary as well as quarantine personnel. In this event, for added safety, material such as shipping containers or bulky plant material should be transported from the quarantine room to the incinerator in sealed multilayer paper bags. Conventional cyanide jars may be used to destroy hyperparasites or other unwanted arthropods as they emerge from shipments.

COLLABORATION WITH COLLECTOR

Value of Preshipment Survey to Quarantine Handling

The collector's notes and observations regarding imported material can be of great benefit to the receiver. Probably the more productive importation programmes occur when collectors can spend a matter of weeks or months in a given region, during which time a better understanding of the ecology and host relationships of the species concerned can be acquired. This knowledge can be applied towards reducing numbers of unwanted species included in shipments. This is particularly important when lepidopterous larvae pupate during shipment, thereby compounding the segregation problems of the receiver due mainly to the difficulty in determining species from pupal characters. Thus, Haeussler (1940, p. 56) was able to import nearly pure stocks of parasitized oriental fruit moth larvae by elimination of other lepidopterous species by means of an inspecting method which utilized the negative phototropic response of the *Grapholitha* larvae. Furthermore, lengthy studies should enable the collector to make adequately large shipments which will greatly aid the receiver in overcoming a major obstacle in the initial establishment of a culture, namely, small numbers.

Regarding the programme of introduction of natural enemies of *Aspidiotus destructor* Sign. into Fiji, Taylor (1935, p. 84) states '. . . the greatest difficulty met with on the voyage arose through more than one species of primary parasite being present in the same cage . . . .' Thus, interspecific competition en route resulted in the elimination of certain species which under field conditions at their destination may have proved to be very efficient controlling agents.

The value of carefully done work by the collector in properly determining host relationships was clearly demonstrated during the importation of the egg parasite

Patasson nitens Grlt. from Australia to South Africa (Tooke 1955, pp. 97 to 99) for biological control of the Eucalyptus snout beetle, *Gonipterus scutellatus* Gyll. In this particular case, study in Australia showed that hyperparasitism in egg capsules of the weevil was completely lacking, thus greatly simplifying and facilitating the work of introducing the mymarid by subsequent justifiable relaxation of quarantine screening in South Africa.

The preliminary survey and bionomic study of parasites of *Promecotheca* in Java by R. W. Paine prior to their introduction into Fiji (Taylor 1937, p. 142) resulted in the importation of only the few really effective parasites.

In 1931, *Ophelosia crawfordi* Riley was propagated in quarantine in California on egg masses of mealybugs and it appeared to be a promising egg predator (Smith and Compere 1931). However, observations by S. E. Flanders, who shipped it from Australia, and H. Compere, who received it at Riverside, showed that it reproduced as a hyperparasite of mature mealybugs, probably through *Anarhopus sydneyensis* (Timb.) which also issued from this material. There was further evidence that *O. crawfordi* could develop on coccinellid larvae. Because of the potential hazards of introducing this parasite, it was destroyed in quarantine.

Collection Data

The data sheet enclosed by University of California collectors in shipments indicates the kind of material to be expected from the shipment as well as the various collection localities and various host species involved. This 5 × 8-inch form, which is of fairly heavy paper, from the collector (or sender) to the quarantine officer (or receiver) has become popularly known in the Department of Biological Control as the 'S. & R. Report' (Sender's and Receiver's Report), and it is illustrated in figure 47. The sender fills out one side and the receiver reports the condition of the shipment and emergence data on the reverse side. One card then contains the complete history of any one shipment and constitutes the original record thereof. Collector's field notes and receiver's laboratory notes relate back to the S. & R. report by the shipper's number and by the chronological S. & R. number assigned by the quarantine officer. If necessary, the receiver notifies the sender by cable concerning the condition of the shipment following the initial quarantine segregation procedure. It is of particular importance to call attention to possible improvements in shipping techniques. If the collector keeps the quarantine officer informed regarding his itinerary, the problem of communicating details regarding shipments and the forwarding of additional shipping supplies to the collector is greatly reduced.

Augmentation of Receipt of Shipments

Receipt of shipments is expedited if senders are careful to affix proper laboratory address, federal importation permits, and postage, as described in chapter 9. Registration of shipments calls for extra handling by postal employees and can delay arrival by one or two days. The receiver can alert local post-office personnel to expect such packages by showing them samples and explaining the need for prompt notification of arrivals. Attention should be called particularly to the label showing the telephone numbers of the receiving laboratory and the home telephone number of the quarantine officer. During periods of high temperature it is most necessary that shipments be picked up without delay. If quarantine officers happen to be unavailable on week-ends or holidays, someone from the laboratory should be delegated to contact the post office regarding the arrival of shipments during such periods and bringing them to the insectary for storage (unopened) at 60° F.

Occasionally a shipment may be sent which does not possess the necessary permits. Such packages are held in customs or quarantine at the port of entry and are not released except to properly authorized persons. If it becomes necessary to go to a port of entry in order to obtain such shipments, it is essential to take along a suitable insect-proof sleeved cage inside of which the package can be opened in the presence of customs officers should they require this.

PREPARATION FOR RECEIPT OF IMPORTED MATERIAL

When institutions plan to send explorer-collectors into the field for the purpose of sending in shipments of living beneficial insects, it is highly desirable that quarantine personnel receive at least six months' advance notice of the pending importations. During this period it will be possible to review the literature relative to the host plant, host (pest) insect, and the natural enemies recorded to date. In addition, it provides an opportunity to examine museum specimens of species expected or of related species.

For new projects, six months is a minimum period to allow for the preparation of host cultures, particularly if growing plants are involved. In this regard, it has been proved of great value to adopt a continuous or overlapping infesting programme on individual natural or substitute host plants so that newly imported parasites may have a free choice of various host stages during initial host-preference and host-relationship studies.

During the preparatory period, renovation of cages or the construction of new cages or specialized equipment can be carried out, and an opportunity to prepare isolation units, ranging in size from small cages to rooms, is afforded. However, it is possible to maintain two or more host species in the same room provided they do not compete, particularly with regard to the host plant. If importations may include species of parasites with males of secondary parasitic habits, colonies of potentially suitable hosts for male parasites also can be initiated during this period.

Probably the most important activity that quarantine people can engage in during the preparatory period is to practise the propagation of species related to those which are expected in shipments. This applies to handling of the host species as well as the entomophagous species.

If a collector has had the good fortune to find sufficient material to make several large shipments in close succession, the receiver may find that additional help is needed to handle it properly. Advance arrangements should therefore be made for the prompt availability of assistance for quarantine personnel should the need arise. Such help would follow initial quarantine screening and propagation and would function in areas of general sanitation, increase of host cultures, routine collections of progeny, and maintenance of cultures. Such a situation invariably develops if two or more collectors are simultaneously in the field.

PROCEDURES FOR HANDLING MATERIAL IN QUARANTINE

Examination and Processing of the Shipment

To minimize the possible transport of organisms into or out of quarantine, it is good practice for quarantine personnel to wear a laboratory coat, particularly during the processing of new shipments. This coat should be white for easy visibility of insects which may alight on it and it may hang in the quarantine room between periods of use. It should never leave the quarantine area without first being fumigated in a large cyanide jar, or being placed in a heavy paper bag which is then sealed and promptly carried to the fumigation chamber. Personnel leaving the quarantine area, i.e. anteroom, should first undergo a decontamination process which may consist of inspection before a full-length mirror, blowing pressurized air over the garments and, if necessary, a change of laboratory coat. This procedure should be carried out where a light trap will attract escaped insects.

Once a shipment has been taken into the quarantine room, it is placed for opening (size permitting) in a large sleeve-cage, which should be stocked continuously with a number of vials, forceps, scissors, collection aspirator, etc., for the purpose of handling the enclosed material (figure 48, facing p. 320).

Opening packages while working through sleeves is important not only in preventing the escape of insects but also for human comfort as was learned during the importation of brown-tail moth parasites (Howard and Fiske 1911, p. 164) when it became necessary to protect personnel from the irritating effects of spines that occur on the host larvae. The show-case type sleeve-cage developed in 1907 by these workers was the prototype of currently widely used isolation, or sleeved, cages. A specially constructed booth may be necessary for the safe opening of large containers. The window booth may be a small room built around an existing window. It is painted white and has one door. The window is double-glazed plate glass—the inner pane is frosted—and the door is a tightly gasketed refrigerator-type door. For ease of collecting, packages are opened before a screened 'transfer cage' which traps nearly all the insects as they fly towards the window. Figure 53 illustrates such an arrangement at the quarantine laboratory of the United States Department of Agriculture Insect Identification and Parasite Introduction Research Branch, Moorestown, New Jersey. If a small room is not available for the opening of large shipping containers, a cloth enclosure (large enough to accommodate the package plus the head and shoulders of the quarantine worker) may be suspended from a light framework within the quarantine room. Such an arrangement has been used by Australian workers particularly in the handling of large quantities of fruit fly parasites shipped from foreign insectaries.

Since shipments destined for the University of California quarantine are usually air-letter packages, the following comments will pertain chiefly to the processing of such containers.

After first gently squeezing or shaking in order to detect broken containers inside, the shipping envelope or wrapping is carefully cut open. If the shipping container is broken, it is possible that insects may be loose within the package. If collectors have observed the precaution of enclosing all shipping containers in stout cloth sacks before placing them in shipping envelopes or boxes, safety in handling at the receiving end is greatly enhanced.

If breakage has occurred, one end of the enclosing cloth sack is cut open and the sack is everted, spilling the contents into a suitable container while working through sleeves, as illustrated in figure 48.

With unbroken containers the collection of parasites which emerged en route is the first concern. Usually the packages are opened within the previously mentioned cage and the parasites or predators allowed to fly to the glass, where they may be collected with an aspirator.

It is particularly important not to use an anaesthetic at the initial opening of a shipment if the natural enemies that emerged en route appear to be weak as expressed by immobility, unsteady gait, or inability to cling to a vertical glass surface, or if dead insects are in the containers. Certain coccinellids are rather easily killed by CO_2. Weakened insects are safely handled only by gentle aspiration or by picking them up with a small brush. The vial into which they are placed should then be provided with a few fine streaks of honey for food, care being taken to avoid large droplets in which the insects could be trapped.

No inflexible rules apply to the feeding of adult parasites. In practice, honey seems to provide moisture and food sufficient to sustain most adults for somewhat long periods. Taylor (1937, p. 234) reports that only enough water should be added to allow the honey to flow freely. This rule of thumb is probably a good one to follow since honeys from different sources vary widely in sugar content. At humidities below 55 per cent most honeys become stiff and must be diluted with water or glycerine in order to enable the parasites to ingest them. Nutritive requirements of adult parasites are more thoroughly covered in chapter 12.

Occasionally, living parasites are observed mired in honey which may be provided in the shipping containers. This probably occurs when the parcel is opened and the contents are suddenly exposed to light, thus stimulating the insects to increased activity. If this situation arises, a drop of distilled water will float the trapped parasite free of the honey. Then it can be retrieved from the water with a fine needle or brush and placed in a dry vial where usually it will preen itself dry.

Segregation of Imported Material

Since the occurrence of biological strains or races is gaining recognition, parasitized hosts should be segregated according to species and stages thereof, host plant, and locality. If anomalous appearance or behaviour is detected, racial or specific differences should be suspected and it may be extremely important to retain discrete cultures of such insects for bio-systematic evaluation.

Just as plant quarantine personnel have to recognize diseased or insect-infested plant material, so should insectary quarantine personnel learn to recognize insects which may be diseased or parasitized. Obviously, dissection is the most positive method of determining the presence of stalkless internal eggs or early stages of endoparasitic development. However, when the amount of host material is small, one is hesitant to sacrifice any of it. In the case of lecaniine and diaspine scale insects, light transmitted through the host as it lies on flashed opal glass is a great aid in detecting quite small internal parasitic larvae and eggs, particularly in nongravid hosts (Fisher 1959). Older parasitic larvae usually cause their hosts to appear swollen or sluggish (or both), or may affect the colour of the derm. Parasites which have pupated are usually easily seen either internally or externally. J. D. Tothill (Howard and Fiske 1911, p. 159) devised a candling technique to select healthy puparia of *Parasetigena segregata* Rond., an introduced parasite of the gypsy moth, and Holling (1958) utilized a radiographic technique to identify and segregate healthy, parasitized, and diseased sawfly prepupae within their cocoons.

Segregated groups are then placed in separate vials or appropriate containers to await emergence of the adult parasites or predators. Figure 50, facing p. 321, illustrates this type of equipment and the emergence record.

Optimum Temperature and Humidity Requirements

Generally, in the quarantine laboratory a constant temperature of 76° F is suitable, if not near-optimal, for culture of many parasites and predators. Higher constant temperatures may limit the continuous propagation of temperate-zone insects.

When selecting a constant optimum temperature for culturing aphids and their parasites, care must be taken to ensure that laboratory conditions will not bring about diapause in the parasites. The primary parasites of aphids often go into diapause while their hosts may continue reproduction (Schlinger 1960a). Examples of 'cold weather' aphids are *Macrosiphum pisi* (Harris), *Myzus persicae* Sulz., and *Aphis spiraecola* Patch; these species may be continuously propagated best if the constant temperature does not exceed 68° to 72° F. Examples of 'hot weather' aphids are *Chromaphis juglandicola* (Kltb.), *Aphis gossypii* Glov., and *Therioaphis maculata* (Buck.); these species may be continuously propagated best if the constant temperature does not fall below 78° to 80° F (Schlinger unpublished notes). If two or more species with widely varying temperature tolerances are to be handled simultaneously in quarantine, the need for temperature control of individual rooms is obvious.

Although little precise information exists regarding relative humidity requirements for optimal development of immature parasites, workers have occasionally reported on the need for humidifying devices in order to increase percentage emergence from shipments. For example, during the importation of parasites of the oriental fruit moth, it was found that emergence from tachinid puparia increased from 22 to 55 per cent when they were suspended on cloth platforms over water in battery jars (Allen, Holloway, and Haeussler 1940, p. 7). According to Howard and Fiske (1911, pp. 158, 213 to 218), *Blepharipoda scutellata* (R. & D.), a tachinid parasite of gypsy and brown-tail moths, at times closely approached 100 per cent emergence when held in a moist environment from the date of collection to emergence at the destination. This was accomplished by first allowing pupation to occur in moist soil before shipment, preserving the moist condition while in transit, and, lastly, at the receiving laboratory by holding the fly puparia in moist earth. Prior to adoption of this procedure, emergence was approximately 3 per cent. Before breaking the diapause of hibernating corn borer larvae it was found to be advantageous to create and maintain a temperature of 80° F and 70 per cent relative humidity (Baker, Bradley, and Clark 1949, p. 48).

At Riverside, the general insectary temperature is maintained at or below 80° F and the relative humidity at 55 per cent. This relative humidity probably is below optimum for most parasites but is a compromise which minimizes rot of certain host-plant material, is not too adverse to parasites, and keeps their food (honey) in a fluid state. This combination ordinarily gives satisfactory emergence from a wide variety of parasitized insects, homopterous pests in particular. During periods of very low outdoor humidity, insectary humidity tends to decrease, so imported material is held over a saturated NaCl solution which creates an atmosphere of approximately 75 per cent R.H. Actually, optimal relative humidities depend on the complex of natural enemies, host insects, and host plants concerned. High humidity usually promotes growth of fungi and causes honey to run so that parasites become trapped. If relative humidity remains too high, it will be necessary to install either a mechanical dehumidifier in a room or to utilize various hygroscopic salts in small cage culture. Even with presumed adequate humidity certain lecaniine scale-attacking aphelinids suffer considerable mortality. For example, *Coccophagus basalis* Comp. suffers at least 60 per cent mortality even when hosts containing fully pigmented pupae are very carefully removed from the laboratory host plant to glass vials and immediately placed at 75 per cent R.H. In this particular instance removal from the substrate may cause a disruption of the delicate relationship between the host–parasite tracheal systems. On the other hand, most immature internal parasites of diaspine scales are not adversely affected by removal of their hosts from the host plant, but ectoparasites, such as species of *Aphytis*, rarely survive when their hosts are removed from the host plant prior to shipment.

Manipulation of Mating

One difficulty inherent in the segregation procedure is that of inadvertently separating males from females of certain parasites. When museum specimens are not available for comparison, the problem becomes one of correctly associating the sexes within a species.

Assuming that a small number of apparently identical virgin females are available along with a heterogeneous group of unknown males, it is a usual practice to place them together in a large vial for observation. If mating will occur, it usually takes place within a short time. This procedure applies to species not requiring flying room for mating stimulus as do certain flies and ichneumonids. A technique that is commonly used to achieve mating parasites is to place 24-hour-old, or older, males with freshly emerged females. Certain coleopterous predators may require several days before mating will occur. Since it is well known that age, space, odour, light, air movement, etc., can exert separate or combined effects on mating, it may be necessary to run a series of tests before the proper mating stimulus is discovered.

Often very few individual insects will survive in a shipment. Small numbers place an immediate limit on the amount of testing and dissection that can be performed. Particularly is this true when attempting to hold virgin female parasites for back-crossing with their own male progeny. Often females will accept the males only upon emergence or shortly thereafter. Sometimes mating can be forced upon reluctant virgins by lightly anaesthetizing them with CO_2, and, as they begin to revive, adding older males. Chilling for 30 minutes at 40° F can also be used for this purpose. Other techniques used to induce mating are given in chapter 11.

If mating is seen to occur, the females should be removed and placed on hosts after allowing one to two hours for sperm to reach the spermatheca.

Determination of Host Preference

If possible, individual mated and unmated females are allowed to run freely among several stages of one or more species of host insects. All attacked hosts are marked for future observation and, if numbers permit, dissection. Numbering the hosts in sequence of attack and making notes on host feeding, oviposition time, etc., can add considerably to an understanding of the biological attributes of the species. Observations such as these must, of course, be conducted in a manner which prevents escape of the parasite or at least provides the means for its easy recapture. For this purpose, a sleeve-cage with a glass top is generally useful. Host material can be supported near the glass by means of a rack so that the activities of the parasite can be observed through a swing-out stereoscopic dissecting microscope. An observation chamber for use with smaller host plants such as potato tubers, potato sprouts, twigs, and small fruits is shown in figure 55. The previously mentioned window booth (figure 49) also may be successfully utilized in such studies.

Observations of the free-moving parasite should be supplemented with trials wherein the female is confined close to the host by means of small cells, tubes, or jars, as shown in figure 52. A series of isolated individuals, if transferred to new hosts daily, can give rather quickly an indication of fecundity, longevity, host feeding, and host preference.

If the closely controlled tests fail to bring about reproduction of the species, it will be necessary to use a potpourri method. This brings into use a reasonably large cage which will accommodate several possible hosts in all stages of development.

This is considered to be the ultimate in free choice of host material, and, in addition, the space, or free flight, factor is likely to be satisfied. Several stubborn species may be introduced into such a situation with the hope that one or more will 'take.' It must be understood that this technique is used as a last resort in attempting to obtain enough insects for further, more closely controlled, studies.

Attention to Abnormal Behaviour Patterns

People who work closely with insects develop a sense of what is right or wrong for the culture, and it is common jargon to refer to particular cultures as 'contented' or 'discontented.' Such subtle observations may be extremely helpful in guiding the quarantine worker along new avenues towards solution of culturing problems. For example, excessive activity is a certain sign that something is wrong. In this event, the first factor to investigate is the food supply—either honey or host material. A stray beam of direct sunlight also can trigger a swarming behaviour, which, if unchecked, can greatly devitalize a culture. As a matter of fact, Tothill, Taylor, and Paine (1930, p. 23) observed that adult *Ptychomyia remota* Ald. readily succumbed to heat from a small spot of sunlight falling on a corner of the fly cages.

Directional artificial light may also attract the natural enemy away from the host, and high intensities may cause abnormal activity. Inadequate light may inhibit oviposition or mating.

Other factors which can be adverse to insect cultures on plants or fruits are webbing of plant-feeding mites, competitive contaminant insects, residues from previous field sprays or dust, air-borne dust, and malodorous plant material such as may result from decomposition. Excessive numbers of beneficial species on continuous cultures will ultimately reduce the rate of oviposition per female through crowding and will quickly exhaust the host supply, and, of course, superabundant oviposition ('overstinging' or superparasitization) can lead to complete loss of cultures.

Screening for Hyperparasites and Other Injurious Organisms

Since the introduction into California of *Quaylea whittieri* (Grlt.), a hyperparasitic encyrtid which attacks *Scutellista cyanea* Mots. and *Metaphycus lounsburyi* (How.), by Craw in 1901 (Flanders 1943a), a controversy has existed regarding the influence of secondary parasites on the effectiveness of their hosts (see chapter 5, section on hyperparasitism). Regardless of these arguments, the strong possibility remains that secondary parasites in a new environment may interfere with effective biological control and may find additional host species in the native fauna to their liking. The problem is aggravated by the fact that only rarely are entomophagous insects of primary habit immune to attack from one or more entomophagous species of secondary habit. Therefore, exclusion of hyperparasites is absolutely essential.

Generally speaking, parasites exhibiting more than cursory interest in parasitized hosts should be suspected of being secondary parasites and very careful tests must be made to confirm or allay the suspicion, particularly if species new to the worker are involved. The literature will be of some help in determining known hyperparasites associated with various primary species.

Chapter 9 presents means by which the foreign collector may safeguard against the importation of hyperparasites. However, in the field, laboratory facilities where host relationships can be studied may be unavailable and probably there will be no taxonomists immediately available for consultation regarding the identity of species new to the collector. For these reasons both primary and secondary parasites may be included in shipments to the quarantine laboratory. Thus the quarantine laboratory must serve as the main line of defence against introduction of hyperparasites.

To the quarantine worker five observations may give clues indicative of hyperparasitism, namely: (1) taxonomic affiliations with families or genera known to contain hyperparasitic species; (2) observation of oviposition in parasitized hosts; (3) empty host 'mummies' which contain two types of meconia and exuviae; (4) dissections which reveal larvae feeding on or within other parasitic larvae or pupae; and (5) increasing preponderance of the species in question over known primary species from a common host as the season progresses, particularly if the suspect species is consistently of smaller size.

The obligatory hyperparasitic habit may be found in species from all the well-known entomophagous chalcidoid families with the exception of the Mymaridae and the Trichogrammatidae. The habit is fairly common in the Elasmidae, Pteromalidae, Eupelmidae, and Signiphoridae (Thysanidae). The Perilampidae are largely hyperparasitic. In the Ichneumonoidea the hyperparasitic habit is relatively rare among the Braconidae, and in the Ichneumonidae it is generally confined to the mesochorine and cryptine species. The habit is seldom encountered in most of the parasitic families of the Diptera, and it is not known among the Tachinidae. It occurs in a few families of the Vespoidea; it is rare among the Proctotrupoidea (= Serphoidea) with the exception of the Ceraphronidae where it predominates. Among the Cynipoidea it is commonly encountered in the Charipinae, many of which attack primary parasites of aphids.

Observation of oviposition in parasitized hosts is a good indication of the hyperparasitic habit. Such behaviour may be observed during the daily inspection of segregated material in the emergence units. Placing these females on hosts parasitized with known primary species which are related to those expected from the shipment will possibly reveal similar tendencies. However, this also may be merely a case of multiple parasitism. If mated females of the parasite in question select parasitized hosts and ignore healthy hosts, they can be classed as direct obligatory hyperparasites and must be destroyed. However, if mated or unmated females of the unknown species oviposit in parasitized as well as healthy hosts, they may be facultative hyperparasites and detailed studies should be conducted in order to learn whether or not this constitutes a threat to the primary parasite or to indigenous parasites in the areas where colonizations are contemplated. If unmated aphelinid females oviposit in parasitized hosts, there is strong probability that males of the species are obligatory secondary parasites. These are not harmful. The problem of culturing species with secondary males is discussed in a following section.

Hosts from which parasites have issued may contain two types of meconia and/or exuviae, as revealed by light transmitted through opalized glass in the case of coccids (T. Fisher 1959), or dissection of larger hosts. Thus, if the known primaries are solitary in habit, secondary parasitism is obviously indicated. A complication arises if young immature primary parasites are attacked, since they may not have developed far enough to void their meconia. Accurate host relationships can be learned only by close study and dissection.

The hyperparasitic habit is positively established if dissection following observed oviposition reveals eggs on or within the immature primary parasite, and later dissections reveal that the eggs have hatched and the larvae are feeding on the immature primary parasite. The technique of dissection involves the use of small, stiff, sharp needles and dissecting medium such as pure water or 0·75 per cent NaCl solution. This work is usually performed under a binocular microscope at 18 to 60 magnifications depending upon the size of the material. Illumination may be provided by a variable intensity lamp and may pass through the host from a substage mirror or be reflected from above. If the latter course is used, light intensity and background colour become important factors. Opaque material is satisfactorily dissected on a white background and translucent objects can be more carefully examined on a black background.

Dry dissection of certain diaspine hosts may be performed by inverting the scale in a drop of fast-drying glue. After a hardening period of 20 minutes the periphery of the ventral shield can be chipped away with needle points and lifted away *in toto*. This method works well with externally feeding secondary parasites and it is possible to follow the complete development of a single individual by holding the material at approximately 75 per cent R.H. Submersion in a fluid medium facilitates dissection but many individuals must be examined in order to follow the life history completely. Larger material, such as Lepidoptera or Coleoptera, can be dissected wet or dry in small dissecting trays, the bottom of which contains a layer of wax. The integument of the host can be spread by inserting pins through it into the wax. The use of various dissecting media may facilitate proper evaluation of the parasite–host relationship.

Several consecutive shipments from a given area usually show an increase in hyperparasites as the season progresses. This should be remembered, particularly if initial shipments from the explorer-collector arrive in late summer, because by then secondary parasites may considerably outnumber primary parasitic species. Provisional separation of primary and secondary parasites is frequently possible by size differences, the secondary parasites being the smaller species. Occasionally, multiple parasitism enters the picture and hosts are found simultaneously containing primary parasites of two or more species.

Facultative hyperparasitism is encountered in a number of the families of the Chalcidoidea, being especially prevalent among the Eupelmidae and Eurytomidae.

FIGURE. 46. During the introduction of parasites of the European corn borer it was necessary to hold in quarantine large quantities of overwintering material in large refrigerated rooms. (Photo copied from Baker, Bradley, and Clark 1949.)

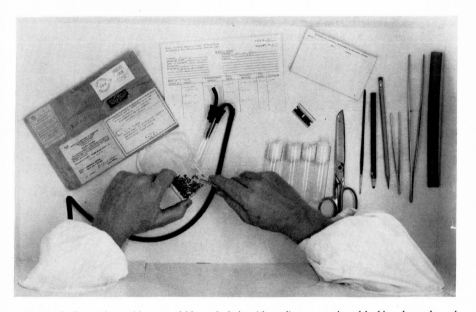

FIGURE 48. Processing a shipment within an isolation (sleeved) cage, as viewed looking down through the glass top.

Beginning clockwise with the left hand, items include plastic packet containing parasite material on leaf fragments, cloth sack which enclosed the packet, shipping envelope, S & R form, collection aspirator, daily emergence form, the length of plastic hose is used to jar insects from shipping vials for re-collection, forceps, pencil (handy for reaching into vials and killing unwanted organisms), waxed pencil, brush for handling very fragile or weak insects, scissors, and razor blade for opening wrappings, 8-dram vials for segregation of material.

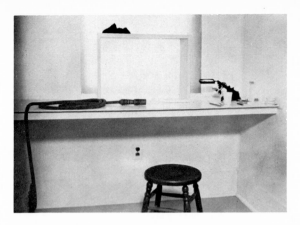

FIGURE 49. Window booth and screened transfer cage used at United States Department of Agriculture quarantine laboratory, Moorestown, New Jersey. Shown are vacuum collector, a self-illuminated low-power magnifier, and various receptacles for segregation of incoming material.

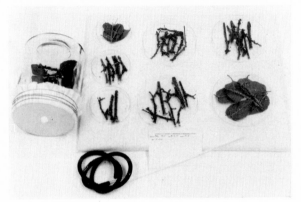

A

UNIVERSITY OF CALIFORNIA--DEPARTMENT OF BIOLOGICAL CONTROL

Note No. ....Date................Noted by........................

B

FIGURE 50.

A. Inverted petri dishes rest on soft padding. The jar at the left serves for larger amounts of material. Note that the cloth top is held in place by a number of separated rubber bands. Emerged material is collected from this container by inserting a long aspirator through a hole in the cloth (shown plugged with cotton). Segregation equipment is not restricted to the containers illustrated. The species of insects as well as the bulk of material will determine the exact method to be used.

B. Emergence record. Emergence is recorded daily on this form. One form is provided for each segregated increment. Data from these forms are summarized on the 'receivers' side of the Senders and Receivers Report (see figure 47).

Again, accurate determination of host relationships can be learned only by dissection throughout the developmental period of the parasites.

The occurrence of facultative hyperparasitism within a genus or species is of interest. For example some species of *Thysanus* exhibit primary habits, while others exhibit secondary parasitic habits (DeBach, Kennett, and Pence 1958). According to Bess and Haramoto (1959) *Eupelmus cushmani* (Crfd.) may have either a primary or a secondary relationship to its host, *Procecidochares utilis* (Stone). Dowden (1935) reported that *Brachymeria intermedia* (Nees) attacks gypsy moth, or other naked lepidopterous pupae as a primary parasite, and as a secondary parasite attacks *Stilpnotia salicis* L. through *Rogas unicolor* Nees (Braconidae). *B. intermedia* has also been reared as a secondary parasite from puparia of five species of Tachinidae.

Parasites of larval or adult predators may be encountered because such material may contain immature parasites which the collector could not detect. For example, species of the genus *Perilitus* attack larval coccinellids but emerge after the host transforms to the adult stage (Balduf 1926a). In New Zealand the usefulness of *Coccinella undecimpunctata* L. was curtailed by the inadvertent introduction of a parasite (Dumbleton 1936). This was reported as a secondary parasite but there is doubt about this.

Neuropterous predators are subject to attack by a considerable number of parasites. For example, larval or pupal stages of *Chrysopa plorabunda* Fitch are attacked by seven species of parasites in five hymenopterous families, and *C. majuscula* Banks is attacked by *Isodromus niger* Ashm. and *Helorus paradoxus* Prov. which attack the larval chrysopid and emerge from the cocoon (Clancy 1946). Delucchi (1954) graphically illustrates the parasites and diseases associated with several species of predators which attack *Adelges piceae* (Ratz.).

Predator material collected in the field in a foreign country should be propagated for at least one complete generation before releasing it from quarantine at the receiving laboratory. With certain coleopterous predators an exception to this rule may be permitted if adults are held and fed at approximately 80° F for two or three weeks following emergence because during this period any latent parasitism should become apparent (Smith 1952) and affected individuals and their parasites can be destroyed.

Manipulation of Species Whose Males are Secondary Parasites

Species of parasites whose females develop as primary parasites, but whose males can develop only as secondaries require specialized handling which must be done initially in quarantine.

An understanding of the phenomenon of the hyperparasitic male was first reported by S. E. Flanders (1936). A later publication (Flanders 1959b) summarizes the known information on this complex and important subject.

Known species having hyperparasitic males occur only in the Aphelinidae and mainly in the genera *Casca*, *Coccophagus*, *Physcus*, and *Prospaltella*. Shipments containing species in these genera should be meticulously segregated into isolated individuals of the various host species because this procedure may give the first clues to the occurrence and source of the hyperparasitic male. Often only females will emerge. These should be given free choice of several stages of their coccid hosts—both healthy hosts and those containing various immature stages of other parasites from laboratory cultures. Of importance at this time is detailed observation of several individual unmated females. Attacked hosts should be marked for dissection.

Virgin arrhenotokous aphelinids deposit only male-producing eggs and, on the healthy coccid host, may place eggs externally (between the host and the substrate) as in *Coccophagus ochraceus* How., whose male feeds primarily on the coccid host and incidentally on the developing internal female parasite or male-producing eggs may be deposited internally, floating free in the blood of the host as in *C. gurneyi* Comp. The author has recently observed that unmated and mated *C. basalis* characteristically oviposit in a specific organ, the suboesophageal ganglion of lecaniine hosts, a habit not known to be evidenced in other Aphelinidae (Flanders, Bartlett, and Fisher 1961). If the coccid contains immature parasites, the virgin aphelinid may lay male-producing eggs in the blood of the host as does *C. compéri* Grlt., on the immature primary parasite as does *C. caridei* Brèthes, or within the immature parasite as does *C. rusti* Comp. The author has observed that *Physcus* n. sp., from Burma (Fisher 1961) requires a dry environment as an oviposition site and selects parasitized *Aonidiella aurantii* (Mask.) which contains very young *Physcus* pupae or pupae of certain other endoparasites and oviposits externally on such pupae.

The intent of the foregoing comments is to convey the idea that the host relationships and life cycle of the hyperparasitic male may be very elusive. The fact that virgins oviposit on certain laboratory hosts does not assure that the male will develop on those hosts. However, once oviposition is observed, daily dissections will reveal any developing males. The first lead indicative of the hyperparasitic male habit comes from observing the first-instar male larva just before eclosion. The presence of functional spiracles (those supplied with branches from the main tracheal system) is positive indication of an external, free-breathing habit, and means that further development can occur only ectoparasitically. In most species of those aphelinid genera mentioned previously, male development occurs at the expense of an immature primary parasite in a relatively dry environment such as would result from a full-fed primary parasite larva having consumed the host's body contents. In known species if functional spiracles are lacking, both sexes can develop only parasitically and as primary parasites of the phytophagous host. Further discussion of the hyperparasitic male habit occurs in chapters 7 and 11.

If the male can be propagated, a culture of the species can often be started by storing the unmated females and later mating them to their own male progeny. If field material is continually coming in, laboratory-reared males can then be utilized to mate with virgins as they emerge from the shipments. In fact, this may be a necessary procedure because of difficulty occasionally encountered in achieving mating with older virgins.

Diapause

Diapause in parasitic entomophagous insects assumes many forms and is closely associated with the physiological state of the host. It has been demonstrated that growth of the parasite is delayed if the host insect enters diapause but is uninterrupted if the host develops without arrest (Salt 1941). This reaction may be of particular importance in the handling of parasites of aphids. The importance of selecting the correct constant temperature for the prevention of diapause in the continuous culture of aphids is discussed in the previous section entitled, 'Optimum Temperature and Humidity Requirements.'

Among the parasitic Hymenoptera, however, there are examples of quiescence and diapause occurring independent of the host's normal development. For example, quiescence occurs in *Comperiella bifasciata* How. which oviposits in all stages of *Aonidiella aurantii*. Development in second moult or older female hosts requires approximately 23 days. Hosts parasitized during the first instar reach the second moult before *Comperiella* emerges. In such hosts 40 days were required for development; the first-instar parasite did not begin active feeding until the host was large enough to provide sufficient food for its maturation. Diapause occurs in species whose hyperparasitic males develop only in the presence of a suitable host, i.e., an immature primary parasite, in a suitable environment (Flanders 1959b). Coccid hosts which contain only the unhatched male larvae of *Coccophagus basalis*, whose males must develop as secondary parasites, will usually complete development and produce progeny.

Since diapause in the host species is usually induced by cyclic or seasonal changes in temperature, light intensity, or food and may be also influenced by parasitization, the occurrence of diapause should be expected when shipping insects either between hemispheres or between sharply contrasting climates (Jaynes 1933; Flanders 1944c). Proper timing of interhemispheric shipments may tend to compensate for the effect of reversed seasons, particularly concerning species which characteristically enter seasonal diapause. For example, during the early 1920's when cactus feeding insects were being sent from the southern United States to Australia, it was reported by Hamlin (1924, p. 455) that the most favourable period for shipment extended from September to December. This procedure, in effect, lengthened the American summer and made it unnecessary to institute costly storage facilities in quarantine in Australia.

In general, diapause is indicated if noticeable delay is detected in completion of development of immatures or by reluctance of adults to oviposit in normal hosts, reduced activity, etc., and the stages concerned appear to be healthy. Usually termination of quiescence in the immature parasite is contingent on causing the host insect to resume its physiological, if not its morphological, development. On the other hand, termination of diapause may require more drastic manipulation such as the use of various kinds of chemical, mechanical, or thermal shock treatments.

Sometimes, to the contrary, it will be necessary to preserve the quiescent or diapause states pending availability of host material from the laboratory or field

(Arbuthnot and Baker 1938). Facilities necessary for the protracted holding of diapausing host material, Lepidoptera in particular, in order to obtain at the proper time the diapausing parasites associated with the various stages thereof have been mentioned previously. Response to diapause-terminating stimuli varies with the species, and in some instances it has been impossible to terminate diapause in the laboratory.

Much has been published concerning diapause in insects and for a summary of the complexities involved the reader is referred to the works of Andrewartha and Birch (1954, pp. 56 to 85) and Lees (1955, 1956).

Storing Adult Parasites

Tolerance of adults of different species of parasites to given temperatures is highly variable and should be investigated for individual species if it becomes necessary to store them.

Most adult parasites of homopterous pests can be held in vials for several weeks at 55° to 60° F in darkness if they are removed to approximately 80° F for 20 minutes for feeding and exercise two or three times weekly; on the contrary, *Meteorus* sp. will tolerate 40° F for 90 days and *Mormoniella vitripennis* Wlk. has produced viable eggs after five months at 4·4° C (DeBach 1943a). Care must be taken to replenish the food, usually honey streaks, and occasionally vials should be changed. In this manner, when males were lacking it has been possible to hold virgin arrhenotokous females after they have deposited male eggs and subsequently to mate them with their own male progeny and thereby initiate a culture. Then, too, subsequent shipments may contain males, thus permitting utilization of the stored virgins. In general, the best storage temperature is one at which appreciable visible activity ceases. This will vary with the species.

Incidental Inclusions—Detection of Disease

A side benefit of the importation of expressly sought exotic natural enemies is the incidental inclusion in the shipments of associated entomophagous species which the foreign collector sometimes has overlooked or about which he has not known if he has lacked the time or facilities to determine just what species were attacking the host. Quarantine personnel should be alert to such unexpected species and where definite host relationships and preferences are learned (a bonus derived from the effort of initial segregation) tests should be conducted comparable with those accorded the sought-after species. The rarest species in a shipment may be an efficient natural enemy in the new environment.

After emergence is complete and before the material has been fumigated, and as a final step before sterilizing or incinerating shipment residues, the host material should be re-examined in detail for evidence of disease. If the services of an insect pathologist are not locally available, suspect material should be sent to a recognized laboratory of insect pathology. Methods of shipping diseased insect material are given in chapter 21.

Termination of Emergence and Disposal of Shipping
Materials and Residues

After parasites begin to emerge from foreign material, the question of how long to hold it for complete emergence must be resolved, especially if only a few individual parasites are being reared out. Experience has taught that it is usually time to dispose of host material if emergence of hyperparasites significantly exceeds that of primary parasites (except in species whose males develop as hyperparasites) or if dissection reveals obviously dead hosts or dead immature parasites concurrent with a sharp drop in numbers of emerging primaries. Proper disposal is extremely important, particularly if shipments are arriving from areas known to harbour plant pathogens which are not present in the area of the quarantine laboratory. Although federal quarantine regulations specifically prohibit entry of the plant host of such diseases, no chances should be taken with the residues (figure 53, facing p. 336).

Already mentioned in the section on facilities and equipment were such items as cyanide jars, incinerator, and autoclave. Incineration is a safe method of disposal for shipping containers and wrappings. Glass and certain wood or metal containers can be re-used if they are sterilized in an autoclave. If shipment residues are not to be retained for the collector's examination upon his return, they, too, should be destroyed by burning.

RECORDING OF QUARANTINE DATA

Written records associated with the quarantine handling of imported material are of utmost importance. The sender's and receiver's form has been mentioned as the original record of importations, and the reader is again referred to figure 51 in order to note the type of information required. Upon the receiver's completing the form at the finish of emergence, the data can be utilized to make a cross index to species of parasite, host insect, host plant, and locality. Names used must be verified by taxonomists. This matter is elaborated later under 'Value of Taxonomy to Quarantine Work.' The receiver's final entry on the S. & R. form is a summary of the daily emergence records (figures 48 and 50) which are initially affixed to the segregated increments. A good practice is to compile a semi-annual or annual summary of shipments received, along with pertinent biological data developed in quarantine. Propagation records include daily observations on testing procedures and become a part of the original data pertaining to importations.

In the Department of Biological Control of the University of California, after a species has been properly screened and its primary habit established, and after a culture has been enlarged to the point where it can be consigned to project personnel, a form entitled 'Quarantine Release Authorization' is filled in and countersigned by the chairman of the department. Copies go to the chairman and the project leader for the purpose of providing a written record of the transaction, as well as a summary of the biological information developed in quarantine, such as notes on fecundity, longevity, host-feeding, sex ratio, and host preference which will be used as a guide by project technicians in the early phases of developing a mass production programme. As a safeguard, upon releasing a species, a small insurance stock of the new species is retained in quarantine until project technicians have their cultures well established.

VALUE OF TAXONOMY TO QUARANTINE WORK

Although in the applied sense the taxonomic status of imported beneficial insects is secondary in importance to their biological attributes, ultimately it is necessary for purposes of communication to have names for them.

Accurate specific determination of imported entomophagous insects and their hosts often involves considerable delay, but since generic identification is usually readily available, the identity of the insects is retained by use of the S. & R. number and the shipment item number, e.g., *Metaphycus* sp. S. & R. 1895-#2. If a large number of the unknown species is derived from several shipments over a considerable span of time from the same area, the species may be referred to by a code name such as *Aphytis* sp. 'A,' *Prospaltella* sp. 'G,' or *Metaphycus* sp. 'C.'

The practical value of rapid determinations is readily appreciated when several shipments arrive during a brief period and it therefore becomes physically impossible to propagate all the species represented. Therefore, if certain importations can be assigned to species which were rather extensively studied or tested in the past, they can be de-emphasized in favour of the newly imported species in the shipments, thus placing maximum effort where it offers the most promise of applied use.

Since it is virtually impossible to identify moving insects accurately, taxonomic determinations are made of dead specimens from shipments and from specimens which died during testing. Specimens of species unknown to the quarantine worker are promptly sent to a taxonomist, as well as specimens for verification of determinations made in quarantine.

In order to maintain accurate records it has become a practice at Riverside to affix vials containing dead insects to the identification memo shown in figure 58. Information from the collector regarding locality, date, host plant, and information from quarantine personnel such as S. & R. No., and host preference are placed on this memo which is then sent to the appropriate taxonomist. The taxonomist returns this form with a determination, and it is then attached to the original S. & R. report. This procedure facilitates changing of names in the records occasioned by subsequent taxonomic information and helps to identify the insect in question, particularly when several shipments over an extended period are involved. Code names are then related to the determination.

RELATION OF QUARANTINE TO OTHER ACTIVITIES

The indispensable role of systematics in quarantine work has been emphasized. On the other side of the coin it can be readily appreciated that the quarantine worker has something to offer the systematist, for it is his privilege to observe biological traits which may be the first indications that the species he is handling is not necessarily what the taxonomist determined it to be (Flanders 1953*b*). Differences may be evident in characteristics of immature stages when adults appear to be identical. For example, differences in pupal pigmentation as well as responses to various temperatures led to critical study of the adults which developed from these immature stages with the result that the number of known species of *Aphytis* has been considerably increased (DeBach 1959).

In the event that new species are successfully propagated, the taxonomist receives adequate series thereof and parallel series can be sent to other taxonomists or museums for their reference collections.

One important bit of information which the quarantine biologist can contribute concerns the correct association of males and females of the species with which he is working, because taxonomic descriptions of parasitic Hymenoptera are primarily concerned with females, the male often being incompletely described or omitted.

Importations are an obvious source of new host and distribution records. Unfortunately, this type of information is rather slow in getting into entomological literature.

The biologies of imported entomophagous insects may be considered of either academic or practical interest, depending upon the host preference and relationships involved. In actual practice, species which show promise of exerting some degree of control over an agricultural pest, as deduced from preliminary laboratory testing, are consigned as soon as possible to the projects concerned in order to implement detailed testing, mass production, and colonization, all of which are beyond the scope of the quarantine laboratory.

CHAPTER 11

Culture of Entomophagous Insects and Their Hosts

G. L. FINNEY AND T. W. FISHER

INTRODUCTION

THE PURPOSES of culturing entomophagous insects are: (1) to study the insect it-self to determine facts pertaining to its habits, life history, and host relationships; (2) to facilitate the establishment of an introduced or indigenous species by providing large numbers for release; (3) to accomplish a wider distribution of a previously established introduced or indigenous species; or (4) to supply routinely or at specified times large numbers of insects for release in the field in order to restore a favourable parasite– or predator–host balance that has been disturbed. The usefulness of laboratory propagation of natural enemies of insect pests is well covered by Baird (1939) who emphatically states that the reproductive qualities of an entomophagous insect under mass culture are not adversely affected by continuous propagation. Upon investigation, reports of degeneration of breeding stock caused by inbreeding were found by Baird to be false and were shown to be an effect of improper handling. At research institutes a suitable plan for maintaining a pilot culture of the beneficial species will usually be suggested by quarantine personnel. Often this will be only a holding procedure and the responsibility of developing a culturing technique of larger magnitude will fall to the insectary superintendent or to technicians on the appropriate projects. Approaches to the problem may be suggested after consulting works of rather broad scope such as those by Bradley (1941), DeBach and White (1960), Finney, Flanders, and Smith (1947), Flanders (1930b, 1949a, 1951), Galtsoff et al. (1937), and Simmonds (1944b).

Large-scale production of a species may not be a requisite for its successful establishment in initial test areas, particularly if it is well adapted in the new environment and its host is at a stage most susceptible to attack. Initially, the efficiency or economy of operation need not be scrutinized too closely, for these factors are not necessarily of prime importance in accomplishing an establishment. The vedalia beetle, *Rodolia cardinalis* (Muls.), provides an excellent example of establishment from release of a few hundred individuals with very little production expense.

When it is desirable to hasten the spread of an established species into wider or more remote areas, a mass-production type of programme may be considered.

Accelerated mass production may be required in carrying out the so-called inundation release which is sometimes necessary in order to correct an upset parasite–host balance. Production projects with these two objectives in view may entail an output ranging from one million to over forty million entomophagous insects annually. To accomplish the latter objective, the major portion of this yield might need to be concentrated into that time of year in which the field host is particularly susceptible to attack.

The level of production attainable with a given species in the insectary depends on the degree to which the beneficial species, host species, and the host-supporting medium are inherently preadapted to the artificial environment. Other determining factors are their interrelationships, ease of manipulation, amenability to simple insectary procedures, and availability of food.

The habits and behaviour patterns of insects vary considerably from species to species. Each has its own particular characteristics and attributes that set it apart, often only to a slight degree, which must be recognized and considered in developing a culture programme.

Because of highly individualized problems encountered in the culture of insect species, it is possible in the space provided only to touch on rather broad implications or principles of insect culture techniques and it will be apparent that most of this presentation is technique-oriented. Although this material is presented under rather comprehensive subject headings, it is not our intent to convey the idea that the development of an insectary propagation programme must follow these phases in sequence, and certainly among species no one phase consistently has greater importance than another. Much of the information in various categories will be derived simultaneously. Because of this inherent characteristic, initial test procedures aimed at achieving greater understanding regarding host preferences, optimal temperatures and humidities, tropisms, mating stimuli, and fecundity should be designed so that such interrelated information will be forthcoming. In essence, this is an elaboration of quarantine handling but with the important difference that greater numbers are involved, hence investigation can cover broader areas, and, of prime importance, the objective is mass production.

Since insectary propagation of entomophagous insects involves three closely interrelated entities, namely, the beneficial species, its host (or pest) species, and the host plant or food substrate, these categories will be considered first in the discussion which follows.

BIOLOGICAL INFORMATION ON THE BENEFICIAL SPECIES

Mating

The principal obstacle to the culture of many entomophagous species is lack of mating under the artificial conditions of the laboratory. The mating habit varies as greatly between species as between families or even orders. Mating characteristics vary from uniparental species that reproduce without mating to those in which culture is precluded because they cannot be induced to mate in captivity. In some species the males develop slightly ahead of the females and are waiting to mate with them as soon as they emerge. Other species, especially those of the Chalcidoidea, mate readily soon after emergence and most are quite amenable to mass culture in this respect.

Copulation or attempted oviposition are not to be taken as conclusive proof that the females are impregnated. Transfer of spermatozoa may not have taken place at all, or perhaps due to interrupted copulation only partial impregnation has occurred. In the latter case, the female may produce a few female offspring and then, in effect, revert to virginity and yield only male progeny. Some species require but one mating and others more than one to provide a balanced sex ratio over their productive life span.

With aged virgins, mating may be induced by special handling techniques such as: (1) brushing their bodies with larval or pupal skins of newly emerged females; (2) withholding nourishment for several hours and then presenting them with food in the presence of full-fed males; (3) partially immobilizing them in an air current in the presence of males; (4) suddenly increasing the temperature from low to optimum in the presence of bright light; (5) subjecting them to anaesthetization, or by chilling and subsequently confining them with males immediately after recovery but before regaining full activity; or (6) merely having a certain ratio of males to females (Flanders 1955).

Special handling is necessary in certain species of the Tachinidae which otherwise will not mate in captivity. Mating may be induced by: (1) shaking the container vigorously to tumble the adults together; (2) placing large numbers of adults, predominantly males, in large screen cages outdoors shaded from the direct sunlight; or (3) transferring screen containers from shaded conditions to a bright sunlit environment.

Species whose mating instincts are influenced by the diurnal light cycle should be held in rooms exposed to the effect of increasing and declining intensity of daylight. A nocturnal or crepuscular species usually will mate in darkness or declining light and those that are diurnal do so when the morning light is increasing.

The majority of species mate most readily at temperatures of 65° to 75° F which may be below the optimum for maximum oviposition and development.

Some species need a period of inactivity during or following copulation in order to consummate impregnation. This usually requires special handling in the unnatural environment of the insectary. For example, in *Macrocentrus ancylivorus* Roh. (Finney, Flanders, and Smith 1947) it was found that the female normally mates but once, after which she secludes herself until impregnation occurs, for in this species the female is not fully impregnated until the spermatophore containing the sperm has been adjusted in such a way that it makes proper contact with the spermathecal duct. The sperm then make their way up the duct to the sperm receptacle or spermatheca. As many as six to seven hours are required to empty completely the spermatophore which is then ejected by the female prior to ovipositing. If the required post-mating rest period is denied her by such factors as excessive heat, light, and parasite density, she remains unimpregnated and accepts the repeated advances of males until she becomes so congested by spermatophores that none can be properly adjusted. These are all ejected previous to oviposition and the female remains in effect unmated and deposits only male-producing eggs in the host.

It was found that *Macrocentrus* would mate and successfully consummate impregnations when allowed to emerge in a closed unit in total darkness at a temperature of 84° F. The progeny of such females were approximately 55 per cent female.

The senior author has observed that females of *Aphidius smithi* Sharma and Rao, in which the presence of spermatophores was not involved, yielded over 95 per cent male progeny when allowed to emerge and oviposit under the influence of bright light at a temperature of 76° F. In this instance, the caged population was quite dense and activity was rather high. However, this species yielded as many females as males when the activity of the parental culture was reduced by placing the cage outside overnight or by covering the cage for a few hours with brown heavy paper.

The females of the Tachinidae and Hymenoptera are usually ready to mate upon emergence whereas the males may not be so disposed for periods up to several days, depending on the species.

In many species the developmental period of the male is usually faster than that of the female and he thus emerges in advance of her. Consequently, the male is for the most part sexually mature and ready to mate when the female emerges.

The males of some species, such as *Opius oophilus* Full., are not sexually mature for five to six days after emergence, and the manipulation and special handling of such species present a serious obstacle to an economical mass-culture programme. In the culture of this species it was necessary to segregate the sexes of *O. oophilus*, hold them to sexual maturity, then mix the males with newly emerged females. Furthermore, effective mating was not accomplished at high densities and only small colonies could be used in the mating units. Apparently the female emits an 'odour,' the gradient of which leads the male to her for mating, and the odour-laden air must be removed from the cage periodically or the gradient will be lost and mating activity will cease. This can be accomplished by a gentle breeze from an electric fan for a brief time between mating periods.

In certain species of the Aphelinidae, mating has a remarkable psychological effect in that it sometimes creates a radical change in the type of host selected by the female as well as causes her to act as a primary parasite instead of a hyper-parasite. *Coccophagus cowperi* Grlt. is an excellent example of a species exhibiting this phenomenon (Flanders 1937a). When unmated, the female oviposits only hyperparasitically in a host which is suitable for the development of the male but not the female; after mating, she oviposits only as a primary parasite in a host in which a female but not a male can develop. In this species, as well as many species of *Coccophagus* and other Aphelinidae, oviposition prior to mating (for male production) is necessary for the perpetuation of the culture in the insectary. Propagation of species with hyperparasitic males is discussed at some length in chapter 10.

Fecundity

The fecundity of a species is seldom fully exploited in a production programme. The females of some species, however, may deposit their entire complement of eggs in a relatively short period of time. For instance, the female of *Dahlbominus fuscipennis* (Zett.) can, within a five-day period, deposit all of her eggs on the cocooned larvae, prepupae, or pupae of her host, *Diprion hercyniae* (Htg.). Each host is able to support to maturity all the progeny of a single parasite (Miller 1940).

An aphelinid species of the genus *Anthemus* lives only four days in the insectary, but within the first 36 hours of her life the female is capable of parasitizing over 150 first-stage individuals of the natural host, *Parletoria oleae* (Colvée), utilizing in that time nearly all of her complement of eggs (Finney, unpublished notes).

On the other hand, in the mass production of *Macrocentrus* only a small fraction of its egg potential was used. The female has a potential of nearly 500 eggs and oviposits an average of 20 per day. However, the newly hatched larvae of the host, *Gnorimoschema operculella* (Zell.), would in three days burrow out of reach in the potato tubers, thus precluding further parasitism.

The entire daily production of the aphelinid *Aphytis lingnanensis* Comp., which consisted of many thousands, was allowed to oviposit in the scale host, *Aspidiotus hederae* (Vallot), for only 24 hours (DeBach and White 1960). They were then re-collected and released in the field. In that brief exposure time each female had deposited two or three eggs, but this ensured a production exceeding the number in the inoculum.

Longevity

The duration of the reproductive life of a species may be a very significant consideration in the development of a mass-culture programme. Some species are still alive and reproducing after their progeny have emerged and are also reproducing.

A hardy species with a long life span usually presents no serious problem in storing and transporting to the field, but a frail species such as *Anthemus* mentioned before must be used in the field immediately after emergence. Adult *Anthemus* could not be successfully transported to the field, hence this species was shipped while in the late pupal stage. The host-supporting potato tubers were fastened to the tree branches and the parasites would emerge and immediately attack the field host with maximum vigour.

Factors Affecting Sex Ratio

In a biparental species the production of males in excess of those necessary to adequately fertilize the females of the culture is superfluous. Therefore, within this limit the more the sex ratio can be made to favour the females the more efficient and effective will be production.

In a gregarious species superparasitism may cause an excess of males due to the selective elimination of the females. This probably occurs because the male can attain maturity on less food than the female. In a solitary species such as *Macrocentrus ancylivorus* the excess parasites are eliminated during the first stage of development through internecine competition. It was found that mated females produce more female progeny when the host is superparasitized than when it is not (Martin and Finney 1946).

In many species the sex ratio is strongly influenced by the host. When *Metaphycus helvolus* (Comp.) was initially mass-produced, the proportion of females increased directly with the size of host attacked. In the early stage of the project the parasite stock was reduced to a dangerously low level because almost the entire production was on small hosts and therefore emerged as males.

Mated females of *Dahlbominus fuscipennis*, a parasite of the spruce sawfly, exhibit definite preference for large hosts. This species oviposits unfertilized male-producing eggs on small-sized hosts.

The aphelinid parasite, *Coccophagus ochraceus* How., attacks young black scale and may deposit several eggs in rapid succession if the host is plentiful. The first egg is fertilized and is deposited inside the host and develops as an endoparasitic female. The remaining eggs, not fertilized presumably due to the rate of oviposition, are deposited externally under the body of the host and develop as ectoparasitic males.

Temperature may influence the sex ratio of certain species by adversely affecting sperm viability. For example, excess males occurred in the progeny of *Trichogramma* exposed for two weeks at 38° to 47° F (Schread and Garman 1933), and in *Aphytis lingnanensis*, a parasite of California red scale, exposure to 30° F for six hours killed nearly all the sperm in the spermathecae of the mated females and a high percentage of males were rendered sterile (DeBach, Fisher, and Landi 1955).

Mutilation and Host Feeding

Parasitic Hymenoptera often use the ovipositor as an instrument for puncturing the host body and lacerating internal structures of the host in preparing to feed on the resultant exudate. This act is referred to as stinging and it may or may not precede oviposition. Certain species must host-feed, presumably to acquire protein for egg production.

In the mass production of certain species, great care must be exercised in presenting the parasites with hosts of the proper size and in maintaining the optimum host–parasite population ratio. *Metaphycus helvolus* will host-feed on about one out of five optimum-sized scale. If smaller scale are used, a greater ratio is fed upon. When an excessive number of *M. helvolus* is used, it is possible for all of the scale population to be destroyed by feeding alone. *Aphytis chrysomphali* (Mercet), an ectoparasite of the citrus red scale, can, in the same manner, completely destroy a host population with no reproduction of either host or parasite occurring. Tests employing various host–parasite density ratios for various times will point the way to increased production efficiency.

Superparasitism and Cannibalism

Superparasitism is not often detrimental in mass cultures. There is, however, a loss of efficiency per female due to the wasting of eggs, especially if a solitary species is involved in which the excess larvae are eliminated in the first stage. As many as 52 dead first-stage *Macrocentrus ancylivorus* were found in a single tuber moth larva in which only one parasite developed. This inefficiency may be alleviated by maintaining a more optimum host–parasite population ratio.

In the mass culture of *Aphytis maculicornis* (Masi), if the ratio of parasites to hosts was excessively high the mortality of the unnatural host, *Hemiberlesia lataniae* (Sign.), would become so great that very few parasites would be produced. The danger of mortality in a gregarious species using the same parasite–host population ratio is greatly reduced if the host can support four or five parasites to maturity rather than only one parasite.

With a solitary species a high percentage of parasitization is usually accompanied by high superparasitism. However, almost 100 per cent parasitism can be obtained with little or no superparasitism with a species that has the ability to discriminate between parasitized and unparasitized hosts. Such is the case with certain species of *Anthemus*, *Chelonus*, and *Aphelinus*.

Control of cannibalism is one of the chief problems in the culture of predators. Since the finding of food is in most cases a result of random search, the detrimental effect of cannibalism may be largely overcome by maintaining an excess of prey available in an ample searching area. Another factor which encourages cannibalism is excessive overlapping of stages, since older instars may attack younger instars when under stress caused by crowding or lack of readily available food.

Host Preference

The host list of certain species when cultured in the insectary is much greater than the number found in nature. These unnatural hosts serve a very useful purpose at times in a culture programme. For example, in the mass culture of *Macrocentrus ancylivorus* the potato tuber moth was found to be much more amenable to insectary techniques than the strawberry leaf roller which is the natural host. Similarly, for laboratory culture of *Aphytis maculicornis*, *Hemiberlesia lataniae* was used in place of *Parlatoria oleae*, the natural host. *H. lataniae* is not recorded as a host in nature.

BIOLOGICAL INFORMATION ON THE HOST INSECT

Special Considerations

The objective in culturing a host species is to provide a pure population of optimum density on, or in, an easily manipulated and acceptable host medium.

The ideal laboratory host insect is one that possesses the following characteristics: (1) is readily accepted by the beneficial species that is to be cultured; (2) may be cultured readily on a host medium which is well adapted to insectary procedures; (3) has a rapid rate of increase (high fecundity or short life cycle or both); (4) is either uniparental or presents no serious mating problem; (5) produces no detrimental by-products, such as honeydew, silk, or wax; (6) is a general feeder (more than one host medium usable); (7) is highly immune to disease; (8) exhibits little internecine activity.

Natural and Unnatural Hosts

Host insects as used in insectary production may be divided into two categories—natural and unnatural. The natural host is usually attacked in nature by the beneficial species. An unnatural host is seldom if ever attacked in nature by the beneficial species, usually because of isolating mechanisms, but will serve as a satisfactory host in the insectary. Convenience and ease of handling are two important criteria which bear on choosing a host for propagation of the entomophagous species.

Although they do not necessarily stimulate deposition of eggs, some unnatural hosts are suitable for the development of the immature stages of the beneficial species. With certain species it is possible to obtain eggs through the use of a natural host or a simulated natural oviposition site. The eggs may then be transferred to the unnatural host for hatching or further development (Simmonds 1944b). The culture of the corn borer parasite, *Exeristes roborator* (F.), was accomplished in this manner (Baker and Jones 1934). In the mass production of *Chrysopa* spp., Finney (1948) utilized coddled and waxed larvae of the potato tuber moth as food for the growing larvae of the predators.

Reproductive Rate of Host

For economy of time, space, and effort, a high rate of reproduction is very desirable in host species. A relatively low 'carry over' on interim stock may be maintained with less danger of loss when the species has a high fecundity. Furthermore, the time required to expand the stock to the large population necessary for a mass-culture programme is greatly reduced.

Rapid build-up of the host population also may be greatly facilitated if the life cycle of the species is of relatively short duration. The quick upsurge of aphid and spider mite populations is largely a product of a combination of short life cycles and high fecundities. Also, aphid cultures usually consist only of viviparous parthenogenetic females.

When the beneficial species is host specific and the host is difficult to culture *en masse*, there is little to be done other than to concentrate on improving old techniques or developing new ones toward a more efficient use of the host. It should not be presumed that the beneficial species is host specific. Instead, all possible hosts known to be amenable to insectary handling should be tested for possible acceptance in the laboratory.

Since a predator usually has a wide range of acceptable hosts, there is often opportunity to choose hosts well adapted to efficient insectary usage. Many millions of coccinellids have been mass-produced in the University of California insectaries. However, since the technique consisted mainly of providing ample food and space, details of procedures used are notably absent in the literature.

An ideal situation is approached when a uniparental host species is used because the rate of reproduction per unit of host medium is increased, the efficiency of parasitization or predation is usually improved, and the host substrate is more effectively utilized.

Examples of two nearly ideal host species are found in the diaspine scale group. One is the latania scale, *Hemiberlesia lataniae*, and the other is the uniparental strain of the oleander scale, *Aspidiotus hederae*. Each of these species develops readily on potato tubers, citron melons, or banana squash.

Although *Hemiberlesia lataniae* is not recorded as a host of *Aphytis maculicornis* in nature, over 18 million parasites were mass-produced in the insectary on this substitute uniparental host in one season (Finney, unpublished notes). Because of biparentalism and higher host specificity, the natural host of *A. maculicornis*, *Parlatoria oleae*, is much more difficult to mass-produce than *H. lataniae*.

Many millions of *Aphytis lingnanensis*, a natural parasite of the California red scale, *Aonidiella aurantii* (Mask.), were cultured in the insectary on the uniparental strain of *Aspidiotus hederae* grown on banana squash (DeBach and White 1960). In this instance this host was utilized not only because of the favourable attributes listed above but also because it was susceptible to attack over a longer period than *Aonidiella aurantii* which serves as an effective host for only a brief interval in the third stage.

The advantages of oleander scale over red scale as an insectary host for the mass production of *Aphytis lingnanensis* are shown in table 3.

TABLE 3

Characteristics of scale species	Oleander scale	California red scale
Sex ratio of scale	All females (uniparental strain)	50% males
Periods of availability to *Aphytis*	Suitable scale available for about 30 days	Suitable scale available for 4-5 days
Effect on substrate	No gumming	Gumming traps parasites
Effect of mutilation by *Aphytis* on scales	Almost nil	High mortality
Aphytis sex ratio	80% females	50% females
Effect on size of *Aphytis*	Larger parasites of uniform size —makes possible volumetric measurement of numbers produced	Smaller adults of various sizes
Number of parasites produced per individual	2 or 3 parasites per host is common	Usually 1 parasite per host

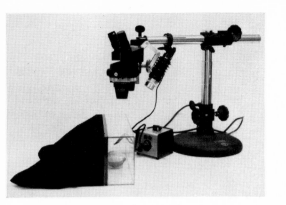

FIGURE 51 (above, left). Observation chamber. This is essentially a glass box with a black cloth sleeve on one side through which material may be manipulated during the observation period. Freely moving individual parasites quickly indicate host stage preferences in this situation.

FIGURE 52 (above, right). Methods of confining parasites close to the host. Left to right: Household canning jar with bottom cut off. Oleander branch trimmed to fit inside 2-inch glass cylinder—cloth glued on top and tied around branch at bottom. Shallow glass or plastic cells, with cloth tops, affixed to melon by bead of beeswax which was applied in the melted state by means of an eye-dropper.

FIGURE 53 (left). Autoclave—a safe means of disposing of shipment residues.

FIGURE 54. Nursery of potted oleander plants used as host of *Saissetia oleae* in the mass production of *Metaphycus helvolus* at Fillmore Citrus Protective District Insectary, Fillmore, California. Each bed contains 500 plants. In the insectary adequate cross ventilation is necessary in order to maintain vigorous plants.

FIGURE 56. Transfer of citrus mealybug crawlers to bleached potato sprouts utilizing branches of *Pittosporum undulatum* as the medium of transfer. Associates Insectary, Santa Paula, California.

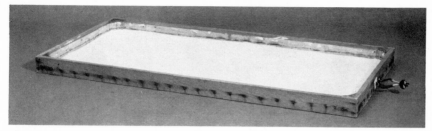

A

B

FIGURE 55. Hot-wire barrier rearing tray.

A. General aspect: size of this one is 20″ × 40″. The sides are 2½″ high. Designed for use with 115 V a.c., this device is extremely useful for open culture of lepidopterous larvae or wingless, non-jumping insects. During operation the barrier is hot to the touch, not glowing red. Its gauge (diameter) is determined by its length.

B. Details of construction: insulated lead-in wires are securely fastened between lock-nuts and arranged as a crude maze in order to prevent escape of insects at that point. Bolts clinched tightly to wall with washers on both sides to prevent any looseness that would lead to arcing of the current. Interior angles rounded at corners and bottom. Small tough wire is used to bind hot wire to the asbestos sheeting on the sides. The binding wire looped over monel wire with ends extending through a small drilled hole and out the other side. The wires are spread apart and a square-shouldered double-pointed tack or staple is driven between them and across the drilled hole. The binding wires are brought together over the staple and twisted together so that the hot wire is held snugly against the sheet rock. The twisted wire is cut off to about ¼″ long, turned down and the end driven into the wood so it will not snag clothes or the person working with it.

A

B

FIGURE 57. Mass production in open rooms.

A. *Macrocentrus* production, University of California, Berkeley.

B. The interior of a *Cryptolaemus* rearing room showing numerous pupae. Associates Insectary, Santa Paula, California.

Hemiberlesia lataniae served as prey in the mass culture of the coccinellid *Chilocorus bipustulatus* (L.) (Finney, unpublished notes). However, the young larvae experienced great difficulty in feeding on adult scale due to the toughness of the armour and almost all feeding was upon immature stages. If the latter stages were depleted, cannibalism became prevalent. The use of *Aspidiotus hederae*, *Parlatoria oleae*, and *Quadraspidiotus perniciosus* (Comst.), all hosts with a more easily penetrable armour, permitted the larval coccinellids to feed upon all stages. The added availability of adult scale provided a greater volume of food per unit of host-inhabited area and, further, deterred cannibalism.

Deleterious Host Products

The lecaniine or soft-bodied scale species, such as the brown soft scale, *Coccus hesperidum* L., or black scale, *Saissetia oleae* (Bern.), present certain cultural difficulties when used as host insects. For example, the accumulation of heavy excretions of sticky honeydew produced by the immature stages may smother the culture as well as trap entomophagous species. In order to reduce such hazards, infested melons are rinsed weekly under flowing lukewarm water, dried by air flow, and replaced in culture rooms. In mass culture this time-consuming practice can be avoided by modifying the infesting technique as follows:

Coccus hesperidum is usually cultured on citron melons. The melon is infested only on one side and is later placed with the infested side turned downward so that as honeydew is produced it will fall away from the culture rather than on it. The melons may be supported on edges of slats spaced 3 to 4 inches apart forming the floor of a rack or by 'hammocks' of 1- or 2-inch mesh poultry netting suspended from a framework.

Scale hosts such as *Saissetia oleae* or the hemispherical scale, *S. hemisphaerica* (Targ.), are usually cultured on green potato sprouts. Such cultures require an occasional thorough washing to remove accumulations of honeydew. The container is tipped on edge and the sprouts washed with a water spray. These washings may be repeated until the culture approaches the oviposition stage. From that point on there is a danger that the dilute honeydew will invade the egg cavity of the adult thereby hindering the escape of emerging crawlers or even precluding the successful incubation of the eggs.

Black scale, although not ideally adapted to mass culture (Smith 1921), has been utilized more than any other species of lecaniine scale in California due to the extensive work done in importing and mass rearing of entomophagous species for release against this pest in the citrus-growing regions of that state. Hundreds of thousands of parasites and predators of various species have been produced on *Saissetia oleae* using green potato sprouts as the host substrate (Flanders 1942c). Currently the insectary of the Fillmore Citrus Protective District at Fillmore, California, utilizes potted oleander plants as the insectary host of *S. oleae* in the mass production of *Metaphycus helvolus* (figure 54, following p. 336).

Other hosts excreting honeydew, but in somewhat lesser volume, are mealybugs, aphids, and leafhoppers. Most of these have a shorter life cycle than the unarmoured scale hosts. Furthermore, unlike the more sessile lecaniine hosts, they tend to move from an unacceptable environment to a more favourable one before they are trapped by honeydew.

Other host species produce a webbing in the immature stages which builds up until the host medium becomes matted with excreta and silk as occurs in the Mediterranean flour moth, *Anagasta kühniella* (Zell.), or the Indian meal moth, *Plodia interpunctella* (Hbn.).

The potato tuber moth, *Gnorimoschema operculella*, also produces silk in the larval stages. The fact that this species normally spins its cocoon in sand facilitates the separation of the host and its parasites, since the chemically inert sand does not react to the sodium hypochlorite (Martin and Finney 1946) used in dissolving the cocooning silk. This technique also made possible the freeing of larvae from the cocoons before pupation so they could be utilized as bare larval hosts in culturing parasites such as *Bracon hebetor* Say, and *Dibrachys cavus* (Wlk.) (Doutt and Finney 1947), or predators such as *Chrysopa plorabunda* Fitch (Finney 1948).

Immunity to Disease

A host species susceptible to virulent micro-organisms should be avoided in favour of one less subject to pathogenic organisms whenever possible even though it may be less attractive to the beneficial species. Because *Prodenia praefica* Grote was extremely susceptible to a polyhedral virus capable of quickly destroying entire cultures, it was not utilized as a host in culturing *Euplectrus platyhypenae* How. The variegated cutworm, *Peridroma margaritosa* (Haw.), was used instead, even though it was not an acceptable host past the fourth instar (Finney, unpublished notes). *P. margaritosa* is a hardy species very resistant to disease and is a general feeder. If handled properly, viable eggs may be obtained for continuous cultures (Waters 1937) (Finney, unpublished notes). Furthermore, *Peridroma*, unlike *Prodenia*, is not subject to diapause which precludes continuity of cultures.

Problem of Diapause in the Host

Certain host species which typically enter diapause in nature may be prevented from so doing by maintaining a sufficient photoperiod in the laboratory. Smith and Langston (1953) prevented *Harrisina brillians* B. and McD. from entering diapause by maintaining 15 hours of steady light in every 24-hour period. As shown by Dickson (1949), codling moth larvae exposed to 14 or more hours of light per day while feeding do not enter diapause. He also reported that either high or low temperatures during feeding prevent diapause in larvae of the oriental fruit moth. Diapause may not be related solely to direct effects of photoperiod or temperature. Schlinger and Hall (1959) are of the opinion that these factors act mainly through the host plant whose physiology may be changed and this change influences onset or termination of diapause in the phytophagous insect and thence in the ento-mophagous species.

Physical Requirements

The temperature and humidity utilized in a culture programme must be adjusted to encompass the tolerance of the entomophagous species, host species, and host medium, separately or in combination. When the host insect is utilized free of its host medium only the beneficial species and host are concerned as in the production of *Dibrachys cavus* (Doutt and Finney 1947). Of course, during the culture of the host species, only it and the substrate are concerned. Compromises must be made as a rule between the optimum environmental conditions of each for the sake of attaining the maximum yield of entomophagous insects per unit of production.

It may be generalized by saying that where only the host and its substrate are involved a temperature of 70° to 75° F and relative humidity of 60 to 70 per cent are beneficial to both, particularly during early development.

Worthy of consideration is the fact that the host's substrate must be maintained in a state acceptable to the host. Therefore, in the final analysis a compromise must be reached regarding choice of a relative humidity which is mutually satisfactory to the substrate and the insect population it supports. Citrus fruits require a relative humidity of over 80 per cent for optimum storage, whereas banana squash and thin-skinned potato tubers are prone to microbial attack if relative humidity is constantly in excess of 60 per cent.

The host attains a greater size with consequent higher fecundity if the substrate is maintained in a more suitable condition. For example, green potato sprouts supporting a culture of *Saissetia oleae* in a dry (45 to 50 per cent R.H.) and warm (78° to 80° F) environment tend to shrivel and toughen. Heavy watering only stimulates an undesirable flush of growth. The scales mature as very small individuals yet for their size produce abnormally large quantities of honeydew. However, if the temperature and humidity are adjusted to approximately 72° F and 65 per cent R.H., the need for watering is greatly reduced and the sprouts become slow-growing and succulent, supporting a thriving scale culture. Host insects such as certain species of mealybugs and aphids also are benefited by a cool humid environment.

During development of the mass production of *Aphytis lingnanensis*, it was learned that the best laboratory host, oleander scale, could be reared satisfactorily only at 75° F during its younger stages. Only scales over 45 days old could tolerate the 80° to 82° F required for rapid development of the parasite (DeBach and White 1960).

Munger (1955) found that it was impossible to rear the citrus red mite, *Panonychus citri* (McG.), over three generations unless the cultures were exposed to fresh outside air drawn into the room. Air recirculated through activated charcoal filters accomplishes the same result and appears to benefit cultures of predators and parasites as well.

Taxes

According to Fraenkel and Gunn (1961), the term taxis (plural taxes) refers to the arrangement assumed by or migration of freely moving organisms in response to a stimulus or stimuli. Taxes of a host species must be studied and utilized to the greatest degree in developing efficiency in the culture programme. For instance, positive thigmotaxis of the six-spotted mite, *Eotetranychus sexmaculatus* (Riley), made it possible to increase the efficiency of ripe oranges as a host medium when the fruit was lightly covered with finely ground kapok lint (Finney 1953). The collection of the eggs of the potato tuber moth, *Gnorimoschema operculella*, was greatly facilitated by the fact that the adults preferred to lay their eggs on rough ventral surfaces, particularly on the underside of a certain type of cloth having a fibrous nap (Finney, Flanders, and Smith 1947). Negative thermotaxis makes possible the open culture of large numbers of crawling insects through use of a hot-wire barrier as shown in figure 55, following p. 336.

Most lecaniine and diaspine scale crawlers exhibit positive phototaxis and as a consequence may be collected by means of shadow-box traps (see chapter 13, figure 81-A). For example, black scale crawlers may be picked up on sheets of paper to which they have been attracted by a source of light and may then be dusted on to potato sprouts. The tray of sprouts should be tipped on edge so that the sprouts will be in a horizontal position during the infesting procedure. The scale crawlers falling through may be picked up on another sheet of paper and the process repeated until most are lodged on the sprouts.

In a similar manner, brown soft scale may be led from one citron melon to another by means of directional light and blocked there by a V-shaped shadow. When the desired number have been transferred, the melon should be taken to a dark cool location until the young have become established. By this method many melons may be infested from one productive 'mother' melon.

Use of hygrotaxis may be demonstrated in large mass-production programmes when mealybugs are used as a host insect because the usual procedure of transferring them is through the use of temporary or transitory host media such as leaves of the pepper tree, *Schinus molle*, or twigs of *Pittosporum* or mustard. When these leaves are laid on trays of bleached potato sprouts which are heavily infested with producing mealybugs, they soon become covered with young crawlers. The infested leaves are then removed and laid upon uninfested sprouts where they quickly dry and the young mealybugs then transfer to the succulent sprouts. This method is utilized at a commercial insectary at Santa Paula, California, and is illustrated in figure 56.

Sources of Host Material

The enormous number of entomophagous insects required in certain mass-production programmes could not be attained without a correspondingly large supply of host material available in the stage most acceptable to them. In order to provide a host in this volume economically it must be easily secured in quantity from field sources when needed, or it must be one ideally adapted to efficient, inexpensive culture procedures in the insectary.

Initial stocks of certain host species perhaps can be secured at little or no cost from an insectary already propagating them at a maintenance level throughout the year. In the interest of expediency, a source of this kind should be sought before resorting to field-collected stock.

Some mass-culture programmes utilize massive quantities of field-collected host material. This is the most inexpensive way if host material is abundant in the area. For example, in Canada vast numbers of field-collected cocoons containing the larval and prepupal stages of the European spruce sawfly, *Diprion hercyniae*, were carefully cleaned and graded for use as host material for culturing *Dahlbominus fuscipennis* (Miller 1940; Wilkes 1947). During that programme from 1935 to 1945 over 889 million parasites were released in the sawfly-infested areas. The European earwig, *Forficula auricularia* L., collected in the field from artificial hiding places were used in the propagation of the tachinid *Bigonicheta setipennis* Fall. (Getzendaner 1936).

The great quantities of black scale crawlers used in the mass-culture programmes of California did not arise from insectary-grown cultures but instead originated from extensive natural infestations of adult populations brought into the laboratory on infested sucker canes or twigs of roadside *Schinus molle*. These infestations were always well attended by colonies of ants which kept the scale populations free of honeydew accumulations and also served to protect them from many species of natural enemies.

Dealing with Field Contaminants

The hazard of incipient contaminations of pest insects and pathogens is coincident with the bringing in of field material to the insectary. Every effort should be made immediately to eliminate these undesirable organisms while the cultures are small. If not done at this time much time and effort must be expended later in trying to suppress these contaminants in expanded cultures.

Perhaps the best approach is to set up several small units, then periodically inspect each closely and remove all undesirable insect parasites and predators and all diseased individuals. To accomplish this will require at least one or two generations, but a mass-culture programme should not be launched until a clean initial stock of host insects is assured.

The safest material to bring in from the field is eggs or field-collected adults producing young which are immediately removed to an isolated location for further development. Even then, in homopterous insects some parasites such as *Aspidiotiphagus* spp. or *Pauridia* spp. which parasitize the very young diaspine scale or mealybugs, respectively, still may persist. For example, *Pauridia* spp. outside a cage will parasitze mealybug crawlers on the inside surface of the cloth cage covering.

Entomophagous species in field-collected black scale egg clusters are prevented from contaminating the insectary stock by placing scale-infested twigs in jars and covering the open end (which faces the light source) with cloth, the mesh of which will permit scale crawlers but not parasites to pass through.

The need for adequate treatment of lepidopterous eggs to offset the ravages of disease is mentioned elsewhere.

INFORMATION ON THE HOST PLANT

The function of the host substrate is to support optimum populations of the host insect and be acceptable to the beneficial species during the culture period.

An ideal host-supporting medium is one that is: (1) amenable to insectary conditions and techniques; (2) able to provide the nutritional requirements of the host insect species; (3) always available at low cost; (4) convenient to handle; and (5) slow to deteriorate.

Types of Host Substrates

There are three types of host substrates: natural, unnatural, and factitious.

A natural host is one that the host insect usually infests in nature such as sugar beets hosting a leafhopper species, a citrus tree or fruit attacked by the California red scale, or the guava fruit supporting oriental fruit fly larvae.

The excessive time and space entailed in growing certain natural plant hosts, the specialized care required in maintaining them in the greenhouse and insectary, and the loss sustained by their occasional collapse can be avoided by substituting whenever possible an unnatural or factitious substrate more amenable to insectary usage. No satisfactory unnatural or factitious host has been found for the following phytophagous species: citricola scale, cottony-cushion scale, most species of aphids, membracids, white flies, and certain lepidopterous larvae. It is probable that species not amenable to artificial culturing occur in all insect pest groups.

An unnatural host is one used in the insectary in place of the natural host mainly for the sake of convenience or amenability to laboratory handling. It is seldom, if ever, attacked by the host insect in nature. The potato tuber, for instance, is an unnatural host to the California red scale and *Peridroma*, as is the citron melon to brown soft scale, purple scale, or long-tailed mealybug.

A factitious host substrate is one that is prepared or formulated by man, such as a synthetic medium for culturing corn borer or fruit fly larvae. Because of the high control potential offered by synthetic nutrient media, there is much interest in their use for the propagation of insects. A review of this subject is presented by Dr. Hagen in chapter 12.

The Potato as a Host Substrate

The potato serves outstandingly as a rearing medium. The punctured tuber is an ideal host for the potato tuber moth, and the scored or sliced tuber is an excellent food for the more advanced stages of various cutworms or armyworms. Bleached potato sprouts grown in darkness from either planted or unplanted tubers support heavy populations of many species of mealybugs. Green sprouts grown under light will support cultures of black scale and other lecaniine scales. The surface of unsprouted tubers is a good substrate for rearing many species of diaspine scales. The more tender growing tips and leaves of potato sprouts grown under fluorescent lights support heavy populations of the green peach aphid.

Varieties or types of potatoes differ greatly; consequently, some are better suited for one purpose than another. For example, the red potato Bliss Triumph yields the best sprouts for culturing mealybugs and has been utilized almost exclusively in the mass culture of *Cryptolaemus montrouzieri* Muls. at a commercial insectary at Santa Paula, California. The smooth skin of the White Rose variety proved most satisfactory for culturing such diaspine scale species as *Aspidiotus hederae* and *Aonidiella aurantii*. The varieties with a textured skin such as the Russet or Burbank are well adapted to the mass culture of the potato tuber moth or the latania scale.

The Russet or Bliss Triumph types grown in the colder areas such as Oregon or Idaho are preferred over those grown in the warmer regions such as central or southern California. The potatoes from the north, especially where excessive irrigation is not practised and harvest follows the first frosts, possess excellent keeping qualities and may be held in storage at 36° to 38° F for 10 to 12 months. Furthermore, these northern potato-growing regions are well outside the incidence of tuber moth infestations so that the potatoes originating there need not be fumigated with methyl bromide as do those from the warmer southern parts of the country.

Reasons for apparent differences in host suitability of potato varieties have not been thoroughly explained. In trying to establish a biological reason for such differences, Tanaka (1953) found that settling of *Ceroplastes ceriferus* (Anderson) on potato tubers was largely determined by distribution of the phloem fibres.

Brown soft scale and San Jose scale do not propagate readily on potatoes. For these and other species with similar traits the citron melon and banana squash are excellent unnatural hosts. Comparing their bulk of approximately 15 pounds with that of a 4- to 12-ounce potato, the greater surface area and easier handling of the potato are readily apparent.

Length of Useful Life and Storage Requirements

Because the life cycles of the various host species of insects differ greatly (that of aphids may be seven days while some scale species require over two months) it is quite essential that the substrate has a long period of usefulness. This becomes even more imperative with sessile species such as diaspine scales that cannot transfer from a collapsing host medium.

Dried seeds of certain plants have been used in culturing a relatively large number of insect species. In the mass culture of *Trichogramma*, wheat was used to culture the host species, *Sitotroga cerealella* (Oliv.) (Flanders 1934). Romanova and Il'Inskaya (1938) give data on the relative merits of rye versus wheat in the mass production of *Sitophilus granarius* (L.) and *S. oryza* (L.), hosts of *Lariophagus distinguendus* (Foerst.). Packaged dehydrated carrots form the basic ingredient of the host medium for the culture of the larvae of the oriental fruit fly, *Dacus dorsalis* Hendel. A common advantage of the above host media is their long useful life. If kept cool and dry, they may be stored over long periods with little or no deterioration.

One of the desirable attributes of the potato, squash, and citron melon is the ability to keep well in storage for several months. It should be noted here that host acceptability and durability after removal to insectary conditions decrease with increasing post-harvest time. Therefore, such material should be used as soon after harvest as is practical.

Effect of Physical Factors

When a mass-culture programme is being developed, first consideration is generally given to the optimum environmental requirements of the beneficial and host insect species. The environment tolerated by the host substrate is usually broader than that of the insects involved. When growing plants are utilized, environmental conditions must in certain instances be regulated to satisfy the more restricted conditions necessary to maintain the useful life of the host plant.

It was found, for example, that potted oleander plants when used as the host for black scale in the mass production of *Metaphycus helvolus* required cross ventilation of fresh air in the room. Otherwise, many of the plants would drop their leaves and deteriorate because of fungi attacking the root system.

Caged sugar beet plants used in the mass production of the beet leafhopper, *Circulifer tenellus* (Baker), required a bank of cool white fluorescent lights to promote green healthy growth while in the insectary.

Ripe oranges, especially the smooth-skinned varieties, serve as an efficient host medium for mites such as *Eotetranychus sexmaculatus* only when lightly covered with finely ground kapok lint (Finney 1953). This same technique with modifications was utilized to induce a better settling of crawlers of *Parlatoria oleae* on potato tubers.

THE MASS PRODUCTION PROGRAMME

Concepts

The goal of a mass-culture programme is to produce with minimum man hours and space the maximum number of fertile females of an entomophagous species in as short a time and as inexpensively as possible.

The mass culture of entomophagous insects involves three closely interrelated and equally important procedures, namely: (1) the propagation or preparation of a medium for supporting the host species; (2) the building up and maintenance of an adequate reservoir of uncontaminated host species; and (3) the maintenance of such cultures of the beneficial species as will meet the needs of the colonization programme.

The development of a single efficient unit for parasite or predator production is usually the basic step inaugurating a mass-production project. Knowing the average yield of such a unit, whether it be a vial, tray, cage, or room, it is only a matter of establishing a series in 'assembly-line' style in order to attain the production level desired. Herein lies our concept of 'mass production,' namely, the skilful and highly refined processing of an entomophagous species and its host and substrate through insectary procedures which result in economical production of millions of beneficial insects, usually expressed in terms of annual production. Economic control of a pest species resulting from periodic colonization of its natural enemies cannot be the standard of measure. For example, in citrus a few dozen *Rodolia cardinalis* per acre can, in two or three generations, reduce *Icerya purchasi* Mask. to non-economic levels, but on the same acre 400,000 *Aphytis lingnanensis* may be required to control *Aonidiella aurantii*.

The unit, or the element of a composite unit such as a room, should be of such size and weight that it can be carried, transported, or manipulated by the insectary worker without difficulty. The number of these units incorporated into the production line is limited by such considerations as floor space, budget, and number of personnel. The type of production unit ultimately chosen depends upon relationships and attributes of the beneficial species, host insect, and host plant, and the susceptibility of each to environmental resistance factors considered singly or in combination.

By 'environmental resistance factors' is meant the stresses that tend to reduce the actual fecundity of the entomophagous population in insectary cultures as the host density is increased. Examples are: (1) sensory interference which depresses the oviposition capacity and retards the rate of oviposition and of development; (2) self-destruction through cannibalism, superparasitism, and host mutilation; and (3) the increased incidence of pest insects and diseases.

The Approach to Mass Production

Development of a mass-production programme demands the acquisition of certain basic knowledge as quickly as possible regarding the beneficial species, its host, and the host-supporting medium, and usually comes as an outgrowth of techniques developed in quarantine and in the initial relatively small-scale culture methods discussed in the first part of this chapter.

Since the attributes and habits of various entomophagous species are highly varied and the interrelationships between the beneficial species, host species, and host-supporting medium are always to some extent different, each insect production project should be adjusted to exploit fully the characteristics of the specific insect species and host medium concerned. Although the details and techniques may differ, certain underlying principles are generally common to most programmes.

There is no substitute for experiment in the formulation of a mass-culture programme. Each new project is a challenge in itself and offers opportunities for the creation of new techniques and concepts as well as reapplication and modification based on previous experience. To the accumulated general information and experience of other workers reported in the literature is added the practical trial and error of basic experimental units.

In approaching a mass-production programme the work is usually developed in the following sequence: (1) the preparation of an adequate reservoir of the host-supporting medium; (2) the propagation of a sufficient and sustained volume of the host species; and (3) the rearing of the entomophagous species in pure culture for use in maintaining insectary cultures at the required level, with the maximum surplus to be utilized in the field colonization programme. Usually each of these procedures, for the sake of efficient operation, is kept separate and distinct, isolated either by time or space, or both.

There are three methods used to integrate these three procedures, namely, 'continuous contact,' 'limited contact,' and 'periodic contact.' All are based on the duration and permitted method of contact between the entomophagous species and its host (Flanders 1955). The 'continuous contact' method requires an unbroken food chain within a single production unit, or cage. A rotation system is utilized wherein the regular removal of a portion of the entomophagous species is accompanied by a concurrent replacement of a portion of the host or its substrate, or both. One example of this method is the routine maintenance of pilot laboratory cultures of *Ephestia* and its parasites. With the 'limited contact' method, an entomophagous inoculum is introduced for a prescribed period into the host population. Duration of the oviposition period is adjusted so that the resulting progeny will consume most of the host population. Adult parasites or predators used in this manner may, when recollected, be released in the field where they may continue ovipositing—as with *Aphytis lingnanensis* (DeBach and White 1960) and *Cryptolaemus montrouzieri* (Fisher, unpublished notes). With the 'periodic contact' method a succession of host populations is exposed to a constant entomophagous population for a prescribed period. In this method the potential fecundity of the parasite or predator can be nearly fully realized, and thus it finds particular use in the rapid build-up of cultures during the beginning phases of a mass production programme. These methods are discussed further in a following section entitled 'Production Efficiency.'

As a general rule, a reservoir of the host species should be maintained in pure culture, isolated and sacrosanct at all costs. The exception would be an instance in which the host insect could be separated from the entomophagous species in pure cultures and in adequate numbers as occurred in the mass culture of the oriental fruit moth parasite, *Macrocentrus ancylivorus*. The separation of the pupae of the potato tuber moth from the parasite cocoons was so clear-cut that no separate host culture units were needed.

However, in the mass rearing of *Cryptolaemus montrouzieri* or *Leptomastix dactylopii* How., a pure culture of *Planococcus citri* (Risso) must be maintained in an isolated room used solely for infesting work. Serious difficulties usually in the form of contaminants have always been encountered when salvaged mealybug crawlers from a predator or parasite production room were relied upon for infesting material.

Standardization

In most culture programmes, and particularly those in which a large volume of material is prepared each day, it is very important that close control of temperature and humidity be maintained. With the standardization of time and temperature the various operations of the day or the week can be scheduled in a well-coordinated and efficient manner.

Factors causing variation in the life cycles of the entomophagous and host species should be reduced to the minimum. The cultures of the host species on or in any given unit of host medium should be initiated in as brief a period as possible by mass-infestation techniques. Individuals of certain host species infested at identical times may, under certain conditions, reach maturity several days apart. The variation in the development of potato tuber moth larvae was materially reduced through the use of standardized egg-sized potato tubers. At the same time the infestation was further standardized by using an even distribution of eggs on an egg sheet exposed to a controlled number of moths for a 24-hour period. Larvae in a small-sized potato would develop much more uniformly than those in a large one.

Lack of adequate humidity will cause variations in developmental time in some host insects. For example, cultures of *Hemiberlesia lataniae* on Russet potatoes develop much more uniformly when the relative humidity is 60 to 65 per cent, whereas at 40 per cent considerable variation occurs in the rate of development.

Internecine action and superparasitism tend to induce uneven developmental rates in some cultures. Cultures of *Sitotroga cerealella* developed rapidly and evenly in wheat, but in corn the growth was slow and more erratic because the wheat was inhabited by only one larva per kernel, whereas the larger corn kernels contained several competing larvae.

Propagating Cage or Unit

The type and size of the production units are determined basically by the attributes, tropisms, and interrelationships of the three biotic constituents involved.

Several of the larger mass-production programmes are conducted in room-sized units. The rearing of *Cryptolaemus montrouzieri* and *Leptomastix dactylopii* on citrus mealybug-infested bleached potato sprouts represents examples of room culture. *Metaphycus helvolus* was cultured on black scale infesting potted oleander shrubs or green potato sprouts in the same fashion.

The open room unit may be feasible: (1) if the reservoir of host material is large enough to infest uniformly all of the host-supporting medium in a very short time so as to establish an even brood therein; (2) if the beneficial species is so strongly attracted to the host that it tends to remain in the area in which it is introduced throughout its period of attack; or (3) if the beneficial species mates and oviposits in total darkness and the host species and host medium are amenable to this environment as in the case of *Cryptolaemus montrouzieri* and *Leptomastix dactylopii.* Sometimes the parasites or predators must be manipulated by light so that they are drawn periodically from one side of the room to the other across the infestations. Most insects exhibit positive phototaxis and tend to migrate towards a directional light source and concentrate there.

The recent trend in insect production, however, is towards the use of smaller replicated units. It is thus possible to exert closer control over the cultures, which is especially desirable if light is required in maintaining the well-being of the host medium, and the parasite or predator exhibits strong phototaxis. The small unit is especially useful when an unnatural, relatively unattractive host is being utilized and the entomophagous species must be confined close to the host culture. Small units also permit the removal of an incipient contamination without jeopardizing the major mass of material. A better control of parasite–host population balance and a quicker and more efficient utilization of the host is also achieved.

The floor space of the laboratory is utilized more effectively both horizontally and vertically with small multiple units. In many instances the collection of emerging parasites or predators is facilitated by anaesthetizing the insects in the smaller units with CO_2-ether gas. Figure 57 illustrates open room culture and figure 63 illustrates smaller enclosed production units. (See pp. 337 and 384.)

Problems Attending Small Units

Certain problems attend the use of small units. Chief among them is ventilation. This is of particular importance where a rooted plant must be held under optimum conditions of light and humidity during and following parasitization of the host. Sleeve cage units may need a ventilation unit (Finney 1960) (see figure 73, chapter 13).

Adequate ventilation alleviates the problem of gases arising from the host medium, such as those emitted by ripening grapefruit which are toxic to some parasite and host species confined in closed units. The gases generated by decaying host media, such as potatoes, squash, or citron, or any plant material for that matter, are likewise detrimental and in some instances permit the invasion of pathogenic organisms into the weakened host.

Production Efficiency

The potential fecundity of the individual entomophagous female is seldom fully exploited in a mass-culture programme. The criterion of efficiency is based primarily not on the inherent fecundity of the parasite or predator, but rather on the yield achieved per production unit.

The entomophagous insects produced in the greatest numbers are generally those having the highest fecundity and utilizing the smallest amount of food per individual. The maximum fecundity of an individual female is attained when the number of suitable hosts available is greater than her productive capacity. In a mass-culture project the inherent fecundity and rate of oviposition are important factors in that they serve to determine the ratio of entomophagous females to the volume or number of host insects per culture unit. The ratio of parasite or predator to host or prey varies greatly with the species involved. Again, the objective is to obtain the maximum production of females per production unit in the minimum of time.

The number of entomophagous insects to be introduced into a given unit in which there is a given volume of host material is determined by experimentation with a series of pilot units stocked with varying parasite–host population ratios. The parasite population in the cage should be adjusted to just lower than the number that causes a reduction in the maximum yield per culture unit due to environmental resistance factors.

If the host is susceptible to parasitism only during a certain stage of its life cycle and the culture is in an even-brooded condition, then a larger number of parasites would be needed to parasitize the host material while it is vulnerable. Often it is not an economical procedure to remove the parasite or predator inoculum for further use. However, with some species it is advisable to remove the inoculum ('sting stock') after a certain time (DeBach and White 1960) in order to prevent superparasitism or a prolonged disturbance of the host insects. Certain predatory coccinellids, such as *Chilocorus bipustulatus*, may be used advantageously as inoculum for brief periods in four or five subsequent units of diaspine scale. Removal and transfer induces a uniform age of developing predator larvae in each cage and this procedure therefore tends to reduce the incidence of cannibalism. Further, this method facilitates more rapid rotation of cages and as a consequence affords a greater degree of sanitation.

With the development of collecting methods, such as with the use of CO_2-ether gas (see figure 76, chapter 13), the re-collection of parasites may, in certain instances, be done economically. Figure 59 illustrates some mass-collection and counting techniques. In the mass culture of *Aphytis lingnanensis*, for instance, the entire daily production was used for a few hours as an inoculum. They were then re-collected by anaesthetization and released in the field (DeBach and White 1960).

There are varying methods of handling the inoculum, the most efficient depending on the attributes and relationships of the parasites or predators and the host species. The inoculum may be introduced into a host population as in the case of *Macrocentrus* and *Cryptolaemus*, or the host insect may be introduced into a parasite or predator population as was done in the rearing of *Chrysopa* larvae with coddled and waxed larvae of *Gnorimoschema operculella* (Finney 1950) and with red scale on potatoes for *Aphytis chrysomphali* (Flanders 1951). Another method may be to maintain in one unit a constant population by adding each day enough parasites to compensate for the daily mortality. The host is separated from the parasites by a thin cloth barrier through which they are parasitized. This method was used in the mass culture of *Dibrachys cavus* on *G. operculella* (Doutt and Finney 1947).

Another nearly self-perpetuating method has been used in which the host and parasite are cultured in a common unit (Flanders 1948c). This has not been utilized, however, in a large mass-culture programme. In order to review the principles exemplified by the cases just given, the reader is referred to a preceding section entitled 'The Approach to Mass Production.'

Factors Responsible for Trouble-Free Insectary Operation

Constant awareness and eternal vigilance should be watchwords for good insectary operation. Here, the 'ounce of prevention' is indeed much more to be desired than the 'pound of cure.' The operator should always assume that trouble is imminent and a daily inspection should be routinely made to detect it in the incipient stage.

The elimination of possible sources of pest organisms in the environs of the insectary is one means of keeping the laboratory free of contaminants. This may be done by eliminating all host plants, culturing only those that are virtually pest-free by nature, or routinely treating the host vegetation if the above means are not feasible. Because of the possibility of insecticides drifting into the insectary, the treating of shrubs in the near vicinity of the building is a definite hazard to the cultures in the insectary and should be done only as a last resort and with great care. Elimination of plant hosts from the immediate vicinity of the insectary is a better approach.

As has been mentioned before, the utilization of small units greatly facilitates the detection of incipient pest invasions in certain cages without threatening the remainder of the cultures.

The rapid turnover of cultures and the immediate destruction of used culture material preclude the building up of possible pest organisms such as secondary parasites, mites, psocids, and disease.

The use of effective barriers, such as the hot wire type (figure 55), will prevent the escape of larvae and crawling insects (Flanders 1945c). Infestation of *Pediculoides* mites, an organism of great concern to insectary operators because of its irritating effect on human skin, can build up into troublesome populations on escaped lepidopterous larvae cocooned in cracks or hidden nooks about the building.

The sterilization of equipment and facilities is essential in preventing the invasion and spread of certain diseases infecting insect cultures.

Insects that have been subjected during their developmental stages to a stress of some sort such as periods of famine or subnutritional diet, incompatible environment, crowding, or injury may be more susceptible to the invasion of certain disease organisms or latent viruses than healthy insects. Steinhaus 1958a and 1958b described the effects of various stressors on certain lepidopterous larvae.

Biological Control of Contaminants

In certain circumstances a biotic agent may be used to control or even eliminate a pest organism in a culture. For instance, the predatory thrips, *Scolothrips sexmaculatus* Perg., was useful against the Pacific mite, *Tetranychus pacificus* McG., in the culture of the red scale parasite *Comperiella bifasciata* How. (Flanders 1943b).

The bethylid *Cephalonomia waterstoni* Gah. completely eradicated an infestation of the beetle *Larmophloeus pusillus* (Schönh.), which was very destructive to the eggs of *Sitotroga* (Schread and Garman 1933).

Other examples of this practice include the use of *Stethorus picipes* Casey to control tetranychid mites, *Metaphycus luteolus* (Timb.) to control *Coccus hesperidum* on potted citrus, and certain species of mealybug parasites to control their unwanted hosts on potato sprouts or potted plants.

Use of Hot Water to Control Contaminants

A hot water bath has on occasion been used to control pest organisms in the insectary cultures. Wheat, the host medium of *Sitotroga*, was dipped in a hot water bath to kill possible pests as well as to add humidity to the medium. Also, in the mass culture of the potato tuber moth newly laid moth eggs were immersed in a hot water bath (118° F for 20 minutes) to prevent the further development of microsporidia in the cultures (Finney, Flanders, and Smith 1947).

Chemical Control of Contaminants

Insecticidal applications for the prevention of pest organisms have been employed with success in several instances. *Sitotroga* eggs were immersed momentarily in carbon disulphide to prevent infestations of mites (Spencer, Brown, and Phillips 1935). Mortality from virus infection can be markedly reduced by immersing eggs of *Sabulodes caberata* (Guen.) in 10 per cent formaldehyde for 90 minutes. General treatment or prevention of disease is discussed by Steinhaus (1953*b*).

Pediculoides ventricosus (Newp.) may be controlled by dusting the infested area with a light film of flowers of sulphur which kills the mobile young attempting to travel through the dust particles. Any field infestations brought into the insectary, especially infestations of lecaniine scale, or lepidopterous cocoon material that includes exhausted material, should be eyed with suspicion and a circle of sulphur dust or of specific insecticides should be placed around the area. Use of such insecticides in the insectary must be conducted with extreme caution.

Rapid turnover and immediate destruction of used material tend to suppress incipient infestations and prevent a flare-up of certain pests.

The recent development of silica gels has been a great help in controlling such pests as cockroaches in the laboratory.

Because of its brief residual action, TEPP has been very useful in controlling greenhouse pests on plants soon to be used with insect cultures in the insectary. Specific acaricides have been used to control mite infestation on plants infested with insect cultures such as spotted alfalfa aphid, *Therioaphis maculata* (Buck.).

Pyrethrum bombs, nicotine fumes, and TEPP smoke generators are used effectively for general fumigation purposes in the greenhouse.

Methyl bromide fumigation is used routinely to defaunate growing plants before bringing them into the insectary as well as to eradicate mealybugs on potatoes and tuber moths in potato tubers destined for rearing scale insects.

Movement of Personnel Throughout the Insectary

Regardless of how insect proof, or how well arranged for isolating competitive insect cultures the insectary rooms are, contamination may still occur if traffic of personnel and visitors is not carefully regulated.

The work for the day should be scheduled to begin with the handling of un-infested host media, and then proceed successively from the least to the most competitive host species, thence to parasite cultures least likely to cause contamination, and then to cultures more hazardous. Obviously, few species under one roof present less likelihood of contamination occurring than when several are being cultured simultaneously.

If personnel is limited, it might be well to work with highly competitive insect cultures such as mealybugs and potato tuber moth on alternate days. Pure cultures should not be jeopardized for the pleasure or convenience of casual visitors. A visiting official with a limited schedule might visit certain cultures before and after lunch, thus lessening the contamination hazard with an interval of time.

Nicotine Hazards

Many entomophagous insect species are very sensitive to the effects of nicotine. Smokers should always wash their hands thoroughly before handling equipment, such as vials, feeding dishes, or cages, which the parasites will contact, and cages as well as materials from which cages will be constructed preferably should be stored in a tobacco smoke-free atmosphere.

Hazards of Dust

As a generalization, parasites are quite sensitive to dust particles. Tubes used for collecting purposes should be well cleaned and stored in dust-free areas. Cages should be wiped free of dust before they are used. Plastic tubes sometimes used in place of glass-collecting tubes are particularly difficult to maintain in a dust-free condition on account of a static electrical charge usually associated with them, and they are not recommended for use in handling dust-sensitive species. Dust clinging to the bodies and wings of certain insects cause death in a matter of a few hours; others are weakened and engage in continuous cleaning activity to the exclusion of normal mating and oviposition. Use of sealed plastic bags for storing freshly washed and dried glassware is strongly recommended.

Sterilization of Equipment

Equipment used in the culture of host material subject to bacteria or virus diseases should be either autoclaved or treated with a good bactericide or virus inactivator before being re-used or placed in storage. Equipment not amenable to autoclaving should be washed clean with a good detergent and immersed in an antiseptic solution such as dilute formaldehyde.

FIGURE 58. Mass production in closed units. Permits maximum control of cultures.

A. Combination oviposition and collection unit used for mass production of *Aphytis lingnanensis*. Each drawer holds five or six banana squash which are infested with *Aspidiotus hederae*. On the open cover can be seen the plastic sheet on which honey is streaked to feed parasites during the 24-hour oviposition period, and their progeny which emerge 14 days later. Drawers on the side shown are covered with cloth. The opposite side is glass. During CO_2-ether anaesthetization a tight-fitting wooden cover is placed over the cloth, as on the top drawer shown. Eccentric levers (shown at the upper corners of all drawers) permit slight elevation of the drawers in order to remove or replace the cardboard bottoms on which anaesthetized parasites fall (DeBach and White 1960).

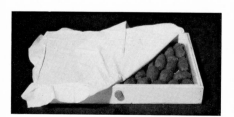 

B. Production of *Aphytis maculicornis*. (Left): Wire trays of latania scale-infested potatoes are placed inside the oviposition unit for the initial sting. (Right): Trays are moved to this type of container shortly before emergence begins. Two additional generations develop and are collected daily after ether-CO_2 anaesthetization from this unit which is called the production-collection unit. Only species which mate and oviposit immediately after emerging may be used to serve a double duty in this manner.

A

B

FIGURE 59. Collecting and counting parasites and predators.

A. CO$_2$-ether anaesthetization permits mass handling of *Aphytis lingnanensis*. Uniform sex ratio and size, made possible by use of the appropriate host, permit volumetric measurement of numbers produced. The larger portion of the device holds several thousand parasites. When rocked back and forth and returned to level position, approximately one thousand female *Aphytis* will remain in the small tube. Prior to and during the measuring out procedure, anaesthetic can be admitted through the small tube in order to completely immobilize the parasites. The thumb is placed over the end of the tube while rocking the device and is removed in order to let the parasites fall into a shipping container. University of California (DeBach and White 1960).

B. Broad scoop facilitates collection of adult *Cryptolaemus* into plastic tube calibrated for volumetric measurement of numbers of beetles. Courtesy of W. C. Beckley, Associates Insectary, Santa Paula, California.

C. Diagram of the collection and counting technique utilized in the mass production of *Chelonus texanus* Cress. in Union of South Africa (Bedford 1956).

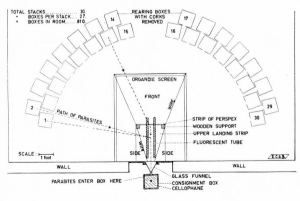

C

Such equipment as metal cages or screen trays may be dipped in a scalding bath for a few minutes in order to kill all insect material such as cocooned larvae, parasites, or mites. This material, along with dried grass and debris, is then sufficiently loosened to be easily removed with a strong spray of water.

Insectary Sanitation

Sanitation regulations strictly enforced will prevent losses from such pests as mites and secondary parasites. Prevention of disease is discussed by Steinhaus (1953*b*). The facilities and equipment of the insectary should be maintained as immaculately as possible. The vacuum cleaner, brooms, brushes, soap and water, and antiseptic solutions should be used unsparingly and routinely.

Hazards of Cage Materials

Before new cages or containers are used they should first be tried out experimentally to determine whether any of the materials used in their construction are toxic to the insects.

The first boxes used in the culture of *Macrocentrus* were constructed of redwood and had to be discarded when experiments proved that they were poisonous to the parasites (Finney, Flanders, and Smith 1947). Copper screen is toxic to some species of insects when used as cage covering. The fumes from acetate sheets made into containers may be toxic to insects. The sheets are usually taken from stocks where volatile gases have been unable to escape. These sheets before they are used must be well aired and cured, preferably in the sun, until all traces of the fumes have been eliminated. A testing procedure for cage materials is presented in chapter 13.

Due to space limitations, details of specific production programmes cannot be included in the text. Shown in table 4 are several selected examples of production programmes of fairly large magnitude which require culturing techniques beyond merely providing sufficient food and space for the species concerned.

TABLE 4

Selected listing of mass-produced entomophagous insects

Pest species	Beneficial species	Insectary host	Literature reference
Diptera			
Dacus spp.	*Opius* sp.	*Dacus* spp.	Finney 1953
Oscinella frit (L.)	*Spalangia drosophilae* Ashm.	*Drosophila melanogaster* Mg.	Simmonds 1953
Hemiptera			
Anasa tristis (DeG.)	*Trichopoda pennipes* Fabr.	*Anasa tristis* (De G.)	Dietrick & van den Bosch 1957
Eurygaster integriceps Puton	*Microphanurus semistriatus* (Nees)	*E. integriceps* Puton	Vodjdani 1954
Homoptera			
Aonidiella aurantii (Mask.)	*Aphytis chrysomphali* (Mer.)	*Aonidiella aurantii* (Mask.)	Bartlett & Fisher 1950
	A. lingnanensis Comp.	*Aspidiotus hederae* (Vall.)	DeBach & White 1960
	Aphytis spp.	*Aonidiella aurantii* (Mask.)	Flanders 1951
	Comperiella bifasciata How.	*Aonidiella aurantii* (Mask.)	Flanders 1943b
	Prospaltella perniciosi Tow.	*Q. perniciosus* (Comst.)	Schlabritzsky 1955
Quadraspidiotus perniciosus (Comst.)			Benassy & Burgerjon 1955
			Finney unpubl. notes
Parlatoria oleae (Colvée)	*Aphytis maculicornis* (Masi)	*Hemiberlesia lataniae* (Sign.)	Smith & Armitage 1931
	Anthemus sp.	*Parlatoria oleae* (Colvée)	
	Coccophagoides sp.	*Parlatoria oleae* (Colvée)	
	Cryptolaemus montrouzieri (Muls.)	*P. citri* (Risso)	
Pseudococcus citri (Risso), and	*Anarhopus sydneyensis* Timb.	*P. longispinus* (Targ.)	Flanders & Compere 1934
Pseudococcus gahani Green	*Chrysopa* spp.	*Gnorimoschema operculella* (Zell.)	Finney 1950
Pseudococcus longispinus (Targ.)	*Metaphycus helvolus* (Comp.)	*S. oleae* (Bern.)	Flanders 1942c
Pseudococcus maritimus (Ehrhorn)	*Aphelinus semiflavus* How.	*T. maculata* (Buck.)	Finney 1960
Saissetia oleae (Bern.)	*Praon palitans* Mues.		
Therioaphis maculata (Buck.)	*Trioxys utilis* Mues.		
Hymenoptera			
Diprion hercyniae (Htg.)	*Dahlbominus fuscipennis* (Zett.)	*D. hercyniae* (Htg.)	Miller 194 o

Lepidoptera

Carpocapsa pomonella (L.)	*Ascogaster quadridentata* Wesm.	*C. pomonella* (L.)	Cox 1932
	Trichogramma minutum Riley	*Sitotroga* sp.	Flanders 1929
Grapholitha molesta (Busck)	*Macrocentrus ancylivorus* Roh.	*Gnorimoschema operculella* (Zell.)	Finney et. al. 1947
			Labeyrie 1957
			Pastrana & Gahan 1950
Ostrinia nubilalis (Hbn.)	*Trichogramma minutum* Riley	*Sitotroga cerealella* (Oliv.)	Schread & Garman 1933
Loxostege frustalis (Zell.)	*Horogenes molestae* (*Uchida*)	*G. operculella* (Zell.)	Allen 1954a
Plutella maculipennis (Curtis)	*Chelonus annulipes* Wesm.	*Anagasta kühniella* (Zell.)	Bradley 1941
Pieris brassicae (L.)	*Chelonus texanus* Cress.	*Anagasta kühniella* (Zell.)	Tardrew 1951; Bedford 1956
Pieris rapae (L.)	*Apanteles plutellae* Kurdj.	*P. maculipennis* (Curt.)	Delucchi et al. 1954
Diatraea saccharalis (F.)	*Apanteles glomeratus* (L.)	*P. brassicae* (L.)	David & Gardiner 1952
	Apanteles rubecula Marsh.	*P. rapae* (L.)	Delucchi 1950
	Trichogramma minutum Riley	*Sitotroga cerealella* (Oliv.)	Tucker 1931
Porthetria dispar (L.)	*Paratheresia claripalpis* (v.d. Wulp)	*D. saccharalis* (F.)	Risco Briceno 1954
	Schedius kuvanae How.	*P. dispar* (L.)	Howard & Fiske 1911

CHAPTER 12

Nutrition of Entomophagous Insects and Their Hosts

K. S. HAGEN

INTRODUCTION

THE CULTURE of entomophagous insects is usually accomplished by rearing the insects on living hosts, either natural or unnatural. Success of this type of programme is a matter of logistics and synchronization of three life cycles: the plant, the phytophagous insect, and the entomophagous insect. The art of manipulating this natural food chain in the insectary has been emphasized in chapter II, but sometimes the use of living or natural food is impractical, uneconomical, or impossible. Of necessity this leads to attempts to modify or substitute for natural foods in the food chain, hence the science of nutrition assumes importance. The actual and potential value of nutrition and artificial diet in the culture of parasites, predators, and their hosts is so great, and the information is so scattered, that more than the usual amount of detail is included in the following discussion.

Replacing or by-passing part of the food chain with artificial diets involves more than just supplying nutritional requirements for growth or reproduction. The diet must first be attractive to the insect. Beck (1956b) proposed several definitions of nutritional requirements in order to prevent confusion. Nutritional requirements should refer only to the chemical factors essential to the adequacy of the ingested diet. Chemical feeding requirements are chemical factors important to normal feeding behaviour, and physical feeding requirements are the insect's requirements as to dietary texture, position, light intensities, and other physical factors influencing feeding behaviour. It is primarily because of these latter two classes of requirements that no universal diet is likely to be found to culture all insects; furthermore, even in one species the diet of the immature stages may be quite different from that of the adult.

The qualitative nutritional requirements are quite similar for most animals. Approximately 30 basic chemicals are required for growth and reproduction. Included are 'essential' amino acids, most of the vitamins of the B group, a sterol, and certain minerals. Luckey (1954) titled an article *A Single Diet for All Living Organisms* and gave the composition. Luckey realized that a diet with the proper formulation of all nutrients required to rear all species may never be known, but

356

because of the similarity in nutritional requirements between animals he proposed 'Universal Diet No. 1.' Undoubtedly, this diet would support growth for some polyphagous insects, for they would probably eat it, but the chemical feeding requirements and physical feeding requirements would not be satisfied for most phytophagous, predatory, or parasitic insects.

The determination of the nutritional requirements of insects has unfolded rapidly in recent years and can be followed in a series of reviews on insect nutrition. Since Uvarov's (1928) review when scarcely a single specific nutritional requirement had been determined, only a few insects have been reared on purely artificial diets in the laboratory. One of the first artificial diets was formulated by Loeb (1915) and Guyénot (1917) for rearing *Drosophila*. A few other workers reared cockroaches, flesh flies, mosquitoes, and some stored-product pests in the laboratory on various artificial diets.

By modifying diets for the insects mentioned above, some specific nutritional requirements were determined in the next ten years by workers reviewed by Wigglesworth (1939), Craig and Hoskins (1940), and Trager (1941). Some of the B vitamins known to be required by higher animals were shown to be definite requirements for insect growth and metamorphosis. One amino acid was distinctly implicated as a requirement. The nutritional importance of certain salts was shown especially in some aquatic insects; as for lipid soluble factors, cholesterol was found to be required by at least one species. The nutritional value of specific carbohydrates was also tested for adult insect utilization. The approach using aseptic techniques and diets greatly added validity to nutritional findings.

In the next decade, insect nutritional studies became more numerous and diets became more chemically defined, as indicated in the reviews by Trager (1947, 1953b). The findings were based on research using the same 'handful' of insect species that could be reared with some ease but did not include any true phytophagous or entomophagous species. However, during this period nearly all the B vitamins known to be required by higher animals were shown to be essential in the diets of most insects tested in the absence of micro-organisms in the diet. The first studies on replacing the total protein by use of amino acids were achieved, and it became apparent that the 10 amino acids required for insect growth were quite similar to those required by higher animals. The importance of some fatty acids was shown in a few insects, and it appeared that a complete chemically defined diet for *Drosophila* had been achieved for supporting growth of the larvae. Since 1950, further strides in insect nutrition have been accomplished as seen in the reviews of insect nutrition literature by Levinson (1955), Lipke and Fraenkel (1956), Hinton (1956), House (1955, 1958a, 1958b), Friend (1955, 1958a, b), and Dougherty et al. (1959). The nutritional requirements for some 15 different species of insects have been more or less completely determined. A synopsis of the specific requirements is shown in tabular form in Albritton (1953) and Spector (1956). For specific reviews of different basic nutritional categories involving insects see Scoggin and Tauber (1950) for lipid studies, Auclair (1953) for amino acids, and E. W. Clark (1958) for certain minerals.

ARTIFICIAL DIETS

All degrees of artificiality in diets have been used for culturing insects from the pure chemical one (defined diet) to media composed of a natural food but mechanically changed (cooked, ground, and blended) which can be termed 'prepared media.'

Aseptic culture involves sterile techniques such as autoclaving the diet and introducing eggs or larvae that have been sterilized, usually with chemical disinfectants. However, known specific micro-organisms can be introduced into the sterile system to serve as food or to provide growth factors for insects to be cultured. Pure culture, known today as axenic culture, is the rearing of one or more individuals of a single species on a non-living medium. The other extreme is xenic culture in which the number of associated organisms in the culture are unknown (Dougherty et al. 1959).

At the present time perhaps the most practical place for artificial diets in biological control programmes is in the culture of the host or prey of the entomophagous insects. The true natural host insect could be used on a suitable artificial medium, or an unnatural host could be used if it were more easily cultured on an artificial diet. This latter approach is particularly useful if the entomophagous species is not strictly host-specific. The advantages of using an unnatural host insect if the natural host insect enters a dormant condition or its cycle is too long are obvious.

Simmonds (1944b) divided the utilization of unnatural hosts (insects) into two categories. The first is where unnatural hosts are attacked by the ovipositing female parasites and the parasite progeny develops normally as in natural hosts. The second is where the parasites will not oviposit on or in the unnatural hosts, but where, by transferring the eggs artificially to the unnatural hosts, the parasite progeny still develops normally.

Therefore, host selection on the part of the entomophagous insects assumes considerable importance in culture methods. In this regard, reference should be made to chapter 6 where this subject is discussed in detail. Host-specificity of phytophagous insects also is a stumbling block when attempting to culture them on artificial media. An enlightening symposium dealing with the physiological relations between insects and their host plants was held in Amsterdam in 1951 with Dethier (1953), Fraenkel (1953), Painter (1953), and Kennedy (1953) participating. Thorsteinson (1953, 1955, 1958), Trager (1947), Hering (1953), Lipke and Fraenkel (1956), Beck (1956a, b), House (1958a, b), and Friend (1955, 1958a) considered the phenomenon of host plant specificity.

If Fraenkel's (1953, 1959) concept is valid, that the basic nutritional requirements are similar for most insects, that these requirements are present in most plants, and that it is the odd chemicals in plants that either attract or repel the phytophagous insect, the use of artificial diets should be simplified. For, to a nutritionally complete medium (which could be almost any plant that satisfied the physical feeding requirements), the addition of a feeding attractant should satisfy the chemical feeding requirements. Removal or 'neutralizing' of repellent chemicals from an unnatural plant medium then should permit the development of an insect. 'Neutralizing' host-plant resistance factors is perhaps possible, for Beck has shown that one resistance factor in corn is not effective in stopping the development of corn borer larvae if a relatively high sugar concentration is present in the plant, even though sucrose is not required by the young larvae (Beck 1957). Fleschner (1952) believes chemical or dust deposits on leaves lowers host plant resistance to mite attack. Fraenkel's basic idea that all plant cells are uniform in nutritional composition requires further evaluation, for although cells may be qualitatively similar in nutrient composition, nutritional imbalances may exist for certain insects ingesting these cells because of quantitative differences in the proportions of nutritional elements. Recent developments on the physiological factors of resistance in a few plants are discussed by Auclair (1958), with emphasis on osmotic (and turgor) pressure of different plant varieties influencing aphid feeding.

In spite of complicating nutritional requirements, host selection factors, chemical feeding factors, and physical feeding factors, some phytophagous insects have been cultured on artificial diets. Furthermore, parasites and predators have, in turn, been reared on insect hosts cultured on artificial diets, and even a few entomophagous species have been cultured directly on an artificial diet.

ENTOMOPHAGOUS INSECTS CULTURED DIRECTLY ON ARTIFICIAL DIETS

Thus far the few parasites most effectively cultured on artificial diets are those that appear to be transitional in their food relations, being either saprophytic or parasitic type feeders. It may never be practical to culture some parasites artificially, for, as Simmonds (1944b) indicated, the most difficult type of parasite to attempt to culture on an artificial diet would be the species the larvae of which enter into anatomical relationships with their hosts.

House (1958a) discussed the nutrition of entomophagous parasites, and later (1958b) reviewed the literature on the nutritional requirements of insects associated with animal parasitism. House (1954a, b, c, d, 1955) concluded from his extensive nutritional studies with *Agria* (= *Pseudosarcophaga*) *affinis* (Fall.), in which the nutritional requirements were largely determined by use of chemically defined diets under aseptic conditions that the nutritional requirements for this parasite do not differ in any important way from those of other insects, and difficulties in culturing parasites will come largely from factors other than a requirement of any special nutritional substance.

Agria affinis, a dipterous parasite of *Choristoneura fumiferana* (Clem.), is one of the few parasites mass-cultured thus far on an artificial diet. House and Traer (1949) found that three parts of pork liver and one part fish (salmon or catfish), each weighed separately, then mixed and reduced to a smooth, paste-like consistency by a food grinder, produced an effective medium for culturing this sarcophagid species. Arthur and Coppel (1953) cultured *Sarcophaga aldrichi* Park., a parasite of *C. fumiferana* and *Malacosoma disstria* Hbn., on the same type medium. R. Smith (1958) reared 40 generations of *Kellymyia kellyi* (Ald.), a sarcophagid parasite of grasshoppers, on pork liver alone. He also reared this species on a mixture of powdered milk, powdered egg, and brewers' yeast moistened with water to the consistency of a thick paste. The flies larviposited freely on the liver and dead grasshoppers but not on the milk–egg–yeast mixture.

A few hymenopterous parasites have been cultured on artificial diets, but only in very low numbers. Simmonds (1944*b*) attempted to rear three ectoparasitic ichneumonids of codling moth pupae by placing the ichneumonid eggs on nutritive gelatine slopes and also on raw beef. The eggs hatched and the first-instar larvae increased in size, but only one larva on raw beef moulted once. Bronskill and House (1957) dissected embryos of *Coccygomimus turionellae* (L.) from parasitized *Galleria mellonella* (L.) pupae, and sterilized them by dipping the embryos momentarily into mercuric chloride solution and then rinsing them four times in a sterile saline solution. After sterilization, the embryos were introduced into a thick watery mixture made from a cooked coagulated homogenate. This was prepared by blending equal parts by weight of liver and saline solution, which mixture was then autoclaved at 15 pounds pressure for 15 minutes. However, only 7 per cent of the embryos developed to adults. The particle size of the liver was considered to be important for acceptance by the larvae.

Some larval growth of *Dahlbominus fuscipennis* (Zett.), an ectoparasite of sawfly larvae, was obtained by feeding them royal jelly of honey bees, but none pupated (House 1958*a*).

Box (1952*a*) was able to feed *Exeristes roborator* Fab. on chopped meat mixed with an extract of pink bollworm, *Pectinophora gossypiella* (Saund.). The parasite laid its eggs on this material when placed in a piece of corn pith containing a groove. The material was covered with a piece of white paper perforated with a pin. The eggs were then removed and placed on pink bollworm larvae 'partially' killed with wet heat, and by this method he was able to raise a large population of *Pimpla* at the time when there was a shortage of *Pectinophora*.

Among the predators cultured directly on artificial diets are a few coccinellids, but to date they have not been mass cultured on any artificial diet. Hawkes (1920) found that adults of *Adalia bipunctata* (Muls.) will eagerly eat pounded dates, upon which they can live for months. The newly hatched larvae could not use the food, but Hawkes managed to bring one larva from the second instar to the adult stage, and most older larvae could be kept for a long time on this diet, but ultimately died without growing. Szumkowski (1952*b*), experimenting with *Coleomegilla* sp. which feeds extensively on various lepidopterous eggs (1952*a*), found that the adults fed well on fresh liver or raw meat and lived longer than those fed aphids, but these beetles did not oviposit, and larvae reared on this medium died before reaching maturity. After supplementing the liver diet with aphids, larval feeding increased from 30 to 70 per cent, and such larvae were able to reach the adult stage. Supplementing the liver with a 'Multivitamin Roche' mixture of liver plus vitamin C increased the number of larvae reaching maturity over liver plus aphids. Szumkowski also obtained greater fecundity and fertility by feeding adults liver plus vitamin E, and liver plus vitamin E plus aphids, than when feeding only liver or raw meat alone. Smirnoff (1958) cultured 19 coccinellid species on a mixture of agar, cane sugar, honey, royal jelly, alfalfa flour yeast, and pulverized dry insects which are natural prey of the species to be reared. For larvae this mixture should be supplemented with three parts beef jelly to one part royal jelly. Hagen (unpublished reports) obtained some egg deposition from *Hippodamia convergens* Guer. adults, that had overwintered, by exposing the beetles to droplets of the following fluid diet mixture: 6 g fructose, 3 g enzymatic protein hydrolysate of yeast, 10 mg choline chloride, 0·1 ml of (50 mg cholesterol plus 25 drops 'Tween 80' plus 1 ml 95 per cent ethyl alcohol), and 10 ml distilled water.

ENTOMOPHAGOUS INSECTS PRODUCED ON HOSTS CULTURED ON ARTIFICIAL DIETS

Host insects cultured on artificial media for use in the propagation of entomophagous insects have been few. But, since new techniques are permitting more and more insects to be cultured on aritificial diets, no doubt more parasites and predators will be cultured on host insects so bred. Simmonds (1944*b*) attempted rearing some parasites on *Drosophila* pupae, and later (1953) he was able to mass-culture *Spalangia drosophilae* Ashm. (which was being released against the fruit fly, *Oscinella frit* (L.)) on *Drosophila melanogaster* Mg. reared in a prepared medium. Maybee (1955) also used *D. melanogaster* as an unnatural host to culture continuously the proctotrupoid *Loxotropa tritoma* (Thoms.) which naturally parasitized the carrot root fly, *Psila rosae* (Fabr.). *P. rosae* itself has an obligatory diapause, and hence is of limited use in rearing this parasite. Maybee used an agar-base medium for culturing the *Drosophila*.

Theron (1947) cultured several ichneumonid species on the larvae and pupae of the false codling moth, *Argyroploce leucotreta* Meyr., and the codling moth, *Carpocapsa pomonella* (L.) which in turn were reared aseptically on an artificial medium supporting introduced moulds. Theron used Ripley's *et al.* (1939) diet technique developed for rearing *A. leucotreta*. The codling moth parasites reared by Theron included *Trachysphyrus sexannulatus* (Grav.), *Cryptus* sp., and *Coccygomimus heliophila* Cam.

The pteromalids *Nasonia* (=*Mormoniella*) *vitripennis* (Wlkr.), *Muscidifurax raptor* Grlt. and Sand. and *Spalangia* sp. were cultured by DeBach (1940, 1942) on housefly puparia. The host material was cultured on Richardson's (1932) medium. Schneiderman and Horwitz (1958) produced *N. vitripennis* on the flesh fly, *Sarcophaga bullata* Park., puparia which were raised from maggots cultured in raw hamburger on brewers' yeast and powdered milk.

Opius longicaudatus (Ashm.) was propagated on *Dacus dorsalis* Hend. cultured in an agar-base drosophila-type medium by using 3 per cent agar and covering the medium with cheesecloth (Marucci and Clancy 1950). These workers also propagated a cynipid, *Trybliographa* sp. and *Tetrastichus dacicida* Silv., on both *D. dorsalis* and *Ceratitis capitata* (Wied.) larvae developing in agar base media. Several other species of *Opius* were propagated on *D. dorsalis* which was cultured in artificial diets developed by Maeda, Hagen, and Finney (1953) and Finney (1956). *O. oophilus* Full., which oviposits in eggs, and *O. vandenboschi* Full., which oviposits in first-instar larvae of *D. dorsalis*, were cultured from sections of either apple or guava which had first been exposed to fruit flies for heavy infestation followed by exposure to the *Opius* spp. adults for parasitization. After parasite oviposition, the fruit sections were placed on nonaseptic media to permit the fly larvae to develop on ample food and parasites to emerge from the fly puparia (Finney and Hagen, unpublished reports).

Several species of grasshoppers of Crytacanthacrinae and Oedipodinae were cultured on an artificial diet which permitted propagation of some of their parasites (R. Smith 1952).

A few predators have been produced by providing unnatural or factitious hosts cultured in artificial media. Readio (1931) reared nymphs of *Reduvius personatus* (L.) on house flies and *Tribolium* larvae grown on artificial media. Struble (1942) was partially successful in rearing a bark beetle larval predator, *Temnochila virescens* (Fabr.), on artificially cultured larvae of *Lucilia sericata* (Meig.). However, the first-instar larvae of this ostomid needed to be fed scolytid larvae, for they could not break the integument of the flesh fly larva. Balduf (1941, 1948) made a series of biological studies in the laboratory of *Phymata pennsylvanica americana* Melin by feeding the bugs on artificial-media-reared adult *Drosophila melanogaster* and *Musca domestica* L. *Sinea diadema* (Fabr.) were fed the same flies (Balduf 1947*b*). Comparing the biological performance of both predatory bugs when fed the flies, Balduf (1947*a*) found that *Phymata* did better, for it ate both fly species as long as they were moving. However, *Sinea* in the fourth and fifth instars and adult stage could not capture *Drosophila* adults because of their small size, while *Musca* was a little too large for easy capture. Thus Balduf concluded that an intermediate size prey would be more suitable for *Sinea*. However, *Sinea* would feed on recently killed *Drosophila* if starved. West and DeLong (1955) reared the reduviid *Zelus exsanguis* (Stål) in the laboratory during the summer by providing miscellaneous insects collected from general sweeping, but in the autumn and winter, *Zelus* nymphs were fed cultivated *Drosophila melanogaster* adults until the fifth instar was reached, and then fed red-pine sawfly larvae, collected from cocoons; the adult bugs were fed cultured house-flies.

ARTIFICIAL DIETS USED IN CULTURING IMMATURE HOST STAGES

The preceding two sections dealt with the relatively few cases where entomophagous species have been cultured on artificial diets or on hosts which have been cultured on artificial diets. However, inasmuch as nearly any insect cultured on an artificial diet potentially represents either a natural or an unnatural host for culture of entomophagous species, it is important for our purposes to examine the use of artificial diets for culture of various potential hosts.

The list of immature stages of phytophagous, mycetophagous, and saprophagous insect species that have been cultured on artificial diets is constantly increasing. · The nutritional requirements of phytophagous insects have been recently reviewed by Friend (1958a, b), and Grison (1948, 1951) and Friend (1955) discuss problems in culturing phytophagous insects on artificial diets. The laboratory culture of a variety of insect species, including some species that have been propagated on artificial diets, has been treated by Galtsoff et al. (1937), Campbell and Moulton (1943), Peterson (1953), and Fisk (1958).

There are a few 'standard' artificial diets that have been used to culture some common test insects. Haydak (1936, 1943) was able to culture *Galleria mellonella*, *Achroia grisella* (Fabr.), *Plodia interpunctella* (Hbn.), *Oryzaephilus surinamensis* (L.), and *Trogoderma* spp., as well as other Dermestidae and grasshoppers on the following diet: four parts fine corn meal, two parts whole wheat flour, two parts skim-milk powder, two parts standard wheat middlings, and one part dried yeast. Equal parts of this dry diet (in grammes) and a liquid mixture containing one part honey and one part glycerine (by volume) are mixed. This is a particularly good diet for wax moths. According to Haydak the dry diet can be mixed in different proportions with the liquid phase depending upon the feeding habits of other insects.

A more purified diet was used by Fraenkel and Blewett (1943) for culturing *Ephestia* moths and five common species of Coleoptera infesting grains and flour. This diet is composed of 50 parts casein, 50 parts carbohydrates (starch or glucose), one part McCollums' salt mixture No. 185, one to three parts sterol (usually cholesterol), five parts dried brewer's yeast, and 15 parts water.

Since these earlier diets, which were employed mainly for propagating cereal-infesting insects, some progress has been made in culturing phytophagous insects on artificial diets. However, such investigations have been along lines of determining nutritional requirements, mostly under aseptic conditions. These research diets do not lend themselves immediately to mass-culture techniques, but provide us with a knowledge of the nutritional, chemical, and physical feeding requirements necessary to permit growth and development. Therefore, substitution of the pure chemicals with cheaper, more whole foodstuffs that would provide similar chemical and physical feeding requirements could be used. Even aseptic conditions employed in culturing insects can probably be circumvented by adding chemical micro-organism inhibitors and altering the pH. The technique of using homogenates and extracts of natural host plants and storing these products in deep freezes has been used successfully in propagating some phytophagous insects attacking host plants that are only seasonally available.

It is appropriate to include a short review of some of the different types of diets used and especially to refer to the different techniques used in the culture of these non-entomophagous forms, for they may be cultured as hosts, or prey for parasites or predators. Instead of treating the insects by their type of food habit, the species will be considered under their taxonomic order.

Diptera

Since many nutritional studies have involved flies, it seems logical to begin with this order, and *Drosophila* culture should be considered first, for not only have the nutritional studies with *Drosophila* led to understanding insect nutritional requirements, but they have yielded important techniques in the use of artificial diets for culturing many other insects. Spencer (1950) lists several important steps in the development of a practical *Drosophila* medium. First, is the addition of an agar base to form a stiff food cake; second, the fortifying of the nutritive value by adding quantities of killed yeast instead of relying upon growing yeasts; and third, the addition of some mould preventive. To this list we should add the altering of the pH for control of bacterial growth. *Drosophila melanogaster* was one of the first multicellular animals for which a chemically defined diet had been determined for its growth (Schultz, St. Lawrence, and Newmeyer 1946; Begg and Robertson 1948, 1950; Hinton, Noyes, and Ellis 1951; and Sang 1956, 1959). Apart from the defined diets there have been many modifications in the techniques for culturing large numbers of *Drosophila* since the original banana-type media. The agar-base medium now usually contains brewers' yeast, a mould inhibitor like parahydroxybenzoic acid, corn meal, corn syrup, molasses, and water. The carbohydrate syrups can be replaced with dextrose (Maybee 1955). Departing from agar-base media, Hodson and Chiang (1948) used fresh cake yeast as larval food. Caldwell (1949) used fresh yeast cake mixed with water and placed the medium in paper towels using a propyleneglycol as a mould deterrent. Bartlett (1951*b*) found that canned custard pumpkin made a good larval medium when placed 2 inches thick in the bottom of 1-gallon glass jars with several paper towels pushed down around the jar sides to serve as pupation strips. Simmonds (1953) used canned tomatoes, corn meal, honey, and water.

The Tephritidae larval media do not greatly differ from the *Drosophila* types. Initially these fruit flies were reared in various fruits. Marlowe (1934) developed an agar-base medium for *Ceratitis capitata* by using honey, crushed papaya, and brown sugar. Marucci and Clancy (1950) reared *C. capitata*, *Dacus cucurbitae* Coq., and *D. dorsalis* on a *Drosophila*-type agar-base diet with banana pulp, sucrose, and mould inhibitors, and found that an agar medium with yeast alone was fairly good. Grison, Feron, and Sacantanis (1950) cultured *C. capitata* on an agar-base medium containing malic acid, salts, sucrose, casein, yeast extract, and a mould inhibitor. He also found that an acid pH of 3 was best for development. Maeda, Hagen, and Finney (1953) cultured the larvae of the above three tephritid species under aseptic conditions on a modified agar-base diet similar to Beck's *et al.* corn borer diet. The purified diet that gave the best response under aseptic conditions—supporting nearly 10 larvae per gramme of medium—contained agar, sucrose, cholesterol, salt mixture, brewers' yeast, and choline chloride. The casein and glucose used in Beck's diet were not necessary. It was also found by Maeda, Hagen, and Finney (1953) that under aseptic conditions *D. dorsalis* larvae could tolerate a wide range of pH. Since a pH adjusted to 4·5 with hydrochloric acid inhibited growth of bacteria and the addition of N-butyl-parahydroxybenzoate repressed mould growth, these modifications permitted the culture D. dorsalis larvae when exposed openly (Maeda, Hagen, and Finney 1953). Blended pumpkin plus brewers' yeast were also found to permit development of the three tephritid species by the same workers. Finney (1956) used blended carrots plus brewers' yeast to mass-culture D. dorsalis and C. capitata under non-sterile conditions by adjusting the pH to 4·5 and adding the above-mentioned mould inhibitor. This medium was much cheaper than the above purified diet. Christenson, Maeda, and Holloway (1956) replaced fresh carrots with dehydrated carrots in the mass-culture of D. dorsalis, D. cucurbitae, and C. capitata. Feron, Delanoue, and Soria (1958) used the same medium for C. capitata, but modified the method of obtaining eggs. Dacus oleae (Gmel.) has been cultured aseptically by Moore (1959) on an agar cellulose medium somewhat similar to Maeda's et al. (1953) medium but containing sitosterol with 'Tween 40' instead of cholesterol; fructose and mannitol were also added.

The Anthomyiidae include some species for which the nutritional requirements are known. Huff (1928) cultured Hylemya cilicrura (Rond.) on potato plugs providing bacteria were permitted to grow on the potato. Friend, Salkeld, and McClanahan (1958) developed a chemically defined diet for this species, but growth was not as rapid as on a control diet of pea seedlings, and attempts to culture H. brassicae (Bouché) on chemically defined diets failed. However, the nutritional requirements of H. antiqua (Meig.) have been determined under aseptic conditions by Friend and Patton (1956), Friend, Backs, and Cass (1957), and Friend (1958b). The larval nutritional requirements of Hylemya larvae are summarized by Friend, Salkeld, and Stevenson (1959).

A few syrphid species that are phytophagous in the larval stage have been cultured in the laboratory. Creager and Spruijt (1935), using aseptic techniques, found that Eumerus tuberculatus Rond. would not grow on sterilized bulb media unless living yeasts were added.

Calliphorid nutritional requirements are reviewed by House (1958b). The culturing of parasitic sarcophagids has already been mentioned. Sarcophaga bullata, a saprophytic species, has been cultured on dog biscuits by Frings (1947) and Frings and Frings (1953). Lucilia sericata larvae have been reared on purified diets under aseptic conditions (Michelbacher, Hoskins, and Herms 1932; Yuill and Craig 1937; Kadner and LeFleur 1951). Culturing large numbers of this species under non-aseptic conditions has been done by Dorman, Hale, and Hoskins (1938) and Hoskins, Bloxham, and Van Ess (1940). Lennox (1939) developed an aseptic method and diets for studying the nutrition of L. cuprina (Wied.). The larval nutrition of Phormia regina (Meig.) has been studied, using various degrees of purified diets, by Hill, Bell, and Chadwick (1947), Brust and Fraenkel (1955), and Hodgson, Cheldelin, and Newburgh (1956). An inexpensive method has been developed for mass-culturing screw-worm larvae, Callitroga hominivorax (Coq.) on ground lean meat, citrated blood, and formalin (Melvin and Bushland 1940; Graham and Dudley 1959).

The culturing of Muscidae has been limited largely to Musca domestica. House-flies in many laboratories are apparently cultured on diets similar to Richardson's (1932) wheat bran, alfalfa meal, water, and yeast-suspension medium. Moreland and McLeod (1957) discuss this type of medium, calling particular attention to the amount of water that should be used. Frings (1948) cultured house-flies on moistened fermenting dog biscuits. Hammen (1956) cultured the entire life cycle of *M. domestica* on a medium comprising dried whole milk, dried brewers' yeast in agar, and water base. Sucrose above 3·5 per cent inhibited larval growth, while cholesterol added to the diet improved it (Hammen 1957). The vitamin requirements of the house-fly and various media used in breeding house-flies are given by House and Barlow (1958) and Hafez (1949). Peterson (1953) covers house-fly production in the laboratory in detail. The larvae of the little house-fly, *Fannia canicularis* (L.), can be cultured in a medium made up of dimalt water, brewers' yeast, commercial laboratory chow, and red wheat bran (Lewallen 1954). The first-instar larvae begin their feeding on ovipositional pads that are soaked with an enzymatic protein hydrolysate of yeast solution.

Lepidoptera

Some lepidopterous larvae that naturally eat living plant tissues, particularly those that bore into tissues, have been cultured on artificial diets. Most of the nutritional requirements have been determined for three borer species by using agar-base media under aseptic techniques. Some species have been cultured in media containing mostly host-plant material, usually foliage, that has been chopped or blended. Some of these media are used under aseptic conditions, and three species have been cultured on specific mould cultures under aseptic conditions.

PURIFIED CHEMICAL MEDIA. The purified chemical media that have been used to culture phytophagous Lepidoptera usually contain a small quantity of the host plant or its extract; cellulose of some type is usually included to make the medium acceptable. Bottger (1942) cultured *Ostrinia nubilalis* (Hbn.) on an agar-base diet containing casein, cellulose, sugars, salts, and water; the borers were transferred to fresh food every second or third day since non-sterile techniques were used. Micro-organisms as contaminants undoubtedly provided the essential vitamins. Beck, Lilly, and Stauffer (1949) improved this agar medium by using glucose, casein, cholesterol, linoleic acid, Wesson's salts, brewers' yeast powder, choline chloride, cellulose, and water. Young unsterilized larvae were introduced on to the sterile medium; therefore a mould inhibitor, N-butyl-parahydroxybenzoate ('Butoben'), was included. In 1950, Beck and Stauffer cultured the corn borer larvae aseptically on the same diet minus 'Butoben' by breaking up egg masses with trypsin and sterilizing the separated eggs chemically.

The larval nutritional requirements of the pink bollworm, *Pectinophora gossypiella*, have been studied by Beckman, Bruckart, and Reiser (1953) who reared a few larvae to adults on a modified chick ration having egg albumin as the protein constituent and provided with cotton linters to induce feeding. Vanderzant and Reiser (1956a) were able to culture the larvae of this species on a sterile, purified, artificial medium containing no plant extracts, using egg albumin as a protein source, and a mixture of pure vitamins. In later diets the same authors (1956*b*) used casein in place of egg albumin. In 1957, they found (with Kerur) that corn oil supplied the essential fatty acid, linoleic acid. Vanderzant and Reiser (1956*b*) describe methods of culturing large numbers of this bollworm on peas, beans, and cotton-seed.

Larvae of the Asiatic rice stem borer, *Chilo suppressalis* (Wlkr.), were cultured aseptically on a modified Beck's corn borer diet by Ishii and Urushibara (1954), but in place of dry corn-leaf extract, rice-stalk meal was included, and cellulose was provided in the form of milled filter paper. The females cultured on this medium have difficulty in emerging from their pupae. Ishii and Hiraho (1955) have determined the amino acids and vitamins required by this pyralid. Matsumoto (1954) cultured *Grapholitha molesta* (Busck) larvae aseptically on a preparation similar to Beck's corn borer diet, but with dried peach leaves rather than corn-leaf extract (Ishii 1956).

PLANT MATERIAL MEDIA. The artificial media today that are perhaps most practical for culturing large numbers of phytophagous lepidopterous larvae are those made up mainly of the natural host plant. The plant parts normally eaten are chopped or blended, and, in most cases, sterilized by autoclaving. In many cases, the lepidopterous eggs are chemically sterilized before introducing them to the medium. In some cases, plant material has been collected in large quantities during the growing season and preserved in various ways for use during seasons when plants are not available.

Wellington (1949) cultured the spruce budworm, *Choristoneura fumiferana*, and two other lepidopterous larvae on a medium containing mostly balsam fir foliage. The foliage is blended with a minimal amount of distilled water to produce a fine suspension, and then is combined with agar and autolysed yeast. Since the medium could not be autoclaved because of the destruction of attractants, sodium propionate was added to inhibit mould growth. Wellington also cultured *Archips fervidana* Clem. on a similar medium based on blended oak leaves of the natural host. He also found that a foliage-water suspension of this deciduous oak could be preserved by 'deep freezing.' Needle miners, leaf rollers, and web spinners could be cultured on this blended foliage medium, but not exposed feeders (Wellington 1949).

Ishii (1956) reviewed the artificial diets used to culture phytophagous insects, mainly in Japan. He reports on Tsutsui's successful culturing of *Chilo suppressalis* by using cut pieces of rice plant stems that have not reached the eared stage of growth. The stems are placed in Erlenmeyer flasks and sterilized, after which the borer eggs are introduced. If rice stalks were used after earing occurred, poor results were obtained. Tsutsui found also that the addition of 2 to 5 per cent dried yeast to the rice stalks gave excellent results. Ishii points out that by obtaining large quantities of rice stalks during the right time of the year and sterilizing them, this material could be used throughout the year. According to Ishii (1956), Saito raised three successive generations of the smaller tea tortrix, *Adoxophyes privatana* Wlkr. on sterilized tea leaves by placing sterilized eggs on this medium. Ishii also cites the aseptic culture of *Barathra brassicae* (L.) by Tsutsui. Here the sterilized eggs were placed in flasks containing sterilized, chopped cabbage leaves.

Elliott (1955) obtained larval growth of *Prodenia eridania* (Cramer) on agar-based media, either containing foliage or purified diets, by piling thin, corrugated strips of solid medium arranged in a criss-cross fashion so that the larvae had access to spaces and crevices below the upper surface.

Probably the artificial media composed primarily of plant-host material that have been used under aseptic conditions could be used under non-sterile conditions if a mould inhibitor were used and the bacteria controlled by adjusting the pH to 3 or 4. Such a technique was described for the culture of certain tephritid species in the preceding section on Diptera.

MOULD MEDIA. Another approach in propagating lepidopterous larvae on artificial diets is the use of certain moulds as food. Ripley, Hepburn, and Dick (1939) mass-cultured the false codling moth, *Argyroploce leucotreta*, by placing sterilized (in formalin) moth eggs on a medium supporting specific mould growth. The medium is prepared by mixing five parts oats (medium grade) and three parts water followed by inoculation with the mould, *Mucor hiemalis* Whemer. Theron (1947) used Ripley's *et al.* technique to culture *A. leucotreta*, but used maize meal instead of oats. Theron (1945), in addition, was able to culture some codling moth larvae on this same medium. He also raised the phalaenid *Euxoa subalba* Wlk. on the same type medium.

Coleoptera

FRESH PLANT FEEDERS. A few elaterids, chrysomelids, and weevils that exist naturally on living plant tissues have been cultured in the laboratory. Elaterid larvae of a few species that dwell in the soil have been propagated in small numbers. According to Davis (1959) agar-base diets such as those used by Grison (1951) to rear *Agriotes* sp. were acceptable to *Ctenicera aeripennis destructor* (Brown), but when the larvae penetrated this type medium too far they could not extricate themselves. Davis (1959) cultured this latter species aseptically by using test tubes containing media and dampened absorbent cotton in which larvae could tunnel. A diet made up of casein, dextrin, brewers' yeast powder, cholesterol, and salt mixture was either placed dry at the bottom of a test tube with the cotton above, or as a pellet of thick paste on top of the cotton.

Among the weevils, larvae of the cotton boll weevil, *Anthonomus grandis* Boh., can be cultured aseptically on an agar-cellulose based medium containing soy-bean protein, cysteine, glycine, sucrose, corn oil, cholesterol, salts, choline chloride, sodium alginate, bacto-yeast extract, pure vitamin mixture, and water (Vanderzant and Davich 1958). This diet was modified by replacing the soy-bean protein with an acetone extract of cotton squares, and with the addition of two mould inhibitors. The diet did not require sterilization, although the eggs were disinfected (Earle, Gaines, and Roussel 1959). In both these cases the adults fed and oviposited on cotton squares. According to Ishii (1956), Tsutsui was able to raise the vegetable weevil, *Listroderes costirostris* Schoen., on a simple diet of sterilized carrot leaves.

STORED PRODUCT FEEDERS. Some species of ptinids, tenebrionids, bostrichids, and silvanids that infest dry cereals are fairly easily reared on their natural foods, and many of these can be cultured on Fraenkel's standard artificial food. Leclercq, Magis, and Rey (1954) reared *Gnathocerus cornutus* F. on a diet containing the extraordinarily high protein level of 90 per cent casein and 10 per cent yeast. An artificial diet of Pablum mixed cereal dried in a thick layer was used by Davis (1956) to rear larvae of *Oryzaephilus surinamensis*. The nutritional requirements of these insects have been reported by Lipke and Fraenkel (1956).

The ostomid *Tenebriodes mauritanicus* (L.) can be propagated by using fine oatmeal that supports moulds, or oatmeal with 5 per cent yeast moistened with a solution of agar and water (Bond and Monro 1954).

The nitidulid *Carpophilus hemipterus* (L.) was cultured on boiled dates with dried yeast added; aseptic techniques were used when propagating the beetles on a more defined diet using a derivative of cellulose as a stiffener (Stride 1953).

Among the dermestids, *Dermestes maculatus* Deg. (=*vulpinus* F.) has been cultured in the laboratory on hides (Grady 1928) and on fish meal (Gay 1938), and *D. maculatus* (=*vulpinus*) was cultured on fish meal by Scoggin and Tauber (1951) who found the moisture content of food to be important. Rapid growth of *Attagenus* sp. larvae on artificial diets containing various protein sources was obtained by Moore (1946). For rearing *A. piceus* (Oliv.) Haydack (1947) found a mixture containing soy-bean flour, casein, dried brewers' yeast, and dried egg yolk to be satisfactory. *Anthrenus scrophulariae* (L.) was cultured through successive generations by feeding adults special diets (see adult-feeding section), and larvae, wool fabric sprinkled with powdered yeast (Sweetman 1956).

Some lathridiid species belonging to three different genera were cultured on media composed of various moulds, mainly *Pencillium* spp. cultured on a rubber substrate that had been dipped in Czapek solution and incubated several days under humid conditions (Kerr and McLean 1956).

The larva of the clerid *Trichodes ornatus* Say is normally restricted in diet to the immature stages of Hymenoptera, especially the prepupae of aculeates. However, in the absence of insect prey the larvae can complete their development on stored pollen (Linsley and MacSwain 1943). The fourth-, fifth-, and sixth-instar larvae of this species, as well as another clerid larva, have been found to live five or six years without food (Linsley and MacSwain 1946).

WOOD FEEDERS. Some wood-boring beetles have been fed on prepared diets. The larval nutrition of the cerambycid *Hylotrupes bajulus* (L.) has been studied by Becker (1949) and Rasmussen (1956a, b, 1957). The latter author used blocks made up of filter paper or wood impregnated with nutrients to determine the influence of peptone concentrations, cholesterol, and yeast extract on larval growth. Chapman and Wilson (1956) used papers of known chemical composition, to which various carbohydrates were added, and fed these to the adult scolytid *Dendroctonus pseudotsugae* Hopk. Sawdust from host trees was mixed with agar and water by

Rivas and Buchanan (1958) and used as an artificial diet for a cerambycid. Warren (1958) reared *Hylobius warreni* Wood on strips of bark blended in water with granulated agar added at a rate of 4 per cent.

Hemiptera and Homoptera

Culturing Hemiptera and Homoptera on liquid artificial diets by using membranes as a surface has been often attempted. Feeding by some leaf hoppers, mealybugs, scales, and aphids apparently has occurred, but no method utilizing membranes has permitted complete growth and development of a single species. Scheel, Beck, and Medler (1957, 1958) review attempts of artificial feeding of plant-sucking insects, and present a technique using semi-solid diets that enabled the successful rearing of the large milkweed bug, *Oncopeltus fasciatus* (Dallas), and the pentatomid *Euschistus variolarius* P. de B. Since these authors did not succeed in propagating plant bugs on liquid diets covered with penetrable membranes, they concluded that these conditions are not necessary. This led them to testing different diet forms, including gels, powders, and semi-solid diets. These bugs were supplied with water by means of dental cotton wicks, and the diets (purified) were provided in pellet form or in shallow plastic dishes. However, the bugs produced were smaller than controls. Beck, Edwards, and Medler (1958) discuss the feeding and nutrition of *O. fasciatus* and conclude that the smaller size was not nutritional but that the purified diets lacked some feeding requirement. Hemiptera may be cultured on semi-solid diets, but in Homoptera liquid diets may be necessary and it has been the lack of suitable pressure of the various media against the membrane that prevented adequate feeding. Kennedy and Mittler (1953) have shown that in certain aphids the flow of plant sap through cut mouth stylets *in situ* is close to the rate of secretion of honeydew. Aphids may therefore be able to rely upon their host plant to feed them, sometimes greatly in excess of their nutrient requirements (Mittler 1958).

Orthoptera

Cockroaches have often been employed as experimental animals for nutritional research and the nutritional requirements are known for some of the common species. The nutritional requirements of *Blatella germanica* L. are covered in detail by Gordon (1959*b*). Stock laboratory cultures of various cockroaches have been reared on dog biscuits and Pablum (Bottimer 1945), Purina Dog Chow supplemented with fresh liver (Sieburth and Bonall 1951), dog food and sections of apples (Dahm 1955), and complete dog foods (Noland 1956).

Crickets of several species were cultured on mixed dry diets, with water separate; however, baby-rabbit pellets, a commercial product, proved to be better than the prepared diet tested by Ghouri and McFarlane (1958).

Some grasshoppers and locusts have been cultured in the laboratory. Haydak's (1942) method of rearing grasshoppers, which employed a small cage for eggs and first instars and a larger cage for growth and reproduction, was modified by R. Smith

(1952) to require only one cage. The food consisted of alfalfa meal, powdered milk, dry brewers' yeast, and sodium chloride. Hunter-Jones (1956) describes techniques for handling and culturing locusts.

Acarina

Some predatory mites will evidently feed on other substances besides their prey. In the field and laboratory, certain species of typhlodromids that naturally prey upon tarsonemid mites have been observed to feed on aphid and white-fly honeydew which permits these mites to survive when host populations are at low densities (Huffaker and Kennett 1953, 1956). These workers (1953) also found that these typhlodromids would eat sugar solutions, egg yolk, and other liquid foods when they were hungry. The typhlodromid mites that Chant (1958, 1959) studied in England usually fed upon tetranychid mites, but he found that they could live for a considerable length of time on apple leaves without other food, and could develop and oviposit in an apparently normal fashion when provided only with fungal spores or plant pollen. Since the predatory mites will feed on liquid and solid foods there exists the possibility of culturing typhlodromids on artificial diets.

Although not necessarily predatory, the two species of tydeid mites studied by Brickhill (1958) were reared on natural honeydew and on a synthetic honeydew composed of a commercial enzymatic protein hydrolysate of yeast plus fructose.

ARTIFICIAL DIETS FOR ADULT INSECTS

Many insect species that have been studied need only to ingest water and a carbohydrate in the adult stage for survival and reproduction. The nutrients essential for reproduction in this type of insect are carried over from the immature stages to the adult. Evidently, there are all degrees of transfer, for some adult insects may not have to feed at all while in others a carbohydrate, protein, minerals, several B vitamins, water, and possibly cholesterol are required for fecundity and fertility. Adult insects requiring such complex diets have received little food reserves from their immature stages.

A clue to those species that require a complex diet in the adult stage for reproduction is that they usually exhibit a distinct preoviposition period. There are some species which will deposit a few eggs after a relatively short preoviposition period, but if fed only carbohydrates fecundity drops rapidly. The initial egg production resulted from a limited amount of stored nutrients; therefore, to have sustained egg production, the essential nutrients must come from extrinsic sources. Some insects, when provided with a simple carbohydrate diet, will never produce eggs. To determine if it really is the deficient diet that is responsible for the failure of egg deposition and not the absence of some extrinsic ovipositional stimuli, an examination of the ovaries will show the extent of ovigenesis.

The preoviposition period can be lengthy in some insects, however, and yet these species do not require a complex diet. Davies and Petersen (1956) found five different types of reproductive readiness in newly emerged adults among different genera of black flies. Some adults emerged with fully developed ovaries and reduced mouth parts; these deposited eggs soon after emergence. An intermediate type was an adult that emerged with much stored nutrients, with eggs one-half developed, and reduced mouth parts; thus, these adults would require some time before the eggs became fully mature, yet the adult did not have to feed on a complex diet before oviposition. At the other extreme, some species upon emerging contained little stored nutrients, eggs less than one-quarter developed, and had piercing mouth parts. These adults took five or more days for ovarian development, and required a blood meal. Many adult predators need complex diets in the adult stage for egg production, whereas many adult parasites frequently can deposit eggs upon emergence. Among the phytophagous insects one would undoubtedly find all degrees of nutrient transfer from the larva or nymph to the adult.

The effects of nutrition on reproduction of adult insects are reviewed by Brues (1946), Trager (1947, 1953b), Dimond, Lea, and DeLong (1958), and House (1958b), and also are discussed in chapter 6 with respect to natural enemies.

The following review of types of artificial diets and techniques employed in handling adult insects is largely limited to the holometabolous insects, for in most cases the adult feeding habits of the latter group are quite different from those of their larval stage.

Diptera

It was apparently in the Diptera that adult nutrition was first discovered to influence reproduction and longevity of insects. Guyenót (1917), experimenting with a different *Drosophila* medium, found that when the adults were fed egg lecithin normal egg deposition occurred. *Drosophila* adults are usually exposed to, and feed on, the same medium in which the larvae are cultured. Special handling of the *Drosophila* adults is covered by Kerr (1954), who fed adults equal parts of honey and compressed bakers' yeast formed in a thin syrup. Gerolt (1957) apparently exposed the adults to the larval medium, but gives detail on handling and sexing adult *D. melanogaster*.

Some agromyzids have been cultured in the laboratory and although the larvae were reared in various plant leaves the adults had to be provided with at least a carbohydrate solution (20 per cent sugar water) to prolong longevity and obtain good egg deposition (Freeman and Guyton 1957).

Some of the economic species of Tephritidae have been mass-cultured successfully, as discussed in the section on culturing immature Diptera. The adults of many species, in order to reproduce effectively, require rather complex diets. It was not until 1931 that adult diets other than fruits and vegetables were used. At this time, Fluke and Allen (1931) found that dead yeast cells plus honey and water not only prolonged the life of *Rhagoletis pomonella* (Walsh) but also stimulated egg deposition. Dean (1938), experimenting with the same species, greatly increased the egg production by adding proteose-peptone to the above diet. Dean principally used two parts of sugar to one part proteose-peptone, with distilled water provided separately. *Ceratitis capitata* can deposit a few eggs on a carbohydrate diet alone

(Hanna 1947; Hagen 1950). When Hanna added a small amount of 'egg protein' to a sucrose solution, egg deposition was increased. Hagen and Finney (1950) found that by using a commercial enzymatic protein hydrolysate of yeast, either mixed with a sugar solution or provided separately in solid form in a small shallow dish, with solid sucrose and distilled water in other dishes, good egg production could be obtained from *Dacus dorsalis* and *D. cucurbitae*. However, to obtain high fecundity from *C. capitata* the food has to be in a solution involving either: (1) mixing 3 g protein hydrolysate with 6 g fructose in 10 ml of distilled water, or (2) providing a 20 to 50 per cent solution of the hydrolysate on one piece of wax paper and honey on another sheet of wax paper. Hagen (1952) also found that enzymatic (trypsin) protein hydrolysate of soy, with a sucrose provided separately, stimulated slightly less egg deposition than the yeast hydrolysate, but usually increased the fertility over the other hydrolysates tested. Hagen (1952, 1958) found that adults of the three last-mentioned species require protein, preferably in the form of free amino acids, a carbohydrate, minerals, B vitamins (thiamin, nicotinic acid, folic acid, and choline) and a male fertility factor, possibly vitamin E, for effective fecundity and fertility. The males required at least a carbohydrate, protein (amino acid mixture), and salts in their diet before they would copulate. Enzymatic protein hydrolysate of yeast with a carbohydrate has been successfully used in an adult diet for reproduction in *D. tryoni* (Frogg.) by Andrewartha and Birch (1954) and *D. oleae* by Moore (1959). The enzymatic protein hydrolysate of yeast is also used in the mass culture of *Anastrepha ludens* (Loew) as part of the adult diet to obtain high egg production. The yeast hydrolysate is provided separately from the dry sucrose which is mixed with orange-juice crystals at the rate of 1:2 with water also separately provided (Rhode 1957). This species does not produce eggs on sucrose and water (Hagen 1958). *Rhagoletis cingulata* (Loew) apparently produced as many offspring on a sugar plus water diet as on either sugar plus yeast hydrolysate or casein hydrolysate (Kamal 1954). Apparently there is an effective larval transfer of metabolites to the adult in this species since a simple diet permits egg production.

In the Tachinidae only a few species have been cultured in the laboratory, and apparently honey, sugar solutions, honeydew, raisins, and water have been provided as food for the adults. Some species evidently require more than a carbohydrate solution to produce eggs. Severin, Severin, and Hartung (1915), studying the stimuli which cause the eggs of the leaf-ovipositing Tachinidae to hatch, fed *Chaetogaedia monticola* Bigot adults ripe bananas and sugar. Dowden (1933, 1934) fed adults of *Blondelia nigripes* (Fallen) and *B. piniariae* Htg., which larviposit on certain caterpillars, and *Zenillia libatrix* Panz., a leaf-ovipositing tachinid, lump sugar and a honey solution made up of one part honey to five parts water; these three species produced progeny on this diet. Allen (1925) found that the red-tailed tachina-fly, *Winthemia quadripustulata* Fabr. fed readily upon diluted honey, mashed banana, and sugar dissolved in water, or upon the honeydew of various species of aphids, but adults reared and maintained in confinement upon sugar, water, and honey alone failed to deposit eggs on host caterpillars, though otherwise living an apparently normal life. Allen did secure some eggs from adults maintained on aphid honeydew combined with other foods, but the eggs were not fertile. Perhaps a synthetic honeydew composed of enzymatic protein hydrolysate of yeast with a carbohydrate and water could be used as an adult food with this species to obtain egg production. The adults of *Paradexodes epilachnae* Ald., a parasite of *Epilachna varivestis* Muls. which oviposits directly on the host larvae, were easily handled under cage conditions but lived longer in dirty cages than in clean ones, indicating that contaminating yeast and other materials were probably beneficial; the adult food provided was sugar and raisins (Landis and Howard 1940). Adults of *Sturmia* sp., a parasite of sawfly larvae, were fed 10 per cent honey solution as well as sugar cubes, with additional moisture provided by spraying the cages daily with water (House 1947). *Phryxe pecosensis* (Tns.) oviposits on *Choristoneura fumiferana* and is cultured readily in the laboratory. The adults are fed 10 per cent aqueous solution of honey and sprayed twice daily with tap water; raisins were crushed and pinned on the inside of the cages to provide protein (Maw and Coppel 1953). *Ceromasia auricaudata* Tns. adults (a microtype egg-laying species) oviposited when fed the same diet as above (Coppel and Maw 1954a). These same workers (1954b) reared *Madremyia saundersii* (Will.) on the same host as the above two tachinids and also on *Pieris rapae* (L.) and *Ostrinia nubilalis* (Hbn.). It deposits macrotype eggs on the integument of its host and these adults were handled in the same manner as the preceding two tachinids. Simmonds (1958a) successfully cultured *Palpozenillia palpalis* (Ald.), a parasite of *Diatraea* spp., by keeping males and females in separate cages supplied with split raisins and dilute sugar water, and obtained mating by introducing a few females at a time into a cage containing 50 or more males. Coppel and Smith (1957) reared another tachinid from the spruce budworm and fed the adults the same diet as above; however, many mated females laid no eggs, possibly because of inadequate food. A leaf-ovipositing tachinid parasite of *Choristoneura fumiferana*, *Phorocera incrassata* Smith, was handled in the same way as the above tachinid adults and oviposited successfully (Coppel 1958).

In the Muscidae, the adult requirements for reproduction vary between species. Roubaud (1922) and Glaser (1923) were evidently the first to find that on sucrose and water *Musca domestica* adults deposited few or no eggs, but if fed peptone bouillon or blood serum with sucrose, longevity and egg deposition were increased. Milk alone is fairly effective (Glaser 1924). An adult food used now is skim milk diluted one-half with water (Frings 1948), or whole milk and dried brewers' yeast in an agar and water base which supports both larvae and adults. Adding cholesterol bettered this diet, but adding sucrose above 3·5 per cent inhibited fecundity and larval growth (Hammen 1956, 1957).

In the Anthomyidae a few species have been reared on artificial diets, and the adults seem to vary in their requirements for egg production. Rawlins (1953) obtained little egg production from *Hylemya antiqua* when he fed the adults honey, but upon adding brewers' yeast to the honey, egg deposition was copious. Sherwood and Pond (1954) reared *H. brassicae* larvae on turnips, but fed the adults a mixture of corn meal, water, molasses, wheat germ oil, liver extract, and extracted turnip juice. However, Foott (1954) apparently obtained eggs from flies fed carbohydrate solutions with water provided separately, but if the flies were fed sugar solutions approximating nectar concentrations (39 per cent) they lived only a few days. Foott concluded that water is just as important as nectar in the diet of the flies.

Adults of *Hylemya cilicrura* were provided with four cotton wicks (absorbent dental rolls) assembled on a wire frame. Distilled water was provided in one vial with a wick, a solution of 10 per cent egg white and 1 per cent sucrose was provided in another vial with a similar wick, a third wick, without vial, was soaked with a 5 per cent yeast suspension, and a fourth with a 1:1:2 solution of molasses, evaporated milk, and water, respectively (McClanahan and Miller 1958). Bardner and Kenten (1957) devised a cage from a lamp chimney to obtain oviposition from *Leptohylemyia coarctata* (Fall.). Oviposition was obtained at the base on filter paper, and food was exposed at the top of the lamp glass. Of several diets tested, the one adopted was made up of beef blood, condensed milk, and honey placed on dental wicks. Long (1958) modified the latter technique for handling adults of the same species by replacing the dental rolls with three vials with wicks suspended in a muslin top over the lamp glass. Diluted sweetened condensed milk, Bovril solution, and honey solution each were placed in the different feeding vials.

Sarcophagid adults, both parasitic and saprophytic, have oviposited under cage conditions and are handled much like the tachinids. The few parasitic species that have been reared oviposited or larviposited when fed honey or carbohydrate solutions. Patterson and Fiske (1911) were able to obtain eggs from various sarcophagids associated with the gypsy moth by spraying a solution of sugar water twice daily into cages. Haub and Miller (1932) and Dorman, Hale, and Hoskins (1938) exposed sugar cubes to flesh flies with water provided separately, but in order to obtain egg deposition the former authors supplied lean meat and the latter provided fish heads. However, Frings and Frings (1953) were able to obtain some reproduction from the same species, *Sarcophaga bullata*, by just feeding adults sugar and water. The nutrition of *Agria* (= *Pseudosarcophaga*) *affinis* has been studied in great detail by House, and apparently House (1951) obtained larviposition by simply supplying a 10 per cent solution of honey and water, and sugar cubes, providing the fly larvae were reared on a liver diet. Additional moisture was supplied by spraying the cages each day with water. The effect of several different carbohydrates on *A. affinis* survival was tested by House (1958a), who found fructose best. Arthur and Coppel (1953) cultured *S. aldrichi* on an artificial medium, but the adults were given, in addition to a 10 per cent honey solution, raisins to provide protein.

The nutrition of flesh flies and blow flies is reviewed by House (1958b). The work of Mackerras (1933) was among the first to show that males of certain flesh flies are not dependent on adult diet for gonad maturation while the females require more than a carbohydrate for egg production. Rasso and Fraenkel (1954) determined many of the adult food requirements for ovarian development in *Phormia regina*. The carbohydrates utilized by blow flies are covered by Fraenkel (1940) and Hassett, Dethier, and Gans (1950). Nicholson (1951) found that freezing liver and grinding it against an emery wheel while frozen made a desirable adult diet for flesh flies. The nutritional requirements for mosquito adults was reviewed by Dimond, Lea, and De Long (1958).

The adult syrphid food requirements for reproduction are not well known. The adults often feed on honeydew excreted from aphids, but perhaps various flower pollens are more important in their diet. Fluke (1937) found that adults need water, light, and a diet of dried yeast with honey (1:1), and certain species required in addition a thin syrup of dextrose and laevulose. The extensive work on syrphids by Schneider (1948) covers the aspect of diapause in the immature stages and shows how important pollen is for egg production in the few species he studied. However, mating is most difficult under cage conditions (Schneider 1948). Lal and Hague (1955) obtained egg deposition from *Sphaerophoria scutellaris* (Fabr.) when the adults were fed only 10 per cent solutions of carbohydrates. Of seven carbohydrates tested, sucrose was the best at 20° C and 70 per cent R.H. *Lampetia equestris* (Fabr.) larvae are bulb feeders, but the adults oviposited when fed various honey-sugar solutions; however, the best egg production occurred when the food was sucrose and pollen (Doucette and Eide 1955).

Neuroptera

Of the Neuroptera, species of *Chrysopa* have perhaps been cultured most extensively. The adults, depending upon the species, vary in what they feed upon (Smith 1922; Balduf 1939b). Some species of *Chrysopa* are direct host feeders while others feed upon liquids such as honeydew, sugar solutions, or extra floral nectaries. Such species as *C. oculata* Say, *C. nigricornis* Burm., *C. rufilabris* Burm., *C. quadripunctata* Burm., and *C. chi* Fitch fed on aphids readily (Smith 1922); *C. majuscula* Banks would not feed on fluid foods but fed naturally on aphids (Hagen 1950). Species such as *C. plorabunda* Fitch, *C. harrisii* Fitch, *C. lineaticornis* Fitch, and *Allochrysa virginica* (Fitch) were never observed to eat live aphids though they fed freely on fluids of crushed aphids, weak sugar water, and plain water (Smith 1922). *C. plorabunda* was mass-cultured and good egg production was obtained by providing adults with mealybug honeydew (Finney 1948). Hagen (1950) found that a commercial enzymatic protein hydrolysate of yeast either mixed with carbohydrates or honey or provided separately permitted greater fecundity than did honeydew of the mealybug, *Planococcus citri* (Risso). Finney (1950) adopted this synthetic honeydew in the mass-culture of *C. plorabunda*. Neumark (1952) used yeast hydrolysate in mass-culturing *C. carnea* St. in Israel. Burke and Martin (1956) obtained egg production from *C. plorabunda* and *C. rufilabris* by feeding a mixture of 'Delmor' nutrient powder, honey, and water.

Coniopterygids are interesting in that three species in different genera, *Parasemidalis flaviceps* Banks, *Conwentzia nigrans* Carp., and a *Coniopteryx* sp., were all found to require a carbohydrate (honey) plus mites or young scales in order to obtain good egg production and to prolong longevity (Fleshner and Ricker 1953). Hemerobiids apparently require live hosts for rearing (Smith 1923).

Lepidoptera

The adults of some species do not feed, and many of the species require only water or carbohydrate solution for egg deposition. Norris (1933, 1934), in her classical papers on *Ephestia*, demonstrated how water and sugar increase longevity and fecundity over water alone or no food. Also, the quantity and quality of larval diets were shown by Norris to influence adult fecundity. Flanders (1930*b*) obtained sufficient egg production from *Sitotroga cerealella* (Oliv.) to mass-culture *Trichogramma* without providing adult moths with food except the dry corn in which the moth larvae were cultured. Walter and La Hue (1939) obtained infertile eggs from *Heliothis zea* (Boddie) adults which were fed 10 per cent honey in water, but 93 per cent of the eggs hatched if moths were exposed to the same mixture that was allowed to ferment or had bakers' yeast added. Ullyett and Merwa (1947) also found that moth size and fecundity were determined by the adequacy of larval feeding. Andrewartha and Birch (1954) state that hepialid species need no food in the adult stage, but Agrotidae require a carbohydrate and water. Vance (1949) found that females of *Ostrinia nubilalis* require water to drink but no sugar. Lukefahr and Griffin (1956) obtained more eggs from *Pectinophora gossypiella* on various combinations of sugars than from those fed only water; the addition of protein hydrolysates did not improve diets. The fecundity of *Gnorimoschema operculella* (Zell.) under constant physical conditions averaged 84 eggs from starved moths, about twice as many eggs from moths fed water, and three times as many from moths kept with water and honey (Labeyrie 1957). However, this species oviposited sufficiently without having food or water specially provided when used in the mass culture of *Macrocentrus ancylivorus* Roh. (Finney, Flanders, and Smith 1947).

David (1957) was able to rear *Pieris brassicae* (L.) continuously; he fed the adults about 10 per cent honey solution in tubes made up as artificial flowers.

Coleoptera

Many of the adult beetles which are predacious feed upon the same prey as their larvae, and the food habits of entomophagous Coleoptera are well covered by Balduf (1935). The adults of many phytophagous Coleoptera also feed upon the same host plant as their larvae, but in both entomophagous and phytophagous species there are adults that do not feed on the same prey or plant hosts as their larvae, and some adults do not have to feed to deposit eggs. Apparently very few Coleoptera other than those feeding on stored grain products have been cultured on artificial foods.

Some general predators such as cicindelids and carabids have accepted bits of raw lean beef (Balduf 1935) and Shough (1940) exposed ten species of six carabid genera on various non-insect diets and obtained some feeding, but it is not known whether they reproduced on such a diet. Some predators evidently will not feed on anything that is not moving, which, of course, precludes use of artificial diets

The elaterid *Conoderus* requires a proteinaceous food for egg production; four or five drops of sweetened water (10 per cent sugar or honey solution) are placed on a strip of blotting paper and powdered yeast is added (Dobrovsky 1954).

Meloid adults of Lyttinae and Meloinae consume large quantities of vegetable materials while the Zonitinae usually consume little or no food (MacSwain 1956). However, *Nemognatha apicalis* LeConte, a species of the latter subfamily, is a nectar feeder in the adult stage, and was kept alive for weeks by the feeding of a solution of honey and water (Linsley and MacSwain 1942).

Carpet beetles were reared through successive generations by Sweetman (1956) who fed adults brewers' yeast, soy-bean flour, honey, and pollen; woollen fabric sprinkled with yeast provided ovipositional stimulus.

Callosobruchus maculatus (Fabr.), given water, lays about 30 per cent more eggs, and with sugar-water available lays about 50 per cent more eggs (Larson and Fisher 1924). *Acanthoscelides obsoletus* (Say) lived for two weeks without food, and lived for about the same period if supplied with water but deposited more eggs; however, egg deposition increased markedly when sugar solutions (Zaazou 1948) were fed.

Adult ptinid beetles require food for continued oviposition and need free water to drink for maximum fecundity (Howe and Burges 1951). *Ptinus californicus* Pic, a depredator of bee larvae in the larval stage, by consuming the stored pollen mass, requires the pollen in the adult stage not only for oviposition but also for copulation (Linsley and MacSwain 1941). The tenebrionid *Tribolium confusum* Duv. produced more eggs if yeast was added to patent flour (Lund and Bushnell 1939).

Hymenoptera

In culturing parasitic Hymenoptera, honey usually suffices as an adult diet, although free water may be necessary as has been demonstrated by Townes (1958) for ichneumonids. The need for a carbohydrate by parasitic adults is usually critical and often is obligatory for egg maturation, oviposition, and longevity. Straight honey streaked on glass in tubes or cages or on wax paper hung in cages is commonly used, although Doten (1911) found that a mixture of equal parts of honey and water was best for the parasite adults he was studying, and one part of strained honey to two parts of water was the most satisfactory food found by Mason (1934) for feeding some *Opius* spp. adults.

If a stiffer honey compound is desired it can be prepared by mixing agar with different proportions of sugar and honey. Holloway (1939) varied the amount of sugar to a mixture of 40 ml of a one per cent agar solution plus 25 ml of strained honey, depending upon the relative humidity (R.H.) of the environment. This agar-honey mixture placed in droplet form on stiff paper with a brush as it begins to solidify is satisfactory at relative humidities not exceeding 40 per cent. If the R.H. is between 40 and 70 per cent, add 10 g of cane sugar to agar-honey mixture; if the R.H. is between 50 and 90 per cent add 25 g of sugar. Adults of some species of tiphiids and scoliids fed on 10 per cent solution of honey and water or a candy made by mixing honey and pulverized sugar (King 1937). Peterson (1953) prepared a stiff honey mixture by adding pulverized sugar to processed strained honey containing no yeast cells. Grosch, La Chance, and Sullivan (1955) included in honey various salts which were evidently detected by *Bracon hebetor* Say adults which showed distinct preference for different salts.

Simple carbohydrate solutions can also be used as adult diets. Pielou and Glasser (1953) exposed various concentrations of dextrose, laevulose, galactose, lactose, maltose and sucrose to *Macrocentrus ancylivorus* adults. A 5 per cent sucrose solution was found to be optimal for longevity. The mean length of life was longer on a 10 per cent sucrose solution than on a 10 per cent honey solution. Barnes (1944) fed adults of *Anastatus semiflavidus* Gah. various mixtures of sugar solutions, honey solutions, citrus juices, soaked raisins, and host eggs with and without carbohydrates. The eupelmids' mean life was longest (43 days) on a sugar-cane syrup solution; a honey solution (1:4) was about as effective as a honey solution plus opportunity to feed on host eggs (39 days). Zoebelein (1956) exposed honeydews from various aphids and scales to *Pteromalus alboannulatus* Ratz., *Dahlbominus fuscipennis*, and *Exidechthis canescens* (Grav.), under different temperature and relative humidity conditions to determine the influence of these factors on longevity. At a relative humidity of 75 per cent, the longevities of these three species, fed various carbohydrates known to occur in honeydew, were compared. Saccharose, glucose, and fructose were found to be the most valuable constituents of honeydew for the insects, but melezitose had a harmful effect. Zoebelein also reviewed other adult feeding tests with parasitic Hymenoptera occurring in forests. Narayanan and Mookherjee (1956) found fructose to be the best carbohydrate for longevity in *Trichogramma minitum* Riley.

In some parasitic hymenopterous adults, the quality of adult food can influence fecundity and apparently can induce diapause in their progeny. Simmonds (1948) provided adult *Trachysphyrus inornatus* (Pratt) with three different diets. Some females were supplied with lumps of cane sugar, others with cane sugar and raisin, and others with raisin alone. All were given, in addition, a dish containing cotton wool soaked in water and a pad of dental cotton dipped in a 1:1 honey water solution. The female *Cryptus* fed cane sugar and raisin or raisin alone exhibited 400 per cent increase in total egg deposition and 100 per cent increase in longevity over the adults fed cane sugar alone, but at the same time the diets including raisins raised the incidence of diapause in the progeny from 2·5 to 36·5 per cent. Finlayson and Finlayson (1957) found that ageing adult females of the ichneumonid *Aptesis basizonia* (Grav.) when fed on honey laid more eggs than when fed on raisins and their progeny showed greater viability.

The presence of host insects is obligatory for some species of adult Hymenoptera for promoting ovigenesis and for preventing inducement of diapause in their progeny. These species feed directly on hosts (for details see chapter 6). The effects of food plant upon the host insect in turn can influence reproduction of certain parasites (Smith 1957).

The nutrition of adult Hymenoptera is perhaps best understood in the honey-bee, *Apis mellifera* L. For years entomologists and beekeepers have attempted to find inexpensive pollen substitutes for bees. Since some parasitic and predatory insect species require pollen in the adult stage at least, research concerning pollen substitutes is important to biological control workers. Haydak and Tanquary (1942) reviewed such attempts and from their tests found that a mixture of soy-bean flour and dry skim milk can be advantageously used in an emergency. Haydak (1949, 1958) obtained better responses when worker honey-bees were fed soy-bean flour fortified with both niacin and riboflavin or dried brewers' yeast. Weaver and Kuiken (1951) compared essential amino acids of royal jelly and six pollens and found no marked difference in essential amino acid composition. They also found that soy-bean protein, casein, and whole egg were very similar in amino acid make-up in pollen substitutes that explains the lack of success in finding a highly effective substitute. However, de Groot (1953) believes the concentration of the amino acid, methionine, in soy-bean flour to be a limiting factor for growth of the honey-bee. The same author (1953) reviews adult dietary studies and gives the amino acids essential for the adult bee in reference to longevity and weight increase. Longevity is substantially increased by adding protein foods to a carbohydrate diet. Pollens from different plants are not the same value for bees, and supplementing various pollens with nutrients offers clues to identifying deficiencies which influence longevity and fat body development (Maurizio 1954) and growth (Levin and Haydak 1958). Honey-bee larvae have been reared on royal jelly in the laboratory (Weaver 1955, 1958).

Formicid nutrition has been studied in only a few species. Smith (1942, 1944) working with colonies of *Camponotus* found that reduced food supply influenced the size of adults produced, and qualitative differences in food composition affected number and size of the progeny. Gösswald (1940, 1951) was able to culture *Formica rufa* L. by providing various insects—i.e., sawfly larvae, *Musca domestica*, and *Tenebrio molitor* L. larvae—or horse meat, plus a carbohydrate such as honey or a sugar solution, and in the field solid sugar placed on artificial nests to aid in colony establishment.

CHAPTER 13

Insectary Facilities and Equipment

T. W. FISHER AND G. L. FINNEY

INTRODUCTION

PRINCIPLES of culturing entomophagous insects were presented in chapter 11. Included for clarity were certain specific facilities or items of equipment relevant thereto. The purpose of the present chapter is to describe and discuss basic features thought to be integral parts of the physical means whereby entomophagous insects can be cultured. Subject matter in this chapter will emphasize development and use of buildings and facilities wherein an attempt is made to alter the existing local climate.

Fundamentally, the word 'insectary' means a place wherein insects are housed or propagated. Therefore, technically the insectary concept would embrace the entire range from caged individual limbs or trees, as the vedalia beetle, *Rodolia cardinalis* (Muls.), was first propagated in California, or *Cryptognatha nodiceps* Mshll. in Fiji, to the opposite extreme of modern climate-controlled installations such as the insectaries of the Canada Department of Agriculture, Entomology Research Institute for Biological Control, Belleville, Ontario, Canada, one of the Commonwealth Institute of Biological Control laboratories at Bangalore, India, and at Rawalpindi, Pakistan, and the insectaries of the University of California, Department of Biological Control at Albany and Riverside.

If justification for the existence of insectaries is necessary, it is clearly given by Beckley (1956) who stated '. . . the primary reason for the existence of the Associates Insectary is to promote biological control.' This statement takes on added significance because Mr. Beckley is responsible for pest control on 10,000 acres of oranges and lemons in or near Santa Paula, California, and therefore views biological control strictly as an effective and economical means of controlling mealybugs and soft scales, particularly *Saissetia oleae* (Bern.). Another growers' co-operative insectary exists in Fillmore, California, and here *Metaphycus helvolus* (Comp.) is propagated for release against *S. oleae* on over 7,000 acres of citrus. These are only two examples of proved commercial insectaries and they clearly represent the ultimate goal of insectaries, namely, to provide safe, economical pest-control service for the grower.

Before discussing the physical facilities helpful in the propagation of entomophagous insects, it would be well to consider the personnel who will use the facilities, for it goes without saying that the success or failure of the programme will depend largely on the capabilities, training, and interest of the personnel involved. Therefore, careful selection of insectary workers is particularly important since the propagation of insects demands highly specialized and extremely varied work. Consequently, no amount of formal training can prepare a person completely for the work. A high degree of interest, curiosity, and enjoyment in working with living animals usually will indicate capability in this direction. Of course, formal training in entomology is highly desirable and usually necessary at the supervisory level. True, practical training is of great benefit, but a somewhat broader background of insect behaviour, physiology, taxonomic affiliations, and biologies will better equip personnel to cope intelligently with insectary problems as they arise.

Further, it is very important that all persons working in the insectary realize the need for the faithful performance of their particular jobs in the over-all propagation programme, and in so far as it is practical, all personnel should develop a basic understanding of all operations within the insectary. Large programmes require a higher degree of specialization among personnel than do programmes where perhaps two or three persons perform all the duties associated with insect propagation—insect handling as well as mechanical knowledge and ability adequate to keep insectary equipment functioning properly.

If the insectary serves several projects under different project leaders or is of commercial scope, it seems desirable to have a superintendent who is responsible for the physical facilities as well as for co-ordination of the various aspects of the propagation programmes, such as making decisions regarding assignment of space in order to minimize intercontamination of cultures.

LOCATION OF INSECTARY

From the standpoint of climate control within the insectary, an area of temperate climate offers the best location. In tropical and subtropical regions, with the exception of certain insular areas, the climatic area chosen should be cool, as in the higher elevations, for it is far easier and cheaper to control heating requirements than to provide facilities for adequate cooling. Experience has shown that inadequate temperature control during climatic extremes usually results in loss of cultures and can neutralize the work of several months.

The ground area occupied by an insectary is determined by the projected purpose and the value placed on such a development by persons interested in it. One or two rooms in an existing laboratory may be considered adequate for certain programmes. By way of contrast, there are over 6,000 square feet in the insectary at Riverside, California (figure 60), and over 61,000 square feet in the quarantine building and new (1955) laboratory building at Belleville, Ontario, Canada (figure 61).

Easy access to the insectary is a necessity. This includes roads, approaches, ramps, and loading areas, which are necessary for convenient handling of host-plant material, lumber, refuse removal, and miscellaneous items of large bulk.

Where possible, consideration should be given to locating the insectary away from the immediate vicinity of agricultural areas. A minimum buffer zone would be perhaps a quarter mile for these reasons: (1) reduces hazard of insecticidal drift from a crop area entering the insectary; (2) reduces chance of contaminant species of parasites or hosts entering the insectary; and (3) reduces chance of hosts (pest insects) moving from the insectary to the crop area. The few preliminary tests which have been concluded to date in order to determine the effect of air pollutants on insects indicate deleterious results to certain aphelinids and coccinellids. Therefore, unless adequate filter systems are contemplated, it would be well to avoid locating an insectary where urban or industrial atmospheric contamination (smog) is a problem.

The terrain of the building site need not be perfectly level. Because of the prime importance of climate control within the insectary, the insulation gained by going below ground may be worth considering. Where contour, water table, and subsoil conditions permit, a basement or cut into a hillside may offer tremendous savings in future air-conditioning costs, as well as permit more accurate climate control.

If the above ground portions of an insectary can be oriented with the greatest length arranged in a true east–west direction, especially in areas with hot summers, natural lighting gains uniformity, the wall on the sunny side can be shaded by an overhanging roof or louvres, and only the short west wall is exposed to the greatest heat source and can therefore be shaded by awnings, louvres, or trees.

Landscaping in the immediate vicinity of the insectary should exclude plant species which serve as hosts of phytophagous insects scheduled for propagation within the insectary. It is well to keep all foliage away from walks and entrances in order to reduce the possibility of carrying contaminant organisms into the insectary on clothing.

BUILDING SPECIFICATIONS

This discussion applies primarily to permanent insectaries. A permanent insectary is one whose projected use will extend over several years. Temporary insectaries are those with a projected short-term use such as for a few seasons.

Exterior Design

Local materials, construction regulations, and architecture will largely decide the exterior features of the permanent insectary. However, facilities of a temporary nature may be needed under certain circumstances and so will be discussed briefly later in this chapter. It is again emphasized that the primary insectary problem is climate control, and many aspects of design revolve around this one necessity regardless of the permanent or temporary status of the insectary. As a consequence of the insectary's highly functional nature, such appurtenances as coolers, louvres on windows, and reflective roofs may be expected to alter somewhat the exterior appearance of the insectary from that of conventional buildings. This need not always happen, however. A field station of the Commonwealth Institute of Biological Control at Fontana, California, is an example of a highly functional insectary in keeping with its residential surroundings (figure 62).

Interior Design

The floor plan will be determined by the proposed use of the insectary. If the intended use is for research and limited mass culture, a quarantine area should be provided and the main insect-handling area may consist of one or more large rooms which may be partitioned into smaller rooms as needed. The insectary at Albany is an example of this type (figure 63).

If the intended use is for large-scale mass-culture programmes, a different design will be called for. The commercial insectaries at Fillmore and Santa Paula illustrate this type (figure 64). Figure 65 shows some of the insectaries given in the listing at the end of this chapter (table 5).

A suggested modest floor plan which meets basic requirements of routine mass production as well as research is shown in figure 66. Because of their varied programmes, federal, state, or university institutions probably would be concerned with both aspects. This concept guided the design of the recent addition (1960) to the insectary at Riverside. Figure 60 shows exterior view and floor plan.

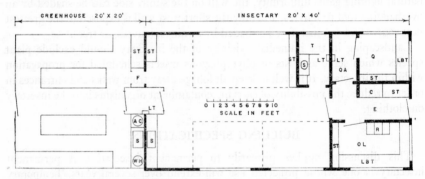

FIGURE 66. Suggested modest floor plan which meets basic requirements of routine mass production as well as research. (Dotted line indicates location of temporary partitions.)
AC Air conditioning. C Clothes closet. E Entry. F Fumigation. LBT Laboratory table. LT Light trap. OL Office-laboratory. Q Quarantine. QA Quarantine anteroom. R Records. S Sink. ST Storage. T Toilet. WH Water heater.

In order to provide ample space for manœuvring bulky items such as carts and racks, corridors are at least 4 feet wide and doorways at least 3 feet wide. Ceiling height is recommended at 7 feet. This height can be reached easily by a person 5 feet 10 inches tall, thus facilitating collection from the ceiling in open-room cultures. Cost of air conditioning is reduced considerably by eliminating excessive head space.

Because fine dust is harmful to beneficial insects, dust control in the insectary is very important, particularly in open-room culture. Since a concrete floor is a major source of dust from the scuffing of its surface, it usually requires covering, at least in rearing rooms. Painting and waxing are adequate only if they are maintained properly. A more satisfactory solution is to cover concrete floors with linoleum or asphalt-vinyl tile. Wooden floors do not present a critical dust problem, but they

A.

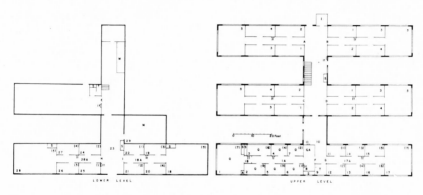

B

FIGURE 60. Facilities of the Department of Biological Control (University of California) at Riverside, California.

A. Exterior aspect as viewed from the north-west. The two wings with the tile roof were erected in 1930. The new addition was completed in 1960.

B. Floor plan. Large rooms for mass culture and small rooms for isolation are provided.

Legend: A Autoclave   M Machinery   S Sink
       I Incinerator   Q Quarantine   T Toilet
     lt Light trap   QA Quarantine anteroom

A

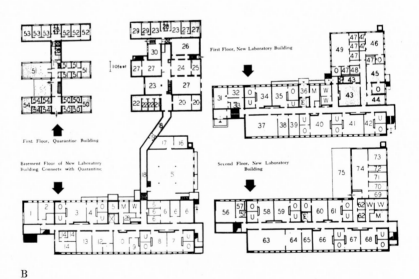

B

FIGURE 61. Canada Department of Agriculture, Entomology Research Institute for Biological Control, Belleville, Ontario, Canada.

A. Exterior of laboratory building. Quarantine building not shown.

B. Floor plan. Details may be obtained from *Agricultural Institute Review*, November–December, 1955.

A

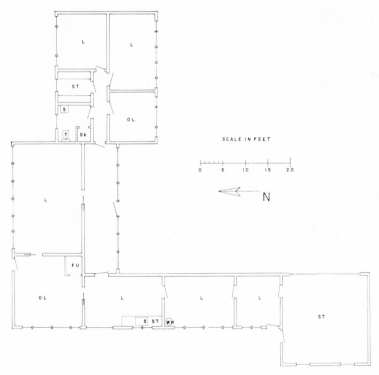

SCALE IN FEET

0   5   10   15   20

N

B

FIGURE 62. Commonwealth Institute of Biological Control insectary located at Fontana, California, is an example of a highly functional insectary designed in the motif of its surroundings—in this instance, a residential area.

A. Exterior—south aspect.

B. Floor plan. Cooling is provided by refrigerated room air conditioner placed in window openings. The larger storage area is cooled by an evaporative cooler.

A

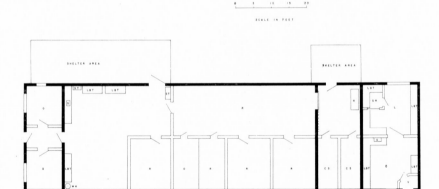

B

FIGURE 63. Insectary of the Department of Biological Control (University of California) located at Albany, California—an example of open planning.

A. Exterior: south aspect.

B. Floor plan. Most of the partitions are temporary and can be moved as propagation needs dictate. The quarantine laboratory is in a separate building (see figure 49 B, chapter 10). Shelter areas are roofed over only and serve as storage for cages, melons, etc.

Legend: CS   Cold storage   R   Rearing   ST   Storage
        L   Laboratory   S   Sink   V   Vestibule
       LBT   Laboratory table   SR   Sterile room   WH   Water heater
       O   Office

A

B

FIGURE 64. Commercial insectaries. The buildings shown plus other similar structures at each location serve the acres indicated.

A. Fillmore Citrus Protective District, Fillmore, California, serves 7,000 acres of citrus.

B. Associates Insectary, Santa Paula, California, serves 10,000 acres of citrus.

A

B

FIGURE 65. Research insectaries selected from the listing at the end of this chapter (table 5).
A. Ministerio de Agricultura, La Cruz, Chile.
B. Landesanstalt für Pflanzenschutz, Stuttgart, Germany.

C

D

C. Commonwealth Institute of Biological Control, Bangalore, India.

D. Commonwealth Scientific and Industrial Research Organization, Division of Entomology, Canberra, Australia.

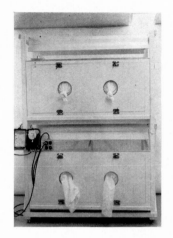

A

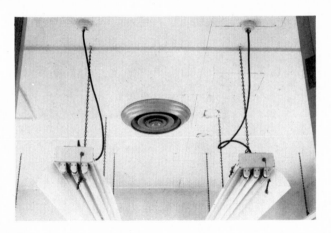

B

FIGURE 67. Methods of providing light for plant growth.

A. Portable lighting. Left: The lighting fixtures above each cage contain two (cool white) fluorescent tubes. A time clock automatically controls hours of light for four cages (two racks). The upper right photo shows the interior of a cage designed for use with this equipment. The sides and back are covered with organdie cloth, the top is heavy cellulose acetate, the door (not shown) is $\frac{1}{4}''$ plywood. This cage sits on a removable bottom of $\frac{1}{2}''$ plywood to which a tight seal is assured by soft rubber gasketing.

B. Fixed lighting. Where space and programming permit, banks of tubes 8 feet in length can be raised or lowered on chains attached to hooks in the ceiling to come within 12 inches of the plants, an optimum distance for many plants.

are far more expensive to maintain and are easily damaged by water. Another source of dust is the water-atomizing humidifier, which provides a fine, rapidly evaporating spray which effectively increases the humidity, but distributes minerals from the water on near-by objects which, in time, constitute a definite dust problem.

Facilities for adequate storage of equipment and supplies are considered when the floor plan is designed. Interior finish of rooms is related to the size of the insects to be handled. Ledges around windows, fixtures, or ducts, can be eliminated by flush design. A smooth plaster finish painted with a glossy moisture-resistant paint coloured off-white (blue or green tint) greatly facilitates the collection of insects and enhances illumination within the room. Paints containing fungicides may be desirable, but paints having insecticidal properties should not be used. All paints used in culture rooms should be thoroughly tested for toxicity to beneficial insects. A convenient screening procedure involves placing in pint-size glass fruit jars a piece of wood or pressed board which has been painted with a sample of the paint to be used and allowed to air-cure for 30 days. Honey streaks are provided on the glass and parasites are added. Control insects from the same culture are placed in an empty glass jar with honey provided. Mortality counts at 24-hour intervals will reveal the needed information. In order to reduce variables, it is necessary to subject both test and control jars to equal conditions of light, temperature, and humidity during the test period.

Window lighting alone is of insufficient intensity for suitable plant growth. Artificial lighting usually will be required for this purpose. An even light gradient, i.e., north light in the northern hemisphere, may be helpful in certain handling procedures such as phototropic collection of hosts or emerging adult beneficial species which exhibit positive phototaxis. On sunny sides of the building's exterior, louvres may be used to achieve a similar result. In order to reduce thermal conductivity and to assure insect-tightness, windows should consist of a rigidly fixed inner pane which is of large dimension and free of cross bars (an aid in collection of insects by aspiration) and flush with interior wall surface, and a removable (for cleaning) but weather-tight outer pane. Approximately 2 inches of air space should separate the panes. If a quarantine area is a part of the insectary, an added degree of safety may be achieved when the outer panes consist of wire-reinforced glass. Improvements in artificial lighting, coupled with the known lack of control over, and inadequacy of, window light to produce healthy plants, have stimulated interest in windowless insectaries. Such a commercial insectary is advocated by DeBach and White (1960). Advantages of below-ground or windowless construction include increased insulation and controllable lighting. Of course, a dependable source of electrical power is a necessity if this type of structure is to be used.

Utilities

The number of ceiling light fixtures will depend on the proposed use. In general, natural lighting should be a secondary consideration mainly because of its unpredictability. Adequate light for growing plants can be achieved by portable racks containing 'cool white' fluorescent tubes, or by providing ceiling hooks from which lights can be suspended directly over growing plants. Figure 67 illustrates such fixtures in use at Albany and Riverside.

It is very important to provide sufficient numbers of electrical outlets. Usually such receptacles will be located just above table or work-bench heights and in the ceiling. A general rule is one double outlet per 8 linear feet of wall.

Where a relatively large installation is contemplated, it is desirable to have a separate power substation provided by the utilities organization which serves the area. By so doing, adequate electricity for the insectary is assured, and the increased line load will not affect other buildings in the immediate vicinity. Where electricity is a primary source of power, power failure can devastate the insectary effort, not only by disrupting air conditioning, but also by freeing several hundred thousand lepidopterous larvae which were confined by hot-wire barriers (see figure 55, chapter 11). Portable gasoline-powered generators can be utilized to maintain minimum operational requirements when such emergencies arise. This also emphasizes the importance of location, design, and insulation, for, if done properly, a building can withstand interruptions in utilities of several hours without suffering damage from fluctuations of temperature.

Related to the lighting problem is the placing of light traps in hallways, wash-rooms, and anterooms to attract and capture escaped natural enemies or hosts and thus reduce the contamination hazard in other rearing rooms. No matter how careful the insectary staff may be, there will be insects at large in the insectary either from cultures or coming in from out-of-doors. Since the hazard of contamination is ever present, it is imperative to reduce this free-living population to the lowest possible level. Chief requisites of construction for light traps are a light source and a baffle system that directs insects into the trap and prevents their leaving it. Light traps ordinarily are placed against or in walls (figure 68), and should be so located that they do not present a collision hazard to personnel or equipment passing near them. Since light traps operate constantly, they should be located away from doors or open windows to which insects out-of-doors may be attracted after dark and thereby gain entry to the insectary.

Domestic (potable) water at 40 to 60 pounds per square inch pressure should be available at all sinks and in all rooms. If possible, hot water should be available to personnel at all sinks.

Distilled water is a necessity for preparing nutrient media for plants. Further, as a last rinse in washing glassware it greatly reduces hard-water film. During warm weather, distilled water can be collected from the cooling coils of refrigerative-type air conditioners. Such water is satisfactory for rinsing glassware but due mainly to a relatively high copper content it may not be used in nutrient media or in hydroponic solutions.

Natural or bottled gas may serve as fuel for the heating system and for conventional burners at laboratory tables. For reasons of safety, gas appliances should be vented to the outside of the building.

Air pressure at approximately 60 pounds per square inch in all propagation

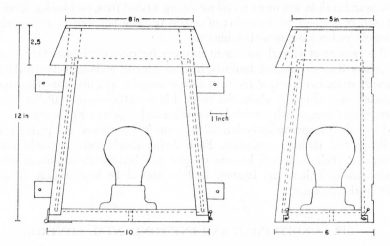

A. This trap is designed for installation on walls or partitions with its top tight against the ceiling. The sloping sides and front are of window glass. The back, top, and bottom may be of wood or sheet metal. The 2½-inch baffle at the top is opaque and may be constructed of wood, pressed fibreboard, or sheet metal. Located at the ceiling-wall angle of corridors, it does not interfere with passing traffic.

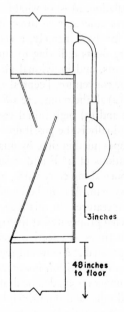

B. This trap is located in the partition between the quarantine room and the anteroom at the Albany laboratory. The lamp is in the quarantine room. The sloping lower pane of glass is removable.

FIGURE 68.

rooms and at sinks will prove useful for drying washed fruit, for blowing debris out of corners of cages, for operation of certain types of temperature and humidity controls, and in water spray humidifiers.

Air vacuum at 10-inch minimum mercury for collectng insects may be more necessary than air pressure facilities, if there must be a choice between the two, because collection is one of the most time-consuming and necessary functions of insectary operation. An alternative method is to make use of available portable electric machines, which provide both positive and negative air pressures.

Floor drains appropriately located in propagation rooms and perhaps main hallways will facilitate sanitation. Such drains should have dirt-tight covers; otherwise, their traps will become clogged and become an additional item of maintenance. Toilets and lavatory facilities should be located away from the propagation rooms.

AIR CONDITIONING AND ENVIRONMENTAL CONTROL

It was emphasized earlier that air conditioning—temperature, humidity, and ventilation—is the most important single problem to be resolved. Only in certain insular locations is there little or no need for supplemental temperature control. Excessive build-up of humidities may be a problem here, but large airy cages usually permit adequate ventilation. Most of what is said here pertains to locations with climate considerably less amenable to insectary operation. Basically, there are two concepts of design involved, namely, a central system which consists of positive and negative pressure ducts radiating to and from all rooms from one or more heating and cooling units, and individual air conditioning for each room. The chief disadvantages of the conventional central system are: (1) lack of adequate control in individual rooms; (2) all the rooms are affected during periods of routine maintenance or breakdown; and (3) high initial cost. The main disadvantage of air conditioning rooms individually is the possibility of higher cost of maintenance per room, which may be compounded in time by unavailability of parts.

Since temperature fluctuations of 2° F and relative humidity fluctuations of 4 per cent are adequate for normal insectary work, moderately priced controls will satisfactorily operate either system. Also to be considered is the possible need of providing for fluctuating temperatures. In this regard, Stein (1960) indicated that *Trichogramma cacoeciae* Marchal propagated at fluctuating temperatures of 16° and 26° C was approximately ten times as effective against codling moth eggs when compared with parasites propagated at a constant temperature of 27° C.

Ventilation, or recirculation of air within insectary rooms, is a vital part of the air-conditioning problem. Munger (1955) demonstrated the need for fresh (filtered) air in the culture of citrus red mite, and the principle appears to have a bearing on the degree of success of culturing certain insects as well. The problem is considered of sufficient importance that a system with several complete air changes per hour with partial or complete recirculation passing air through spun glass and carbon filters to remove particulate and chemical pollutants, respectively, has been incorporated into the planning of the new addition to the Department of Biological Control insectary at Riverside. Such an arrangement calls for highly specialized temperature-control equipment, which would be too costly for other than large insectaries at research institutes.

'Heat pumps' which automatically control both heating and cooling are increasingly available on the American market. The 1960 cost (installed) is approximately $600 per ton cooling capacity for household units. In a temperate climate, a 3-ton unit of this type could be used to air-condition an insectary of 1,000 to 1,600 square feet, providing insulation and ceiling height were proper. Since this is a forced-air system, a certain amount of duct work is required. A return duct to the machine insures a degree of recirculation. Air filters and humidifiers can be supplied for 'heat pumps.' Only time will tell the story on maintenance costs and efficiency, but it appears that 'heat pumps' have much to offer in the area of packaged climate control.

A related matter is that of circulation within the individual rooms in addition to that provided by the main heating or cooling source. This becomes especially important if many large cages and tables occupy a room and as a consequence dead air spaces, or stratification, develop. Fans located in such a manner as to keep air moving at various levels will smooth out temperature and humidity gradients.

In general, methods used for achieving climate control will depend on the type and permanency of the insectary.

Temporary Facilities

Temporary facilities should conform to the general planning of a permanent installation and in practice should give several years' dependable service. For example, many existing laboratories have ceilings 8 feet or more in height. The construction of a false ceiling at the suggested 7-foot height will make air conditioning easier and more satisfactory. The false ceiling may be made of light-gauge gypsum board, $\frac{1}{4}$-inch plywood, or $\frac{1}{8}$-inch masonite nailed to the lower edges of properly spaced joists and furring strips. The seams can be covered with tape and the entire surface then painted. Additional mechanical features, such as wiring, plumbing and duct work can occupy the space above the false ceiling.

Heating may be achieved by household-type electric or gas heaters. If the latter are used, it is important to have them vented to the out-of-doors. At Riverside, one thermostatically controlled 1,200-watt electric heater with a built-in fan adequately heats a well-insulated 14 ft. × 30 ft. room with a 7-foot ceiling. Smaller rooms (12 ft. × 12 ft. × 7 ft.) can be heated with similar but smaller heater fans or by bare wire heat cones with a fan behind them. A simple wiring diagram for inclusion of thermostats with such heaters is shown in figure 69.

When considering cooling for small areas, the prevailing relative humidity out-of-doors must be known. Evaporative coolers are useful in arid climates, but are much less effective where the humidity is in excess of 50 per cent during hot weather. Air conditioners of the refrigerator type, although more costly, are effective regardless of existing outdoor humidities.

Relative humidity may be regulated by either reduction or increase to a desired level. The former may be accomplished by either a refrigerative cooler which locks free moisture as ice on its cooling coils, or an exhaust fan in the attic which can reduce relative humidity to the level of outside conditions by pulling air through the building.

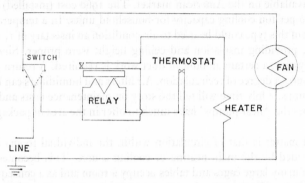

FIGURE 69. Wiring diagram for simple laboratory heaters. If assembled as indicated, the fan will operate continuously and the heating element will be energized only when the contact points of the thermostat close.

In arid climates it is relatively simple to increase humidity by using evaporative coolers housed completely within the building. Figure 70 shows a wiring diagram of such apparatus. Minor mechanical changes of the evaporative cooler allow the fan to operate constantly, and the recirculating water pump operates only when an increase in humidity is called for by a humidistat. Additionally, desirable features of both systems are increased air circulation and filtration of the air. A 2,000 CFM evaporative unit is considered adequate to humidify approximately 4,000 cubic feet, providing insulation and vapour sealing are adequate. As previously mentioned, circulation of air within rooms is necessary if stratification is to be prevented.

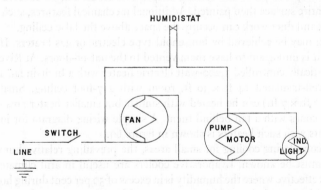

FIGURE 70. Diagram of evaporative cooler used indoors to increase relative humidity. If wired in this manner, the fan runs continuously. Water recirculation pump is activated by humidistat.

Recirculation may include or exclude outside air. If outside air is to be forced into the insectary, it is necessary to provide adequate filtration in order to prevent the entry of unwanted organisms or particulate matter. In arid areas, especially during periods of high temperature and low relative humidity, it may be necessary to exclude outside air and recirculate the air within the building in order to maintain the desired relative humidity unless air enters through an evaporative cooler. If evaporative coolers are used, it is necessary to provide filtered openings, such as partially opened windows or doors, in order to assure a flow of cooled air through the building. Otherwise, excessive humidities as well as heating will result.

Permanent Facilities

Larger permanent insectary installations may be provided either with central systems of climate control or with individual room air conditioners. If the insectary consists of more than one wing, or group of rooms, a 'heat pump' for each wing may be desirable. In the original insectary at Riverside a system of dampers in the supply and return ducts permits the recirculation of air solely within one wing or through the central humidifying and heating units.

At Riverside the recently completed insectary addition is equipped with a central steam-heating system and a central chilled-brine cooling system with individual rooms controllable $\pm 2°$ between 60° and 90° F and ± 4 per cent between 40 and 80 per cent R.H. Heated or cooled air and steam for humidity enter rooms through a common duct as thermostats or humidistats dictate. The central cooling system actually consists of two operating units each of which has two compressors. The designed capacity of the compressor is such that three of them will provide adequate cooling. The fourth compressor is a reserve or safety feature which guarantees continuous operation of the air-conditioning equipment if one unit becomes inoperative. Because of excessive summer heat, additional features include insulation of ducts and ceiling as well as a provision for cooled air to be continually blown through the attic space from a large evaporative cooler. The roof is covered with light-coloured crushed rock embedded in tar over four layers of asphalt-impregnated paper. In the older portion of the insectary the central evaporative cooling system failed to give adequate temperature control. Therefore, it was necessary to install household refrigerated room air conditioners in several of the existing rooms, and they have been quite satisfactory during the past five years.

Maintenance and Safety

The foregoing discussion of various types of rather specialized devices leads naturally to the problem of maintenance. Preventive maintenance needs to be planned and practised throughout the year, and it is highly desirable to have a person of varied mechanical interests on the insectary staff. Replacement of items of equipment and anticipated maintenance costs must be considered in projected budgets.

Because of the mechanical features pertinent to insectary operation, safety to personnel becomes an important consideration. To this end, all moving machinery should be well shielded. Indeed, the initial design should include all possible safety features, such as fire prevention, low electric-shock hazard, well-lighted stairwells and entrances, and non-opposing doors. Miscellaneous safety facilities include a well-stocked first-aid kit (all personnel should be well trained in emergency first-aid techniques), adequate fire extinguishers at appropriate locations, fire blankets, and mild alkaline solutions for neutralizing the effects of acid burns.

FURNISHINGS AND EQUIPMENT

Insectary furnishings include standard items such as work tables, storage cabinets, chairs, and basic office equipment. Specialized equipment items pertaining to specific quarantine or mass-culture problems are mentioned in chapters 10 and 11.

Mobility is a desirable feature for bulky items such as laboratory tables, large racks, and plant-growth lighting devices. Retractable wheels present added versatility for such equipment. For most efficient use of space, cages, racks, or tables should be designed in equal multiples of dimension. Figure 72 illustrates such portable equipment.

Peterson (1947) describes a great many insect-rearing aids. The present writing will touch mainly on technical aids of a general nature as utilized in biological control for the propagation of entomophagous insects.

Cages for housing insect cultures are perhaps the items most used in the insectary and range in complexity from those which can be made easily by laboratory personnel from such articles as glass jars, lamp chimneys, cellulose acetate, and a great miscellany of small cages for limited propagation, to those requiring the services of an experienced carpenter or cabinet maker. Examples of both general types are shown in figure 71.

Principles of Cage Design

In order to have assurance that an insect cage is escape-proof, particular care must be given to such matters as mortised and glued joints, glazing, properly attached cloth areas, and well-sealed doors. Door gaskets may consists of felt cloth or of light sponge rubber. Cloth and gasketing should be glued and stapled, or tacked to the cages. Ease of cleaning is important and is possible if the bottom of the door is flush with the floor of the cage.

An isolation or sleeved cage was developed for handling parasitic insects by workers in the U.S. Department of Agriculture in 1907 (Howard and Fiske 1911, plate IX, figure 2). S. E. Flanders, in 1934, redesigned this type of cage, and since then several modifications of it have been made, but this is the type most often used in insectary rearing programmes at the University of California. Figure 71 B shows some of these cages.

Worthy of further emphasis is the fact that when insects are propagated indoors, proper ventilation and filtration of air can be prime factors of success. This is true in open culture where an entire room serves as a cage (previously discussed under recirculation), as well as with conventional rearing cages, each with its own particular micro-environment. The size mesh of cloth or screening to be used is determined by the size of the smallest insect to be contained in or excluded from the cage. If the inclusion of growing plants causes excessive humidities or unfavourable odour concentrations, exhaust apparatus similar to that shown in figure 73 should provide the needed ventilation. In addition, it may be necessary to pass the air through activated carbon filters in order to get rid of chemical pollutants.

As was previously stressed with regard to paint for interior walls, paint for cages also should be thoroughly tested in the cured state for toxicity to insects. The same precaution should be exercised if insects contact raw wood, as may be the case with wooden nursery flats. As a general rule, no cages are used if any paint odour can be detected. Sizing or dyes in cloth, as well as various plastic materials, are suspect unless proved safe. Inasmuch as all insects do not react similarly to various toxicants, representative species should be tested. Experience at Riverside has shown that micro-Hymenoptera, such as species of *Aphytis* and *Coccophagus*, serve as good insects of such effects.

Because many adult and immature beneficial insects are quite small, certain optical aids, together with adequate illuminators, are necessary for efficient insectary procedure. Magnifications of 9× to 54×, as provided by conventional stereoscopic dissecting microscopes, are sufficient for most routine needs. Adequate extension supports provided with a rack and pinion focusing mechanism, and ball and socket swivel mounted for vertical and horizontal swinging give added usefulness to the instrument. Other optical aids that are useful are hand lens of 14× or 20×, head lens of 3× or 4×, a reading glass, and illuminated magnifiers. The research laboratory will, of course, have need of instruments of greater power. Basic optical aids are shown in figure 74.

COLLECTION, PACKAGING, SHIPPING, AND STORAGE EQUIPMENT

Certain specialized techniques and items of equipment have been developed regarding procedures for collection, packaging, and storage of beneficial insects pending shipment.

Collection in the insectary may be accomplished by three general methods used singly or in combination, namely: (1) utilization of insects' inherent behavioural taxes; (2) anaesthetization; and (3) aspiration.

Perhaps the most commonly used behavioural taxis utilized for insect collection is phototaxis. The first-instar, or crawler, stage of many scale insects as well as adult entomophagous insects exhibit strong positive phototaxis. The light source may be an even light gradient from a window or an artificial light. Figure 75 shows equipment and methods designed to collect insects by light attraction.

Because most adult beneficial insects are attracted to light, care must be taken in open culture to shield hot light bulbs with cloth or panes of glass to prevent parasites from contacting them.

Strong anemotaxis may be taken advantage of for concentrating large numbers of insects. Use of this response was utilized in the collection of *Aphytis* (Flanders 1951). In a different and novel application, artificial air currents were useful in obtaining large numbers of eggs of the moth, *Sitotroga* (Flanders 1934). Moving air pressed the females' abdomens against a wire screen and the resulting pressure stimulated egg deposition. Although currently not used, a collection technique which utilizes the chemo- and phototaxic responses of adult *Cryptolaemus montrouzieri* Muls. was developed by W. C. Beckley, manager of Associates Insectary at Santa Paula, California. The chemo-stimulant consisted of smoke from smouldering rags in a bee smoker which stimulated the beetles to fly to the nearest light source, in this case a cloth-covered window. A large, flat funnel is utilized to scoop them into plastic tubes (see figure 59 B, chapter 11).

Anaesthetization by combining CO_2 and ether was developed by Finney, Flanders, and Smith (1947) in connection with the mass production of *Macrocentrus ancylivorus* Roh. and its host, *Gnorimoschema operculella* (Zell.), the potato tuber moth. CO_2 used alone will anaesthetize insects for only short periods and is consequently of limited value in mass-production work. However, it is adequate and safe for handling small numbers of insects rapidly, for instance in making quick sex-ratio counts or for removing contaminant organisms. Ether used alone may weaken or kill insects and when used repeatedly or in quantity in a poorly ventilated room constitutes a definite explosion and fire hazard. Mixing the two gases by means shown in figure 76 greatly extends the anaesthetization period as compared with CO_2 used alone and minimizes the danger of explosion.

Collection by aspiration may be by simple mouth aspiration or by utilizing mechanical suction such as that provided by household vacuum sweepers, portable devices designed for laboratory use, or piped-in vacuum. Collection by use of a modified hair dryer is illustrated in figure 77. Mouth-operated aspirators should be equipped with filters in order to protect the operator from inhaling fine debris. Several types of aspirator collectors are shown in figure 78.

In mass-culture work, large numbers of a beneficial species can be collected by anaesthetization in a closed unit (figure 58, chapter 11), measured (counted), and placed in storage containers during one continuous operation. Volumetric counting of parasites or predators is convenient and accurate but can be used only when size and sex ratio are uniform. Some counting devices are shown in figure 59, chapter 11. In a technique developed by Bedford (1956) for the collecting, counting, and packaging of *Chelonus texanus* Cress. (see figure 59, chapter 11), the parasites were attracted by a double light source directly into the shipping container, and were easily counted as they passed through slots in cork on the way.

After insects are counted they are placed in containers for transportation to colonization sites. Choice of container depends on the mode of transport. Insulation against lethal temperatures extremes and an available food supply for the insects while in transit are prime considerations. Convenient storage containers are small, heavy paper cartons of one-half-pint or one-pint size. Glass or plastic tubes and vials can be used for small numbers of beneficial species. Containers must be supplied with streaks of honey or honey-agar as food for the insects as well as bits of shredded wood or paper for resting sites. Paper or shredded wood which have been impregnated with honey may be used satisfactorily to provide both food and resting surface (B. R. Bartlett, unpublished notes). Such containers may be packed in sturdy boxes or cartons for shipment (figure 79).

Most adult entomophagous insects may be satisfactorily stored at 50° to 60° F and at approximately 75 per cent relative humidity. At this temperature they are relatively inactive and consume little food. Conventional household refrigerators equipped with modified thermostats are usually adequate for this purpose. If it is necessary to accumulate collections for several days or, in some cases, weeks before shipping the insects or taking them to the field for colonization, they will remain in good condition if the containers are removed two or three times weekly from 60° F and warmed to approximately 80° F for 20 or 30 minutes. During this time the insects become active, feed, and defecate. With this procedure it is always important to provide a supply of food and moisture. Otherwise, loss of vigour and increased mortality may follow. Honey seems to provide both requirements.

Packing and shipping of entomophagous insects from an established insectary for the purpose of intrastate colonization will constitute the major portion of the following discussion. Techniques of shipping natural enemies to the home insectary as utilized by collectors in foreign areas are discussed in chapter 9.

Typically, shipments from insectaries will be for direct release at the destination. Because of the hazards inherent in such procedure, the matter of proper quarantine handling enters the picture. Although immature parasites may survive adverse conditions better than adults, detection of potentially harmful species is most accurately performed by screening the latter. Shipments of parasitized hosts can be safe under closely controlled conditions as in mailing cards to which are attached eggs of *Sitotroga* parasitized by *Trichogramma*. It is presumed that collections of beneficial species will be thoroughly checked by the shipper and only pure cultures of the beneficial form included. As an added precaution, such material, prior to field release, should be re-examined at the destination for the presence and removal of unwanted species.

The problems of shipping are concerned with local transportation which may involve insectary, institutional, or local growers' vehicles, and utilization of public or governmental transportation facilities. Prevailing weather has a profound influence on the chosen mode of shipment, particularly when extremes of temperature prevail.

Since containers in which parasites or predators are collected and stored in the insectary will usually be too fragile to serve as shipping containers, local shipment of beneficial species requiring not over 8 hours in transit may be satisfactorily accomplished by placing the containers of insects in a small, insulated, prechilled chest. The addition of a frozen gel packet will prolong the effectiveness. In order to avoid subjecting the insects to lethal or weakeningly low temperatures, some sort of insulation between the insect containers and the frozen gels or ice should be provided. This technique was developed by Brennan and Mail (1954), who made shipments of adult *Culex tarsalis* Coq. with low mortality in up to 50 hours in transit. Figure 81 A shows an insulated chest and gel packets as used at the University of California.

Instead of using an ice chest for storage of the insects, wrapping the insect containers in wet cloth will adequately cool them by evaporation for a few hours in arid areas if temperatures do not exceed 110° F. This is effective if such preparations are transported in wire baskets within the shaded vehicle, for its movement causes air flow around the package of insects, thereby increasing the rate of evaporation. A convenient carrying case, employing the evaporative cooling principle, for local transport has been developed at Riverside and is shown in figure 81 B. An automobile which was provided with mechanical refrigeration was used for redistributing large numbers of parasites of the spotted alfalfa aphid throughout the hot interior valleys of California. Holloway (Allen, Holloway, and Haeussler 1940) reported a high degree of success in shipping parasites of oriental fruit moth by surrounding the insect containers with a thick layer of moist cotton and corrugated paper which was held in place by light canvas.

Shipments requiring commercial or governmental freight or mail services, as with interstate transport, must necessarily be handled in a somewhat more formal manner and must display proper shipping permits in order to expedite prompt delivery. For long distances, air mail and air freight offer the most rapid means of transportation. Adult parasites often suffer a rather high mortality from starvation or temperature extremes while en route. Unless these problems can be satisfactorily solved it will be necessary to ship immature stages. When quarantine regulations permit, parasitized hosts on portions of their host plant may be shipped. Such material may be mailed in small flat packages contained in large cloth-reinforced paper envelopes and shipped via air mail—a technique utilized by foreign explorers. It is sometimes more satisfactory to place bulky material in small porous boxes and send them air freight. The latter method is well adapted to shipping of adult predators and large adult parasites which seem to require more room for relatively unrestricted movement than do small parasites. The reader is referred to chapter 9 for further discussion of shipping techniques.

SANITATION AND SAFETY EQUIPMENT

In order to prevent contamination of cultures of entomophagous species or their hosts, one of the most important principles to observe rigidly is never to bring field material or host-plant material into the insectary unless it has been fumigated or is securely caged.

Continuous successful insectary operation can be achieved only if one is constantly aware of the interrupting factors which may be encountered and may need appropriate preventive measures. Disease can quickly neutralize a propagation programme by either: (1) assuming devastating epizootic proportions with immediate effect, as virus diseases of lepidopterous larvae; or (2) acting as an insidious devitalizing agent, as microsporidian diseases of eggs or larvae. Entomophagous mites can have an equally devitalizing effect on their insect hosts. Fine dust from poor-quality concrete floors or from free-spraying humidifiers can settle on host material and greatly reduce activity of parasites. This subject is elaborated upon under 'contaminants' in chapter 11 and is re-emphasized here because of its profound importance.

Facilities and equipment which will improve sanitation for the building are vacuum cleaners, brushes, brooms, sweeping compounds, mops, buckets, antiseptics, such as aqueous solutions of formalin or chlorine, and also adequate storage space for these items. The best sterilization method for glassware is autoclaving. Next best are deep sinks or trays wherein glassware and plastic cages can be immersed in antiseptic solutions.

Waste disposal presents a special problem. A safe procedure to prevent living insects leaving the environs of the insectary is burning or fumigating host-plant material used in the culture programme. Arrangements for regular removal of trash should be made with local agencies.

SUBSIDIARY FACILITIES

Greenhouse

Greenhouse facilities may be necessary for culturing host plants. In general, however, a plant propagation greenhouse does not provide an ideal environment for the mass culture of entomophagous insects because of factors which are largely beyond the control of the insectary operator, namely: (1) light and humidity conditions cannot be economically standardized; (2) contaminant species of phytophagous insects will invade the plants; and (3) predators or secondary parasites cannot be excluded. Specially designed greenhouses for the quarantine handling of imported weed-feeding insects would overcome the disadvantages just mentioned, but the cost probably would prevent their being used for commercial production of entomophagous insects.

Storage

STORAGE OF EQUIPMENT. Storage of equipment has been mentioned previously and is here re-emphasized for it is a most necessary facility both within the insectary in the form of reasonably dust-proof cabinets or drawers for storage of cloth and glassware, and outside as weather-proof sheds or buildings for unused cages, certain host material, and tools.

STORAGE OF HOST MATERIAL. Storage of host material may require considerable space and is usually provided independently of the insectary building. A commercial insectary may require several hundred square feet for such purposes. Because of the necessity for maintaining several insect species simultaneously, a research insectary also may require relatively spacious facilities for storage of a variety of host-plant materials such as banana squash, melons, potatoes, citrus fruits, and grains, and, in addition, lath house or greenhouse space for leafy plants.

Seasonally available host materials such as melons and other cucurbits require dry storage. Ordinarily, an open shed with a water-tight roof provides adequate protection. Material of this sort is safest when placed in layers one or two deep on sturdy, airy racks. Thorough screening will minimize rodent damage.

Grains and cereal products should be fumigated upon receipt and then placed in insect-proof containers for storage.

In warm regions certain host materials such as potatoes and citrus fruits do not keep well without refrigeration. Refrigerated rooms will be required to maintain the necessary 38° to 42° F.

Fumigation

Fumigation facilities are necessary if proper sanitation and prevention of contamination by insects are to be achieved. Nicotine and HCN fumigation chambers can be easily and economically constructed. For example, a large box or framework enclosed by a plastic tarpaulin will suffice. Injury to potted plants from methyl bromide usually can be averted if relative humidity in the fumigation chamber does not fall below 80 per cent. A general-purpose fumigation chamber used at Riverside is shown in figure 82.

Persons who conduct fumigation must be thoroughly conversant with the dangers of the materials used and the necessary antidotes, and must understand what constitutes adequate fumigation for the particular material being tested. Except for the occasional necessary fumigation of insectary rooms, fumigation should be performed well outside of the insectary. If a permanent fumigator is contemplated, it should be located downwind of the main building and equipped with an exhaust stack high enough so that discharged fumes will not endanger personnel or cultures in the insectary or near-by installations.

Workshop

If research is to be a major insectary function, facilities for construction and repair of cages and other paraphernalia are necessary. Power tools such as table saw, grinders and sanders, jointer, bandsaw, and drill press require the services of someone trained in their uses. A collection of conventional hand tools such as hammers, saws, chisels, planes, screwdrivers, wrenches, brace, bits, and clamps of various sizes will suffice for most repairs. Electrical and plumbing facilities also will need occasional attention. In addition, painting supplies will be needed, and safe storage is required for flammable materials. In short, the insectary programme will greatly benefit from the services of a skilled handyman.

Specialized Research Equipment for Controlled Environment Studies

BIOCLIMATIC CABINET. Of proved value for determining biological potentials of insects is the bioclimatic cabinet (figure 83). The following description is taken from Messenger and Flitters (1957, pp. 119–127): 'Each chamber is similar to a walk-in refrigerator, being fitted with two doors separated by a 4-foot vestibule, and having an inner work space providing floor area 6 feet by 6 feet for conducting experiments. Attached to the chamber are various air-conditioning controls and devices that permit the air circulating within the chamber to be heated, humidified, cooled, or dried, as desired. A major feature of these chambers lies in their capability of controlling temperatures and humidities in smoothly varying patterns such as occur naturally. Temperatures may be controlled to within plus or minus one degree Fahrenheit over the range from −5° to +125°. Humidities, within this same temperature range, may be controlled to within plus or minus 3 per cent relative humidity over the range 20 per cent to 98 per cent. At temperatures above freezing, humidities may be controlled to as low as 10 per cent. Lights within the chambers are automatically turned off and on by means of time clocks, and the settings of these clocks are periodically varied in order to duplicate the variations in photoperiod as these occur naturally.'

Detailed descriptions of mechanical features are given in Flitters, Messenger, and Husman (1956). Three bioclimatic cabinets are at present located at the University of California, Department of Biological Control laboratory at Albany, California.

Biotrone (Bio = life ; trone = balance). In order to study the plant–insect complex under a wide range of combinations of sunlight, temperature, and humidity, this highly specialized greenhouse was conceived by S. E. Flanders and C. A. Fleschner. Although this useful research facility has been mentioned in scientific literature (Clausen 1954a) and popularly in various trade journals, no detailed description has appeared since it was placed in use in mid-1953. The following description was provided by C. A. Fleschner:

'The biotrone is a 12 ft. × 12 ft. glasshouse covered by a cubical lath-house consisting of 165 interlocking aluminium louvres. The main purpose of the louvres is to prevent excessive direct solar radiation, and they may be opened and closed automatically in three ways, namely, by direct solar radiation, by a combination of direct solar radiation and temperature within the glasshouse, or by a time clock. As a means of heat conservation all louvres are closed at sunset and opened at sunrise the year around by the time clock which is self synchronizing for seasonal change in length of day. In addition, the clock energizes a remote bulb thermostat circuit which contains three separately located thermostats. These thermostats are located on the tops of the lath house and shielded to face east, south, and west. When a thermostat is closed by solar radiation in excess of a predetermined intensity, only the louvres controlled by that thermostat are closed. The east thermostat controls the east side and the easterly half of the top. The south thermostat controls the south side and the entire top. The west thermostat controls the west side and the westerly half of the top. The north, or entry, side is opened and closed by the clock and stays open all day.

'Heating or cooling within the glasshouse is accomplished by a thermostatically controlled electric heater and a refrigerative cooler. A humidistat adds humidification by means of fog-nozzles.

'Fluorescent and incandescent lights within the glasshouse provide simulated sunlight should the need arise.'

The biotrone is located at the University of California, Department of Biological Control, in Riverside.

INSECTARIES OF THE WORLD

The following listing (table 5) does not include all known insectaries and the final date of compilation was December 1960. The intention here is to present a well-distributed selection of biological control insectaries in several countries. Installations having known quarantine facilities are indicated by an asterisk. Those which produce material mainly for insecticide screening are not included. Presented elsewhere in this chapter are photographs and diagrammed floor plans of insectaries which, in our opinion, cover a wide range of design and therefore demonstrate methods used to cope with a variety of problems.

This information was derived mainly from answers to questionnaires sent to the institutions listed. Co-operation of all correspondents is hereby gratefully acknowledged. It is regrettable that information regarding biological control insectaries in China was not received in time for inclusion in this listing. The practical use of insectaries in Russia was reported by Dr. Carl B. Huffaker of this department. In 1959 he visited certain Russian agricultural research institutes and he stated (department files) that there is considerable production of *Trichogramma* on collective farms in the Ukraine with the reported result of a complete saving of winter wheat from cutworm attack.

Because rearing programmes change we chose not to indicate the organisms being propagated but rather the listing is intended to illustrate that Biological Control is of world-wide interest and has been supported by government and private funds for a considerable period. A listing of national (state and private) organizations which includes brief summaries of the scope of their works is given in the admirable work by Franz (1961a).

A list of selected propagation programmes is given in the closing section of chapter 11.

TABLE 5

A partial list of biological control insectaries

Country	Sponsoring organization	Date founded	Full-time personnel
Argentina	Instituto National de Tecnologia Agropecuaria, Buenos Aires	1935	22
Australia	Queensland Dept. of Lands, Brisbane,* Qld.	1924	7
	CSIRO,		
	Canberra,* A.C.T.	1927	7
	Samford,* Qld.	1958	3
	Sydney,* N.S.W.	1953	3
Canada	Canada Dept. of Agr. Res. Branch, Belleville,* Ont.	1928	79
Chile	Ministerio de Agricultura, La Cruz	1937	20

A

B

FIGURE 71. General types of cages.

A. Adaptations of glass and plastic containers. Upper row, left to right: Three conventional lamp chimneys and one hard plastic box (holes may be punched out by using a heated tin can, cloth is attached with a soluble plastic cement, such as DuCo Household Cement). Lower row, left to right: Four glass tubes with cloth glued on one end; one-gallon pickle jars are used entire, or cut and placed on a pad of cellucotton, cotton, and cloth. Positioning the rubber bands as shown on the battery jar at the right permits a tight fit of the cloth top. Other items shown are a household one-pint fruit jar, and a section of glass cylinder on a padded board.

B. Cages requiring services of skilled cabinet makers. Left: Sleeved cages showing modifications. The longer types can be used in a vertical position to accommodate potted plants. Right: By starting a culture in one side of this duplex cage, it can later be given additional space by removing the centre partition, thereby avoiding a possibly disturbing move. The ruler is in inches.

A

B

FIGURE 72. Portable equipment designed to allow for maximum use of available floor space.

A. Upper: Rolling laboratory tables of counter height. Lower: The tall rolling rack was designed for battery jars of one- or two-gallon capacity.

B. Combination propagation cage and storage for glassware, cloth, and other supplies.

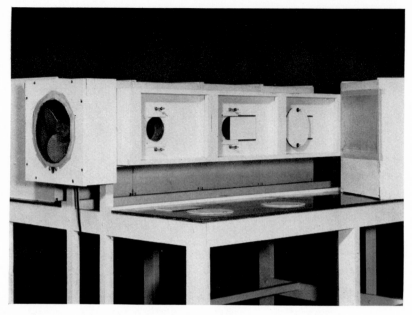

FIGURE 73. Apparatus used for ventilation of sleeved cages. The fan creates a negative pressure in the common duct with the result that air is pulled through the cages which are placed with their cloth backs against the ports. It is doubtful if aphids or mites can be continuously propagated indoors in numbers sufficient for economical insectary procedure without providing adequate ventilation (Finney 1960).

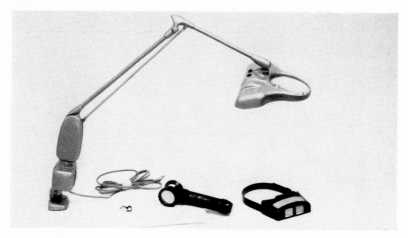

A

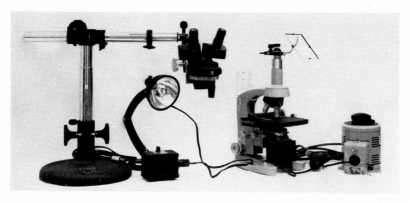

B

FIGURE 74. Basic optical aids necessary for efficient insectary work.

A. Low-power magnifiers used in routine mass culture. Left to right: Illuminated magnifier (fixed), hand lens, portable self-illuminating magnifier, and head loupe.

B. Higher power magnifiers used in research insectaries. Left to right: Stereoscopic dissecting microscope gives 9× to approximately 100× magnification; the supporting mount permits adjustment in three planes; flood lamp illuminator with variable transformer control. At the right is a compound microscope with its substage illuminator. Shown attached are a card for converting ocular micrometer readings to microns and a camera lucida. The variable transformer can be used for adjusting light intensity which is of particular value when working with the latter.

A

B   C

FIGURE 75. Phototaxic collection of insects.

A. Left: Shadow collection of black scale crawlers (Fillmore Citrus Protective District Insectary, Fillmore). Crawlers leave the drying twigs and collect below the light at the shadow line. Right: Shadow box used for collection of smaller numbers of lecaniine crawlers. When the double-walled cover is in place ventilation is provided through cloth-covered holes in the interior wall. Crawlers move towards light which enters through the glass or celluloid front and collect at the V-shaped shadow. The interior is painted with non-reflective black paint.

B. Amphitheatre—oleander scale crawlers (University of California). Crawlers are attracted towards the vertical fluorescent tube and collect in windrows at the shadow line case by broad V's of cardboard.

C. Leptomastix (Associates Insectary, Santa Paula). The demountable box is at floor level. When the slide is removed, the parasites which are positively geotaxic (and therefore on the floor) and positively phototaxic move into it. When a predetermined number of parasites have entered the box, the metal sliding covers are replaced. The box is then removed and taken to mealybug-infested citrus groves where the parasites are released.

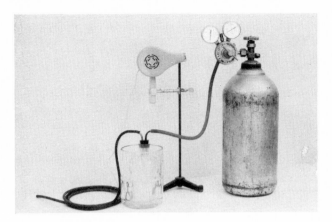

FIGURE 76. Apparatus for blending CO_2 and ether for anaesthetizing parasites. From right to left: CO_2 cylinder with pressure regulator, warm air source to prevent pressure regulator from freezing up during prolonged use, flask of ether in water bath at room temperature (80 degrees), tubing in the rubber stopper of the ether flask. CO_2 does not bubble through the liquid ether, but passes in and out of the flask, picking up sufficient ether to produce the desired effect.

FIGURE 77. Modified hair dryer used to collect parasites directly into a carton for storage prior to shipment (U.S.D.A., Moorestown).

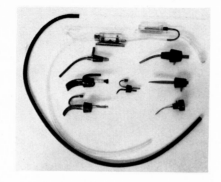

A

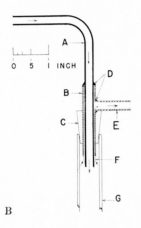

B

C

FIGURE 78.

A. Collecting devices utilizing air flow. At the top is a glass tube with the end narrowed. The hose holds a bit of fine mesh cloth over the opposite end of the tube. Just below is the collecting device developed by A. J. Nicholson (C.S.I.R.O., Div. of Ent., Canberra, Australia) in conjunction with population studies utilizing blow flies as test animals. Air pressure only is needed as direction of air flow can be controlled by the two-way valve arrangement beneath the major tube either to suck insects in or blow them out. The other devices are made from copper tubing of various sizes and they fit into standard straight-sided shell vials. The three at the right were designed for collecting predaceous mites. The small one in the centre fits into a 1½-dram shell vial.

B. Diagram of aspirator. A construction diagram of the uppermost aspirator in the group on the left in figure 84 A.

Legend: A Intake tube
        B External shell of suction line
        C Stopper
        D Bead of solder around tube
        E Suction line
        F Cloth or 100-mesh screen
        G Receptacle

C. Portable collector. This portable collector is made from a clothing vacuum cleaner. Two size-D flashlight batteries provide power to run the tiny rotary fan. This collector is very useful in the insectary as well as in the field.

FIGURE 79. Containers for storage and shipment of beneficial insects pending field colonization. Cartons of various sizes can be utilized. They should contain a lining of waxed paper streaked with honey for food and shredded wood to provide added resting surface during storage and in transit.

FIGURE 80. Biotrone.

A

B

FIGURE 81. Methods for counteracting lethal high temperature during local shipment of parasites.

A. Prechilled chest and frozen gel packet utilized in shipments requiring added protection from excessive heat. Note buffer between frozen gel and containers of insects.

B. Carrying case which cools by evaporation. The plastic hose is used for jarring the insects out of the tubes at the release site.

FIGURE 82. Fumigation chamber. The interior volume of this double-walled and insulated box is 250 cubic feet. The interior is lined with galvanized steel and all seams are soldered. The door is double gasketed. The exhaust valve at the upper right and air intake valve at lower left are gas tight. Air within is circulated past a thermostatically controlled electric strip heater. A perforated false floor permits the fumigant to completely surround the material. Methyl bromide is admitted via a coiled copper tube which is immersed in a one-gallon size warm water bath. The arrangement assures accelerated volatility of the fumigant and a relative humidity adequate to prevent plant damage. Safety features include interior lighting, an alarm bell, a padlock on the door, and a tall exhaust stack. The exhaust fan and its motor are located on top of the corrugated roof which covers the fumigation chamber.

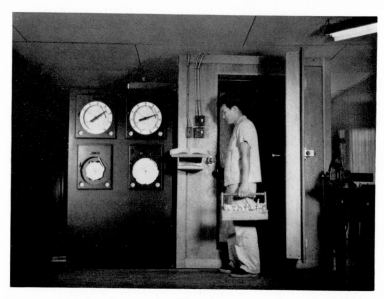

A

B

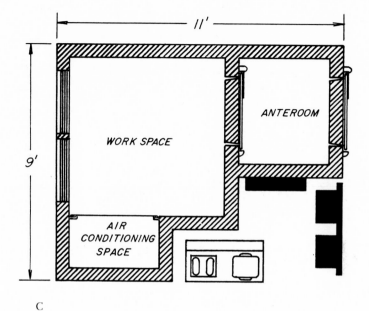

C

FIGURE 83. Bioclimatic cabinet (Albany, California).

A. Front view of bioclimatic cabinet, showing main control panel at left, and outer door opening into air-lock vestibule. The switches at centre control the ultra-violet, infra-red, and ordinary tungsten lights within the cabinet.

B. Side view of bioclimatic cabinet showing control panel at far right, motor and power switches at centre, chimney coil, solenoids and relays at left, and freon refrigerator pumps below.

C. Plan of bioclimatic cabinet.

FIGURE 84. An easily transportable, large organdie-cloth colonization cage used in field colonization of natural enemies of pests of vegetable and field crops. A vacuum machine collector is utilized to remove all insects from the plants within the caged area. The organdie cage is then fastened to a board base and soil is used to close the space between the boards and the ground. Host insects are then introduced into the cage. Natural enemies may be colonized at the same time or at any later date. The best results are obtained if a sequence of several releases are made to ensure all stages of the parasites or predators being present in the colony. One or several generations of the host and natural enemy may be reared before removal of the colonization cage.

A

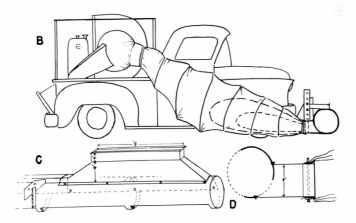

FIGURE 85. Mechanical collector developed for large-scale field collection of imported parasites of the spotted alfalfa aphid: (A) collector in operation; (B) diagrammatic side view of collector—broken line invaginations in air duct indicate positions of collecting sacks; (C) diagram of one side of 'scoop' showing the adaptive collar with which it is connected to air duct; (D) lateral view of 'scoop'—note anterior opening (broken line) for entry of insect material and posterior opening through which material is drawn via adaptive collar into collecting sacks in air duct (van den Bosch *et al.*, 1959).

FIGURE 86. Emergence cages for recovery of natural enemies from samples of parasitized host material. The containers are made from corrugated cardboard cartons with a false floor sloping to the lip of the funnel. Adult parasites attracted to the light source collect in the removable glass vials. (Courtesy of E. C. G. Bedford, Union of South Africa, Division of Entomology Parasite Laboratories.)

Country	Sponsoring organization	Date founded	Full-time personnel
France	USDA, ARS, Nanterre, Seine	1919	7
	Ministère de l'Agriculture, La Minière, S. et O.	1957	5
	Institut National de la Recherche, Agronomique Antibes (A.-M.)	1917	7
Germany	Institut für Biologische Schädlings- bekämpfung, Darmstadt	1953	18
	Landesanstalt für Pflanzenschutz, Stuttgart*	1951	2
India	CIBC, Bangalore	1956	2
	Indian Agricultural Research Institute, New Delhi	1938	11
Israel	Citrus Marketing Board, Rehovot	1960	2
Japan	Faculty of Agriculture, Kyushu University, Fukuoka	1920	—
Kenya	Dept. of Agr., Nairobi	1941	—
Mauritius	Dept. of Agr., Reduit	1924	—
New Zealand	Dept. of Scientific and Industrial Research, Ent. Div., Nelson*	1956	29
Pakistan (West)	CIBC, Rawalpindi	1957	8
Peru	Estacion Experimental Agricola de la Molina, Lima	1935	3
Switzerland	Swiss Federal Agr. Exp. Sta., Nyon, Changins	1960	4
Trinidad	CIBC, St. Augustine	1945	5
Turkey	Zirsi Mucadele Enstitudu Parazit, Laboratuari Diyarbakir	1956	4
Union of South Africa	Dept. of Agr. Tech. Serv., Div. of Ent., Pretoria	1957	6
Union of Soviet Socialist Republics	Ministry of Agriculture,		
	Tashkent*	1947	8
	Pyatigorsk*	1958	6
	Batumi*	1947	5
United States	Univ. of California,		
	Albany*	1943	33
	Riverside*	1929	27
	Associates Insectary, Santa Paula, California	1928	3
	Fillmore Citrus Protective District, Fillmore, California	1924	3
	USDA, Moorestown*, New Jersey	1928	3
	CIBC, Fontana, California	1949	2
	Bd. of Agr. & Forestry, Honolulu*, Hawaii	1913	7
Yugoslavia	Inst. for Plant Protection, Beograd (Zeman)	1954	6

* Has known quarantine facilities.

CHAPTER 14

Methods of Colonization, Recovery and Evaluation

PAUL DeBACH AND B. R. BARTLETT

COLONIZATION

IN BIOLOGICAL CONTROL the term 'colonization' refers to the attempted establishment of a community of organisms in a new locality. It includes the field release of the imported species and such manipulation as is necessary for favouring their general increase and spread. Experience has shown that unplanned or random release of new parasite stocks is, in the main, uneconomical and that colonization should be based upon an intimate knowledge of the biological and ecological interrelationships of the natural enemies and their hosts.

In the colonization of a new importation the primary objective is to obtain permanent establishment in at least one locality which may be used as a focal point for natural spread or as a source for further manipulated distribution of the species.

Relation to Introduction and Culture Procedures

Insectary propagation of the species ordinarily provides sufficient numbers of the natural enemies to afford an opportunity for the species to be given a fair trial in the field. At times, however, repeated importations of the species from abroad may be substituted for insectary culture. The circumstances under which this direct release programme may be preferable to insectary culture at the destination depends upon the conditions encountered, involving at times economic expediency, host or natural-enemy culture difficulties, or the availability of adequate culture facilities. Where at all possible, any detour of the process of insectary propagation of a new species at the destination is not recommended. Insectary propagation generally provides the optimum conditions conducive to successful colonization. It permits the greatest latitude in the timing of releases and makes available the most vigorous stocks; it also affords the best opportunity for intimate observation on the biologies and host relationships of the species.

Although in an importation project it is sometimes necessary to be prepared for a rearing programme of somewhat indefinite duration, the proper techniques of colonization may materially shorten the period of insectary propagation. As soon as the first insectary stocks are established so that cultures will not be subject to loss and the exclusively beneficial nature of the species is definitely determined, some initial releases of adult material are often made on an exploratory basis. On occasions this simple trial, even with very limited numbers, may be found to be all that is needed to achieve establishment, and the relatively complex procedures of insectary propagation may be profitably discontinued. In the majority of cases some insectary propagation of the species will be necessary, both to establish the best conditions for release of the species and to work out the host relationships and intricate biologies of the species upon which a sound colonization programme should be based. Since at times some colonization is carried on concurrently with the detailed insectary studies on the newly imported species, there have been a number of cases of natural-enemy establishment which have proceeded with little or no basic study of the insect biology beyond that of the simple host relationships involved. This has not, however, been the general rule. Often, a complicated set of bio-ecological requisites must be met before the establishment of a beneficial insect species can be effected, and it is rare that such a fortuitous set of conditions is encountered accidentally and without guidance.

Ecological Factors to be Considered in Colonization

It is not always a simple matter to decide upon the soundest precepts for efficient colonization of newly imported species of natural enemies. Much of our information on the comparative value of different colonization policies has been drawn from a study of the specific causes of failure in previous trials, the most desirable procedures often being implied by inductive reasoning. Clausen (1941) and Flanders (1959a) have discussed this subject. Some of the difficulties involved in colonization procedures are considered below as a basis for suggested practical policies and techniques favouring release and permanent establishment.

Experience has shown that unfavourable environmental conditions are the most prevalent causes for failure in colonization.

THE CLIMATE. Failure to adapt to the new climate is responsible for more failures in colonization than any other single factor, and to some extent the effects of climate are interwoven with all other factors of adaptation to the new environment. This is particularly true in cold or temperate areas or areas subject to extremes of temperature or aridity. The extremes act both directly as deterrents to natural-enemy survival, and indirectly to disrupt synchronization of seasonal development of natural enemies with their hosts. Seemingly minor changes in climate may produce differential effects upon the natural enemy and its host so as to give significant differences in the period of emergence of the two species as, for example, the unsynchronized emergence of the tachinid *Centeter cinerea* Ald. and its Japanese beetle host, when this parasite was introduced to eastern United States from Japan (Clausen 1956a). At times the disruptive influence of climate may be reflected in an unsynchronized hibernation or diapause period in the host and the entomophagous species. Diapause adaptation may be very complete, being induced or delayed exactly with its host as in certain species of *Chelonus* (Bradley and Arbuthnot 1938).

Frequently, diapause may be a requisite for satisfactory development on a host in a temperate climate, but may be lacking entirely in many of the natural enemies otherwise capable of successfully attacking the host. The lack of this type of climatic adjustment in many of the opiine parasites of fruit flies prohibits their successful utilization against some of the tephritids inhabiting the continental United States (Clausen 1956b).

It is now recognized that very few natural enemy species are capable of controlling their host over its entire range. This is well illustrated by the diverse effectiveness of the black fly parasites in Mexico where four effective parasite species were required to cover the variable climatic conditions encountered throughout the range of the host (Clausen 1958b). In retrospect it can readily be seen that many of our most generally effective species could not have been colonized permanently in certain areas had the initial releases been confined to a single area and a single period. Even the efficient vedalia and *Cryptolaemus* beetles are eliminated by especially unfavourable winter seasons from a number of the areas where they ordinarily keep their hosts in check. In this regard, also, it is known that a number of normally efficient natural enemies survive severe climatic extremes only by virtue of their sheer abundance and the discovery by some individuals of particularly protected 'shelters' during unfavourable seasons. *Rodolia cardinalis* (Muls.) and *Cryptochaetum iceryae* (Will.) on cottony-cushion scale may be used as examples to illustrate how such reservoirs are preserved. In some particularly cold winter areas these species can be found only on host colonies upon ornamental plants near buildings where they are protected from the normal temperature extremes.

From the above examples it may be recognized that the initial release of a new species should be made to cover as diverse a climatic area as is practical so that the most suitable environment will be encountered. Also, it should be recognized in some cases that until a certain minimum abundance has been attained the chances for extinction of the species may still prevail.

ALTERNATIVE HOSTS. It is frequently suspected that many failures in the colonization of newly imported natural enemies have been due to the absence in the new environment of alternative host species needed to carry the natural enemies over periods of unsuitability or scarcity of the principal host. The mandatory need for alternative hosts among parasites appears as a requirement more often in cold or temperate climates where specialized climatic adaptations of the hosts are common. The polyphagous habit in varying degrees is not uncommon among parasites, and some species rely heavily upon a range of hosts for maintaining population reservoirs when their principal hosts are in unsuitable stages.

Since it is relatively impossible to foretell exactly how a species may react to a new environment, the common procedure in colonization is to set up a reasonable number of liberation sites with varied environmental conditions and concentrate the initial releases in these locations. This policy offers the best advantages for the natural discovery of alternative hosts when they are required by the newly imported species. Under certain circumstances, when the requirement for alternative host insects is recognized, it may be feasible to supply artificially the desired species to the immediate colonization area to favour initial establishment as described in chapter 15.

BIOLOGICAL COMPETITORS. It is obvious that sufficient quantities of the host species should be available and exist in the correct stages for attack by the species released, and that the host voltinism should correspond to the seasonal biology of the natural enemy. This, ordinarily, is simply arranged for in the choice of the first releases at a selected location. However, it is not uncommon to find that at new sites or as releases at a site are continued, certain biological competitors for the host may develop which may reduce the chances of establishment. At low host densities, especially, many of the competitors may severely handicap the initial establishment. Already-established entomophagous species often present severe competition to new species even though the latter may have seasonal or other general advantages not possessed by the original species. This is particularly the case where they compete for the same host stages (DeBach and Landi 1959a). To minimize the difficulties in obtaining permanent establishment under such cases of competition, either particularly large numbers of the natural enemies may be colonized at a single release site or special locations may be selected which are not so subject to competing organisms. Under certain conditions it may at times be possible to establish natural enemy-free host colonies under field cages so that the initial colonization will not be opposed by competing species. This procedure also offers the advantage that additions of host material can be made to the cage so that large numbers of the natural enemies may be produced before their final release from the cage.

The somewhat unpredictable action of predatory insects and insect pathogens is often favoured by high host densities, these agencies at times so reducing the host supply that newly colonized species cannot gain a foothold (van den Bosch et al. 1959). Spiders and birds at times play a role in restricting the abundance of a host so that colonization procedures are made difficult. Ants often have to be eliminated from the colonization area by ground or tree trunk treatment with chemicals or by entanglement barriers so that they will not interfere with the action of the natural enemies to be released. Hyperparasitism rarely becomes a significant factor until the new species has become abundant.

SUITABILITY OF THE HOST PLANTS. The possible unsuitability of certain host plants to a newly imported species of natural enemy should be considered in the planning of colonization. This subject is considered in detail in chapters 5 and 9. From the standpoint of colonization, an unsuitablity of the host plant for a natural-enemy species may be due to its undesirability as a source of shelter or food for the adults, or a degree of physiological immunity may be imposed by the plant through the host insect upon the natural enemy. A classical example of the latter effect is found in the failure in development of *Apanteles congregatus* (Say) on *Protoparce* spp. feeding on dark-fired tobacco (Gilmore 1938).

PHYSIOLOGICAL SUITABILITY OF THE NATURAL ENEMY TO ITS HOST. It appears very likely that if all facts were known, physiological unsuitability of natural-enemy species to their hosts has been the cause of a great many of the failures in colonization of imported species of parasites and possibly some predators. The adaptiveness may range from nearly perfect to highly imperfect and still not always be readily distinguishable in the insectary culture of the species. The attribute is hard to assess as is the closely allied phenomenon of accidental or 'casual' parasitism in nature.

DISPERSAL. The dispersal habits of an imported species are of great significance in colonization procedures, since they are intimately connected with the problem of adequate mating of the progeny of the released individuals. Slowly dispersing species are less handicapped in this respect. Even with uniparental species there seems to be some danger that small initial populations may be so diluted through dispersal losses that establishment will not be favoured.

Procedures of Colonization

THE COLONIZATION SITE. Ordinarily a limited number of alternative sites are chosen for colonization with a view towards both diversification of environmental features and suitability to specific requirements as revealed by biological studies of the species, as well as to the ultimate ease of natural spread.

The choice of release sites is frequently complicated by the temporary nature of the plantings upon which the natural enemies are to be colonized, as well as by unexpected pesticide treatment of the site. Frequently, the single most important requirement for a prospective colonization site is the owner's assurance that it will not receive applications of toxic chemicals. Also, unusually inclement weather conditions sometimes cause extermination of the host or natural enemy, so protected sites should be chosen. Signs or placards requesting co-operation or sometimes even shelters may offer some security against these hazards; however, the desirability of full control over the colonization site, even to direction of the cultural practices, is frequently the only sure way of maintaining optimum conditions for colonization. Some degree of security is achieved by working through the larger agricultural organizations which will ordinarily assume a high degree of responsibility in the project. In some instances only rental or other legal arrangements supply appropriate security for the site. Private gardens are often very favourable locations for obtaining diversified host plants and alternative hosts in colonization. Neglected or abandoned plantings, in some instances, have proved to be desirable release sites.

TIMING RELEASES. Releases are timed to coincide with the earliest seasonal availability of host stages suitable for attack and the occurrence of favourable weather. If the period of occurrence of suitable host stages is short, it is sometimes difficult, but nonetheless important, to synchronize perfectly the insectary production of the natural enemy with the development of the host in the field. Colonization sites selected from diverse climatic areas will often widen the period during which the required host stages will be available. This may be particularly advantageous when direct release of imported species is the method used, and shipment schedules do not coincide with the periods most opportune for local colonization.

Ordinarily, a number of consecutive releases are planned for each colonization site so that a continuity of both sexes of the developing natural-enemy progeny will occur during the optimum period for host attack. Emigration losses will be less critical and favourable weather will be more certain. It is generally considered more advisable to limit the number of colonization sites than to release very few natural enemies at many locations. The timing of consecutive releases of parasitic species having hyperparasitic males is particularly important so that the two sexes of the parasite may be synchronized in development (see chapter 10).

Releases are often made in the morning, since that is a common period for parasite emergence and mating, and it gives the warm daytime hours for oviposition, orientation, and the seeking of protected microhabitats. Clausen (1941) suggests that release in the evening around dusk restricts dispersal while still providing a period of orientation to the new surroundings. This might be the more desirable procedure during the hotter part of the year. Release in brilliant sunlight is known to stimulate rapid dispersal of some species, so this factor should be evaluated. Obviously, wind, prospects of rain, frost, or extreme hot weather indicate that colonization should be delayed until the weather is satisfactory.

STORAGE OF NATURAL ENEMIES. As just indicated, it is frequently desirable to hold adult entomophagous insects for more appropriate times of release. For many species this is accomplished by keeping them under refrigeration at about 60° F and about 75 per cent R.H. Honey is ordinarily supplied as a source of food. At this temperature, activity usually is curtailed, but enough movement occurs to permit some feeding to take place. Where lower temperatures are needed for storage, the insects must be removed at intervals to permit normal feeding. Very low temperatures may cause sterilization of both males and females (see chapter 11). Emergence of adults from the pupal stage may be delayed safely for periods varying up to several months, depending upon the species.

TYPES OF RELEASE MATERIAL. Colonization is usually made of the adult stages of parasites and predators since immature stages are more difficult to colonize and may be more subject to destruction by unfavourable meteorological conditions and by predators. The pupal stages of coccinellids are sometimes, however, put out at the colonization site since they are rarely attacked by predators. Trichogrammatids and other egg parasites are sometimes colonized as immature stages within the eggs of their host because of the ease of handling. Sometimes various developmental stages of parasites within the hosts are colonized to provide a continuity of emerging adults which may facilitate mating. When immature stages of natural enemies are colonized, mating is ordinarily satisfactory, since the earlier emerging males ordinarily await the emergence of females.

MATING PRIOR TO RELEASE. Mated female parasitic Hymenoptera usually give rise to both male and female progeny, often with a preponderance of females. Before release it should be ascertained that functional mating has occurred so that there will be a favourable sex ratio among their offspring as they develop in the field. Overmating can, under certain circumstances, result in non-fertilization of eggs, which produces a preponderance of males in the offspring (Flanders 1956). The mating instinct is ordinarily well developed at emergence, but with some species it may be considerably delayed or require special light, temperature, or space conditions.

OVIPOSITIONAL CAPACITY. Some parasitic species can oviposit shortly after emergence. In other species gestation is delayed for variable periods of time. Also, some examples are known in which reproductive degeneration of parasites occurred during prolonged holding of adults (Clausen 1941). The presence of ripened eggs in the oviduct as determined by dissection or by ovipositional response to suitable hosts should be determined for the species prior to field release.

FOOD AND WATER. Variable food requirements must be met with certain species for egg development before oviposition can proceed. Ordinarily these requirements are satisfied by constant supplies of honey and water. However, some species require special nutritional elements found in fresh honeydew or substitutes (see chapter 12). Other species may need special nutrients gained by feeding upon the body fluids of their hosts. Ordinarily this will occur automatically in the process of culture. Food should be available during transport to the field for release.

TRANSPORT TO THE FIELD. Some protection from excessive heat and aridity is frequently given to adult natural enemies during their transport to the point of colonization. Natural-enemy containers, enclosed in a waterproof plastic bag or metal box, are ordinarily kept cool during transport by cloth gauze wrappings which provide evaporative cooling when wetted. Iced boxes and even refrigerated automobiles have been used for transport of imported natural enemies to the point of release.

OPEN FIELD RELEASE. Natural enemies are released in the field in the immediate vicinity of suitable hosts. Their orientation and search habits should be followed at the time of release. It is most important to observe attempted oviposition. If dispersal occurs without host attack, confined release is usually advantageous.

CONFINED RELEASE. Colonization under cages is very frequently used in the initial phase of release of a new species. With this method it is possible to examine the conditions of attack and to get accurate information on the effects of critical climatic factors and variable host-plant effects. The technique has had wide usage since the earliest periods of natural-enemy importation. It was the method used in the original colonization of vedalia in California in 1889 and of *Opius humilis* Silv. against *Ceratitis capitata* Wied. on coffee in Hawaii in 1913. Release under field cases or in sleeve cages, where practical, permits the investigator to follow the biological development and normal increase of the species in detail under field conditions even when only small numbers of the natural enemies are available for release. Under cloth or screen confinement the abundance of the host can be controlled by adding more hosts as needed. Competitive natural enemies often can be eliminated from the sleeves or cages. The example shown in figure 84 (following p. 400) was used by van den Bosch et al. (1959). Sometimes the confinement area is fumigated previously with calcium cyanide and subsequently restocked with the host before use to assure freedom from competitive natural enemies. Some increase in temperature and some changes in humidity may occur under sleeve cages in direct sunlight.

RELEASE NUMBERS. There are no means by which one can reliably estimate the minimum number of any natural enemy which must be released in order to procure establishment. Permanent colonization is accomplished very readily with only a few individuals of certain species. Ten mated females of vedalia are commonly considered enough to establish that species in a new locality. In contrast, the Canadian releases of *Dahlbominus fuscipennis* (Zett.) against the spruce sawfly consisted of 10,000 adults per colony.

Great difficulty was encountered with open-field colonization of parasites of the spotted alfalfa aphid in 1955. Somewhat better results were obtained by concentration of releases under field cages the following year. However, permanent colonization at all release sites was almost consistently successful after millions of the species were available for distribution from established colonies (van den Bosch *et al.* 1959). The conclusion was reached that a minimum 'inoculation charge' might be needed for establishment of the species involved.

CONTINUATION OF RELEASE PERIOD. As a very general rule, excessive difficulty in the initial establishment of a species indicates a lack of adaptability to the new environment and the probability of subsequent ineffectiveness in providing complete control. Clausen (1951) has suggested that on the basis of practical experience most species that turn out to be highly efficient become established readily, given suitable release conditions, and indicate their potential ability to give control of the host within a period of three years following the initial releases. There appear to be very few exceptions to this rule among those species destined to play leading roles in the control of their hosts. However, with species of lesser effectiveness where a desirable partial control effect may be obtained, visible results may not be expected so rapidly. It still appears, however, that there is little advantage to continuation of releases beyond the period of three years when repeated failures are experienced. Within this period all reasonable possibilities of establishment should have been explored. Greater perseverence might eventually accomplish the purpose, but a species that requires such effort is unlikely to be very rewarding.

DISTRIBUTION FROM ORIGINAL SITE OF ESTABLISHMENT. With certain natural-enemy species, spread from the point of initial establishment is sometimes limited. The restriction may be caused by an exceptionally slow dispersal rate of the species, as with the egg parasite of the gypsy moth, *Anastatus disparis* Ruschka, which showed a normal spread of only 200 feet per year (Howard and Fiske 1911). Also, other unrecognized barriers to natural spread may exist. After establishment has been obtained in one locality, it is frequently possible materially to increase the rate of distribution of the species by bulk movement to other localities. This may involve extensive transfer of field-collected adults as was successfully done in the Klamath weed beetle programme in California and Oregon from 1949 to 1952, or it may involve movement of hosts containing immature stages of the natural enemy. This procedure worked exceptionally well in 1956 and 1957 when all stages of the parasites of the spotted alfalfa aphid were transferred first by bulk movement of cut alfalfa to new colonization sites and later by the mechanical vacuum collector shown in figure 85, following p. 400 (van den Bosch *et al.*, 1959). Grower co-operation in this phase of the project is highly desirable, since it generally assures better care of the colonies when the responsibility is shared with those who are to benefit.

RECOVERY

Recovery attempts are usually undertaken soon after the initial release of newly imported natural enemies so that any progress towards establishment may serve as a guide in colonization efforts. The objective is to obtain a simple qualitative assessment of the presence or absence of the species with little or no reference to its probable efficiency.

Sampling for Recovery

Recovery operations are conducted at a time and place where the species is most likely to be encountered, and the simplest techniques available are used. Close observation for adults or immature stages of a species will often reveal its presence. Frequently, parasitization will produce symptoms on the host which will distinguish it from unparasitized individuals. Where these procedures do not suffice for detection, the natural enemy may have to be reared from or dissected from its host. When no further feeding of the host is required, rearing is commonly employed since large numbers of hosts may be handled easily. Emerging adult parasites can often be induced to go to light sources for ready collection, or as with most scale insect and mealybug recovery samples, where the host is collected in association with the plant source, the entire infested plant material may be held in sealed containers until the natural enemies emerge, die, and drop to the bottom of the container where they may be examined at any convenient time after collection (figure 86, facing p. 401). Berlese funnels are sometimes used to separate living insect material from included plant material preliminary to examination for parasitization. Adults of newly introduced parasites and predators may be sorted from sweep net and other gross material in a similar fashion. This was done by Dietrick, Schlinger, and Garber (1960) in connection with their highly efficient field suction collecting machine.

Dissection of host material for detection of the immature stages of internal parasites may sometimes be necessary to establish the presence of the parasite. Such dissections are preferably made in saline solution. At times, treatment of the host with xylene, benzene, or standard insect clearing solutions for insect tissue may permit identification of immature forms of the parasite within the intact body of the host.

Temporary Establishment

The first field generation from a newly colonized species, represented by the direct descendants of the released individuals, is very frequently recovered at the immediate colonization site. Often, however, no further reproduction occurs, so little significance is generally attached to these initial recoveries. Failure to obtain a second generation on multivoltine hosts in the field is generally an indication of poor physiological or ecological adaptation to the host. If the general suitability of the host for attack is known from preceding insectary propagation, and, as is so often the case, repeated colonization attempts under presumably favourable conditions give unchanged results, it must be assumed that the introduced species is encountering an ecological barrier to establishment.

Early abundance of second-generation individuals in the field is encouraging in view of the general rule that species destined to be highly effective ordinarily start out quickly and easily. However, as previously emphasized, many species otherwise well adapted to their hosts turn out to be great disappointments in their susceptibility to climatic extremes. For this reason all establishment of newly introduced natural enemies is considered provisional until they have demonstrated their capacity to survive periods including unusually severe winter and summer climatic conditions.

The decline of newly imported natural-enemy populations after a very favourable beginning sometimes presents a perplexing problem in biological control. Suitable explanation for these reversals is often lacking. The striking retrogression of *Metaphycus lounsburyi* (How.) upon its black scale host, *Saissetia oleae* (Bern.), in California following its early abundance after colonization affords such an illustration. The thesis that hyperparasitism by *Quaylea whittieri* (Grlt.) was responsible for the rapid subjugation of the beneficial species (Essig 1934, p. 834) finds little support today when the general ineffectiveness of *M. lounsburyi* persists while the hyperparasite is a rarity. Some few other examples of parasite population reduction after reaching a high initial abundance have been recorded by Clausen (1951). These are both examples of good biological control, hence the decrease is to be expected after the host is reduced. The complete loss of colonies of *Lixophaga diatraeae* (Tns.), a parasite of the sugar-cane borer, after it had persisted for five years (Clausen 1956a) and of *Rodolia koebelei* (Ol.) after a number of years of general abundance in California, may possibly be explained by ultimate exposure to devastating climate extremes.

In connection with the significance of early recovery operations there are some examples wherein many years intervened between releases and the first recovery of the colonized species. Howard (1924) lists two such examples, both of which almost assuredly were due to inadequate recovery attempts. Fullaway and Krauss (1945) record seventeen years as intervening between release and recovery of *Tiphia segregata* Cwfd. colonized in Hawaii against the anomala beetle, and eleven years intervening between release of *Apanteles glomeratus* (L.) and its recovery on *Pieris rapae* (L.). Inadequate recovery attempts and later accidental introductions, respectively, might well account for these examples.

Where to draw the line between temporary and permanent establishment of a newly introduced species of natural enemy is a question. Because of the vagaries that may be expected claims for beneficial insect establishment before the passage of at least three years may, in many cases, prove to be incorrect. Certainly, predictions of future abundance of the species based on early recovery abundance are even more hazardous. It is believed, however, that after three years' time the effects of the newly introduced species should ordinarily be self-evident, if the species is destined to be very efficient.

The Probability of Permanent Establishment

The expectation of permanent establishment of imported species is of interest, although statistics on this subject merely tend to emphasize that establishment is and probably always will remain a highly empirical process. As more modern procedures are utilized, enabling importation and colonization of larger numbers of species, it is possible that the percentage of failures may increase rather than diminish because less likely prospects may be emphasized with the greater ease of handling. This tendency has been exemplified in some of the most intensive campaigns where less success in establishment has attended the later trials involving species obviously less well adapted to the particular hosts.

Clausen (1956a), in considering 390 species of natural enemies imported into the United States, lists 94 or 24·4 per cent as having been established. Flanders (1953d) records permanent establishment of 23 out of 63 (36·5 per cent) of the hymenopterous parasites imported into California against citrus-infesting coccids. In the intensive campaign against *Dacus dorsalis* Hend. in Hawaii from 1947 to 1951, Clausen (1956b) lists 11 out of 23, or 47·8 per cent, of the released species of natural enemies as having become permanently established. In the campaign against sugarcane leafhoppers in Hawaii, 38·1 per cent of the imported natural enemies were established. Of the natural enemies imported into Hawaii for scale and mealybug control, 33·9 per cent became established, and of all the coccinellids introduced into the same area, 33·8 per cent were established (Swezey 1925).

EVALUATION OF EFFECTIVENESS OF NATURAL ENEMIES

Discussion

One of the first general discussions of this subject was given by Smith and DeBach (1942), and many of their remarks still seem apropos as the following rather extensive quotation will indicate: '... workers in the field of biological control are sometimes reproached for failing to present statistical evidence in support of their claims. Critics contend, quite justifiably, that a reduction in the population of an insect host, following the establishment of one or more of its insect enemies, is not necessarily proof that the enemy was the cause of the reduction. Failure to present convincing evidence in support of conclusions with reference to parasite introduction is not, however, an indication of lack of appreciation of the desirability of some method of measuring, statistically, the effect of parasites or predators on their host populations. It is rather an indication of the difficulties inherent in the problem itself, difficulties far greater than those ordinarily encountered in research in other fields of economic entomology, such as toxicology. .... By studying the oscillations, fluctuations, and other population changes and correlating them with the various causes of variation in mortality and in fecundity, we may learn how to evaluate the epidemiological effect of enemies or diseases of an organism. The difficulty in the development of such a method lies in the multiplicity of factors and the complexity of their interrelations. Some factors, for example, are density-dependent and others are density-independent. Some produce their effect almost immediately; others, only after a considerable lag. The effect of some is super-imposed on the effect of others. Mortality resulting from one factor often overlaps that from another. There remains, also, the general difficulty of developing population-sampling techniques which satisfy the statistical requirements. We believe thoroughly that this can and will be done, but that its consummation is largely in the future.

'Proof is an intangible thing. The number of times that event B must be observed to follow event A before the conclusion that A *caused* B is justified, is arbitrary, and differs with different conditions and with different persons. Repeated observations merely increase the *probability* that the conclusions are in accord with the facts. A single observation that the population of the cottony-cushion scale, *Icerya purchasi* Mask., dropped after the introduction of vedalia, *Rodolia cardinalis* (Muls.), would not, in itself, have been very convincing to those entomologists who had observed that the populations of the scale rose and fell before the introduction of vedalia But when it was observed that, in many different parts of the world, the scale population invariably dropped and remained at a low level after the establishment of vedalia, most entomologists were satisfied to accept this as proof that vedalia determined the population level of its host. This conclusion was not reached, of course, without the knowledge that vedalia fed voraciously on the cottony-cushion scale, and that reductions in populations of the prey were associated with ample evidence of destruction by vedalia. Perhaps the most convincing evidence of all, however, was the demonstration that on trees where vedalia was excluded, the host became extremely abundant, whereas on trees to which vedalia had access, the scale population remained at a low level.

'Pending the development of more satisfactory quantitative methods of popula-tion analysis, it would seem reasonable to expect those who are engaged in bio-logical-control research to submit evidence of the following kinds:

'(1) Gross data showing that, generally speaking, as the [introduced] entomo-phagous species spread from place to place, its establishment was followed, in each limited area and within a reasonable period of time, by an appreciable reduction in the host population.

'(2) Gross data showing that, after the general establishment of the entomo-phagous species, the host population remained at a much lower level, on the average, than before such establishment.

'(3) Detailed, or more exact, data showing decidedly higher survival of the host when protected from attack by the entomophagous species than when exposed to attack.

'If these studies indicate that, as the enemies spread to new areas, the pest density has almost invariably dropped in those areas, and that, after general dis-persal of the enemy, the pest in most of the areas has reached and maintained a level appreciably lower than that existing previous to the establishment of the enemy, there is considerable justification for the conclusion that successful biological control has taken place. But there is always a *possibility*, no matter how remote, that the lowering of the population density of the pest after the establishment of the enemy, was only a coincidence; that some other factor, such as a weather cycle, a change in cultural methods, or a disease epidemic, took place synchronously with the establishment of the enemy; and that, in reality, the enemy had little or nothing to do with the change in status of the pest. Arguments based on such contentions are often advanced by those who oppose the idea of biological control, and, unless it can be shown that the presence of the parasite or predator actually materially reduces the survival of the host population, it must be admitted that there is always some basis, however far fetched, for such arguments. This is because the destruction of large numbers of the host, or a large percentage of the host population, by an insect enemy does not *necessarily* affect the *net* survival of the host population. The insect enemy may simply replace some other cause of mortality without materially influencing the numbers of host individuals that *survive*.

'What is really needed, therefore, to make conclusions with reference to the practical effect of introduced entomophagous insects more convincing is the development of a technique whereby the effect of the entomophagous species on the density of its host population can be satisfactorily measured.

'Briefly, the method [described herein] consists of the excluding of the parasites from hosts on certain branches of the host plant, while permitting them to have access to hosts on other branches in the immediate vicinity.

'It will not be possible . . . in every case to use the procedure outlined in the present paper. The application of ingenuity should, however, result in the development of techniques by means of which the differential between presence and absence of introduced enemies on the survival of their host or prey populations within the same area can be measured and recorded. Biological control will not receive the recognition it merits from entomologists and ecologists until satisfactory methods of measurement of these effects are utilized and the results recorded.'

Although this section on the evaluation of the effectiveness of natural enemies in the regulation of population densities of their hosts is included in a chapter dealing primarily with newly imported natural enemies, the need for and use of adequate evaluation techniques covers a much broader field than the evaluation of results accruing from importation and colonization alone.

Evaluation of the relative effectiveness of natural enemies of all pests of a given crop or in a given ecosystem is a fundamental prerequisite to intelligent attempts to manipulate insect populations ecologically. Evaluation should be one of the first procedures, if not the first, to be carried out in any new biological control project. It furnishes a scientific ecological basis for applied biological control which otherwise would be largely empirical. Thus, if the *potential* capabilities of all natural enemies on a given crop become known, the need for new importations or manipulation becomes apparent. Evaluation should also point out or help delimit the reasons why certain natural enemies fail to attain their potential. It is especially important with crops receiving regular, and often many, annual pesticide applications, that evaluation techniques take into account the adverse effects of treatment on natural enemies.

Thus, in any attempt at evaluation, the first step is to isolate, analyse, and preferably when possible to eliminate experimentally from the study those factors adverse to natural enemies. Obviously weather factors must be analysed, usually with supplementary laboratory experiments, but certain adverse factors such as pesticide application, dust, or ants can be greatly reduced or eliminated altogether from study plots. Only in this manner can the actual ultimate potential of natural enemies in control of the host be clarified. The single most important qualification is to carry out studies in plots free of pesticidal treatments, and this includes drift residues. Such an approach has been emphasized previously (DeBach 1951), and it was pointed out (p. 444) '. . . an untreated grove is not considered to be one in which pest-control treatment has been skipped for one year or two. Indications are that three or four years may pass before a natural balance that has been upset is completely reattained. It is desirable, therefore, to restrict basic studies of this type as much as possible to groves that have received virtually no insecticidal, fungicidal, or deficiency treatments for five or more years.' Again it was emphasized (DeBach 1958b, p. 188), 'The first step toward an understanding of the complex faunal relationships on citrus was to learn the potentialities of the entire natural-enemy complex in control of all pests in the complete absence of chemical treatments and to analyze the effect of insecticidal treatments on the balance of arthropod populations.

'After it was determined what natural enemies could do in the absence of treatment, it became possible to evaluate their intrinsic weaknesses and to determine other environmental factors adversely affecting natural enemy populations. This information led to the exploration of various possibilities of increasing the effectiveness of established natural enemies as well as of reducing the adverse effects of insecticidal applications.'   Various methods have been used for evaluating the effectiveness of natural enemies. These will be discussed in the following sections under qualitative methods, quantitative methods, and experimental methods.

Qualitative Methods of Evaluation

Qualitative evidence based on frequent, detailed, and widespread field observation may furnish the investigator with the most rapid and least effort-causing means of obtaining some idea of the importance of natural enemies in the control of their host. At best this method will provide indications only—never formal proof—and at worst it will be highly misleading. Much will depend on the wisdom, training, and experience of the individual investigator. The main advantages of this method are that a much broader survey can be made of field populations in a short period of time.

The observational method may be most applicable and reliable when used to evaluate the effectiveness of newly introduced natural enemies. Evaluation of results following introduction probably have been made most frequently by this method.

The effectiveness of vedalia in the control of the cottony-cushion scale, as well as many other successful cases of biological control, have been established in this manner. If establishment is followed by obvious increase in natural-enemy populations, at the expense of the host, followed by obvious decrease in the host population and the same relationship holds as the natural enemy spreads to new areas, this is strong presumptive evidence of cause and effect. When the host population remains low and the same performance perhaps is repeated in other countries, this would usually be accepted as adequate proof of control by natural enemies.

When evaluation of already-established natural enemies is attempted, spread is not involved, so the same type of phenomenon cannot be observed because a balance between host and parasite has already been reached. In such cases the entomologist, by repeated observation of host-parasite trends, may form an opinion of the effectiveness of one particular natural enemy or of that of a group. Rarely would he be sure that the average host population density observed was a resultant of natural-enemy activity because other factors might just as well have been responsible.

Quantitative Methods of Evaluation

Quantitative methods are in a sense observational but the observations are made by taking samples of the host and parasite, predator, or pathogen populations and determining the mortality to be ascribed to these as well as to other factors, and: (1) by means of correlation of the population changes of the host and natural enemies, attempts are made to show the effect of the natural enemy, or enemies, on the host population, or (2) by analysis of life table mortality data, the effects of various environmental factors are interpreted.

To begin with, the quantitative method can at best be only as good as the extent to which the samples taken actually represent the populations being studied. Sampling methods and statistics cannot be covered here, but it is of utmost importance that adequate samples be obtained or the study will be largely wasted. Morris (1960) reviews sampling of insect populations and thoroughly covers the literature. Really adequate sampling techniques are not easily developed even for one species of insect and, in biological control, many entomophagous species may have to be considered along with any given host insect. Any statistician will affirm that development of proper sampling techniques which cover a variety of species and situations over a period of time can become a full-time job. It also frequently turns out that apparently valuable information from certain intensive sampling methods may, with additional biological knowledge, prove to be inadequate or misleading. Difficulties in obtaining accurate samples of natural populations and possibilities of erroneous conclusions based on inaccurate samples are pointed out by Lewis (1960) who states '... Methods of estimating parasitization of the spruce budworm, *Choristoneura fumiferana* (Clem.), by *Apanteles fumiferanae* Vier. and *Glypta fumiferanae* (Vier.) have yielded different answers, depending on the manner and timing of collections. ... Observations in northern Maine during 1950 and

FIGURE 87. The chemical exclusion method utilizing DDT as a selective insecticide to depress natural enemy populations while having little if any direct effect on the host, the California red scale. The increase in scale populations following inhibition of natural enemies by DDT is indicated in the photos by the increasing amount of defoliation shown from left to right. The tree at the left shows the appearance of untreated trees in the grove both before and after the experiment started. Such trees have very low red scale populations. The centre photo shows considerable defoliation due to red scale increase 6 months after the initial application of DDT to eliminate natural enemies. The photo on the right shows extensive defoliation due to an extremely heavy red scale infestation after 11 months of inhibition of natural enemies by DDT.

FIGURE 88. The paired comparison sleeve-cage check method of mechanical exclusion of natural enemies. *Upper:* The enclosed sleeved-branch on the right has been artificially infested with black scale but parasites are excluded. The open sleeved-branch on the left was similarly infested but naturally occurring parasites have ingress and egress. *Lower:* The same sleeved-branches as above shown one year later (with sleeves pulled back); *right*—entire branch from closed sleeve is dead and defoliated owing to unrestricted increase of the black scale in the absence of parasites; *left*— original artificial infestation of black scale in open sleeve has been reduced by parasites (mainly *Metaphycus helvolus*) to a very low level equivalent to that on the remainder of the tree.

Figure 89. The biological check method utilizing ants to inhibit natural enemies. Comparison between orange trees without ants (left) and trees with ants (right) depicts the degree of biological control by natural enemies. The tree at left—which is representative of the entire grove—has all potential pests under excellent biological control; the nearby tree at right—which is of the same age—has been stunted and partially defoliated by increases in mealybugs, soft scales, and particularly the California red scale due to inhibition of their natural enemies by ants.

1951 indicated higher parasitization by *Apanteles* and *Glypta* in fourth-instar bud-worm collections . . . than in second-instar collections immediately after emergence from hibernation. Since both species of parasites attack the budworm in the late summer prior to hibernation of the host, it is impossible for an actual increase in the amount of parasitization to occur in the following spring.' Another excellent case in point is furnished by Dietrick, Schlinger, and Garber (1960) who developed a new mechanical suction sampling method for use on alfalfa insects and their natural enemies to replace the old and widely used sweep-net method upon which many conclusions regarding host–natural-enemy populations have been based. The new method collects from several to several hundred times as many hosts and natural enemies as the sweep-net method for the same unit area. Additionally, the sweep-net method does not sample different co-existing species populations with the same accuracy. Sweeping gave about 66 per cent accuracy with spotted alfalfa aphid adults but only about 10 per cent accuracy with the female parasites of the aphid. Needless to say, data from such sampling could lead to completely misleading con-clusions. This is not to discourage the sampling method, but to encourage proper sampling and interpretation, otherwise not only are time and money wasted but, worse yet, false conclusions may result. Simmonds (1948*b*) has pointed out some of the many difficulties involved in obtaining adequate samples of parasite populations and the misinterpretations that can result. He has concluded (p. 439) '. . . to avoid misleading results care must be taken to secure samples of host material in the field with due consideration to the habits of both host and parasite. This point in sampling is not simply one of size of samples but one of the necessity of ensuring that samples taken really represent all the situations occurring in the host–parasite relationship.

'It is not claimed that the defects outlined above are the only ones inherent in the method of sampling field populations of insects to obtain an estimate of controlling action of parasites. Nor is it claimed that in no instance can a valid estimate of parasite activity be obtained by a simple sampling method. The object of this note is merely to stress the fact that values obtained in this way should be viewed with caution, and that no estimate of the controlling value of any individual parasite species should be based on the results from a few such samples. In order to gain some true idea of the value of a parasite species as a controlling agent it is necessary to study it in the field over a range of conditions, when its effectiveness may usually be expressed far better in general terms than by a series of "percentages of parasit-ism," although these latter may be of use in conjunction with such a general description.

'As with attempts at the mathematical prediction of fluctuation of insect popula-tions, narrowly changing environmental conditions may have such a marked effect on the interaction of parasite and host that figures for percentage parasitism, etc., have little significance outside the peculiar circumstances occurring at the point in time and space where the sample was taken, and again description in general terms gives a better indication of the effectiveness of a parasite. . . .'

We would emphasize here that figures on per cent parasitization used alone—as

18—I.P.W.

so often is done—are of little value in predicting host population trends in the next generation. It can be shown by simple arithmetical models that in one case 98 per cent parasitization will be insufficient to keep the host from increasing in the next generation, whereas with another species of parasite and host, 60 per cent parasitization could result in a decrease. This merely serves to illustrate that a high degree of parasitization in itself does not indicate an effective parasite.

Ideally, population sampling, i.e., partial census, should show long-term trends of actual mortality caused by the parasite, predator, or combination being studied. In order to do this, periodic samples usually must be taken over a period of several years and should take into account the number of generations of natural enemies to one of the host. Thus, a parasite population may have to be sampled several times during one host generation. Mortality caused by ovipositional probing and host-feeding by adult parasites must also be taken into account with many parasites. Various workers (Johnston 1915; DeBach 1943b) have shown that such mortality may be much greater than that caused by parasitism. DeBach (1943b) pointed out that the value of the introduced black scale parasite, *Metaphycus helvolus* (Comp.), in control of its host was seriously questioned initially because a much larger proportion of black scales was found to be dead from unknown causes than from parasitism. He showed that this 'unknown' mortality was caused by host-feeding and mutilation by adults of *M. helvolus* and that about three and one-half hosts were killed in this manner to each one killed by parasitism. In the case of predators the number of hosts fed upon should be known for a range of host densities inasmuch as individual hosts may be completely consumed at low host densities by hungry predators, but when hosts are abundant the predator may go from one to another, taking just a little food from each but killing all those fed upon. Thus, the number of hosts killed per individual predator can never be assumed to approximate a constant.

After more than ten years of study of a single species of parasite (*Aphytis lingnanensis* Comp.) of the California red scale we have been unable to develop a practical sample which will accurately depict *total* parasite-caused mortality. The many complexities involved, such as host-feeding and multivoltinism of the parasite, render impractical anything other than a sample which gives parasite and host population trends.

Many of the attempts to evaluate natural-enemy effectiveness have been based upon periodic partial census of the host–natural-enemy complex without taking into account mortality caused by other environmental factors. Assuming that a really representative and adequate sample is used, and this would be unusual, this method will show relative trends in host–natural-enemy populations which can be graphed, and correlations between changes of the host and natural enemy can be drawn. Such data, when correlated with other factors, may be very valuable as aids in indicating which environmental factors, including the host, may be adversely influencing natural-enemy populations, but they rarely, if ever, will *prove* that natural enemies are responsible for regulation of the host density at any particular observed average population level. The reason for this is that the same type of host–

natural-enemy population trends will be obtained whether a seasonal upward trend of the host actually is halted and reversed by natural enemies or is halted and reversed by other factors, such as unfavourable weather. Nevertheless, such data, along with other observations made while collecting them, may thoroughly convince the investigator that one or more natural enemies are the key factors in host-population regulation. However, convincing others of the correctness of his interpretations is a much more difficult problem. Perhaps Morris (1959) has helped clarify this problem in an interesting analysis of the evaluation of parasites as key factors (i.e., single factor analysis) in population dynamics. He concludes that parasitism is a key factor in population regulation if parasitization in one generation can be used to predict host-population density in the next.

A somewhat more detailed and intensive quantitative method of evaluation involves the development of life tables. The objective of life table development is to show for a period of time, natality, age groups, different causes of mortality, and amount of mortality per age group attributable to each mortality factor. From such data, attempts are made to determine the relative importance of various mortality factors and to predict future population trends of the host. This method again is only as good as the periodic partial censuses, i.e., the samples upon which it is based. Such studies furnish extremely valuable demological and bioecological data regarding hosts, natural enemies, and other mortality factors, but the complexities of accurately sampling a faunal complex in various habitats and accurately determining degrees of mortality caused by various factors often will require so much work as to make the method impractical, even if it should supply a valid means of accurately evaluating the effectiveness of a given factor in population regulation. It is doubtful, however, that the investigator can *prove* by this method that any particular mortality factor is responsible for maintaining the 'host' population at a lower level than otherwise would attain were that factor absent from the complex. Some method of proving such cause and effect is the goal of the current discussion.

Morris (1957) has carefully analysed the subject of interpretation of mortality data in studies on population dynamics and has stressed the use of life table data. He has emphasized an analysis of mortality from the standpoint of how given percentage mortalities may affect changes in populations, and, from such an analysis, attempts to determine how natural control comes about. Some of his main points are: (1) Variations in mortality from generation to generation are stressed as being of utmost importance in producing *changes* in population trends. (2) Conversely, a constant mortality each generation, regardless of magnitude, is considered to be unimportant. (3) Level of mortality is considered important: (a) variation or increments at high levels of mortality are more important than equal variations at low mortalities; and (b) small variations in mortality can be very important at high mortality levels.

After developing these and other points to show the significance of variation in total generation mortality, Morris (1957) states, 'We are [now] in a better position to consider the effects of variations in individual mortalities ... [but] ... The problem at once becomes more difficult and cannot be solved in any general way unless we are willing to make assumptions of such a simplifying nature that they fail to represent real situations.' Thompson (1955) expressed similar difficulties when he stated, 'In fact, all we can reasonably hope is that formulations such as those discussed here may provide convenient patterns of thought, serving for the provisional integration of data and indicating lines of research.'

Morris disagrees rather completely with the ideas on interpretation of mortality data expressed by Bess (1945) and Bodenheimer (1938), and partially with those of Nicholson (1933) and Thompson (1955). We would disagree on a few points with Morris as well. For instance, his theoretically based conclusion (1957, p. 63) that '. . . the majority of factors affecting insect defoliators are of a density-independent type. If this were not so, we would experience much more violent fluctuations from generation to generation than we do. This is obvious from the [theoretical] examples presented . . . where a decrease of only 10% in egg mortality resulted in a 10-fold increase in population.' His contention that additional density-dependent factors acting against insect defoliators would result in more violent fluctuations ignores the possibility of effective biological control. Additionally, it is highly improbable, to say the least, that a decrease in egg mortality of 10 per cent (from 15 per cent to 5 per cent) would result in a ten-fold increase in population. These calculations and conclusions were possible only because Morris unjustifiably assumes that density-dependent factors produce constant absolute mortalities, even if an earlier cause of mortality is removed. This, of course, is not a description of density-dependence. When it is all 'boiled down,' Morris has really expressed some mathematical facts which must follow if one considers various percentage mortalities which *might* occur in natural populations. To draw an absurdly obvious example, an increase in generation mortality of 1 per cent from 99 to 100 per cent is more important than a similar 1 per cent increase but from 1 to 2 per cent.

It appears that we have no deductive means as yet of determining the relative importance in population regulation of mortalities occurring in different age groups of the 'host,' i.e., larval vs. pupal parasites, or of contemporaneous mortalities caused by different factors acting in the same 'host' age group, i.e., egg parasite sp. A vs. egg parasite sp. B. This is because mortality factors may replace each other, so that if an egg parasite responsible for causing 30 per cent parasitization of the host eggs were to disappear, more first-instar larvae might result, but this increased larval density might be responded to by larval parasites in a manner largely or entirely to make up for the missing egg mortality. Thus, the simplest and surest way to be certain just what role the 30 per cent egg mortality played in population regulation would be to eliminate the egg parasite experimentally and compare the ensuing average host population density with the former one.

Experimental Methods of Evaluation

The preceding discussion has emphasized the authors' belief that the qualitative or quantitative evaluation methods outlined usually are inadequate for the precise determination of the importance of any one or a combination of natural enemies in regulation of an insect's average population density. This leaves the paired comparison experimental approach involving plots having natural enemies present and plots having them excluded.

MECHANICAL EXCLUSION. This is the earliest type of experimental check method used for the evaluation of natural-enemy effectiveness. Two procedures usually are involved: (1) ridding the plot of natural enemies, and (2) excluding natural enemies for a more or less lengthy period by the use of screening or other physical barriers. The first formal report on the use of this method was given by Smith and DeBach (1942). They eliminated natural enemies as well as the host from citrus branches by fumigation of 10 closed cloth sleeves, then reinfested the branches with the host. Subsequently they opened five of the cloth sleeves to permit access to the parasite and then studied host trends in the closed parasite-free sleeves and host and parasite trends in the open sleeves. They were able to demonstrate that host survival was very greatly reduced by the parasite, as is shown in figure 88. Later, DeBach, Dietrick, and Fleschner (1949) modified this procedure to enable the original host population to go undisturbed by fumigation. They used closed sleeves impregnated with DDT to eliminate the originally present natural enemies which were highly motile and would contact the impregnated cloth. Inasmuch as the host insect was sessile, it was unaffected by the DDT-impregnated cloth. Host population trends in closed DDT-impregnated sleeves were then compared with trends in open untreated sleeves to which natural enemies had access.

Other workers have successfully employed similar techniques. Franz (1958b) in Germany, in studies of the balsam woolly aphid, *Adelges piceae* Ratz., in fir trees, used open 'plots' (marked out only) on the trunks, closed 'plots' protected from predators by a wire-mesh shelter treated with a contact insecticide, and 'plots' with similar, but untreated, wire-mesh shelters but which had two small holes to allow access of predators. The latter plot allowed for evaluation of microclimatic effects. Franz considers that the effects of predation were proved conclusively by comparison with populations protected from predators, and that the marked influence of predation could be measured and the time of action of the predators defined. Way and Banks (1958) describe a method for evaluating the effectiveness of natural enemies of *Aphis fabae* Scop. Parasites and predators were excluded from some cages by dieldrin-treated terylene netting. Other cages, given comparable climatic conditions, had slatted walls to allow free access of natural enemies. Means of exclusion of natural enemies other than cages of one sort or another may be possible through the use of barriers of moving air, electrically heated resistance wire, or sticky materials.

The cage-exclusion method may have limitations involving either the applicability to larger and highly motile hosts or an influence on factors other than natural enemies. Smith and DeBach (1942) pointed out that dispersal may be limited and the physical environment may be modified. Fleschner (1958) found that even in the absence of predators the citrus red mite population density became greater within closed sleeves than it did in the open. This was ascribed in part to limitation of migration by closed sleeves and a modification of the microclimate within the sleeves making the leaves more suitable as food for the mites. Thus, with these mites he considered that the method may not give an accurate measure of the efficacy of natural enemies, i.e., that natural enemies might appear more efficient by comparison than they actually are.

Each particular use of the mechanical exclusion method will present different problems. The possible limitations must be considered, investigated, and evaluated. In many cases it will be found that the limitations, such as modification of the microenvironment, can be by-passed by suitable planning so that the only variable factor will be the presence or absence of natural enemies.

CHEMICAL EXCLUSION. Apparently the first formal use of this method was described by DeBach (1946), who employed DDT as a selective insecticide to demonstrate experimentally the biological control of the long-tailed mealybug and the cottony-cushion scale. The procedure involves the use of chemically treated insecticidal check plots which greatly reduce or eliminate natural-enemy populations but have little or no effect on host populations. Thus, a selective insecticide is necessary. Host population trends on such plots are compared with trends on plots having natural enemies operating undisturbed. The difference between the two types of plot directly shows the effect of the natural enemy on the host population as is graphically illustrated in figure 87, between pp. 416 and 417.

Various investigators have since successfully used this method to demonstrate, in a visual and striking manner, biological control of a variety of insects, including the California red scale (DeBach, Fleschner, and Dietrick 1950), the yellow scale (DeBach 1955), the six-spotted mite (Fleschner, Hall, and Ricker 1955), the cyclamen mite (Huffaker and Kennett 1956), phytophagous mites (Lord 1956), the olive scale (Huffaker and Kennett 1960), and the cabbage root fly (Wright, Hughes, and Worrall 1960).

This method has certain advantages over mechanical exclusion methods. There is no interference with host dispersal, plots can be of nearly any desired size, and the microclimate is not modified. The possible effects of climate and host-plant resistance on the host, of course, are measured by this method. Aside from the problems of developing satisfactory sampling and experimental techniques, and choosing suitable selective insecticides, only one possible limitation has been suggested which might qualify the validity of this method of evaluation of the efficacy of natural enemies. Briefly stated, chemical residues on a plant, aside from any adverse effect on natural enemies, may *possibly* favour host-population increase, either directly by favouring the physical environment (e.g., a better substratum), or indirectly by modifying the physiology of the plant in a manner to make it nutritionally more favourable. DeBach (1946) pointed this out, and DeBach, Fleschner, and Dietrick (1950) stated, 'Should such effects be demonstrated their values will have to be subtracted from the total mite increases following DDT applications in order to arrive at the results caused by elimination of predators alone.' Since this time, certain results, especially with mite species, have shown that such effects do occur (Fleschner 1952), but that this is not consistently true (Fleschner 1958). Warren and King (1959), in a study of natural control of pecan aphids and mites, concluded that there was no direct beneficial physiological effect of DDT on the aphid or mite populations, nor was there any indirect beneficial effect which might possibly have come from the DDT spray residue having a physiological effect on the tree. DeBach (1955, 1958*b*) discussed experimental tests on the validity of the insecticidal check method, especially as a measure of the effectiveness of natural enemies of certain diaspine scale insects, and concluded that DDT residues had no direct or indirect beneficial effect on scale populations except through selective elimination of natural enemies.

As a balance against the problematical beneficial effects of selective insecticides in promoting host population increase, it should be emphasized—and this has been the authors' experience many times—that the insecticides used are rarely, if ever, absolutely selective. That is, some hosts are usually killed and some natural enemies are not killed. This tends to minimize the role of natural enemies when the plots are compared. Constant immigration of natural enemies from the outside into chemical exclusion plots produces similar effects because most of the insecticides used do not kill natural enemies instantly.

We would conclude, therefore, that the chemical exclusion method gives us one of the finest tools for evaluating the effect of natural enemies in the regulation of host population densities. Careful planning and evaluation of the method in each particular case should enable the investigator to eliminate from the study (or to analyse the effect of) any variable factors involved besides natural enemies.

TRAP METHOD. A variation of the above-described chemical exclusion method, which removes most of the limitations previously discussed, has been tested by the authors (unpublished data). It is referred to as the 'insecticidal trap method.' The procedure involves the use of a chemically poisoned area or border surrounding an untreated area. Virtually any size of area can be employed, depending upon the floral and faunal complex involved. The poisoned-border area traps natural enemies which are dispersing to or from the untreated central area, thus tending to eliminate or reduce them over a period of time. The efficiency of this method will be greatest with fairly sessile hosts having highly motile natural enemies, but rarely will complete elimination or exclusion be attained. Thus, a less-than-maximum picture of the total degree of biological control will be obtained. Inasmuch as no chemical residues or any other factors are known to be involved as variables in this type of comparison, it is highly suitable where practical. Its successful use depends to a large extent on obtaining suitable chemical poisons for the natural enemies which one desires to eliminate.

EXCLUSION BY HAND REMOVAL. The elimination of natural enemies from a plot by hand removal probably provides the best evaluation method of all, when it is possible or practical to use this method. No serious objections concerning the validity of the method are known, although certain cases might occur where hand removal of natural enemies would so seriously disturb host populations as to cause considerable dispersal. Aside from this, the only limitation is the practical one of a man or men having the time and ability to maintain consistently a host population free of natural enemies in the field for a lengthy period. Fleschner, Hall, and

Ricker (1955) obtained striking results following hand removal of natural enemies of avocado pests from certain plots (portions of trees) for a period of 84 days. Biological control was demonstrated to be responsible for the normally low host populations in the grove studied. This applied to the omnivorous looper, *Sabulodes caberata* Gn., the six-spotted mite, *Eotetranychus sexmaculatus* (Riley), the long-tailed mealybug, *Pseudococcus adonidum* (L.), the avocado brown mite, *Oligonychus punicae* (Hirst), and the latania scale, *Hemiberlesia lataniae* (Sign.). According to Fleschner (1958), 'The hand-picking method of removing mite predators has proved to be the most dependable one used thus far in measuring the efficacy of natural enemies of plant-feeding mites. Its greatest weakness lies in the amount of time required.'

INHIBITION OF NATURAL ENEMIES BY ANTS. This has been referred to as the bio-logical check method (DeBach, Fleschner, and Dietrick 1951). It is based on the fact that honeydew-seeking ants constantly interfere with or kill natural enemies. The authors' observations indicate that by far the greater adverse effect is by inter-ference. Parasites contacted or disturbed by ants invariably jump or fly but seldom are captured. Comparisons between ant-infested and ant-free plots definitely de-monstrate, in some cases at least, whether or not natural enemies are producing biological control (see figure 89). It has been shown that this method is not limited to studies only of the honeydew-producing insects which the ants are tend-ing. The biological control of associated but non-honeydew-producing insects, such as diaspine scales and mites, also can be evaluated because the ants' effect on natural enemies in a given area is indiscriminate. A five-year comparison between population trends of a non-honeydew producer, the California red scale, *Aonidiella aurantii* (Mask.), in the presence and absence of ants was used by DeBach (1958b) to demonstrate conclusively the degree of biological control by natural enemies. Steyn (1958) obtained similar results in South Africa. Bartlett (1961) discusses ex-periments on the influence of ants upon parasites, predators, and scale insects.

Several pros and cons relate to the use of this method. One of the important points is that microclimate is not affected by ants. Although in a sense this is com-parable to the hand-removal method, the apparent effectiveness of natural enemies is minimized because ants are never 100 per cent effective in natural-enemy in-hibition. Their adverse effect on natural enemies depends on the species of natural enemy, the number of ants involved, and their rate of activity. This varies con-siderably, but even in the heaviest ant infestation natural enemies are never com-pletely excluded; merely inhibited to a greater or lesser extent. However, if the host population is higher in the presence of ants, this shows (with certain possible exceptions) that the population level observed in the absence of ants is due to natural enemies, and this, of course, is what the investigator is trying to determine. However, it does not show how high the host population would go if natural enemies were completely excluded.

Obviously the method is limited to situations where ants can be employed, either naturally or by the use of artificial colonies. Thus, use of an artificial colony in a plot in which suitable food is placed to constantly attract the ants may broaden the potentialities of the method. Ingenuity could replace man with ants in the hand-removal method.

Where naturally occurring ants are utilized, honeydew-producing insects are usually present and a certain amount of honeydew, fungus, and dust will accumulate in this habitat, which may affect other host populations in the same microhabitat. Some hosts, such as mites and diaspine scales, will be covered with honeydew and die, but mites also possibly may be favoured by the dusty deposit which sometimes accumulates. Such variables can usually be taken into account and evaluated.

It has been suggested (Banks 1958) that ants, when tending aphids, are responsible for increase in aphid fecundity and rate of population growth. If true, this could affect the relative rate of increase, but in view of the usually great reproductive capacity of aphids, it should have little effect on average population densities attained. On the other hand, Bartlett (1961) showed that ants caused no physiological stimulation of scale development. Ants also remove excess honeydew which may save some newly hatched aphids, mealybugs, or scale insects from drowning (Bartlett 1961). There is no satisfactory field evidence, however, that drowning would limit populations of honeydew producers at low levels, although the levels observed may be somewhat higher than would have occurred in the absence of ants, providing also that natural enemies were absent.

All in all, a lower aphid population in the absence of ants would seem to be referable to the effect of natural enemies, unless it is claimed that aside from effects on natural enemies, ants *enormously* affect not only the rate of increase but the average density of aphids. Banks (1958) indicates that these effects are not great. Therefore, it appears that, in cases where natural enemies are not involved, certain aphid populations may be somewhat higher in the presence of ants than in their absence, but if natural enemies are present and strikingly lower aphid populations occur in ant-free plots as compared with ant-infested plots, the low level in the ant-free plots can for the most part be attributed to biological control.

In non-honeydew producers, such as diaspine scales in which the ants show absolutely no interest, it seems obvious that no beneficial effect from ant-tending is involved.

Bess (1958) studied population trends of a honeydew producer, the green scale, *Coccus viridis* (Green), in the presence and absence of ants. He found that the experimental scale populations were much lower in the absence of ants than in their presence but had no satisfactory explanation of how the ants aided or protected the scales. He concluded that there was little or no evidence obtained to indicate that ants reduced parasite or predator attack even though his data show a decidedly higher ratio of parasites to hosts in the absence of ants than in their presence. He did not consider the possibility of host-feeding mortality caused by adult parasites (rather than predation) nor of interference by ants with parasites.

It would appear that in many comparisons using ants, host populations would be somewhat less on ant-infested plots (because some natural enemy activity still occurs) than would be the case on plots which had natural enemies *completely* excluded by some other method. Hence, the effectiveness of natural enemies tends to be minimized in this method.

In the authors' experience, ants have never been responsible for as great or as sustained host populations as have chemical- or mechanical-exclusion methods. This applies to both honeydew-producing and non-honeydew-producing hosts. Nor have we seen evidence of self-regulation of host populations at low levels as a result of honeydew production. In other words, populations of honeydew producers can attain and maintain high average levels in the absence of the sanitary action of ants. Their failure to do so, in our experience, has been due to the action of natural enemies.

Thus, the relative differences between ant-infested and ant-free plots in the biological check method as often as not will present a minimized picture of the degree of biological control. In any event, the validity and accuracy of this method in a particular case will depend on the care, thoroughness, and objectivity of the investigator.

OTHER METHODS. On rare occasions it may be possible to find naturally occurring localized situations having natural enemies absent. This would be a case of natural exclusion. Comparison may then be made with nearly similar habitats having natural enemies present and the effect of the natural enemies thereby evaluated. Another possibility is purposely to place host-infested plants in areas not having natural enemies present (perhaps because of the absence of the host plant or host insect); to follow host-population growth trends in these areas in the absence of enemies and to compare these with trends on host-infested plants placed in areas having normal natural enemy activity. Inasmuch as in such cases plots are likely to be separated from each other by considerable distances, care must be taken to choose comparable habitats.

SECTION V

The Conservation and Augmentation of Natural Enemies

CHAPTER 15

Manipulation of Entomophagous Species

PAUL DeBACH AND K. S. HAGEN

INTRODUCTION

THIS CHAPTER encompasses something more than the usual procedure involved in the introduction and colonization of new natural enemies, even though the latter could be called manipulation. Usually in importation work the parasite, predator, or pathogen is left to its own resources after it has been adequately colonized. It succeeds or fails without additional help from man. We reserve the term 'manipulation' to apply to special procedures which may be necessary to help a natural enemy become established or to become a more effective biological control agent. These procedures can involve manipulation of the natural enemy itself or manipulation of the environment. In this chapter, manipulation of the natural enemy itself as a means of enhancing biological control is emphasized. Chapter 16 deals with manipulation of the environment.

Many introduced natural enemies fail to become established—about 60 to 80 per cent according to the figures of Clausen (1956a)—or, if established, fail to control the host because of some slight shortcoming in adaptability or because of disadvantage caused by an adverse environment. Unfavourable effects caused by the environment may be obvious, but frequently they are so slight as to go virtually unnoticed. One of the great puzzles of biological control work is why so many natural enemies which have been transferred from one country to a new one having a very similar climate fail to become established. It seems logical to assume, in some cases at least, that by means of manipulation of one sort or another natural enemies can be made to overcome certain inherent or environment-induced disadvantages.

NEED AND JUSTIFICATION FOR MANIPULATION ATTEMPTS

Before undertaking a manipulation programme to enhance natural enemy effectiveness, the need and justification for the work should be established on a sound scientific basis unless some obvious and easily corrected defect is involved. Detailed biological and ecological data must clearly indicate the need for and the reasonable possibility of success of manipulation, especially if natural enemies are to be mass produced. Manipulation will often be expensive. In the long run, the costs should be more than balanced by the increased control attained. In the beginning, the initiation of such a programme must be based on sound estimates of probable success. Justification for undertaking research towards this end may be determined by several considerations including whether: (1) the natural enemy is considered potentially effective (i.e., has demonstrated a high searching ability in the country of origin or other areas and is well adapted in most respects) but is rendered ineffective periodically by adverse environmental conditions or by some relatively minor lack of adaptation; (2) the pest (host) is not easily or successfully controlled or is too expensive to control by other methods; (3) the level of control desired (i.e., below the economic injury level) may be so low as to be impractical; (4) other methods are undesirable for various reasons such as direct or indirect damage to the crop, plant, or soil from chemical application; the presence of poisonous residues on crops from chemical applications; or the occurrence of serious faunal 'upsets' resulting in biological 'explosions' from the use of chemicals; or (5) treatment is necessary for only one or two pests in the faunal complex and successful manipulation of natural enemies might result in complete biological control.

FACTORS INVOLVED IN NATURAL ENEMY INEFFECTIVENESS

If preliminary studies indicate that manipulation of an apparently particularly promising natural enemy might be justified, the exact reason or reasons for failure or lack of adjustment to the environment must be determined. Various factors or combinations may be responsible. In the general habitat these include: (1) adverse climatic factors such as heat, cold, low humidity, rain, or wind; (2) unfavourable host plants which may fail to provide sufficient shelter or otherwise may be un- attractive; (3) scarcity of water or of food for adult parasites because of lack of pollen, honeydew, or floral nectar; (4) severe competition with other species which may be constant or intermittent; (5) adverse toxic effects from chemicals applied to the crop or habitat (see chapter 17); and (6) adverse effects of cultural practices (see chapter 16). The host insect may be unfavourable or unsuitable: (1) because of unsynchronized voltinism between the host and natural enemy or because of unsynchronized diapause; (2) because the host plant confers resistance on the host insect to the natural enemy; (3) because the host insect represents a biological strain unsuitable to the natural enemy; or (4) because suitable stages of the host are periodically unavailable or scarce, so that enemy populations are depressed. On the other hand, the entomophagous species itself may have some inherent unsuitability not connected with factors already mentioned. It may exhibit: (1) ovarian diapause, migration, or aggregation away from the host population for a portion of each year as certain coccinellids do; (2) a low rate of reproduction either seasonally or constantly which, if further reduced by periodic environmental unfavourability, enables the host population to reach outbreak levels easily; and (3) disadvantages at low densities concerned with inability to find mates or with a tendency to dis- perse. A discussion and review of some cases of adaptive weakness are given by DeBach (1958a, pp. 759 to 761).

DETERMINATION OF THE ADVERSE FACTORS INVOLVED IN NATURAL ENEMY INEFFECTIVENESS

The determination of the type of manipulation necessary will depend primarily on basic ecological, biological, and physological studies which show why the natural enemy is kept from its full potential. When entomophagous species fail in establishment, laboratory studies on temperature and humidity responses are indicated in order to show whether the species can tolerate the conditions of the physical environment. Investigations should be made of the preference for and suitability of the habitat and host plant and the presence of necessary requisites, such as food for adult parasites. Studies are also necessary to show whether the species is physiologically well adapted to develop in the host insect (host suitability) and is synchronized with the host's life cycle. The attractiveness or desirability of the host as an oviposition site (host selection) must be determined. Competition with already-established natural enemies should also be considered, as well as possible adverse effects of insecticides or cultural practices. If the newly introduced natural enemy came from the same host plant and host insect species in its native home, and was colonized in adequate numbers in various habitats, then failure of establishment can usually be charged to unsuitable climatic conditions.

With already-established natural enemies which appear to be operating below their potential effectiveness, the first approach is to acquire detailed bio-ecological data on host–natural-enemy populations and biologies over a period of time in representative ecological areas in the field. In addition to purely biological studies such as those just mentioned, this should include the taking of periodic partial censuses to establish life-table data and host–natural-enemy population trends as well as experimental comparisons to demonstrate the degree of natural-enemy effectiveness (see chapter 14—'Evaluation of Effectiveness of Natural Enemies'). When studies are planned to exclude or at least to explain the role of any possible adverse environmental effects including chemical applications, dust, ants, or cultural practices, the actual potential of the natural enemy under 'normal' environmental conditions will become apparent. Long-term untreated controlled plots normally suffice for this purpose. Analysis of field population trends and experimental results, including correlation with climatic or other possible adverse factors or with a lack of some necessary requisite, should indicate the relative effectiveness of various natural enemies and help point out the reasons, if any, for lack of efficiency. When the field studies are followed up with appropriate laboratory studies, possible means of manipulation should become clear.

If, however, such studies indicate the predator, pathogen, or parasite to be markedly incapable of economically successful biological control of the host under the ecological conditions generally prevailing, manipulation should not be attempted. That is, if the ineffectiveness is not caused by some periodically unfavourable environmental factor, by some lack of a requisite which can be supplied, or by some simple and relatively minor lack of adaptation, but rather is caused by some serious disadvantage inherent in the species itself, such as inability to find hosts at low host densities or a marked lack of tolerance to prevailing weather conditions, then manipulation would appear impractical. It is probable that a rather large proportion of ineffective natural enemies will be found to fall in this category, but each case must be determined on its own merits.

VARIOUS METHODS OF MANIPULATION

There are various possible ways of enhancing the effectiveness of natural enemies, depending upon the leads furnished by the basic studies just outlined. Some major possibilities include: (1) periodic colonization, using either mass-produced or field-collected natural enemies; (2) development of adapted strains by artificial selection; (3) provision in the habitat of supplementary food for adults or other scarce or inadequate requisites; (4) artificial use of alternative hosts such as: (a) the normal host plant with an alternative host insect colonized, (b) use of an alternative host plant with the normal host insect occurring either naturally or as a result of being colonized, (c) use of an alternative host plant with an alternative host insect; (5) artificial inoculation of the normal host plant with the normal host insect; and (6) modification of the habitat to eliminate or mitigate adverse effects of cultural practices. The first two possibilities are treated in this chapter because they involve manipulation of the natural enemies themselves; the remaining possibilities, which are concerned with manipulation of the environment to favour natural enemies, are covered in chapter 16.

The objective of periodic colonization is to increase artificially the natural-enemy population by releasing entomophagous insects or applying pathogens periodically. This would be done at critical periods, especially when adverse conditions have depressed the natural enemy and it is scarce in respect to the host.

This seemingly simple technique of manipulating a single biotic factor in order to overcome some weakness and thus enable it to control the host insect is a most complex phase of applied biological control. In a sense it is necessary to insert a 'cog' of the correct structure, at the right place and the right time into the machinery of the ecosystem. If the 'cogs' mesh, the pest will be controlled before damaging the crop. Therefore, as already mentioned, the ecology and the life history of the pest as well as those of the natural enemy must be understood before attempting a particular type of release.

TYPES OF PERIODIC COLONIZATION PROCEDURES

Two types of periodic colonization of natural enemies used to obtain biotic reduction of a pest have been categorized: (1) inundative release, and (2) inoculative release. The source of natural enemies can be either from mass culture or translocated from one locality to another in the field.

Inundative releases are made to control a pest, largely, if not entirely, by the natural enemies released, not by their progeny (Flanders 1930*b*, 1951). This type of control is similar to that obtained by use of chemicals since the mortality of the pest is more or less immediate and there is no prolonged interaction of the populations. When used in an inundative manner, natural enemies have been termed as biotic insecticides (Stern *et al.* 1959). Flanders (1951) sees the economic use of this type, specifically involving parasites or predators, to be limited to the control of pests infesting crops of high value having relatively light infestations. This release method is probably best suited to pest species that are univoltine, or, if multivoltine, to ones that reach injurious numbers during but a singe generation a year. The necessity of making several very large releases during a given year would probably be economically unfeasible. The cost of production is the critical factor here; however, inundative releases with pathogens appear more promising.

Control from the use of inoculative releases is dependent upon progeny being produced for more than one generation following the colonization of individuals of the beneficial species. The control action usually persists longer with the inoculative-type release as compared with inundative releases. However, the two intergrade and the distinction between them is somewhat arbitrary.

The periodic colonization of small numbers of natural enemies against low populations of pests has been termed an 'accretive release' by Flanders (1930*b*, 1951), and he believes that this is the only type of periodic release that could be economically used against pests of crops such as sugar cane that are characterized by relatively large host-infested surfaces per acre. This is an inoculative release to us. Marlatt (1901) suggested this type of release for he believed that it is theoretically possible to obtain a certain degree of control of insect outbreaks by assisting the multiplication of natural enemies through releases made at the beginning of the outbreak.

The colonization of an entomophagous species along with its host or prey is of value when a crop has a history of being damaged by pests that periodically immigrate to an area or are too sparsely distributed in the area to maintain the natural enemies during a certain season or a certain planting phase. The objective here is to have a population of beneficial species dispersed and existing in the crop along with their hosts in order to offset immigration or to reduce highly localized pest foci which, if unchecked, would explode to damaging proportions rapidly. Huffaker and Kennett (1953, 1956) used this technique to control the cyclamen mite in strawberries. This is discussed further in chapter 16.

PERIODIC COLONIZATION REQUIREMENTS

Evolution of a periodic colonization programme usually has its origin in field studies. When a pest is noted to be effectively controlled by some natural enemy in certain areas, or during certain seasons, and not in other areas or seasons, periodic colonization is suggested as an appropriate approach. Such procedure appears especially appropriate when injury to the crop is found to be correlated with an obvious lag or absence of the beneficial species. The points mentioned earlier under 'Need and Justification for Manipulation Attempts' should be considered when contemplating a periodic colonization programme.

The lowest population density of the pest that will cause economic damage, which is called the economic injury level, must be known, for the goal is obviously to keep the pest population from attaining this level. With some pests the economic injury level may be set so low, either by marketing standards or yield losses, that it is impractical to consider any form of periodic colonization.

The selection of the natural enemies to be utilized should be based on carefully conducted field population studies which furnish life-table data on the host and natural enemies over an adequate period. The beneficial species may either be endemic or imported. Frequently a single 'key' natural enemy will be apparent as the one which should be colonized. If several species appear to have equal potentials, the one that can be mass-cultured most cheaply should be tried first. In some cases it may be necessary or desirable to release more than one species if they can be easily cultured. If the pest to be controlled infests a crop that normally receives, or is likely to receive, a chemical treatment for a plant disease or another insect pest, the beneficial species selected for release should be able to tolerate the treatments, or else the timing of the releases should be made to circumvent this problem. There is an alternative of finding a substitute chemical that is more selective and spares the species being liberated.

Determining the colonization dosage, the distribution and the frequency of releases are the most difficult problems encountered. Before determining what colonization ratio of natural enemy to host would be effective, it must first be decided what colonization type is appropriate.

If the inundative method is to be employed, the ratio is not so critical as long as sufficiently large numbers of the entomophagous species are released to prevent the pest from doing damage. The greater the number of individuals released the further the pest should be repressed, remembering, however, that searching success of the natural-enemy population reaches a point of diminishing returns (DeBach and Smith 1947). Factors that limit the maximum number liberated are expense and possible detrimental intraspecific interactions, depending upon the species used. Only by testing releases in the field can it be determined what minimum number of individuals, spacing of releases, and timing of releases will give control. This requires making releases in replicated plots against different densities of hosts or prey. Serial releases may be necessary if there is a prolonged oviposition by the host, or if the ovipositional period of the natural-enemy is extremely short. Serial releases will help in the latter situation by offering some freedom in the exact timing of a release.

If the inoculative method (i.e., continuing reproduction for several generations following colonization) is being considered, the determination of an effective colonization ratio between pest and biotic agent is more complicated, for not only can too few be released to cope with the pest's power of increase, but, equally important, it is possible to liberate too many entomophagous individuals in relation to the pest population. Also, serial releases are more likely to be necessary in this case. If the proportion of the beneficial species to the density of the pest is too great, the pest population may be drastically reduced, but because of subsequent starvation of the enemy, resurgence of the pest is certain to occur quickly under favourable climatic conditions. For example, if predator adults are released in too great a number, there will not be enough prey to induce reproduction, hence no predator progeny will be present to act against the next pest brood or generation. Effective ratios between the pest population and natural-enemy population can suddenly be disrupted if there is a large immigration of the pest or of natural enemies into the plot.

The natural enemies to be used must be produced cheaply, or consistently found in the field in sufficiently large quantities to be translocated, to make periodic colonization economically feasible. The methods of mass-culture of beneficial species are covered in chapter 11. In the translocation of enemies, the individuals to be released must be of good quality and free of their hosts and parasites.

The methods used to evaluate the effectiveness of periodic colonizations are similar to those used for evaluating the effectiveness of indigenous or of newly established, imported beneficial species. These techniques are discussed in chapter 14. Before a periodic colonization programme is ever recommended, the researcher should have *demonstrated* conclusively by field tests that the desired control is being attained only as a result of the colonizations and that the programme is economically feasible.

PERIODIC COLONIZATION ATTEMPTS

A number of attempts to colonize beneficial species periodically in crops has been made, but the number of projects that have persisted are few. The reasons for their discontinuance appear to fall into four categories: (1) the procedure was not based on adequate research, was not scientifically sound, and early apparent success was coincidental or was never actually demonstrated; (2) inconsistency in control; (3) effective and cheaper chemical controls being developed that formerly were not available; and (4) effective biological control achieved by newly introduced natural enemies.

It seems appropriate to discuss specifically many of the various attempts at control by periodic colonization. Even though some of these failed, perhaps we can learn from their shortcomings. Projects that have ended because new chemicals replaced them should be kept in mind in case insecticidal resistance of the pest develops or because of disruptive influence to the balance of other insect or mite species present in the crop. Even though a chemical may have solved the problem in one area or country, the use of this same chemical may be more expensive than the cost of labour for mass-culture and liberation in another locality. The differences in marketing standards may permit release in one area while in another country it would not be feasible.

The periodic colonization projects following are discussed under the type of release, either inundative or inoculative. This division has some overlap, since some beneficial species have been tried under both methods, and under the so-called inundative method, progeny are undoubtedly often produced for more than one generation. Furthermore, biotic reduction from inoculative releases may last more than one year, thus approaching in degree the action of a conventional established biological control agent. Hence, the use of these two terms should be recognized as being more a matter of convenience than of especial significance. The place of periodic colonization in relation to the field biological control programme is discussed by Boyce (1950), Clausen (1956a, 1958b), DeBach (1958a), Flanders (1930b, 1951), Fleschner (1959), Franz (1958a), Imms (1931), Sandner (1958), Smith (1946), Smith and Armitage (1920), Shepetilnikova (1960), Sweetman (1958), and Telenga (1958).

Inundative Releases of Natural Enemies

Most of the natural enemies periodically colonized in large numbers to control pests primarily by the action of the individuals released have been egg parasites. However, some species of *Dahlbominus*, *Chrysopa*, and various pathogens have been used against other host stages. The use of diseases is discussed in chapter 21. In a sense inundative releases act as biotic insecticides.

TRICHOGRAMMA SPP. There probably have been more of the egg parasites, *Trichogramma* spp., cultured by man than parasites in any other genus. The following species have been mass-cultured and periodically colonized: *T. minutum* Riley, *T. evanescens* Westw., *T. semblidis* (Auriv.), *T. cacoeciae* Marchal, and *T. pallidum* Meyer. Many of these species have apparent physiological races that evidently have to be considered in developing a colonization programme. The variability in form, colour, and developmental rates has not only led to synonymy of species but has contributed to the confusion as to what species actually were liberated. The influence of physical factors, nutrition, seasons, and habitats, upon species variability has been studied by Flanders (1931, 1938a), Marchal (1927a, b, 1936), Peterson (1930), Quednau (1955, 1956a, b, 1957), and others.

In 1895, the possibilities of 'farming' the parasite *Trichogramma* for the control of lepidopterous pests were discussed in detail by F. Enock at a meeting of the London Entomological and Natural History Society.

Howard and Fiske (1911) were evidently first to release large numbers (thousands) of *Trichogramma minutum* which were obtained from field-collected eggs against the brown-tail moth. However, the nature of the brown-tail moth egg mass precluded any high degree of parasitization of any one egg mass. They found that host eggs with parasites could be cold-stored for long periods, and also suggested the possible control of greenhouse pests by releasing *Trichogramma*. Mokrezeckie and Bragina (1916) believed that the number of *Trichogramma* which it is possible to rear in the laboratory is theoretically unlimited, and these workers in Russia released *T. semblidis* against the codling moth.

Various techniques were used by subsequent workers to culture or rear *Trichogramma*, but apparently no method had been developed for its mass culture until

Flanders (1929, 1930b) found that *Sitotroga cerealella* (Oliv.) eggs provided an excellent host and the moth could be mass-cultured rather easily. Modifications of this method permitted producing a million parasites at a cost of $5 to $10 (Spencer, Brown, and Phillips 1935).

Since large quantities of *Trichogramma* could be cultured rather inexpensively, this stimulated periodic colonization programmes in many countries against many different pest insects. It now appears from studies in Russia (Shepetilnikova 1960) and Germany (Stein and Franz 1960; Stein 1960) that *Trichogramma* reared under diurnal alternating high and low laboratory temperatures give considerably better results in the field than parasites cultured under constant temperature conditions. This important possibility should be checked in all *Trichogramma* projects. Following are various hosts against which *Trichogramma* has been tried.

CODLING MOTH, *Carpocapsa pomonella* (L.). In the United States, Flanders (1930c) obtained some reduction of this pest, but the results were not encouraging. Alden and Webb (1937) also obtained reduction. In Russia, Sidrovnina (1938) reports substantial reductions of this pest by releasing *Trichogramma evanescens* on two or three days during the moth oviposition period. Kovaleva (1957), referring to early releases of *Trichogramma* against *C. pomonella* on apple in Russia, obtained disappointing results and attributes the inefficiency to using the wrong form of *T. evanescens* which is naturally adapted to parasitize the eggs of noctuids in open fields. In 1938 to 1940, with a local form of *Trichogramma* reared from *C. pomonella* and released at 2,000 per tree, a reduction was obtained in percentage of fruits infested from 77·7 to 20·1 and from 87·7 to 52 per cent. A young orchard on higher ground receiving liberations showed no effect. Kovaleva concluded that conditions in low-lying valley orchards were more favourable to the parasites than those on higher ground. Eggs laid on smooth upper leaf surfaces were more heavily attacked. Telenga (1956) reports that *T. pallidum* is a naturally effective parasite of the moth eggs in the wet steppe zone, but is released in the dry steppe areas to supplement other controlling measures. In Spain, Urquijo and Dadin (1943) achieved some reduction of codling moth by releases as did Stein (1960) in Germany.

ORIENTAL FRUIT MOTH, *Grapholitha molesta* (Busck). In the eastern United States, Peterson (1930) concluded from his experiments that 300 to 1,000 adult *Trichogramma* released per tree were not sufficient to produce parasitization of host eggs in adjacent trees. Schread's (1932) releases resulted in 50 per cent parasitism; however, at times natural parasitism attained this level. Allen and Warren (1932) made mass liberations of 400 parasites per tree 24 days before harvest in New Jersey. A slight reduction in moths occurred, but it was concluded that the results did not justify recommending this method.

PECAN NUT CASEBEARER, *Acrobasis caryae* Grote, PECAN LEAF CASEBEARER, *A. juglandis* (LeB.), AND HICKORY SHUCKWORM, *Laspeyresia caryana* (Fitch). These received *Trichogramma minutum* releases for several years in Georgia and Florida (Spencer, Brown, and Phillips 1949). Between 1931 and 1936, 30,000,000 *Trichogramma* were released against *A. caryae* using from 2,500 per tree to 200,000 per tree, and both yellow and dark varieties of *T. minutum* were used. Although significant reductions in infestation were obtained, the method was concluded to be impractical. Millions of additional *Trichogramma* were released against the other two pecan pests, but the results indicated that releases would not be satisfactory as a method of control.

CUTWORMS, *Euxoa segetum* (Denis and Schiff.) AND *Barathra brassicae* (L.). These pests of grain in the Russian Ukraine are controlled by periodic colonization of *Trichogramma evanescens*. When the parasite is introduced on 'fallow land,' 60 to 80 per cent egg parasitization is achieved and this saves stands of winter grains even at high egg densities (Telenga 1958).

COTTON LEAF-WORM, *Prodenia litura* (F.). In Egypt the cotton leaf-worm was not controlled by periodic colonization of *Trichogramma evanescens* (Kamal 1951).

EUROPEAN CORN BORER, *Ostrinia nubilalis* (Hbn.). Egg parasitization in Connecticut from colonization of 10,000, 20,000, and 30,000 *Trichogramma* per acre was higher in check plots than in release areas (Schread 1935).

SUGAR-CANE BORER, *Diatraea saccharalis* (F.). This borer, which also attacks corn and rice, has received numerous releases of *Trichogramma minutum*. The lack of parasitization of the borer eggs early in the season by *Trichogramma* prompted most release programmes. In British Guiana, Cleare (1929) seems to have made the first mass releases against the borer and obtained some control, but later (1934) he apparently felt that this method of control was inadequate. The following authors reported positive results from periodic colonization against the borer: Hinds and Spencer (1928, 1930), Hinds, Osterberger, and Dugas (1933) in Louisiana, Smyth (1939) in Peru, Tucker (1939a) in the Barbados, and Wolcott and Martorell (1943b) in Puerto Rico. However, Jaynes and Bynaum (1941) in Louisiana liberated 10,000 to 45,000 parasites per acre of sugar-cane for three seasons and found that borer damage was the same between release plots and check plots. They do not recommend periodic colonization. Dugas (1940) speculated on reasons why benefits from artificial colonization decreased as compared with the outstanding gains obtained from *Trichogramma* in the past. He believed that the lower general population levels of the borer in recent years (late thirties) was attributable to initially higher parasite populations occurring earlier than in the past, and this may have resulted from either a selection of a strain from the vast numbers cultured and released that could tolerate early season conditions, or possibly increased alternative host populations became available with increased planting of winter legumes. In India, Narayanan (1957), evaluating reports of *Trichogramma* releases against stem and root borers of cane sugar, finds inconsistency in results. Clausen (1956a) calls attention to the different cultural practices of harvesting sugar-cane and the possible influence on *Trichogramma* release results. In the United States the cane is harvested at the end of each growing season, whereas in the Tropics (Peru, Barbados) the crop is permitted to grow for 18 to 24 months before cutting.

The widespread use of *Trichogramma* and claims of control based on inadequate data provoked Smith and Flanders (1931) to publish a paper titled, 'Is *Trichogramma* Becoming a Fad?' They called attention to factors that must be considered in evaluating the effectiveness of releases. Morrill (1931) wrote a rebuttal to the above citation claiming that the criticisms were too general and that control of the 'leaf worm' infesting Arizona and Texas cotton is an example of the value of releases.

According to Sandner (1958), the lack of earlier success with *Trichogramma* in the Ukraine is explained by Kovaleva (1954) and in Central Europe by Mayer (1955). In the Ukraine mistakes have been attributed to applications at too large doses of parasites (up to 300,000 per hectare) and degeneration (shortened longevity) of parasites as a result of culturing *Trichogramma* under stable temperature and humidity conditions. Mayer (1955) evidently demonstrated that doses over 100,000 per hectare decrease effectiveness because of superparasitism. The optimum number for releases he recommends is about 20,000 females per hectare. Mayer also points out that in central Europe *T. semblidis* and *T. cacoeciae* in various forms are far superior to the American *T. minutum*.

We have to agree with Clausen (1958b) that in general the results obtained from experiments with *Trichogramma* releases against fruit insects have not been sufficient in the extent of control or consistency to warrant general recommendations for the use of these parasites by growers.

There appear to be basically at least two reasons why many releases have failed. First, the provoking motive to use this parasite was not based on field studies indicating that *Trichogramma* was potentially capable of controlling the pest unaided, but its use was based on the ability to produce an inexpensive mass of parasites that would seem sufficient to kill nearly every egg of the pest if enough of the parasites were released. Secondly, in most cases no attention was given to culturing and releasing a particular species or strain that was known to attack the specific pest eggs against which they were being released. Evidently serious consideration has to be given to ascertaining the correct species or strain, optimum number for release, correct timing of releases, temperature responses, nature of the structure of the host eggs, where they are deposited, and suitability of the habitat. Some other natural enemy species which have been used in the inundative manner follow.

Lathromeris senex (Greze). In Russia this trichogrammatid is released against pea bruchids. Field parasitization is increased by late plantings of narrow strips of peas along margins of regular earlier planted pea crops (Karpova 1950).

Telenomus emersoni (Grlt.). This scelionid was found to be an egg parasite of tabanid eggs during an investigation of a tabanid problem in Texas (Parman 1928.) Tabanid eggs were so common in 1914 that about two million eggs could be collected in one day, and 97 per cent of these eggs were parasitized by the *Telenomus*. Six to 83 parasites emerged from each mass. Parman speculated that control of the fly may be achieved by collecting the horsefly eggs and placing them along streams in vessels which would allow the parasites to escape but would retain the fly larvae to be destroyed. For fourteen years the tabinid population did not attain the level it did in 1914. This general decrease was believed to be in part the result of general distribution of the parasite, supplemented by egg collections. The parasite was found to be most effective during seasons with a higher percentage of sunshine (Parman 1928).

Microphanurus semistriatus (Nees). This Old World scelionid is mass-cultured and released periodically against the eggs of the scutellarid *Eurygaster integriceps* Put. in Iran, Russia, and elsewhere. The scutellarid adults are collected in huge quantities from mountain aggregations during the winter months (December, January, and February) and brought to the laboratory for feeding and oviposition. The bug eggs are then exposed to previously collected hibernating *Microphanurus* adults. Millions of parasites are produced and released at the rate of 10,000 per hectare when the *Eurygaster* begin to oviposit in the field (Vodjdani 1954). This method of control was used in Russia in the early 1900's against the same pest (Vassiliev 1913). In Iran, according to Vodjdani, this method was initiated in 1945 by Alexandrov (1948) and is still a large-scale operation, widely controlling the wheat pest, particularly in the Esfehan province.

The scelionid *Telenomus gifuensis* Ashm. This is an egg parasite of the pentatomid *Scotinophora lurida* Burm. in Japan. The scelionid emerges earlier in central Honshu than in southern Kyushu. Therefore, Hidaka (1958) could translocate *T. gifuensis* from the former locality to paddyfields in southern Kyushu. The results indicate clearly that the parasites thus liberated are effective in control of the bugs in southern Kyushu. Mass-culture and periodic colonization is also suggested by Hidaka.

Telonomus verticillatus Kief. This is a gregarious egg parasite of the lasiocampid moth *Dendrolimus pini* (L.). In Russia an outbreak of *D. pini* occurred between 1930 and 1940 and ceased in 1940 to 1941. *T. verticillatus* was found to be important in control of the moth. The parasite adult can be found hibernating beneath loose bark. Since three to five generations of *T. verticillatus* can be produced in the insectary before the pest oviposits in the field, many parasites are released 110 to 160 yards apart at the rate of 1 female to every 14 eggs of the moth. This is based on sampling the egg population in a whole area. The parasite population can also be increased by introducing into pure stands other plants supporting alternative hosts of the parasite, or by setting out parasitized egg batches of *D. pini* obtained in the laboratory (Ryivkin 1950).

The eulophid *Dahlbominus fuscipennis* (Zett.) and the ichneumonid *Exenterus oriolus* Htg. These two, which attack larvae of *Diprion pini* (L.) in cocoons, were found to be the most important parasites of the sawfly in Spain. Two tons of cocoons were collected in October and November in one year and stored during the winter. In February the cocoons were placed in parasite emergence boxes. These boxes were placed around the perimeter of the infested area to increase the numbers of parasites, some three million, where they were most needed. Sawfly cocoons collected during the autumn were also exposed to *Dahlbominus fuscipennis* in the laboratory, and these cocoons were added to the parasite emergence boxes in the spring. Parasitization amounted to 64 per cent in the field with no damage occurring in 1950 (Ceballos and Zarco 1952).

Chrysopa plorabunda Fitch (=*C. californica* Coq.). It was observed in central California that *C. plorabunda* was able to control *Pseudococcus maritimus* (Ehr.) on pears when plots were left untreated with insecticides (Doutt 1948). The *Chrysopa* larvae were found to survive the regular DDT codling moth sprays, but the adults were destroyed by the insecticide. Natural oviposition by *Chrysopa* was prevented by the first season treatments, thus the mealybug populations increased rapidly.

Mass culture of *Chrysopa plorabunda* by Finney (1948, 1950) permitted colonizing eggs in test plots that were receiving the regular spray programme. These egg colonizations gave promising results (Doutt and Hagen 1949). Refined releases, particularly as to the timing, were made the next year. Colonizations of 250 eggs per tree, placed in the crotches of the trees, made at the proper time and repeated at two successive periods gave the most effective results. For proper timing *Chrysopa* larvae should coincide with the presence on the trees of the immature mealybugs of the first generation. The mealybugs were suppressed to such a point by the releases that they did not even rebound during the following year (Doutt and Hagen 1950). This method was not adopted by the growers, for at about this time parathion was found to control mealybugs and the use of insecticides was preferred.

Inoculative Releases of Natural Enemies

The control using this type of release comes from the accumulative action by the progeny produced over several generations following the release of relatively small numbers of natural enemies as compared to the host. Besides predators and parasites, the use of some pathogens falls under this category of release (see chapter 21). The cases following are reviewed under the natural enemy involved.

THE MEALYBUG DESTROYER, *Cryptolaemus montrouzieri* Muls. This was introduced into the United States in 1892 by Albert Koebele. It was distributed over much of California wherever mealybugs infested crops. By 1915 only an occasional specimen could be found except along the southern California coast. Repeated attempts to reintroduce this species into valleys not immediately adjacent to the coast resulted in failure, since they could not survive the winter period (Clausen 1915).

In the narrow zone where the beetles were more or less permanently established, Armitage (1919), Smith and Armitage (1920), and Essig (1931) observed at times that mealybugs infesting citrus were controlled by the beetles. However, *Cryptolaemus* usually did not reduce the mealybug populations in time to prevent damage. Clausen (1915) observed that this predator lacked the ability to spread to any extent from tree to tree or from grove to grove. Smith and Armitage (1920) logically assumed that if large colonies of *Cryptolaemus* could be supplied at the proper time, periodic abundance of the pest could be avoided. With success of a preliminary release by Armitage (1919) in two acres of lemons located in Ventura County, great interest was stimulated in this control method. In the meantime, efficient techniques were being developed in the insectary of the California State Board of Horticulture to mass culture *Cryptolaemus* by rearing them on mealybug cultured on potato sprouts (Branigan 1916; Smith and Armitage 1920).

The first insectary to be built and operated aside from the state insectary was that of the Limoneira Company of Santa Paula, California, in 1916. During the early twenties the introduced citrophilus mealybug was beginning to do extensive damage. This stimulated building additional insectaries for mass culturing *Cryptolaemus*. By 1931, 14 insectaries were devoted almost exclusively to the production of *Cryptolaemus* for use in the control of mealybugs attacking citrus in southern California (Smith and Armitage 1931). More than 40,000,000 beetles were produced from July, 1926, to July, 1927, alone and released over some 50,000 acres of citrus (Essig 1931).

Ten beetles were usually released per tree. This number of adults produced enough larvae in the second generation to control light and medium mealybug infestations, which represented 90 per cent of the total infestation. During the spring, 90 days are required to reach the second generation, and a minimum of 60 days is necessary during the summer months. The period of beetle liberations was between April 1 and September 1. Other months were too cool for *Cryptolaemus* to be effective. The optimum period for release was April, May, and June. The time of the release was more or less geared to the degree of infestation on an orchard basis. If only a trace of mealybug was found, the orchard often was skipped, and the properties that had the heaviest populations in the early spring received the first releases.

Banding tree trunks with burlap strips was the common practice for measuring the citrophilus mealybug populations, since the adults would collect beneath the bands, and counts of these and their egg masses under the bands furnished a good population index. Also, these bands provided good pupation sites for *Cryptolaemus*, as well as other predators. Along with banding the trees, ant control was also practised, which further increased the effectiveness of the natural enemies (Smith and Armitage 1920, 1931; Armitage 1929).

The periodic colonizations of *Cryptolaemus* in California reached their peak in the late twenties. During the early thirties the number of beetles produced and released decreased following control of the citrophilus mealybug by imported parasites. In recent years 1957 to 1959, five insectaries in southern California cultured several million *Cryptolaemus* each year. The largest operation is the Associates Insectary of Santa Paula, California. During the 1958 to 1959 season, this growers' association cultured over 31 million *Cryptolaemus* at a cost of about $36,000. An average of 23 adults was released per tree, and over one million trees received liberations. This same insectary cultured over 56 million *Leptomastix dactylopii* How. which were released along with the beetles for mealybug control (Beckley 1959). The periodic colonizations at present are directed primarily towards controlling the citrus mealybug, since over the years biological control of the other mealybugs in citrus has been accomplished by introduced parasites. Continued releases against this mealybug might not be necessary if upsets due to insecticides and ants did not occur.

Also, the number of outbreaks of *Pseudococcus citri* (Risso) has been reduced not only by *Cryptolaemus* but by the introduced parasite *Leptomastidea abnormis* (Grlt.) and by periodic colonization of the encyrtids *Leptomastix dactylopii* and *Pauridia peregrina* Timb. (Clausen 1956a). In Russia, *Cryptolaemus* is cultured and released on the shore of the Black Sea for the control of *Pseudococcus gahani* Green and *Pulvinaria aurantii* Ckll. on citrus (Telenga 1958).

Cryptolaemus montrouzieri has also been periodically released in greenhouses for control of mealybugs. Whitcomb (1940) obtained practical control of mealybugs, *Pseudococcus citri*, on gardenias and *Phenacoccus gossypii* Town. and Ckll. on chrysanthemums. The temperature has to be above 70° F and the mealybug infestation should be great enough to provide adequate food but not high enough to cause damage. One adult was liberated per gardenia plant and one for each two chrysanthemum plants. As in citrus, Whitcomb obtained control of greenhouse pests mainly by the second generation larvae that developed. Pritchard (1949) reported some use of this predator against mealybugs infesting gardenias in greenhouses in California, but the results were variable, with mealybugs being reduced but not eliminated, thus necessitating new releases each spring. In some gardenia ranges, the *Cryptolaemus* survived winter conditions in California but still were not effective enough to give control unaided because of too cool conditions (Doutt 1951*b*). Doutt released *Exochomus flavipes* (Thunb.), *Anagyrus kivuensis* Comp., and *Chrysopa plorabunda* in these greenhouses and obtained effective control of *Pseudococcus citri*. *Cryptolaemus*, liberated along with *Leptomastix dactylopii*, effectively controlled *P. citri* infesting *Stephanotis* in greenhouses in California, but since the near eradication of the pest occurs, annual periodic releases are suggested (Doutt 1952*a*).

THE VEDALIA BEETLE, *Rodolia cardinalis* (Muls.). The vedalia beetle is usually spectacular in its ability to control the cottony-cushion scale, *Icerya purchasi* Mask., unaided. In Iran, however, it appears that annual periodic release is necessary. In 1932, Jalal Afshar and M. Kaussari found a large infestation of the scale on citrus near the Caspian Sea. The same year the vedalia was introduced and quickly reduced the scale (Kaussari 1946). However, the following spring the coccid populations evidently increased faster than the few beetles that did not starve and that survived the winter. During the summer months small citrus trees are purposely infested in greenhouses with *Icerya*, and in the autumn the vedalia adults are introduced. When the new beetles emerge they are held at 15° C until the next spring, at which time they are released in citrus groves wherever there is an obvious infestation (Kreokhin 1947).

Hippodamia convergens Guér. The convergent lady beetle has attracted much attention since 1912 when Carnes wrote a paper titled 'Collecting Ladybirds by the Ton.' Between 1908 and 1914 Carnes and others collected huge quantities of *H. convergens* adults from winter aggregations in the Sierra Nevada Mountains of California. The beetles were easily collected, and they could be held in cold storage for months until shipped. Any California grower could obtain 30,000 beetles free for every 10 acres of crop in which he wished to control aphids, by just writing to the superintendent of the state insectary.

The service of translocating the beetles began when cantaloupe growers in the Imperial Valley of California had no means of controlling the melon aphid, *Aphis gossypii* Glover, which was ruining their crops. The common observation in many parts of the country of naturally occurring *H. convergens* controlling aphids in crops, coupled with finding an easy source of masses of beetles, sparked the release programme. This same logic generates the same feeling today in spite of experimental evidence that such translocations of *H. convergens* do not give control.

Many growers who received beetles from the state in the early 1900's felt that they were obtaining control. However, such releases were not critically studied until 1918. Davidson (1919) carefully followed releases of thousands of beetles in southern California and found that about 10 per cent of the beetles remained where liberated. Later, he (Davidson 1924) marked the beetles by spraying them with paint before liberating them. After three days scarcely any of the marked beetles could be found in the area where released. Some marked beetles were found as far away as $4\frac{3}{4}$ miles from the point of release. When the beetles were released at night they dispersed the following day when it became warm.

Packard and Campbell (1926), Garman (1936), Knowlton, Smith, and Harmston (1938), and Eddy (1939) are among some of the other entomologists who studied releases of *Hippodamia convergens* and concluded that such liberations do not ensure aphid control because of the rapid dispersal.

However, there is still much interest in using this species, and private collectors make their living in the western states by selling *H. convergens* collected from the mountains. Some dealers sell as many as 10,000 gallons of beetles a year (a gallon contains about 70,000 individuals).

Hagen (unpublished reports), experimenting with *H. convergens* releases, duplicated Davidson's work by marking beetles with paint and releasing them against aphids in alfalfa, hops, and lettuce. When the beetles were collected from mountain aggregations in December, January, February, and March, these beetles upon release flew extensively when temperatures reached 65° F and above. However, Hagen also found that if the beetles were collected in May, June, July, August, or September from mountain aggregations, they did not exhibit the same flight behaviour, for the majority of beetles remained where released. However, they tended to reaggregate if suitable habitats could be found, and those that did feed, fed very lightly. These releases did not prevent relatively low aphid populations from increasing to damaging numbers. The reason for the reduced beetle-appetite appears to be correlated with the amount of stored fat they had produced prior to aggregating. They normally exist on this fat for about nine months while they are in the mountains.

By feeding synthetic diets in the laboratory to *Hippodamia convergens* adults that were collected from aggregation during the winter, the number of beetles taking off from a release point was greatly reduced over those not fed, but this method is far from being practical at this time (Hagen, unpublished reports). If practical methods could be developed to prevent the initial flight when released, this method would be considered inoculative, for here again the control would have to come from larval progeny produced.

THE COCCINELLIDS *Brumus octosignatus* (Gebler) AND *Semiadalia undecimnotata* (Schneid.). These coccinellids, which form aggregations in the mountains of

Central Asia, have been observed to feed on *Hypera postica* (Gyll.) larvae infesting alfalfa, and on aphids on cotton in the U.S.S.R. These beetles are collected from the mountain aggregations and released in the valleys earlier than the times at which they normally arrive. One adult coccinellid to 20 to 50 *Hypera* larvae gave successful control of the weevil (Yakhontov 1937).

Brumus suturalis (F.) and two species of *Scymnus* are not numerous enough until the end of the dry season in Java to control the mealybug, *Pseudococcus citri*. De Fluiter (1939) indicates that these coccinellids can be bred in large numbers during the rainy season on *P. lilacinus* Ckll. and liberated against *P. citri* at the beginning of the dry season.

Sympherobius amicus Nav. This was mass cultured and released against *Pseudococcus citri* infesting citrus in Israel by Bodenheimer and Guttfeld (1929). The results from releasing adults were encouraging and were more effective than those obtained from *Cryptolaemus montrouzieri* which evidently could not become established.

Aphidius testaceipes (Cress.). This endemic braconid of North America was one of the first entomophagous species to be translocated in large numbers for release against a pest. In 1907 an outbreak of the greenbug, *Toxoptera graminum* (Rond.), occurred in the small grains of the Mississippi Basin. Hunter and Glenn (1909) obtained parasitized aphids in Oklahoma and southern Kansas, where the aphids appeared earlier in the season in large numbers, and transported them north in the hope of reducing aphid populations in the rest of Kansas. During the aphid outbreak to the south, it was observed that the braconid reduced the aphid, but too late to prevent damage. The hypothesis was formulated that artificial distribution of the parasites should not only eliminate the lag period of the parasite activity, so advantageous to the greenbug, but would also establish the parasite in the field with the first greenbugs as hosts, and thereafter the parasite would protect the crop by attacking subsequent greenbugs as they appeared. Several hundred million mummified aphids were estimated to have been released. The effectiveness of these releases in preventing damage by the aphids is problematical because even though results were interpreted by farmers as being good, as Clausen (1956a) points out, farmers in general are eager to believe in the efficiency of biological control as it relieves them of using other more laborious and costly methods.

Aphidius granarius Marsh. This parasite was released for the control of aphids attacking wheat in South Wales where the natural parasitization by this braconid was low. Increased parasitism was obtained in the release plots where 10 adult *Aphidius* were released in small cages arranged in a block in the central portion of the grain fields. After about 23 days the cages were removed to permit the emerging parasites to work in the rest of the field (Arthur 1945).

Macrocentrus ancylivorus Roh. This braconid is one of the 56 recorded primary parasites found to attack the immature stages of the exotic oriental fruit moth, *Grapholitha molesta*, in North America (Haeussler 1930). This larval parasite is an endemic species in eastern United States, attacking the strawberry leaf roller, *Ancylis comptana fragariae* (W. & R.). *M. ancylivorus* was first recorded from

G. molesta by Garman (1917) in Maryland. Bobb (1939), Boyce and Dustan (1958), Daniel (1932), Driggers (1941), Haeussler (1932), Stearns (1919), and others found this parasite to dominate all others from Virginia to Ontario. None of the seven parasites imported from Europe, the two from Australia, or the 17 species from Korea and Japan parasitized the oriental fruit moth to the extent that *M. ancylivorus* did (Allen *et al.* 1940). This is one of the few examples of a parasite of a native pest proving effective against an introduced pest attacking another crop (Clausen 1956a).

The correlation between high *Macrocentrus ancylivorus* parasitization of early broods of *Grapholitha molesta* larvae in peach twigs with less fruit infestation by subsequent moth broods was observed by most of the above workers, and also by Yetter and Allen (1940) and Stearns and Amos (1941). The same correlation was observed by Daniel (1936a, b) and Brunson (1940) when *Macrocentrus* was released. However, Driggers (1940) found no strict correlation in the above sense, but nature of planting and percentage fruit infestation were correlated. In view of these observations and absence of generally accepted insecticidal control measures, Brunson and Allen (1944) made large-scale periodic colonizations in New Jersey peach orchards to determine if fruit injury could be decreased. The releases involved mainly *M. ancylivorus* but some *Agathis diversus* (Mues.) imported from Japan were also liberated. The former parasites released were mass-reared from *Ancylis* larvae, the latter from *G. molesta* larvae. The parasites were released for five years at an average rate per year of 3·3 females per tree or 330 females per acre of orchard. Most of the parasites were released against the second-brood larvae. Over the five-year period an average of 47 per cent less fruit was injured per tree in release plots as compared with check orchards.

The releases of *M. ancylivorus* could be considered as inundative releases if the parasitization were always directed at the second-brood moth larvae, but since some releases were made against the first brood only, the control action in this case was dependent upon the parasite progeny attacking the second-brood pest larvae.

Since this work, apparently very little has been done along the lines of periodic colonization in the eastern states. The development of spray programmes using organic phosphorus insecticides in bearing peach orchards has permitted but very scanty *G. molesta* populations during the first three generations, much less than those prevailing before insecticide control was available (Allen and Plasket 1958).

In the west, when the oriental fruit moth invaded California in the early forties, *M. ancylivorus* was mass cultured (Finney, Flanders, and Smith 1947) and 49 million were released over a three-year period in infested orchards in the attempt to eradicate the pest or stop its spread. The parasite evidently failed to become established, and other factors have been responsible for maintaining the pest at a generally low level (Clausen 1958b).

Rhogas dendrolimi Mats. This highly effective parasite of the lasiocampid moth, *Dendrolimus sibiricus* (Tshetv.) is found in the Irkutsk district of the U.S.S.R. Boldaruev (1958) states that artificial propagation of the braconid is not feasible, but suggests gathering parasitized *Dendrolimus* caterpillars during their non-flight year and transporting them to plantations where massive increases of the pest are beginning. During the spring of the flight year, he suggests the transport of the mummified caterpillars containing the parasite larvae, but only the early mummies should be gathered to avoid transporting secondary parasites.

Encarsia formosa Gahan. This internal parasite has been employed widely to control the greenhouse white fly, *Trialeurodes vaporariorum* (Westw.) in greenhouses. Though this parasite was first collected in the United States, its importance as a controlling agent of the white fly in greenhouses was discovered in England by Speyer (1927). He increased the effectiveness of the parasite by moving parasitized aleurodids into glasshouses where it was absent. Techniques for propagation and distribution were improved and several million parasites were used by the Nursery and Market Garden Industries Development Society.

In 1928 a stock of parasites was sent to Canada where Baird (1935) reports that distribution of the *Encarsia* was made to growers upon request, and that complete success was reported in almost every instance where the parasites were released sufficiently early in the season before the white fly increased to destructive numbers. McLeod (1938) reports on nine years' use of *E. formosa* in Canada, and discusses rearing methods, as well as the number of parasites necessary for white fly control. The number used depends upon the area under glass, area infested, crops infested, degree of infestation, stage of development of the crops, and the temperature. After considering this information, McLeod found that usually from 1,000 to 2,000 parasites per thousand square feet of greenhouse space are sufficient to control an infestation. If more parasites are required, better results can be expected if a light fumigation is carried out before parasites are introduced. Good results are still being obtained in Canada, but recolonization is necessary each year (McLeod 1954).

In Belgium the liberation of *E. formosa* in greenhouses gave complete control of the aleurodid (Van Den Brande 1939). In the United States, Milliron (1940) studied some factors affecting the efficiency of the parasite, including plant pubescence, honeydew, and temperature.

Miles and Miles (1948) suggest storing old plants bearing parasitized aleurodids in a frost-proof shed and returning the plants when the heat is again turned on in the greenhouse and plants set out. The most intensive research in the influence of temperature upon the *Encarsia* and white fly populations has been performed by Burnett (1948, 1949). He found that 27° C not only increased the fecundity of the parasite to the level of the white fly, but that the parasite developmental rate was doubled over that of the host.

Encarsia flavoscutellum Zehnt. Hazelhoff (1927) found that in older sugar cane fields *E. flavoscutellum* often controlled a woolly aphid, *Oregma lanigera* Zehnt. The lack of biological control in young cane fields was the result of parasite lag. Therefore, he translocated the *Encarsia* to these sites. Hazelhoff favoured the parasites by using chemical treatments only when the percentage parasitism was below 40, and after the insecticide treatment, he also released parasites against the few remaining hosts. This prevented a rapid resurgence of the pest.

Prospaltella perniciosi Tower. This has been mass cultured and colonized against the San Jose scale, *Quadraspidiotus perniciosus* (Comst.), in parts of Germany since 1954, but economic control had not occurred by 1956 (Franz 1958*a*).

Aphytis spp. These diaspine scale parasites have received much attention by biological control workers in California. The golden chalcid, *Aphytis chrysomphali* (Mercet), was found by DeBach *et al.* (1950) to control the California red scale, *Aonidiella aurantii* (Mask.), in untreated citrus orchards in certain coastal areas of southern California but usually not in intermediate or particularly in interior climatic areas. Periodic colonizations of *A. chrysomphali* and *Aphytis* 'A' (= *lingnanensis* Comp.) were shown to be capable of solving the problem in intermediate areas where abiotic factors were periodically adversely influencing the *Aphytis*. In interior climatic areas colonizations appeared economically impractical. In addition to adverse climatic periods, the more uniform the development of the scale generation, the more necessity there is for periodic colonization of parasites. This is because the gravid females and the first developmental stages of scale are not susceptible to parasitism, thus creating a period when parasite populations are depressed. It was demonstrated by DeBach *et al.* (1950) that liberating about 100,000 parasites per acre of citrus resulted in a satisfactory degree of commercial control of California red scale in several test orchards. Later (DeBach, Landi, and White 1955) 400,000 *Aphytis* per acre was determined to be more certain. DeBach (1954) found that *Aphytis* 'A' (= *lingnanensis* Comp.) was superior to *A. chrysomphali* in field colonization tests.

In the interior climatic area of the Santa Clara Valley, Ventura County, in southern California, the black scale, *Saissetia oleae* (Bern.), has only a single generation annually which results in a period of several months during the summer when susceptible hosts are not available for the otherwise effective parasite, *Metaphycus helvolus* (Comp.). As a result, the parasite population becomes drastically reduced. Smith (1942*a*) suggested colonization of this parasite each autumn in order to overcome the lack of synchronization. This is now being done regularly by the Fillmore Citrus Protective District Insectary. They colonized over 5,400,000 parasites during the 1958 to 1959 autumn and winter and over 3,350,000 during the 1959 to 1960 season and claim beneficial results. No critical evaluation has been made of the control benefits derived from this programme.

Inoculative Releases of Natural Enemies Plus Host or Prey

There is apparently only one example of this type release which involves spidermites.

Typhlodromus reticulatus Oud. and *T. bellinus* Womer. These are indigenous predatory mites in California. These predators were found to control the cyclamen mite, *Steneotarsonemus pallidus* (Banks), infesting third- and fourth-year strawberry fields when not inhibited by detrimental chemical treatments used to control other pests (Huffaker and Spitzer 1951; Huffaker and Kennett 1953).

The latter authors felt that the erratic biological control of the cyclamen mite in second-year fields was the result of the lag in appearance of the predatory mite and of the more vigorous treatment practices which are applied to the crop during the second year. To compensate for the predator lag, Huffaker and Kennett (1956) stocked plots with predators during the autumn of the first-year growth and in other plots stocked the typhlodromids during the spring of the second-year growth. In both cases complete economic control was obtained in the second-year crop. The actual releases of these predators plus varying densities of prey were stocked on one-fifth of the plants in the field. This gave an average inoculation of about two or three predators per plant throughout the 30,000 plants per acre.

Deliberate introduction into the fields of the pest mite along with the predator early in each planting will achieve the earliest possible establishment of equilibrium at the low prey densities, thereby effecting economic control. Huffaker and Kennett (1956) suggest using clippings from normal winter pruning of berries, for the clippings have both the predator and prey. The growers' reluctance to purposely introduce the mite pest has precluded the adoption of this technique, although it was used commercially in a few instances.

DEVELOPMENT OF ADAPTED STRAINS

This phase of biological control is new and unexplored; what little has been written about it is enthusiastic but often conjectural. No biological control investigator has specialized in this phase and as yet no outstanding field results have been demonstrated clearly. Nevertheless, we consider this area of research to be a most promising one in biological control whether from the viewpoint of pure or applied research.

Various authors have suggested selective breeding for adapted strains as a promising method of approach to the enhancement of biological control, including Box (1956), DeBach (1958a), Heimburger (1945), Mally (1916), Muir (1931), Rubtzov (1947, 1960), Sailer (1954), Urquijo (1946, 1951, 1956), Wilkes (1942), and Wishart (1949). Theoretical considerations relating to artificial selection are discussed by Robertson (1960).

Two phenomena occurring in natural populations probably have been largely responsible for the emergence of the idea of selective breeding for improved strains of entomophagous species. These are : (1) the occurrence of natural enemies showing obvious lack of adaptation, and (2) the occurrence of definite races having different adaptations.

Cases of Adaptive Weakness

Various environmental factors to which natural enemies may be poorly adapted, as well as certain biological weaknesses, have been mentioned earlier in this chapter. Obviously, all organisms are adapted to a more or less narrow set of conditions and will fail to survive if there is much departure from the tolerable range. That there are many natural enemies which might be improved should be self-evident. The fact that the majority of introduced enemies fail to become established and that only a small proportion of established or indigenous species is effective has had sufficient emphasis. If, however, a species is ill adapted in some minor respect, there may be hope for improvement. Evidence that such is common is seen everywhere in the varying parasite faunas of a given host between areas which appear superficially similar.

Some few examples among many of poor adaptiveness of natural enemies to conditions which do not differ greatly from favourable ones follow. The principal parasite, *Aphidius testaceipes* (Cress.) (= *tritici* Ashm.) of the grain aphid or greenbug, *Toxoptera graminum*, can overtake and control the aphid during warm summer weather. However, low temperatures are more unfavourable to the parasite than to the aphid, thus favouring population increase of the aphid over the parasites (Hunter and Glenn 1909; Headlee 1914). In Britain, similar results were obtained for a coccinellid predator. During the summer the lady beetle was able to overtake and reduce the aphid populations, but at temperatures below 50° F aphid populations increased noticeably and predator populations lagged behind (Dunn 1952). Laboratory population studies on the Mediterranean flour moth, *Anagasta kühniella* (Zell.), and its parasite, *Bracon hebetor* Say, showed that at high temperatures the parasite had a decided advantage over the host, but at low temperatures there was no possibility of the parasite overtaking the host (Payne 1933*a*). Similarly, in the laboratory Burnett (1949) showed that the parasite *Encarsia formosa* could increase more rapidly than the host, *Trialeurodes vaporariorum*, and dominate it at high temperatures but at low temperatures the host increased more rapidly than the parasite population. Within the citrus areas of southern California the parasite *Aphytis lingnanensis* Comp. may control successfully the California red scale, *Aonidiella aurantii*, in some localities but not in others. Climatic differences are definitely responsible for this but the differences in climate are slight (DeBach, Fisher, and Landi 1955). In Nova Scotia, *Aphytis mytilaspidis* (LeB.) usually produces good biological control of the oystershell scale in the Annapolis Valley but not in colder central New Brunswick (Lord and MacPhee 1953).

The habitat or host plant may be directly or indirectly unsuitable to a parasite or predator even though a preferred host insect is present. *Protoparce sexta* (Johan.), feeding upon dark-fired tobacco, becomes physiologically conditioned so that it no longer is a suitable host to its parasite, *Apanteles congregatus* (Say) (Gilmore 1938). Similarly, the California red scale grown on *Cycas revoluta* is not suitable to its parasite, *Habrolepis rouxi* Comp., whereas successful development of the parasite occurs in California red scale on citrus according to Smith (1957) who cites other cases as well. The leafhopper egg-predator, *Cyrtorhinus mundulus* (Bredd.), has a strong tropism for the sugar cane plant and will choose sugar cane having relatively few suitable hosts present over adjacent maize plants on which suitable hosts are numerous (Muir 1931.)

Cases of Adaptive Races in Nature

Inasmuch as there is a growing list of known cases of adaptive races among entomophagous species, it might be logical to assume that better adapted races might be developed artificially. It should be borne in mind, however, that what an author considers to be a race may later be found to represent a sibling species, or for that matter a difficult-to-distinguish morphological species. This merely means, of course, that the 'race' has progressed somewhat further along the evolutionary path.

The existence of naturally occurring races of entomphagous species is of paramount importance in biological control. Bio-ecological differences between races may make them the equivalent of distinct species from the standpoint of practical biological control. First Clausen (1936), then Smith (1941), and later Flanders (1950b), and DeBach (1953), emphasized the importance of obtaining and utilizing all possible races or strains of entomophagous species, and Tucker (1939a), Box (1952b), and other specialists on biological control of the sugar cane borers, *Diatraea* spp., in the Caribbean area, followed such a policy. The existence and possible utilization of such races should preferably be thoroughly investigated before undertaking the artificial development of an adapted race. The former procedure will usually be cheaper than the latter and, of course, desired results from artificial selection are never guaranteed.

Naturally occurring races show various types of adaptations, some of which have been reviewed by DeBach (1958a). Climatically adapted races of *Trichogramma minutum* are described by Lund (1934), who showed that the Louisiana grey race develops more slowly than the California yellow race at low temperatures but more rapidly at high temperatures. The grey race was more susceptible to low humidities than the yellow race, but the former showed slightly greater survival at high humidities than the latter. A wet-area Amazon strain and a dry-area Sao Paulo strain of *Metagonistylum minense* Tns. from Brazil are presumably adapted to different climates and vary in colour and fecundity according to Tucker (1939b). Appreciable differences in reproductive capacity and time of emergence of *Tiphia popilliavora* Roh. were shown by Clausen (1936) to exist between races imported from Korea and Japan. Clausen suggests that the late emerging form should be of much greater value because of the larger number of Japanese beetle grubs that are in the proper stage for attack when the late-form wasps are ready for oviposition. Host-preference adaptation has been shown between races of *Trichogramma*, one attacking the eggs of *Tortrix rosana* (L.) but the other not (Marchal 1927b), between races of *Comperiella bifasciata* How., one of which prefers the California red scale, *Aonidiella aurantii*, and the other the yellow scale, *A. citrinia* (Coq.) (Smith 1942b); between races of *Prospaltella perniciosi*, one of which is limited to the San Jose scale, *Quadraspidiotus perniciosus*, and the other to the California red scale, *Aonidiella aurantii* (Flanders 1950b; DeBach 1953); between races of *Aspidiotiphagus citrinus* (Craw), one race of which is known to attack the oleander and yellow scales but not the California red scale in California, whereas an oriental race commonly parasitizes the California red scale in the Orient (Flanders 1950b); between races of *Metaphycus luteolus* (Timb.), one of which parasitizes the black scale, *Saissetia oleae*, in Mexico and the other the brown soft scale, *Coccus hesperidum* L., in California (DeBach 1958a); and between races of *Paratheresia claripalpis* (v.d. Wulp), which show preferences for different species of *Diatraea* and *Zeadiatraea* in Venezuela (Box 1956).

Certain races may be more effective against the same host in the field than other races. The New Jersey strain of *Macrocentrus ancylivorus* has been demonstrated to be more effective than other strains against the oriental fruit moth, *Grapholitha molesta*, when colonized in various states (Clausen 1936). Three strains—perhaps sibling species—of *Aphytis maculicornis* (Masi) have been found to differ considerably in biological characteristics. The one from Persia is much more effective against the olive scale, *Parlatoria oleae* (Colvée), than the others (Hafez and Doutt 1954; Doutt 1954a). A similar case involves *Aphytis mytilaspidis* as a parasite of the fig scale, *Lepidosaphes ficus* (Sign.). One race was naturally distributed throughout California and other states on *Lepidosaphes* but was ineffective in California against *L. ficus*. A race of *A. mytilaspidis* imported on fig scale from Italy proved much more effective in California (Doutt 1954b; Huffaker 1956). In China the imported Russian race of *Aphelinus mali* (Hald.) was found to have a much greater reproductive potential and to produce better biological control than the already established Tsingtao race (Lung, Wang, and Tang 1960).

Concepts and Procedures of Selective Breeding

The art and science of selective breeding to produce strains of domestic animals and cultivated plants better suited to man's needs is so well developed that it is now usually taken as a matter of course. The genetics, procedures, and techniques involved can be found in many standard texts. Aside from work by apiculturists, little has been done along this line by applied entomologists. The possibilities in such work were first clearly emphasized by Wilkes (1942), who stated, 'It seems probable that the method utilized in this investigation . . . could be applied to other characteristics involved in the relations between parasite and host. The work of Thorpe and others has shown that the host preferences of parasites . . . are relatively plastic. Further analysis, combined with constructive breeding work on Mendelian lines, might allow us to duplicate in regard to parasites the results obtained with domestic animals and provide material far better adapted to the needs of the economic entomologist than that which Nature provides.'

One common question concerning attempts to develop adapted strains of parasites or predators is whether man is likely to be able to do in the laboratory something that natural selection would not do in the field. The authors implicitly believe that genetic manipulation and selective breeding in the laboratory can result in adaptations which would rarely if ever occur in the field and that the development of desirable adaptations can be greatly speeded up by laboratory selection. In the latter regard, usually many more generations per year can be obtained in the insectary than occur outside. Dobzhansky's (1951, pp. 118–121) discussion of population genetics furnishes a basis for the hypothesis—which we put forth here—that selection for tolerance to climatic extremes may be more feasible under planned laboratory conditions than in nature. Dobzhansky has shown that the gene population in *Drosophila* shifts as seasons change. *Drosophila* populations tend to become adapted to winter conditions as a result of natural selection—which implies considerable cold-induced mortality—but the following summer the reverse must occur, accompanied again by considerable heat-induced mortality. Thus, the species temporarily adapts to survive either more extreme heat or more extreme cold, but only one condition at a time and in different seasons; hence, a greater adaptation of *individuals* to both heat and cold is unlikely to occur. However, in the laboratory the *same individuals* can be subjected to both heat and cold extremes with the expectancy of ultimately developing a strain having a greater tolerance to both sets of conditions (see p. 455 and figure 90). Such a strain, having a wider range of temperature tolerance when placed in the field, should not have to suffer the mortality that a wild strain would in response to seasonal changes.

Genetic variability, which is a basic prerequisite for any selection work, may be increased in various ways in the laboratory over what might be found occurring in nature. Irradiation may produce new or rare gene mutations, gross mechanical changes within the chromosomes or duplication or losses of whole chromosome sets. Interspecific or interracial crosses may also be brought about in the insectary which would not occur in nature, resulting in a potentially tremendous source of new genetic variability (Sailer 1954). This becomes possible because of the existence of geographically or ecologically isolated species or races which are capable of interbreeding when brought together and because physiologically, morphologically, or psychologically reproductively isolated species or races may sometimes be forced to cross in captivity when this would never occur in nature. Handschin (1932) was unable to cross the species *Spalangia orientalis* Graham from Australia with *S. sundaica* Graham from Java until he isolated a special strain of *S. sundaica* which successfully crossed with *S. orientalis*. Other things may be done with laboratory cultures such as forced oviposition on unnatural hosts to change host-preference (Allen 1954a) which would be unlikely to occur in nature.

Four principal considerations must be met for the successful development and use of an improved strain of natural enemy: (1) what are the characters needing improvement; (2) is genetic variability of the stock to be selected adequate and can it be increased; (3) what are the most adequate, yet practical, culture and selection techniques; and (4) will the new strain maintain its integrity in the field?

It has been emphasized earlier in this chapter that any of a multitude of causes may be responsible for poor adaptability, and approaches were suggested for the determination of these causes. Probably poor adaptation to climate is the most common failing, which may be improved by selective breeding, but host-preferences may conceivably be changed, host-unsuitability improved, resistance to insecticides increased, fecundity improved, diapause modified or eliminated, and any of numerous other biological characteristics might be improved.

Some means of improving genetic variability in the laboratory have just been suggested. The other principal means is to acquire as many stocks as possible from localities throughout the geographical range of the entomophagous species and combine these into a master mixed culture. Such a culture should be maintained at a high population level in order that maximum genetic variability be retained. Selection pressure can then be applied against this culture or its subcultures. Success in selection can be sharply curtailed by lack of genetic variability, until in genetically homozygous lines, selection becomes inoperative. Thus, a natural enemy stock imported from only one locality may represent a more or less pure line with distinctly limited possibilities for improvement through selection. Adverse effects from inbreeding may occur with such stocks as suggested by Simmonds (1947a).

Selection procedures cannot be predicted in advance, unless perchance it is known just which and/or how many genes determine the inheritance of the character in question. If polygenic inheritance is involved, good selection techniques would involve low selection pressures each generation in order not to eliminate certain genes from the population which might be necessary for the best ultimate combinations. Dobzhansky (1937, p. 182) has shown that the effectiveness of selection may be very low in small populations. This would also indicate the use of cultures containing the maximum number of individuals practical to work with. Selective pressures causing about 50 per cent mortality and other desirable procedures are indicated by the work and references of J. King (1958) on the development of resistance to insecticides by *Drosophila*. In the case of a simple dominant-recessive gene pair controlling the character in question, or at most a few genes being involved, then selective pressures can be rather drastic, ranging above the 90 per cent mortality level in each generation, and culture population levels can be lower.

One important consideration is that the selection pressure be adjusted to a level which will not drastically reduce initial culture populations in the succeeding generation, otherwise a non-selected generation for recovery of culture numbers must be interposed. The reproductive capacity of the species thus will be an important factor in determining what selective pressure can be used.

Care should be taken during the selection work to ascertain that unfavourable modifications are not occurring at the same time as the desired character is being favourably modified. Therefore, periodic checks should be made for viability, sex ratio, rate of development, fecundity, or other biological characteristics not purposefully undergoing selection.

When the results of artificial selection are finally thought to be satisfactory, field trials are in order and the maintenance of the integrity of the new strain assumes importance if the species is already established in the area to be colonized. This is, of course, no problem when newly introduced species, which previously have failed to become established, are being used. Otherwise, one possibility—albeit a difficult one—of ensuring the integrity of the improved strain would lie in further selection to develop some sort of reproductive isolation. Isolating mechanisms are extremely diversified and include failure to interbreed because of differences in habitat preference, differences in breeding seasons or times, lack of attraction between sexes, physical or psychological bars to copulation, physiological failure of fertilization, and failure of development of the fertilized egg or embryo (Dobzhansky 1951, chapter 9). The best type of genetic isolation would be to select an apomictic strain of the adapted strain. Uniparental races or sibling species of hymenopterous parasites producing only females are not uncommon in several groups. The isolation of large numbers of virgin females may reveal that an occasional case of apomixis occurs in normally biparental species.

The number of individuals of the adapted strain colonized in a given area in relation to the already established 'wild' population may be of importance. Studies on population genetics indicate that, given equal survival values, particular genes will tend to remain in the population in proportion to their original ratios. This is known as the Hardy-Weinberg Law (Dobzhansky 1951, p. 53). Should the artificially selected strain have a greater survival value in the field, as we expect, then it should become dominant over the 'wild' form as a result of natural selection. In any event, it does not necessarily follow that field crossing of the 'wild' form with the selected laboratory strain will eventually result in the loss of the increased adaptiveness developed in the laboratory.

Results of Selective Breeding

Very little of a practical nature has been done thus far with artificial selection of natural enemies, but the work which has been done indicates interesting possibilities and directions for future research. Handschin (1932) not only recognized the potential importance of races but of interspecific crosses. Working with two species, *Spalangia orientalis* of Australia and *S. sundaica* of Java, he found that crossing did not occur between individuals of the two species reared from field-collected puparia of a number of muscid flies which inhabit dung. However, he obtained a special race of *S. sundaica* living only on the buffalo fly, *Lyperosia exigua* de Meij., and reared it through many generations; then when the *Lyperosia* strain of *S. sundaica* was crossed with *S. orientalis* (especially *S. orientalis* females with *S. sundaica* [*Lyperosia* strain] males), good progeny production consisting of nearly 50 per cent females resulted. Handschin stated, 'Now, since these crossings had successfully produced a fertile progeny, the idea grew that it would be possible to secure a combination which should possess not only the greater egg capacity and longer lifetime of *S. sundaica* but also the adaptation to North Australian conditions of *S. orientalis*. . . . From July to November, 1931, five generations were bred through, using all possible combinations of the parent and derived stock. . . . The results obtained, . . . are so striking that they deserve confirmation by further experiments, and should stimulate further research along these lines. . . .'

Wilkes (1942) was perhaps the first to employ artificial selective pressure in the laboratory in order to develop a better adapted strain of parasites. His problem was to increase the effectiveness of *Dahlbominus fuscipennis* in cooler field locations. When *Dahlbominus*, which parasitizes the European spruce sawfly, *Diprion hercyniae* (Htg.), was tested in the laboratory in a temperature-gradient, two principal groups congregating around 8° and 25° C were obtained. Selection of individuals congregating in the 8° C (6° to 10° C) zone resulted, after four generations, in a strain in which over half of the adults preferred temperatures below 12·5° C. This is virtually a complete reversal of the response of the original stock. Subsequent studies comparing the selected strain with a wild one from a low-temperature area showed that both had nearly identical low-temperature preferences. In this case, such results might have been expected, inasmuch as original stocks came from the same source and natural selection in the field was operating in much the same manner as the type of artificial selection employed in the laboratory. The rapidity of adaptation indicates a simple type of inheritance, especially since further selection did not appreciably lower the temperature preferendum.

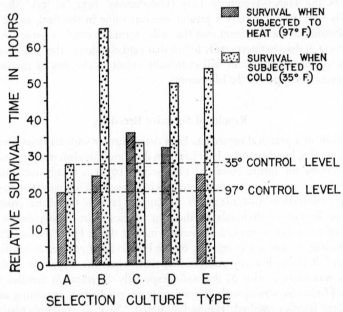

Figure 90. The relative development of tolerance to heat and/or cold in various cultures of the parasite *Aphytis lingnanensis* Comp. following 85± generations of selection in the laboratory as measured by the LD$_{50}$ at 97° F for heat tolerance and at 35° F for cold tolerance. The control culture (A) received no selection treatment. In the other cultures, selection treatments involved subjection of (B) to cold (40° F) in each generation, of (C) to heat (94° F) in each generation, of (D) to heat, then to cold in alternate generations, and of (E) to heat and cold in each generation.

Currently, DeBach *et al.* (1960 unpublished data) are engaged in artificial selection trials to develop climate-tolerant strains of *Aphytis lingnanensis* for use against the California red scale on citrus in areas of southern California in which the parental strain of *A. lingnanensis* is ineffective because of lack of adaptability to climatic extremes. Strains have been selected for increased tolerance to cold alone, to heat alone, but particularly to both cold and heat. It is considered that the type of artificial selection employed should produce results which would not be expected to occur from natural selection in the field. Results after about 85 generations show definite, and in some strains striking, increases in tolerance to cold alone, to heat alone, or to both. Figure 90 shows the degree to which the better strains have responded. It is notable that even where selection has been made for cold adaptation only, or for heat adaptation only, increased tolerance has developed in both directions. Field trials will not be conducted until it appears that near maximum tolerance has been developed.

Sex ratio improvement in laboratory cultures was obtained by Simmonds (1947a) and Wilkes (1947) by selective breeding. The stocks had reached the point where males almost entirely were being obtained. Wilkes showed that inbreeding in the laboratory cultures was responsible for high male sterility, which, of course, results in decreasing proportions of females. By outbreeding and selection for high female production, he found that the percentage of sterile males could be drastically reduced. The mean number of progeny per female was increased from 34 to 68 and oviposition and longevity improved. This resulted in a great increase in the efficiency of mass production of *Dahlbominus fuscipennis* for field release. Simmonds selected families having high proportions of females and thus increased the sex ratio favourably. The results were ascribed to the breeding out of factors inducing male sterility. Mass-rearing of parasites was greatly improved as a consequence.

Host-preference modification has been discussed by Simmonds (1944b) and was obtained by Allen (1954a) in an extremely significant piece of work which points the way for further trials with other species. Allen first had to use attractants to induce the oriental fruit moth parasite, *Horogenes molestae* (Uchida), to oviposit in the potato tuber worm, a foster host. After employing this method for about 11 generations, it was found that an artificial stimulus was no longer required to induce oviposition on the foster host. Further selective breeding for 39 generations produced a strain which reproduced 24 times as efficiently as the original on the potato tuber worm. Earlier, Meyer and Meyer (1946) had changed the host preference of *Chrysopa carnea* St. (=*vulgaris* Schr.) by selection. If similar results could be carried over to field application in biological control, there is no predicting what beneficial results might be accomplished. If highly efficient parasites of one host species can be artificially selected to change their host preference to a related host species, then the second species automatically obtains a parasite of proved past capabilities.

Potential resistance to insecticides constitutes an important capability of most natural enemies, which may be improved through selective breeding. Pielou and Glasser (1952) increased the tolerance of *Macrocentrus ancylivorus* to DDT by several times after nine months of selection. It is to be expected that natural enemies may develop increased resistance to insecticides in the field just as so many pest species have in recent years. However, this can be speeded up in the laboratory and greater levels of tolerance undoubtedly built up by appropriate selective procedures and the use of original stocks having maximum genetic variability.

Other results of interest include the work of Box (1952b, 1956) who crossed races of the tachinid fly *Paratheresia claripalpis* from Trinidad, Mexico, Venezuela, and Peru. The Venezuela-Trinidad hybrid was the most vigorous and suited to Venezuelan conditions and showed improved host-preferences. There is some indication that increased field effectiveness resulted. Urquijo (1946, 1951) practised artificial selection on *Trichogramma minutum* for several years and developed strains in the laboratory which showed a five-fold increase in 'ovotropismo' (host-finding ability) from 1946 to 1949.

QUALIFICATIONS FOR USE OF MANIPULATION

The possibility of manipulation is one which catches the popular fancy, especially the ideas of mass production and periodic colonization or of the field translocation of entomophagous organisms. The potentialities involved or the results obtained are commonly magnified by the layman and sometimes by the entomologist. When such manipulation procedures are carried out, true cause and effect may be difficult to ascertain. The fact that higher parasitization or mortality follows periodic colonization of a parasite or predator does not necessarily mean that they were responsible. The work previously cited with respect to the periodic colonization of *Trichogramma* or translocation of *Hippodamia convergens* is sufficient evidence of this. It must be borne in mind that increase of natural enemies already present may be responsible for the results that are accredited to manipulation.

Trichogramma has been mass produced and colonized in countries all over the world and, in spite of the fact that it has been naturally present in nearly all these situations, rarely have adequate field studies been carried out to show whether or not the colonizations in themselves have been responsible for increased control.

Similarly, *H. convergens* is collected from natural aggregations and sold on a large scale in the United States, even though the practice has been shown by entomologists to be ineffective at best.

It is just as important—perhaps more so—to demonstrate that manipulation is really efficacious, as it was during the initial phases of such a study to determine its need and a logical method of approach. Generally, this can best be done by using untreated paired-comparison field plots involving manipulation tests in one series versus no manipulation in another. In periodic colonization, the proper timing of releases and the best numbers for colonization will have to be determined first in such a manner.

If manipulation is successful, paired-comparison plots will show the relative degree of success by differences between the two series of plots. This, in effect, is a demonstration, and it can be used effectively to convince other entomologists as well as agriculturalists of the soundness of the method.

One final consideration remains. The cost of manipulation should be as cheap or cheaper than other methods and the results as good or better than other methods, to make it really worth while. Evaluation of the economic significance of results, however, should not be restricted to the effect against the main target alone, i.e., the pest toward which manipulation is directed. This pest may well be a key one, that is, one originally requiring major insecticidal pest control applications. Its successful control by manipulation can result in widespread improvement in biological control throughout the entire faunal complex.

CHAPTER 16

Environmental Modification and Biological Control

R. VAN DEN BOSCH AND A. D. TELFORD

INTRODUCTION

INNUMERABLE potentially injurious insects are effectively controlled by entomophagous and entomogenous organisms in a wide variety of habitats. On the other hand, as pointed out in chapter 15, in many habitats prevailing environmental conditions discourage satisfactory biological control. Certain habitats of a highly artificial nature may be so transient and unstable as virtually to preclude the effective activity of natural enemies and, consequently, require frequent pesticide applications. There is, however, an intermediate category of insect habitats which may lack only certain key requisites and it is with these that adversity may be favourably modified for effectual action by entomophagous species.

To a large extent, the efficacy of natural enemies depends upon the degree of permanence, stability, and general favourability of environmental conditions. The many successful biological control programmes against pests of field and forage crops, and particularly of horticultural crops and forests, illustrate the utility of this method in amenable environments. We deduce, then, that the environment, its physical and biological properties as well as its stability and relative permanence, can determine the efficacy of natural enemies. Departures from the natural environment, whether intentional or incidental, by influencing entomophagous species, are often reflected in the degree of depredation caused by injurious arthropods. Such effects may be restricted to a single field or may be so extensive as to bridge continental boundaries. In this chapter, we shall examine some of the environmental changes which affect entomophagous arthropods and show, whenever possible, how environmental manipulation may be applied to increase their effectiveness.

Effects of Regional Changes in Agriculture on Biological Control

Agricultural changes on a grand scale can profoundly affect the entomophagous faunas of entire regions. In many cases replacement of natural biota or diversified agriculture with large monocultures has caused general faunal impoverishment, yet certain species of phytophagous arthropods have become extremely abundant

(Schneider 1939; Voûte 1946; Silvestri 1949; Franz 1951; Smith 1956; and Elton 1958). The reaction of natural enemies to these gross changes is of particular interest to us.

The North American western wheat stem sawfly, *Cephus cinctus* Nort., became practically immune to its local parasites following the introduction and extensive planting of wheat (Criddle 1922). Such escapes may occur because indigenous parasites frequently do not adapt to newly created agricultural environments as quickly nor as easily as their hosts (Myers 1931, 1935; Smith 1956). As the cultivation of peas spread in Europe, the cecidomyid gall midge, *Contarinia pisi* Winn., increased in abundance. However, unlike the parasites of the wheat stem sawfly, its parasite, *Pirene graminea* Hal., readily adapted to the agricultural environment following the ubiquitous increase of *C. pisi*. This previously rare chalcid shortly became one of the most common and effective natural enemies of the pea gall fly in Central Europe (Kutter 1934).

The western yellow-striped armyworm, *Prodenia praefica* Grote, a phalaenid moth native to western North America, has also changed its habits with agricultural development. Subsequent to the introduction and widespread cultivation of alfalfa in western United States, this previously innocuous insect has damaged a variety of crops and has become particularly destructive in California (Weldon 1914; Blanchard and Conger 1932; van den Bosch 1950).

Although it was formerly restricted to limited niches during the dry season, *P. praefica* now reproduces in vast acreages of irrigated alfalfa. Its increase in California is also attributed to the introduction of range plants, particularly those of the genus *Erodium*. These filarees are available for egg deposition early in the year, when dormant or winter-grazed alfalfa is unavailable as a host. As the filarees produce seed and wither with the approaching dry season the moths return to alfalfa. The introduction of alfalfa and filaree have allowed *P. praefica*, once a comparatively rare species, to become one of the most abundant lepidopterous insects in the great Central Valley of California (van den Bosch 1950).

The increase of *Prodenia* has had a significant effect upon the complex of parasites which attack it and other lepidopterous species. Frequently, these parasites, which include the tachinids *Eucelatoria armigera* Coq. and *Archytas californiae* Wlkr. and the hymenopterous species *Hyposoter exiguae* (Vier.), *Apanteles marginiventris* (Cress.), and *Chelonus texanus* Cress., develop in immense numbers on *P. praefica* in midsummer and late summer. At such times, in alfalfa and contiguous crops, they unquestionably affect populations of such pests as the corn earworm, *Heliothis zea* (Boddie), the beet armyworm, *Spodoptera exigua* (Hbn.), the cabbage looper, *Trichoplusia ni* (Hbn.), and the variegated cutworm, *Peridroma margaritosa* (Haw.). Without the impetus it gains on populations of *P. praefica*, it is questionable whether this parasite complex would be as important in the biological control of a variety of lepidopterous pests in Central California.

Graham (1929) and Tothill (1922, 1958), in discussing causes of insect outbreaks, stress the effects of environmental modifications on natural enemies. Concerning the spruce budworm, *Choristoneura fumiferana* (Clem.), they, as have others, take the view that recent outbreaks of this pest have been caused primarily by a change in forest composition in eastern North America. The spruce budworm shows a definite preference for balsam fir over its namesake host tree, spruce. Conditions in unmolested forests of the region indicate that, prior to the coming of civilization, balsam fir was a minor and occasional component. Clean-cut logging practices and forest fires have greatly favoured balsam fir regeneration over spruce, so that there now exist vast areas of almost pure stands of the preferred budworm host plant. Under these conditions of massed food supply in a changed environment, natural enemies appear to be incapable of preventing or controlling outbreaks. The best they are able to do is to lengthen the periods between outbreaks. Graham and Tothill also postulate that similar basic causes have encouraged outbreaks of the gypsy moth, *Porthetria dispar* (L.), the tent caterpillar, *Malacosoma disstria* Hbn., the walking stick, *Diapheromera femorata* (Say), and the Colorado potato beetle, *Leptinotarsa decemlineata* (Say). It is suggested that properly planned and enforced cultural practices and cropping systems can ultimately relegate these serious pests to their former endemic status.

The Habitat and Biological Control

Most beneficial species achieve their greatest efficiency within habitats where conditions are most suitable for their well-being. Parasites and predators may be commonly associated with particular climates or microclimates, kinds of vegetation, soil types, geographic faciation, and so on. Normally, these frequented places provide a source of prey but, in addition, they must satisfy all the other vital requirements of their entomophagous inhabitants. Quite often, through astute observation, we can identify the requirements which restrict beneficial species to the places where they live. Sometimes, however, these basic needs elude us and we cannot explain why certain natural enemies do not occupy additional habitats which, to us, appear suitable for them. With many species we tend to consider that the selective forces which have determined their characteristic habitats no longer exist and that habitat choice has become wholly innate or genetically set. For want of a better phrase, it has been said that the animal is psychologically attuned to its habitat.

In our text we shall accept habitat as the place or kind of place where an animal lives, and be content to discuss only the more obvious environmental factors which determine habitat choice and suitability, whenever they are pertinent. Thus, we choose to distinguish habitat, a dwelling place, from 'niche' (Elton 1947), the status or role of an organism in a habitat.

The importance of parasite and host habitats in biological control is discussed by Flanders (1940, 1959a) and Townes (1958). Flanders notes that an introduced parasite may never become efficient because it does not frequent its host's habitat in the new environment. He recommends, therefore, that collectors attempt to obtain natural enemies from pests infesting the species (or variety) of host plant on which they are to be established in a foreign country (see also chapter 9).

Townes, on the other hand, encourages us to broaden our search for natural enemies to include habitats similar to those infested by the pests but not necessarily within the range of the pest species. Here, different emphasis is placed on methods of searching for efficient parasites and predators; nevertheless, each entomologist recognizes the importance of natural enemy-habitat relationships. Although the diversity of biological control problems requires flexibility in our methods, we must realize the general significance of habitat selection and compatability in determining the effectiveness of natural enemies. The creation of undesirable natural-enemy-habitat relationships by environmental modification or by introducing exotic species into new environments must be avoided whenever possible. Some examples of how changes in the habitat have affected natural enemies follow.

The pale western cutworm, *Agrotis orthogonia* Morr., under natural conditions on Alberta prairies lives above the surface of the ground and feeds chiefly on the stems and leaves of native grasses. Various natural enemies have access to the larvae and effect a considerable degree of biological control. In crop areas, however, where soil cultivation is customary, the cutworm has been able to move under-ground with ease and feeds upon the stems of plants about an inch below the soil surface. Under agricultural conditions this insect has apparently begun a new mode of life in a different habitat where its natural enemies cannot reach it. Effective biological control of the pale western cutworm in cultivated soil is restricted to those times when excessive soil moisture temporarily forces the larvae to the surface (Seamans 1926).

An analogous situation regarding parasitization of the sugar cane froghopper, *Tomaspis saccharina* Dist., is described by Pickles (1931) and Myers (1935). In the West Indies this insect occurs naturally on grasses in shaded tropical forests but has managed to invade agricultural areas where it attacks sugar cane. The froghopper has adapted to the new habitat by inserting most of its eggs into the soil where they resist the arid conditions of the dry season. In the soil these eggs are also protected from parasites which will attack them above ground and in the cane trash.

Discussing parasitization of the sugar cane borer *Diatraea saccharalis* (F.), Myers (1935) remarks that the borer was primitively attracted to much more hygrophilous plant associations than its near relatives. In the course of time it has adapted itself to cane-growing conditions. Its reduced parasitization in the new environment is attributed to the fact that its parasites were unable to adapt to the much drier habitat created by sugar cane culture.

O'Connor (1950) working with the predacious ant *Oecophylla smaragdina subnitida* Emery, an enemy of the coreid *Amblypelta coccophaga* China, in the Solomon Islands, found that its colonies were being eliminated by another ant, *Pheidole megacephala* (F.), where coconut groves were under clean culture. He observed further that during World War II, when neglected groves developed a heavy undergrowth, they were reoccupied by *Oecophylla*. It was apparent that undergrowth provided a more favourable habitat for this ant as well as a means for it to avoid *Pheidole* while moving from tree to tree. On the basis of O'Connor's

A

B

C

FIGURE 91. *Polistes* shelters used to increase the efficiency of the wasps in hornworm control on tobacco in North Carolina. A. General aspect of shelter. B. Shelter turned upside down to show method of protective screening (note wasp nest at left). C. A shelter used also for transporting colonies. Screen can be replaced with a short board to prevent escape of adults. (Courtesy of F. R. Lawson.)

FIGURE 92. *Coccinella novemnotata franciscana* Casey feeding on exudations of *Xanthium spinosum* L. (× 6).

FIGURE 93. Strip-farming alfalfa to conserve natural enemies. (Schlinger and Dietrick 1960.)

conclusions, palm fronds were placed tip-end-up against tree trunks so that *Oecophylla* might escape *Pheidole* predation. This practice resulted in a 'remarkable' re-establishment of *Oecophylla* and a subsequent control of the coreid. As a consequence, O'Connor recommended that a cover crop with a tangled growth form be employed in coconut groves in order to improve the biological control of the coreid pest. Way (1958) recommended a similar procedure in Zanzibar.

Schwenke (1958) considers the effect of the host 'biotop' upon the qualitative and quantitative parasitization of lepidopterous tree defoliators. His experiences indicated that a given parasite species reaches its maximum density in one type of 'biotop,' within which environmental conditions are most favourable for the parasite; it occurs at lower and lower densities as the environment becomes less favourable to it. Thus, he observes that only a few of the known parasite species of a given host occur in any single locality.

Schwenke suggests that an understanding of biocoenotic ('biotop') differentiation by parasites is valuable for three principal reasons: (1) By recognizing the dependence of parasites upon local environmental conditions we may study its causes and apply the results to favour parasites by influencing environmental factors. (2) Through studies of this kind, parasites may be selected for export on the basis of a greater host dependence and a minimum 'biotop' dependence. (3) Realizing the existence of biocoenotic differentiation, the effects of biological control, with respect to parasite density, can be compared only in biocoenotically equivalent localities.

An example of how a habitat change may favour a natural enemy is afforded by the predacious earwig, *Labidura riparia* (Pallas). This predator is indigenous to warm moist regions of the world and has only recently been recorded from the arid south-western desert valleys of California. It is believed that *L. riparia* has been able to invade California and flourish in the formerly barren valleys because a favourable habitat was produced with the development of irrigated agriculture in these regions (Schlinger, van den Bosch, and Dietrick 1959). In California, *L. riparia* seems principally associated with alfalfa fields where microclimatic conditions appear to be near optimum for its nesting and foraging habits. Were it not for alfalfa and other vegetation which provide suitable habitats for this predator, it would almost certainly be excluded from the dry desert regions of western United States.

The effects of habitat changes upon insectivorous mammals have received only limited attention by zoologists and entomologists. Myers (1931) remarks that the mahogany shoot borers, *Hypsipyla* spp., in the West Indies produce an entire generation in the fallen fruits. In the virgin forest the agouti, *Dasyprocta* sp., devours the fallen fruit and thereby is a very important agent of biological control by destroying a great number of larvae and reducing the food supply of the remainder. Forests encroached upon by man evidently become unsuitable to the agouti and it is now rarely found in civilized areas where mahogany is grown.

Graham (1929) comments that drainage of swamp forests changes the condition of ground cover and therefore may have an effect upon the overwintering stages of pests that hibernate in the layer of duff or surface vegetation. If tamarack swamps were drained, the surface vegetation of moss and grass would give way to other plants and become more varied. This change in vegetation, by improving food conditions, would, in turn, bring about an increase in the number of mice per unit area. Because mice destroy large quantities of sawfly cocoons, their increase as a direct result of drainage would aid in reducing sawfly abundance.

Buckner (1955a, b) offers further information regarding insectivorous mammal populations on tamarack bogs in Canada. In wet bogs with a heavy crown closure, the masked shrew, *Sorex cinereus cinereus* Kerr., is the most abundant insectivorous mammal. It is an efficient predator of the larch sawfly, *Pristiphora erichsonii* (Htg.), because it rejects over 60 per cent of the parasitized cocoons. The drainage of one such bog resulted in an interesting change in its small mammal inhabitants. Subsequent to drainage, the saddle-backed shrew, *Sorex arcticus laricorum* Jackson, gained dominance and the red-backed vole, *Clethrionomys gapperi loringi* (Bailey), increased noticeably. It was believed that this change may have had significant effects upon the sawfly population because *S. arcticus* does not discriminate between parasitized and unparasitized cocoons while *C. gapperi* is discriminate in less than half its choices.

Conservation and encouragement of small insectivorous mammals in forests of north-eastern United States are advocated by Hamilton and Cook (1940). Shrews, mice, chipmunks, squirrels, and moles are widely distributed and numerically well represented in a variety of forest types of that region. They are an aid to the control of forest insect pests that spend some part of their lives in or on the soil. It was found that insects comprised up to 20 per cent of the diet of rodents whereas with the shrews and moles the proportion of insect food was above 50 per cent. Populations of these small mammals can exceed 200 per acre in wooded areas where conditions are favourable. Hamilton and Cook point out that those factors which go to make an excellent forest—adequate growing stock, good representation of species and age classes, satisfactory shrub and herb layers, the best possible soil—also tend to maintain the heaviest and most varied mammal populations.

Bess, Spurr, and Littlefield (1947) impressively correlate the efficacy of predators of the gypsy moth, *Porthetria dispar*, to the availability of vegetative cover on the forest floor. Large gypsy moth larvae feed mostly at night, and during the day retire to cool, moist, secluded places to rest and ultimately to pupate. In eastern United States, mesophyllic woodlands with a moist and deep forest floor support an abundance of insect-eating small mammals and arthropods. Here the short-tailed shrew, *Blarina brevicauda brevicauda* (Say), and the deer mouse, *Peromyscus leucopus noveboracensis* (Fischer), consume a major proportion of the gypsy moth larvae and pupae. Consequently, in stands supporting a good undergrowth and abundant litter, gypsy moth defoliation is seldom severe. In more xeric open stands brought about by poor site conditions and poor management, insufficient undergrowth decreases predator populations and discourages the descent of gypsy moth larvae to the forest floor. As a result, these stands consistently suffer severe defoliation.

Raquel Dexter (1932) concluded that the giant toad, *Bufo marinus* (L.), could be used effectively against sugar cane grubs, *Phyllophaga* spp., in Puerto Rico, provided certain habitat changes were initiated. She suggested that the banks of water reservoirs and main irrigation ditches should be planted with bananas and other plants attractive to *Phyllophaga* adults which would inevitably fall prey to the toads in their preferred haunts. Wolcott (1934) observed that the toad, as a decisive factor in *Phyllophaga* control, has been practically eliminated in certain urban areas of Puerto Rico because of heavy street traffic, the few areas in which they may hide during the day, and the scarcity of pools where the immature stages may be passed.

Many authors contend that the elimination of nesting sites and perching places in favour of crop production has reduced insectivorous bird populations in agricultural areas. They generally recommend the planting of hedges and trees as well as placing out artificial perches and nest boxes in crop lands in order to enhance insect control by avian species.

Unfortunately, there have been only a few investigations which clearly demonstrate the potentialities of vertebrate insectivores as agents of biological control. These, however, indicate that, in silvic habitats, some insect-eating birds and small mammals can respond numerically and functionally to insect populations (Gibbs 1958; Morris *et al.* 1958; Simmonds 1958*b*; Holling 1959). It has been shown by these authors that predator response can be manifested by an intensity of predation which is relative to host availability. The whole picture of vertebrate predation of pest arthropods deserves further investigation. It is a field where the habitat seems to be of prime importance and where there are certainly greater opportunities for initiating desirable environmental modifications conducive to increased utilization of vertebrate insectivores—a virtually untapped and insufficiently evaluated resource.

ENVIRONMENTAL MODIFICATIONS RELEVANT TO INCREASED NATURAL ENEMY EFFECTIVENESS

In Importation and Colonization Programmes

The colonization and establishment of introduced entomophagous species already have been treated in chapter 14. However, because success in these highly important phases of biological control relies so closely upon certain aspects of environmental modification, some repetition seems apropos.

It cannot be overemphasized that colonization and field releases of introduced entomophagous species should be attempted under conditions most favourable for their survival and reproduction (Flanders 1940; King and Parker 1950; Sweetman 1958; Franz 1961*b*). Successful rearing under controlled laboratory conditions, however encouraging, gives little assurance of establishment in a more rigorous field environment. The success of an exotic natural enemy may be seriously handicapped if the requirements for its field establishment are not carefully predetermined (Clausen 1936; Wolcott 1948; King and Parker 1950; Flanders 1940, 1959*a*). As a general rule, colonization sites should provide an abundance of susceptible host stages for an adequate period of time, an attractive host habitat, maximum protective cover for beneficial species, and sufficient food and moisture. The area of the colonization or release site may determine the number of natural enemies it is necessary to introduce and the frequency of their liberation in space and time.

Whenever these requirements or others pertinent to establishment are sub-optimum, favourable environmental modifications must be given every consideration. Although each introduction programme has its unique problems, previous endeavours have given rise to many techniques that are now generally employed. Some, for example, are: caging, shading, providing artificial cover (moss, litter, and paper or cloth tree bands) for protection against desiccation, cold, wind, natural enemies, and other adversities, supplementing inadequate food and moisture, and maintaining advantageous ratios of beneficial species to pests by reintroductions of one or the other. Not infrequently, simple, yet very important environmental modifications employed by observant entomologists have greatly facilitated introduction programmes. Indeed, they have even produced excellent results from otherwise unsuccessful projects.

Artificial Structures as Aids to Biological Control

The use of artificial structures for the encouragement of established and indigenous parasites and predators has received limited consideration. Myers (1931) comments that the most important predators of the cotton leafworm, *Alabama argillaceae* (Hbn.), in the West Indies are *Polistes* wasps. On St. Vincent Island, *Polistes annularis* (L.) was so efficient in this respect that no insecticide was used against the leafworm for ten years. The cotton growers on the island erected substantial sheds in their fields for *P. annularis* to nest in. Myers felt that the good work of the St. Vincent wasps was not necessarily due to the greater efficiency of this local species, but rather to the especially favourable environment for the maintenance of large *Polistes* populations.

In order to reduce the hazard of insecticide residues on natural leaf tobacco in North Carolina, Lawson *et al.* (1961) investigated the practicality of biological control against hornworms, *Protoparce sexta* (Johan.) and *P. quinquemaculata* (Haw.). Tests showed that indigenous *Polistes* wasps, principally *P. exclamans* Vier. and *P. fuscatus* (F.), could substantially reduce hornworm population levels and the degree of injury caused by the hornworms to the tobaccos. *Polistes* predation was increased locally by erecting nesting shelters adjacent to tobacco fields (figure 91 A, B). It was also shown that local predators could be supplemented by transporting occupied *Polistes* shelters to fields where they were most needed (figure 91 C).

During the biological control programme against the citrophilus mealybug, *Pseudococcus gahani* Green, Smith and Armitage (1931) found that banding citrus trees benefited its principal predator, *Cryptolaemus montrouzieri* Muls. The application of 5-inch burlap bands around the trunks of infested trees attracted the mealybugs which tended to concentrate beneath them to oviposit. The bands also attracted the coccinellid predators, thereby increasing the intensity of predation. In groves where bands were not used the beetles pupated in cracks in the bark and in the ground litter and, consequently, were exposed to heavier attack by omnivorous predators.

One of the most active efforts to encourage beneficial insects by the provision of artificial nesting sites is that involving the predacious ant, *Formica rufa* L., an enemy of forest insect pests in Europe. This work was pioneered by Gösswald in Germany (Gösswald 1951) who developed techniques for the production and release of large numbers of *F. rufa* queens as well as means of protecting their nesting sites from predacious vertebrates.

The recent increase in crop pests on smallholdings in France is attributed to the substitution of hedgerow boundaries by wire fences (Janvier 1956). Janvier feels this pest increase has resulted from a reduction in hymenopterous predators that utilize hedgerows and other relatively natural nesting sites. He recommends supplying nesting sites for these predators by the use of pithy plants, ditches with vertical banks, and sand piles on or around small farms.

Spencer (1958) considers that biological control of grasshoppers by nemestrinid flies in British Columbia has been restricted by a lack of favourable oviposition sites for the flies. *Trichopsidea clausa* (O.S.), for instance, has been known to attack over 90 per cent of *Camnula pellucida* (Scudder) in localized areas. The parasitic fly oviposits in cracks and crevices and in beetle emergence holes in dead trees and fence posts. The newly hatched larvae are distributed by the wind and ultimately enter grasshoppers through the intersegmental membranes. Sheep and cattle ranchers have been urged to increase localized nemestrinid populations by placing old barkless, cracked, beetle riddled fence posts in known *Camnula* egg beds and breeding grounds.

Artificial structures have also been utilized to increase the numbers of vertebrate insectivores in areas where their predatory activity has been considered beneficial. Myers (1931) points out that the introduction of exotic insectivorous birds into the West Indies would be of doubtful value. Rather, efforts should be directed towards the active protection of indigenous species, the numbers of which have been depleted in some cases. Above all, protective cover should be provided, and on the drier islands, artificial drinking places established. Although birds are plentiful on some of the islands, perches and cover are not available in large acreages of sugar cane. On many plantations kiskadees and flycatchers have been encouraged to enter the cane fields by providing them with perches. At planting time, many-branched bamboo perches up to 15 feet tall are erected at various intervals within the fields. In some areas these perches are supplemented by plantings of shrubs along field margins to provide additional nesting sites.

Taylor (1938), in an account of insectivorous birds of British forests, first draws attention to successful bird management in Germany. An infestation of the red-tailed beech roller moth, *Dascychira pudibunda* (L.), in Hainish Forest north of Eisback was checked after three generations of defoliation at the edges of a bird sanctuary. Thus, in Seebach Wood, in areas where artificial nesting sites and protective management were employed, the defoliator remained innocuous although the surrounding forest was severely damaged. In the Langhangen Division near Neustrelitz an outbreak of the pine moth, *Bupalus piniarius* (L.), occurred during 1928 and 1929. Population samples in bird sanctuaries average 50 caterpillars per tree as compared with 5,000 per tree in unmanaged areas. The infestation was stopped at 30 to 50 metres from the last row of nesting boxes in a managed block. It was concluded therefrom that it is possible to protect pine forests by colonizing insectivorous birds. The German investigations indicate that at least two nesting boxes per acre are needed in order to secure successful protection against caterpillar damage. The effective range of a pair of insectivorous birds at breeding time extends within a radius of 50 metres from the nest.

Taylor disagrees with the opinion that birds cannot be important insect predators in pure coniferous forests because of the paucity of species and lack of water in some regions. He maintains that providing artificial drinking places will attract more birds to these dry forests. The provision of nesting boxes for the hole-nesting tit, the starling, robin, nuthatch, and redstart, he feels, should be included in forest-protection planning, particularly in Britain's coniferous forests.

In conclusion, this author emphasizes that the Germans have demonstrated that the protection and encouragement of birds promises success in combating insects only when used as a preventive and not as a curative measure. That is, success is to be expected only if the birds are brought in before an infestation can assume the proportions of a calamity.

Further work with the management of birds in British forests is reported by MacKenzie (1951). As a result of providing nesting boxes in the forest of Dean from 1942 to 1946, there was a steady increase of tits and flycatchers occupying boxes until every nesting site was in use. Before the boxes were put out, flycatchers were almost entirely absent in the forest. It was concluded too that providing suitable nesting sites can also increase the numbers of insectivorous birds in broad-leafed forests. MacKenzie claims that similar results were also obtained in coniferous forests in Scotland and East Anglia.

In the United States, McAtee (1940) in an attempt to control a nut weevil, was able to increase the song-bird population of an experimental chestnut orchard in Maryland. The installation of bird houses attracted song birds so that, in some seasons, the normal population of the area was quadrupled. Of 98 nest boxes on a three and one-half acre site, 46 were occupied during a typical year.

In their studies, Hamilton and Cook (1940) found a dozen species of small insectivorous mammals widely distributed in a variety of forest types in eastern North America. They were eight to thirty-five times more numerous than birds in the same habitat during the summer and much more abundant during the winter. Mice, shrews, chipmunks, squirrels, and moles often numbered 50 to 200 or more per acre depending upon forest type and site conditions. The authors remark that, when applied to certain environmental deficiencies, artificial aids can be used to increase the numbers of these small mammals. Some success has been achieved towards inducing deer mice to move into young larch and pine plantations by supplying nest boxes. Shrews are encouraged by lopping and scattering brush. Although the cost of these operations may be high, the authors suggested that it might be vastly cheaper and more effective than sporadic insecticidal control for certain forest pests.

Supplementary Food for Natural Enemies

Numerous entomologists have observed the utilization of plant products such as nectar and pollen by beneficial insects as a source of nourishment and moisture (see also chapter 6). Box (1925) points out the importance of nectar-bearing plants adjacent to sugar cane fields as food supply for adult scoliid parasites of cane grubs (*Phyllophaga* spp.) in Puerto Rico. Later, Wolcott (1942) attributes the greater abundance of *Tiphia* in Haiti as compared with Puerto Rico to the greater abundance of wild parsley, *Pastinaca sativa* L., on the former island. Wolcott (1941) advised Puerto Rican sugar-cane growers to allow a limited growth of weeds bordering their fields to provide a food source for *Larra americana* Saussure, an introduced parasite of the mole cricket, *Scapteriscus vicinus* Scudder.

King and Holloway (1930) found nectar of wild carrot, *Daucus carota* L. to be highly preferred by *Tiphia popilliavora* Roh., an introduced parasite of the Japanese beetle, *Popillia japonica* Newm., in eastern United States. They suggested that an abundance of wild carrot in beetle-infested areas would favour the efficiency of *T. popilliavora*.

Myers (1931) comments that roadsides adjacent to sugar-cane fields in Guiana favoured abundant growth of razor-grasses (*Paspalum* spp.). *Diatraea saccharalis* and *D. canella* Hmps. attacking these grasses were significantly parasitized by *Ipobracon* spp. which were strongly attracted to the flowers of the wild-grass hosts. In reference to the biological control of sugar-cane borers, Jepson (1954) emphasized a need for a study of parasite behaviour in the field under prevailing monocultural conditions. He points out that among a parasite's requirements is the need for the nectar of flowers, which is not provided for by young graminaceous plants under cane-growing conditions. For this reason, sugar cane growers in Mauritius have for some time attempted to aid parasites by taking suitable food and shelter plants into the fields.

Recent Soviet experiments show that the vast majority of adult parasites require supplementary nourishment in order to reproduce effectively. In a review of biological control in the U.S.S.R., Telenga (1958) remarks that *Scolia dejeani* Lind. may be attracted to its grub hosts by sowing honey plants (*Phacelia* and *Eryngium*) in commonly infested areas. From an interview with Telenga at the Kiev Laboratory, Huffaker (1959a) reports that Soviet entomologists are investigating interplanting of pumpkin with corn to provide food for adult corn borer parasites in fields devoid of nectar sources. As a substitute for bare fallowing Telenga also recommends the planting of nectar crops in orchards. In this regard, Huffaker (1959a) also reports the statements of Mrs. Yelezarova at the Tashkent Laboratory. She comments that *Aphytis proclia* (Wlkr.) becomes asynchronous with its host, the San Jose scale,

Quadraspidiotus perniciosus (Comst.) because of the paucity of adult food. This condition is improved by planting a *Phacelia* cover crop in orchards. Three crops of *Phacelia* will increase the proportion of parasitized scales to 76 per cent from 5 per cent where cover crops are not used. Uncompleted experiments utilizing four seasonal plantings of *Phacelia* were expected to bring about full parasite–host synchrony and even more favourable increases in parasitization.

Pollen is another important food for adults of various entomophagous insects. Perhaps adults of more species of syrphids rely upon pollen for egg production than any other group of predators. In order to obtain eggs from his laboratory-reared syrphids, Schneider (1948) had to supply them with pollen. Weems (1953), while collecting syrphids observed that the distribution of plants whose flowers are favoured by certain species of the flies often does not coincide with the distribution of these species. Thus, it would seem that the distribution and effectiveness of certain syrphids might be increased through the timely planting of pollen plants favoured by potentially useful aphidophagous species.

Coccinellids also feed upon pollen as Forbes (1883) and subsequent authors have reported. K. S. Hagen (personal communication) adds that certain species of *Hippodamia* shift to such plant foods when aphids become scarce and that this type of nourishment permits survival but not reproduction. We may conclude, then, that the maintenance of pollen as well as nectar-producing vegetation can be advantageous in certain agricultural areas.

The role of plants as a source of honeydew for parasite food has been noted by several authors. Clausen, Jaynes, and Gardner (1933) explain that one of the main limiting factors bearing upon the *Tiphia* parasites of the Japanese beetle is that of the food supply of the adults. Although the summer and autumn species can take advantage of floral and extra-floral nectaries, the spring species generally feed upon insect secretions. It is thus evident, they say, that the maintenance of large *Tiphia* populations throughout the season is entirely dependent upon the presence of aphid-infested plants and various weeds bearing suitable blossoms and nectar glands. This condition is, however, in opposition to what these authors then considered the best agricultural practice—that is, the elimination of weeds as a possible source of insects injurious to cultivated crops.

In the economy of the forest biocoenose, honeydew is considered a very important food for many beneficial insects. Germany's mixed woods which are rich in tree species and ground vegetation provide an optimum supply of honeydew. It is proposed, therefore, that various timber species be added to pure stands of pine, beech, and others in order to approach this more desirable condition which favours biocoenotic stability (Zoebelein 1956, 1957).

Allen and Smith (1958) relate the percentage of parasitized alfalfa caterpillars, *Colias eurytheme* Bdvl., to the availability of nectar and honeydew to the parasite *Apanteles medicaginis* Mues. In the Central Valley of California, fields adjacent to the San Joaquin River often have more highly parasitized *Colias* populations than those in the western valley plain. Riparian fields which are characteristically smaller and more irregular in shape support abundant marginal vegetation. This vegetation and its associated aphids provide ample nectar and honeydew for *A. medicaginis* adults. Sufficient food, a critical factor limiting this parasite's efficiency, is not available in the larger fields of the western plain which are kept relatively free of weeds.

The merits of forest insect predation by omnivorous rodents have been subjected to much debate. Hamilton and Cook (1940), who favour the encouragement of small forest mammals, report that logging practices which fail to retain an adequate proportion of seed-bearing trees reduce not only the growing stock but limit populations of polyphagous rodents by reducing certain elements of their food supply.

Grange and McAtee (1934) are of the opinion that certain omnivorous birds can benefit the farm as objects of beauty, sources of game, and as predators of harmful insects. They recommend the maintenance of vegetation on farm lots of a type that will furnish food as well as shelter for these birds and other wild life. Taylor (1938), on the other hand, remarks that artificial feeding of polyphagous birds seldom proves practicable for improvement of insect control in British forests. However, he adds that under exceptional circumstances such efforts may not be fruitless.

Alternative Hosts for Natural Enemies

The importance of alternative hosts to laboratory studies and colonization programmes is amply treated in other chapters. Here we are interested in how manipulations of the field environment affect biological control through their influence upon alternative arthropod hosts of natural enemies. Fundamentally, alternative hosts ameliorate conditions of asynchrony between preferred hosts and their non-specific parasites and predators. The secondary manifestations of this function are numerous and often essential to effective biological control. A few of these factors are: (1) damping of extreme oscillations in natural enemy and host densities; (2) maintaining functional natural enemy populations during low density periods of preferred hosts; (3) providing suitable overwintering hosts; (4) facilitating maximum natural enemy distribution; and (5) reducing natural enemy cannibalism and combat.

Silvestri (1909b), an early exponent of the biological control method, recommended cultivation of plants within Italian olive groves which would support alternative hosts for parasites of the olive fruit fly, *Dacus oleae* (Gmelin).

In his investigation of parasites of the boll weevil, *Anthonomus grandis* Boh., Pierce (1912) emphasized the fact that surrounding each cotton field there are numerous plants harbouring weevils which normally produce broods of parasites that are capable of attacking the boll weevil. He believed that the elimination of certain alternative hosts of boll weevil parasites at the proper time would force these parasites to attack the cotton pest. By cutting hedges of *Ambrosia trifida* L. infested with the weevil *Lixus scrobicollis* Boh., he obtained a 10 per cent increase of boll weevil parasitization by *Eurytoma tylodermatis* Ashm. in two test plots of cotton adjacent to the hedgerow. Pierce commented that there are a few plants without objectionable qualities, that might be planted adjacent to cotton fields in order to attract alternative hosts of boll weevil parasites. Hedges of blackberries or dew berries would support the blackberry bud weevil, *Anthonomus signatus* Say, with its numerous parasites, all of which attack *A. grandis*. These parasites would produce a spring generation which could mature sufficiently early to attack the first developing stages of the boll weevil. For a similar purpose, planting of *Amorpha fruticosa* L. was also recommended.

Concerning a cropping system in cotton areas, Pierce suggested the planting of a forage or hay crop adjacent to cotton fields. He contended for instance, that cowpeas would undoubtedly encourage build-up of several important parasites which attack the cowpea pod weevil. In the case of a hay field, the process of harvesting would enable the parasites present in various weeds to escape and attack the most abundant host, the boll weevil.

Pierce's ideas for a cropping system, although progressive at the time, are vulnerable to some criticism in view of present knowledge. However, the merits of this approach were more conclusively demonstrated by Hambleton (1944) against *Heliothis virescens* (F.) in the Cañete Valley of Peru. Here cotton cultivation had become so intensified and the habitat so modified that conditions were favourable for the development of the boll-worm but unfavourable for its natural enemies. Parasites and predators were unable to multiply sufficiently to become effective. Development of natural enemies during the winter months was reduced to a minimum, since there was little vegetation and few alternative hosts existed to provide food or shelter for them. At Hambleton's recommendation the ecological status of the valley was changed to modify the entire insect situation with respect to *H. virescens*. Flax was introduced as a winter crop and was followed by summer propagation of corn, beans, sweet potatoes, or weeds on fallowed land. This succession of vegetative growth provided more suitable conditions for natural enemies.

The cultivation of corn was encouraged because it served as host to many insect species which were ideal for the reproduction of entomophagous forms such as *Nabis punctipennis* Blanch. and *Paratriphleps laeviusculus* Champ. These predators of bollworm larvae gradually increased as they found other hosts to prey upon after the cotton crop had matured.

Similarly, parasitization by two or more tachinids of the genus *Archytas* became noticeable. These flies were able to produce a generation or more on the flax cut worms *Agrotis ypsilon* (Rott.), *Euxoa bilitura* (Guen.), and *Spodoptera frugiperda* (J. E. Smith) by the time *Heliothis* again became active on cotton.

The changes in the cropping system in the valley reduced *Heliothis virescens* to a non-pest status within three years. This pest decline was attributed primarily to the increased activity of its natural enemies through a more balanced type of agriculture and changes in cultivation.

Later, Wille (1951) was able to achieve equally successful bollworm control in another Peruvian valley by following Hambleton's example. Subsequent to these successes Beingolea (1957) concluded that natural enemies encouraged by cropping corn in conjunction with cotton also contributed to the biological control of two Peruvian cotton leaf rollers, *Argyrotaenia sphaleropa* Meyrick and *Platynota* sp.

Ullyett (1947) observed that the relative abundance of aphids on cabbage in South Africa can determine the effectiveness of general predators against larvae of the diamond-back moth, *Plutella maculipennis* (Curtis). Syrphid flies, staphylinid beetles, and anthocorid bugs are important predators in the cabbage fields but are attracted principally to aphids. When few aphids are present these predators concentrate more on the *Plutella* larvae. In practice this often occurs, so that, unless the aphids themselves cause an appreciable financial loss, their presence must be regarded as a favourable factor. It is Ullyett's opinion that in order to maintain these predators within the environment, it would seem desirable to have sub-economic, fluctuating populations of aphids permanently present in the crop.

Since its introduction into North America, the oriental fruit moth, *Grapholitha molesta* (Busck), has been particularly injurious to deciduous fruit crops. The status of the oriental fruit moth and its parasites in the new habitat has attracted the interest of numerous entomologists. It was found that an indigenous braconid, *Macrocentrus ancylivorus* Roh., had adapted itself to this new host and had become its most effective parasite. However, *M. ancylivorus* and other fruit moth parasites overwinter principally in alternative hosts, which include the strawberry leaf roller, *Ancylis comptana fragariae* (W. & R.), and the ragweed borer, *Epiblema strenuana* (Wlkr.). Allen (1932) observed that the dominance of *M. ancylivorus* in peach orchards in New Jersey was largely dependent upon the extensive growing of strawberries in relatively close association with peaches. He felt that the ploughing under of second-year strawberry beds following harvest destroyed vast numbers of the parasite when it was most valuable to the control of the fruit moth. Pepper and Driggers (1934) added that in New Jersey peach orchards, where clean cultivation was not practised, a much greater control of the oriental fruit moth was obtained. This was attributed to the availability of alternative hosts for *M. ancylivorus* and other fruit moth parasites on the dominant weed species (ragweed, *Ambrosia artemisiifolia* L., smart weed, *Polygonum* spp., lambs quarter, *Chenopodium album* L., and golden rod, *Solidago* sp.). Driggers and Pepper (1936) similarly showed that larvae and pupae of the codling moth, *Carpocapsa pomonella* (L.), were more highly parasitized in a heavily sprayed and weedy apple orchard than in a heavily sprayed and clean-cultivated orchard. An unsprayed and uncultivated orchard showed four and one-half times as much larval parasitism as either of the heavily sprayed orchards. From these comparative data it can be speculated that alternative hosts in weedy orchards might also favour greater codling moth parasitization. Contrary to the reports of other entomologists, Haden (1935) reported that the presence or absence of the strawberry leaf roller and the ragweed borer had no appreciable effect upon oriental fruit moth control by parasites in Delaware. Bobb (1942), however, reconfirmed the association of weedy orchards and effective parasitism of the oriental fruit moth control by parasites in Virginia. Clausen (1936), citing the oriental fruit moth as a prime example, emphasizes the general importance of maintaining a weed source for alternative hosts of orchard pest parasites. In essence, he affirms that the destruction of plants harbouring alternative hosts of pest parasites may bring about a high mortality among the parasites without a corresponding effect upon the pest host. Consequently, overwintering parasites are at a particular disadvantage because they must build up the following spring from a very low population level.

DeBach (1951, 1958c) suggests that the utilization of permanent cover crops in citrus groves in southern California might provide alternative hosts for general predators of citrus pests. DeBach (1951) explains the theoretical basis for his suggestion in the following manner. General predators may act as a sort of balance wheel in a pest-enemy complex. They tend to feed on whatever pest may be present in abundance. Although, in themselves, they are perhaps incapable of causing biological control below economic levels, they slow down the rate of increase of potential pests or reduce peak infestations when more specific natural enemies may be limited by other factors. If general predators are to be effectively beneficial, they must have a continuity of food available to them. This may not be practicable on the citrus tree itself, but the use of prey-infested cover crops could be the answer to an appreciably higher average general predator population. The application of DeBach's principle obviously need not be restricted to the citrus groves of southern California.

The advantages of maintaining plant species for alternative hosts of teak de-foliator parasites are discussed by Beeson and Chatterjee (1939). Caterpillars of *Hapalia machaeralis* Wlkr. and *Hyblaea puera* Cram. periodically build up to epidemic proportions that seriously damage teak in the tropical plantations of India. Under the prevailing conditions, the addition of monospecific or polyphagous parasites to the pre-existing complex improves pest control, but alone they cannot stabilize populations to the extent that characteristic wide oscillations productive of epidemics will not occur. These authors suggest that a solution might lie in the existence of a mixed undergrowth in teak plantations. In suggesting silvicultural changes to improve teak undergrowth they outline characteristics of plants that might be utilized. The plants must support insects which are either: (1) alternative hosts of parasites of teak defoliators; or (2) alternative food for polyphagous predators; and (3) they should provide a suitable shelter or niche for these species. Moreover, undergrowth plants must be alternative hosts of pests feeding on teak.

Improvement of Pest–Natural Enemy Synchronization

Occasionally, the effectiveness of an entomophagous species is reduced or lost because it becomes partially or wholly separated from its host in time or space. Infrequently, synchronization may be re-established by natural means. More often it is necessary to attempt to rectify or at least lessen asynchronous relationships by manipulating the environments in which they occur.

Probably the greatest difficulty in achieving synchronization between crop pests and their natural enemies has been encountered in attempts to control scale insects with introduced parasites in California citrus groves. Early mention of host–

parasite synchrony is made by Quayle (1911) with respect to citrus fumigation for the black scale, *Saissetia oleae* (Bern.). He comments that in southern California it is not uncommon to find a citrus grove with its borders and avenues lined with pepper or olive trees. These serve as an excellent breeding ground for the black scale because they remain untreated. Although these trees perpetuate a pest insect, *S. oleae*, they are believed to be a distinct benefit because they also ensure the continued breeding of its parasite *Scutellista cyanea* Mots. This is a particularly important function during periods when a grove may be recovering from the effects of an insecticide treatment. Quayle inferred that the maintenance of *Scutellista* on these alternative host trees tended to decrease the number of insecticide treatments necessary for the control of black scale in the groves.

The matter of synchronization of the black scale and its parasites is given further attention by Flanders (1942*b*). In 1919, the parasite *Metaphycus lounsburyi* (How.) was established in southern California. It reproduced rapidly and within a year or two had brought damaging infestations of the scale under control. It followed, however, that heavy reinfestations occurred. *M. lounsburyi* was not completely effective, partly because it brought about discrete, uniformly aged generations of *S. oleae*. The elimination of overlapping scale generations created long periods when there was a scarcity of suitable hosts. The longevity of the females of *M. lounsburyi* was not sufficient to enable them to bridge the gap between the occurrences of acceptable host stages.

Metaphycus helvolus (Comp.) is confronted with a similar situation in the arid interior region of southern California. Here the climate extremes limit the black scale to a single annual generation. Smith (1942*a*) points out that, during the summer, this may result in the near elimination of *M. helvolus* from inland orchards. However, with the approach of autumn when the scale becomes large enough to be successfully parasitized, field liberations of insectary-reared parasites might solve the problem.

Flanders (1949*b*) suggests the planting of oleander in proximity to citrus trees. When watered frequently, this alternative host plant will create a humid environment which will encourage continuous generations of the scale and its parasite. It is felt that this will prevent the parasite from lagging behind the build-up of its host on citrus. In a hot climate the scale thrives only on oleander branches which are recumbent on the moist ground and covered by fallen leaves. In such an environment *S. oleae* exists in all stages and is protected from *M. helvolus*. However, crawlers that go from the hidden colony to exposed parts of the plant serve as parasite hosts. Flanders remarks further that the planting of large acreages solely to a single species of plant tends to produce a less favourable balance than that which occurs in a mixed planting which more nearly approaches a natural condition. The addition of oleanders to a citrus grove, therefore, is a return to a more natural state and, consequently, to better biological control.

DeBach (1958*c*) applies a similar principle to the control of the California red scale, *Aonidiella aurantii* (Mask.), and the oleander scale, *Aspidiotus hederae* (Vallot), on California citrus. English ivy is being tested as a ground cover to serve as an alternative host for these pests. Both of the scales are attacked by *Aphytis lingnanensis* Comp., the principal red scale parasite. Artificial inoculation of scales on the ground cover provides peak host populations when they are needed to increase parasite populations in citrus groves.

Artificial infestation of the crop host plant with the pest insect at suitable periods also has been suggested as a means of solving the problem of asynchrony. Smith and DeBach (1953) tested this method with the univoltine black scale and its parasite *M. helvolus* on citrus in interior regions of southern California. By artificially infesting the trees with newly hatched *S. oleae* just before and during the summer period of critically low host density, they were able to extend the activity of the parasites for a considerable length of time. However, *M. helvolus* was too efficient and eliminated the artificially inoculated scales too soon to permit carry-over of the parasites through the entire summer. Although the trials were not successful from a practical viewpoint, the authors felt that '. . . the satisfactory demonstration of the principles involved is highly encouraging, and that slight additional manipulation might result in complete success.'

In experiments analogous to those of Smith and DeBach, Huffaker and Kennett (1956) artificially inoculated strawberry plants with cyclamen mite, *Steneotarsonemus pallidus* (Banks), in order to achieve successful biological control of that pest. The results of these studies were so encouraging that they suggested deliberate infestation of new plantings as a possibly practicable technique in the control of this pest. Through this technique a sub-economic equilibrium between the cyclamen mite and its principal predators, *Typhlodromus reticulatus* Oud. and *T. cucumeris* Oud., could conceivably be achieved before periods of highest yield and potentially greatest mite damage were reached. These authors speculate that it might be feasible to introduce only the predators into strawberry fields. However, they believe that when this method is employed it must be certain that the cyclamen mite is rather generally present in new plantings if the predators are to survive and be of benefit. Consequently, both components of the ultimate equilibrium should be introduced in order to obtain quick and satisfactory results.

The artificial infestation or inoculation of crops in order to augment the efficacy of natural enemies will generally be useful only in those cases where an otherwise efficient entomophagous species is periodically depressed because of lack of suitable stages or insufficient numbers of the host. Smith and DeBach (1953) remark that no doubt there are many insect pests which have in their habitat enemies possessing the qualities necessary to bring about control were it not for the asynchronization of their populations with those of their enemies. This fact is the basis for the belief that asynchronization may be overcome and biological control achieved, not only by mass-culture and periodic colonization of enemies, but also by culture and colonization of the pest insects themselves. Fundamentally, this process differs little from vaccination, since it has as its objective the production of a mild, non-injurious infestation in order to prevent a heavy injurious one.

Synchronization with respect to the effectiveness of general predators in citrus is discussed by DeBach (1951, 1958c). Although general predation may not regulate pest populations in the strict sense, it can effectively retard the rate of pest increase and militate against explosive outbreaks. To act in this capacity general predators must be constantly available in sufficient numbers. The utilization of prey-infested cover crops in citrus groves, it is believed, would achieve this end. Thus, it is suggested that the biological control of the citrus red mite, *Panonychus citri* (McG.), be augmented in experimental plots by planting permanent cover crops. This method provides alternative host mites and other prey on the herbs and grasses as food for general predators found associated with citrus.

The importance of a cropping system for the maintenance of synchrony between a dipterous leaf miner, *Liriomyza* sp., and its parasites is recognized by Hills and Taylor (1951). Lettuce and cantaloups furnish an almost year-round environment for the leaf miners in the Salt River Valley of Arizona. However, the damage caused to lettuce is of little concern since leaf miner parasitization reaches a high level on this crop in the winter and early spring. The lettuce crop in this region is considered responsible for the successful overwintering of large numbers of parasites which ordinarily attack *Liriomyza* on young cantaloups in April. Conditions that interfere with the overwintering of the parasites on lettuce can result in damage to the cantaloup crop.

The separation of harmful arthropods from their natural enemies in space is not an uncommon occurrence. The most successful biological control programmes have been based upon the reuniting of accidentally introduced exotic pests with their parasites and predators by searching for these natural enemies and purposely introducing them. It has been found, however, that a host plant preferred by an exotic pest may not be attractive to parasites introduced from its native locale. Thereby, a spatial breach may be effected between the host and its natural enemy. We have also learned that certain insects, by adapting to new agricultural environments, have become more harmful because their natural enemies could not adapt with equal facility. Thus, the pale western cutworm in Alberta escaped its parasites by occupying a subterranean habitat in cultivated areas; the sugar-cane froghopper escaped its egg parasites by ovipositing in the soil in cane fields; and the sugar-cane borer moth, by adapting to a drier agricultural habitat, left certain of its parasites behind in its primitive aquatic environment.

Aside from the work concerned with parasite and predator introductions for the control of exotic pests, the problem of uniting pests and their natural enemies in space has not been widely studied. However, as mentioned earlier, Raquel Dexter (1932) recommends that habitats of the giant Surinam toad be planted with vegetation favoured by *Phyllophaga* beetles, thus improving the spatial relationship between the toad and its principal prey.

An interesting environmental change has provided for a possible improvement of the spatial relationship of the beet leafhopper, *Circulifer tenellus* (Baker), and its egg parasites, *Aphelinoidea plutella* Grlt. and *Abella subflava* Grlt., in southern Idaho (Henderson 1955). Outside cultivated lands these egg parasites survive the winter in areas occupied by Russian thistle, *Salsola kali* L. var. *tenuifolia* Tausch. Thus, with comparatively few eggs of the overwintering generation available for parasitization in the spring, enormous numbers of egg parasites emerging in Russian thistle areas were largely wasted. Within recent years, however, the breeding areas of the beet leafhopper have been changed. Today, Russian thistle has invaded over-grazed rangeland and to some extent has overlapped the mustard areas where the spring generation of leafhoppers develops. This change should be advantageous to the leafhopper egg parasites because it will bring them into contact with the eggs of the spring generation of the host.

In a somewhat different way attempts have been made to improve the spatial relationships between the lima bean pod borer *Etiella zinkenella* (Treit) and its parasites by Viktorov in Russia. In this case leguminous trees were removed from the vicinity of agricultural hosts of the pod borer because the parasites were only effective near the ground whereas the pest persisted at crown level (Franz 1961a, b).

Control of Honeydew-Feeding Ants

The inhibitory effect of honeydew-feeding ants upon biological control is often of critical importance. When honeydew-secreting insects infest crops, ants that attend and protect them can seriously deter the natural enemies of these homopterous pests. This problem has been studied particularly in citrus culture but is commonplace on other crops, ornamentals, and in nature. Flanders (1942b, 1945a, 1958), DeBach (1951, 1958c) and DeBach, Dietrick, and Fleschner (1951) show that ants, especially the introduced Argentine ant, *Iridomyrmex humilis* (Mayr), must be eliminated from California citrus groves in order that full benefit be realized from natural enemies of the California red scale, the yellow scale, the citrus red mite, the citrus mealybug, the brown soft scale, the black scale, and citrus aphids. DeBach, Dietrick, and Fleschner state that '. . . biological control will be rendered completely unsatisfactory if honeydew-seeking ants are abundant.' Steyn (1958) discusses similar problems in South Africa. In the citrus groves near Letaba, ants also interfere with the biological control of California red scale and the brown soft scale. *Anoplolepis custodiens* Smith disturbs *Aphytis chrysomphali* (Mercet), *Chilocorus distigma* Klg., and *C. wahlbergi* Muls., as well as other coccinellids and spiders. In the same way, *Pheidole megacephala* is shown by Annecke (1959) to be harmful in South African citrus orchards.

Modification of Adverse Agricultural Practices

It is our intention here to offer only a general outline of the large subject matter pertaining to this phenomenon. This will be done by selecting from the literature references to some of the representative and more important ways in which agricultural practices can affect biological control.

PLANTING AND SEED BED OPERATIONS. Until recent years, biological control in truck and field crops has, on the whole, been subordinated in the light of concentrated efforts in more permanent crops. Consequently, the effects of planting and seed-bed operations upon natural enemies have not been generally investigated.

Ullyett (1947), however, does give this matter consideration. After a thorough investigation of mortality factors affecting *Plutella maculipennis*, he concluded that cabbage seed beds should be left undisturbed after removing plants needed for the crops. In this way a suitable reservoir is provided from which the parasites can disperse later. Parasitism is usually so high in the seed beds that few moths escape.

CULTIVATION AND DUST. Cultivation, a basic agricultural operation, is of questionable value to some permanent crops in which entomophagous species effect a significant pest reduction. *Aphelopus* sp., a parasite of the white apple leafhopper, *Typhlocyba pomaria* McA., passes the winter in the cocoon just beneath the soil surface. Armstrong (1935) observed that a large percentage of these parasites is killed by discing and other methods of orchard cultivation in the autumn. Autumn discing in an orchard where 30 per cent parasitization has been recorded was followed by a spring in which no parasitization could be observed. Later, Steiner (1938) further substantiated Armstrong's observations. He recommended that cultivation be confined to June of the following year or that a portion of the soil beneath the trees be left undisturbed. Muma (1961) demonstrated in preliminary experiments in Florida citrus groves that six major injurious insects and mites may be reduced in number or partially controlled by reducing cover crop cultivation. His data did not, however, give evidence that there was a consistent favourable effect on natural enemy abundance or effectiveness in the under-cultivated groves.

It was experimentally demonstrated by Pepper and Driggers (1934) that parasitization of the codling moth, *Carpocapsa pomonella*, is appreciably reduced by cultivation in apple orchards in eastern United States. This is attributed to the removal of necessary alternative hosts of the parasites in the weedy undergrowth.

In the U.S.S.R. the problem of using *Caenocrepis bothynoderes* Grom. against the beet pest *Bothynoderes punctiventris* Germ. is being studied. It has been found that in the process of sugar beet cultivation, especially during mould-board ploughing in the autumn, the *Caenocrepis* are shifted to the deeper soil layers and subsequently cannot reach the surface. As a consequence, the pteromalid is ineffective in that country. However, experimental deep ploughing without mould-board has brought about a great increase in parasite survival with a corresponding decrease of 50 to 70 per cent in the weevil population. Contrary to the situation with *Caenocrepis*, *Perilitus bicolor* West, a parasite of the hemp flea beetle, *Psylloides attenuata* Koch., increases after mould-board ploughing of hemp fields. In this case, the beetles are caused to emerge from hibernation later than they would normally, at a time when temperatures are less adverse to parasite activity (Telenga 1958).

Some authors indicate that cultivation can affect natural enemies secondarily through the condition of the host plant. Osburn and Mathis (1946) made a comparison of the numbers of Florida red scale, *Chrysomphalus aonidum* (L.), on orange trees in uncultivated plots to those growing on cultivated plots in the same grove. Scale infestations were markedly greater on trees growing under cultivation. Nevertheless, orange trees subjected to intensive cultivation were more vigorous and in better physical condition than those left uncultivated even though they were more heavily infested. The difference between the percentage of parasitized scales as well as those infected by an entomophagous fungus in the two treatments was small. However, there was some evidence that a greater percentage of parasitism was associated with the infestations on cultivated plots. One might speculate that perhaps greater tree vigour resulting from cultivation produced scale hosts which were more acceptable to the parasites. In this regard, Flanders (1940) explains that the condition of the host insect can determine the success of parasite establishment. Hymenopterous parasites tend to deposit fertilized (female) eggs only in preferred host individuals. Characteristics such as small size, age, or other factors that cause the host to become unfavourable decrease the possibility of establishment, since unfertilized (male) eggs are deposited in less desirable hosts.

Evenhuis (1958) believes that cultivation in apple orchards favours the increase of woolly apple aphid, *Eriosoma lanigerum* (Hausm.). The resultant new tree growth promotes aphid reproduction, while disturbing the soil beneath reduces the relative numbers of natural enemies.

The nature of the more transient truck and field crops makes it mandatory that many of them be cultivated frequently. Whatever harm this practice might inflict upon natural enemies in such crops must be overlooked. On the other hand, under these conditions, it is probable that frequent cultivation eliminates many soil-inhabiting pests mechanically and, as well, exposes them to the elements and to omnivorous entomophagous species. Based upon mathematical reasoning, Thompson (1927) claims such mechanical controls as cultivation should not adversely affect the efficacy of parasites so long as at least as many hosts as parasites are eliminated.

Dust is an inevitable companion of cultivation and of unpaved access roads for farm machinery. Plank (1929), Driggers (1930), Fleschner (1952), Flanders (1940), Bartlett (1951c), and DeBach (1951, 1958c) report the inhibition of effective parasitism and predation by dust. DeBach (1958c) artificially increased California red scale populations by purposeful road dust applications. As a means to discourage dust production in citrus groves he suggests overhead sprinklers, cover crops, and dust-reducing road surfaces.

IRRIGATION. The importance of proper irrigation practices to the enhancement of biological control has been demonstrated in a variety of crops. Michelbacher and Smith (1943) report that poor irrigation schedules in California during 1941 prevented some alfalfa fields from achieving normal growth for about seven weeks following harvest. This allowed the alfalfa caterpillar prolonged periods for egg deposition which were followed by heavy larval damage. In this case, tardy irrigation enabled *Colias* populations to increase to the extent that the parasite *Apanteles* was unable to suppress them in the normal manner.

The effect of irrigation in determining the occurrence of fungas epizootics in aphids infesting alfalfa is of great significance. Davis *et al.* (1957) and Hall and Dunn (1957b) suggest timely irrigation to induce outbreaks of fungus in populations of the spotted alfalfa aphid, *Therioaphis maculata* (Buck.). It is noteworthy that such epizootics frequently occur in populations of the pea aphid, *Macrosiphum pisi*

(Harris), as well as in those of spotted alfalfa aphid following routine irrigation of alfalfa in California.

Hambleton (1944) and Willie (1951) stress the need of a strict irrigation schedule for the successful biological control of *Heliothis virescens* in Peruvian cotton. A minimum of irrigation water is applied during the growing season in order that succulent growth of the leaves and stems can be avoided. This succulent growth attracts ovipositing females of *Heliothis* over wide areas, and as a result such rapid increase of the pest follows that natural enemies cannot overtake them in time. This effect is compounded by the fact that the principal predator, *Paratriphleps laeviusculus*, an anthocorid bug, apparently lacks the capacity to work actively in the humid microclimate of heavily irrigated fields.

Careful attention must be given to the proper irrigation of cabbage in South Africa so that full benefit might be obtained from diamond-back moth predators (Ullyett 1947). Some of the most important predators of this lepidopterous pest live in the soil. It is possible to drown these insects or drive them away if the crop is irrigated too freely at one time or too frequently. When the plant mounds between the channels are not inundated, this danger is not too great. The worst possible conditions are produced when the fields are flood-irrigated.

Within citrus groves in arid regions of California, adequate moisture is an important requirement of scale parasites. DeBach (1951) contends that sufficient relative humidity can be maintained in the groves through the use of sprinkler irrigation supplemented by cover crops and the encouragement of more dense foliage.

CLEAN CULTURE. Many of the agricultural practices which are placed in the ambiguous category of 'clean culture' are unfavourable from the point of view of effective parasite and predator activity. Common sense should allow that cultural methods which are beneficial in one crop may not be universally profitable. There is little doubt that weed removal in and around certain truck crops and seed crops is a necessary precaution. We have already pointed out, however, that weed removal in apple and peach orchards and the early ploughing under of near-by strawberries eliminates necessary alternative hosts of overwintering codling moth and oriental fruit moth parasites.

Ullyett (1947) condemns the practice of eliminating cruciferous weeds in the cabbage-growing regions of South Africa. In this case, the importance of weed hosts of *Plutella maculipennis* does not lie in the reservoir of the pest that they might provide. Natural-control factors act in the weed environment in much the same way as in the cultivated crop. Hence, the weeds serve to maintain the balance attained between the host and its mortality factors in the cultivated crop which has preceded them as a food medium. Consequently, where no cabbage crops are available for *Plutella* over a considerable period, the weeds serve to preserve the natural balance during this period so that when cabbage is again planted the presence of adequate numbers of natural enemies in the area is assured.

Davis et al. (1957) warn that the annual clean-up of weeds along the edges of alfalfa fields, fence rows, stand pipes, etc., is destructive to predators. Certain ladybird beetles pass a period of dormancy in such places and are disturbed or destroyed when the weeds are removed. These authors do not advocate that weed clean-up associated with California alfalfa be abandoned. Rather they suggest that it be delayed until after mid-March when aggregations of dormant ladybird beetles have largely dispersed.

The popular conception of clean forestry is criticized by Hanson (1937). Except when large-scale operations are carried out, it is not considered beneficial to remove felled or fallen pole-sized pine timber in British forests. Leaving the small-diameter thin-barked trees on the ground provides a sustained but limited supply of breeding material for the maintenance of a permanent population of natural enemies of pine beetles.

The practice of burning harvest residue is associated with clean culture in various crops. The effects of burning sugar-cane trash on beneficial organisms has been a controversial issue for over thirty years. Those against trash burning claim that it is harmful to parasites of the sugar-cane borer, *Diatraea saccharalis*, particularly the trichogrammatid egg parasites. Those in favour claim that burning does not select against the parasites and therefore has no harmful effect upon the host–parasite ratio. It would appear that regional differences in cane-growing conditions might determine whether or not cane trash burning inhibits *Diatraea* parasites. Hence, the advantages of burning in Louisiana may not be realized in Mexico (Holloway 1929; Abarca, Iturbe, and Caceres 1958). Wolcott and Martorell (1943a) comment that when non-burning of cane trash in Puerto Rico was first recommended, only its effect on the moth borer and *Trichogramma* was considered. However, the giant toads which have been subsequently introduced to the island are rarely able to escape from between crossfires. Thus, the non-burning of trash is of even greater importance in order to preserve the effective predation of white grubs by toads in the cane fields.

The burning of grain stubble is usually employed as a means of disposing of harvest residue. Marchal (1908) remarks that the destruction of grain stubble may have unfortunate consequences in the natural control of the Hessian fly, *Phytophaga destructor* (Say). Should this be done in a tardy manner there is a risk that all of the flies will abandon the stubble, leaving only the parasites to be destroyed. Marchal discusses an analogous case concerning a cecidomyid (probably *Sitodiplosis mosellana* (Gehin) (=*Contarinia tritici* Kirby)) which attacks the wheat grain. In this case, burning of the debris after threshing has an injurious effect upon the parasites of the fly. Although the debris contains pupae of the midges it is probable that they are parasitized because the healthy non-parasitized larvae of these flies pupate in the soil.

McColloch (1923) also condemns the burning of wheat stubble in Kansas because about 66 per cent of the 'flaxseed' (Hessian fly puparia) are at the crowns of the plants and are not destroyed. Although a significant reduction of the pest was not attained, its parasites were destroyed by stubble-burning.

Shaking apple blossoms from the trees and burning them in order to control the apple blossom weevil, *Anthonomus pomorum* L., is considered undesirable by

Imms (1918). Because the parasites are destroyed by this procedure, Imms suggests boxing the blossoms in such a way that parasites may escape while the weevils remain confined.

To combat the Malaysian coconut zygaenid, *Artona catoxantha* Hamps., the lower, more heavily attacked fronds are often pruned and burned. Gater (1925) claims that this only prolongs the infestation because the parasites, principally *Ptychomyia remota* Ald., a tachinid, are killed. When left undisturbed the parasites eventuolly control *Artona* outbreaks. Gater claims that cultural practices such as burning, smudging, and spraying will cause outbreaks of this pest.

The removal of pests by hand is considered detrimental to biological control by some authors. Holloway (1929) and Plank (1929) believe the 'cutting of dead hearts' or removal of young sugar-cane plants killed by moth borers reduces the abundance of *Diatraea* parasites and is therefore of little value. For the same reason, le Pelley (1934) and Kirkpatrick (1937) rule out the hand-picking of *Antestia* eggs from coffee plants in the plantations of Africa. Because the amount of parasitized bug eggs commonly attains 90 per cent, it is felt that hand-picking merely removes parasites from the fields.

MOWING. The mowing of large contiguous acreages of alfalfa at harvest in California has been shown by Schlinger and Dietrick (1960) to affect adversely most of the beneficial insects inhabiting the fields. These authors recommended a strip-farming practice as a means of conserving natural enemies of alfalfa pests. Strip-farming as shown in figure 93 is essentially the process of cutting and harvesting hay from alternate strips in the same field. When each set of alternate strips of hay matures and is cut, the other strips are about one-half grown. Thus, strips of growing hay are always available for the pest species as well as the natural enemies, and a more satisfactory population balance between each pest and its natural enemies can be obtained and retained during the entire growing season.

An example of the adverse effects of mowing the entire field at one time (regular farming) as compared with mowing a field in alternate strips (strip-farming) is shown in table 6, with reference to some of the natural enemies of the spotted alfalfa aphid, *Therioaphis maculata*. The aphid host was of a similar density in both fields earlier in the experiment, but later the aphid rose to such densities as to cause considerable damage to the regular-farmed hay, while at the same time the aphid density in the strip-farmed hay became insignificant. The data from table 6 reveal, among other things, that there were 1,809,000 more natural enemies per acre in the strip-farmed field than in the regular-farmed field. In other words, there was an increase of 42 natural enemies per square foot due to the conservation of beneficial species. It was also pointed out by these authors that several species of parasites were found effectively working in the strip-farmed field that never appeared in the regular-farmed field.

In regions of North America where the alfalfa weevil, *Hypera postica* (Gyll.), is a pest, well-timed mowing can augment the effectiveness of the parasite, *Bathyplectes curculionis* (Thoms.) (Hamlin *et al.* 1949). With proper timing of the harvest, the younger weevils which are least parasitized sustain a greater mortality, while nearly mature weevils which are highly parasitized are least affected. Thus, when the first seasonal cutting of alfalfa is promptly undertaken the parasite is of greatest value in minimizing the production of adult weevils from the tremendous larval population of the first crop.

TABLE 6

A comparison of the average number of the more important natural enemies of the spotted alfalfa aphid, Therioaphis maculata (Buck.), per acre during June, 1959, at Brawley, California (Schlinger and Dietrick 1960)

Species	Regular farming	Strip-farming	Number increased by strip-farming
Lady beetle adults	46,000	205,000	159,000
Lady beetle larvae	11,000	232,000	221,000
Green lacewing larvae	195,000	206,000	11,000
Aphid wasp parasites	70,000	287,000	217,000
Big-eyed bugs	199,000	401,000	202,000
An aphid-eating spider	105,000	1,094,000	989,000
Totals	626,000	2,435,000	1,809,000
Total per sq. ft.	14	56	42

SILVICULTURAL PRACTICES. Silviculture, although somewhat unique, must be looked upon as a phase of agriculture. This takes greater significance in light of recent second-growth timber and permanent logging enterprises which have been initiated to counterbalance the decreasing virgin forest resource.

DeLeon (1935) considers the effects of standard bark beetle control methods upon natural enemies. The fell-peel method exposes larval broods to natural mortality factors—the elements, ants, shrews, voles, chipmunks, and other insectivorous species. The deck and burn method, however, does not depend upon the natural mortality factors. When the latter is employed with lodgepole pine against the mountain pine beetle, *Dendroctonus monticolae* Hopk., it is practically totally destructive to the parasite, *Coeloides dendroctoni* Cush. Autumnal burning, however, destroys few parasites. The predacious dolichopodid, *Medetera aldrichii* Wh., is destroyed by both spring and autumn burning. DeLeon, therefore, concludes that although artificial control is always necessary, a method that is effective and at the same time will inflict the least injury to the beneficial insects is to be desired. He recommends that the deck and burn method be used only in the autumn because at least the spring brood of *Coeloides* is spared. It is noteworthy that the method of fell and treatment with an insecticide is generally employed today. Bark beetle control by this method is apparently deemed adequate without the help of natural enemies because timing of treatments for parasite conservation no longer receives general consideration.

Hanson (1937) presents a very interesting report of the amalgamation of biological control and silvicultural practices against beetles (*Myelophilus* spp. and others) in second-growth pine forests in Great Britain. From the silvicultural point of view, the nearest approach to the natural state in second-growth Scots pine forests occurs in young pole crops before the first thinning. At this growth stage natural enemies are very numerous and for a time satisfactory biological control exists. The duration of this condition is determined by the growth rate of the crop. The rate of beetle increase is determined by the availability of suitable breeding material. When breeding material is at a minimum, overcrowding of the broods occurs and a higher beetle mortality results. Overcrowding of the broods also is distinctly advantageous to the natural enemies. If the supply of breeding material is equal to or exceeds the requirements of the beetles, overcrowding ceases and biological control diminishes. Suitable breeding material in the second-growth pole stand takes the form of suppressed trees and occurs at a stage later than the proper time for thinning the stand. It follows that each pole crop should be thinned according to local growth conditions. The desirability of maintaining an equilibrium between the beetles and their natural enemies is of primary importance. Consequently, from the entomological point of view it appears beneficial to defer the first thinning until the time approaches when the combined effects of overcrowding and biological control threaten to break down. This point is reached when the quantity of suitable breeding material (suppressed poles) tends to equal the minimum requirements of the resident beetle population.

Hanson also points out that the sudden increase of available breeding material produced by thinning provides abnormally favourable conditions for the sudden increase of beetles, and outbreaks are caused. This is especially true when felled trees are allowed to remain in the area that has been thinned. Should thinning be done in strips so that a limited amount of breeding material is available, outbreaks are not encouraged and a permanent population of natural enemies may be maintained in the stand.

As a measure against spruce budworm, *Choristoneura fumiferana*, in eastern Canada, Heimburger (1945) suggests the planting of hardwood barriers. The installation of hardwood barriers of 30 miles or more in width should be effective against approaching spruce budworm outbreaks largely by reducing the availability of susceptible balsam fir. The barriers should be located at the periphery or in the paths of outbreaks where the population pressure is highest. It is felt that even a retardation of the budworm in some cases should allow its parasites to catch up to the periphery of the outbreak before the barriers become ineffective.

In areas where the method is feasible, solar-heat treatment of felled ponderosa pine is recommended against *Dendroctonus brevicomis* Lec. by Person (1940). This method allows many of the clerid predator *Thanasimus lecontei* Wolc. to escape but kills a high percentage of the beetles. It was found that bark beetle mortality was highest on the tops of the logs; however, it also increased on the undersides because the clerids tended to concentrate there. When the bark was peeled from the exposed logs more predators were killed. Because high air temperatures are needed, the solar-heat treatment of felled and infested logs can be used only against the summer generation of bark beetles and is limited to open stands on favourable slopes.

Keen (1952) aptly summarizes the modern approach to forest insect control through wise silvicultural practices. In order to prevent destructive insect outbreaks in a managed forest, the first objective of forest insect control is to regulate conditions so as to maintain a natural balance between the insect population that is destructive and its natural enemies as well as between the insects and their food supply. This objective will be attained more fully in the future through silvicultural practices which involve such measures as prompt disposal of slash and correction of other insect-breeding conditions, the regulation of stand density and competition, the regulation of environmental factors through drainage or other methods, and the selection of insect-resistant varieties and species of trees.

If native insects already have a full complement of natural enemies, an effort can be made to create favourable conditions for the manipulation of these beneficial agencies. Direct methods, such as burning or sun curing, can be modified so that beneficial insects will not be destroyed in as large numbers as the harmful species. Sometimes only a slight change in this direction will give the beneficial insects the upper hand, and they will quickly bring an epidemic back to normal balance.

CHEMICAL PESTICIDES, MICROBIAL INSECTICIDES, AND ENTOMOPHAGOUS SPECIES. One of the most acute problems contemporary entomologists must face involves the effect of pesticides on the natural balance of arthropods in agricultural regions. Since the early 1940's revolutionary new pesticides have been highly effective against injurious arthropods. Unfortunately, many of these materials suppress beneficial species as well. Consequently, reinfestations may follow treatments quickly and repeatedly. Environmental modification or imbalances caused by pesticide application are coming to be recognized as primary problems in pest control. Suffice it to say here that such modifications are frequent and often strikingly detrimental to the efficacy of arthropod natural enemies. Because of its tremendous importance, this subject is given detailed consideration in chapter 17.

In view of the increasing interest in applied insect pathology, it is important to consider the effects of diseases, especially the microbial insecticides, on other agents of biological control. Current knowledge indicates that insect pathogens, particularly the polyhedral viruses, often exert their greatest effect at high host densities. They are potentially most useful, therefore, in environments conducive to rapid and sustained pest increase as, for example, environments brought about by regional crop specialization or in forests where silvicultural practices tend to restrict the number of tree species. In certain of these environments arthropod parasites and predators are normally quite effective. How does the introduction into the environment of another control factor—insect disease—affect other entomophagous species? Steinhaus (1954), in an extensive review of the effects of diseases on insect populations, comments that there are situations in which parasites and disease are antagonistic and there are those in which they work in concert. In fact, the combined effects of parasites and disease, in certain cases, have exceeded the effect of either agent alone.

Steinhaus (1954) points out that Niklas observed that fifth-instar larvae of the nun moth, *Lymantria monacha* L., infected with a polyhedral virus were not attacked by a tachinid parasite in Europe. Similarly, this author reports that Masera found that larvae of the butterfly, *Pieris brassicae* (L.), infected with a microsporidian were not parasitized by *Apanteles glomeratus* (L.). Michelbacher and Smith (1943) indicate that in California when the polyhedrosis of the alfalfa caterpillar is epizootic in the larvae it kills parasitized hosts before the parasite, *Apanteles medicaginis*, can complete its development.

The effects of a fungus disease of *Plutella maculipennis* upon its parasites and consequently upon outbreaks of this pest are given much attention by Ullyett and Schonken (1940) and Ullyett (1947). The disease, *Entomophthora sphaerosperma* Fres., periodically causes heavy mortality of *P. maculipennis* on crucifers in humid districts of South Africa and, under epizootic conditions, is severely detrimental to the parasites of its host. Parasite populations are drastically reduced through direct mortality within the host's body and indirectly by the near elimination of hosts for the subsequent parasite generation. Following fungus epizootics, reinfestation and recurrent outbreaks of *Plutella* occur rapidly as a result of its release from parasite control.

On the surface, it seems paradoxical that an entomophagous agent can perpetrate a more serious pest outbreak than that which it has eliminated. Nevertheless, there exists here a condition analogous to pest resurgences caused by chemical application (chapter 17). As a consequence, Ullyett and Schonken do not endorse a general acceptance of the *Plutella* fungus as a biological control agent. Rather, they recommend a fungicidal control of the pathogen in humid areas, in order to prevent serious outbreaks of its pest host.

Reports of the disastrous effects of a pathogen on the biological control of an insect are, as yet, extremely rare. By no means should they be regarded as a stigma upon increasingly successful microbial pest control. We are reminded, however, that the panacea of pest control eludes us still.

The combining of pathogenic agents with other natural enemies towards the common goal of more permanent pest reduction would seem to merit greater attention. A few authors give us insight into the possibilities for this approach. From an investigation of the red-backed cutworm, *Euxoa ochrogaster* (Guen.), in Saskatchewan, King and Atkinson (1928) conclude that the presence of disease in certain populations greatly increased the proportion of emerged parasites to emerged moths. This, they feel, would favour the possibility of high parasitization in the following year. Apparently, the observations of King and Atkinson are very similar to those of Ullyett and Schonken. However, the residual populations of *Euxoa* and its parasites were evidently in ratios more conducive to sustained effective parasitism.

Michelbacher and Smith (1943), while inferring that *Apanteles* larvae were killed because of the polyhedrosis disease of their hosts, also observe that there were cases in which the parasite dominated the situation after the wilt disease had first reduced the number of *Colias* larvae. When this occurred there was no further build-up in the host population. In this regard, Steinhaus (1954) cites the unpublished data of Thompson. When correctly timed, a virus application greatly reduces populations of the alfalfa caterpillar without having a marked effect on the parasite. In nature and in controlled field treatments, the parasite larvae usually emerge and pupate before the infected host dies. Furthermore, Thompson feels that the available data indicate that virus treatment of economic populations of the alfalfa caterpillar increases the chances of the parasite, *Apanteles*, in controlling the following generation of host larvae.

Bird and Elgee (1957) report on an interesting series of events which led to the control of the European spruce sawfly, *Diprion hercyniae* (Htg.), by the harmonious effects of an entomogenous virus and two parasites. Initially two introduced parasite species, *Dahlbominus fuscipennis* (Zett.) and *Exenterus claripennis* Thoms., were established in Canada and showed ability to cause sawfly mortality at high host population levels. These, however, were eliminated as control factors by the severe epizootics of an introduced polyhedrosis on the sawfly during 1940 to 1942. Since the virus has become the controlling agent at high host densities, the parasites *Drino bohemica* Mesn. and *Exenterus vellicatus* Cush., which are active at low host densities, have replaced the formerly dominant parasite species. Here we have an outstanding example of how, with a proper ecological balance, parasites and disease together can effect a near perfect biological control.

To terminate the extensive and ramified subject matter of this chapter, the words of Tothill (1958, p. 531) seem especially appropriate, '... while we have the clear duty to control, as best we may, outbreaks of injurious insects of all kinds, yet the time has come, at least for some of them, to set our sights toward prevention rather than control. ... To bring about such ... prophylaxis, we need to work with nature and not against her, and we need to give very serious thought indeed to changes in the environment that have made the outbreaks possible. We have changed the environment once; we have it in our power to change it again; and we should now, I suggest, be making long-term plans for doing so. Such an inspiring objective may be difficult to achieve but is well within the compass of modern biological science.'

CHAPTER 17

Integration of Chemical and Biological Control

B. R. BARTLETT

INTRODUCTION

THE DEVELOPMENT of powerful new contact insecticides has been one of the most spectacular recent advances in the field of scientific agriculture. The near elimination of insect life from entire crop areas, which has long been considered the ultimate goal of chemical pest control, can now be accomplished. However, the expected permanence of pest control results achieved by this process of virtual sterilization has been disappointing. New pests have risen quickly to prominence, and some of those for which treatment was applied have recurred with unusual rapidity. Toxicologists have sought to avoid these unfavourable consequences of chemical treatment by increasing the persistence of the pesticides used or by more frequent applications to sustain toxic residues. These approaches have not always provided the longer-lasting pest control expected, and have frequently led to mounting pesticide usage and to increased residue problems of produce and soil. These results along with the alarming development of resistance of pests to insecticides have stimulated interest in pesticide programmes designed to work harmoniously with biological restraints on pest increase.

By combining the advantageous features of both chemical and biological control methods, i.e., reducing the pests while causing a minimum disruption of the natural-enemy activity, a greater permanence of pest suppression may be obtained. Treatments so designed have been termed complementary or integrated control programmes. Although most chemical treatments produce some unfavourable change in the subsequent natural enemy–pest ratio, certain pesticide manipulations have been shown to reduce this adverse effect with corresponding gains in the future pest restraint. Inquiry into the processes of integrated chemical and biological control has established the rules governing its successful operation. The application of these principles to pest-control practice deserves greater attention.

Many of the initial experiments in promoting a favourable balance between pests and their natural enemies following the use of pesticides have been carried out by entomologists with a partisan interest in biological control. Biological control investigations in the past have been primarily concerned with the development of long-term reductions in average population density levels, while toxicologists' interests have been mainly concerned with the rates of fluctuation of relatively discontinuous pest population systems where experience has demonstrated the threat of crop injury. Equal consideration to the two viewpoints demands of the toxicologists that they give full recognition to the significant role played by natural enemies in pest suppression (Metcalf 1959), and that biological control interests recognize the necessity for positive assurance of pest suppression without risk of economic damage to the crop. The successful development of integrated chemical and biological control programmes requires the conciliation of these two viewpoints as much as it requires the combination of knowledge of natural-enemy evaluation and pesticide toxicity.

The Manifestations of Natural Enemy Disruption by Pesticides

Pest outbreaks following the disruption of favourable natural enemy–pest balances by pesticides may be separated into two types for convenient identification. The first, characterized by the rise to economic prominence of an insect which is relatively unaffected by the pesticide while its normally efficient natural enemies are destroyed, is commonly termed a 'pest upset.' These outbreaks, often publicized as 'traded' pests, have occurred at one period or another upon practically all cultivated crops where pesticides have been used. Although readjustment from such upsets eventually follows cessation of the inciting treatment, the general practice has been to recommend the addition of still another pesticide to counteract the effect of the first. This practice has had some interesting results. Today, a number of current pest control recommendations consists of measures directed against such normally biologically suppressed species. The peak of irony seems to have been achieved in California when malathion, which as a drift contaminant had been responsible for the initial upset of the cottony-cushion scale, *Icerya purchasi* Mask., through destruction of its vedalia predator, was recommended at a higher dosage for corrective control of the same pest infestations that it had originally provoked (Bartlett and Legace 1960).

The second type of pest outbreak associated with the destruction of natural enemies by pesticides is that referred to as a 'resurgence.' Resurgences are characterized by an abnormally rapid return to economic abundance of a pest that was initially suppressed by a pesticide which also destroyed that pest's natural enemies. This type of outbreak is a frequent response to pesticide treatment wherever natural enemies supply a partial degree of pest destruction but do not have the capacity to provide full and complete biological control. Resurgences are easily overlooked in their initial stages, but as the effect of additional natural-enemy destruction accumulates, an ever-increasing need for more frequent pesticide treatment is required.

That there are other long-term detrimental effects of pesticides on the natural-enemy–pest balance which are less easily observed than those mentioned above is certain. However, proof of these effects is difficult and for the most part can only be inferred from either theoretical or circumstantial evidence without clear documentary proof. Studies on population dynamics indicate that pesticides cannot exert long-term effect on subsequent pest populations except those detrimental effects resulting from reduced natural-enemy influence; a subtraction which eventually leads to a higher rate of pest increase and a greater intensity of fluctuation of the pests around a higher average population density. Therefore, any pesticide unfavourable to parasites and predators would be expected to show a decreasing effectiveness with prolonged use (Nicholson 1940). Empirical evidence supports this theoretical view of long-range effects from pesticides (Woglum *et al.* 1947). Other long-term effects of pesticide use over large areas are suggested by the fact that untreated acreages enjoying a natural control advantage may lose this benefit as surrounding areas come under treatment. Also, attempts to regain a pre-existing favourable natural-enemy–pest balance by returning to a less provocative treatment after long usage of a disruptive insecticide with a broad toxicity spectrum often demonstrate that over-all long-term natural-enemy efficiency has been lessened.

THE NATURE OF PESTICIDE INTERFERENCE WITH BIOLOGICAL CONTROL

The History of Pesticide-Induced Outbreaks

A survey of the disrupted balance of pests and their natural enemies by the use of the old-line pesticides employed before the development of DDT is most revealing. The individual literary references will not ordinarily be cited here in detail since they are adequately reviewed by Brown (1951) and by Clausen (1936). It is desirable, however, to review some effects which demonstrate that responses to the more recent wide toxicity spectrum pesticides have, in many cases, had similar counterparts among treatments utilizing old-line pesticide materials, and to show how the patterns exposed as the result of the early studies have supplied us with ready causal explanations of the mechanics of upsets as they were encountered with the newer contact insecticides.

Many of the early records of detrimental pesticide influences were poorly documented for a positive correlation of natural-enemy destruction and observed pest increase. It was often automatically presumed that beneficial-insect destruction was directly responsible for the pest increase even when this assumption was unjustified. A common error in the early studies was that of ascribing pest increase, following a change of pesticide materials, to natural-enemy destruction, when actually the previously used material may have had an unrecognized influence on the suppression of the pest. The common inference that spider mite or aphid increases were always due entirely to natural-enemy destruction also was sometimes an unjustified assumption.

Much of our present knowledge on the mechanics of pesticide-induced insect outbreaks was provided by early studies using stomach poisons as the historical models. Evidence for the destruction of certain species of parasitic Hymenoptera by stomach poisons was well documented. Lead arsenate was shown by a number of the early investigators to be detrimental to parasites of the genera *Trichogramma* and *Ascogaster* in their attack on the eggs of codling moth and other lepidopterans. Calcium arsenate destruction of the braconid parasites of aphids was well documented following early studies (Folsom and Bondy 1930). In general, parasite destruction by stomach poisons was fairly well traced to an effect upon adult parasite stages presumably associated with ingestion of toxic quantities of the poison obtained either during parasite self-cleaning activities or by their feeding on contaminated honeydews. Contrary evidence, however, was presented by some workers to show that with a substantial number of important species of parasitic Hymenoptera no destruction was associated with the use of stomach poisons. These observations were confusing but were, in general, properly ascribed to the distinctive habits of the individual species.

Evidence for the destruction of certain species of coccinellid predators by stomach poisons was well substantiated. Arsenicals destroyed vedalia and other species of coccinellids, cryolite destroyed *Cryptolaemus*; and in the laboratory, tartar emetic destroyed certain scale-feeding lady-beetles. These effects again were fairly well traced to the ingestion of lethal amounts of the poison in the feeding by the lady-beetles on contaminated material. There was also, however, some contrary evidence that certain of the coccinellids were not detrimentally affected under field conditions by some of the common stomach poisons employed at that time. It was an almost inescapable conclusion that in the feeding habits of the various beneficial species differences were responsible for the confusing variations in field susceptibility of both parasitic Hymenoptera and predacious Coccinellidae to stomach poisons.

The studies of the effects of the old-line contact insecticides on natural enemies showed that, although generally the influences were of lesser intensity, the results were very similar to those we now encounter with the newer potent contact materials. Comstock (1880) pointed out that pyrethrum spray against scale insects did more harm than good by destroying the beneficial insects. Koebele (1893) observed that spraying or fumigation to kill red scale resulted in the destruction of beneficial insects, and those not killed outright would leave in search of food; the consequence was that in a few months the trees again would be infested, with no natural enemies present, and retreatment would be required.

A comparatively complete and basic knowledge of how the early pesticides influenced natural enemies was available to most of the early field toxicologists. Elemental sulphur and lime-sulphur were shown to have a long-term detrimental effect, associated with the persistence of residues, on the adults of some of the delicate internal parasites of scale insects, while pyrethrum, and particularly nicotine, were less harmful. Rotenone was denounced for its specific effect on coccinellids. Petroleum oil, despite its favourable selectivity by modern standards, was shown to be detrimental to some delicate internal parasite species, and especially to parasites of codling moth eggs. Even kerosene emulsion was associated with a more rapid resurgence of a whitefly pest in which all the parasite-susceptible stages were destroyed by the treatment. Tar oils were incriminated in the destruction of overwintering immature *Aphelinus mali* (Hald.) within its woolly apple aphid host.

Chemically treated tree bands were condemned since they killed the general predators preferring their shelter. The protection afforded to the late larval and pupal stages of internal parasites within their killed host bodies was established for fumigants and for nicotine, pyrethrum, rotenone, and even to a degree for lime-sulphur, although the latter material, with its persistent residues, also destroyed the emerging adults. Less protection was afforded these stages of internal parasites when petroleum oil was used.

The role played by some of the early fungicides in the destruction of both beneficial insects and pathogenic fungi was never fully established. Sulphur and lime-sulphur were associated with the destruction of some species of natural enemies—not others. The significance of the destruction by fungicides of beneficial fungi attacking scale insects and whiteflies was confused by the controversy over whether the fungus species were predominantly saprophytic or truly parasitic in nature. A separate argument involving the reasons for spider mite increases following the use of some fungicides was clarified with the demonstration that these increases were associated with a stimulation of the pest provided by the granular nature of some fungicidal residues (Holloway, Henderson, and McBurnie 1942).

In the present era of unrestricted use of new potent contact pesticides, more or less complete elimination of natural enemies from treated areas has become commonplace, and a great amount of detailed but disconnected information on the disruption of individual species of natural enemies by certain modern pesticides has been accumulated. The range of these effects has been well reviewed by Ripper (1956). In general, these data have merely served to demonstrate that there are few crops to which pesticides are applied that do not benefit from an unexpectedly high measure of biological control, and that because of the great seasonal, geographical, and biological variations in the potentialities of hosts and their natural enemies it is necessary that each problem be dealt with on an individual and local basis. Therefore, further recounting of specific examples of natural-enemy disruption by currently used pesticides is unnecessary. Only those examples will be further stressed which are necessary models for establishing the general concepts of diagnosis and correction of pest outbreaks associated with pesticide use.

Methods Used in the Study of Detrimental Pesticide Influences

In the study of adverse pesticide influences some techniques and plot designs reveal better than others the detailed processes of how and why detrimental effects sometimes occur with pesticide use. Some of these specialized techniques are still in the process of development. Familiarity with the relative advantages and disadvantages of the different methods is a requirement for integrated pest control experimentation and proper interpretation of results.

In the past, one of the major sources of information on this subject was from randomized plots designed primarily for assessing toxicological effects upon pest populations. These plots, designed as they are for another purpose, often leave much to be desired in the quality of information they reveal. The major drawbacks to this type of comparative plot design are, first, that often there is no control plots which will accurately reflect the potentialities of natural control, and secondly, that usually only very short-term effects come under observation. These deficiencies can be largely offset by having: (1) large treated and untreated plots with adequate buffer areas intervening to minimize trap and migrational effects upon the natural enemies; and (2) adequate census data on the natural enemies and their hosts for sufficient periods both before and after treatment.

In evaluating effects of treatment it is desirable to distinguish between natural-enemy elimination from direct kill and that due to subsequent migration because of lack of suitable host material, even though the end result is similar. Discrepancies in reporting elimination because of migration as due to toxicological kill confuse the pesticide–natural-enemy record with apparently contradictory reports of toxicity. Census counts taken within a day or so after treatment are most important, since they often provide the only source of information upon the effects of pesticides on immature or cannibalistic predators which cannot be determined other than through field studies. The period of persistence of toxic residues to the various beneficial species should be carefully recorded as shown by continued toxicity or by re-entry of the natural enemies.

Much can be learned from reports of the exact details surrounding insect out-breaks following pesticide use. Ordinarily these details are given little attention. References customarily consist of citing the pest increase seemingly associated with treatment, accompanied by the statement that the disturbance was presumably connected with natural-enemy destruction. This type of record may even be in-correct in the assumption that natural-enemy destruction caused the observed effect. However, pest upsets following treatment are often important indicators of the presence of efficient natural enemies. Accurately acquired population data on the hosts and natural enemies may well serve as the foundation for future integrated control programmes or indicate the usefulness of the beneficial species as intro-ductions to other areas. Even where a complete analysis of the causes of the pest upset in its initial development has not been obtained, still a study of the host–natural-enemy readjustment following the upset may provide a reasonable explana-tion of the mechanics of the disturbed balance. A good indication of the causal nature of the pest upset may be obtained from the earliest possible examination of the abundance and variety of natural enemies present in both upset fields and in differently treated or untreated fields to determine the extent of natural-enemy interruption. Particular attention should be paid to evidences of previous natural-enemy work in the upset fields. Examination of field margins may indicate the attempted re-entry of some species. Upsets due to host stimulation or those associated with changeovers from previously used pesticides having an unrecog-nized deterrent effect upon the host may sometimes be recognized by the sharp breaks in pest upset conditions at the borders of treatment and non-treatment areas.

Since almost all natural enemies exhibit pronounced seasonal differences in effectiveness, there is sometimes considerable variation in the conditions of adjustment and recovery from a pest outbreak caused by the destruction of natural enemies. After the upset has occurred it is not always a simple matter to establish that the destruction of a certain species was responsible for the pest outbreak. It may be misleading to assume that natural-enemy dominance during the period of recovery from pest upset is representative of corresponding efficiency of the same natural-enemy species under normally undisturbed circumstances. Following an upset by natural-enemy elimination, normally less efficient or sometimes even rare species often gain a temporary superiority by earlier ingress and may maintain the numerical advantage for long periods. The earliest influx of natural enemies usually consists of the most mobile and seasonally abundant forms, or sometimes those species (frequently coccinellid predators) which are ordinarily attracted to high host densities. One should beware of predicating natural-enemy efficiency strictly upon temporary abundance, particularly following recovery from pesticide upset.

In experimentation designed particularly for study of the adverse influences of pesticides, it is necessary to establish a reference point of optimum natural balance from which deviations may be measured as pesticide influences are introduced. A crop area undisturbed by previous treatment is generally assumed to represent the most favourable balance attainable. Where such crop areas are available, experimentation can be handled by direct treatment of a portion of the area with a pesticide, and the natural-enemy and pest population changes in both treated and untreated areas can be compared through periodic census data.

A modification of this study method has been used on a practicable and effective scale in the outstanding investigations on integrated control of apple pests in Nova Scotia (Pickett and Patterson 1953; Pickett, Putman, and LeRoux 1958). With one or more typical properties having minimum requirement pesticide programmes to serve as reference standards or controls, changes in the entire faunal complex were examined on the treated properties with each substitution or addition of a pesticide. Observed changes were measured in response to the intact ecosystem so that host interactions under the modified conditions of treatment could be accurately assessed. Also, responses to surrounding natural-enemy reservoirs were included in the assessment, while local interaction effects, such as may occur with small plot systems, were largely avoided. This experimental plan provides a very desirable approach to the solution of a unique problem, but a very great amount of population census data must be obtained if the basic causes of the changes are to be shown and interpreted accurately. Census data obtained from this type of experimentation provide a correlation of natural-enemy and host abundance from which the efficiencies of specific natural enemies (and hence the desirability of their protection) can be inferred. It should be recognized that with these types of correlation data it is very difficult to obtain exact knowledge of the effectiveness of low host-density feeders in restraining incipient pest increases. Also, the methods do not isolate any possible effect of host stimulation by the pesticides from host increases due to natural-enemy destruction.

For further detailed examination of the particular components involved in the adverse influences of pesticides, some specialized techniques are available.

Specifically, they are modifications of the insecticide check methods which are described in detail in chapter 14. By a suitable choice of certain pesticides applied at very low dosages which will destroy natural enemies without harming the pests, it is possible, on a portion of undisturbed crop area, to estimate the over-all pest suppression potential of all the natural enemies on the crop from the pest increase following removal of the beneficial insects. By further modifications of the technique as explained in chapter 14, it is at times possible to isolate the influences due to indirect host stimulation through the plant.

These indirect methods of assessing adverse pesticide influences have interesting potentialities, but up to the present time have been little used. Their usefulness lies principally in the fact that with them it is possible to measure mathematically not just the mere reduction in natural-enemy numbers resulting from treatment by a pesticide, but actually to measure the efficiency in pest restraint attributable to the natural enemies.

How Pesticides Act to Cause Pest Outbreaks

A clear definition of the manner in which pest outbreaks may be provoked by the use of pesticides has been obtained partly through experimental processes as previously described, but to an even greater extent from a study of the mechanics of upsets as they have been produced accidentally in various ways from field treatment.

In any attempt to systematize the causes of pest outbreaks following the use of pesticides, it is first necessary to recognize that pesticide-induced outbreaks may be brought about by natural forces other than those creating an unfavourable influence on the natural enemies. Foremost among such cases are those of stimulated host reproduction or survival potentials as suggested by experiments showing that the nutritive value of plants to mites or certain homopterous insects may be changed by pesticidal action (Hueck 1953; Fleschner 1952). The degree to which this stimulating effect may be responsible for these pest increases as opposed to natural-enemy inhibition has not been completely resolved. In certain cases an appreciable systemic effect through the plant is indicated by the results of the tests. In other instances a direct stimulation of the pest by the insecticide is shown (Löcher 1958). In still other tests better physical habitats for host survival and lodgment are presumably afforded by the residues. The isolation of possible host stimulation effects from the superimposed restrictive influences of pesticides upon natural enemies must be distinguishable if significant progress is to be made towards the correction of all types of pesticide-induced outbreaks. Attempts to isolate the extent of each influence constitute an important line of current research (see chapter 14).

The common mechanism by which pest upsets are provoked with both contact and stomach-poison insecticides is predominantly through direct destruction of natural-enemy adults. As a general rule, therefore, pesticide residues continue to destroy natural enemies only as long as they remain fatal to the newly maturing adult individuals. Because of the delicacy of many natural enemies, their complete elimination by pesticides occurs much more frequently than does that of the pest species. It is through complete elimination of natural enemies within the treated area that most of the severe pest upsets are produced by treatment.

Seasonal activity and dispersal characteristics of the beneficial species may handicap their re-entry into treated areas even after toxic residues are no longer present. Some relatively non-migratory predatory mites may not re-enter treated areas for extremely long periods. The dispersal of some very effective aphelinid parasites of scale insects has been shown to extend to a distance of little more than 10 tree rows per year as deduced from spread after colonization (DeBach 1954). These are extremes, but even under ordinary circumstances beneficial species rarely become re-established immediately upon dissipation of toxic residues. This frequently permits the pest to increase to outbreak proportions before effective natural enemies can make their way back into a treated area after having been completely eliminated.

The complete elimination of natural enemies through disruption of their food chains is not uncommonly the cause of pest outbreaks following treatment. With the near eradication of a pest by treatment, the natural enemies are eliminated by starvation or through their dispersal. When pests become re-established, an outbreak occurs before they are found and overtaken by the natural enemies. This course of events has been demonstrated to occur on many occasions. It has even been recorded with aphicides which, while temporarily eliminating the aphids, were virtually harmless as direct poisons to the natural enemies (Knowlton, Smith, and Harmston 1938). Any catastrophic elimination of a pest would appear likely to produce a similar response. Outbreaks have followed pest eradication by insect pathogens through a comparable chain of events (Ullyett 1947), and Taylor (1937) has even found the same course of events to be associated with the elimination of an effective parasite by a seasonally competitive predator. A rather unusual example of a whitefly pest outbreak following treatment with kerosene emulsion, which is practically non-toxic to the parasites, has been suggested by C. P. Clausen as being due to the temporary elimination of all susceptible stages of the host which caused the dispersal of the parasites with pest outbreaks preceding their re-establishment (Clausen and Berry 1932).

Much interpretative information on the mechanics of pest upsets has been gained through detailed studies on the effects of pesticide drift from treated to neighbouring untreated properties, and a study of the contributing factors provides some basic concepts for the successful integration of biological and chemical control.

The first of these is that usually the persistence of the toxic residue is the most critical factor in the destruction of natural-enemy reservoirs within a treated crop-area. It is often surprising that frequent reapplication of such trace quantities of drift pesticides can cause the elimination of certain species of natural enemies. Even materials with reasonably fugitive residues have produced this effect through frequent exposure. It is also plain, as long as the toxic residues persist, that near-by reservoirs of natural enemies lose their significance, and that the initiation of recovery will be retarded.

A significant concept of the mechanics of pesticide-induced outbreaks may be demonstrated from the changed natural-enemy–host ratios that have at times been shown to accompany upsets caused by drift contaminants. This effect was illustrated in upsets of the cottony-cushion scale, *Icerya purchasi*, by malathion drift. This scale insect was susceptible only to high dosages of malathion. At the light drift dosages the natural enemies were reduced in numbers but no balancing pest reduction occurred and there were serious outbreaks of the pest. Although a nearly similar natural-enemy disruption was shown with parathion, an appreciable amount of the pest was destroyed by drift dosages of that material so that very few immediate deleterious effects occurred. Similarly, little or no upset occurred when parathion or high dosages of malathion were applied directly to the trees as a scale control. A very comparable example of an unfavourable natural-enemy–host ratio was illustrated in the increases of *Coccus hesperidum* L. by parathion treatment which did not destroy the scale insect. No increases followed treatment by a combination of malathion and parathion which destroyed a reasonable proportion of the scale. This difference in upset occurred even though the effects of the two treatments against the natural enemies of the scale were almost identical. It follows, then, that where there is a greater reduction percentagewise of the pest species than of the natural enemy there is little or no tendency towards upset. This, of course, applies only to cases where constant reservoirs of the natural enemies are available for re-entry as soon as the toxic residues are lost. Materials inducing pest upsets are generally those to which the specific natural enemies involved are extraordinarily susceptible while the pest is not. Natural-enemy decimation without any balancing destruction of the host, combined with persisting residues restricting natural enemy re-entry, produce the most serious pest upsets. The pattern by which upsets are induced by pesticides is thus seen to differ radically from that of pest resurgence, although the concept of a disadvantageous natural-enemy–host ratio may be applied to both.

Closely allied with the responses observed with local drift upsets are those associated with the trap effect of treated upon untreated portions of a crop. On a number of occasions observations have been made of upsets of pests along the borders of untreated properties, which resembled in some respects those caused by pesticide drift. That these were not always due to drift contamination but at times were due to the trapping out or depletion of natural enemies as they dispersed into or through the toxic residue area was confirmed by experimental tests (DeBach and Bartlett 1951; Bartlett 1957).

The recognition of drift and trap effects in causing pest upsets leads to speculation as to the extent to which these effects can be expressed as area-wide deterrents on natural-enemy increase. There was evidence that the vedalia predator of *Icerya purchasi* was nearly eliminated from much of the Imperial Valley of California during the period of widespread use of parathion against the spotted alfalfa aphid in that area in 1955. A comparable destruction of this predator was observed earlier during the period of blanket use of DDT on citrus, grapes, and as a mosquito-abatement treatment in the central California citrus district (DeBach 1947a).

Observations on the progress of recovery from upsets illustrate another basic pattern in the mechanics of pesticid-induced outbreaks. As previously mentioned, many upsets do not immediately correct themselves once the cause of the upset is removed. Periods of up to three years have been required for reattainment of normal balance on orchard crops following particularly upsetting treatments. During this period, seasonal upsets often occur each successive year with gradually lessening intensity. This has been true even though the natural enemies involved were very efficient as with those of *Icerya purchasi* (DeBach and Bartlett 1951), *Lecanium pruinosum* Coq. (Bartlett and Ortega 1952), and *Coccus hesperidum* (Bartlett 1951a). In a study of the three cases of upsets listed above, the period required for reattaining a normal balance appeared to be associated with variable seasonal efficiencies of the natural enemies so that once eliminated there were long seasonal periods unfavourable for the natural enemies but favourable for increase of the host.

There are undoubtedly other ways besides those mentioned above by which pest outbreaks can be caused by pesticide treatment. Folsom and Bondy (1930) pointed out that aphidophagous species were destroyed by certain pesticide formulations while their aphid hosts were attracted to the treated plants. That some pesticides repel natural enemies under field conditions has been shown (Sysoev 1953). Unfortunately, there is little information on this subject. The unique quality of sulphur in impairing the host recognition of a parasitic species as reported by Flanders (1942b), and the impaired ability of natural enemies to cling to and traverse residue-contaminated surfaces, indicate many possible unexplored ways in which natural-enemy functions may be inhibited by pesticides without apparent direct destruction.

THE SELECTIVITY[1] OF PESTICIDE TREATMENTS TO NATURAL ENEMIES

The Nature and Measurement of Selectivity

Selectivity is the measure of the capacity of a treatment to spare natural enemies while destroying pests. The term is ordinarily used in a relative sense to express the differential favourability of a natural-enemy–pest ratio evoked by one treatment compared with that occurring on a reference or standard treatment. (High selectivity = favourable; low selectivity = unfavourable natural-enemy–pest ratio.)

Ordinarily, selectivity is considered with respect to the entire effects of treatment; however, under controlled laboratory conditions the toxicological selectivity of a pesticide may be expressed quantitatively as the dosage differential required to give a predetermined percentage destruction of the pest and of its natural enemy (Barlett 1958).

For convenience of discussion, selectivity in pesticide treatment has been separated into two classes according to the manner in which the preferential toxicity to pests and their natural enemies originates. These are: (1) physical

[1] As used here, selectivity is distinguished from the term 'specificity,' the latter being considered the capacity of a material to express extraordinary toxicity to particular species.

selectivity which originates from differential exposure of pests and natural enemies to the pesticide; and (2) physiological selectivity which originates from an inherent physiological difference in susceptibility of hosts and natural enemies to a toxicant.

Physical Selectivity as a Means of Natural Enemy Protection

The physical factors contributing to differential natural-enemy and pest exposure to pesticide treatment are complex, but their manipulation offers many promising opportunities for favouring natural-enemy conservation in integrated control programme. A discussion of these factors and the ways in which they may be used to implement favourable selectivity rests heavily upon our knowledge of the conditions favouring pest–natural-enemy imbalance and, by inference, the processes through which it may be avoided. The practical application of the principles as outlined below presupposes that reasonably efficient natural enemies are present and that the relative performance of pesticides against the host species is accurately known.

Regardless of the individual enthusiasm for any single line of approach to the problems of integrated control, successful application of the method requires detailed study of at least the key pest–natural-enemy relationships on the infested crop. This type of study is necessary to uncover specialized or distinctive biological characteristics distinguishing the pests and their natural enemies. Although to date the use in integrated control practices of distinctive characteristics between the life histories and ecology of the pests and their natural enemies has been practised in only relatively few isolated cases, involving for the most part simple ecosystems, it is believed that particularly good opportunities exist in this less intensively developed field of study. For this reason these features as discussed below may be inordinately emphasized and include much circumstantial evidence in the desire to stimulate more exact and discriminating investigation.

SELECTIVITY DERIVED FROM PRESERVATION OF NATURAL ENEMY RESERVOIRS OUTSIDE THE TREATED AREA. All integrated control programmes have as their goal the preservation of natural-enemy reservoirs while simultaneously destroying a satisfactory portion of the pest species. For best results natural-enemy reservoirs are maintained within the treated area so that the beneficial species are immediately available as a restraint against pest increase. It is apparent, however, that closely parallel results may be obtained by the retention of reservoirs within easy migrational distance of the treated areas.

A number of practices have been recognized as furthering the rapid re-establishment of natural enemies to areas from which they had been eliminated by treatment or by temporary elimination of sources of food. The value of adjoining untreated acreages of a similar crop as a valuable source of natural-enemy supply has long been recognized as, at times, are untreated alternative host or 'foster' plants (see chapter 16). Recolonization from laboratory-reared stocks was also shown to be effective after elimination of the parasites. Parasite recolonization programmes following elimination of parasites of California red scale, *Aonidiella aurantii* (Mask.), and the brown soft scale, *Coccus hesperidum*, on citrus by parathion were successfully used. Later, staggered application of parathion to alternating portions of contiguous citrus areas was recognized as very effective in restricting the intensity of brown soft scale upsets. To this end, schedule recommendations for the use of parathion were purposely broadened from otherwise advantageous timing so that contemporary area-wide parasite destruction would be minimized.

Some field practices, taking advantage of the benefit provided by near-by natural-enemy reservoirs, have been used to enable growers to withdraw from overburdensome pesticide schedules and gradually to attain better integrated control programmes. In general, most of these practices have involved the policy of spot treatment at high-density pest locations until increasing natural-enemy activity permits some retreat from pesticide use. This, for example, was the general approach pursued in the establishment of milky disease, *Bacillus popilliae* Dutky, for control of the Japanese beetle, *Popillia japonica* Newm.

Manipulations of application for preservation of near-by reservoirs range from rather simple to complex procedures, depending upon the pest–natural-enemy relationships. Methods have been variously referred to as 'skip,' 'spot,' or 'strip' treatments, depending upon the physical plan used. DeBach and Landi (1959*b*) have applied these methods successfully to a number of difficult citrus scale insect problems in combination with other integrated control practices. Dowden (1952) has considered comparable processes in relation to forest insect control. These manipulated treatments to preserve near-by natural-enemy reservoirs have the advantage that under certain circumstances they permit the use of otherwise relatively non-selective toxicants when less disruptive materials are not available.

SELECTIVITY DERIVED FROM DIFFERENTIAL SUSCEPTIBILITY OF DEVELOPMENTAL STAGES OF NATURAL ENEMIES. The developmental stages of natural enemies vary greatly in their susceptibility to pesticides, and manipulations of treatments to take advantage of these tolerances to pesticides offers favourable opportunities for integrated control programmes. Ordinarily, it is the adult stage of parasites and predators which suffers most severely through pesticide action. Nymphal heterometabolous predators are an exception to this rule since they are ordinarily more readily destroyed with contact poisons than are adults. The same is true for a few species of coccinellids (Bartlett 1958). Larval neuropterous and dipterous predators and many of the coccinellids follow the general pattern of greater adult susceptibility to both contact and stomach poisons. Extraordinary tolerance to most toxicants is found with larvae of some syrphids, chrysopids, and certain coccinellids such as those of the genus *Stethorus*.

With most all holometabolous natural enemies the prepupal and pupal stages are relatively immune to all types of toxicants. This applies to fumigants as well as to most contact pesticides and is particularly advantageous to the protection of internal parasites where even the late larval forms as well as the pupae protected within their host remains may survive treatment.

The eggs of some predators are protected to a large extent by position, especially so in certain anthocorid and mirid predators where the eggs are laid inside plant tissue. Eggs of many other predators are ordinarily destroyed with difficulty even when directly exposed to pesticide action.

Surviving pesticide treatment by virtue of their immaturity, both parasites and predators can often be relied upon to help control those pests missed in treatment, and supply a restraint against pest resurgence.

SELECTIVITY DERIVED FROM DISTINCTIVE FEEDING HABITS OF NATURAL ENEMIES. Specialized feeding habits of natural enemies are among the most distinctive features which confer upon this group a degree of physical selectivity to pesticide treatment. The feeding habits of immature internal parasites obviously contribute to contact-poison immunity while they are protected within their hosts' bodies. With parasitic species the variable feeding and cleaning habits of adults affect to a large extent their susceptibility to stomach poisons, which are ingested only more or less accidentally as contaminants. Hosts contaminated with certain poisons are lethal to predators which consume those hosts in their entirety. This has been shown to be the case with the scale-feeding *Lindorus lophanthae* (Blaisd.) (Henderson and Holloway 1940 to 1943), and with *Rodolia cardinalis* (Muls.) (Smith 1929*b*). Much remains to be learned about the tolerance of the varied entomophagous species to contamination of the honeydews which nearly all of the adults of both parasites and predators subsist upon wholly or in part. Some few pesticides, when mixed with honey in the laboratory, are distasteful to certain parasites and predators. This feature may be of considerable consequence in adult natural-enemy destruction with stomach poisons. This was strongly indicated by early work, but with the current reliance upon contact poisons this consideration has become of secondary interest to that of direct destruction. By and large there appears to be less destruction associated with stomach-poison action, an observation which has even led to the suggestion that cellulose-coated contact poison particles should substantially increase selectivity between chewing insect pests and their carnivorous natural enemies (Ripper *et al.* 1948).

Systemic toxicants favour the conservation of natural enemies when they are applied so as not to be contact poisons. The reported destruction of some predators by feeding upon hosts poisoned with systemics (Ahmed *et al.* 1954) has not appeared to be of critical significance in the destruction of natural enemies where these materials have been used. The possible danger of systemics to some predators which are intermittently phytophagous has not been demonstrated. Bait sprays, particularly those including special pest attractants, have been responsible for surprisingly few recorded pest upsets. Although the detailed mechanics of apparent natural-enemy tolerance to bait sprays have not been adequately examined, there is little doubt that distinctive pest and natural-enemy feeding habits play an important role in the selectivity.

SELECTIVITY DERIVED FROM DISTINCTIVE SEASONAL LIFE HISTORIES AND HABITATS OF NATURAL ENEMIES. Distinctive seasonal life histories and habitats of natural enemies relative to those of their hosts may offer favourable avenues for obtaining more auspicious natural-enemy–host ratios with pesticides and preserving reservoirs of the beneficial species.

Pesticide timing is ordinarily quite rigidly fixed by the susceptibility of the pest, control most commonly being directed against recently hatched larvae, if they can be reached; otherwise against the adult stages. These are not, in general, the stages of heaviest parasite attack although they may at times represent periods of predator activity. There is, therefore, often relatively little opportunity to change the timing of treatment to periods of lower parasite activity except in some cases where pesticide schedules are extended dangerously into the period of natural-enemy activity. Remedies suggested for the correction of inferior control from this cause ordinarily consist of eliminating in so far as possible the treatments during periods of high natural-enemy activity and emphasizing better pest destruction when there is less natural-enemy efficiency (Gösswald 1935; Steiner 1938; Gäbler 1948). In cases where widely dispersing predators are involved or where there is an upset of a secondary pest, the remedy has been to shorten the toxic-residue period by fewer treatments and reduced dosages to give less interference to the natural enemies (DeBach 1947a; Michelbacher and Middlekauff 1950; Bartlett and Ortega 1952).

The examples listed above illustrate some of the manipulations so far reported, which may be construed as taking advantage of pesticide timing schedules to confer a selective advantage to natural enemies in chemical treatment. They involve only the principle of avoiding treatment destructive to natural enemies in so far as possible during periods of effective parasite or predator activity. This practice was formerly of necessity incorporated into most empirically developed control programmes, but since the advent of potent contact poisons less attention has been paid to the danger of broadened timing schedules. Unquestionably, more concentrated attention to detailed life history studies with special emphasis upon seasonal natural-enemy–host ratios would not only expose many of today's errors of pesticide timing, but also would indicate many other ways in which differential habits and biologies of pests and natural enemies could be used to advantage in complementary chemical and biological control.

There is very little exact information on the general principles by which selective timing of treatments might be used in integrated control. The activity of natural enemies compared with that of their hosts is frequently delayed, particularly in the spring season, followed later by an increase to a peak period of activity. The conservation of natural enemies requires avoidance, where possible, of deleterious treatment during the late increase and peak periods of parasite or predator activity. However, the question of the potential danger of treatment at the beginning of the period of natural-enemy activity has not been completely established. Although there is some contrary circumstantial evidence, most recorded evidence suggests that relatively non-persistent residue treatment in the early period of parasite increase usually does not seriously affect over-all efficiency of natural enemies, although it may cause a very temporary setback in their numbers (Ullyett 1947; H. Allen 1958). It is considered significant that in the cases cited, reservoirs of natural enemies were retained within the treated area. Where a material completely eliminates natural enemies, its use during any part of the parasite activity period should be avoided when this is at all possible.

SELECTIVITY DERIVED FROM DISTINCTIVE PHYSICAL FEATURES OF PESTICIDES AND THEIR APPLICATION. Dosage plays a complex role in the physical selectivity exhibited by pesticide treatment. Field recommendations for pest control customarily include a margin of overdosage which may be contrary to the concept of complementary biological control. Relatively simple dosage adjustments can frequently reduce the adverse effects of pesticide treatment by either preserving adequate natural-enemy reservoirs otherwise destroyed, or by permitting earlier natural-enemy re-entry after extermination. In either case, subsequent natural-enemy multiplication may more than offset any sacrifice in initial pest destruction through a lowered dosage. Application of this principle has been the basis of a most successful programme for obtaining long-range control of the spotted alfalfa aphid, *Therioaphis maculata* (Buck.), in California (Stern *et al.* 1959). It has been profitably used, also, on other occasions in field- and orchard-crop protection to provide favourable natural-enemy–host ratios (Michelbacher 1954).

Dosage reduction to favour natural-enemy–host ratios depends upon a proper evaluation of the pest-control needs and of the choice of pesticide. Since most natural enemies, except for the more rugged predators, are much more easily destroyed than are their respective hosts, their temporary extermination might still occur with reduced dosages. This, in combination with reduced pest kill, represents the exact mechanism through which the most intense pest upsets have been provoked by treatment. On the other hand, if a reasonable dosage reduction will, to any degree, favour the ultimate natural-enemy–pest ratio after toxic residues have disappeared, there is the possibility of a long-range economic advantage. The extent to which dosages may be reduced and still provide satisfactory host kills and advantageous natural-enemy–host ratios has not been resolved for other than a few unique test circumstances. The decision as to the tolerable minimum pest reduction level rests upon the degree of natural-enemy destruction and the effectiveness of the beneficial species as well as upon the fixation of an economic injury level arbitrarily set for the crop. There seems to be little doubt, however, that there are many circumstances in which it is not desirable to undertake complete pest destruction. In this connection it appears likely that much of the selectivity associated with the old-line pesticides can be attributed to the fact that overdosage, designed to kill 100 per cent of the pests, was impractical with the relatively weak toxicants available.

Closely allied with the question of dosage is that of pesticide persistence. The stress put upon this quality of pesticides by chemical industries in their research and development programmes for new materials has been contrary to the advantageous use of the materials for complementary chemical and biological control. The most generally selective contact insecticides in use today consist of those materials which have reasonably fugitive residues. Ordinarily, if the toxic residue retention period does not exceed the time required for the parasite species to pass through the protected prepupal and pupal stages into the vulnerable adult stage, some reservoir of the parasites will be retained. The period of protection, in general, is seldom less than 7 to 10 days under optimal growth conditions for the multivoltine parasitic Hymenoptera, and is extended appreciably by weather unfavourable for parasite development. The toxic residue persistence periods of most of our present-day contact insecticides greatly exceed this value, particularly since the toxic residue retention period for delicate, susceptible parasitic species is generally much greater than would be expected on the basis of general pest toxicity. For example, parathion dosages toxic to diaspine scale insects have been shown by bioassay to be toxic to the adults of the internal parasites of the scale insects for from 5 to 7 weeks.

There is little information on the subject of pesticide degradation with regard to natural enemies, since rather difficult bioassays are required for assessment of the minute quantities affecting susceptible species. In a number of cases with the very delicate parasitic species it appears that the exponential curve for toxicity degradation must level off at a point considerably exceeding the minimum lethal dosage. That the quantities effective against susceptible natural enemies are small can be readily seen from the frequency with which pests are upset by drift contamination from adjoining acreages where multiple treatments are applied. (Upsets from this cause are ordinarily easily corrected by attention to prevailing directional winds during treatment, or by changing from dusts to sprays or from airplane to ground application.) Dual or multiple pesticide treatments are particularly destructive since the periods of toxic-residue persistence are extended so that no reservoirs of protected immature forms are retained. An unexplainable extension of toxic-residue persistence in such cases has been demonstrated using highly susceptible parasitic Hymenoptera in bioassay tests. For example, repeated mist applications of DDT to citrus were still toxic to some of these species a full year after application ceased.

Aside from the recognized effects in extending the persistence of toxic residues, virtually nothing is known about the comparative destructiveness to natural enemies of the various types of pesticide formulations and different types of application. No consistent differences have been recognized between emulsives and wettable powders. The value of pelletized or granular materials for application to the ground without leaving deleterious residues on plant foliage has been recognized. Dusts have been shown to be exceptionally toxic initially to parasitic Hymenoptera, but sprays may often equalize this disadvantage by virtue of the persistence of their residues. No information is available on the comparative merits of mist concentrates versus thorough coverage sprays. Virtually nothing is known about the possible advantages of pesticide combinations and of bait sprays in natural-enemy conservation. These subjects should afford interesting and productive fields for future study. The advantages of soil application of systemics are obvious. Considerable progress has recently been made in this direction (Metcalf 1957).

Physiological Selectivity of Pesticides as a Means of Natural Enemy Protection

Physiological selectivity is obtained when a pesticide is preferentially more poisonous to pest species than to natural enemies. In a general sense, this is not as frequent in occurrence as might be expected since many natural enemies are very susceptible to small amounts of toxicants. However, this kind of selectivity has had great popular appeal. Early optimism was stimulated by the pest specificity found with a number of acaricides, systemics, and insect pathogens.

Extensive laboratory studies have been made to examine the tolerance of natural enemies to pesticides. Although exceptional tolerance of natural enemies to pesticides has been rare, exceptional susceptibility has been more frequently encountered, and it has been interesting to find that where this extraordinary susceptibility of a species has been demonstrated in laboratory toxicity tests, a parallel upset with the material and a similar natural-enemy–host complex has very frequently been recorded from the field. The studies have shown that most natural enemies respond to pesticides in a way readily predictable from their size, general vigour, and from the responses to the same material of some fairly comparable pest species. Occasionally a natural-enemy species will show exceptional tolerance to a wide toxicity spectrum pesticide, but, as with pest species, these particular responses do not follow any determinable pattern and such few isolated cases as have been found are of little practical use where, as is usually the case, many host–natural-enemy associations must be considered in the treatment of a crop. Unless the natural enemies showing this exceptional tolerance to an otherwise wide-toxicity-spectrum pesticide are particularly effective against major pests on the crop, the gains from their individual preservation ordinarily will not outweigh the over-all loss from the destruction of other natural enemies.

It is now recognized that the physiological selectivity of pesticides to natural enemies is, in general, inversely proportional to the so-called 'toxicity spectrum' or generality of purpose of the toxicant.

This does not mean, however, that a favourable selectivity cannot be obtained with the wide spectrum contact materials by taking advantage of manipulations to create a favourable natural-enemy–pest ratio. As previously pointed out, skip- and spot-treatment programmes often very effectively utilize these materials. Furthermore, it has been suggested by the results of a very few experiments even with wide-toxicity-spectrum pesticides that under certain circumstances of restricted dosage (and consequently restricted persistance) the resulting natural-enemy–pest ratio is *more* advantageous than before treatment. The conditions for obtaining this advantage sometimes are delicately balanced on the seasonal preponderance of protected immature parasite stages and susceptible host stages, but the principle of lowered dosage designed to kill not all of the pests but only a greater proportion of them than of the natural enemies may confer a favourable selectivity advantage to a number of the wide-spectrum materials not ordinarily considered suitable for integrated control use.

It also may be concluded from the studies available that the most useful physiological selectivity is associated with an extraordinarily high susceptibility of the pest species to a particular pesticide which in turn tends to affect natural enemies in a less spectacular or more normal fashion. If the highest degree of differential toxicity between pests and natural enemies is associated with high pest specificity and more normal or predictably low effect upon all the natural-enemy species, it is plain that the so-called narrow-spectrum pesticides are more likely to fill these requirements.

The Toxicity of Some Commercial Pesticides to Natural Enemies

Information on the toxicity of commercial pesticides to natural enemies is limited. In many cases, conflicting evidence has been reported because of different conditions of use. It should be kept in mind that exceptional tolerances shown by individual natural-enemy species to a particular pesticide, unless they represent key relationships, are very often of little consequence in integrated control practices since ordinarily a complex natural-enemy fauna must be considered with application to an agricultural crop. The check list of commercial pesticides presented in table 7 is designed to serve as a general guide for development and trial of prospective integrated chemical and biological control programmes. The general rating given each pesticide was compiled from many sources and is accurate only for the dosages which have been most frequently used in protection of commercial crops.

A Summary of the Selectivity Associated with the Different Types of Toxicants

The types of pesticides are broadly characterized by different degrees of selectivity. Both the physical and physiological patterns of selectivity associated with each type are presented in the following summary as a general review of their merits and shortcomings. The manner of use of the pesticide will determine the ultimate favourability of any individual toxicant in integrated control practice.

Systemic insecticides, when applied to seed or through the soil or in other fashions so as to avoid contact effect, are highly selective. Currently available systemics generally have fugitive residues, but exhibit some contact toxicity which destroys delicate adult parasites without seriously affecting their protected immature stages. Coccinellids and adults of the robust predators frequently survive limited dosages of the currently used systemics applied as foliage treatments.

Insect pathogens, when applied as formulated sprays or dusts, afford exceptional prospects for selective toxicity favouring natural enemy species (see chapter 21). Virus pathogens of insects are exceptionally specific in their action. Some of the fungi and bacteria exhibit relatively broad ranges in pathogenicity to pest species, but no response has been shown to some of these pathogens in laboratory feeding tests with coccinellids and parasitic Hymenoptera, nor have the pathogens shown any destruction of natural enemies when applied in the field.

Some of the so-called 'inerts' are at times very detrimental to certain natural enemies. Desiccating powders destroy thin-cuticled natural enemies by dehydration, presumably following disruption of epicuticular films. Many parasitic species are highly susceptible to this action which is generally lost once the pesticide has been wetted with dew or moisture. Coccinellids and hemipterous predators are generally less responsive to the dehydration effect, but show decreased effectiveness presumably from inhibited traction and reduced searching activity associated with the powdery residues.

TABLE 7

Degree of pesticide toxicity to natural enemies *

Pesticide	Toxic residue persistence	Recorded pest upsets	Coccinellidae	Hymenoptera	Hemiptera	Neuroptera	Phytoseiidae	Thysanoptera	Syrphidae	Tachinidae
Aldrin	M-L	Mites, leaf rollers	M-O	M	H	—	L-O	—	—	—
Aramite ®**	L	—	L-O	L-O	—	—	M-L	O	—	H
BHC	H-M	Aphids, bollworms, mites, scale insects	H-L	H-L	H	—	M	—	—	H
Bordeaux mixture	H	Aphids	O	O	O	O	O	O	—	—
Calcium arsenate	H	Aphids	H-O	M-O	O	M	—	—	—	—
Captan ®	H	—	O	L-O	M	—	M-O	O	—	—
Chlorbenside ®	H	—	—	—	—	—	—	—	—	—
Chlorobenzilate ®	H	—	O	O	O	O	M	—	—	—
Chlordane	M-L	Aphids, leafhoppers, mealybugs, mites	M-O	H-M	H-M	O	—	—	—	—
Chlorthion ®	M	—	H	H	H	—	O	O	—	—
Copper oxychloride	H	—	—	—	—	—	O	O	—	—
Cryolite	H	Aphids, mealybugs, mites	M-O	M-O	—	—	O	—	—	M
DDT	H	Aphids, arctiids, bollworms, leaf miners, mealybugs, mites, scale insects, leaf rollers	H-M	H-M	M	H-L	H-M	H	M	H
Delnav ®	H	—	H-L	M	—	—	H-M	—	—	—
Demeton	L	Scale insects	H-L	M-L	M-L	—	H-M	—	—	—
Diazinon ®	M-H	—	H	H-M	H-M	—	H	—	—	H
Dieldrin	H	Mealybugs, mites, leaf rollers, scale insects	M-O	M	H-M	—	M	H	—	H
Dilan ®	M	Aphids	H	H-M	H-M	—	M	—	—	—
Dimite ®	H	—	L-O	—	—	—	H	—	—	—
DN-111 ®	M	—	L-O	L	L	L	—	—	—	—
Dylox ®	L	—	O	M-L	L	L	M	—	H	—
Endrin	H-M	Leaf miners, mites	H-M	H	H	—	—	—	—	—
EPN	M	—	H	H	H	—	M	—	—	—
Ethion	H-M	—	H-M	—	—	—	—	—	—	—
Ferbam ®	H	Mites	O	L-O	O	—	H-M	O	—	—

Table of relative toxicity of pesticides to beneficial insects, with pests controlled.

Material									Pests controlled
Genite ®	M-L	O	L	M-O	—	M-O	M-L	—	—
Glyodin ®	M	H	O	O	—	O	O	—	—
Guthion ®	H-M	M-O	M	M	—	M	—	—	—
Heptachlor	M-L	L-O	M	M-O	—	M	—	—	Mites, leaf rollers
Karathane ®	H	L-O	M-L	L-O	—	L-O	L-O	—	—
Kelthane ®	H	M-O	H-O	H	—	H-O	H-O	L-O	Aphids, scale insects
Lead arsenate	H	L-O	M-O	H	—	H	H-M	—	Leaf miners, mites
Lindane	M	O	M-L	H	H	H	M	—	Mites, scale insects
Lime-sulphur	H	H	H	H	—	H	H	—	Mites, scale insects
Malathion	M	H	H	M	H	M	M	M-L	Aphids, mealybugs
Methoxychlor	H-M	O	M-O	O	O	O	M	M	Mealybugs
Neotran ®	M	O	M-O	M-O	O	M-O	M-O	O	—
Nicotine sulphate soln.	L	—	H	—	—	—	L	—	—
Oil (petroleum)	L	L-O	L-O	L-O	L-O	H-M	H-M	L-O	Mites
Oil (tar)	O	O	H-M	H-M	H-M	O	O	O	—
Ovex (Ovotran)	M	L-O	L-O	O	—	M-O	M-O	—	—
Parathion	H	H	H	H	H	H	H	H	Aphids, bollworms, leaf miners, mites, scale insects
Perthane ®	M	L-O	M-L	H-L	—	M	H	—	Aphids, mealybugs
Phosdrin ®	L	H	H	—	—	H	—	M	—
Pyrethrum	M	M-O	M	M-L	—	M-L	L-O	—	—
Ryania	L	L-O	H	M	—	M	—	—	—
Rotenone	L	H-L	O	—	—	H-O	—	—	Scale insects
Sabadilla	L	O	L-O	—	—	—	—	—	—
Selocide ®	M	L-O	M-L	—	L-O	—	L-O	—	—
Schradan	L	O	H	—	—	H	H	—	Mites, scale insects
Sevin ®	H	H	M	—	M	M	M	—	Mites
Sulphenone ®	H	M-O	H-M	M-O	O	H-M	H-M	O	Leafhoppers, mealybugs, mites, scale insects
Sulphur	H	L-O	H-M	L-O	O	H	H-M	—	Mealybugs, mites, scale insects
Tartar emetic	L	M-O	L-O	L-O	—	—	L-O	—	—
TDE	H	M-O	H-M	H-M	—	—	M	—	—
Tedion ®	L	L-O	L-O	L-O	—	L	L-O	L	—
TEPP	L	H-M	H-L	H-L	M	H-M	H	—	—
Toxaphene	H-M	H-L	H	H	—	H	H-M	H-M	Aphids, bollworms, mites
Trithion ®	H-M	H-L	M	H-L	—	H	M-O	—	—
Zineb ®	—	O	O	O	—	O	—	—	—

* H = High   M = Medium   L = Low   O = None   ** ® = Registered trade name

A number of acaricides are almost totally non-toxic to entomophagous insects. A few show enough natural-enemy toxicity to be undesirable in complementary control practices. Some high-potency contact insecticides, when used at very light acaricidal dosages, have, under certain circumstances, destroyed enough of the small stages of other concurrent pests to compensate for the temporary restriction of the natural enemies of those pests. Little is known about the effect of acaricides upon other than a very few species of the predatory mites. Toxicities of acaricides to predacious mites may vary considerably between species (Huffaker and Kennett 1953).

There is little general information concerning the selectivity of ovicides to natural enemies. Petroleum and tar oils do not afford any advantageous differential toxicity to the immature forms of internal parasites over that shown to the hosts regardless of whether the parasite inhabits eggs or exists within the body of its host. Oils show variable degrees of toxicity to adult parasites or predators depending on the species. Application of ovicides during times of plant dormancy generally does not coincide with periods of high natural-enemy activity.

Stomach poisons spare many natural enemies. Both parasitic and predatory species may, at times, be destroyed by feeding on contaminated hosts or honey-dews. Immature parasites are usually protected by their position, and because parasitization often retards further host feeding upon poisoned foliage, a preponderance of parasitized hosts frequently survives treatment with stomach poisons. The slow rate of stomach-poison toxicity where expressed directly against parasites or predators often permits some oviposition before death so that satisfactory natural-enemy reservoirs are carried over toxic-residue periods. Bait sprays with contact-poison bases have, on occasions, shown favourable conservation of natural enemies for reasons not yet satisfactorily explained.

Fumigants ordinarily fail to destroy late larval and pupal stages of internal parasites. The negligible residual toxicity of fumigants strongly favours survival of parasites which emerge as adults following treatment. Coccinellid pupae are ordinarily somewhat tolerant of fumigants.

Fungicides are generally innocuous to natural enemies, with the exception of the beneficial fungi which constitute effective control agencies in some climates. Granular residues associated with some fungicides have stimulated certain pest increases. A few fungicides show limited insecticidal toxicity which is usually undesirable for natural-enemy conservation. A few fungicides with acaricidal suppressant activity have indirectly favoured the predator–spider mite balance.

Contact insecticides with transitory residues may permit the conservation of natural-enemy reservoirs. Some contact insecticides have such extraordinarily high toxicity to certain pest species that dosage can be reduced to kill a high fraction of susceptible stages of the pest and still permit some natural-enemy survival. This is rarely possible with wide-spectrum contact poisons unless they have non-persistent residues. The generally unfavourable selectivity of contact pesticides may be most readily offset by manipulated use which avoids exposure of at least a porton of the natural enemies to pesticide treatment while destroying most of the pests.

Combinations of pesticides with independent modes of action will inevitably come into wider use. This will not necessarily result in less favourable selectivity although this generally has been the case where combinations of different contact poisons have been applied in the past. Stomach poisons and a non-persistent contact poison, for example, would theoretically provide a favourable combination.

CONCLUSION

There are many pathways to effective integrated chemical and biological pest control, the principles of which have been established in the preceding discussion. Approaches and procedures for perfecting integrated programmes are not stereotyped, nor are they likely to become so. Each distinct problem will have to be considered on the individual basis of natural-enemy–pest life histories, habits, and interrelationships in order to establish the pesticide programme best complementing existing biological control. A suitable choice of pesticides with desirable toxicity characteristics must be made, but without proper use of the material the full capacity of the treatment to give well-integrated chemical and biological control cannot be realized.

It is firmly believed that sufficient ammunition in the way of pesticide materials is now available to permit the development of harmonious chemical and biological control methods wherever they are needed. The development of new chemicals has, for the time being, outstripped the development of the biological and ecological information required for their proper use. Obtaining this information is not too formidable a task for the ultimate reward of long-lasting crop protection.

SECTION VI

Insect Pathology

CHAPTER 18

Microbial Diseases of Insects

EDWARD A. STEINHAUS

INTRODUCTION

IT IS TO BE EXPECTED that the advent of man's knowledge of insect parasites and predators preceded that of the microbial pathogens of insects. Not only the matter of size differences but the later development of high-powered microscopes contributed to this. Nevertheless, many early naturalists were appreciably aware of the fact that insects had diseases.

From the time of Aristotle, the honey-bee was known to suffer from disease, and we know that maladies of the silkworm were recognized during the Middle Ages. The first insect pathogen of which we have record was a *Cordyceps* fungus on a noctuid, reported and illustrated by de Réaumur in 1726. One hundred years later, in 1826, Kirby included a chapter on the diseases of insects in the famous treatise, *An Introduction to Entomology* (Kirby and Spence, 1826). And in 1835 Agostino Bassi, the 'father' of insect pathology, published his great work on muscardine, a fungus disease, of the silkworm. Louis Pasteur gained fame, and the appreciation of his countrymen, for his monumental studies (1870) on pébrine and flacherie of the silkworm and for devising methods of controlling the former, thereby saving the silk industry of France from ruin.

That destructive insects were also subject to disease was recognized by such early biologists and entomologists as Walsh, LeConte, Hagen, Metchnikoff, Forbes, Snow, Howard, and Fiske. However, prior to World War II, most of our knowledge concerning the nature of different diseases in insects, and the nature and properties of the causative agents, was provided by a small group of men among the more prominent of whom were d'Herelle, Metalnikov, White, Paillot, Masera, and Glaser. Their contributions did much to establish the foundations of insect pathology and to furnish basic information on the essential character of microbial diseases in insects. Furthermore, the work of the United States Department of Agriculture on the milky diseases of the Japanese beetle helped hold attention on the potentialities of micro-organisms as biological control agents.

In recent years insect pathology and microbial control have received increased attention and support throughout the world. Following the establishment of the Laboratory of Insect Pathology at the University of California in 1945 and a similar laboratory by the Canadian Department of Agriculture in 1946, numerous projects and laboratories for the study of insect diseases were organized in many countries of the world. Virtually every group concerned with the biological control of insects eventually came to include at least some phase of insect pathology or microbial control in its research programme. Today, entomogenous micro-organisms are beginning to receive their just proportion of concern as biotic agents affecting insect populations.

The use of micro-organisms in the control of insect pests will be considered in the final chapter of this section; it is therefore appropriate that in our consideration of the diseases themselves (the subject of the present chapter) we limit our discussion to those diseases and infections which have been, or potentially are, of importance in microbial control. (See also the extensive review by Franz, 1961a.) An entire book itself would be required on this subject if it were to be treated in the same detail as is being done in this volume with the insect parasites and predators. It would be impractical to attempt to cover any but the seemingly more important or best studied diseases, especially those that have some potentialities in the control of insect pests. Nor shall we attempt to any degree to make the present chapter bibliographically complete. As a matter of convenience we shall consider these diseases according to the nature of the causative agent, thus: the bacterial, fungus, virus, protozoan, and nematode diseases of insects.

BACTERIAL DISEASES

The first bacterial diseases of insects that have been studied to any extent were those of beneficial insects. Pasteur's (1870) elucidation of the cause of flacherie of the silkworm and Cheshire and Cheyne's (1885) study of European foulbrood of the honey-bee mark the beginning of our knowledge of how bacteria can infect and cause the death of insects. Much was learned through the study of these diseases (including American foulbrood of the honey-bee) that could later be applied to the study of the bacterial diseases of harmful and destructive insects. On the basis of our present knowledge, the bacteria associated with insects may be divided into certain arbitrary categories or groups (Steinhaus 1959a): non-entomogenous bacteria regularly present in the insect's normal external environment, bacteria regularly or occasionally present in the healthy insect's alimentary tract, non-spore-forming pathogens (mostly facultative), spore-forming facultative pathogens, spore-forming obligate or stabilized pathogens, and crystalliferous spore-forming pathogens. Bucher (1960) has grouped the bacterial pathogens of insects as to obligate pathogens, crystalliferous spore-formers, facultative pathogens, and potential pathogens.

The first major study of a bacterial disease of a destructive insect was the dysentery and septicaemia of grasshoppers reported by d'Herelle in 1911 from Yucatan, Mexico. He observed extensive epizootics of the disease among locusts (*Schistocerca*) arriving from Guatemala. They were of such proportions that by 1912 the populations were reduced to a point where no invasion into Mexico occurred. From the diseased locusts d'Herelle isolated a small gram-negative rod which he named *Coccobacillus acridiorum*. When inoculated into healthy locusts the bacterium quickly caused a septicaemia and killed the insects. In the field, d'Herelle claimed to have successfully used this organism in initiating epizootics among grasshopper populations in Mexico, Colombia, and Argentina, and less so in Algeria and Tunisia.

Since d'Herelle's time what apparently is the same bacterium has been isolated from diseased grasshoppers on several occasions by other workers. The causative bacterium is now recognized (see Lysenko 1958a; Bucher 1959) as one of the coliform group and according to modern nomenclature is identical with, or close to, *Cloaca cloacae* var. *acridiorum* (d'Herelle).

This disease of grasshoppers is typical of that group of bacterial infections in insects that manifest themselves in the form of either a dysentery or a septicaemia or both. Gram-negative small rods are frequently found to be the cause of such conditions, commonly occurring in cutworms and other lepidopterous larvae. In most instances the identity of the causative bacterium has never been determined. It would appear that in most cases a coliform is involved, but species not capable of fermenting lactose are commonly isolated. In laboratory and insectary rearings the red-pigmented bacterium *Serratia marcescens* Bizio, is frequently encountered as the cause of septicemia in many insects (Steinhaus 1959b). In most infections caused by gram-negative small rods the symptoms are those of septicaemia. The infected insect ceases to feed, becomes sluggish in movement, may exhibit diarrhoea or vomiting, or both, gradually becomes flaccid and dies usually within 24 to 72 hours. The cadaver turns dark brown to black in colour, is filled with the causative bacterium, and eventually dries down to a hard black scale.

The Milky Diseases

Although the larva of the Japanese beetle, *Popillia japonica* Newm., was known to be susceptible to disease since 1921, the first significant reports on what are known of the milky diseases of this insect appeared in 1935 (Hawley and G. F. White) and 1938 (Hadley). R. T. White and Dutky (1940) showed that two principal types of infections were involved; these have been designated as type A and type B milky diseases. The causative bacteria of these two types were described by Dutky (1940), who named them *Bacillus popilliae* and *Bacillus lentimorbus*, respectively. Certain other scarabaeid grubs, notably *Amphimallon majalis* (Razou.), are also susceptible to these bacteria. A third milky disease, caused by an unnamed bacillus, has been reported in *Odontria* grubs from New Zealand. *Bacillus fibourgensis* Willie, a bacterium similar to *B. popilliae*, causes a 'milky disease' in the cockchafer *Melolontha melolontha* (L.). And Beard (1956) has reported two milky diseases in Australian Scarabaeidae. One, in *Sericesthis pruinosa* (Dalm.), is caused by *Bacillus lentimorbus* var. *australis* Beard; the other, in *Heteronychus sanctaehelenae* Blanch., is caused by *Bacillus euloomarahae* Beard.

Of the two types of milky diseases of the Japanese beetle (fig. 94), type A, caused by *B. popilliae*, has received the most attention and study, primarily because of its importance in the control of this insect. *B. popilliae* is a slender, nonmotile (motile strains have been reported), gram-positive rod which becomes swollen at the time of sporulation. In addition to the formation of a spore, a refractile body forms at one end of the sporangium which, in unstained preparations, suggests a footprint in outline. The bacillus may be cultured under aerobic, as well as under anaerobic or semi-anaerobic, conditions. However, it appears to be more truly an anaerobe than an aerobe. (Incidentally, true anaerobes of the genus *Clostridium* have, so far, not been found frequently as pathogens of insects although recently Bucher (1961) has reported two such species from diseased tent caterpillars (*Malacosoma*).) The typical spore stage of the bacillus develops on artificial media only with difficulty. The spores are highly resistant to adverse environmental conditions.

Infection of Japanese beetle grubs occurs through ingestion of the bacteria which penetrate the insect's gut wall in their vegetative form. After a period of development in the haemocoele, the bacteria sporulate. The blood of the infected grub assumes a milky-white appearance. Although sporulation usually begins on the third or fourth day after infection, the number of spores reaches its maximum after about 13 to 16 days. The turbidity of the blood can usually be detected beginning about the sixth day. If one pulls off the leg of a diseased larva, the drop of body fluid oozing from the opening is opaque white, as distinguished from the water-clear or only slightly cloudy aspect of a similar drop from a healthy larva.

Externally, a diseased grub exhibits an increased turbidity and opacity in the pericardial region and posterior segments. The dorsal vessel and rectal sac, readily visible in the healthy insect, become obscured. The opacity of the legs is also increased. The diseased grub turns almost uniformly opaque, its activity is reduced, and the insect becomes moribund. Although some infected grubs may transform to pupae and adults, metamorphosis is usually inhibited and prevented. Eventually, the insect dies; grubs infected during the earlier instars usually die more quickly than do older ones.

Type B milky disease is caused by *Bacillus lentimorbus*, a gram-positive rod the sporangium of which is spindle-shaped and does not contain a refractile body as does *B. popilliae*. Japanese beetle grubs infected with *B. lentimorbus* are difficult to distinguish from those infected with the agent of the type A disease until the diseased larvae have overwintered. Type B diseased larvae then assume a muddy-brown coloration instead of remaining milky white. Attempts to cultivate *B. lentimorbus* on artificial media have failed. The pathogenesis of the type B disease is similar to that of the type A disease, except that *B. lentimorbus*, in addition to developing in the blood, also attacks other tissues. Also, brown to black blood clots are formed, and accumulate in the appendages of the insect, blocking circulation of the haemolymph.

Diseases Caused by Crystalliferous Bacteria

In recent years, among the more interesting and important bacteria used in the biological control of insect pests are those which form toxic protein crystals at the time of spore formation. These crystals are highly toxic for certain insects, especially certain Lepidoptera, but are apparently harmless for other forms of life. The bacteria are in many respects similar to the common soil spore-former, *Bacillus cereus* F. and F., but are differentiated from this species by the presence of the crystal in the sporangium, their characteristic pathogenicity for insects, and certain minor physiological differences.

Although some authorities believe that *Bacillus bombycis* Auctt., the cause of flacherie in the silkworm as observed by Pasteur (1870), was a crystalliferous bacterium, the currently best known species, *Bacillus thuringiensis* Berl., was isolated in 1911 by Berliner (1911, 1915) from diseased larvae of the Mediterranean flour moth, *Anagasta kühniella* (Zell.), received from a flour mill in Thuringia, Germany. Later, Mattes (1927), also in Germany, reisolated the bacillus and made a more detailed study of it. As early as 1902, however, Ishiwata (1905) isolated from diseased silkworm larvae in Japan a spore-forming bacillus that came to be known as *Bacillus sotto* Ishiwata. This, too, is a crystal-bearing bacterium. In 1951, Toumanoff and Vago reported, as the cause of flacherie in the silkworm, the isolation of a bacterium which they designated as *Bacillus cereus* var. *alesti*. This was subsequently found to be a crystalliferous strain. The last three of these spore-formers, obviously related to each other, were difficult to distinguish from the common soil bacterium *Bacillus cereus* except that the latter does not contain the crystalline inclusion in its sporangium (Steinhaus 1951*b*; Steinhaus and Jerrel 1954). In 1958, the taxonomy and nomenclature of insect pathogens related to *B. cereus* were studied by Heimpel and Angus who proposed that these three crystalliferous bacteria be designated as varieties of *B. thuringiensis* thus: *Bacillus thuringiensis* var. *thuringiensis*, *Bacillus thuringiensis* var. *sotto*, and *Bacillus thuringiensis* var. *alesti*.

In 1949, Steinhaus (1951*a*, *b*) isolated from *Aphomia gularis* (Zell.) a crystalliferous bacterium which Heimpel and Angus (1958*b*) considered to be a new species, *Bacillus entomocidus* var. *entomocidus*. Previously, in 1945, a similar strain had been isolated by Steinhaus from the Indian-meal moth, *Plodia interpunctella* (Hbn.), and this Heimpel and Angus decided was a new variety, *Bacillus entomocidus* var. *subtoxicus*. Another species, in which the crystals remain attached to the spore and are not toxic for Lepidoptera, was named *Bacillus finitimus* Heimpel and Angus. In Russia, Talalaev (1956) isolated from the Siberian silkworm, *Dendrolimus sibericus* Tshetv., a spore-forming bacterium which he named *Bacillus dendrolimus*. This bacillus has since been found to be crystalliferous, and apparently closely allied to *B. thuringiensis*.

The crystal, or parasporal body, is formed by the bacillus at the time of spore formation. It is characteristically diamond-shaped, but in some strains the shape may be rhombohedral to cuboidal. Usually each sporangium contains but one crystal. The latter is freed from the cell wall with the spore, and appears to persist indefinitely. It is protein in nature, consisting of over 17 per cent nitrogen, and at least 17 amino acids, but no phosphorus. It stains readily with most biological dyes, and is easily demonstrated with negative stains or by means of phase microscopy.

As early as 1906 and 1915 Japanese scientists (Ishiwata, and Aoki and Chigasaki) observed that old cultures (sporulated and thus having formed crystals) of *B. thuringiensis* var. *sotto* contained a substance toxic for the silkworm. Both Berliner (1915) and Mattes (1927) observed the crystal (Restkörper) in *B. thuringiensis* var. *thuringiensis* but did not associate it with the toxicity or the pathogenicity of the bacillus. This was suggested by Hannay (1953; see also Hannay 1956, and Hannay and Fitz-James, 1955). Toumanoff and Vago (1951, 1952*a*, 1953) reported the toxic action of *B. thuringiensis* var. *alesti*. Angus (1954, 1956*b*, *c*) established a relationship between the crystallized toxin of sotto and the paralysis that occurs in this insect following the ingestion of the crystal-bearing sporangium. He also found that whereas isolated toxic protein caused paralysis upon ingestion, it did not have this effect when injected into the body cavity. The crystal is soluble in alkaline solutions, and there is some indication of a correlation between the pH of the insect's gut and its susceptibility to the toxicity associated with the crystal. As suggested by Hannay (1956), there exists a triangle of variables (insect host, bacillus, and crystal), the relative importance and limitations of which have yet to be fully established. The durability of the crystal is indicated by the fact that dried spore preparations of *B. thuringiensis* var. *thuringiensis* may retain their ability to kill susceptible insects for at least 10 years (Steinhaus 1960*c*). (For other aspects of the historical development and modern significance of the crystalline toxin, see Steinhaus 1960*a*.)

The toxicity of the crystal for certain insects, primarily Lepidoptera, has been well demonstrated. There is some disagreement, however, on the additional invasive role played by the bacillus in the course of infections. It appears probable that while the crystal is the active toxic principle responsible for paralysis and other symptoms in the susceptible host, in many cases the bacillus invades the tissues and body cavity of the insect accelerating the lethal process. It should be noted that *B. thuringiensis* also produces a heat-stable, water-soluble, dialysable substance, distinct from the crystal and from lecithinase, which is toxic for insects when injected (McConnell and Richards 1959).

The toxicity of the different species and strains of crystalliferous bacteria for insects appears to vary. Thus, in several tests (Steinhaus 1960*c*) with the silkworm, *B. thuringiensis* var. *alesti* was usually the most virulent, a strain of *B. thuringiensis* var. *thuringiensis* isolated from *Anagasta kühniella* in California was only slightly less virulent. Next in virulence was *B. thuringiensis* var. *sotto*, then *B. entomocidus* var. *entomocidus*, and then the original Mattes strain of *B. thuringiensis* var. *thuringiensis*. This relationship may differ according to the insect species concerned.

Depending upon the insect, it appears that there are at least three different modes of action by which the crystalliferous bacteria kill their insect hosts. The distinctions between these modes of action have been elucidated largely through the work of Heimpel and Angus (1959) who have designated them as Types I, II, and III. In Type I there is a paralysis of the midgut within a few (5 to 20) minutes after the ingestion of the sporulated bacillus. This is followed in one to seven hours by a general paralysis of the entire insect body. The general paralysis is accompanied by an increase in blood pH from 1·0 to 1·5 pH units, indicating a leakage of alkaline gut contents into the blood. This mode of action has been seen in such insects as *Bombyx*, *Protoparce*, and *Antheraea*. In Type II, the insects (e.g., *Malacosoma*, *Anisota*, and *Nymphalis*) suffer no blood pH increase, but there is paralysis of the gut, and the insects die in from two to four days without a general paralysis. This type of action is probably the most common of the three. Type III so far is known in only one insect, *Anagasta kühniella*, which dies in two to four days without any symptoms of general paralysis. It is not killed by the toxin in the absence of spores, as can happen in the case of Types I and II. It appears that the spores must germinate (in the presence of toxin) and grow in the midgut before causing death.

The range of insect hosts susceptible to these crystalliferous bacteria is continuously widening. Most of the susceptible species are Lepidoptera but certain Diptera, Hymenoptera, and Coleoptera may be susceptible upon receiving large doses of spore preparations. Among the most susceptible species so far known are those belonging to the genera *Bombyx*, *Anagasta*, *Colias*, *Pieris*, *Thaumetopoea*, *Hyphantria*, *Protoparce*, *Plodia*, and *Plutella*. Other invertebrates, as well as vertebrates and plant life, have not been found to be susceptible. The successful use of these bacteria in the biological control of pest insects is described in a subsequent chapter.

FUNGUS DISEASES

Although fungi belonging to the ascomycete genus *Cordyceps* were the first entomogenous species known, they have not been used extensively in attempts at biological control. Most study has been devoted to certain fungi found on scale insects and whiteflies, to the so-called white and green muscardine fungi, and to a few of the entomophthoraceous fungi. Accordingly, our discussion will largely be limited to these groups.

It is important to realize that, as with many bacteria, many of the fungi associated with insects are not true pathogens, or are pathogenic only under certain conditions. Saprophytic species frequently develop in or on insects that have died of other causes. Some fungi are, in essence, parasitic but not lethal in their association with insects; thus, the large order Laboulbeniales (Ascomycetes) is made up of species that live primarily on the external surfaces of insects. The genus *Septobasidium* (Basidiomycetes) consists of species associated with scale insects which, although some are parasitized, live beneath the stromata of the fungi. And, of course, some fungi, such as the ambrosia fungi of certain termites and wood-boring beetles, are definitely mutualistic in their relationship with insects.

Also the fact is to be kept in mind that in the majority of instances fungus pathogens infect their insect hosts not so much through ingestion (however, see Sussman 1952; Gabriel 1959) as by the penetration of the body cavity through the integument. This requires conditions of adequate moisture or humidity. Once within the body cavity the fungus proliferates, invades the tissues, and fills the body of the insect with thickly grown hyphae or hyphal bodies. In most cases the fungus then sends conidiophores to the exterior where fruiting bodies develop, enabling the organism to contact new hosts. The infected insect usually assumes a dried mummy-like appearance, frequently becomes covered with conidia-bearing mycelium, and sometimes contains resting spores which enable the fungus to survive periods of adverse environmental conditions or the absence of a suitable host. However, these statements are generalizations only and each group of entomogenous fungi has its own peculiarities and its characteristic association with the insect host. The physiological characteristics of these fungi are as interesting and as important as the morphological characteristics. As pointed out by Madelin (1960), a greater knowledge of the behaviour and physiology of entomogenous fungi is essential for their successful use in the microbial control of insect pests.

Entomophthorales Infections

As the name would imply, the order Entomophthorales includes the most important group of entomogenous fungi in the class Phycomycetes, although such fungi also occur in the orders Mucorales, Blastocladiales, and Chytridiales. Most authorities recognize the single family Entomophthoraceae made up of several genera of which *Empusa*, *Entomophthora*, and *Massospora* are composed primarily of entomogenous species. There has been some vacillation in the use of the names of the first two of these genera. The name *Empusa* has been widely used since it was first proposed by Cohn in 1855 for a fungus parasite, *Empusa muscae* Cohn, of the housefly. It has been challenged by some writers because of its previous use for a genus of orchids. Although Thaxter, the leading early authority in the group, considered the name nevertheless acceptable, some recent authors (e.g., Bessey 1950; Hall and Dunn 1957a) feel that it must be rejected because of the homonym rule of the International Rules of Botanical Nomenclature. Accordingly, they advocate the use of the generic name *Entomophthora* rather than *Empusa* assuming, apparently, that only one genus is involved. There is some reason to believe that actually the fungi concerned fall into two generic groups, but as yet such distinction has not been generally recognized. In view of the unsettled aspects of the nomenclature and taxonomy of these fungi we shall consider it expedient here to conform to the conclusions of Hall and Dunn and use the name *Entomophthora*.

It appears that the first entomophthoraceous fungus infection in insects was reported by De Geer in 1776 and 1782, and Latreille in 1805 in flies. These were probably infections caused by the well-known *Empusa muscae* Cohn (now *Entomophthora muscae* (Cohn)). Species of *Lucilia*, *Calliphora*, and certain syrphids are susceptible but the best-known host is the housefly, *Musca domestica* L. Infected flies are commonly found indoors attached to the walls and ceilings of buildings in a lifelike position. Close inspection of flies killed by the fungus usually reveals on the wall or windowpane a distinct halo of discharged spores (conidia) encircling the insect. This phenomenon illustrates a very interesting characteristic of most *Entomophthora*. After the conidiophores have emerged through the integument of the insect, conidia are formed which are discharged from the terminal portion of the conidiophores. The conidia are discharged violently into the air thus forming a halo or ring of conidia about the dead insect.

When a discharged conidium lands on or contacts a susceptible insect, in the presence of adequate moisture, it begins to germinate, sending out a conidial hypha that penetrates through the integument into the body cavity. Here the hypha breaks down into segments called hyphal bodies, and invades the tissues of its host, and kills it. If conditions of temperature and moisture are not favourable, instead of completing its development, the fungus may thicken its wall and form chlamydospores to preserve its vitality until conditions for growth are appropriate. Ordinarily the hyphal bodies develop with great rapidity into hyphae which penetrate to the outer air (frequently through the thin intersegmental membranes) and form conidiophores each of which produces a single conidium. Sometimes the hyphal bodies develop into either sexual or asexual resting spores.

The life histories of other species of *Entomophthora* are, in general, similar to that of *E. muscae*. The genus consists of a large number of species some of which have been well studied, but most of which have had only a minimum of study aside from taxonomic considerations. Most of them have not been grown on artificial media although some species have been cultured on such material as potato, swordfish, and pork. Hall and Halfhill (1959) have not only cultivated five species of *Entomophthora* on artificial media (10 per cent Sabouraud dextrose agar), but have succeeded in obtaining on such media the germination of resting spores of one of these, *Entomophthora virulenta* Hall and Dunn.

Among the most noteworthy known species of Entomophthora (in addition to *E. muscae*) are: *E. grylli* Fres. found on various Orthoptera and Lepidoptera; *E. sphaerosperma* Fres. common on Diptera, Hemiptera, Lepidoptera and other insects; *E. aulicae* (Reich.) found infecting caterpillars of the brown-tail moth and other insects; *E. fumosa* Speare on mealybugs; and *E. aphidis* Hoffman and *E. exitialis* Hall and Dunn on aphids. Another interesting Entomophthoraceae, *Massospora cicadina* Peck, is a parasite of the periodical cicada. Unlike species of *Entomophthora*, it produces conidia within the body rather than on the surface of its host. The conidia are exposed and disseminated when the insect's abdominal segments drop off as a result of the infection.

Blastocladiaceous Infections

The entomogenous Blastocladiales are confined largely to one group, the family Coelomomycetaceae, which parasitizes mainly mosquito larvae. About twenty species are known, all in the genus *Coelomomyces*. They have been found infecting species of *Aëdes*, *Anopheles*, *Culex*, *Psorophora*, and *Uranotaenia* in the Federated Malay States, India, Russia, the United States and Africa. The natural incidence of infection in mosquito populations may vary from very low to as high as 95 per cent in pool environments.

The principal development of *Coelomomyces* occurs within the body cavity of its insect host. Certain regions of the body cavity or virtually the entire haemocoele may become filled with the spores and mycelium of the fungus. Such larvae become white to yellowish-orange in colour, and opaque. Ordinarily the fungus completes its development in the larval stage of the mosquito, but sometimes it continues on through the pupal and adult stages. (See Keilin 1921*b*; Couch 1945, 1960; Couch and Dodge 1947.)

Another primitive phycomycetous fungus (a Chytridiales) causing infection in insects is *Myiophagus ucrainicus* (Wize). This fungus, or close relatives, has been found in certain Coleoptera in the Ukraine, in certain Diptera in England and the United States, and in scale insects in Bermuda, Canada, and the United States. The body contents of many of the diseased insects are almost completely disintegrated and replaced by an orange to reddish mass of fungus material.

Cordyceps Infections

Species of the genus *Cordyceps* (class Ascomycetes) were among the first entomogenous fungi known. Their frequently large size and colourful appearance brought them early attention. Approximately 250 species are known (about 50 species in the United States), and these have been studied primarily from a taxonomic standpoint. (One of the principal American workers in this group is E. B. Mains.) *Cordyceps* is cosmopolitan in distribution and occurs on representatives of several orders of insects, principally Hemiptera, Diptera, Lepidoptera, Hymenoptera, and Coleoptera.

Members of the genus *Cordyceps* are characterized by the fact that the stroma arises from a sclerotium formed within the body of the infected insect. At the end of this stroma or stem is a fertile portion, the 'head,' which may be brightly coloured. The perithecia are contained in this structure, and within them are slender asci, each of which contains eight slender spores. After escaping from the ascus, the multiseptate spores usually break up into their component cells, which eventually germinate. Some species of *Cordyceps* are believed to have conidial stages which are at present included in such imperfect fungal genera as *Spicaria* (=*Isaria*), *Botrytis*, and *Hirsutella*. One of the best-known species is *Cordyceps militaris* (Fr.) Lk., the conidial stage of which is believed to be a *Cephalosporium*.

The life history of most cordyceps is similar to that of entomogenous fungi in general. The germ tube of the germinating spore penetrates the integument of the host within the body cavity of which the fungus develops and forms a sclerotium which eventually gives rise to fresh stromata and spores.

Other Ascomycete Infections

In considering infections by Ascomycetes it should be remembered that most entomogenous species have, in addition to the perfect or sexual form, an imperfect or asexual form. Unfortunately, for many of these sexual forms the corresponding asexual forms have not been recognized and, conversely, the sexual forms, if they exist, are not known for most of the entomogenous Fungi Imperfecti. However, a number of such correlations have been made in the case of the Ascomycetes found on scale insects and on whiteflies. The true pathogenicity or invasive capacity of some of these species has been questioned, and in some cases it does appear that the fungi are secondary invaders or grow only on weakened insects or those dead or dying of other causes. Some species, however, are true pathogens.

The fungi found on scale insects belong to a number of genera, and some have been known by a number of synonyms. Among the more important species are those belonging to the genera *Sphaerostilbe*, *Nectria*, *Podonectria*, *Lisea*, *Hypocrella* (all of the order Hypocreales), and *Myriangium* (of the order Myriangiales). In the United States, most of our knowledge of these fungi originates with studies made in the citrus-growing areas of Florida where it was believed they provided a sub-stantial measure of biological control of citrus scale insects. They are, however, known in other parts of the world.

Sphaerostilbe species are commonly called the 'red-headed scale-fungi' because of the orange-red to red colour of the perithecia. The conidial stages of these fungi are generally considered to be in the imperfect genus *Fusarium* (= *Microcera*). They are found on a large number of different scale insects. *Nectria*, commonly known as the 'pink fungi' in Florida, is particularly common on the Florida red scale. *Podonectria* are known as the 'white-headed scale-fungi.' They occur on a number of scale insects, and are sometimes found on purple scale that had been killed by the endoparasitic chytrid, *Myiophagus* sp. Members of the genus *Hypocrella* have their imperfect stages in *Aschersonia*. In the scale-insect group of fungi, about 25 species of *Hypocrella*, with about 15 corresponding species of *Aschersonia* are known. Species of *Myriangium* are common on scale insects throughout the tropics.

Again in Florida, considerable attention has been given to the fungi on whiteflies or aleurodids. In this case the fungi are known primarily in their imperfect form. *Aschersonia aleyrodis* Webber, the so-called 'red aschersonia,' is found on *Dialeu-rodes citri* (Ashm.) and other whiteflies. Its perfect stage is in *Hypocrella libra* Sydow. Soon after a nymph becomes infected with the fungus, it becomes swollen and may secrete more honeydew than usual. As the fungus develops internally, the interior organs of the nymph appear to contract away from the margin. After the insect dies the hyphae break through the body wall and form a dense marginal fringe around the edge of the insect. Subsequently the red pustule with its spores develops. *Aschersonia goldiana* Saccardo and Ellis, the 'yellow aschersonia,' is parasitic especially on *Dialeurodes citrifolii* (Morg.). It resembles the red ascher-sonia in habits and general appearance, except that its pustules are yellowish in colour. Other fungi found on whiteflies include *Aegerita webberi* Faw., 'Webber's brown fungus,' *Fusarium aleyrodis* Petch, and *Verticillium cinnamomeum* Petch.

The Muscardine Diseases

The word 'muscardine' may refer either to a type of disease caused by certain fungi, or to the fungi themselves. In such diseases the fungus emerges from the body of the insect, covering the animal with a characteristic kind of fungus mat resembling, in a way, a French bonbon or candy mint (French *muscardin*). The word was first used as it applied to the well-known disease (white muscardine) of the silkworm caused by the fungus *Beauveria bassiana* (Bals.) Vuill. It has also been used in reference to the disease (green muscardine) of the wheat cockchafer and other insects caused by *Metarrhizium anisopliae* (Metch.) Sorokin. Mycoses caused by certain other closely related fungi also fall in this category. All of the fungi involved are Fungi Imperfecti.

Until recently, about 14 species of *Beauveria* were recognized. In 1954, MacLeod revised the genus and reduced the 14 species to synonymy with *Beauveria bassiana* and *Beauveria tenella* (Del.) Siemaszko. *Beauveria bassiana* was named after Bassi who, in the first half of the nineteenth century, performed his classic experiments proving not only that white muscardine (or, as the Italians called it, 'mal del segno' or 'calcino') was caused by this fungus but also, by so doing, that microorganisms could cause disease in an animal. Since then innumerable studies have been made of the disease as it occurs in the silkworm, and most of our knowledge stems from these studies. It should be clearly understood, however, that the same fungus is responsible for disease in a large number of other insects (at least 175 known species in North America alone), and that in certain situations has shown some promise as a means of controlling certain pest insects. Inasmuch as this book is concerned primarily with the principles of biological control we shall not concern ourselves here with the fascinating story of muscardine of the silkworm.

Among the destructive insects known to be susceptible to *Beauveria bassiana* are the European corn borer, the codling moth, and the chinch bug. The latter, *Blissus leucopterus* (Say), is subject to natural outbreaks of muscardine that may markedly reduce destructive populations. The strains of *Beauveria* primarily concerned have been known by the name *Beauveria globulifera* (Speg.) Picard, but this species has now been placed in synonymy with *B. bassiana*. It was first definitely observed on chinch bugs by Forbes (1890), in Illinois, in 1882. It has also been found causing natural epizootics in Minnesota, Iowa, and Kansas.

On the chinch bug, the *globulifera* strains of *B. bassiana* usually appear as loose white cottony or mealy growth, at times almost completely enveloping the insect. The conidiophores form closely packed conidia, creamy white in colour. The fungus grows readily on artificial media where it produces a somewhat more 'fluffy' type of growth than do most other strains of *B. bassiana* which typically produce a flat, mealy, chalky, pulverulent growth. On the integument of the chinch bug, and under conditions of appropriate temperature and humidity, the conidium sends out a germination hypha that penetrates the body wall of the insect. The insect dies of the infection in about three days. Hyphae fill the body cavity of the bug, finally penetrating to the outside, where the body is covered with the typical white mycelial growth. Numerous conidia are formed on the conidiophores, and when these land on other insects the cycle is repeated.

In the European corn borer and larvae of other Lepidoptera, the course of the infection is similar to that in the silkworm, and similar to that just mentioned in the chinch bug. An infected larva becomes sluggish in movement, fails to respond to most external stimuli, and frequently assumes a somewhat pinkish colour. The larva remains soft and pliable until the mycelium has grown throughout the animal's body. Following this, the insect becomes rigid and mummified, and the body contents are white and chalky. As long as the mummified larva remains in a dry atmosphere, no external sign of the fungus is evident. Upon exposure to moist air, however, the conidiophores break through the integument and the white mycelium becomes apparent over the surface of the insect. Within a day or two conidia are produced giving the insect a mealy, powdery appearance. The conidia remain viable for as long as 128 weeks at 4° C and for about 7 weeks at 23° and 38° C (Steinhaus 1960c). The conidia of *B. tenella* have a somewhat higher degree of germination than do those of *B. bassiana* after three or four months on artificial media (Müller-Kögler 1960).

Infections with *Metarrhizium anisopliae*, the cause of green muscardine, are similar in most respects to those caused by *Beauveria bassiana*. The green muscardine fungus was discovered by Metchnikoff, in 1879, infecting larvae of the wheat cockchafer. This Russian worker studied the disease and envisioned the practical use of it by man in the control of insects. He also evidenced an appreciation of the significance of natural epizootics in reducing insect populations. Since his discovery a large number of insects have been found infected with *Metarrhizium* —at least 75 species in North America alone.

Metarrhizium anisopliae has a taxonomic position near *Penicillium* in the family Moniliaceae. Its perfect stage is not known; the report that it is a *Cordyceps* is generally discounted. It grows readily on artificial media, and its germination, growth, and development are promoted by high humidities and warmth.

Other Mycoses

Of necessity we have been able, in this chapter, to consider only a few of the many fungus diseases known in insects. It is difficult to predict which groups are likely to be the most important from the standpoint of biological control and this aspect of the subject will be treated in chapter 21. Before concluding this section of the present chapter, however, there are a few other mycoses that should at least be mentioned.

A disease, sometimes known as the 'red muscardine,' has been observed in *Cleonus, Euxoa*, and other insects. It is caused by *Sorosporella uvella* (Krass.), a verticiliacious Hyphomycete for which no perfect stage has yet been observed. Larvae killed by this fungus become pink to brick red in colour. If the body is opened or ruptured, the host's internal tissues may be seen to have been largely replaced by a mass of brick-red resting spores which are readily dispersed in dust-like fashion. Under appropriate conditions the resting spores germinate, forming conidiophores and conidia. The fungus may be cultivated on a variety of non-living media.

Other genera of Fungi Imperfecti that contain important entomogenous species include *Spicaria* which is found infecting a number of Lepidoptera and Coleoptera.

About 15 species are known in North America. The generic name *Isaria* has now been largely discarded in favour of *Spicaria*. *Vermicularia* occurs on cicadas, *Acrostalagmus* and *Cladosporium* on aphids, *Aspergillus* and *Pericystis* on bees, *Acremoniella* on the clover leaf weevil, *Stemphylium* on coccids, and *Synnematium* on various Hemiptera. For other interesting examples the reader is referred to the recent book by Aoki (1957).

VIRUS DISEASES

From the standpoint of basic research, perhaps the most active area of investigation in insect pathology during the past decade has been that of the insect viruses (see reviews by Bergold 1958; Smith 1959; Krieg 1961). One of these diseases, the nuclear polyhedrosis (jaundice) of the silkworm, has been known for several centuries, but, of course, was not recognized as virus-caused, until the second decade of the twentieth century (von Prowazek 1907, 1912; Escherich and Miyajima 1911; Glaser and Chapman 1913; Acqua 1919). Today, at least 250 virus infections have been recognized in approximately 175 insects and arachnids. Of this number, about 170 of them are nuclear polyhedroses, 30 are cytoplasmic polyhedroses, 35 are granuloses, and 8 are known that do not appear to be associated with inclusion bodies of any kind. There are a few infections suspected of being caused by viruses, but definite proof is lacking. Annotated lists and bibliographies of insects reported to have virus diseases have been presented by Hughes (1957) and Martignoni and Langston (1960).

For the most part, the hosts of these viruses are Lepidoptera, although a few Hymenoptera and Diptera, and one or two Coleoptera (*Melolontha*, and possibly *Oryctes*), also suffer infection with these agents. Virus diseases have also been reported in the citrus red mite and in the European red mite (*Panonychus*). Only the immature stages (larva and pupa) are highly susceptible; adults may carry the virus but they are usually not killed by it. In general, many insect viruses exhibit a fairly high degree of host specificity, but some authors have reported many instances of successful cross infectivity. Some of these experiments, however, did not take into consideration the possibility that latent infections were being activated in the test insects.

The Polyhedroses

The polyhedroses are characterized by the formation of polyhedron-shaped inclusion bodies in the infected tissues of the host. These inclusion bodies contain, embedded in their matrix, the virus particles which may be rod shaped or spherical. Two general types of polyhedroses are recognized: the nuclear polyhedroses in which the virus multiplies in the nuclei of the infected cell, and the cytoplasmic polyhedroses in which the virus multiplies in the cytoplasm of such cells. As far as is known at present the viruses causing nuclear polyhedroses are rod shaped while those causing cytoplasmic polyhedroses are more or less spherical in shape.

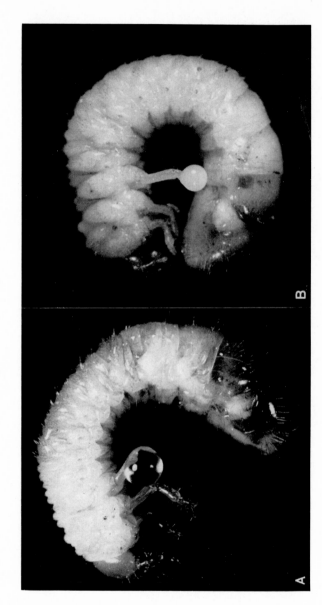

FIGURE 94. Healthy (A) and milky-diseased (B) grubs of the Japanese beetle, *Popillia japonica* Newm. A drop of body fluid from each grub is shown oozing from the tip of a cut leg. The drop from the diseased grub shows the cloudy, opaque aspect of the fluid characteristic of type A milky disease. (From Wheeler and Adams, 1945.)

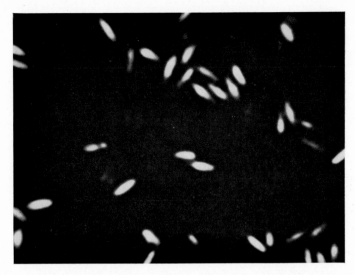

FIGURE 95. Spores of *Bacillus popilliae* Dutky as seen in a nigrosin-stained smear. Towards left centre may be seen a spore with the footprint appearance.

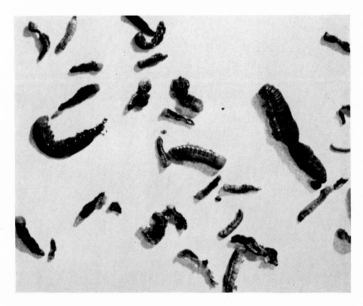

FIGURE 96. Larvae of the alfalfa caterpillar, *Colias philodice eurytheme* Bdvl., dead of infection with *Bacillus thuringiensis* Berl.

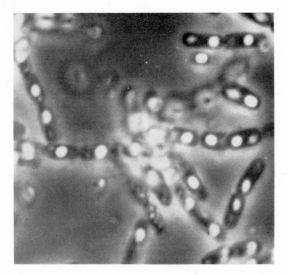

A

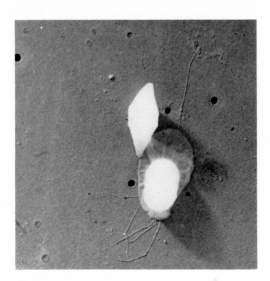

B

FIGURE 97. A. Sporangia of *Bacillus thuringiensis* showing spores (larger bright objects), and crystals (smaller
dim objects), as seen with a phase microscope. B. Electron micrograph of spore and diamond-shaped crystal.
The latter has just been released from the sporangium of
the Bacillus.

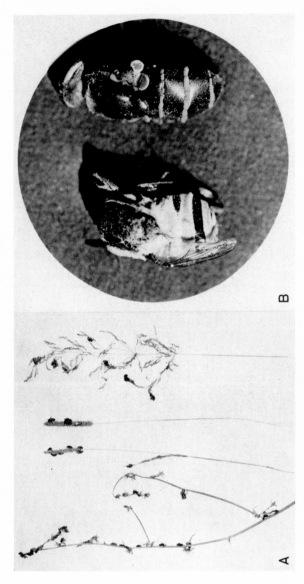

FIGURE 98. Adult blowflies, *Phaenicia mexicana* (Macq.), killed by an entomophthoraceous fungus, *Entomophthora americana* (Thax.). A. Blowflies clinging to stalks of chicory and grasses. B. Close-up view of specimens killed by the fungus. Note tendency of conidiophores to break out of the body cavity along intersegmental membranes. (Photos courtesy of E. Dresner.)

FIGURE 99. Examples of *Cordyceps* parasitizing insects. (A) *Cordyceps dipterigena* Berk. & Br. on a fly. (B) *Cordyceps stylophora* Berk. & Br. on the larva of a beetle. (C) *Cordyceps clavulata* (Schw.). (D) and (E) *Cordyceps unilateralis* (Tul.) on ants. (From E. B. Mains, 1939, 1941.)

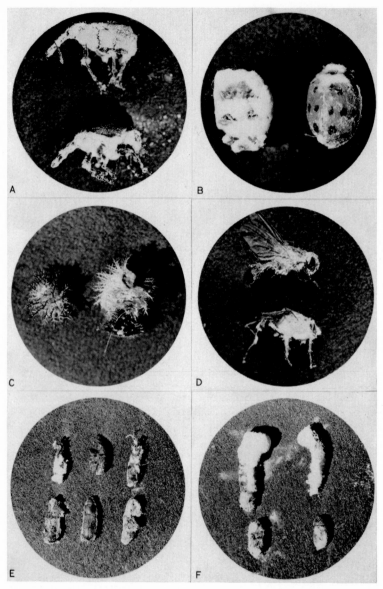

FIGURE 100. Insects attacked by *Beauveria bassiana* (Bals.), showing the layer of white spores that may cover the specimen. A. *Rhyncites*, B and C. *Epilachna*, D. *Musca*, E. *Sitophilus*, F. *Attagenus*.

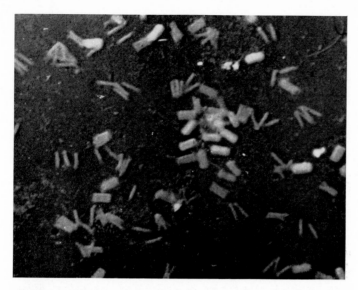

FIGURE 101. Electron micrograph of virus of a nuclear polyhedrosis of the alfalfa caterpillar, *Colias eurytheme* Bdvl. Virus bundles as well as individual virus particles may be seen.

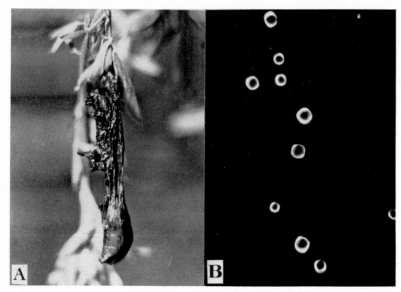

FIGURE 102. (A) Armyworm, *Prodenia praefica* Grote, dead of a nuclear polyhedrosis. (B) Dark-field preparation showing polyhedra from diseased *Prodenia* larva.

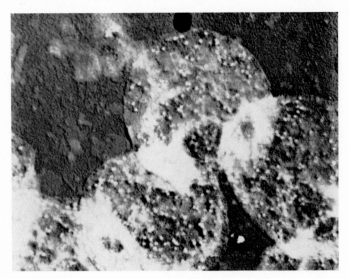

FIGURE 103. An electron micrograph of dissolved cytoplasmic polyhedra showing presence of spherical virus particles, the cause of a cytoplasmic polyhedrosis of the alfalfa caterpillar, *Colias eurytheme* Bdvl.

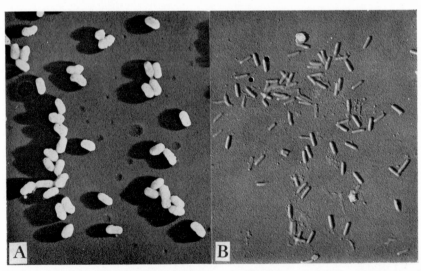

FIGURE 104. Granulosis virus of the omnivorous looper, *Sabulodes caberata* Guen. (A) Untreated capsules (granules) containing virus rod within. (B) Freed virus particles after capsules have been treated with dilute alkali.

THE NUCLEAR POLYHEDROSES. Larvae infected with the virus of a nuclear poly-hedrosis usually show few distinctive symptoms until a few hours before death. The incubation period varies in different host species between 5 and 20 days, usu-ally it covers a period of about a week. In some species of insects, the infected larvae may cease feeding, become somewhat sluggish in movement, and become yellowish or pale in colour. They may swell slightly, then become limp and flaccid. Shortly before and after death the integument is very fragile and easily ruptured, emitting the liquefied contents which are filled with disintegrating tissue and poly-hedra. The dead larvae are usually found hanging by their prolegs from the host plant or other support. Eventually, they may dry down to a dark brown or black cadaver.

In 1856, Cornalia and Maestri separately described the crystal-like polyhedra in jaundice-diseased silkworms and related them to the malady. Since then there has been little question as to their association with the disease, but the virus particles themselves were not demonstrated until 1947 when Bergold showed their presence by means of analytical ultracentrifugation and electron micrographs. Polyhedra formation occurs in the nuclei of infected cells of certain of the host's tissues, usu-ally the fat body, epidermis, tracheal matrices, blood cells, and sometimes the cells of the midgut and other organs. The Malpighian tubules and silk glands do not appear to be involved. Four or five days after infection small granules may be seen within the infected nuclei, gradually increasing in size, sometimes forming a ring about the periphery of the nucleus, and then filling the nucleus which increases greatly in size. Eventually the nuclear and cell membranes break, liberating the polyhedra into the body cavity of the insect.

The polyhedra are insoluble in water, alcohol, ether, and acetone, but soluble in acids and alkalis. They stain with difficulty with most aniline dyes unless pretreated with acids, or stained for a relatively long time. In size they range from 0·5 to 15 microns. They vary greatly in shape although usually the picture for any one polyhedrosis is rather uniform. Their many-sided shape is usually readily apparent. The crystalline nature of the polyhedra has been verified by the demonstration of a macromolecular paracrystalline lattice. Chemically, the polyhedra are nucleo-proteins; analyses have fairly well revealed their chemical constitution, including that of their amino acid make-up (Bergold 1958, 1959).

If the polyhedra are treated properly with dilute alkali, the rod-shaped particles within them can be demonstrated. From very few to over a hundred virus particles may be found, distributed at random, embedded within the polyhedron. In general, the size of these virus rods ranges from about 20 to 50 millimicrons in width to about 200 to 350 millimicrons in length. The rods are surrounded by an outer, or 'developmental,' membrane, and an inner, or 'intimate,' membrane. With some viruses, such as the virus in the silkworm, usually only one rod is in one develop-mental membrane; in the case of other viruses, such as the virus in the gypsy moth, up to eight rods may occur within a single developmental membrane. There is some evidence that the virus rod itself may have a substructure since in certain preparations it may be seen to break up into what appear to be six to eight spherical subunits. There is some evidence that these rod-shaped viruses also possess a slender protrusion extending from one end and which may be associated with the mechanism of attaching the virus particles to the host cells. The virus rods contain deoxyribonucleic acid (DNA); no ribonucleic acid (RNA) has been found.

Within the cell nucleus the virus appears to develop according to a definite cycle, first indicated by Bergold (1950). In brief, the rods attach themselves to unused chromatin material, lose their developmental membranes, and release the spherical subunits. Membranes are formed about these subunits which continue to multiply and develop within the chromatin which is utilized during the process. Within the nuclear sap the virus particles complete their development inside their membranes, forming into rods. The dense mature rods again attach to the chromatin material and shed their membranes, and the entire process is repeated until all the chromatin is used up. Polyhedra begin to form as dense material gathers about the bundles of virus particles and embeds them. Not all of the virus rods are occluded by the polyhedra; those not occluded may aid in transmitting the virus to other cells.

Many of the nuclear polyhedrosis viruses appear to be highly specific while others are capable of causing infection in two or more insect species. It is believed that infection is frequently latent in insects and that the occult virus may remain with an insect for several or many generations before it is triggered into activity by some stressor. Within the polyhedra the virus may retain its activity for years, in some cases up to 25 years or even longer. The occluded virus is fairly well protected by the polyhedral protein from the action of chemicals, drying, sunlight, putrefactive enzymes, and moderately high temperatures. The free virus particles are much less stable, being readily susceptible to all these agents.

Of the approximately 170 known nuclear polyhedroses, the best-known examples include those in the silkworm, the nun moth, the gypsy moth, the alfalfa caterpillar, and the European spruce sawfly. Although minor differences occur, in general the pathogenesis of the disease is essentially the same in all cases.

An interesting type of nuclear polyhedrosis has been observed in larvae of the crane-fly, *Tipula paludosa* Meig. The polyhedra, found in the nuclei of leucocytes and fat cells, are more or less crescent-shaped. When they are treated with alkali they swell, elongate, or become filamentous, but return to what was essentially their original shape upon modification of the pH or suspension in water. The virus particles appear to be rods approximately 12 by 60 millimicrons in size. The disease has an incubation period of about 14 days. No distinctive symptoms are present in the early stages of the disease; gradually the infected insect becomes pallid and chalky white, and eventually dies.

THE CYTOPLASMIC POLYHEDROSES. The first cytoplasmic polyhedrosis was discovered by Ishimori in 1934 in the silkworm. He observed polyhedra in the cytoplasm of the midgut cells of the insect and considered them to represent a disease different from that characterized by the presence of polyhedra in the nuclei of infected cells. Polyhedra were similarly seen in the cytoplasm of gut cells of larvae of the clothes moth (*Tineola*) by Lotmar in 1941. Since then, approximately 30 species of insects have been found susceptible to cytoplasmic polyhedrosis viruses.

The cytoplasmic polyhedroses are, in general, not so fulminating as are the nuclear polyhedroses. In the cases so far known, the infection is largely limited to the midgut epithelium. This structure usually shows signs of infection by becoming smoky white, opaque white, or yellowish in colour and fragile in consistency.

The polyhedra are similar in most respects to those present in nuclear polyhedroses, although in some cases they apparently stain more readily with methylene blue than do the latter. The virus particles, on the other hand, are quite distinct. They tend to be spherical in shape, from about 20 to 70 millimicrons in diameter, and appear to contain ribonucleic acid (RNA) rather than deoxyribonucleic acid (DNA).

Although not considered to be a cytoplasmic polyhedrosis, a disease in *Pieris brassicae* (L.) is characterized by the presence of refringent bodies of very irregular form in the cytoplasm of the blood cells and fat cells of the affected larvae. The disease is known only in France where it was reported by Paillot (1924, 1926a). Although the causative virus has never been isolated or demonstrated with the electron microscope, Paillot described certain granular elements which he related to the virus. Similar polymorphic inclusions have been reported in the blood cells of *Malacosoma neustria* (L.).

Granuloses

In 1926, Paillot (1926b) observed a disease, in the European cabbage-worm, *Pieris brassicae*, characterized by the presence, in the infected cells, of numerous small granular inclusions. He designated the disease as 'pseudo-grasserie,' but it and about 30 similar infections are now known as 'granuloses.' They have been observed only in larvae of Lepidoptera, and are being found in an increasing number of species throughout the world. Susceptible species are found in such genera as *Pieris, Euxoa, Peridroma, Cacoecia, Eucosma,* and *Junonia.*

Compared with the nuclear polyhedroses, the symptoms associated with the granuloses are more subdued; they vary somewhat according to the host species, and the diseased larvae usually become less active than healthy larvae, somewhat flaccid, and assume a pallid or whitish translucent aspect. The period from infection to death ranges from 6 to 20 days.

The principal tissues affected by granulosis viruses are the adipose tissue, epidermis and frequently the tracheal matrix and blood cells. There is some disagreement as to whether the virus develops in the nucleus or in the cytoplasm of the affected cells. Some workers believe that there is a dichotomy here and that some granuloses are what might be called nuclear granuloses and others are cytoplasmic granuloses. In any case, in an infected cell there is an accumulation of small granular inclusion bodies, called 'capsules,' each of which contains a virus particle. These ellipsoidal inclusion bodies are about 200 by 500 millimicrons in size. In the fat cells these capsules may gather in vacuoles or 'bubbles' several microns in diameter. The infected tissue eventually disintegrates and the body fluids of the diseased larvae become filled with the inclusions. Except for their size and shape, the properties of the capsules are essentially the same as those of the nuclear polyhedra.

In all of the granuloses so far studied, each capsule typically contains a single rod-shaped virus particle. These virus rods, in their main particulars, are similar to those causing nuclear polyhedroses. They possess developmental and intimate membranes, and pass through developmental stages. In size they range from 40 to 80 millimicrons in width by 200 to slightly over 300 millimicrons in length.

Tanada (1956a, 1959) describes what appears to be a case of synergism between a nuclear polyhedrosis virus and a granulosis virus in the armyworm, *Pseudaletia unipuncta* (Haw.), the granulosis virus being the synergist. The addition of the granulosis virus to the remains of larvae dead of the nuclear polyhedrosis greatly increases the virulence of such remains for the armyworm. An initial oral administration of the granulosis virus followed by the inoculation of the nuclear polyhedrosis virus increases the susceptibility of the armyworm more than the initial inoculation of the nuclear polyhedrosis virus followed by the granulosis virus. Inasmuch as the heat-inactivated virus is still capable of reacting synergistically with the unheated nuclear polyhedrosis virus, Tanada has suggested that the granulosis virus is composed of two components, an invasion portion and an infective portion.

Non-inclusion Virus Infections

Not all viruses capable of causing disease in insects are manifested by the presence of inclusion bodies. At the present time there are not more than eight recognized virus diseases of insects not characterized by the presence of cellular inclusions, and in only two of these has the virus been demonstrated by means of electron microscopy. It is not unreasonable to expect additional examples of non-inclusion virus infections to be found as techniques improve.

The first non-inclusion virus disease to be recognized in insects was sac-brood of the honey-bee. The viral nature of the causative agent of this disease is evidenced by the fact that filtrates from diseased honey-bee larvae are infectious when fed to healthy larvae. The virus particles have not been demonstrated with the electron microscope, unless the 60-millimicron spherical particles observed by Steinhaus and Wasser (Steinhaus 1949c) represent this agent. Another disease of the honey-bee—a paralysis of the adult bee—is also believed to be caused by a non-inclusion virus. Although not generally accepted, and certainly needing confirmation, Paillot (1930a, b) believed that the primary cause of both gattine and flacherie in the silk-worm was a virus, and that the distinctiveness of the two diseases depended upon the particular bacteria (streptococcus or spore-forming bacillus) that happened to act as a secondary invader.

A disease of the armyworm, *Pseudaletia unipuncta*, was found (Steinhaus 1951a) to be caused by a non-inclusion virus which Wasser (1952) showed, by means of the electron microscope, to be a small spherical particle about 25 millimicrons in diameter. The disease is apparent in the late larval instars and in the pupal stage. Infected larvae are somewhat swollen and darker than are healthy insects. Death occurs within 6 to 14 days after infection.

In 1954, Xeros described a non-inclusion virus disease in larvae of the crane-fly, *Tipula paludosa*. Through the wet skin of the diseased larva the fat body appears purple. There is increase in the size of the lobules of the fat body which becomes nodular in character. Death occurs two to four weeks after infection.

The virus appears to develop in the cytoplasm of the fat-body cells, which may be observed to be filled with somewhat irregular spheres having a diameter of about 100 to 130 millimicrons. In cross section, dehydrated and embedded virus particles exhibit a hexagonal outline. The designation TIV (*Tipula* Iridescent Virus) is sometimes given this agent because of its unusual optical properties (Smith and Williams 1958). Centrifugate pellets of the virus particles appear orange or amber in colour by transmitted light, and iridescent or turquoise by reflected light. Another peculiarity is the fact that an exceptionally large amount of virus is produced in the host tissues. From 5 to 10 mg of virus (up to 25 per cent of the insect's weight) can be obtained from one larva.

Another type of non-inclusion virus should be mentioned, the so-called σ-virus (sigma-virus) of *Drosophila melanogaster* Meig. (see l'Héritier 1958). The only known symptom caused by this virus is that it renders the infected flies sensitive to carbon dioxide. Normal *Drosophila* can be held in CO_2 for hours without showing any ill effects, but an exposure of only a few seconds causes an irreversible paralysis in infected flies. About one-third of the field-collected *Drosophila* in France are sensitive to CO_2. The virus is transmitted by the gametes without following Mendelian segregation; it is an example of cytoplasmic maternal inheritance. Some infected flies (called 'stabilized' females) consistently transmit the virus to all of their progeny. However, most females are 'non-stabilized' and transmit the virus to only 22 per cent of their progeny, and for only a short period of their life. Normal flies can be made sensitive by injecting them with an extract from sensitive flies. The size of the virus has been estimated to be between 40 and 50 millimicrons, but it may be larger.

Latent Virus Infections

There is considerable evidence that insect viruses frequently remain occult and cause latent infections in their hosts. Some authorities believe that a virus can survive in a host, even for several generations, without causing recognizable symptoms, but that under the influence of certain stressors or incitants can be 'triggered' into causing an active or frank infection. It is thought that some of the confusion and inconsistencies in experimental results might be explainable on the basis of these latent infections.

A variety of stressors have been reported as capable of transforming a latent virosis (usually a polyhedrosis) into an acute form of the disease. Among these stressors are heat, cold, excessive moisture, crowding, chemicals, ultra-violet light, and quality of food (Vago 1951; Gershenson 1956; Yamafuji 1958; Bergold 1958; Steinhaus 1958*a*, *b*; 1960*c*).

Insect Virus Classification and Nomenclature

In keeping with efforts in recent years to classify and name viruses, several attempts (Paillot 1926a; Holmes 1948; Steinhaus 1949c, 1953; Zhdanov 1953; Andrewes 1954; Bergold 1953, 1960; Weiser 1958b; Vago 1958; and Krieg 1961) to handle the insect viruses in a systematic manner have been made in classifying these agents along phylogenetic lines, there has been significant progress in placing the insect viruses into fairly distinct and useful groups. Because virus taxonomy is in the early stages of its evolution, many changes and realignments are expected yet to come. Some progress in the international understanding of the problems concerned, criteria to be used, as well as in agreement on the form of generic nomenclature has been arrived at through the activities of the sub-committee on viruses of the International Nomenclature Committee. This Committee, agreeing to the proposal to end all generic names with the suffix '-virus,' has accepted the following generic names:

> *Borrelinavirus* (Paillot) (nuclear polyhedrosis viruses)
> *Smithiavirus* (Bergold) (cytoplasmic polyhedrosis viruses)
> *Bergoldiavirus* (Steinhaus) (granulosis viruses)
> *Moratorvirus* (Holmes) (non-inclusion viruses)

Weiser has recognized additional genera as follows: *Birdia* (nuclear polyhedrosis viruses affecting the midgut epithelium), *Xerosia* (viruses characterized by crescent-shaped polyhedra), and *Steinhausia* (nuclear granulosis viruses). The genus *Paillotella* Steinhaus awaits the definite isolation of the virus particles before it receives final recognition by the Committee. If and when any of these names are accepted by the Committee they will presumably be used with suffix '-virus' ending.

Rickettsial Infections

In recent years it has become clear that rickettsiae, or rickettsia-like organisms, are capable of causing frank infections in insects. The fact that the rickettsia of typhus fever reduces the life span of the louse has long been known, but the rickettsiae to which we refer here, as far as is known, have insects as their definitive hosts. Rickettsial infections have been reported in larvae of the Japanese beetle (*Popillia*), the forest May-beetle (*Melolontha*), two coccinellids (*Stethorus*), and the crane-fly (*Tipula*). All four species of rickettsiae have been named after the genus of their host and have been placed in the genus *Rickettsiella*. It is possible, on the basis of symptomatology, that a rickettsial infection occurs in larvae of the rhinoceros beetle (*Oryctes*) but the agent has not yet been isolated (Surany 1960). The diseases caused by these rickettsiae are rather slow in developing, may give the fat body of the insect a bluish-green coloration, and kill their hosts in from one to four months. Sometimes peculiar crystalline bodies occur in association with the rickettsiae, but their significance is not yet known, other than they may represent a disturbance in the metabolism of the host caused by the rickettsiae (Dutky and Gooden 1952; Willie and Martignoni 1952; Hall and Badgley 1957; Müller-Kögler 1958; Kreig 1958, 1961; Huger 1959).

PROTOZOAN DISEASES

Protozoan infections in insects are probably of considerably more importance than is generally realized. To be sure, many of these infections are benign and cause little morbidity or mortality, but many are severe and are highly fatal. Some may frequently appear in epizootic proportions and others may be represented by only a local invasion of tissue by the protozoan. Generally, protozoan diseases are relatively slow in developing, and frequently they may become somewhat chronic in nature. On the other hand, certain sporozoan infections may develop rapidly and kill the insect host within a short time. Protozoan-infected insects may show few, if any, external signs of infection, or they may be stunted in growth and development, change in transluscency and colour (usually becoming opaque and whitish because of the accumulation of spores or cysts in the internal tissue or fluids); in addition they may exhibit loss of appetite, abnormality of movement, and may remain in a moribund condition for long periods prior to death.

Unfortunately, the great majority of entomogenous protozoa have not been cultivated on artificial media. This has handicapped the study of these microorganisms, and, as a result, we know very little about their physiology. Their taxonomy and life histories are fairly well known, but even here there is much confusion and many gaps to be filled. Information concerning their specific distribution and occurrence is fragmentary, but it is evident that they are widespread and that they occur in numerous species of insects in a wide range of ecological niches.

Diseases Caused by Flagellates

Very few flagellates (Mastigophora) cause actual infection, disease, or pathological changes in insects. A significant number of flagellates are found associated with healthy insects, but these live in either a commensal or mutualistic relationship with their arthropod host. Sometimes a flagellate, such as *Leptomonas pyrrhocoris* (Zotta) found in certain plant bugs, can cause a fatal infection when inoculated into the body cavity of another insect, such as the larva of the wax moth. In some insects, flagellates may attach themselves to the gut wall or occur abundantly in the Malpighian tubes and cause but minor disturbances of the host's life processes. Sometimes certain so-called vertebrate flagellates, when in their invertebrate hosts, invade individual gut cells, eventually destroying them. However, little general harm to the insect is apparent.

Diseases Caused by Amoebae

Only a few diseases of insects are known to be caused by members of the order Amoebida (class Sarcodina), but these are very interesting infections. Although the diseases of the honey-bee are not being considered in this chapter, the so-called amoebic disease of this insect, known primarily in Europe, has given us valuable information pertaining to this type of infection in insects. The same can be said of the amoebic disease of grasshoppers (*Melanoplus*). The latter disease was discovered in 1936 by King and Taylor in Iowa. It has not been found to be a common disease in nature, and even after artificial distribution of the cysts of the amoeba an incidence of only about 5 per cent was observed. This figure may not be too significant, however, since movements of the insects in and out of the infected area might have lowered it considerably.

Taylor and King, after originally designating the amoeba as *Malpighamoeba locustae*, later (1937) proposed for it a new genus, *Malameba*. The parasites occur in the lumen of the grasshopper's Malpighian tubes, and in the epithelial cells of the midgut and those lining the gastric caeca. The Malpighian tubes become swollen, somewhat glassy in appearance, and packed with cysts. The swollen tubes eventually burst, liberating the cysts (4·6 to 6·2 by 8·5 to 10·0 microns in size) into the hemocoele. The trophozoite, or vegetative stage, of *M. locustae* is from 5 to 10 microns in diameter, hyaline, containing from 8 to 30 highly refractile globules, and moves by pseudopodia.

Diseased grasshoppers may, if lightly infected, show few symptoms. If heavily infected, they become increasingly sluggish, lose their appetites, become 'comatose,' and are unable to remain upright. Just before death the jumping legs twitch. In nymphs death usually does not take place until the fifth instar. Transmission takes place through the ingestion of the cysts previously discharged from an infected grasshopper along with its feces. The time from an infective feeding to the development of cysts in Malpighian tubes is usually from 14 to 18 days. At least 37 species of grasshoppers have been found to be experimentally susceptible to the amoeba.

Gregarine Infections in Insects

The earliest Sporozoa to have been observed were the gregarines. Nevertheless, our knowledge concerning them is limited largely to their taxonomy and life histories. Their host distribution is fairly well known in some instances, but of their physiology and biological relationships we know very little. The order Gregarinida is generally separated into two suborders: Eugregarinina and Schizogregarinina. The latter group is the more important from the standpoint of their potential use in biological control, although the former is by far the larger.

The eugregarines do not undergo asexual reproduction, or schizogony, but multiply sexually by sporogony. The trophozoites may consist of a single compartment (Acephalina), or be divided into two compartments by a septum (Cephalina). Most of the eugregarines in insects are cephaline gregarines. They inhabit the alimentary tract where they are most commonly observed in the relatively large, vermiform, sporadin (sporont) stage. Transmission occurs through the ingestion of spores liberated from a cyst. In general, the life cycle proceeds from the ingested spore to sporozoite to trophozoite to sporadin to gamete to zygote to spore. Aside from the damage caused to individual midgut cells in which the trophozoite develops, usually no great harm comes to the insect host. Most eugregarines have been described from Coleoptera, Orthoptera, and Diptera.

The schizogregarines may be markedly pathogenic for their insect hosts. The members of this group undergo both sporogony and schizogony. Sporogony is of a type similar to that occurring in the eugregarines. Schizogony, which may occur either outside or inside of the host cell, may take place by binary fission, multiple fission, or budding. Of the 25 or 30 species of schizogregarines described from insects, most have been found in Coleoptera, Diptera, and Hemiptera. When one spore is formed from the union of two gametocytes, the schizogregarine is placed in the family Ophryocystidae; when two or more spores are formed, it belongs to Schizocystidae. *Mattesia dispora* Naville is a well-known example of the latter. When a spore of *M. dispora* germinates, the emerged sporozoite penetrates an adipose cell of the host insect (e.g., the Mediterranean flour month, *Anagasta kühniella*), undergoes schizogony, forms gamonts which associate in pairs around which a cyst is formed; gamete formation occurs, followed by zygote formation, and each zygote develops into a spore. Infection of a new host takes place through the ingestion of spores liberated from the disintegrating dead insects. For a generic classification of schizogregarines the reader is referred to that proposed by Weiser (1955).

Coccidian Infections in Insects

The order Coccidia belongs to the same subclass (Telosporidia) of Sporozoa as do the gregarines. They differ in numerous respects, however, one of the principal differences being that the mature trophozoite of the Gregarinida is large and extracellular while that of the Coccidia is small and intracellular. Reproduction takes place both asexually and sexually. Most species of coccidia that parasitize insects belong to the family Adeleidae, of which the genus *Adelina* is the most important. About 12 species of this genus are known in insects. Other Adeleidae parasitic in insects are included in the genera *Legerella*, *Chagasella*, and *Ithania*.

The effect of the coccidian on its host may be slight or marked, depending upon the intensity of the infection. Even in heavy infections, however, the insect is usually able to continue its development and metamorphosis and to maintain most of its activities for long periods of time. Heavily infected insects are frequently sluggish in movement, their reproductive capacity may be reduced, and they sometimes show slight colour changes. The protozoa may be present in nearly every part of the body, and especially in the fat body. It is important to avoid the rather insidious infections caused by these organisms in insectaries and other places where insects are being reared.

Microsporidian Infections in Insects

One of the most famous of all maladies known in insects is *pebrine*, a disease of the silkworm, caused by *Nosema bombycis* Naegeli. Another well-known infection is nosema disease of the honey-bee caused by *Nosema apis* Zander. Intensive studies

of these diseases in the two beneficial insects that serve as their hosts have taught us
a great deal about the group of protozoa concerned: the microsporidia. The order
Microsporidia contains several families of which the most important from the
standpoint of insect pathology is Nosematidae, consisting of about 10 genera. These
genera are separated largely on the basis of the number of spores formed from each
sporont. Thus, species of the genus *Nosema* form a single spore from each sporont,

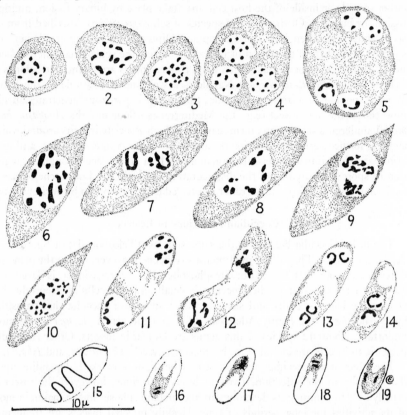

FIGURE 105. Different stages in the life history of *Nosema carpocapsae* Pail., as it occurs in the
larva of the codling moth, *Carpocapsa pomonella* (L.). 1–5. Schizogony. 6–13. Sporogony. 14–19.
Spores (redrawn from Paillot 1939).

Glugea and *Perezia* produce two spores, *Gurleya* four, *Thelohania* eight, *Stempellia*
one, two, four, or eight, *Duboscqia* and *Trichoduboscqia* 16, *Caudospora* several,
and in the case of *Plistophora* a variable number of spores are formed, often more
than 16.

   Microsporidian infections have been found in species of at least 14 orders of
Hexapoda. The most common known insect hosts are Diptera and Lepidoptera.
Approximately 150 species of entomogenous Microsporidia are known. Some of

these are widely distributed geographically and others appear to have rather limited distribution. Some are rather specific as to their insect hosts, while others are capable of infecting insects in different genera or even in different orders. A list and brief description of the Microsporidia infecting insects has been presented by Thomson (1960).

The most commonly seen form of any Microsporidia is the spore stage, the characters of which are of great importance in distinguishing the different species. It serves as the resistant stage of the organism and is able to tide the pathogen over periods of unfavourable environmental conditions, and during the period between the change of host individuals. The average microsporidian spore is from 3 to 6 microns long by 1 to 3 microns broad. Some species exhibit two distinct spore sizes. The form and shape of the spore is usually oval or pyriform, although it may be spherical, bacilliform, or any of several other shapes. The spore consists of a spore membrane or covering surrounding a sporoplasm, and a polar filament coiled directly in the spore or encased within a polar capsule. The polar filament is capable of extrusion as a very fine, long, thread that may be several hundred microns in length in some species. Electron microscope studies on the cytology of the microsporidian spore have been made by Weiser (1959b) and Huger (1960).

The life cycles of microsporidia vary, but a generalized description may be as follows: Soon after a microsporidian spore is ingested by a susceptible host, the polar filament is extruded, becomes detached, leaving a small opening through which the sporoplasm creeps out as an amoebula. (Recent evidence indicates that in some cases at least, the sporoplasm is pulled or dragged out of the spore by the polar filament.) The two nuclei of the amoebula fuse into one, and a uninucleated planont is formed. The planont passes between the epithelial cells of the insect's intestine (in some species the midgut cells are infected), into the haemocoele where it multiplies by binary fission. Various tissues of the body are then invaded, and the parasite is now designated as a schizont or meront. In their intracellular location the spherical to oval meronts divide actively by fission, budding, or multiple division, filling the cytoplasm of the host cell. This period of schizogony ends in the formation of sporonts, each of which produces a single or a number (depending on the genus) of sporoblasts. Each sporoblast becomes a spore. This is the sporogony part of the life cycle. The entire life cycle is usually completed in about four days. For a more complete exposition of the different life cycles of Microsporidia, the reader should consult such papers as those by Kudo (1924) and Weiser (1946, 1947, 1959a).

The most common natural route by which insects are infected with microsporidia is through the mouth. However, some of these protozoa are also transmitted from one generation to the next via the egg, and instances are known in which they are transmitted from diseased to healthy individuals by the contaminated ovipositor of parasitic Hymenoptera.

The symptoms exhibited by an insect infected with a Mircosporidia may vary according to the degree and extent of the infection. Insects normally having somewhat transparent body walls commonly assume a dull milky-white, opaque appearance as the result of the accumulation of spores in the tissues underlying the integument. Greyish or yellowish colour is assumed by some infected insects, and the appearance of dark mottled areas or spots of dark-brown coloration is common- As a result of infection, the host may remain small or dwarfed, or it may become distended or swollen. The activity of the insect becomes impaired either because the muscles themselves are affected or because they have been pushed aside by pressure from near-by distended tissues. Although infected insects may complete their metamorphosis, infected larvae frequently are unable to pass into the pupal and adult stages. Sometimes only certain tissues are invaded by the pathogen, but in many cases nearly all of the tissues of the body are affected. Ordinarily, the fat body and other adipose tissue are the favourite seats of infection by microsporidia; the fat body may diminish in size and at times may be almost completely replaced by the protozoan. Commonly, the infected cells become enormously enlarged, and the nuclei may become hypertrophied. Depending largely on the extent of tissue destruction, the time from infection to death may be prolonged, or it may occur with great rapidity.

Although only about 200 species of insects are known to be susceptible to Microsporidia, some important economic species are included among them. (Undoubtedly, many more Microsporidia and hosts remain to be discovered.) The classic examples of microsporidioses in the silkworm and the honey-bee have already been mentioned. Among the destructive species, microsporidian diseases have been recorded in such insects as the European corn borer, cabbage-worms, codling moth, Mediterranean flour moth, potato tuber-worm, corn ear-worm, gypsy moth, brown-tail moth, and numerous others. Especially noteworthy is the fact that many species of mosquitoes are prominent hosts of Microsporidia. Many of these protozoa seen in mosquitoes have not been described, named, or identified. These infections are widespread among mosquitoes and are undoubtedly of considerable significance in the ecology of these important insects.

Other interesting Sporozoan infections include the *Mycetosporidium* infections in certain weevils, *Helicosporidium* infections in certain Diptera, and those infections, in a variety of insects, caused by certain Haplosporidia of the genera *Haplosporidium*, *Coelosporidium*, *Nephridiophaga*, *Serumsporidium*, and *Coelomycidium*. Although usually considered as pathogens of vertebrates, it should not be forgotten that some of the members of the order Haemosporidia invade the tissues of their insect host and bring about pathological changes in them.

Ciliate Infections in Insects

Several species of Ciliata have been found causing disease in insects. The two best-known are *Glaucoma pyriformis* MacArthur and *Lambornella stegomyiae* Keil. The latter infects larvae of *Aedes scutellaris* (Walkr.), and was first observed in the Malay States by Lamborn in 1921, and described by Keilin in the same year. The ciliate invades all parts of the body cavity of its host, and infection usually results in the death of the larva, which is unable to pupate and complete its development.

The *Glaucoma* infection was reported in 1922 by MacArthur in larvae of *Culiseta annulata* (Schr.) in England. Two years later it was observed in France in larvae of *Chironomus plumosus* (L.). In Northern Rhodesia it parasitizes *Aedes fulgens* Edw., and probably other culicine mosquitoes. The ciliate invades most of its host's body cavity, but is found particularly abundant in the head. A rather constant feature of the infections is the destruction of the insect's eyes, although this has not been found to occur in all hosts. The ciliate has been found experimentally infectious for larvae of the wax moth or other insects. The organism may be held or cultured in water, hay infusions, and in the liquid on the surface of agar plates.

Other ciliates found parasitizing insects include species of *Ophryoglena* in ephemerids, *Operculariella* in dytiscids, *Colpoda* in a hemiptera, and *Balantidium* and *Nyctotherus* in cockroaches.

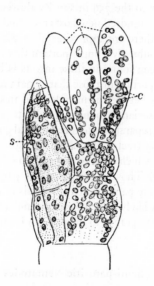

FIGURE 106. The ciliate *Lambornella stegomyiae* Keilin parasitizing the posterior end of a larva of *Aëdes scutellaris* (Wlkr.). *S*, siphon; *G*, gills; *C*, ciliates (from Keilin 1921).

NEMATODE DISEASES

Those Nemathelminthes (roundworms) for which insects serve as primary hosts are included in the classes Nematoda and Nematomorpha. Some members of the third class, Acanthocephala, spend their larval stage in an insect host, and the adult stage in mammals. Well over a thousand species of roundworms have been reported from insects; most of these belong to Nematoda which frequently kill or seriously harm their host.

All nematodes are similar in their general external appearance. Their elongate, unsegmented body has little or no variation in diameter, although it does taper towards one or both ends. There are three main stages in the developmental cycle of most nematodes: eggs, juvenile (larva) (including four growth stages), and adult. Usually the young larvae spend a short period as free-living organisms, frequently in an aquatic environment of water or mud. Most nematodes are bisexual, the females producing fertile eggs after copulation.

At least 16 orders of Hexapoda are involved as hosts to nematodes. About one-third of the known species have been reported from Lepidoptera. As pointed out by van Zwaluwenburg (1928), who presented a host list of entomophilic nematodes, this is probably because of the intensive work of Schultz (1900) with this group of insects, and does not necessarily represent their true distribution in nature. The next largest number of hosts are found in the order Coleoptera, followed by Orthoptera, Diptera, Hymenoptera, and others. La Rivers (1949) added over a hundred species of insects to the 759 in van Zwaluwenburg's host list, and there have been approximately a hundred new hosts recorded since then. Therefore, it is probably safe to say that there are approximately 1,000 insects known to serve as hosts to nematodes—undoubtedly a small portion that actually exist. The number of nematodes that have been found in these insects is believed to approach 1,500 species—again but a tiny portion of those that remain to be discovered.

The biological relations between nematodes and insects vary all the way from those of mere fortuitous association to those of obligate parasitism. For convenience, these relationships may be separated into three general groups: (1) Those nematodes which live in the alimentary tract of the insect in a more or less commensal association. (2) Those nematodes which have a combination of saprophagous and parasitic habits; semi-parasites. (3) Those nematodes that parasitize the body cavity or tissues of their host; obligate parasites. On the basis of our present knowledge the first of these groups is not likely to be of great significance from the standpoint of biological control. In the paragraphs to follow a few examples of the last two groups will be considered briefly.

Semi-parasitic Nematodes

Two of the best-known members of this group are species of *Neoaplectana*. *Neoaplectana glaseri* Steiner was first discovered in dead Japanese beetle grubs, *Popillia japonica*, by Glaser and Fox (1930). Larvae of certain other beetles are also susceptible. When infected with the nematode, Japanese beetle grubs become less active and have a diminished appetite. They assume a mottled to uniform rusty or ocherous brown colour. Upon microscopic examination the body contents are found to be swarming with nemas.

The infective second-stage forms of *N. glaseri* are acquired by the grubs through the mouth. The nematodes soon develop into mature males and females and copulate. The new parasites become so numerous that the insect dies and the worms invade the entire body, and pass through one or two or more generations in the cadaver of the host. (Since further development continues in the dead host, the nematode is considered a saprozoic or semi-parasitic organism rather than a true parasite.) As the cadaver disintegrates the nemas invade the soil and remain in a free-living state until they are ingested by another grub.

N. glaseri can be grown on artificial media (e.g., fermented potato mash, infused veal pulp), and in this manner enough nematodes can be obtained to make possible its field distribution for use as a control measure.

The second example of a semi-parasitic nematode has been known by the designations 'Dutky's nematode' or DD136 (Dutky and Hough 1955). Apparently it is a species of *Neoaplectana*, but its identity has not been finally determined. It was first observed by Dutky in 1954 in diseased codling moth larvae. The infectious stage is the ensheathed second-stage larva which seeks out the insect host, is ingested, penetrates the gut wall, and injects a small gram-negative bacterium into the body cavity. The host usually dies of a bacterial septicaemia in about 24 hours. Thus, the disease is primarily a bacterial septicaemia in which the bacterium is carried by the nematode which acts as a sort of micro-syringe introducing the bacteria into the insect's body cavity. Incidentally, the bacterium not only kills the insect but also serves as food for the nematodes. It also produces an antibiotic substance that prevents the insect cadaver from decaying so rapidly that the nematode could not complete its development.

The nematode is capable of killing the codling moth and at least 40 other species of insects, including the corn earworm, the boll weevil, the pink bollworm, the vegetable weevil, and cabbage-worms. It is a very hardy nematode, and can live for a long period under favourable conditions in the absence of its insect host. It is resistant to the action of many chemical insecticides and fungicides, and hence can be used in combination with them. It is harmless to plants and to higher animals. It can move over moist surfaces for considerable distances seeking an insect host. The nematode can be mass-produced in the laboratory on wax-moth larvae.

Nematodes Parasitic in the Body Cavity of Insects

Those species of nematodes that obligately parasitize the body cavity and tissues of insects are, for the most part, included in the families Tetradonematidae, Mermithidae, and Allantonematidae. Of these the mermithids are best known. Two examples may be cited, both of which infect grasshoppers: *Agamermis decaudata* Cobb, Steiner and Christie, and *Mermis subnigrescens* Cobb. *A. decaudata* is sometimes found in insects other than grasshoppers, but *M. subnigrescens* appears to be strictly a grasshopper parasite.

The free-living stages of *A. decaudata* coil up (usually one female and up to eight males) in small cavities in the soil. After copulation, egg-laying takes place. The next spring the newly hatched second-stage larvae migrate to the surface of the soil, climb grass and other low vegetation when wet, and seek out newly hatched grasshopper nymphs. The nemas penetrate the integument of the insect and grow rapidly in its body cavity. There is usually only one parasite per host. About one to one and one-half months later the males force their way through the body wall of their insect hosts, followed one or two months later by the females from their hosts.

The host grasshopper always succumbs when the parasite emerges from it. An infected insect may show few outward symptoms; the abdomens may appear distended, and the insects may be sluggish and incapable of sustained flight. Internally, the gonads are visibly affected, particularly in the females in which the ovaries are always greatly reduced in size.

The life cycle of *Mermis subnigrescens* is similar to that of *Agamermis decaudata*, but differs in one important respect. Instead of depositing its eggs in the soil, the

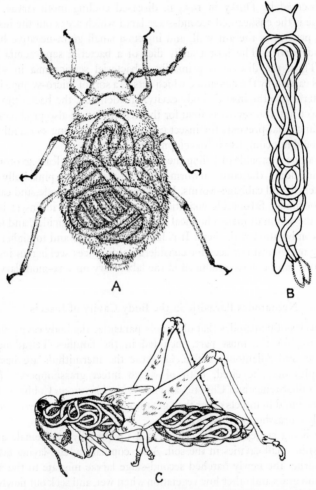

FIGURE 107.   Insects infected with nematodes. A. A root aphid (*Anoecia*) infected with an undetermined nematode. (Redrawn from Davis, 1916.) B. Larva of *Aëdes aegypti* (L.) infected with two nematodes (*Mermis* sp.), one of which is about to emerge via the anus. (Redrawn from Muspratt, 1945.) C. Grasshopper nymph (*Melanoplus*) containing one fully grown female *Agamermis decaudata* C.S. & Ch. (Redrawn from Christie, 1936.)

gravid females of *M. subnigrescens* migrate to the surface of the soil, climb the vegetation, and deposit their eggs thereon. The eggs are swallowed by grasshoppers which feed on the vegetation.

A large number of other nematodes, obligately parasitic in insects, have been observed. Unfortunately, most of the information we have about them is limited to their taxonomy. Many of these, such as the mermithids and allantonematids undoubtedly constitute an important factor in the natural control of insects. Among the best-studied infections, in addition to those already mentioned, are the mermithid parasites of ants, and the allantonematid infections in Coleoptera, Diptera, and Hymenoptera. The Nematomorpha, or 'hair-worms,' are common parasites of small aquatic insects (e.g., Chironomidae, Ephemeridae, and Trichoptera), but also occur in terrestrial species. A few flatworms (Platyhelminthes) also occur in insects, but in most of these cases the insect serves merely as an intermediate host.

DIAGNOSIS OF INSECT DISEASES

The art or act of distinguishing one insect disease from another may be executed at different levels or in different ways. That is, a diagnosis may be based on the symptoms of the disease as shown during the life of the insect, or the diagnosis may be based on changes occurring after death, or it may be based on the information obtained from a laboratory examination of various body fluids, tissues, or secretions of the insect. Frequently, of course, a diagnosis involves all three of these procedures; or one can make a differential diagnosis by which one of two or more diseases are identified by systematically comparing their symptoms or post-mortem changes, or the laboratory findings. In any event, the accurate diagnosis of insect diseases and the identification of the causative agents involved constitute an important part of insect pathology.

To obtain an accurate and certain diagnosis, the safest procedure is to submit appropriate specimens to an insect pathology laboratory (Steinhaus 1960*d*, 1962). As a practical field procedure, however, one can frequently gain a fairly accurate idea of the nature of the disease by observing certain gross symptoms and post-mortem changes. The following paragraphs summarize the general identifying characteristics of the principal groups of infectious diseases in insects:

The first signs of the onset of a bacterial disease in an insect are usually reduced activity and a decreased appetite, followed by the discharge of fluids from the mouth and anus. The infection may begin as a dysenteric condition with an accompanying diarrhoea, but in most instances the invading bacterium eventually enters the body cavity of the insect and causes a septicaemia that terminates in the death of the host. Following death, the insect's body, especially that of the larva, usually darkens to brown or black. The freshly dead insect is usually soft and may become shapeless. The internal tissues may disintegrate to a viscid consistency, sometimes accompanied by odour, but ordinarily they do not 'melt' or liquefy as do insects dying of certain virus infections. The cadaver of the insect usually dries and becomes shrivelled, the integument remaining intact. Microscopic examinations

24—I.P.W.

of smears or histological sections of an insect dead or dying of a bacterial disease usually show large numbers of the causative bacterium present. If the bacteriological examination is delayed too long, care must be taken to differentiate the true pathogens from possible similar-appearing saprophytes which may flourish in the tissues of the dead insect.

Some virus infections may be distinguished from bacterial infections by the fact that the affected larvae frequently 'melt' and rapidly disintegrate. Whereas the integument of an insect suffering from a bacterial infection is often rubbery and relatively resilient, that of insects infected with nuclear polyhedroses and certain granuloses is extremely friable, disintegrating rapidly upon the slightest touch or stress, the liquefied body contents running out as a cloudy or opaque fluid. Virus-infected insects frequently become pallid or yellowish in colour; sometimes the accumulation of inclusion bodies within the insect's body cavity lightens the colour of the insect or gives it an opaque whitish appearance. Most of the virus diseases known in insects are characterized by the presence of inclusion bodies (e.g., polyhedra and capsules) within the tissues of the infected host. These bodies can be visualized with ordinary high-powered light microscopes. The virus etiology of the disease can usually be confirmed by the demonstration, by means of the electron microscope, of the virus particles themselves.

Insects that have been killed by entomogenous fungi vary somewhat in appearance depending upon the kind of fungus concerned, and the stage or degree of development of the fungus. When optimum conditions for its growth and development prevail, the fungus usually appears in the form of conidiophores, hyphae, or mycelium on the surface of the insect's body. Sometimes the animal's entire body is enveloped, at other times the fungus may be apparent only at areas where the body wall is thin, such as at the intersegmental membranes. In the absence of adequate atmospheric moisture there may be no external evidence of the fungus, although the body cavity of the insect may be filled with it. Shortly after the death of such an insect, consistency of the body contents may be cheesy; eventually the insect becomes hard, brittle, and mummy-like. Unlike the appearance in most bacterial and virus infections, the insect infected with a fungus usually retains its general body shape and colour, except that it may be covered or partially covered by the fungus. Of course, definitive diagnoses of a fungus infection can usually be made upon microscopic examination of the diseased insects, especially when this is accompanied by appropriate culturing of the fungus.

Protozoan diseases of insects frequently run a slower or more chronic course than do most other types of infections. Nevertheless, beginning in the early stages of such a disease the insect may show the usual signs of reduced activity and loss of appetite. If slow acting, the protozoan may affect the rate of growth and development of its host; groups of infected insects frequently show considerable variation in size and development as compared with the more uniform appearance of a similar group of non-infected insects. Because of the presence of spores or cysts, the infected insect may assume an opaque, whitish appearance, or show other discoloration. In some cases, the infected insect may exhibit virtually no outward symptoms other than perhaps some sluggishness. After death the diseased animal may become darkened in colour, and may dry to brittle remains, but usually these changes are considerably slower than in bacterial infections. Microscopic examinations of protozoan-diseased insects usually reveal the presence of spores or other stages in the infected tissues.

The symptoms and diagnostic signs associated with nematode infections vary greatly and it is difficult to generalize concerning them. In some nematode diseases there are virtually no external evidences of infection; in others the changes are marked and dramatic. Usually it is necessary to confirm the diagnosis by microscopic examination of the body contents of the affected insect, although sometimes the worm is so large as to be readily apparent without the aid of a microscope. Ordinarily, infected insects have a diminished appetite and are less active than normally. Infected larvae may become flaccid, coloured, and somewhat mottled in appearance. In the case of *Neoaplectana* infections, for example, the insect larvae take on a characteristic rusty or brown colour; at first the coloration is spotty in distribution but later, just before and after death, the colour is more uniform. Larvae turning black as in the case of some bacterial infections, are usually not parasitized by nematodes.

CHAPTER 19

Epizootiology of Insect Diseases

Y. TANADA

INTRODUCTION

EPIZOOTIOLOGY is the science dealing with disease dynamics involving animal populations both in time and space. Inasmuch as the population and its environment are intimately associated in epizootiology, this science connotes an ecological outlook. Thus, an incessant interrelation exists between host population, pathogen population, and environment.

The progress of morbidity or mortality from disease is expressed in time in the form of an epizootic wave. The wave when expressed graphically may be more or less symmetrical, or may be asymmetrical with ascending and descending phases of unequal lengths. The shape of the epizootic curve is generally governed by a complex of factors, such as the increasing or decreasing virulence of the pathogens, the increasing or decreasing resistance of the host, the rate of transmission, the rate of emigration and immigration of the host, the density and spatial distribution of the host, and the effect of environmental factors which may increase or decrease the rate of infection.

When the disease is continually present but at low incidence, it is designated as an enzootic disease. A disease may, therefore, oscillate between enzootic and epizootic phases depending primarily on the relationship between host population, pathogen population and environment.

Both infectious and non-infectious diseases are concerned in epizootiology, but the present treatment is limited to the epizootiology of infectious diseases in insects. Non-infectious diseases may be caused by genetical, physical, chemical, physiological and other factors. In some cases, epizootics of infectious and non-infectious diseases may occur together in an insect population.

One of the important goals of insect pathology is to determine the fundamental principles governing the epizootics of infectious diseases in insect populations. With a knowledge of these principles: (1) epizootic diseases could be initiated for the control of insect pests; (2) diseases of beneficial insects could be controlled; and (3) the insect pathologist may be able to predict how diseases may regulate insect populations. Lack of knowledge concerning the epizootiology of insect diseases has caused insect pathologists (including insect ecologists) to adopt many principles from epidemiology (see Steinhaus 1949a, 1954; Franz 1961a). This is understandable, in

548

spite of the early knowledge that insects are susceptible to diseases (see chapter 18), because of the large numbers of different insect species and pathogens involved. The early investigations on the epizootiology of insect diseases were concerned mainly with the diseases of the domesticated silkworm, *Bombyx mori* (L.), and the honey-bee, *Apis mellifera* L. Even in these insects, the causes (agents) of certain of their diseases were not clarified until recent years. Since 1945, there has been a great increase in the knowledge of the fundamental nature and characteristics of many insect pathogens, especially those of viral and protozoan nature. With this knowledge, one can predict that the progress in the study of the epizootiology of insect diseases will be greatly accelerated in the next decade. Recently, Franz (1961*a*) and Krieg (1961) have presented simplified diagrams depicting the occurrence and cessation of epizootics among insect populations.

Three primary factors are concerned in an epizootic: (1) the pathogen or infectious agent; (2) the susceptible hosts within the population; and (3) efficient means of transmitting the pathogens to the susceptible hosts. These three primary factors are in turn closely affected by the physical and biotic environment which may favour or inhibit the spread of infection from host to host. These factors, as they are concerned with the epizootiology of insect diseases, will be dealt with in detail.

THE INFECTIOUS AGENT

Virulence and Infectivity

There is a fine distinction between virulence and infectivity. Virulence may be defined as the disease-producing intensity or power of a micro-organism, and infectivity as the capacity of a pathogenic micro-organism to spread from one insect host to another (Steinhaus 1949*a*). Occasionally these terms have been used synonymously because pathogens with high virulence also possess high infectivity but this may not always be true. Such may be the case when insect pathogens are applied as microbial insecticides without proper coverage to plants supporting a susceptible host population. This often results in a low mortality among the individuals of the population. The pathogens may be highly virulent to the individual insects but because of their poor capacity to spread or their low infectivity, they may fail significantly to reduce the insect population.

Infectivity or the capacity to spread is one of the most important factors concerned in epizootics within an insect population. In epidemiology the term *epidemic strain* has been employed to define a strain with the capacity to spread naturally among a herd (host population) giving rise to a severe and fatal epidemic (Wilson and Miles 1946). In epizootics of insect populations, this term can be replaced with *epizootic strain*. The epidemic strain is characterized by two attributes —high virulence and high infectivity—but it may lose its epidemic character by losing either attribute. However, Webster (1946) has concluded from his studies in experimental epidemiology that the host population with its individuals of variable susceptibility to diseases may be of more fundamental importance than the changes in the virulence and infectivity of the pathogens.

The infectious agent or pathogen may exhibit variations in virulence. Steinhaus (1949a) has listed four general ways in which to increase the virulence of insect pathogens: by (1) passing it through susceptible insects or possibly other animals; (2) causing it to dissociate into its more virulent or less virulent strains; (3) introducing, together with the micro-organism, substances (mucin, starch, etc.) that may aid in increasing its invasive powers; (4) associating it in a mutualistic relationship with other micro-organisms that may render it more capable of invading tissues than it would be otherwise. Some of the methods by which the virulence may be decreased are by: (1) passing it through insects or animals unfavourable for its growth and development; (2) causing it to dissociate into strains of low and high virulence; (3) cultivating it at abnormally high temperatures; (4) cultivating it under abnormal nutrient conditions. Examples of the use of most of these methods in increasing and decreasing the virulence of insect pathogens can be found in the literature of insect pathology.

Insect pathogens with strains of variable virulence are known largely in the bacteria and fungi, and to a lesser extent or not at all in viruses, rickettsiae, protozoa, and nematodes. Among the early reports of the existence of strains in entomogenous non-spore-forming bacteria is that of Glaser (1918) for the grasshopper bacterium, *Cloaca cloacae* (Jordan) Castellani and Chalmers (= *Coccobacillus acridiorum* d'Herelle *Cloaca* Type A). Lysenko (1958a) and Bucher (1959) also have thoroughly studied this bacterium. The entomogenous spore-forming bacteria, *Bacillus cereus* Fr. and Fr. and *Bacillus thuringiensis* var. *thuringiensis* Berl., have been investigated extensively in recent years. Strains of *B. cereus* have shown differences in their virulence to insects (Steinhaus 1951b; Stephens 1952; Heimpel and Angus 1958a, b). Heimpel and Angus (1958b) after biochemical and infectivity tests have concluded that *B. thuringiensis* var. *thuringiensis*, *B. thuringiensis* Berl. var. *sotto* (Ishiwata) Heimpel and Angus, and *B. thuringiensis* Berl. var. *alesti* (Tou. and Vago) Heimpel and Angus should be included as varieties of *B. thuringiensis*.[1] This has also been suggested by Delaporte and Béguin (1955). However, Toumanoff and Le Corroller (1959) maintain that the differences are not sufficient to separate *B. thuringiensis* var. *thuringiensis* from *B. cereus*.

The pathogenicity of *B. cereus* is associated with the production of a toxic enzyme, lecithinase (a phospholipase type C), which breaks down tissue phospholipids; whereas *B. thuringiensis* var. *thuringiensis* and other related crystalliferous species produce a crystalline proteinaceous compound toxic for insects (Heimpel and Angus 1958a). Another toxic component has been detected by McConnell and Richards (1959) in cultures of *B. thuringiensis* var. *thuringiensis* and in non-pathogenic strains of *B. cereus*. It is distinct from the heat-labile inclusion bodies

---

[1] The form in which the authors of these scientific names are cited follows the Botanical Code of Nomenclature. The Bacteriological Code is not clear concerning the citation of authors especially where varieties or subspecies are concerned. We understand the forthcoming revison of the Bacteriological Code will make the matter of author citations unambiguous.

and lecithinase and is toxic by injection but not by oral feeding. A similar toxin has also been reported by Tamashiro (1960). Apparently nutrient-broth cultures of *B. thuringiensis* var. *thuringiensis* produce a filterable principle that interferes with the development of the house-fly (Briggs 1960).

The milky disease organisms, *B. popilliae* Dutky and *B. lentimorbus* Dutky, are known to have strains with variable virulence for the Japanese beetle, *Popillia japonica* Newm. and the European chafer, *Amphimallon majalis* (Raz.) (White 1947; Tashiro and White 1954; Tashiro 1957).

In addition to the differentiation of the entomogenous bacterial strains by means of their pathogenicity, such strains can also be differentiated with the use of antibiotics and bacteriophage. Toumanoff and Lapied (1954) have observed that *B. thuringiensis* var. *thuringiensis* and related varieties are all resistant to penicillin and varied in their tolerances to terramycin, chloromycetin, aureomycin, and strep-tomycin. With the use of bacteriophages, Gochnauer (1958) has demonstrated the presence of several strains of *B. larvae* White and of *B. alvei* Cheshire and Cheyne. The former bacillus causes American foulbrood of honey-bee and the latter, according to some authorities, is associated with the European foulbrood.

One of the significant studies demonstrating the wide variability in the strains of a fungus species is that of MacLeod (1954*a*, *b*). He has concluded that 14 allegedly different species of *Beauveria* should be reduced to synonymy to two species, *B. bassiana* (Bals.) Vuill. and *B. tenella* (Del.) Siem. For many years these 'so-called' 14 species have been known to vary in their pathogenicity to different insect species. Other fungi, such as the white halo fungus, *Cephalosporium lecanii* Zimm. (Ganhao 1956), and the green muscardine fungus, *Metarrhizium anisopliae* (Metch.) Sor. (Rockwood 1950*b*; Radha, Nirula, and Menon 1956), are known to possess strains with different pathogenicity for insects. In the case of the green muscardine fungus, Radha *et al.* have observed long-spored and short-spored forms, the former appearing to be specific in their pathogenicity for *Oryctes rhinoceros* (L.).

Although little is known about the presence of strains among the entomogenous viruses, recent reports indicate that such may exist. Ossowski (1957*a*, 1958, 1960) has observed that specimens of the nuclear polyhedrosis virus of the wattle bag-worm, *Kotochalia junodi* (Heyl.), obtained from various localities differed in their pathogenicities from the one present in the area which was treated. He believes that there are different strains of the bagworm virus, and that a given population of bagworm differs in its susceptibility to these various strains. Apparent mutations in viruses have been reported by Aruga (1957), Aizawa (1958), and Gershenson (1959*a*, *b*).

It is common knowledge that the virulence of many pathogens of man and other animals is reduced by repeated culture on artificial media, and that such loss in virulence is regained when passed through a susceptible host. Information is gradually accumulating that this is also generally true for many insect pathogens. The reader should consult chapter 20 for a detailed account of the effect of culture methods on the gain and loss in the virulence of insect pathogens.

Several investigators have considered the possibility of increasing the invasive property or the virulence of certain pathogens by combination with certain incitants and with other pathogenic or non-pathogenic micro-organisms. The ingestion of triturated glass has increased the infection in insects by certain micro-organisms (Weiser and Lysenko 1956; Steinhaus 1958a). Mucin is known to enhance infection in vertebrates, but the manner in which it promotes the infection of *Pseudomonas aeruginosa* (Schr.) Mig. in insects has not been determined (Stephens 1959a).

Virulence has also been increased by the synergistic associations of two or more micro-organisms. In some cases not all the micro-organisms are primary pathogens. The armyworm, *Pseudaletia unipuncta* (Haw.), is more susceptible to virus infections when fed a mixture of a granulosis virus and a nuclear polyhedrosis virus (Tanada 1956a). In this synergistic association, the granulosis virus appears to be the important synergist that enhances the virulence of the nuclear polyhedrosis virus (Tanada 1959b). Inasmuch as this property is retained even after the granulosis virus has been heated at 80° C for 10 minutes, which is beyond its thermal inactivation point (75° C for 10 minutes), Tanada has proposed the hypothesis that the granulosis virus consists of two portions, an infective and an invasive portion. Further tests are necessary to verify this hypothesis. Preliminary field observations have indicated that the synergistic association between the two viruses plays an important role in the virus epizootics of the armyworm (Tanada 1959b, 1961).

Although Bird (1959) has obtained greater mortality by feeding the larvae of the spruce budworm, *Choristoneura fumiferana* Clem., a mixture of a nuclear polyhedrosis and a granulosis virus than by feeding them only one of the viruses, he believes that there is no evidence of synergistic effect on the development of the second virus. He assumes that the individuals are not equally resistant to both viruses, and those which might have survived exposure to one virus, die from exposure to the second virus. Vago (1956) has observed that the occurrence of virus infections in certain insects increases the possibility of infections by other pathogens.

Isakova (1954) has isolated from diseased *Eurygaster integriceps* Puton three bacterial species, *Chromobacterium prodigiosum* Top. and Wil. (= *Serratia marcescens* Bizio), *Pseudomonas pyocyanea* Mig. (= *P. aeruginosa*), and a spore-former resembling *Bacillus mycoides* Flügge (= *B. cereus* var. *mycoides* (Flügge) Bergey *et al.*). A mixed culture of these three bacteria, especially when raised in liquid medium, is more pathogenic to several species of insects than that of the individual bacterium. When a mixture of *Serratia marcescens* and *Bacillus thuringiensis* var. *thuringiensis* Berl. is fed to wax moth larva, *Galleria mellonella* (L.), the former inhibits the development of the bacillus but the latter nevertheless enables *S. marcescens* to develop more freely (Steinhaus 1959b). Since this phenomenon occurs in the absence of vegetative rods, it is the toxic crystalline inclusions that are responsible for increasing the susceptibility of the wax moth larva. On the other hand, Stephens (1959c) working with *Pseudomonas aeruginosa*, *S. marcescens*, and a coliform bacterium has reported that in the combined feeding of two pathogenic bacterial species to the grasshopper, *Melanoplus bivittatus* (Say), the LD_{50} obtained is no lower than the LD_{50} of either bacterium alone. When fed a combination of two pathogenic bacteria, the grasshoppers generally die from an infection produced by only one organism which alone is present in the blood. The organism taking precedence is generally that fed in greater numbers. When *P. aeruginosa* and *S. marcescens* are fed in equal numbers, all of the deaths are caused by *S. marcescens*.

Bailey (1956, 1957*a*) has recently presented evidence that the European foul-brood of honey-bee is caused by a mixture of *Streptococcus pluton* (White) and *Bacterium eurydice* White, rather than by *Bacillus alvei* which was formerly recognized as the etiological agent. Both organisms have to be grown together in mixed anaerobic culture in order to be infectious. Bailey (1957*b*) has also shown that *S. pluton* is not a variety of *B. eurydice*, as believed by previous workers.

In the case of the protozoa, Weiser (1956) has reported that mixed infection by two or more microsporidian species in the gypsy moth, *Porthetria dispar* (L.), is not more virulent than infection by the individual microsporidian. However, some host-specific microsporidia (e.g. *Nosema lymantria* Weiser) can be transferred to other hosts (e.g., *Euproctis chrysorrhoea* (L.)) by combining with another micro-sporidian (e.g., *Thelohania similis* Weiser) pathogenic for these hosts (Weiser 1956, 1957*a*).

The mutualistic association between bacteria and a number of species of nematodes of the family Steinernematidae has been observed by Dutky (1937, 1959) and Weiser (1955). The nematode has the bacteria in its oesophagus, and usually after entering the host through the mouth it injects the bacteria into the body cavity of the host and this results in a septicaemia. The bacteria not only serve as food for the nematode but also produce an antibiotic which prevents the growth of micro-organisms inimical to the development of the nematode.

The standard and usual method for measuring differences in virulence of insect pathogens is the dosage-mortality test or some modification of it. In 1952, Sussman proposed the quantitative measurements of virulence based on the respiratory gas exchange of the infected host during the disease. He has found that the pupa of *Hylaphora cecropia* (L.) undergoes a twenty-fold increase in oxygen uptake as a result of infection by the fungus *Aspergillus flavus* Link. The loss in weight of the infected pupa is roughly parallel to the respiratory increase and is the result mostly of water loss through the spiracles. Lysenko and Sláma (1959) have utilized the respiratory gas exchange method in accurately determining the duration of the incubation period of *Serratia marcescens* infection in diapausing pronymphs of the sawfly, *Cephalcia abietis* L. This duration is inversely correlated to the infectious dose of the pathogenic bacteria which is injected into the host.

Capacity to Survive

The frequency with which epizootics break out among insect populations is closely associated with the survival capacity of the pathogens among the host and within the host environment. There are numerous examples in insect diseases where the pathogens are continuously present in the host population and epizootics occur repeatedly at periodic intervals.

The survival capacity of the insect pathogens may be separated into: (1) survival in the host habitat, and (2) survival within the individuals of the host population and the associated insect parasites, predators, and other animals. In general, insect pathogens possessing a spore or resistant stage in their life cycles are capable of surviving and persisting for long periods in the environment of their hosts. The resistant stages may be the spore stage of the bacteria, protozoa, and fungi, the inclusion bodies of insect viruses, and the cyst and ensheathed stages of the nematodes.

There is abundant information on the storage capacity of insect pathogens under laboratory conditions but much less is known about their survival capacity or persistence in the habitat of the insect host. Thompson and Steinhaus (1950) have found that the soil in alfalfa fields contains nuclear polyhedrosis virus that is infectious for the alfalfa caterpillar, *Colias eurytheme* Bdvl. When the alfalfa fields are irrigated by flooding, the virus particles may be deposited on the plants and may later infect alfalfa caterpillars feeding on such plants. Although no tests were conducted, it is highly probable that the virus may persist in the soil for some years. The nuclear polyhedrosis virus of the Great Basin tent caterpillar, *Malacosoma fragile* (Stretch), may successfully persist throughout the winter on the host plants (Clark 1955, 1956, 1958). In the case of the wattle bagworm, *Kotochalia junodi*, the nuclear polyhedrosis virus may persist in virus-killed larvae remaining in the bags on the trees for more than a year (Ossowski 1957*b*). Such infected cadavers appear mainly responsible for carrying the infection from season to season. On the other hand, the viruses of the European spruce and pine sawflies (*Diprion hercyniae* (Htg.) and *Neodiprion sertifer* (Geoff.)) are apparently incapable of surviving on the host plants during the winter (Bird 1954, 1955).

The long-term persistence of the spores of the milky-disease organisms, *Bacillus popilliae* and *B. lentimorbus*, is indicated by the enduring control of the Japanese beetle once the spores have been introduced into the habitat (turf) of the host (White 1940; Beard 1945). Very little is known of the persistence in nature of other entomogenous spore-formers, such as *Bacillus cereus*, *B. thuringiensis* var. *thuringiensis* Berl. and their related varieties. Stephens (1957*b*) has found that some spores of *B. cereus* which were applied to apple trees apparently germinated and the bacteria multiplied after the second and later sprays. The variation in persistence seems to be caused mainly by factors affecting the viability of the bacteria.

It is generally assumed that non-spore-forming bacteria have low survival capacity outside their hosts or in the absence of suitable media. This is apparently not so of *Bacterium noctuarum* (White) Steinhaus (= *Serratia marcescens*), the cause of cutworm septicaemia, which is capable of remaining viable in moist soil over long periods (White 1923*b*). D'Herelle (1914, 1915) has found that *Cloaca cloacae* (= *Coccobacillus acridiorum*) remains virulent in dried cadavers of grasshoppers for about two years. The survival of *Pseudomonas aeruginosa* is increased if it is combined with 1 per cent casein, 5 per cent sucrose, and 1 per cent granular mucin (Stephens 1957c). With the use of such a protectant, approximately 29 per cent of the bacteria survive after 24 hours and 9 per cent after one week.

Streptococcus pluton, one of the pathogens causing European foulbrood, is capable of surviving at least 15 months in the dried faecal deposits of infected larvae (Bailey 1959a, b). This ability of *S. pluton* to survive desiccation may provide an explanation of how a honey-bee colony, even after a long period of broodlessness, may develop European foulbrood in its new brood. *Bacterium eurydice*, whose presence is also necessary for the development of the disease, is endemic in the alimentary tract of the normal adult bees, and from which source larvae almost certainly become infected.

The ubiquitous fungi, such as the white muscardine, *Beauveria bassiana*, the green muscardine, *Metarrhizium anisopliae*, and certain entomophthoraceous fungi, appear to persist successfully in the host habitat. This has been indicated by the recurrent outbreaks of disease each year under favourable conditions among susceptible hosts of these fungi. The white muscardine, when applied to the hibernating quarters of the bug, *Aradus cinnamomeus* Panz., has remained effective for at least two years, and the fungus infection has spread out considerably from the treated foci (Smirnov 1954). The fungi of the spotted alfalfa aphid, *Therioaphis maculata* (Buck.), when introduced into a fungus-free population have persisted for several years, even during periods of host scarcity (Hall and Dunn 1957b). One of the striking features of the autumn fungus epizootic caused mainly by *Entomophthora exitialis* Hall and Dunn among the populations of spotted alfalfa aphid, is the very sudden appearance of the epizootic after an unfavourable dry period of more than five months, during which not a single diseased aphid can be found in the samples (van den Bosch et al. 1959b). The fungus probably remains in the resting spore stage throughout the unfavourable dry period in the field.

Among the protozoa, the Sporozoa with their resistant spore stages are capable of persisting in nature for a relatively long period. Weiser (1956) has reported that microsporidian spores in the soil may survive for at least 12 months. The presence of water is important in maintaining the spore, because the spore dies within a few months when dried. It is of interest that certain entomogenous flagellates may remain alive over long periods when their resistant bodies (metacyclic forms) are embedded in the dry faecal particles of their hosts (Gibbs 1948, 1957). Certain nematodes are capable of surviving as ensheathed larvae for long periods in the soil, under bark of trees, and in the stems or whorls of plants where some moisture is available (Glaser and Farrell 1935; Hoy 1954; Dutky 1959). Such nematode larvae, however, are killed in a short time by desiccation.

The persistence of insect pathogens within infected hosts, uninfected healthy carriers, parasites, and predators has received considerable attention in recent years. More and more examples are being found for this type of survival, and in some cases, it may be more important than the persistence of the pathogens in the host habitat. Thus Bird (1954, 1955) has found that the nuclear polyhedrosis viruses of the European spruce and pine sawflies do not successfully overwinter on the host plants, and the survival of part of an infected population, therefore, plays a major role in the spread of infection. The persistence in infected hosts may be especially important for pathogens whose host lives on annual or deciduous plants and each year's host generations live on new host plants or plant parts. Such is the case with the Great Basin tent caterpillar, where the ovarial transmission plays an important role in carrying the virus through the 9- to 10-month period during which no susceptible stage of the insect is present (Clark 1955). This important aspect of epizootiology will be discussed in greater detail in the sections on the latent infections, the dispersal capacity, and the transmission of pathogens.

There is some question of how long a pathogen is capable of spreading and surviving in an insect population. In native insects, any disease associated with them in nature may be considered to have survived with such insect populations for many years. In these cases it is generally difficult to estimate the length of the association between host and pathogen. However, in the case of exotic insect species which had migrated considerable distances into a new habitat, the disease can often be detected early and its progress studied. Such has been the case with the milky diseases of the Japanese beetle, and the virus diseases of the European spruce and pine sawflies in North America. In these cases, the pathogens have shown marked capacity to survive in the host population and habitat.

Capacity to Disperse

The dispersal ability of insect pathogens or their capacity to spread throughout the host population or host environment is very important in the occurrence of epizootics among insects. This characteristic is closely associated with the persistence of insect pathogens in nature. Dispersal in nature occurs by various methods, such as the movements of healthy carriers and infected hosts (primary, secondary, etc.), by being transported on the bodies of non-susceptible insects and animals, by climatic and physical factors (wind, rain, snow, and streams), and by their own motility or by special discharging apparatus (fungi). However, automotility is rather limited, and, in general, insect pathogens do not possess properties comparable with the searching capacities of insect parasites and predators. Exceptions are the entomogenous nematodes and fungi but it is unlikely that they exhibit a definite search pattern. In the case of certain entomogenous nematodes, the infective larval stages apparently seek out or are attracted to the host (Dutky 1959), but it is not known to what extent they are attracted nor how great a distance they travel.

Dispersion by the movement of healthy carriers and infected primary and secondary hosts is one of the principal methods of dissemination of insect pathogens. The infected hosts may distribute the pathogens through their eggs, faecal matter, regurgitations, and, after death, their disintegrating bodies may deposit the pathogens in the insect's habitat. It is obvious that if insect pathogens are transmitted by the infected adults to their offsprings, such adults serve in the dissemination of the pathogens. This aspect will be discussed under the section on 'Transmission'. It is merely sufficient to say that congenital transmission has been shown to occur mainly with viruses, bacteria, and protozoa.

In addition to the examples cited previously for the dispersal of entomogenous bacteria, it should be mentioned that the adult Japanese beetles are also susceptible to the milky diseases of the grub and may disseminate the bacteria (Langford, Vincent, and Cory 1942). Most nematodes are presumably spread by the movements of their hosts, as has been demonstrated for various species of *Neoaplectana* (Bovien 1937; Glaser, McCoy, and Girth 1940; Girth, McCoy, and Glaser 1940). However, the extent to which parasitized hosts may be hindered in their flight or movement needs further investigation. This may suggest why nematode parasitism may be more or less localized.

The inadvertent reaction of insects to certain types of pathogens, such as the nuclear polyhedrosis virus and certain entomogenous fungi, seems to facilitate the distribution of these pathogens. Many lepidopterous and hymenopterous larvae when infected with nuclear polyhedrosis tend to die attached to the tops of plants, including trees, and after death their bodies disintegrate and the remains are scattered to the lower parts of the plants. Because of this tendency for the cadavers to remain on the tops (*Wipfeln*) of trees, such virus diseases are sometimes designated in German as *Wipfelkrankheit* or *Wipfelsucht*. A somewhat similar situation occurs with certain entomophthoraceous fungi. It is rather common to find dead bodies of flies and other insects which are killed by fungi clinging to the tops of plants. Any wind passing over such plants may carry the fungus spores. With the entomophthoraceous fungi of certain aphids, the infected alate aphid may be impelled to migrate in an early stage of infection (Rockwood 1950a).

The ovipositional characteristics of the insect species may effect the dispersal of the pathogens which are transmitted through the egg. Bird (1955) has found that the European spruce sawfly, *Diprion hercyniae*, which lays its eggs singly, when infected with the nuclear gut polyhedrosis virus establishes a larger number of foci of infection through the infected eggs than the infected adults of the European pine sawfly, *Neodiprion sertifer*, which lays its eggs in clusters. The nuclear polyhedrosis virus of *D. hercyniae* is, therefore, more effective at low population levels.

In general, the faecal matter of infected insects may contain infectious pathogens which may survive in such faeces for certain periods of time. This occurs especially with pathogens which infect the gut, malpighian tubules, and silk glands. The nuclear polyhedrosis viruses of the sawflies and of certain Lepidoptera, and the cytoplasmic polyhedrosis viruses have been shown to infect the midgut cells. As these viruses destroy the midgut cells, they are discharged into the lumen and eliminated with the faeces. In certain bacterial infections (e.g. European foulbrood and bacterial infection in grasshoppers) faecal contamination is important in the dispersal of the pathogen, but in others, as in *Pseudomonas aeruginosa*, the bacteria cannot persist in large numbers in the gut, and the faeces of the infected individuals are often free of bacteria. A fungus, *Zygaenobia intestinalis* Weiser, has been found to discharge its conidia into the lumen of the larval gut of *Zygaena carniola* Scopoli, and the conidia are distributed through the faeces (Weiser 1951). In many protozoan infections, the faeces of the infected hosts are highly contagious (Weiser 1956; Günther 1956).

Although some insect pathogens are rather host specific, others are capable of infecting several different insect species. Such alternative hosts, if present in abundance in the biotops, may be important in disseminating the pathogens. The microsporidian, *Thelohania hyphantriae* Weiser, in addition to its principal host, *Hyphantria cunea* (Drury), infects the lackey moth, *Malacosoma neustria* (L.), the brown-tail moth, *Euproctis chrysorrhoea*, and the apple tree web-moth, *Hyponomeuta malinellus* Zell. The movements of these alternative hosts serve in spreading the infection in nature (Weiser and Veber 1955). Certain hymenopterous parasites of the European cabbage-worm, *Pieris brassicae* (L.) (Blunck 1952), the imported cabbage-worm, *P. rapae* (L.) (Tanada 1955a), and *Aporia crataegi* (L.) (Lipa 1957) are also susceptible to the microsporidians which attack their insect hosts. The incidence of the fungus disease, green muscardine, in the autumn culture of silkworms is closely associated with the abundance of the alternative wild insect hosts, especially *Naranga aenescens* Moor, in the areas of silkworm culture (Tateishi, Murata, and Hirano 1954; Tateishi 1957).

In addition to the alternative hosts, many other non-susceptible insect species and other animals in the biotope may aid in the dissemination of the insect pathogens by serving as mechanical carriers of the pathogens either within or on their bodies. These include parasites, predators, scavengers, and birds. Examples will be cited later of certain insect parasites and predators which are capable of transmitting pathogens to their common hosts and they would be expected also to disseminate the pathogens.

Dissemination of the nuclear polyhedrosis viruses of the European spruce and pine sawflies is aided by insect parasites, predators, and scavengers, and by birds (Bird 1953a, 1955). The parasites of the European spruce sawfly, *Diprion hercyniae*, are considered responsible for the introduction of the nuclear polyhedrosis virus of the sawfly into North America from Europe (Balch and Bird 1944; Balch 1958). After feeding on virus-infected sawfly larvae, the stomach contents of the catbird and the cedar waxwing may be highly infectious for the larvae of the European pine sawfly, *Neodiprion sertifer* (Bird 1955). The larvae of *N. sertifer* are also highly susceptible to the virus, even after the virus has been fed to the predatory bug, *Rhinocorus annulatus* L., and the robin, *Erithacus rubecula* L. and has been eliminated with the faeces (Franz, Krieg, and Langenbuch 1955; Franz 1956).

Birds, insects, skunks, moles, and mice have been connected with the dissemination of the milky disease organism, *Bacillus popilliae*, of the Japanese beetle (White and Dutky 1940; White 1943; Polivka 1956). Adults of *Tiphia* spp., which have been obtained from soil containing milky disease organisms of the Japanese beetle, have been found to carry the spores on their bodies (White 1943). The hymenopterous parasites, *Dibrachys* sp. (Metalnikov and Metalnikov 1935) and *Apanteles glomeratus* (L.) (Toumanoff 1959), may act as mechanical carriers of *Bacillus cazaubon* (Metalnikov, Ermolaev, and Schobaltzyn) and *B. thuringiensis* var. *thuringiensis* Berl.

Protozoa may be distributed also by non-susceptible carriers such as scavengers, insect parasites, and predators (Weiser 1956). The spores of *Thelohania hyphantriae* may retain their virulence even after being excreted with the faeces of such insects as *Calosoma sycophanta* L., *Xylodrepa quadripunctata* L., *Cantharis fusca* L., and *Formica rufa* L., and the mite, *Tyrophagus noxius* Zakhvatkin (Weiser 1957*b*). Similarly the spores of *Nosema polyvora* Blunck and *Plistophora schubergi* Zwölfer pass with little or no loss in virulence through the alimentary tracts of a bird (*Parus major* L.) and an earwig (*Forficula auricularia* L.) (Günther 1959).

Climatic and physical factors in the environment may also play a part in the distribution of the pathogens. In many cases, the importance of these factors has not been evaluated for the various types of insect diseases. Wind is of primary importance in the movement of infected hosts and of certain pathogens. Many fungi are dependent to a large extent upon wind and air currents for their dispersal. The nuclear polyhedrosis viruses, especially in cases where the hosts die suspended from tree tops, may be scattered by wind and rain. Pathogens capable of surviving for some time in dusts may be carried by the wind. The action of rain may distribute certain pathogens, but in general it would be expected to wash the pathogens off the plants.

Streams and rivers may carry the pathogens from place to place. In this connection, an interesting observation has been cited by d'Herelle (1914) that a river or stream acting as a physical barrier to migrating grasshoppers, which have a bacterial epizootic raging among them, may temporarily arrest the epizootic by preventing the grasshoppers, which are weakened with bacterial infection, from crossing the river and continuing with the vigorous individuals. In this manner, most of the sources of infection are removed from the population. In the case of the nuclear polyhedrosis of the alfalfa caterpillar, Thompson and Steinhaus (1950) have observed that the practice of irrigation by flooding the alfalfa fields may distribute the virus from the soil on to the plants. They consider the population density of the alfalfa caterpillar and the stage of growth of the alfalfa at the time of irrigation as important factors in initiating an epizootic.

THE HOST

Information is gradually accumulating on the susceptibility and resistance of insects to the various diseases. In some cases, the mechanism for the susceptibility or resistance of the insects has been worked out. However, very little is known as yet about the susceptibility of the insect population taken in its entirety. Thus Steinhaus (1949*a*) has stated: 'If we are to understand the true nature of epizootics and their spread among insect populations we must take into consideration what epidemiologists of human disease call "herd infection" and "herd immunity". . . .' He has suggested the terms 'population infection' and 'population immunity' as they relate to the interacting of diseases and insect populations.

An insect population has characteristic property, structure, and composition. The population interacts with other insect species (parasites, predators, scavengers, and competitors), other animals, plants, and micro-organisms (pathogenic and non-pathogenic). It is affected by certain physical and climatic factors of the environment. The immunity or susceptibility of a population to an epizootic, apart from the susceptibility or resistance of the individual hosts, may be governed by the specific structure of the population. A population whose individuals may be susceptible to infection may not be subject to disease outbreaks because of direct resistance by the individuals to the introduction and spread of the disease or because the population is so located or distributed that infection cannot reach them. Direct resistance of the population to infection may also be associated with the movement (emigration and immigration) and spatial distribution (aggregation) of the insects. The more closely together the individuals are, the more likelihood of contact and spread of the disease. Indirect resistance would be associated with climatic conditions unfavourable for the development of an epizootic (as with fungus diseases) or physical barriers which prevent the migration and introduction of pathogens into a susceptible host population.

The various types of individuals that make up an insect population, as far as their susceptibility to disease is concerned, have been classified by Steinhaus (1949a) as: (1) the typically diseased insect; (2) the atypically diseased insect; (3) the uninfected immune; (4) the uninfected susceptible; (5) the latently infected insect; and (6) the healthy carrier. Among the six classes of individuals, the only fully susceptible hosts at risk are those classed as uninfected susceptibles. These classes have been adopted from those set up by epidemiologists for the individuals in an infected human population. At the time Steinhaus presented the classification, he observed that latent infections and individuals that act as healthy carriers are inadequately known in insect populations. Since then evidence has been presented, especially with the virus diseases, that latently infected and healthy carriers do occur in insect populations. However, it is not known whether all six classes of individuals are present in every insect population and for the different types of diseases.

The resistance of the population may be affected by all those factors that act on the resistance of the individual insects. Resistance in individual insects to infectious diseases may result from natural (innate) or acquired resistance. Insects are naturally resistant to nearly all diseases of plants and other animals, and these organisms are generally not affected by diseases of insects. Certain diseases of insects, especially virus and protozoan diseases, are highly specific for a single host species or restricted to a few related insects. As in other animals, insects are able to acquire immunity, either naturally or artificially, and this may come about through the active or passive participation of the insects.

The natural resistance is associated with biological and physical characteristics which go to make up the insect's resistance to infection. For example, immunity may be associated with the different stages of the insect's life cycle or to the presence of a more or less impermeable exoskeleton. In general, young larvae are more susceptible to infection than older larvae (i.e., maturation immunity) to most diseases. This is true in spite of the fact that the individuals may die at an older instar or even in the pupal and adult stages. In the European spruce and pine sawflies, the prepupal stage is immune to infection by polyhedrosis viruses (Bird 1953b; Bird and Whalen 1953). The temporary prepupal midgut is composed of resistant embryonic cells, but the new digestive cells, which develop from the embryonic cells and which appear later in the pupa and adult, are susceptible to the viruses.

There are several exceptions to the increase in resistance with the age of the larvae, but some of them need confirmation. Grasshoppers in their early instars are more resistant to infection by *Cloaca cloacae* than older instars, and the period of least resistance is reached at the last nymphal moult (d'Herelle 1914; DuPorte and Vanderleck 1917). The adult grasshoppers are less susceptible than the nymphs but they are most susceptible to infection by *C. cloacae* during the period of oviposition. The hornworms, *Protoparce sexta* (Johan.) and *P. quinquemaculata* (Haw.), are most susceptible to infection with septicaemia as fifth-instar larvae (White 1923*a*, *b*). Ullyett and Schonken (1940) have observed the earlier larval instars of *Plutella maculipennis* (Curtis) to be more resistant than the older instars to infection by *Entomophthora sphaerosperma* Fres. According to Billings and Glenn (1911), the old chinch bugs, *Blissus leucopterus* (Say), which have finished depositing their eggs succumb more readily to *Beauveria bassiana* than do the younger ones The young larval stages of the silkworm are more susceptible to the fungus. *Spicaria farinosa* (Fr.) Vuill. (= *Isaria farinosa* (Dickson) Fr.), and other *Isaria* spp. than the older stages (Aoki, Sasamato, and Nakasato 1955).

Older pupae of some Lepidoptera are resistant to infection by *Beauvaria bassiana*, *Aspergillus flavus*, and *A. luchuensis* Inui (Sussman 1951; Tanada 1955*b*). This resistance is apparently accounted for by a waxy epicuticular layer (Sussman 1951; Koidsumi 1957) in which the free medium-chain saturated fatty acids, presumably caprylic or caproic acids, seems to act as antifungal agents (Koidsumi 1957). This antifungal agent seems to be generally present in the epicuticle of insects.

Good examples of maturation immunity are found in the diseases of the honey-bee. Certain brood diseases, such as the American and European foulbroods, are restricted only to the young. On the other hand, in *Nosema* disease, the microsporidian, *Nosema apis* Zander, infects the intestinal epithelium of adult bees but does not infect the brood.

In virus diseases, the general assumption is that adult insects are resistant to acute infections even though they may transmit the virus in an active or latent state to their offspring. The question of the adult immunity to virus infections still awaits thorough investigation. Szirmai (1957) has reported that when mated with healthy males, the females of the fall webworm, *Hyphantria cunea*, which have developed from larvae presumably with virus infections have laid fewer eggs than females from uninfected larvae. But, it was not determined whether the reduction in fecundity was caused by the direct effect of the virus on the adult or by the effect of the virus on the larval development in such a way as to weaken the adult.

The female scolytid, *Stephanoderes hampei* Fer., when infected with the white muscardine fungus, *Beauveria bassiana*, lays fewer eggs than uninfected adults (Pascalet 1939). In microsporidian infections, the infected adults of the spruce budworm, *Choristoneura fumiferana* (Neilson 1956; Thomson 1958), and the European corn borer, *Ostrinia nubilalis* (Hbn.) (Zimmack, Arbuthnot, and

Brindley 1954; Zimmack and Brindley 1957) have a lower rate of oviposition than normal adults. Reduction in fecundity is of common occurrence in many insects with nematode infections.

It is generally known that both the honey-bee and the silkworm possess strains which exhibit resistance to certain diseases of these domesticated insects. Confirming evidence of the presence of genetically resistant lines of honey-bee to American foulbrood has been obtained recently by Lewis and Rothenbuhler (1961) through the use of artificial insemination. They inoculated sperms from susceptible and resistant drones into sister queens from each of two resistant, genetically distinct lines. Their results indicate that there are genetically determined differences in the resistance of honey-bee to the American foulbrood. Very little is known about the occurrence of resistant strains of wild insects or the acquired resistance of wild insects to disease, despite the long association between the hosts and pathogens. This stems evidently from the lack of extensive investigation of infectious diseases of insects in the field. In his early work with *Cloaca cloacae*, d'Herelle (1911) has shown that grasshoppers which have survived the feeding of a low virulent culture of the bacterium cannot be killed by the ingestion of very virulent cultures. He has also found that about 20 to 25 per cent of the grasshoppers in a population infected with the bacterium may have acquired an immunity to *C. cloacae*. Moreover, attenuated cultures are believed to immunize the grasshoppers against the virulent strains of the bacterium. Some grasshoppers are apparently symptomless carriers of the bacterium (d'Herelle 1914). The grasshoppers may also acquire immunity against *C. cloacae* after a natural infection by closely related bacteria (Sergent 1916; DuPorte and Vanderleck 1917). However, Pospelov (1926) has concluded that *C. cloacae* is a normal inhabitant of the blood of grasshoppers, and becomes pathogenic only when the host is under stress. Bucher (1959) considers the bacterium as a common inhabitant of the gut flora and not a true pathogen.

Bird and Elgee (1957) have speculated that the recent continual increase of the European spruce sawfly without a subsequent rapid rise in polyhedrosis suggests for the first time an increase in the resistance of the sawfly to the disease. This was indicated because previous observations showed that the virus disease was density-dependent and was independent of stress factors such as weather, overcrowding, and lack of food. In a population of the larch bud moth, *Eucosma griseana* (Hbn.), the LD_{50} of a granulosis virus has increased from 1954 to 1955 (Martignoni 1957). This seems to indicate that the larch bud moth population which has been declining because of a granulosis epizootic since 1954 has apparently developed some resistance to the virus. A laboratory stock of *Pieris brassicae* which survived an outbreak of granulosis has been found more resistant to this virus than *P. brassicae* cultures obtained from different localities (Rivers 1959; David and Gardiner 1960). This resistant *P. brassicae* stock is also less susceptible to a cytoplasmic polyhedrosis virus (Sidor 1959). Martignoni and Schmid (1961) after comparing different populations of *Phryganidia californica* Pack. and of *Pieris rapae* for their resistance to virus infections, conclude that the two populations of *P. californica*, a native species, show differences in susceptibility to a nuclear polyhedrosis virus, while the two populations of *P. rapae*, a recent immigrant, do not differ in their susceptibility to a granulosis virus. According to Ossowski (1960), there exist not only strains of nuclear polyhedrosis virus of the wattle bagworm, but there are also bagworm populations which vary in their susceptibility to the virus.

In connection with the immunity to pathogens acquired by the insect hosts, the pathogens are also capable of mutating to more or less virulent forms and this may cause some difficulty in evaluating the development of resistance in the field. In the case of chemical insecticides, the changes would be reflected only by the insects themselves.

The susceptibility of the larvae of certain insects to the entomogenous strains of *Bacillus cereus* (non-crystal-bearers) and to *B. thuringiensis* var. *thuringiensis*, var. *sotto*, and their close relatives (crystal-bearers) is apparently associated with the pH of the midgut. Insects susceptible to the non-crystal-bearers have midgut pH (less than pH 9) close to the optimum (pH 6·6 to 7·4) for the toxic enzyme, lecithinase, produced by these bacteria (Heimpel 1955), and those susceptible to the crystal-bearers have midgut pH towards the alkaline (pH 9·0 to 10·5) which is necessary to dissolve the toxic crystals (Angus 1956a). The reaction of different insects to the crystal-bearing bacteria has been discussed in chapter 18.

There is apparently a bactericidal, bacteriostatic, and fungicidal substance produced in the intestinal fluid of the silkworm (Masera 1954). This substance may also act on the nuclear polyhedrosis virus of jaundice and on the microsporidian of pebrine. The nature and origin of this substance are unknown. Certain aerobic bacteria present occasionally in the guts of insects, such as grasshoppers, are potential pathogens which have difficulty in multiplying in the relatively anaerobic conditions of the midgut thus reducing their likelihood of invading the haemocoele (Bucher 1960).

Temperature, as it increases, is known to accelerate the infectious process in insects and thereby usually shortens the period from infection to death. A rise in temperature may increase the susceptibility of insects to infection, especially to certain bacterial diseases (Steinhaus 1958a). However, in certain diseases, continuous rearing of insects at high temperatures seems to increase the resistance of the insects to infections. The cabbage looper, *Trichoplusia ni* (Hbn.), can resist infection by the fungus, *Spicaria rileyi* (Farlow) Charles, when reared at 30° C (Getzin 1961).

The imported cabbage-worm, *Pieris rapae*, when exposed to the granulosis virus and reared at 36° C (Tanada 1953), the European spruce sawfly, *Diprion hercyniae*, when exposed to the nuclear polyhedrosis virus at 85° F (29·4° C) (Bird 1955), the cabbage looper, *Trichoplusia ni*, and the corn earworm, *Heliothis zea* (Boddie), to their respective nuclear polyhedrosis viruses at 39° C (Thompson 1959) show resistance to virus infections. These insects, however, become susceptible to their respective viruses when the temperature is lowered or alternated between high and low. In the case of the yellow-striped armyworm, *Prodenia* sp., the nuclear poly-hedrosis virus is capable of infecting the hosts even at temperatures as high as 46° C (Thompson 1959). Inasmuch as the viruses are capable of withstanding the high temperatures outside of the insect's body, the inhibition of disease at high temperatures does not appear to be due to inactivation of the virus. Thompson (1959) has concluded that, since the cabbage looper and the corn earworm when exposed to their respective viruses and reared for two days at 26·7° C before being placed at 39° C die of virus infections, the high temperature appears to affect the mechanism or mode of invasion of the viruses. However, in the case of the imported cabbage-worm, some larvae when exposed to the granulosis virus two to five days at room temperatures and then transferred to 36° C, do not die from granulosis (Tanada 1953). Accordingly, the exact mechanism by which the insect resists infection at high temperatures may not necessarily be the inability of the virus to invade the host, but may be the inability of the virus to multiply in the host at high temperatures or may be due to increased cellular and humoral immunity which are brought into effect by the high metabolic rate of the host.

The resistance of honey-bee to the microsporidian, *Nosema apis*, has been associated with high temperatures. Previously it has been assumed that recovery from *Nosema* disease is indirectly associated with warm weather because the brood nest is kept cooled by the worker bees. Recently, Schulz-Langner (1958) has observed that the internal body temperature of bees, even within the hive, may extend beyond 37° to even 44° C. She has shown that the development of the microsporidian infection is retarded proportionately to the hours the bees spent at 37° C. This indicates that high temperature may have a direct rather than indirect effect on *Nosema* infection. However, Bailey (1959c) has obtained some evidence that *Nosema* infection is not naturally suppressed by increased environmental temperature, but by reduction of infective faecal matter of the bees, which do not transmit the infection to young individuals in the summer.

One of the important physiological bases for natural immunity is 'cellular immunity' which is expressed by phagocytosis carried out mainly by certain blood, fat, and pericardial cells. Steinhaus (1949a) has given a detailed discussion of this subject.

In contrast to natural resistance, very little is known about acquired immunity in insects. Acquired immunity is dependent on humoral responses (antibodies) which may be acquired either naturally or artificially. Various types of antibodies have been reported in insects, but in most instances they need confirmation.

A kind of resistance in Japanese beetle grubs has been observed by Beard (1944). He has found that when grubs fail to acquire the disease after an injection of *Bacillus popilliae* spores, they may be less susceptible to a second injection. However, it is not known if such resistance can develop after the oral ingestion of the spores, which is the normal route of invasion by the bacteria into the grub.

That acquired immunity may be a more complex phenomenon than was originally assumed has been indicated by the works of Briggs (1958) and Stephens (1959b) which question the presence of certain antibodies in insects. Working with 11 species of Lepidoptera, Briggs has used live and attenuated bacteria (pathogenic and non-pathogenic) and solutions of ovalbumin as antigens which were injected into or fed to the insects. He has not been able to demonstrate natural or acquired immune properties in the haemolymph with serological techniques, such as agglutinin, precipitin, and complement-fixation tests. He has found, however, that vaccinated insects possess an extremely heat stable antibacterial principle, demonstrable *in vitro*, in the sera of insects. This specific antibacterial principle is retained throughout larval life, resists exposure to acid and alkali, but is suspended when exposed to pepsin. This immunological response develops only by injection and not by feeding of the antigen. The thermostability of the artificially acquired antibacterial principle sets it apart from vertebrate antibodies. Stephens (1959*b*) also has not been able to detect any true antibodies in the blood of the larvae of the wax moth, *Galleria mellonella*, when *Pseudomonas aeruginosa* was injected as an antigen into the larvae. The larvae are actively or passively immunized against lethal doses of *P. aeruginosa* within 20 to 24 hours. However, unlike Brigg's findings, the immunity lasts for only a brief period of about three days. *P. aeruginosa* antigen remains in the blood of larvae of the wax moth during the resistant period of the insect. The active portion that enhances the antigen is contained in the serum and probably bound to a blood fraction. The immunity is more specific than non-specific and it is not possible to protect wax moth larvae with non-specific substances, such as broth, though it is possible to immunize them passively with the blood of rabbits immunized against the homologous antigen (vaccination).

Stress factors may affect the resistance of insects and may be of great importance in epizootiology. This involves a study of the relation between disease and certain stressors and incitants in the environment (see Steinhaus 1958*a*). These aspects will be discussed in the section on the 'Effect of Environmental Factors' on epizootics.

METHODS OF TRANSMISSION

In general, the transmission of pathogens in insects is through the external openings, through the integument, and by congenital or parental transmission. These methods of transmission may be modified, as in the case of transmission through the stings of insect parasites or bites of predators or through cannibalism. Although the respiratory route is one of the most common means of transmission of human diseases, especially those of the viruses and bacteria, there is very little information, if any, that insect pathogens are transmitted by this route. The most common method of transmission of the various insect pathogens, aside from the fungus, appears to be through the mouth. However, the passage of pathogens from one host generation to another through the eggs of the host insects, especially in the case of viruses and protozoa, has been shown in recent years to occur rather commonly among insects.

In oral infection, the susceptible host may become infected through cannibalism on infected individuals and by feeding on food contaminated with: (1) the decomposed remains of infected insects; (2) the faeces from infected larvae; and (3) the infectious micro-organisms carried to the food plants by wind, rain, and by other animals. Cannibalistic behaviour among species of grasshoppers is apparently an important method of transfer of certain bacteria (d'Herelle 1914; Béguet 1916; Velu and Bouin 1916; Stevenson 1959; Stephens 1959*c*). Cannibalism may also play a role in the transmission of the protozoan, *Mattesia dispora* Naville, in the Mediterranean flour moth, *Anagasta kühniella* (Zell.) (Weiser 1954).

Transmission through the integument occurs commonly in fungus and nematode diseases. Previous claims of the transmission of fungi through the mouth have been questioned; however, Gabriel (1959) has succeeded in experimentally infecting several insect species with fungi by microfeeding them conidia of *Metarrhizium anisopliae* and *Beauveria bassiana*.

The infectious micro-organisms may also gain entrance into the insect's body cavity with the aid of the piercing or chewing mouth parts of predators and the stings of parasites. *Pilophorus uhleri* (Knight) (order Hemiptera) which feeds on the larvae of the sawfly, *Neodiprion swainei* Midd., is capable of transmitting a nuclear polyhedrosis virus through its feeding to the sawfly (Smirnoff 1959). Predatory wasps, *Vespula rufa consobrina* (Saussure) and *V. vulgaris* (L.), are also suspected of transmitting the virus (Smirnoff 1961). A common parasite of the alfalfa caterpillar, *Apanteles medicaginis* Mues., is able to transmit the nuclear polyhedrosis virus to the alfalfa caterpillar by stinging the host with its contaminated ovipositor or by carrying the virus on its body to the food plant of the caterpillar (Thompson and Steinhaus 1950). Smith *et al.* (1956) strongly suspect that the granulosis virus of the western grape leaf skeletonizer, *Harrisina brillians* B. & McD., is transmitted by the insect parasites, *Sturmia harrisinae* Coq., and *Apanteles harrisinae* Mues. According to Metalnikov and Metalnikov (1935), the insect parasite, *Dibrachys* sp., can transmit *Bacillus cazaubon* and *B. ephestiae* (M. and C.) (= *B. thuringiensis*) through its ovipositor into larvae of *Galleria mellonella*.

Paillot (1933) was the first to suggest that certain microsporidia could not be transmitted by way of the mouth, but either by: (1) transovarial transmission, or (2) transmission through the action of insect parasites. Inasmuch as the incidence of the microsporidian *Glugea legeri* (Pail.) (= *Perezia legeri* Pail.) in cabbage-worms was closely associated with the parasitization by the braconid wasp, *Apanteles glomeratus*, Paillot has proposed that the wasp is essential to the transmission of the protozoan parasite. Additional observations that protozoa are transmitted by parasites have been presented by Payne (1933*b*) for *Thelohania ephestiae* Mattes by the braconid parasite, *Bracon hebetor* Say, to the Mediterranean flour moth, *Anagasta kühniella;* by Toumanoff (1950) for *Coelogregarina ephestiae* Ghél. by *Dibrachys cavus* (Wlkr.) (= *Dibrachys bouchéanus* (Ratz.)) to *Galleria mellonella;* by Blunck (1952*b*, 1954) for *Nosema polyvora* by *Apanteles glomeratus* to the European cabbage-worm, *Pieris brassicae;* by Tanada (1955*a*) for *Glugea mesnili* (Pail.) (= *Perezia mesnili* Pail.) by *A. glomeratus* to the imported cabbage-worm, *Pieris rapae;* and by Lipa (1957) for *Nosema aporiae* Lipa by *Apanteles* sp. to *Aporia crataegi*. In the case of *Apanteles glomeratus*, both *Nosema polyvora* and *Glugea mesnili* can heavily infect this insect parasite, but infected adults are still capable of laying viable eggs.

In many other cases, insect parasites, predators, and even vertebrates have been suggested as transmitting pathogens to insect hosts. However, in most of these cases, the animals probably serve as carriers which disseminate the pathogens on to the food of the insect host rather than directly transmit the pathogens into the host.

As insect diseases are studied in greater detail, more and more of them have been found to be transmitted through the parents, especially through the female by way of the egg. Since the classic work of Pasteur showed that, in pebrine of the silk-worm, the microsporidian, *Nosema bombycis*, is transmitted through the egg of the silkworm, others have found this to be a rather common occurrence among protozoan infections. Such maternal transmission of protozoa has been observed in the European cabbage-worm (Blunck 1952); the imported cabbage-worm (Tanada 1955a); the European corn borer, *Ostrinia nubilalis* (Zimmack, Arbuthnot, and Brindley 1954; Zimmack and Brindley 1957; Kramer 1959a); the spruce budworm, *Choristoneura fumiferana* (Thomson 1958); the fall webworm, *Hyphantria cunea* (Weiser 1957b); and the alfalfa snout beetle, *Brachyrhinus ligustici* (L.) (=*Otior-hynchus ligustici* L.) (Weiser 1958a). Apparently the microsporidia are not transmitted through the infected males of the European corn borer (Zimmack, Arbuthnot, and Brindley 1954) and the silkworm (Machay 1957), but are transmitted to a certain extent by infected males of the spruce budworm (Thomson 1958). Weiser (1956), however, considers that congenital transmission of protozoa occurs in only a few cases in wild insects. In certain microsporidia which infect only the midgut, the spores are transmitted to the egg surfaces with the faecal matter or by the con-taminated anal hairs (Günther 1956).

A few bacteria have been found to be transmitted through the parent insects. According to d'Herelle (1914), the faecal matter containing *Cloaca cloacae* eliminated by infected female grasshoppers may contaminate the surface of the eggs or the mucilaginous matter which is secreted around the eggs. The bacterium, *Pseudomonas aeruginosa*, is intimately associated and transmitted with a small percentage of grasshopper eggs (Bucher and Stephens 1957). In the nun moth, *Lymantria monacha* (L.), the unidentified *Schlaffsucht* bacteria are transmitted through the egg (Janisch 1958). According to Bailey (1959a), *Bacterium eurydice*, which is associated with *Streptococcus pluton* in European foulbrood, is endemic in the alimentary tract of normal adults bees, particularly at the anterior end, from which source the larvae become infected.

An increasing number of reports have appeared on the transmission of viruses through the egg (see Bergold 1958). In some cases, the virus appears to be trans-mitted on the surface of the egg. Thus, Steinhaus (1949b) has observed that disinfection of the eggs with 10 per cent formaldehyde by weight for 90 minutes greatly reduces the incidence of polyhedrosis in the emerging larvae. However, a small percentage of the treated eggs still developed polyhedrosis (Thompson and Steinhaus 1950). In many instances, the viruses are transmitted within the egg, especially those in the occult (latent) state, which are passed from one host genera-tion to another. There is, however, much controversy on the question of latency, The confusion exists to some extent because of insufficient knowledge of the process of latent infections in insects. Some investigators consider latent virus infections widespread throughout the population of certain forest insects (Roegner-Aust 1949; Bergold 1953a, 1958; Grison and Vago 1953, Vago 1953b; Krieg 1956,

1957*b*; Franz and Krieg 1957; Janisch 1958). Assuming that such widespread infections exist in nature, Roegner-Aust (1949) has expressed the futility of the artificial application of viruses for the direct control of the latently infected insects.

Aside from the viruses, there are only a few reports of latency in other insect diseases. The reports of latent bacterial infections in several insect species (Vago 1952; Janisch 1958), of latent amoeba infection (*Malpighamoeba mellificae* Prell) in the honey-bee (Giordani 1959), and of latent microsporidian infections in the spruce budworm (Bergold 1951) and in the African migratory locust, *Locusta migratoria migratorioides* R. and F. (Canning 1953), need further confirmation.

The mere transmission of the pathogens through the eggs to the next generation does not necessarily indicate that such pathogens are in an occult state. Evidence must be presented that the pathogens are not actively causing symptoms of infection while being in the so-called occult state. In insects, the adults generally do not show any visible signs of infections, especially with virus diseases; therefore, passage through such adults is usually considered as being in an occult condition. However, this may not be so. Observations of virus polyhedra in adult insect tissues may indicate an active infection (Sager 1960; Tanada and Chang 1960). Evidence of latency is generally assumed when the pathogen cannot be detected and the disease develops because of certain stresses. This aspect will be discussed in the following section on the effect of environmental factors on latent infections.

EFFECT OF ENVIRONMENTAL FACTORS

There are innumerable statements in the literature that environmental conditions are important in governing epizootics in insect populations. However, very little quantitative data are available on the specific factors and mechanisms involved. Nevertheless, there is no doubt that the environmental factors affect the initiation and development (or prevention and suppression) of disease outbreaks. The extent of their influence may vary with the nature of the three primary factors: pathogen population, host population, and method of transmission. Some of these aspects have been discussed previously under the sections dealing with the pathogen, its virulence, its capacity to survive, its capacity to disperse, and methods of transmission, and with the host, its resistance and susceptibility.

Environmental factors may act not only on active infections but also may activate latent infections in insect populations. In the epizootics of some diseases, the influence of environmental factors is not clearly apparent (e.g., certain virus diseases), but in others, such factors play a prominent role (e.g., fungus diseases). In many cases, the outbreak of disease is the result of a combination and interaction of many factors in the environment, and it is often difficult to separate the importance of the various individual factors.

Inasmuch as the phenomenon of latency is closely associated with the influence of environmental factors on disease outbreaks, let us first discuss latent infections in insects. Prior to the study of latent infections in the virus diseases of insects, there was little or no information along this aspect of insect diseases. The recent extensive investigations on latency, especially in virus infections, have brought out the importance of this phenomenon in epizootiology. There is some confusion, however, because of the insufficient knowledge of the process of latent infections in insects. Bergold (1958) in discussing insect viruses said: '. . . probably the most problematic subject in the whole field is that of latency and provocation of insect viruses.' The definition of latency is not necessarily uniform in all fields. It has been defined by Walker, Hanson, and Evans (1958) as non-apparent infections (which give no overt sign of their presence) which are chronic and in which a certain virus–host (or pathogen–host) equilibrium is established.

Latency is indicated when the disease is expressed after an apparently healthy insect has been placed under certain stress conditions. Bergold (1958) has listed five different ways in which an occult insect virus has been activated: (1) by physical conditions during rearing; (2) by food quality; (3) by application of various chemicals; (4) by infection with insect viruses from other host species; and (5) by super-infection with the species-specific virus. Because of space limitations the historical background of latency and the numerous laboratory tests claiming the induction of latent infections will not be considered here, but the reader is encouraged to consult the comprehensive treatment by Bergold (1958).

In order to distinguish the action of the various environmental factors on the host and pathogen, Steinhaus (1958a, 1960b) has suggested the usage of 'stress' to refer to a state manifested by a syndrome, or bodily changes, caused by some force, condition, or circumstance in or on an insect or on one of its physiological or anatomical systems. The agents can be called 'stressors' and 'incitants.' According to Steinhaus, a stressor may also be thought of as any stimulus, or succession of stimuli, that tends to disrupt the homeostasis of an animal. The environmental factors may become stressors or incitants as they fluctuate from one level of intensity to another. It is, therefore, important to determine as precisely as possible, not only the action of the environmental factors on the host and pathogen, but also the level of intensity at which disease is caused to break out in insect populations. There is a great paucity of such precise data.

There are occasional statements that the effectiveness of certain diseases appears independent of stress conditions and secondary factors, such as kind of food and weather. This is presumably the case with the virus diseases of the European spruce- and pine sawflies (Bird 1955). According to Weiser (1956), weather and host food plant have no effect on microsporidian infections.

Humidity is the most frequently cited physical factor affecting the initiation and development of epizootics among insect populations. This is especially true of fungus diseases but there is some evidence that it also may affect other diseases. In general, epizootics of fungus diseases are dependent mainly on humidity, with other physical factors, such as temperature, sunlight, and wind maintaining secondary roles. Thus, Hart and MacLeod (1955) have demonstrated with a specially built apparatus that optimum germination of *Beauveria bassiana* spores occurs at relative humidity above 94 per cent and at a temperature of 28° C, with negligible germinations at 10°, 38°, and 44° C. With certain fungi, high humidity alone is not sufficient to cause germination but the occurrence of free moisture in contact with the conidia is necessary for germination (Ullyett and Schonken 1940). Schaefer (1936), however, reports that high humidity may not be very important because he obtained infection of the red locust, *Nomadacris septemfasciata* (Serv.), with *Entomophthora grylli* Fres. at relative humidities below 60 per cent. He considers the health or natural resistance of the insects to be of great importance, and climatic and other factors to stimulate infection by lowering the resistance.

In the field, the humidity of the microclimate is often more important than that of the general climate. This has been observed by Snow (1896) among chinch bugs, *Blissus leucopterus*, attacked by *Beauveria bassiana;* by Domenichini and Vago (1955) among grasshoppers attacked by *Empusa grylli;* and by Hall and Dunn (1957b) among the spotted alfalfa aphids attacked by various entomophthoraceous fungi. The successful use of irrigation water to initiate fungus epizootics in populations of the spotted alfalfa aphid has been mentioned previously.

Neither excessively wet nor extremely dry conditions has lessened the effectiveness of the type A milky disease organism (*Bacillus popilliae*) of the Japanese beetle (White 1940).

The possible association between high humidity (and/or rainfall) and the development of virus epizootics has been indicated in the California oakworm, *Phryganidia californica* Pack. (Harville 1955); in the gamma noctuid, *Plusia gamma* (L.) (Vago and Cayrol 1955); in the fall webworm, *Hyphantria cunea* (Szirmai 1957; Schmidt and Philips 1958); in the gypsy moth, *Porthetria dispar* (Wallis 1957); and in the armyworm, *Pseudaletia unipuncta* (Marcovitch 1958). Humidity apparently has little effect on the nuclear polyhedrosis virus diseases of the European spruce sawfly (Balch and Bird 1944; Bird 1955), and of the alfalfa caterpillar (Thompson and Steinhaus 1959).

Nematodes, like the fungi, are greatly dependent on high humidity and moisture at moderate temperatures (60° F (15·5° C) and higher), especially during dispersal outside their hosts and during the long free-living periods (Girth, McCoy, and Glaser 1940; Couturier 1950; Schvester 1957; Welch 1958; Dutky 1959). In humid years, Schvester (1957) has found the infection of the scolytid beetles, *Ruguloscolytus rugulosus* Müller by the nematode, *Parasitylenchus dispar rugulosi* Schvester may be over 30 per cent, but during dry years may be as low as 12 per cent.

The direct effect of temperature on epizootics in insect populations is not adequately known. As indicated previously, only within certain temperature ranges does humidity become important in initiating fungus diseases. In general, at high temperatures the progress of infection is greatly accelerated within the individual host insect. In certain diseases, which were mentioned previously, high temperatures may increase the resistance of insects to infections. In others, the pathogens invade the body of the host insect more frequently when the host is under a stress of high temperature (Steinhaus 1958a). Grasshoppers, hornworms, and cutworms seem to be predisposed to septicaemia during warm weather (d'Herelle 1914; White 1923a, b). However, certain insects are more susceptible to fungi, bacteria, and viruses when reared at low temperatures (Pospelov 1926; Franz 1961a). It is rather interesting that the larvae of *Melolontha* spp. when infected with rickettsia rise to the surface of the ground in late autumn (Wille and Martignoni 1952; Niklas 1956a, 1960). The stimulus appears to be one of a lowering of the temperature. More microsporidian-infected European corn borers, *Ostrinia nubilalis*, are killed by the low winter and the high summer temperatures in Illinois than uninfected individuals (Kramer 1959b).

The action of sunlight, especially the ultra-violet rays, may have a direct effect on insect pathogens. This is especially true with pathogens which have no resistive stages in their life cycle (e.g., non-spore-forming bacteria (d'Herelle 1914; White 1923a, b)), and with the non-resisting stages of other pathogens. However, the spores of the milky disease organism, *Bacillus popilliae*, when exposed to the sun for over 8 hours, begin to show a reduction in their viability, which may be greatly affected after 48 hours in sunlight (White 1946). In *Entomophthora pseudococci* Speare, the presence or absence of daylight at the time of maturity of the hyphal bodies predetermines to a large extent the type of reproductive body that is formed (Speare 1912). Azygous spores of the fungi are produced when the fungus cultures are placed in a dark location a few hours before the hyphal bodies are ready to germinate.

In the case of insects inhabiting the soil, the occurrence of disease epizootics may be associated with the physico-chemical characteristics of the soil, in addition to such factors as temperature and humidity. A milky disease organism similar to that of the Japanese beetle, when applied for the control of the grubs of *Melolontha melolontha* (L.), is more effective in soil rich in humus than in sandy or clay soils (Hurpin 1955). According to Beard (1945), it may be that the soil colloids are an aid in fixing the spores of the milky disease organism (*B. popilliae*) to the soil, and that in light sandy soils, there is a leaching out of spores rather than an actual mortality of the spores. Beard (1945) has reported that low pH adversely affects the spores of *B. popilliae*, but such pH is usually not encountered in the soils in Connecticut. Certain nematodes (Mermithidae) apparently favour calcareous soils (Théodoridès 1952).

Soils of high organic content are more favourable for fungus diseases than those with low organic matter, such as sandy soils (Schaerffenberg 1952; Bünzli and Büttiker 1959; Dutky 1959). The presence of organic matter, such as humus, increases the water-retention property of the soils and the resulting high humidity within such soils would favour fungus infections. In the green muscardine fungus, *Metarrhizium anisopliae*, however, in addition to humidity, another factor, the contact between spores adsorbed on soil particles and the insect cuticle, is important for the infection of the insect (Dutky 1959). Bünzli and Büttiker (1959) have found that soils with an abnormally high content of nitrogenous organic matter favour the breeding of *Anomala exitialis* Per. and *Schizonycha profuga* Per., but at the same time provide a suitable medium for the survival and development of a high degree of virulence in the fungi, *Torrubiella* sp., *Beauveria bassiana*, and *Metarrhizium anisopliae*. The grubs of the beet weevil, *Cleonus punctiventris* Germ., are killed chiefly by *M. anisopliae* in acid-reacting soils whereas they succumb mostly to *Tarichium uvella* Krass. (=*Sorosporella uvella* (Krass.) Gd.) in alkaline soils (Pospelov 1940; Pyatnitzkii 1940). According to Pyatnitzkii (1940), by changing the acidity of the soil with mineral fertilizers, P. F. Mende has succeeded in varying the incidence of the two fungi. Meier (1940) has concluded that fungus diseases among soil pests may follow a change in acidity of the soil by suitable manures. In the soils in Southern Rhodesia, Bünzli and Büttiker (1959) did not observe such a correlation between soil acidity and fungus disease incidence.

Under certain conditions—when the insect population increases in size and also when there is a continual disappearance of food—the spatial requirement may become critical and the insects may be subjected to the stress effects of crowding. The general association between insect population increase and the development of disease may at times be correlated with the phenomenon of crowding. Such a condition may greatly influence the spread of infection among insects which have tendencies towards cannibalism (e.g., grasshoppers). But on the whole, information along this line from field observation is lacking.

Under laboratory conditions, Steinhaus (1958a) has concluded from his studies on stress factors, that crowding of certain insects increases the incidence of disease among them. In some cases, the disease is induced from a latent state, and in others, the micro-organisms normally present in the environment (including the insect's alimentary tract) are able to invade the host which is weakened by the stress of crowding. These situations may be distinct from the transmission of pathogens from one insect to another, as it may occur under crowding. A secondary effect resulting from crowding may be the unfavourable accumulation of dead individuals in the habitat regardless of the cause of death. Such a situation may occur among populations of Japanese beetle grubs, and the accumulation of dead grubs in the soil creates an environment unfavourable not only for the living grubs contained therein, but also for the development and spread of disease (Beard 1945).

Although the nutritional requirements of insects would be expected to play an important role in the outbreak of diseases among insect populations (aside from the example of depleted food and cannibalism), information confirming this is generally lacking. The incidence of infection by the microsporidian, *Glugea pyraustae* (Pail.) (=*Perezia pyraustae* Pail.), is lower in European corn borers on borer-resistant corn varieties than those on susceptible varieties (Chiang and Holdaway 1960). During the past decade, certain chemicals and types of food have been used in laboratory tests to provoke virus diseases in insects (see Bergold 1958). Most authorities believe that such diseases develop from the activation of latent virus infections, but a few (Shvetsova 1950; Yamafuji 1957) maintain that the virus diseases result from physiological changes due to disrupted carbohydrate–protein metabolism or by the conversion of a cellular host component to an active virus.

A rather interesting investigation conducted by Krieg (1956) with two field populations and a laboratory culture of *Neodiprion sertifer* has indicated that only the field populations develop polyhedrosis when fed thioglycolic acid, sodium fluoride, and hydroxylamine. Larvae from one of the field populations where the virus is endemic developed the virus disease more readily than the larvae from the other field population. The laboratory culture which did not develop disease had not been exposed to the virus before. Krieg has concluded that the field populations exposed to the virus contain the virus in a latent state among some of the larvae.

The reader may recall that Wallis (1957) has claimed a close correlation between relative humidity and the incidence of virus disease among the gypsy moth populations. On the other hand, others have reported that the host plant or the type of food eaten by the gypsy moth larvae may be more important than weather in activating the virus infections (Schmidt 1956; Vago 1953a; Shvetsova 1954; Kovacevic 1954, 1956).

The demonstration of latent virus infection in tissue culture can be considered as one of the most convincing evidences that such a phenomenon occurs in insects. That this may be so has been indicated by Grace (1958). He selected at random explants from the ovarian tissue of the white-marked tussock moth, *Hemerocampa leucostigma* (J. E. Smith), and transferred one set of explant to Eagle's basal medium to which blood plasma had been added. Such cultures in which the medium had been changed developed an infection with nuclear polyhedrosis virus, but the others remained healthy. He had postulated that the larvae carried a latent virus infection and the 'physiological shock' resulted in activation of the virus when the tissue explant was transferred to a medium with blood plasma.

Certain compounds, such as glucose and citric acid, apparently act as inhibitors to virus infection (Krieg 1957b). Certain antibiotics, such as penicillin, aureomycin, streptomycin, or terramycin, seem to have no effect (Bergold 1953a; Krieg 1957b). However, Ueda et al. (1955) have observed that the antibiotic 'grasseriomycin' produced by *Streptomyces* sp. is effective against the nuclear polyhedrosis virus of the silkworm.

Other than virus diseases, the few reports on the effect of nutrition on host susceptibility have been on certain bacterial and protozoan diseases of honey-bees. Bailey (1959b) has speculated that the annual epizootic of European foulbrood may be associated with pollen shortage during which time the larvae are probably fed freshly collected pollen in which *Bacterium eurydice* is present. *B. eurydice* dies within a few days in stored pollen. The natural outbreak and cessation of European foulbrood are also governed by the removal of infected and dead larvae by the worker bees (Bailey 1960). The rejection of infected larvae occurs more frequently when larval food is merely adequate, as it may be when a colony is growing rapidly; and occurs less frequently when larval food is more abundant, as it may be when brood rearing is retarded. According to Matuka (1959), the vegetative forms of *Bacillus* larvae cannot survive more than six hours in royal jelly because of its unfavourable pH. The American foulbrood apparently develops when the brood is no longer fed royal jelly. During the rainy season in Venezuela, the rains affect the nectar and pollen of the flowers and make them unfavourable to the bees (Stejskal 1959). During such rainy seasons the protozoan diseases caused by *Nosema apis*, *Malpighamoeba mellificae*, and cephaline gregarines begin to increase in incidence among the honey-bees.

On the other hand, the virulence with which microsporidia (Weiser 1956) and certain viruses (Balch and Bird 1944; Bird 1955) are capable of infecting their hosts is not influenced by weather and food.

INTERACTION BETWEEN PATHOGENS, PARASITES, AND PREDATORS

In many cases the insect parasites and predators are generally unaffected by diseases of their hosts, and they occur commonly in areas where epizootics are reducing their insect hosts. There are several outstanding examples of the regulation of insect populations by the combined effect of diseases and parasites. Such is true in the control of the red-backed cutworm, *Euxoa ochrogaster* (Guen.) (King and Atkinson 1928), the Japanese beetle (White 1943; Fleming 1958), the alfalfa caterpillar (Thompson and Steinhaus 1950), the sawflies (Bird and Elgee 1957; Balch 1958), and the spotted alfalfa aphid (Hall and Dunn 1957b).

A highly compatible association between disease and insect parasites has been reported by King and Atkinson (1928) in the natural control of the red-backed cutworm, *Euxoa ochrogaster*. The disease, which is probably a cutworm septicaemia, destroys a much greater proportion of unparasitized than parasitized larvae, and thereby greatly increases the proportion of parasites to moths emerging. This results in an increase in the rate of parasitism of the host the following year. The disease is the most important factor in causing the rapid decline from the peak of an outbreak of the cutworm; the parasitism is important in reducing subsequent rate of increase. Most of the insect parasites are capable of completing their development before maximum disease mortality. The *Gonia* spp., however, are not favoured by the presence of the disease. King and Atkinson have speculated that the parasites lower the vitality of the host some time before the completion of their own development, and thus increase the host's susceptibility to the disease. Paillot (1925) has observed that the presence of *Apanteles* larva in the European cabbage-worm seems to predispose the cabbage-worm to invasion by entomogenous bacteria.

Insect pathogens may affect other biological control agents: (1) indirectly, by reducing the host population to such a low level that the number of insect parasites and predators is drastically reduced, and (2) directly, by infecting them or competing with them in the host tissue. Occasionally the pathogens may reduce the host population to such a low level that certain parasites have been eliminated from the area. Such a case has occurred in South Africa with the insect parasites and predators of *Plutella maculipennis* when the population of *Plutella* was reduced to a low level by an outbreak of the fungus, *Entomophthora sphaerosperma* (Ullyett and Schonken 1940). According to Ullyett and Schonken, '. . . The intervention of the disease in an existing equilibrium system resulted in the replacement, by destruction, of permanent mortality factors by a temporary mortality factor (the fungus). When the latter disappeared, the host population was able to recover more rapidly than its parasites and thus to swing to a higher density level than before.'

The implication brought out by Ullyett and Schonken that disease is destructive to the existing biotic control by predators and parasites is probably restricted to the conditions under their observation and may not necessarily apply to all fungus and other diseases. The effective co-existence of fungi and parasites and predators in the control of citrus pests has been brought out by Muma (1955). In other instances, such as the nuclear polyhedrosis of the European spruce sawfly, two introduced parasites, *Dahlbominus fuscipennis* (Zett.) and *Exenterus claripennis* Thoms., which had become established in 1938 and 1939, were apparently eliminated as control factors during the severe virus epizootics of 1940, 1941, and 1942. However, since 1944 other introduced parasites, *Sturmia* (*Drino*) *bohemica* Mesn. and *Exenterus vellicatus* Cush., became successful control factors and were able to maintain themselves at low levels of sawfly populations (Bird 1955; Bird and Elgee 1957).

The action of diseases and parasites as control factors in forest insects may occur at different levels of population (King and Atkinson 1928; Bird and Elgee 1957; Martignoni 1957; Balch 1958; Baltensweiler 1958). The diseases are more effective at high population levels and the parasites at a low population level. In some instances, certain parasites move out to the periphery of an epizootic area where more hosts are available (Niklas 1939; Franz and Krieg 1957).

Certain insect parasites because of their biological characteristics are more capable of surviving within an insect host population exposed to infectious microorganisms. Thus, *Tiphia vernalis* Roh. actively oviposits on Japanese beetles in May when the soil temperatures rarely exceed 65° F (18·3° C) (White 1943). At this temperature, the development of the milky disease organisms is retarded and the *Tiphia* parasites are able to emerge from their infected hosts. This may account for the abundance of *T. vernalis* in areas in which the incidence of milky diseases has been consistently high. On the other hand, *Tiphia popilliavora* Roh., which is active in the latter part of August when the soil temperatures range above 70° F (21·1° C), will suffer much more from the milky diseases because the rapid development of the diseases may destroy the host tissue before the *Tiphia* larvae have completed their development.

It is generally assumed that insect pathogens usually do not directly attack the insect parasites and predators of their hosts. Several insect parasites and predators have been observed developing on hosts infected with fungi, bacteria, and virus (Ullyett and Schonken 1940; White 1943; Dresner 1949; Biliotti 1955, 1956*a*, *b*; Tanada 1956*b*; Guthrie, Rabb, and Bowery 1959). These parasites show no apparent symptoms of infection by the pathogens and appear able to mature to adults, generally, if their hosts are killed by the disease after a certain stage in the development of the parasites. The parasites may fail to mature when the hosts are killed at an early larval stage of the parasites.

Direct infection of insect parasites and predators has been observed with the microsporidia of the cabbage-worms (Blunck 1952*b*, 1954; Tanada 1955*a*), of the fall webworm (Weiser 1957*b*), of the potato tuber-worm *Gnorimoschema operculella* (Zell.), and of *Aporia crataegi* (Lipa 1957). Although the reproductive capacities, in the infected parasites, may be reduced, the parasites are still capable of parasitizing the host insects. However, in certain cases such as in the insectary rearing of the parasites, the production of the parasites may be seriously affected (Allen 1954*b*). Other than the microsporidia, certain omnivorous fungi such as *Beauveria bassiana* and *Metarrhizium anisopliae*, are known to infect parasites and predators.

Inasmuch as the predators of the fall webworm select microsporidian-infected larvae over healthy ones, their actions may be harmful because they remove the potential source of infectious material from the area (Weiser 1956; Weiser and Veber 1957). On the other hand, some parasites are capable of selecting host larvae which are healthy or only slightly infected with disease. Thus Niklas (1939) has presented convincing evidence that such is the case with the tachinid parasite, *Parasetigena segregata* Rond. Masera (1948) has observed that *Apanteles glomeratus* is apparently capable of selecting healthy European cabbage-worms from those infected with pebrine (microsporidian infection).

Mixed or multiple infections of several different pathogens within the same host are frequently observed under laboratory conditions. The mixed infections may vary from co-existence to antagonism to synergism. Several examples of synergistic association in viruses, bacteria, and protozoa have been mentioned previously. An example of antagonism is the case of the milky diseases, types A and B, of the Japanese beetle (Beard 1946). If a mixture of type A and type B spores are injected into a host larva, only type A disease or only type B disease develops, not both of them. The relative spore dosage largely determines which type is successful. Time is also a factor. If type B is injected first and type A two days later, only type B develops, except when large dosages of type A are used. If the time advantage is in favour of type A, only this type will develop in the grub. Beard has suggested an antibacterial action for this antagonism. The antagonism between *Pseudomonas* and *Serratia* has already been mentioned (Stephens 1959*c*).

Antagonism between different viruses when fed together have been observed in *Pieris brassicae* (Vago 1959*a*), in *Pseudaletia unipuncta* (Tanada 1959*b*), in *Choristoneura fumiferana* (Bird 1959) and in *Bombyx mori* (Auruga *et al.* 1961). Depending on whether the first virus has an advantage in time, dosage or virulence in infecting the host, the second virus may or may not succeed in infecting the same host. Lists of examples of two or more viruses occupying the same host insect have been compiled by Martignoni (1957) and by Steinhaus (1957*a*)

The importance of the insect parasites, predators, and other animals in the dissemination of insect pathogens has already been discussed in a previous section of this chapter.

DISEASE IN RELATION TO HOST DENSITY

It is generally accepted that, under natural conditions, the disease-producing micro-organisms affect a greater proportion of the insects as the host population increases in density, i.e., they are density-dependent mortality factors. However, insect pathogens may also act as density-independent mortality factors under some conditions, such as when they are applied as 'living or microbial insecticides.' In this latter case, nevertheless, the action of the pathogens may develop into one of density-dependence because when certain adaptable pathogens are applied to a small segment of a susceptible host population, they can multiply and spread as a density-dependent mortality factor.

On the other hand, Ullyett and Schonken (1940) have concluded: 'Although the *spread* of the fungus among the population of hosts is largely dependent upon the density of the latter, the *appearance* of the disease is wholly dependent upon the extraneous factor of weather conditions.' From this, fungus disease may be classed as a density-independent mortality factor. However, Ullyett and Schonken have failed to recognize that even though the appearance or the initiation of infection (i.e., for fungus diseases) is dependent on weather and climatic conditions, this has no bearing on the density-dependence of disease. For example, certain insect parasites and predators are capable of acting on their hosts only under certain weather conditions, yet they are certainly not considered as being density-independent mortality factors. In other words, weather and climatic factors should not be considered as causing disease to act as a density-independent mortality factor, but only as permitting or not permitting disease to act, that is, as a conditional factor of natural control. Later, Ullyett (1953) has stated that, because the appearance of disease is dependent on weather conditions and the spread of the disease upon the host density, the disease factors are peculiar and belong to a class of their own; they are neither wholly density-dependent nor density-independent but pass through phases which include both characteristics.

Epizootics among insect populations occur generally under a high host density. However, in recent years the investigations on the viruses of the sawflies (Bird and Elgee 1957), of the Great Basin tent caterpillar (Clark and Thompson 1954; Clark 1955), and of the armyworm (Tanada 1961), and on the fungi of the spotted alfalfa aphid (Hall and Dunn 1957*b*) have indicated that epizootics can occur at low host densities. Apparently, after a severe epizootic in an extensive population of susceptible hosts over a wide area, these pathogens are so widely distributed in the environment or within the surviving host population that they are capable of preventing the increase of the following host generation which may be at a low density.

In the milky diseases of the Japanese beetle, Beard (1945) has observed the importance of heavy grub populations for a rapid spread of the diseases. A high inoculum potential of spores also favours the spread of the diseases. However, a heavy grub potential can compensate for a low inoculum potential, and, conversely, a heavy inoculum potential can compensate for a low population in causing a resultant high incidence of milky diseases. The incidence of 'Lorsch disease' caused by *Rickettsiella melolonthae* (Krieg) Philip is highest in populations of the scarabeids, *Melolontha* spp., which exhibited a continuous regression in density (Niklas 1960). There is high mortality by rickettsiosis among the residual populations in the year preceding their final disappearance.

Epizootics may also depend, not directly on the absolute host density, but on the relative density determined in relation to the environmental capacity for the species (Martignoni 1957). According to Martignoni, the population of the larch bud moth,

25—I.P.W.

when approaching the capacity of the biotope, is apparently affected by stress factors, such as starvation, which encourage the development of virus epizootics. Certain environmental factors may trigger epizootics among insects with latent virus infections independent of the density of the insects (Roegner-Aust 1949; Kovacevic 1956; Wallis 1957; Janisch 1958; Bergold 1958). However, the effect of such stress factors needs further substantiation. With fungi, they may be capable of initiating epizootics at low and high host densities. This has been shown to be the case especially with certain ubiquitous fungi such as the white muscardine and entomophthoraceous fungi (Billings and Glenn 1911; Hall and Dunn 1957*b*).

Although epidemics in human populations are closely associated with host density, it is the relative spatial arrangement of the hosts which may be of greater importance than the actual number of individuals in the spread and development of epidemics. The closer the individuals are to one another, the greater the opportunity for contact and the spread of infection. Likewise in an insect population, the distribution and the number of the various types of individuals (typically diseased insect, atypically diseased insect, uninfected susceptible, and healthy carrier) may affect the development of an epizootic.

The maximum opportunity for the spread of infection in animal populations will occur when a centre of close aggregation of susceptible hosts is associated with marked dispersal of such hosts (Stallybrass 1931). The closely aggregated centres serve as nodal points from which the infection may radiate throughout the population or to fresh populations. In the case of epizootics in insect populations we may speculate that similar situations may have resulted in the dramatic and rapid spread of certain diseases. It is highly probable that the epizootics of the fungus diseases of the spotted alfalfa aphid may have resulted initially in this manner in California. During the first year or so after the invasion of the spotted alfalfa aphid into California little or no fungus disease was apparent among the aphid population. But shortly after the first pathogenic fungus species was discovered on the aphid, epizootics of fungus diseases became rather widespread throughout the southern part of the state. The high dispersal capacity of the aphid has been indicated by its rapid spread throughout California and the initial dissemination of the fungi was very likely associated mainly with the dispersal of infected aphids. However, supporting evidence for this speculation is lacking at present.

In contrast to the fungus epizootics of the spotted alfalfa aphid may be the epizootics of milky diseases of the Japanese beetle grub. Here is a situation of a close host aggregation associated with slow dispersal. The relatively slow dispersal of the milky disease organisms is caused by the high mortality rate of the grubs which remain in the soil, and hence the pathogens have little opportunity for distribution to fresh populations. A limited dispersal may occur by means of the few surviving and infected adults and by other animal carriers. This may be one of the reasons why the mechanical distribution of the spores to uninfected populations of the Japanese beetle is so highly successful, whereas in the case of the fungi of the spotted alfalfa aphid, the mechanical distribution may not be so effective after an initial introduction because of the high dispersal capacity and persistence of the fungi.

CHAPTER 20

Mass Production of Insect Pathogens

MAURO E. MARTIGNONI

INTRODUCTION

THE STATEMENT by Krassilstschik (1888): 'The idea of controlling insects by means of artificially induced epidemics, idea expressed some twenty years ago by the scholars, has become a practically feasible one, which in the future will be perfected and broadly utilized,' appears to come remarkably early in the history of insect pathology. What differentiates this idea from similar earlier 'visionary suggestions' is the fact that it is based on what can be called, according to Steinhaus (1956a), the first successful attempt, by Metchnikoff and Krassilstschik, to mass-produce an insect pathogen, *Metarrhizium anisopliae* (Metch.) Sor.

The approach of Elie Metchnikoff and Isaak Krassilstschik is so remarkably modern that it is worthy of detailed description. We know today there are numerous problems, besides the one of nutritional requirements, that must be solved before micro-organisms can be grown on a large scale. Metchnikoff (1880) was faced with these difficulties at the very beginning of his work. He found that *M. anisopliae* would grow and sporulate easily in a sugar solution, in hanging drops; but this could not be reproduced in larger volumes of fluid. A. Werigo, a chemistry professor at Odessa, suggested beer mash as a medium for large-scale production. The experiment was successful. Metchnikoff must have used conventional laboratory methods for his work; in his 1880 paper he mentions the use of flasks stoppered with cotton or asbestos. [Some other very interesting first-hand information on the efforts of Metchnikoff during this phase of his work is given by Marion (1880, pp. 24–28).] After this major breakthrough, it was up to Krassilstschik (1888), who succeeded Metchnikoff '... when work of another type distracted him from these experiments...,' to develop methods for large-scale production. His main concern being, naturally, to produce a large amount of viable spores at small cost, he was faced immediately with three major problems: (1) the development of simple procedures which could be carried on by unskilled labourers; (2) the development of large unbreakable containers; and (3) the elimination of contamination. These three problems were solved admirably by Krassilstschik. In Smela, in a small experimental plant built in 1884, the major culture operations were carried on through a closed system of pipes inaccessible to dust and unwanted spores. The large containers were of metal. Thanks to his procedures the workers performed only very simple operations. To avoid frequent sterilization, fresh sterile medium was injected into the containers without previously sterilizing them, after having collected the old medium with the spores; the fungus spores remaining in the vessel would automatically start the next culture. Here are some of the data quoted by Krassilstschik: 14 to 15 days elapsed between seeding and harvesting, at 25° C; 180 to 220 grammes of spores were produced per square metre of medium (10·76 square feet); 8 kilograms (17·64 pounds) of spores were needed to control the sugar beet curculio, *Cleonus punctiventris* Germ., on a hectare (2·47 acres) of sugar beet culture. It is known that the Smela plant produced 55 kilograms (121·25 pounds) of spores in four months during the summer of 1884. From these data it can easily be calculated that the experimental plant had something in the order of 25 square feet of fresh medium surface available daily.

The work of the two Russian biologists demonstrated early the feasibility of large-scale microbial control. Many have written on the need for large-scale production methods for insect pathogens. From Krassilstschik (1888) and Giard (1892) to Clausen (1954a), Steinhaus (1956b, c, 1957c), and Fleschner (1959), this need has been reaffirmed over and over. 'Ease and cheapness of production and application' are among the principal characteristics of a 'desirable pathogen' (Bucher 1958), and *Bacillus thuringiensis* Berl. is an 'admirable pathogen' because, first among other characteristics, it is '. . . easily cultivated on various media and by mass techniques' (Dutky 1959). Dustan (1924a) who planned to control *Lygus communis* var. *novascotiensis* Knight with *Empusa erupta* Dustan stated, after having mentioned the failure of culture experiments, that the culture work will be continued, '. . . for the final success or failure of the whole investigation may depend on our ability or inability to induce growth under artificial conditions.' Dustan's statement may be repeated today in a different context for it is the success or failure of microbial control as a whole which often depends on the production of pathogens in marketable amounts and at competitive prices.

The method of mass culture developed by Metchnikoff and Krassilstschik was later applied in France by Gaillot (Giard 1892), to the culture of *Beauveria tenella* (Delacr.) Siem. (=*Isaria densa* (Lk.) Fr.). In his very interesting paper, the exuberant Giard raised many points which have not lost actuality. First, there was the possibility of diminution of virulence after many passages in culture *in vitro*. Then there was the problem of standardization of the spore mixtures when marketed. (Giard used the word 'titrés' but he probably meant a spore count or a germination test; in fact, he recommended that besides this 'titration' the package should also indicate the number of passages of the fungus in culture, in order to give an idea of the degree of virulence of the pathogen. A thorough discussion of standardization may be found in Steinhaus (1957d) and also in Stern, Hall, and Peterson (1959)). Also the problem of infectivity of the insect pathogen for farm animals and for plants was mentioned; this, too, was recently reappraised by Steinhaus (1957d, 1959a) and by Fisher and Rosner (1959). (It may be interesting to note that Giard performed one of the first peroral pathogenicity tests on humans and other vertebrates with an insect pathogen.) Finally, the touchy problem of government intervention in the production of microbial insecticides was raised. Giard was against private industry; he thought that, due to the imprecise knowledge of the culture methods, industry would voluntarily or involuntarily take too much advantage of the credulous public. Remarkable is the answer of Giard to those who asked him why the white grub had not been completely eliminated by the fungus: 'Well,' said he, 'there are still Englishmen in London after the great plague of 1665!'

Metchnikoff and Krassilstschik experienced special problems in large-scale production. They evolve, it is true, from laboratory-scale investigations but nonetheless it is clear that large-scale production is not simply an enlargement of laboratory-scale culture methods. The present chapter will not discuss—with some exceptions—those methods developed for laboratory cultures by the bacteriologist, the mycologist, and the protozoologist but rather will examine the common problems which arise for bacteria as well as for tissue cell cultures once they are prepared in large quantities. Those who are interested in growing some fastidious micro-organism in culture tubes or Petri plates should consult the specific literature and the monumental bibliography in certain monographs (e.g., Cochrane 1958; Dougherty et al. 1959; Hutner et al. 1953; Levine and Schoenlein 1930; Pelczar et al. 1957; Steinhaus 1946, 1949a; and certain good manuals prepared by private laboratories as Difco 1953). The readers who are planning to do work towards large-scale production of an insect pathogen should instead consider such books as the ones by Prescott and Dunn (1959), Smyth and Obold (1930), and Steel (1958) as part of their required reading. A vivid review of some of the problems of commercial production of insect pathogens has been completed recently by Briggs (1963).

Whereas some of the terms to be used in the following pages may be well known, certain others probably need explanation. While 'pure' applied to cultures of bacteria and other simple protists has a clear meaning, it no longer does when applied, for instance, to nematodes grown in the presence of yeasts. Therefore, I prefer to avoid the use of the words 'pure', favouring 'axenic' and its relatives 'synxenic' and 'xenic,' terms that avoid ambiguity and are beginning to have widespread use among zoologists and microbiologists as well (see Dougherty 1959a). Axenic cultivation is the rearing of one or more individuals of a single species on a non-living medium. Cultures of organisms associated with one or more known species are called synxenic; if unknown species are associated with the one species of interest, then the culture is xenic.

The non-living medium may be of known or partly known composition. Dougherty (1959b) suggests the following simple terminology: holidic are media whose intended constituents, other than purified inert materials, have exactly known chemical structure before compounding; meridic are media composed of a holidic base to which is added at least one substance or preparation of unknown structure or of uncertain purity; oligidic are media in which crude organic materials supply most dietary requirements.

THE USE OF LIVE INSECTS

The infection of living insects for the mass production of pathogens has been widely used in the past and is still in use today, even in industry. Usually the viruses, the protozoa, and the rickettsiae are propagated in living insects, but there are also good examples of mass production of bacteria, fungi, and nematodes by this method. With our advancing knowledge in nutrition, more and more so-called obligate parasites will be grown axenically. I agree with Trager (1957) that the obligate intracellular parasites represent an extreme of nutritional specialization. '... The simplicity of *Escherichia coli* is deceptive. It grows nicely on a little ammonium salt and a carbon source, but it has within itself the means for synthesis of nearly all the vitamins required by mammals in their diets. Mammalian cells have lost these synthetic mechanisms. ... Intracellular parasites have lost still more synthetic mechanisms.' In some cases, it is easy to grow the vegetative stages of a micro-organism axenically but no resistant stages (e.g., bacterial spores) are produced. As a method of mass production, the use of live insects seems to be successful only in cases where it is impossible to obtain, with our present knowledge, the desired stages of a micro-organism in a non-living medium. If it is possible to grow the pathogen in non-living media, this will be preferred for large-scale production. Already Giard (1892) and Forbes (1895) realized the disadvantages of *in vivo* production and recommended propagation *in vitro*, wherever possible.

There are commonly three ways of using insects as substrate for the mass production of pathogens: (1) healthy specimens are collected in the field and infected in the laboratory; (2) insects are reared and infected in the laboratory or production plant; and (3) diseased or dead specimens are collected in field populations subject to natural or artificially induced epizootics.

The first system has been in use since the earliest times of microbial control and is still in use today. The field collection of insects for the mass production of pathogens is usually preferred when the insect species involved is difficult to rear on a large scale in the laboratory, such as miners and budmoths, or has a very long life cycle, as some cockchafers.

A pathogen which very early became available on the market as a microbial insecticide is, interestingly enough, *Bacillus popilliae* Dutky, the causative agent of type A milky disease of the Japanese beetle, *Popillia japonica* Newm. *Bacillus popilliae* does not sporulate readily on bacteriological media; however, it can be mass-produced in its insect host. Three patents were issued by the United States Department of Agriculture covering the major features of the techniques and several licences have been issued for the commercial production of the material (Dutky 1959). The insecticide has been or is marketed under the names 'Japonex,' 'Japidemic,' and 'Doom Milky Disease Spores.' The very ingenious procedure for the preparation of spore-dust mixtures (figures 108 and 109, between pp. 592 and 593) has been developed mainly by Dutky (1942).

A tremendous number of grubs of *Popillia japonica* have been used in the production of this microbial insecticide. White and McCabe (1943) report that during 1942 alone some 500,000 grubs of the Japanese beetle were used to produce 12,980 pounds of the talc-spore mixture of *Bacillus popilliae*, standardized to contain one hundred million spores per gramme. In total, 184,000 pounds of spore dust have been produced since the start of the Federal-State programme of distribution of bacterial spores in 14 eastern states of the United States and the District of Columbia (Dutky 1959).

Rickettsiella popilliae (Dutky and Gooden) Phillip can be mass-produced in larvae of *Popillia japonica*, giving yields up to 330×10^9 rickettsiae per larva (Dutky 1959). The diseased larvae are killed and ground about 35 days after inoculation. What is considered now to be the same species of rickettsia was isolated in Europe from *Melolontha melolontha* (L.) (Wille and Martignoni 1952); this micro-organism could be produced in the European cockchafer, in the absence of *Popillia japonica*. The disease seems, however, to have a slower course in *Melolontha* (two or three months, according to Wille (1954)), a fact which makes improbable the use of this particular host–parasite system in large-scale production programmes.

Viruses, too, are sometimes mass-produced in the laboratory using healthy, field-collected insects. Martignoni and Auer (1957) placed larvae of *Eucosma griseana* (Hbn.), which had been collected originally for statistical purposes, in large trays isolated with hot-wire barriers according to the method of Finney, Flanders, and Smith (1947). The larvae were fed branches of larch previously sprayed with a suspension of granulosis virus. A similar method, on a larger scale, has been used by Martouret and Dusaussoy (1959) for the production of a virus (cytoplasmic polyhedrosis) of *Thaumetopoea pityocampa* Schiff. This technique can be improved considerably by infecting full-grown larvae, just prior to pupation; thus, the virus will multiply in the non-feeding pupal state (Vago and Atger 1961).

Entomophthora aulicae (Reich.) has been mass-produced in caterpillars of *Nygmia phaeorrhoea* (Donov.) by Speare and Colley (1912).

Field-collected insects can be used repeatedly for the mass production of certain micro-organisms when these can be recovered from the insects' faeces. Taylor and King (1937) kept in rearing cages large numbers of grasshoppers infected with *Malameba locustae* (King and Taylor). The excrements were collected at intervals and thoroughly mixed with bran and a small amount of molasses. This mixture was scattered along roads and fences providing a successful control of the pest.

Another use of healthy, field-collected insects should be mentioned; when only a limited amount of cultured material is available, insects are collected in the field and infected by placing them in contact with the culture. These insects are then released in the field before they die to assure a good dispersal of the infective agent. It was Snow's belief (1891) '. . . sick bugs would prove more serviceable in the dissemination of the disease than dead bugs.' Snow distributed chinch bugs, *Blissus leucopterus* (Say), which had been killed by the fungus *Beauveria bassiana* (Bals.) Vuill. (= *Beauveria globulifera* (Speg.)) with instructions to place the dead bugs in a jar for 48 hours together with 10 to 20 times as many live bugs from the field. The infected bugs would then be deposited in different portions of the field and, in their turn, communicate the disease to healthy bugs. Forbes (1895) and

Edington (1899) recommend an analogous method. Similarly, trans-ovum transmission of nuclear polyhedrosis virus was achieved by application of a virus paste to the genital armature of healthy adult females of *Colias eurytheme* Bdvl., the alfalfa caterpillar (Martignoni and Milstead 1962).

Weiser and Veber (1957) have a very interesting and important use for field larvae which is indirectly connected with the mass production of pathogens. The short-lived spores of *Thelohania hyphantriae* Weiser, a parasite of *Hyphantria cunea* (Drury), can be maintained virulent from one year to the next by passing them through one alternative host, the browntail moth, *Nygmia phaeorrhoea*. *H. cunea* overwinters as a pupa and infected pupae die usually during the winter with the protozoan following the fate of its host. The brown-tail moth overwinters as a young larva. First-instar larvae infected in the autumn are not killed by the microsporidian until the following spring. The infectivity of the pathogen is thus preserved intact in the small diapausing larvae for up to 240 days through the winter. Speare and Colley (1912) kept the fungus *Entomophthora aulicae* alive through the winter by infecting the larvae of successive generations of the brown-tail moth.

The second system—the mass production of insects in the insectaries and their subsequent infection—is more reliable and more suitable to large-scale production than the collection of large numbers of field insects, provided the insect species can adapt itself to laboratory rearing procedures and has a short life cycle. This system may become even more attractive when additional data on the nutritional requirements of insects have become available and these can be propagated in non-living media (see chapters 12 and 15 in this book; and Dougherty *et al.* 1959).

Problems in mass production of certain pathogens *in vivo* can be greatly simplified if the disease agent concerned does not exhibit strict species specificity but has a wide host range. If this is the case, it is possible to select the host which presents the smallest amount of rearing difficulties. However, a watchful eye should constantly be kept on possible loss of pathogenicity. Giard (1892) expressed the hope that the passage of *Beauveria tenella* in hosts other than *Melolontha melolontha* might enhance its virulence for the white grubs. But this is rarely the case. Hall (1954), trying to mass-produce *Nosema infesta* Hall in what are possibly its two natural hosts (the fawn-coloured lawn moth, *Crambus bonifatellus* (Hulst) and the fiery skipper, *Hylephila phylaeus* Drury), discovered soon that both these species which appeared to offer the greatest potential from the standpoint of spores produced per insect were difficult to propagate on a large scale. Hall, therefore, selected more easily cultured host insects and produced the protozoan in *Junonia coenia* Hbn., mass-reared in the laboratory, and in the potato tuber-worm, *Gnorimoschema operculella* (Zell.). The rearing method for this last species was adopted from Finney, Flanders, and Smith (1947) with some modifications. After a few passages in the tuber-worm the spore yield started to decrease indicating a reduction in virulence at least for *G. opercullella*. Production operations had to be stopped.

Clark and Thompson (1954) treated populations of *Malacosoma fragile* (Stretch), the Great Basin tent caterpillar, with polyhedrosis virus produced in an alternative host, *Malacosoma californicum* (Pack.), the California tent caterpillar. Actually, in this case the larvae were infected as part of a wild population in a heavily infested orchard and reared in the laboratory for only part of their life. Chamberlin and Dutky (1958) successfully treated larvae of the tobacco budworm, *Heliothis virescens* (F.), with polyhedrosis virus which, according to Dutky (1959), was mass-produced in corn earworm larvae, *Heliothis zea* (Boddie).

McEwen and Hervey (1958, 1959a) and Hofmaster and Ditman (1961) were able to produce large amounts of polyhedrosis virus of the cabbage looper, *Trichoplusia ni* (Hbn.), and of granulosis virus of *Pieris rapae* L., the imported cabbage-worm, in greenhouse-reared larvae of these species. The yield per larva of *T. ni* is 8×10^9 polyhedra and two to five diseased larvae provide sufficient material to treat one acre of crop (McEwen and Hervey 1959b).

The nematode DD-136, a member of the family Steinernematidae closely resembling *Neoaplectana chresima* Steiner (Dutky and Hough 1955), has been mass-produced in one of its hosts in the laboratory. Experimentally, the nematode has shown a wide host range; among its hosts is the greater wax moth, *Galleria mellonella* (L.) which is easily propagated in the laboratory in a medium containing Pablum, honey, glycerine, and water. With the method of mass production developed by Dutky (Anonymous 1956; Dutky 1959), one wax moth larva yields about 160,000 ensheathed, second stage juvenile nemas or 1·5 millions per gramme. The maximum yield in monoxenic culture (a bacterium is associated with this nematode) is 300,000 infective juveniles per gramme or approximately one-fifth of what can be obtained from the wax moth.

The third system, the collection of diseased or dead specimens in the field, has been extensively used in microbial control. Its feasibility depends mainly on the ease with which large numbers of insects can be collected. Extremely small insects, or insects which live inside parts of a plant or in special structures they build (like miners, budworms, bagworms), as well as insects living high in the crown of trees, do not lend themselves to this type of production because of the obviously great amount of manual labour involved in the collecting.

Viruses for use in control tests are often collected in large quantities in the field during epizootics; most of the references concerning insect viruses will be found in the lists by Gershenson (1960), Hughes (1957), and Martignoni and Langston (1960). Probably Giard (1892) is among the first to recommend mass collecting of diseased insects in the field. He has suggested the use of mummies of *Melothalon melolontha* to obtain spores of *Beauveria tenella*. Dupont (1913) recommends a similar method for the distribution of *Cephalosporium lecanii* Zimm., *Hypocrella* sp., and *Microcera* sp. Surprisingly, the paper by Dupont contains a controversial footnote by the entomologist A. Vuillet, who disagrees with Dupont regarding the usefulness of the distribution of entomogenous cryptogams among susceptible insect populations. Vuillet claims that such a distribution programme could be successful only if the environmental factors are favourable to the development of the fungus infection. If these factors are not favourable, epizootics could not be produced by artificially distributing the pathogen. With these remarks, Vuillet proved to have had great insight; epizootics cannot always be produced at will in insect populations, particularly when the pathogens are entomogenous fungi. The collection and distribution of dead insects in considerable amounts for the propogation of fungus diseases has been tried by Burkill (1914) with *Artona catoxantha* (Hmps.) infected with *Beauveria bassiana* (= *B. globulifera*) and has been a widely distributed method with the so-called 'red aschersonia,' *Aschersonia aleyrodis* Webber, and other fungi pathogenic for several species of whiteflies and scale insects. *A. aleyrodis* can be stored easily during the winter (from December to July) on dry leaves both at room temperature and in cold storage (Berger 1911; Watson 1915). The collection of locusts killed by *Empusa grylli* (Fres.), which were then ground into meal and used to infect other swarms, is reported by Edington (1899).

The transfer of cut alfalfa bearing dead and living infected aphids (*Therioaphis maculata* (Buck.)) from a field where an epizootic of *Entomophthora* spp. was in progress to fields having a disease-free aphid population was tried by Hall and Dunn (1958*a*) with considerable success.

To my knowledge, the most spectacular use of field-collected infective material was realized with a polyhedrosis virus of the alfalfa caterpillar, *Colias eurytheme* Bdvl., in California (Steinhaus and Thompson 1949; Thompson and Steinhaus 1950). Early in the season an initial supply of virus was produced by rearing the alfalfa caterpillars in large numbers in an insectary. Once an initial supply of virus was accumulated, the least expensive and easiest way of building up a large supply of virus was effected by spraying the virus on a field containing a high population of caterpillars. By collecting the infected larvae with a sweeping net the day before they were expected to die of the disease, a large quantity of virus was obtained. According to Thompson and Steinhaus (1950), 7 gallons of infective material were recovered in four hours' time on the sixth and seventh days after the application of one-half pint of a suspension of polyhedra. The bodies of approximately five diseased caterpillars provide enough virus to cover an acre of alfalfa (Steinhaus 1956*b*).

Steinhaus and Thompson (1949) recommend the following method for the preparation of infectious material for field distribution. The larvae, which undergo putrefaction and soon become semi-liquid, are triturated to a thick homogeneous suspension in a Waring blender. The material is then diluted 1:3 with distilled water, passed through cheesecloth to remove large particles and a hemocytometer count made of the approximate number of polyhedral inclusion bodies in the suspension. While the count of inclusion bodies is not the most accurate estimate of the virulence of a suspension, it is nonetheless the most convenient means of arriving at an approximate evaluation of the potency of a suspension for field use. Dosage-mortality tests would, of course, provide a better estimate of the virulence of a preparation and have been used in field tests by some workers (e.g., Martignoni and Auer 1957); such tests require, however, much work and time.

Weiser and Veber (1957) report that one field-collected third- or fourth-instar larva of *Nygmia phaeorrhoea* infected with *Thelohania hyphantriae* yields from 37 to 100 million spores. Sprays used by these authors in the control of *Hyphantria cunea* contain about 200 to 300 larvae per gallon (3 to 6 million spores per ml). The large number of larvae required for sprays containing protozoan spores may be a serious limiting factor in the production of this type of microbial insecticide.

A very exceptional use of field-collected material (not insects) has been reported by Gerhardt (1955). An abundant growth of blue-green algae of the genus *Anabaena*, and particularly *Anabaena unispora* Gardn., seems to have a deterrent effect on mosquito larvae in rice fields. Gerhardt achieved an abundant growth of blue-green algae in various test plots throughout a rice-growing season by transporting stubble from one rice field to another. Gerhardt, however, feels that greater success could be achieved when it becomes possible to utilize mass-cultured algae as the source of inoculum.

In conclusion, it may be stated that the utilization of live insects for the mass production of microbial insecticides is by no means a thing of the past, as exemplified by *Bacillus popilliae*, the nematode DD-136, and the polyhedrosis virus of *Colias eurytheme*. The use of live insects as a substrate requires considerable manual labour, and is, therefore, economically acceptable only when: (1) the infective or resistant stages of the pathogen cannot be mass-produced in non-living media; (2) the pathogen is highly desirable as a unique control possibility; and (3) the infective agent is extremely virulent (see Bucher 1958), a factor which in this case may be best expressed by the number of larvae or other insect stages needed for the production of the material required to treat an acre of crop or forest.

AXENIC CULTURE

Provided that the infective stages or resistant stages of a pathogen can be produced on non-living media, axenic cultivation is the choice method for their mass production. Back in 1888, Krassilstschik showed the feasibility of this method for large-scale production of spores of an entomogenous fungus. Few other examples of axenic mass production of insect pathogens can be found in the literature and not until recently were true industrial methods applied to the production of microbial insecticides. J. Howard Flint, the patent lawyer who wrote a chapter on the relation of patent law to biological processes in Smyth and Obold's book (1930), stated: 'The micro-organisms appear to have gone into business. Imperceptibility their myriads have crept into industry, where they are nourished and pampered for the work that they do.' Truly, also insect pathogens seems to have crept into business, possibly not so imperceptibly but definitely pampered, and they are now an important part of what Duddington (1961) calls 'the livestock of industry.' In fact, the first industrial insect pathology laboratory has already been established (Anonymous 1959).

The big step forward in the axenic mass cultivation of micro-organisms came with penicillin; it is one of the indirect benefits which this drug has given us. The principal advances in the technology of aerobic fermentations made in the course of the development of methods for the production of penicillin have evolved along three closely interrelated lines according to T. Jackson (1958): (1) at the laboratory level, biological and biochemical studies; (2) at the pilot-plant level, the establishment of optimal conditions and scale-up practices through the study of the influence of environmental factors; and (3) at the plant level, the development of rigidly aseptic techniques for mass culturing.

Of the many problems encountered in large-scale axenic culture of micro-organisms (and Hastings (1958) lists a long series of these difficulties) only a few have been solved for the insect pathogens. And usually they have been solved at the lowest level, the laboratory level. However, the fast developments in biochemical engineering (see Prescott and Dunn 1959; and Steel 1958) along with the success obtained with one insect pathogen, *Bacillus thuringiensis*, promise much for the future. By now the industry is aware of the potentialities of microbial control (Steinhaus 1959*b*, *c*), and has devoted much research to the aspects of mass production of at least one pathogen. The first microbial insecticide to be produced axenically in marketable amounts has been granted a coveted designation: the exemption from tolerances by the United States Food and Drug Administration (Anonymous 1959; Harvey 1960). Of course, quite a few risks and much speculation remain; but this is innate in the dynamics of the industry. It must not be forgotten that one year of successful research can pay, as Hastings said, dividends for several years!

So far, axenic cultivation on an industrial scale seems to have been developed only for fungi and bacteria. However, there are indications that other micro-organisms can be mass-produced, as shown by the recent success in the mass culture of cells from tissues of vertebrates, for virus production.

Substrates

Media utilized for the mass culture of micro-organisms are either solid or liquid. Diphasic media, used in some special cases, are not likely to be used in the mass production of insect pathogens. There are innumerable holidic and meridic media for the culture of micro-organisms (see e.g., Levine and Schoenlein 1930) but most of them are very expensive and therefore not suitable for plant-production uses. Media used in the large-scale production of micro-organisms are mostly oligidic, containing crude organic materials. The micro-organisms are produced in surface culture (on solid and on liquid media; in the last case one may speak of 'still' culture) and in submerged culture, in liquid media. Surface-culture methods had their blaze of glory during World War II, in the production of penicillin, before all the obstacles of aerated submerged fermentation could be eliminated. Now, surface-culture methods are considered too laborious and expensive for large-scale production. Most fungi, however, are known to produce only mycelium in submerged culture which usually fails to sporulate while submerged. These organisms present difficult problems from the standpoint of mass production. In the case of the fungi, a combination of a submerged phase (for mycelium production) and of a surface phase (for sporulation) may be preferable industrially to surface culture alone for the production of large amounts of spores. The bacteria, which can sporulate abundantly in submerged culture, have a definite advantage over the fungi! Today, surface-culture methods are used for laboratory-scale production, when only limited quantities of a pathogen are needed for preliminary field tests. In the past, most insect pathogens have been produced in large quantities by surface-culture methods; some examples will be mentioned in the following pages, but we must realize that the future lies in submerged fermentation.

Fungi. The most frequently used raw materials for the culture of entomogenous fungi in quantities are sweet potato, Irish potato, corn meal, oats, bran, rice, bread, middlings, lima beans, molasses, radish, prune, stems of *Canna* and of *Caladium*, beer mash, sawdust, beef broth, pork, blood, dog dung, swordfish, and herring. Some workers have used more expensive media, such as Sabouraud dextrose agar, but their use in large-scale production is questionable from the economical standpoint. Although true plant-production methods have never been reported for entomogenous fungi, some of these have been grown on a scale larger than at the laboratory level (see table 8). The media utilized by the various workers combine a good environment for growth and sporulation with ease of preparation and low cost.

TABLE 8

Entomogenous fungi produced in quantities

Species	Literature
Phycomyceteae, Entomophthorales	
Entomophthora coronata (Cost.) Kevorkian	Hall and Dunn 1958
Entomophthora exitialis Hall and Dunn	Hall and Dunn 1958
Entomophthora virulenta Hall and Dunn	Hall and Dunn 1958
	Hall and Halfhill 1959
Fungi imperfecti, Sphaeropsidales	
Aschersonia aleyrodis Webber	Berger 1910, 1921
	Fawcett 1908; Newell 1921, 1923
Aschersonia cubensis Berk. and Curt.	Berger 1921
Aschersonia goldiana Sacs and Ellis (often mentioned in literature as *Aschersonia flavocitrina* P. Henn.)	Berger 1921
Fungi imperfecti, Moniliales	
Beauveria sp.	Wikén, Bovey, Wille, and Wildbolz 1954; Wille 1954; York 1958
Beauveria bassiana (Bals.) Vuill.	Bartlett and Lefebvre 1934; Dresner 1949; Hall 1954; McCoy and Carver 1941
Beauveria globulifera (Speg.) Picard (today this is considered a strain of *B. bassiana*, according to MacLeod 1954)	Billings and Glenn 1911; Forbes 1895
Metarrhizium anisopliae (Metch.) Sorokin	Krassilstschik 1888; Metchnikoff 1880; Rorer 1910, 1913a, b; Vouk and Klas 1931

The corn meal mush medium has been in use since Forbes' time (1895). Forbes used a corn meal batter mixed with beef broth for the propagation of *Beauveria bassiana* (= *B. globulifera*). Bartlett and Lefebvre (1934) used the same medium (without the addition of beef broth) for *B. bassiana*.

Bran was used by McCoy and Carver (1941), by Dresner (1949), and by York (1958) for species of *Beauveria*.

Potato, both sweet and Irish, has been used by numerous workers, particularly for the mass-production of species of *Aschersonia*. Fawcett (1908) prepared his medium according to the following method: the sweet potatoes were washed, peeled, washed again, and put through a meat chopper. This ground-up mass was then washed in running water to eliminate fine particles, and the moist medium was sterilized in an autoclave at 110° C for about 20 minutes or more.

Rice has been extensively used by Rorer (1910, 1913*a*, *b*) and by Gough (1911). The rice was thoroughly washed and boiled for 10 to 15 minutes. Then it was drained dry and placed, still warm, in the culture vessels, and autoclaved for one hour at 100° C on three or four successive days. In earlier experiments, the boiled rice was not autoclaved but contamination was likely to occur. Pascalet (1939) used rice with the addition of peptone for the culture of *Beauveria bassiana*, for the control of *Stephanoderes hampei* Fer. Schaerffenberg (1959) was able to produce large amounts of spores of *Metarrhizium anisopliae* on a rice-agar medium.

Some idea on the economics of spore production in surface culture may be obtained from table 9. If we take the ratio (spores produced per square foot of medium):(spores used to treat one acre) we notice that a quotient of about *one* is the maximum which has been attained using the media described above. Krassilstschik used the highest amount of spores per acre.

The large-scale culture of fungi as well as that of bacteria requires a good knowledge of the environmental conditions responsible for: (1) germination, (2) growth, and (3) sporulation. The identification of the responsible nutritional factors becomes feasible only when the micro-organism concerned can be grown on a holidic medium. This unfortunately has been done only in rare instances, with entomogenous fungi. Most studies (with meridic or oligidic media) are limited to spore germination and growth and little is known on sporulation. Hall and Halfhill (1959), Masera (1937), Sawyer (1929, 1931), Schweizer (1947), and Vouk and Klas (1931) are among the few who have conducted studies on some aspects of germination and growth of entomogenous fungi. MacLeod (1959*a*, *b*) has initiated a nutritional study on the genus *Hirsutella* with meridic media in submerged culture; it is exactly this type of work which is urgently needed if industrial production is to be realized.

Evidently much more has to be known about sporulation because the spore is the end product of the fermentation process in the microbial insecticide industry. The most inclusive generalization, as Cochrane (1958) points out, is that sporulation is initiated by factors which check the growth of an established mycelium without too drastically poisoning its metabolism. But the intimate mechanism remains to be defined. That humidity plays a role in the sporulation of entomogenous fungi has been reported by Bartlett and Lefebvre (1934), Dresner (1949), and Sawyer (1929). The spore yield is lowered by culturing on fluid media or on solid media in presence of high relative humidity. The ideal condition for spore production was found to be a very moist but not wet medium with a low humidity maintained after germination of the seedling spores. Nutritional factors play an important role in sporulation, too. While it is true there is no conclusive evidence for a specific nutritional factor

TABLE 9

Spore production in surface culture calculated from data available in the literature

Species	Culture medium	Spore production (g/sq.ft of medium)	Spores used in dusts or sprays	Literature
Metarrhizium anisopliae (Metch.) Sorokin	Beer mash, in still culture	16·7–20·4	3237·5 g/acre	Krassilstschik 1888
	Rice, trays in special cabinet	1043·3 (spores and starch)	907·2–1360·8 g/acre (spores and starch)	Rorer 1913*a*
	Rice, Erlenmeyer flasks	30·2	400 g/acre (14,500 corn plants)	Vouk and Klas 1931
Beauveria bassiana (Bals.) Vuill.	Bran, 20 cm Petri dishes	8·9	20 g/acre	McCoy and Carver 1941
	Beans, 9 cm Petri dishes	21·8	20 g/acre	Dresner 1949
	Rolled breakfast oats, 20 cm Petri dishes	15·2	26·6–484 g/acre	Hall 1954

required for sporulation and not required for growth (see Cochrane 1958) the absolute amount of some nutrients required for sporulation is higher than that which supports growth. Shanor (1936) found that perithecia-bearing stromata of *Cordyceps militaris* (Lk.) are produced on dead pupae but never on autoclaved ones. Strains of *Beauveria bassiana* (= *B. globulifera*) produced the highest amount of spores on Sabouraud maltose agar, followed by Molish medium, blood agar base, Raulin-Thom and Czapek-Dox media, potato dextrose, and corn meal agar (MacLeod 1954a). Hall and Dunn (1958a) found Sabouraud dextrose agar to be the most suitable for growth and conidial spore production of *Entomophthora coronata* and *E. virulenta*, while this same medium had to be fortified with a rich breakfast cereal in order to obtain fair growth and good production of spores of *E. exitialis*.

Entomophthora muscae Cohn seems to be more fastidious; good growth, conida, and resistant stages have been produced by Schweizer (1936, 1947) on a medium containing blood and meat broth gelatine. Instead of blood, use may be made of urea, uric acid, hippuric acid, hypoxanthine, creatine, xanthine, and lecithin. The author considers the enzymatic activity of the medium essential to growth, along with fats and *d*-glucosamine; therefore he recommends cold sterilization of the medium. According to Hall and Halfhill (1959), however, Schweizer's findings cannot be generalized for the entire group of entomophthoraceous fungi (see also Müller-Kögler 1959).

Sawyer (1929) finds carbohydrates and fats not essential to the growth of two species of *Entomophthora* while protein is required for the completion of their life cycle. Organic nitrogen is required for the mycelial growth of *Hirsutella gigantea* Petch (MacLeod) 1959a). Schaerffenberg (1957) recommends the addition of 3 per cent peptone to a malt-extract medium, for the large-scale production of spores of *Beauveria bassiana*. *Metarrhizium anisopliae* seems to have a better synthetic machinery; it shows no special requirements for carbohydrates (glucose, laevulose, arabinose, galactose, saccharose, inulin, and glycerine do equally well) and uses both organic and inorganic N sources (Vouk and Klas 1931) as far as growth is concerned.

BACTERIA. Although mass production of entomogenous bacteria is a relatively recent achievement, there seems to be a greater knowledge of the requirements for spore germination, vegetative growth, and sporulation of these than there is, e.g., for the fungi. Bacterial physiology is of an older tradition than fungal physiology and the idea of a bacterium as 'a small bag of enzymes' has forced its way even into the minds of the most inveterate taxonomists.

One of the first bacteria to have been grown on a large scale for the microbial control of insects was *Cloaca cloacae* var. *acridiorum* d'Hérelle (= *Coccobacillus acridiorum* d'Hérelle). While the preservation of the virulence of this microorganism presented many difficulties, which will be discussed later, this form is not fastidious and can be grown easily in submerged culture (d'Hérelle 1912, 1914, 1915, 1916). The bacterium has been used extensively by d'Hérelle and by other investigators (e.g., Sergent and Lhéritier 1914) against various species of grasshoppers. D'Hérelle used three different broths, all peptonized, for his work (see

FIGURE 108. Inoculation of grubs of *Popillia japonica* Newm. with spores of *Bacillus popilliae* Dutky. The grubs, foreground, are kept on ice. The stereoscopic microscope and microinjector are secured to a board so the point of the needle appears in the microscope field when the syringe is clamped in place. The entire apparatus is tilted so that the operator does not have to look straight down all day long. Inoculated grubs are placed in individual compartments in the incubating tray, background. (Photograph courtesy of Fairfax Biological Laboratories, Clinton Corners, New York.)

FIGURE 109. Experimental plant-scale equipment used in processing diseased grubs of *Popillia japonica* Newm. infected with *Bacillus popilliae* Dutky. (A) Meat grinder for crushing diseased larvae. (B) Batch mixer for incorporating crushed grub suspension with precipitated chalk. (C) Hopper through which the preliminary mix is fed. (D) Classifying chamber (note the muslin-covered blast gates for controlling direction and quantity of air flow). (E) Cyclone dust collector. (F) High speed paddle-wheel impeller pressure fan. (G) Bag collector. (H) Gas-fired furnace for heating air blast to flash-dry moist dust. (Photograph courtesy of Japanese Beetle Laboratory and S. R. Dutky, Entomology Research Division, Agricultural Research Service, U.S. Department of Agriculture, Beltsville, Maryland.)

FIGURE 110. Culture cabinets used for the mass production of *Metarrhizium anisopliae* (Metch.) Sorokin. (A) Closed cabinet, ready for sterilization. (B) Open cabinet with shelves removed; the holes in the back are for inoculation; central pipe for steam. (C) Open cabinet, showing rice covered with growth of green muscardine; in this cabinet the steam pipes run along the sides and are joined under each shelf by a cross pipe. (From Rorer, 1913.)

FIGURE 111. Povitsky flasks containing nutrient agar upon which *Bacillus thuringiensis* Berl. is being grown and spores produced. Total surface of medium amounts to about 70 square feet. (Photograph courtesy of E. A. Steinhaus, Laboratory of Insect Pathology, Department of Biological Control, University of California, Berkeley.)

FIGURE 112. General view of a group of twelve 20-litre fermentors. Each group of four fermentors, with their accessory equipment, operates as a unit. (Photograph courtesy of R. G. Dworachack, Industrial Products Investigations, Fermentation Laboratory, Agricultural Research Service, U.S. Department of Agriculture, Peoria, Illinois.)

table 10). A first medium (simple meat broth with peptone) was soon abandoned because the bacterium lost its virulence if cultured for periods over two to three days. The culture in broths described in table 10 were still virulent after 15 days. The bacteria, with the broth in which they were cultured, were sprayed on grass tufts, distributed throughout the infested area; the amount of broth used varied from one litre to 50 ml per hectare; small infestations required relatively higher amounts of culture.

TABLE 10

The composition of three media used by d'Hérelle for the large-scale culture of Cloaca cloacae *var.* acridiorum *d'Hérelle. Reactions of media were 'slightly alkaline.' Incubation of media was at room temperature.*

Ingredients	Year published		
	1914	1914	1915
Water, ml	1,000	1,000	1,000
Meat extract (Liebig), g	—	—	5
Potato, g	—	10	—
Gelatine, g	30	20	—
Peptone (Chapoteau), g	40	5	5
Glucose, g	5	5	—
Sodium chloride, g	5	5	5

Métalnikov and Métalnikov (1935) considered the use of vegetable raw materials less expensive than meat extracts. They recommended potato broth and a potato-gelatine medium. Quantities of spore dust of *Bacillus thuringiensis*, *B. galleriae* No. 2 (Chorine), *B. cazaubon* (Métalnikov), and other bacteria were produced on these media. Similar media may also have been used for the mass production of a microbial insecticide 'Sporeine,' which was sold in France before 1940 (Jacobs 1950) by the now defunct Laboratoire L.I.B.E.C. then located at 26 Rue d'Alleray in Paris. This firm was headed by S. Métalnikov (Toumonoff, pers. comm., 1960). Günther (1958), too, used a medium containing potato and other substances of vegetable origin for the large-scale production of a spore-former.

Solid media and standard laboratory methods were used by Husz (1931) who mixed spores of *Bacillus thuringiensis* from 224 Petri dishes with 6 kg of talc for the production of dusts. Steinhaus (1951b) and Hall (1954) produced *B. thuringiensis* on a somewhat larger scale on plain nutrient agar, sometimes with the addition of one per cent dextrose. Dextrose, however, did not seem to increase the final amount of spore yield. Cultures in nutrient broth gave a smaller spore yield (due to improper aeration, probably) than they did on the solid medium. One 6-litre Povitzky flask, with an agar surface of 75 square inches, gave from 0·2 to 0·3 gramme (Steinhaus 1951b) to 0·7 gramme (Hall 1954) of dry spore powder.

Fortunately, as it has been pointed out, *Bacillus thuringiensis* is not as fastidious as some other bacterial insect pathogens. Recently mass production of *B. thuringiensis* spores (and parasporal bodies) in industrial quantities has been achieved in media that are not too complex and certainly not too costly. Complete details of the mass-production methods are not available, because some of the media are factory secrets (in some cases, patents are pending). Bioferm Corporation (personal communication, 1959) propagates the bacterium in 500-gallon quantities, in a medium containing beet molasses and corn steep liquor. This culture is then used to inoculate larger fermentors. Sporulation occurs rapidly and uniformly (90 per cent in less than two days) in a 'sporulation medium.' Briggs (1963) gives further details concerning media and procedures.

Wikén and Wille (1953, 1955) did a long series of quantitative investigations on the metabolism of a *Bacillus* sp. (pathogenic for *Melolontha melolontha*) during growth and sporulation. This is probably the only instance of a nutritional study with holidic media on a bacterium pathogenic for insects. The strains of the species investigated have been found by the authors to be heterotrophic for (+) biotin and thiamine, and to need organic N in form of *l* (+) glutamic acid and *dl*-cystine for growth and sporulation. The medium developed by the investigators for the large-scale production of the pathogen in aerated culture has the following composition (Wikén, Bovey, Wille, and Wildbolz 1954; Wikén and Wille 1953, 1955; Wille 1954):

glucose	2·0 grammes
l (+) glutamic acid	4·0 grammes
dl-cystine	0·06 gramme
K_2HPO_4	0·5 gramme
KH_2PO_4	0·5 gramme
$MgSO_4 \cdot 7H_2O$	0·2 gramme
NaCl	0·01 gramme
$MnSo_4 \cdot 4H_2O$	0·01 gramme
$FeSO_4 \cdot 7H_2O$	0·01 gramme
$Ca(H_2PO_4)_2 \cdot H_2O$	2·0 millilitres of a saturated solution at 25° C
thiamine	0·5 milligrammes
(+) biotin	25·0 microgrammes
dist. water	1,0000·0 millilitres

The pH of the solution was adjusted at 6·5 to 7·3 by means of NaOH. With sufficient aeration, after 8 to 14 days a sporulation of 50 to 60 per cent was obtained; the spore production amounted to 10^9 per millilitre of substrate. The amount of sporulation decreased rapidly when the bacterium was cultured on common nutrient agar. In submerged non-aerated culture, the amount of spores formed did not exceed 20 per cent of the cell population. The addition of more oxygen and the addition of trace elements can increase sporulation to 80 per cent and shorten the incubation time to about five days (Wille 1954).

Basically the same medium has been used by Krieg (1957) for the mass-production of *Bacillus thuringiensis*. Krieg observed that sporulation started within 48 hours and was completed by 96 hours in heavily aerated cultures.

A mass culture of *Pseudomonas aeruginosa* (Schroeter) Migula was prepared by Baird (1958*a*) in a medium consisting of:

Bacto nutrient broth, dehydrated	8 grammes
gastric mucin	10 grammes
casein	10 grammes
sucrose	50 grammes
distilled water	1,000 millilitres

The cultures were incubated at 36° C for 24 hours. For field usage against grass-hoppers the cultures were diluted 1:10 with distilled water. Sucrose, casein, and mucin were added in order to preserve the viability of the bacteria when dried in thin films in the field.

Serratia marcescens Bizio, which at times is an important insect pathogen (Steinhaus 1959*b*) and may have a future in microbial control, has been produced on a large scale in media containing skim milk powder, protopeptone, and glucose (Benedict *et al.* 1957). The medium must be highly oxygenated; under these conditions up to 260×10^9 cells per millilitre were obtained. Smith and Johnson (1954) have obtained yields up to 38 per cent of the total substrate, using a holidic medium and very efficient aeration. Neopeptone, which has been long in use for the culture of *S. marcescens*, can be substituted by soy products, which are much cheaper, in a medium containing mannitol or sorbitol as carbon source (Harned 1954).

A very interesting series of investigations towards the axenic cultivation of *Bacillus popilliae* has been initiated by Steinkraus. The outcome of this research project is very important for the production of spores in large quantities, *in vitro*. When Dutky (1940) isolated and described the agents of type A and type B milky diseases of *Popillia japonica*, he succeeded in culturing only one of the two species, *B. popilliae*. However, no sporulation occurred. Steinkraus and Tashiro (1955) obtained spores in axenic culture, on a medium which evolved from studies on sporulation *in vivo*. Particular attention was given to pH, oxygen tension, growth factors, and carbohydrates and nitrogen requirements of the micro-organism. Since sporulation in a diseased larva occurs after the vegetative cells have become very numerous in the blood, it seemed that a nutrient deficiency might be a factor inducing sporulation. It was observed that good sporulation resulted when vegetative cells were transferred from the rich 'growth medium' as a thick paste to the 'starvation medium.' In addition to starvation (and crowding), high temperatures also promoted sporulation. The composition of the two media is given in table 11.

It is impossible to mention here, even briefly, the many factors influencing germination, growth, and sporulation of bacteria. The reader is referred to the monograph edited by Halvorson (1957) for more information on this subject. In general, as for the fungi, sporulation of bacteria may be obtained under various conditions which have in common the effect of reducing or stopping growth. Grelet (1957) infers that sporogenesis is the response of a genetically apt bacillus to an increase in the generation time. It should be pointed out that 'starvation' (meaning the sum of various deficiencies) does not always end in sporulation; the scarcity of some elements like Mg, Mn, K, or, in the case of some aerobic spore-formers, lack of oxygen, does not allow sporulation. With *Bacillus cereus* var. *mycoides* (Flügge) insufficient concentrations of glutamate, or disequilibrated concentrations of valine, leucine, and isoleucine, hinder growth without promoting sporulation. According to Grelet one may distinguish two sets of conditions for sporulation: (1) conditions which appear at a definite stage of a culture, causing vegetative growth to stop and promoting sporulation; and (2) conditions which are

TABLE 11

Media for the axenic culture of Bacillus popilliae *Dutky*
(Steinkraus 1957; Steinkraus and Provvidenti 1958).

Ingredients	Growth medium	Starvation medium
Tryptone	10 g	—
Yeast extract	6 g	0·2 g
K₂HPO₄	3 g	—
(NH₄)₂HPO₄	—	1
KCl	—	0·2 g
MgSO₄	—	0·2 g
Soluble starch	10 g	10 g
Activated carbon	6 g	3 g
Glucose	1 g	—
Fructose	1 g	—
Mannose	1 g	—
Maltose	1 g	—
Sucrose	1 g	—
Salicin	1 g	—
Agar	15 g	15 g
Distilled water	1000 ml	1000 ml

necessary for the accomplishment of spore formation and which can be realized continuously from the beginning of the culture. The addition of certain substances promotes sporulation as shown by studies on a *Bacillus* sp. made by Wikén and Wille (Wille 1954); the addition of trace elements increased both sporulation rate and spore production in the holidic medium described above. Sporulation of a *Clostridium* has been increased up to 99·9 per cent by the addition of 1·5 per cent trypticase (a peptone derived from casein); also casamino acids and casitone gave good results (Hitzman, Halvorson, and Ukita 1957).

Extremely interesting and important investigations were made by Fitz-James (1957) on the sporulation of species from the *Bacillus cereus* group, including *Bacillus thuringiensis* Berl. var. *thuringiensis*[1] and *B. thuringiensis* var. *sotto* (Aoki and Chigasaki) Heimpel and Angus. These studies show that the composition of the

---

[1] See footnote 1, page 550.

medium has an influence on the size and composition of the spores of the varieties studied. Particularly, the RNA content of the spores is influenced by the medium while the DNA content remains constant. It was also evident from the studies made by Fitz-James that those varieties with the smallest spores and least amount DNA also produced the smallest crystals. Further studies on the development of the parasporal protein crystals have been reported by Young and Fitz-James (1959). Studies on protein turnover by Monro (1961) show that crystal formation in *Bacillus thuringiensis* is part of a general process occurring during sporulation; the crystal protein is synthesized from amino acids which are derived largely from the breakdown of vegetative-cell proteins.

From the standpoint of large-scale production, the study of germination and growth factors is at least as important as the study of factors influencing sporogenesis. Studies on various *Bacillus* spp. have shown, for example, that it is possible to stimulate growth by the addition of autoclaved solutions of glucose and phosphate to growth media. This stimulation has been referred to a reduction in the lag phase, whereas the growth rate and the maximum cell density are generally independent of glucose-phosphate (Sergeant, Lankford, and Traxler 1957). The germination of spores of *B. thuringiensis* is not inhibited by *d*-alanine, in spite of the reported inhibitory effect of this form on some bacteria. Germination with *d*-alanine occurred as well as in the presence of *l*-alanine, but at a slower rate. The well-known inhibition by *d*-alanine in strains responsive to *l*-alanine has been shown to be temporary only, for *B. thuringiensis*, due to the probable presence of alanine racemase, resulting in racemization to the stimulatory *l* form (Wolf and Mahmoud 1957). Recently, a 1:1 chelate of calcium and dipicolinic acid has been shown to induce rapid and complete germination of both aerobic and anaerobic bacterial endospores (Riemann and Ordal 1961). The mechanism of the chelate action is not yet understood, but the use of such agents may prove advantageous for the synchronization of spore germination in mass cultures.

PROTOZOA. It is still premature to speak of media for the mass culture of protozoa under axenic conditions. However, some protozoa have been grown axenically, and there is much research going on in protozoan nutrition, so that the outlook is promising (Hutner *et al.* 1953). Provasoli (1958) has published a very useful catalogue of laboratory strains of free-living and parasitic protozoa; of the many species listed, the only one known to cause infection in insects, so far, has been grown axenically—*Tetrahymena pyriformis* (Ehren.). The literature on the effect of amino acid balance on the growth of this ciliate has been reviewed recently by Gordon (1959*a*).

Herpetomonas muscarum (Leidy) (=*Herpetomonas muscae-domesticae* Burn.), a commensal in the gut of flies, has been grown aerobically in a medium prepared from full-grown silkworm larvae, and on horse-blood agar by Glaser (1926). The method of axenization described by Glaser is very interesting; he injected suspensions from the fly alimentary tract in the general cavity of silkworm larvae; within 72 hours nearly all silkworms died of septicaemia. The survivors usually contained a few *Herpetomonas* without bacteria. In this connection it may be well to mention that Neff (1957) axenized an *Acanthamoeba* sp. by an agar-surface migration method, a technique which may also prove valuable for some of the protozoa pathogenic for insects.

Another species living within insects, *Crithidia fasciculata* (Léger) has been grown *in vitro* by Cowperthwaite, Weber, Packer, and Hutner (1953). The holidic medium used has a degree of complexity comparable with that required for exacting bacteria such as *Streptococcus* or *Lactobacillus*.

Work on protozoa should take into consideration not only liquid or solid media, but also diphasic media, which in some cases have proved superior to the monophasic ones (Wallace 1956).

Also certain intracellular parasitic protozoa have been cultured *in vitro* in absence of host cells. This has not yet been accomplished with an insect pathogen, but Trager (1953a, 1957) has succeeded in maintaining *Plasmodium lophurae* Coggeshall *in vitro*, up to four days, in a complex medium containing a suspension of haemolysed duck erythrocytes. How much of the intactness of the host cell is required for the development of an intracellular parasite? Are the physical structure, labile metabolic intermediates, or its enzymes and coenzymes of the host cell necessary? Trager's work is an attempt to answer some or all of these questions. Studies of this kind may lead, some day, to the mass production of microsporidia and of other protozoa having good potentials as microbial insecticides.

NEMATODES. To simplify the discussion of substrates for nematode culture, a separation line, even though artificial, has to be drawn between axenic and synxenic cultivation of nematodes. Therefore, cultures prepared with media containing fragments of non-autoclaved organ tissue will be considered synxenic, while cultures in media free of (living) cells will be considered axenic (see also Dougherty 1959a, p. 39). Of course, cultures of nematodes associated with other microorganisms are synxenic or xenic by definition.

So far, only two nematodes, pathogenic for insects, have been grown in large quantities under axenic conditions; *Neoaplectana glaseri* Steiner, a parasite of *Popillia japonica*, and *N. chresima*, a parasite of *Heliothis zea* and of other insects. Glaser, McCoy, and Girth (1940) briefly mentioned a method for axenic cultivation of *N. glaseri*, using liquid media containing kidney extracts devoid of particulate matter. Glaser, McCoy, and Girth (1942) later described in detail methods for the axenic cultivation of the two species of *Neoaplectana*. The medium is a semi-solid gel at pH 7·0 containing 20 grammes ground beef kidney or liver, 0·5 grammes sodium chloride, and 0·5 grammes agar in 100 millilitres water. This medium is autoclaved and may be stored for two weeks prior to use. Both species of nematodes grew well in this medium.

Axenic culture of *Neoaplectana glaseri* in a fluid medium has been achieved by Stoll (1953, 1959). Stoll's medium (1959 formula) consists of heat-stable infusion broth made from veal or beef heart, with a 10 per cent supplementation of heat-labile raw liver extract at an acid pH (6·0 to 6·5). Especially favourable in promoting growth has been raw liver extract made from the livers of rabbits sacrificed in late pregnancy or early *post partum*.

Equipment and Procedures

Often, in the past, insect pathogens have been produced at the laboratory level in quantities sufficient for experimental field tests; only recently has the industry shown an active interest in their production on a larger scale. In the next pages the discussion of the equipment and procedures will be divided into two sections: at the laboratory level and at the pilot-plant and industrial levels.

AT THE LABORATORY LEVEL. Routine laboratory techniques have often been used for the production of small batches of bacteria and fungi for field tests (e.g., *Bacillus thuringiensis* by Husz 1931; *Beauveria bassiana* (= *B. globulifera*) by Hall 1954). The final products are very expensive because of the high amount of manual labour involved, but the operation may be justified if the value of pathogen for field use in not fully known. At this stage of research, cost is not the limiting factor. The procedure is simple; after appropriate incubation (in Petri dishes) the spores are scraped from the surface of the medium as a thick paste, in the case of the bacteria, or as a powder, in the case of the fungi. The spores are then dried, pure or mixed with talc or starch, and the dry mass pulverized gently in a mortar. The final product may be used dry, as a dust, or suspended in water, as a spray.

With less manual labour and less danger of contamination one may use somewhat larger vessels which offer a greater medium surface. Roux and Povitzky bottles are handy and have been used (figure 111, between pp. 592 and 593) for the production of *Bacillus thuringiensis* (Steinhaus 1951b, Hall 1954).

Other vessels, particularly useful for the still culture of fungi, are the Fernbach flask and the large Carrel flask; the latter can be conveniently stacked during incubation or storage. Fernbach flasks have been used by Wikén, Bovey, Wille, and Wildbolz (1954) for the production of spores of a species of *Beauveria*. Benedict et al. (1957) used Fernbach flasks with 16 indentations, on a rotary shaker, for the production of *Serratia marcescens* in highly aerated conditions. Corman et al. (1957) studied the various factors limiting oxygen absorption rates in flask fermentation, as turbulence (determined by the size of the flasks in relation to the eccentricity of rotary shakers) and closure.

Other containers may be used, if the glass resists autoclaving. Milk bottles, selected on the basis of ready availability in wartime, have been used for the mass production of penicillin. Beer bottles have been used too, for the production of *Cloaca cloacae* (d'Hérelle 1916). Erlenmeyer flasks have been used for the culture of fungi by some investigators (Vouk and Klas 1931), but Dresner (1949) finds them impractical. Metal containers were used by Krassilstschik (1888), but unfortunately no details on their shape and size have been found in the literature (see 'Introduction' to this chapter).

Forbes (1895) used Mason fruit jars for the production of *Beauveria bassiana* (= *B. globulifera*). Wide-mouth bottles ($\frac{1}{4}$, $\frac{1}{2}$, and full pint) have been used for one of the early extensive distribution programmes of *Aschersonia* spp. The spores of the fungi were introduced into the bottles either by spraying them suspended in sterile water, or by streaking them with a platinum needle. Newell (1921) mentioned that 956 such cultures were distributed in 1918–19, and 1,332 in 1919–20. The bottle cultures, on a sweet potato medium, were sold for 75 cents each; one bottle would provide enough material for the treatment of an acre of citrus trees (Newell 1921; Berger 1919, 1921). Budget difficulties for biological research are not new: 'The nominal charge of seventy-five cents per culture, to cover actual cost of production, is made necessary because the Plant Board has no appropriation for this work.' Newell (1921) writes that the lack of more suitable quarters has forced him to prepare the cultures of *Aschersonia*, '. . . in the attic of Language Hall at the University . . .' with some contingent adverse effects; an abnormally large number of cultures spoiled because of high summer temperatures.

Circular tin dishes and tin pudding dishes were used by Gough (1911) for the preparation of rice cultures of *Metarrhizium anisopliae*.

A practical method of preparing cultures of entomophthorous fungi for distribution to farmers has been developed by Hall and Dunn (1958a). Disposable $\frac{1}{4}$-pint waxed food containers were used for the culture procedures; the same containers were shipped to the field after a four-day incubation period at 25° C. The cartons were sealed by dipping them in melted paraffin, to maintain high humidity.

A remarkable detailed account of the preparation of mass cultures of *Cloaca cloacae* under field conditions has been given by d'Hérelle (1914, 1916). The transportation of the material necessary for one complete grasshopper control operation required 15 mules!

Much larger amounts of bacterial cells or spores can be produced at less cost in aerated cultures. This is the choice method for the production plant, but some simple devices have been developed also for small-scale experiments. Wikén *et al.* (1954) used Kluyver's aerated culture apparatus for the production of quantities of spores of a *Bacillus* sp., and the same method was used by Krieg (1957a) for the culture of *Bacillus thuringiensis*. Wille (1954) and Krieg report that strong aeration of the medium is essential to sporulation, while in absence of oxygen there is only vegetative growth.

The collection of spores may present some problems. McCoy and Carver (1941) devised a simple apparatus for collecting spores of *Beauveria bassiana* (= *B. globulifera*) grown on solid media. Hall (1954) considers this method as impractical, because one attempt to obtain fungus spores terminated in a serious spore-dust explosion causing injury to the operator!

AT THE PILOT-PLANT AND PLANT LEVEL. Once the value of a microbial control agent has definitely been established, pilot-plant and eventually plant production may be undertaken by laboratories specially equipped for this purpose. The necessary apparatus usually requires a considerable investment of funds and of specialized knowledge. A new type of specialist particularly concerned with the fermentation processes at the industrial level is on the scene: the biochemical engineer. Courses are being given on this subject and many books have been published (see e.g., Prescott and Dunn 1959; Steel 1958). Like the chemical engineer, the more modern biochemical engineer may be defined as a man who talks biochemistry to engineers and engineering to biochemists (Hastings 1958).

Undoubtedly both biochemistry and engineering are needed to put fungi and bacteria to work on large surfaces, on solid media and liquid media, and in deep cultures in fermentors having up to 80,000 gallons of working volume! There are a few successful examples of large-scale production of entomogenous fungi in surface cultures; Krassilstschik (1888) has already been mentioned. Rorer (1910, 1913a, b) has described cabinets (figure 110, between pp. 592 and 593) for the mass production of *Metarrhizium anisopliae* on rice cultures. The scaling-up procedure was as follows: (1) Petri dish culture; (2) potato slab cultures, rather dry; and (3) production cabinets. Maximum spore production was obtained two or three weeks after inoculation in tropical temperatures. A detailed description of Rorer's method can be found also in Gough (1911).

Even though a system as the one just described is relatively simple and requires only a limited amount of manual labour, it is not suitable for the production of industrial quantities of spores. The plant-production level is characterized by highly complex and highly mechanized systems; the operation of a great amount of equipment by a few people has been made possible by the development of submerged culture methods.

Since among the bacteria some aerobic spore-formers have a high potential as microbial insecticides, the methods for their production will be given special attention here. For the large-scale production of anaerobes, the reader is referred to the book edited by Steel (1958).

The large vessels used for the culture of micro-organisms in industrial plants are called fermentors; their working volume is from 5 litres to 80,000 gallons. In the fermentor, or connected with the fermentor, one finds baffles, spargers, agitators, sample lines, and control systems for temperature, pH, and foam. Small fermentors may be built of glass and metal parts, but large ones are stainless steel or mild steel. The main problem during culturing is the maintenance of aerobic conditions; accordingly, fermentors may be divided into four categories:

(a) forced aeration without mechanical agitation,
(b) forced aeration with propeller-type agitation,
(c) forced aeration in a rotary drum,
(d) closed-system circulation of the medium by air-lift pump.

Wikén (1956) and Wille (1954) were able to obtain an increased amount of spores from cultures of a *Bacillus* sp. pathogenic for *Melolontha melolontha* in a fermentor of type (b) developed in co-operation with the firm Kerag in Richterswil, Switzerland. A simple and inexpensive fermentor of type (d), to be used in pilot-plant production, has been devised by Lundgren and Russell (1956). The high cost of the fermentors is due to the fact that both the equipment for aeration and mechanical agitation are necessary for maximum growth. The use of an air-lift pump (as proposed by Lundgren and Russell) which circulates, agitates, and aerates the medium in a closed system eliminates most of the costly equipment which is justifiable for large-scale production but less so for exploratory pilot-plant cultures.

The main characteristics of a 20 to 50 litre fermentor (figures 112 and 113) have been described in detail by Dworschack, Lagoda, and Jackson (1954). Since (1) agitation, (2) aeration, and (3) geometric characteristics are essential factors in the transition from pilot-plant to production-scale culture, it is important that pilot-plant-scale fermentors establish conditions and anticipate yields for future production-scale work. This fermentor has facilities which permit adequate variation of temperature, agitation, aeration, sterilization, foam control, and pH. The control and recording of pH in small-scale fermentations has been discussed in a subsequent paper by Dworschack, Lagoda, and Jackson (1956).

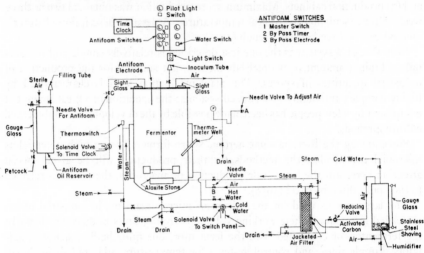

FIGURE 113. Operating diagram of a 20-litre vat fermentor. (*Courtesy of R. G. Dworschack, Industrial Products Investigations, Fermentation Laboratory, Agricultural Research Service, U.S. Department of Agriculture, Peoria, Illinois.*)

In one instance (Bioferm Corporation, personal communication, 1959) the development of production methods for *Bacillus thuringiensis* has been undertaken in 50-litre fermentors of a type similar to the one described by Dworschack, Lagoda, and Jackson (1954). Geometrical similarity, however, does not seem to be an essential factor in the case of *B. thuringiensis*. Twenty-litre and 200-litre fermentors have been used by Vaňková (1959) in pilot-plant studies for the production of *B. thuringiensis*.

Hastings (1958) gives a list of the common problems which arise in plant-scale fermentors:

(1) Handling and preparation of raw materials for fermentation.

(2) Selection, maintenance, and preparation of cultures of the desired organism.

(3) Provision of services, including steam, electric power, water supplies, compressed air, refrigeration.

(4) Design of fermentation vessels to suit the particular process.

(5) Control of the fermentation when in progress.

(6) Harvesting the fermentation and recovery of the product in saleable form.

(7) Disposal of effluents and recovery of by-products.

It is beyond the aim of this chapter to go into details. Only a few aspects among the most important will be treated here briefly.

STERILIZATION. Liquid media are usually sterilized by heat or by filtration prior to use. In large-scale fermentations the loss of nutrient values by overheating and some undesirable physical changes in the medium may be avoided by using chemical sterilants, particularly beta-propiolactone and ethylene oxide (Toplin and Gaden 1961).

AERATION. The amount of aeration is usually measured as OAR (oxygen absorption rate), which is the amount of mH oxygen absorbed per litre per minute. The OAR can be measured by various procedures, polarographically or by the sulphite oxidation method (Arnold and Steel 1958; Corman et al. 1957). Installation of baffles in a fermentor improves the utilization of the air supplied, especially at low aeration rates. Since antifoam agents markedly depress the OAR, they should be added judiciously. Inasmuch as certain media tend to foam more than others, it may be possible to manipulate the composition of the medium to diminish foaming (Corman et al. 1957). With Serratia marcescens, for example, the per cent yield of cells based on substrate utilized, the total cell concentration, and the live cell count have been shown to vary directly with OAR (Smith and Johnson 1954). Benedict et al. (1957) came to similar conclusions working with Fernbach flasks having 16 indentations, as well as with a 20-litre fermentor. A critical evaluation of some aeration problems is presented by Phillips and Johnson (1961).

FOAMING. The development of much more efficient agitation systems and aeration systems for fermentation processes has made foam control a serious problem. Foam accumulation causes a decrease in OAR denaturation of protein, and flocculation of bacteria. There are two conventional methods for foam control: (1) addition of antifoam agents, and (2) mechanical foam-breaking vanes attached to the stirrer shaft. If large amounts of foam are formed, mechanical foam breaking can assist foam breakdown by a chemical antifoam. Foam production occurs when the surface tension of the medium is lowered, and in the presence of a certain degree of heterogeneity of molecules at the gas–liquid interface. High viscosity and the presence of long-chain molecules aid foam formation (Boyles and Lincoln 1958). Pirt and Callow (1958), in studies made with Aerobacter aerogenes (Kruse) Beijerinck, found that intense foaming occurred when the OAR was 2·17 or more. Intense foaming was stopped at values of 1·67 or less. The authors developed a foam-prevention method, by single additions of antifoam (autoclavable silicone emulsions) at two-hour intervals. With their method, intense foaming never occurred at OAR values of 2·17 to 2·83. Foam prevention enables the culture vessel to be filled almost to capacity. Besides silicones, which sometimes cause deposits, animal or vegetable oils are used as defoaming agents; these must be sterilized and added aseptically to the culture vessels. For the production of Bacillus thuringiensis lard oil (Bioferm Corporation, personal communication 1959) and silicones (Vaňková 1959) have been used as antifoam agents.

HARVESTING. Most spore-forming bacteria cultivated in a medium favourable for the formation of heat-resistant forms will produce some spores before the maximum population of vegetative cells is reached; and, for a considerable length of time there will be simultaneous growth of vegetative cells and production of spores. Some of the spores may germinate and start a new growth cycle. Also, if the culture is started with a spore inoculum, not all of them will germinate initially. Biochemical processes occurring during vegetative growth are different from those taking place during sporulation; these conditions make it rather difficult to harvest clean spores from the mixture of cell forms present. Halvorson (1957b) was able to obtain rapid and nearly complete sporulation of a *Bacillus* sp. and of a *Clostridium* sp. by using a very heavy inoculum from an actively growing culture. The inoculum was of sufficient size to give an initial population equal to approximately 10 per cent of the maximum population attainable following growth. In the initial step from the spore suspension, a medium was used that would induce at least 90 per cent of spores to germinate in less than 15 minutes. Since sporulation is a multiphase process, harvesting must not be done before spore maturation. The process should be followed on smears taken from sampling lines. With *B. thuringiensis* and other crystalliferous spore-formers the parasporal crystal must be fully formed before harvesting. The oxygen demand of a *Bacillus* culture, as determined polaro-graphically by Halvorson, gave a bimodal curve when plotted against time. The first maximum occurred during vegetative growth of the cells, the second maximum, which was higher, appeared at the beginning of sporulation. According to Halvorson, if oxygen is depleted at this time, the cells often lyse and form no spores. In *B. thuringiensis* sporulation occurs rapidly and uniformly, at levels of 90 per cent or higher, in less than two days in large fermentors (figure 114). The scaling-up procedure (Bioferm Corporation, personal communication, 1959, and Gemmill 1960) is as follows: (*a*) culture tube; (*b*) Erlenmeyer flasks of 0·3, 1, and 6 litres; (*c*) 80-gallon and 500-gallon fermentors; (*d*) final stage in a sporulation medium in a 12,000-gallon fermentor. Once rapid and simultaneous sporulation is achieved, the spores (and, in the case of crystalliferous spore-formers, the parasporal body, too) must be separated from the medium (continuous separation by means of Sharples centrifuges, or filtration) then dried, and formulated. Cohen (1953) describes a rapid and simple method for harvesting mass culture of micro-organisms at the pilot-plant level. The culture medium with the micro-organisms is passed through a Selas-type FP filter suspended in the culture vessel. Aseptic filtration is achieved by suction. Foam flotation may be used to separate spores or vegetative cells from the medium and from the debris produced by cell autolysis. Just as foam flotation is used in the mining industry and in certain procedures of biological industry, Boyles and Lincoln (1958) developed foaming chambers for the collection of spores of *Bacillus anthracis* (Cohn) Koch. Also cells of *Serratia marcescens* and of other bacteria can be concentrated by this system. The selective nature of the flotation process should be emphasized, as it appears to furnish much cleaner spore lots, from the morphological standpoint, than does centrifugation. McConnell and Richards (1959), as well as Briggs (1960), reported the existence of a heat-stable, water-soluble, non-volatile toxic substance in final whole cultures of *Bacillus thuringiensis* and *B. cereus*. Preservation of this toxic fraction in the commercial microbial insecticide (along with bacterial spores and parasporal crystals) is desirable, and can be achieved by absorbing final whole cultures to suitable inert materials.

SYNXENIC AND XENIC CULTURE

Viruses

One of the restrictive criteria in the definition of a virus is that these sub-microscopic entities reproduce inside living cells. Therefore, the mass production of viruses is linked indisputably to the mass production of the host cells. In a few cases insect tissue cells have been cultured successfully *in vitro*; reviews of this work have been published by Day and Grace (1959) and Martignoni (1960). Up to now, however, repeated subculturing of rapidly proliferating insect cell colonies has eluded all workers. Insect cell strains for virus production are not available, so far, and a method for the routine preparation of primary monolayers of susceptible cells (comparable with the preparation of some vertebrate cell cultures) was developed only recently (Martignoni and Scallion 1961*b*). Propagation of nuclear polyhedrosis virus *in vitro* is possible (Trager 1935; Martignoni and Scallion 1961*a*) but the methods are not yet suitable for large-scale production.

On the other hand, tissue culture methods for vertebrates have evolved rapidly, in the past decade, and today mammalian cells can be propagated routinely in 5-litre and 20-litre fermentors (McLimans *et al.* 1957; Ziegler *et al.* 1958). As soon as an insect cell strain and a suitable culture medium become available, the long-awaited step to mass culture will not be difficult.

Certain problems in methodology have to be solved during the transition from test-tube cultures to fermentor cultures. For example, the frequent change of nutrient medium presents no difficulties in small volumes, but it is a major obstacle in submerged culture in fermentors. Circumventing the necessity of making such frequent changes is particularly important from the standpoint of economy or ease of manipulation, in the mass production of viruses. Since in some tissue culture systems certain amino acids are rapidly depleted, the replacement of these limiting substrates may be a means of maintaining high rates of cellular proliferation without renewing the media. This was recently demonstrated by Thomas *et al.* (1958); addition of *l*-arginine alone maintained active cellular proliferation for periods up to 9 days, and cells continued to proliferate up to 20 days through the addition of arginine and new media.

Nematodes

Mass production of *Neoaplectana glaseri*, a most important nematode in the microbial control of *Popillia japonica*, the Japanese beetle, has been achieved outside the host insect in fresh, non-autoclaved animal tissue or on living cultures of yeasts. There are at least five methods, which have been used at one time or another for the culture of this nematode, and similar methods have been adopted for the culture of *Neoaplectana chresima* (since 1942), and of the nematode DD-136 (since 1955).

(*a*) Agar-yeast (Glaser 1931, 1932; Glaser, McCoy, and Girth 1940; McCoy and Glaser 1936). Petri plates of dextrose-veal infusion agar are inoculated with a culture of Fleischmann's yeast, purified from bacteria by plating on dextrose agar. After 24 to 28 hours the yeast forms a luxuriant growth; the plate is then inoculated with the nematode and incubated at 21 to 24° C. After six to seven days, second-instar juveniles are formed. Living yeast undoubtedly furnishes the necessary accessory growth factors; when the nematodes become extremely abundant, in about two weeks, the yeast cells are completely grazed off, and the development ceases. On continuous *in vitro*-culture, however, there is a slow decline in fecundity. Cultures of *Neoaplectana glaseri* have never been obtained on living or dead bacteria, but the nematode DD-136 has been propagated on cultures of an associated bacterium (Dutky 1959).

(*b*) Agar-yeast-ovary (Glaser, McCoy, and Girth 1940; McCoy and Glaser 1936). Desiccated cow's ovaries, sprinkled over the moistened surface at the time of nematode inoculation (about 1 mg per cm^2 of culture surface), have made it possible to maintain the nematode *in vitro*, on yeast cultures, for many more transfers than with the simple agar-yeast method.

(*c*) Potato-yeast (Glaser, McCoy, and Girth 1940; McCoy and Glaser 1936). The potato medium consists of a mixture of ground raw Irish and sweet potatoes. This mixture is inoculated with bakers' yeast before placing the nematodes on the cultures (see (*a*) above). A preservative is added to avoid appreciable mould growth. The cultures are incubated over a period of 6 to 10 days at a temperature of about 21° C. Before inoculating with the nematodes and during incubation the pH of the medium must be adjusted within the limits of 7·0 to 7·6. For their mass-production system, McCoy and Glaser recommended covered trays of glavanized sheet iron, $33 \times 61 \times 3\cdot8$ centimetres, with an inner protective coating of Bakelite enamel. A steel rack (figure 115, following p. 624) was used to store 42 trays. The inoculum consisted of 200,000 to 400,000 nematodes, and the production per tray averaged about 4-million nematodes, but under optimum conditions occasional cultures yielded as high as four times this figure. The original agar-yeast-ovary technique is expensive, and does not yield the large quantities of material desirable for field distribution. The potato-yeast method is not well adapted for maintaining a stock. Consequently, the stock of nematodes is regularly maintained by the agar-yeast technique, and the potato medium is used for large-scale production.

(*d*) Veal pulp (Glaser, McCoy, and Girth 1940; McCoy and Girth 1938). Fresh veal, free of fat, is ground three times in a food chopper. It is weighed, mixed with twice its weight of distilled water, and kept in the ice box for 18 to 48 hours. The infusion is then poured on a clean flannel cloth, drained, and squeezed as dry as possible by hand or in a press. A preservative is added to the pulp, the mass thoroughly mixed, and placed in the culture vessels. The cultures are now ready for the nematode inoculum. The yield of the veal cultures prepared by McCoy and Girth ranged from 9,000 to 12,000 nematodes per cm^2 of culture area (the potato cultures described above produced about 2,000 nematodes per cm². The average yield per tray (see (c)) was about 20-million second-stage juveniles. No appreciable decline was evident on continued subculturing, at least up to 10 or 12 transfers. However, it is good practice to replace older cultures by agar-reared nematodes, as this maintains a higher average yield and more uniform development of the large-scale cultures.

(e) Sterile animal tissue (Glaser 1940; Glaser, McCoy, and Girth 1942). A piece of tissue, weighing 1 to 2 grammes, is placed in the condensation water at the bottom of an ordinary nutrient agar slant, and the surface of the tissue is inoculated with nematodes sterilized in dilute sodium hypochlorite. Evaporation should be prevented by trimming the cotton plug, pushing it down, and covering the surface with sealing wax. A small perforation is later made through the hardened wax. An 18- to 20-day old mouse embryo, beef kidney, rabbit ovary or kidney may be used. Both species of *Neoaplectana* were grown on sterile animal tissue.

About 3,600 million juveniles of *Neoaplectana glaseri*, all produced on veal pulp, were distributed by the New Jersey Department of Agriculture in the autumn of 1936 and spring of 1937 (McCoy and Girth 1938). The six-year-long colonization programme was completed in 1939 (Dutky 1959). Responsible for its discontinuation was *Bacillus popilliae*, which proved to be superior to the nematode in controlling *Popillia japonica*. Dutky rightly remarks: 'It is most unfortunate that these promising studies were directed against a host that could be attacked by an even more remarkable pathogen.'

VIABILITY, VIRULENCE, AND PRESERVATION OF MICRO-ORGANISMS

In order to be an active microbial insecticide, a micro-organism must be viable and virulent. Already in 1879 Metchnikoff wrote: 'For a practical solution to the problem of disseminating the muscardine fungus it is extremely important to know how long the green spores preserve their ability to germinate.' The best estimate of the pathogenicity of a micro-organism for a given host is, of course, an LD_{50} determination. This test is time-consuming, and therefore not always practical. In the case of bacterial and fungus spore preparations, germination tests give a good estimate of the viability (Müller-Kögler 1960), but do not necessarily indicate the degree of virulence. The number of spores in two preparations of *Bacillus thuringiensis*, for example, may be identical, but the insecticidal activity of the two may vary greatly, due to differences in size or composition of parasporal crystalline inclusions or in concentration of crystals and other toxic substances in the preparation (Stern, Hall, and Peterson 1959). Recently, a '*Pieris brassicae* unit' has been proposed as a measure of the activity of *Bacillus thuringiensis* preparations (Krieg 1961). Bioassay is a must in industrial production control; not only can there be a change in virulence of the microbe being produced in large quantities, but also contamination by a similar strain may inadvertently occur. Heimpel (in Heimpel and Angus 1960) reports that in experimental culturings of mixed inocula of

Bacillus thuringiensis varieties and *Bacillus cereus*, in time the latter species outgrew the pathogenic crystal-formers.

Cloaca cloacae has not been in great demand as a microbial insecticide because of its rapid loss of virulence. The bacterium remains viable up to two years in culture, but its virulence is lost after a few days (d'Hérelle 1914). It was necessary to enhance the virulence of the bacterium before mass production, by repeated passage through grasshoppers; the method has been described in detail by d'Hérelle (1914). Later, d'Hérelle (1915) found that dry cadavers of infected grasshoppers were a source of highly virulent bacteria, even after long periods of preservation. This finding, of course, greatly simplified mass-production techniques, by eliminating the time-consuming passages through the insect host. Through repeated passage in insects, Toumanoff (1956) and Le Corroller (1958) were able to transform common strains of *Bacillus cereus* into crystalliferous strains pathogenic for insects.

Loss of virulence in bacteria pathogenic for insects has often been connected with the pH of the culture medium. *Bacillus thuringiensis* loses part of its virulence after passages in acid media (Métalnikov and Métalnikov 1935), as well as in basic media (pH 9) (Toumanoff and Vago 1952*b*). Neutral reaction of the medium is considered most satisfactory for the preservation of virulent strains of this pathogen. Most investigators agree that on nutrient agar, under normal conditions of temperature and nearly neutral pH, the production of crystals by pure cultures of crystalliferous bacteria is a surprisingly constant character (Heimpel and Angus 1960). However, under certain conditions, crystalliferous bacteria have been converted to acrystalliferous forms. Sometimes other factors may be involved, as in the case of the nematode *Neoaplectana glaseri* cultured in veal pulp. In tests with beetle grubs, distinctly and consistently better parasitism resulted with nematodes reared using the sodium derivative of methyl-*p*-hydroxybenzoate (0·05 per cent) plus formaldehyde (0·06 per cent) as preservative, than using hydroxybenzoate alone. This difference was not due to a higher soil survival, which was the same in both cases (McCoy and Girth 1938).

The adaptation to certain culture media is a desirable characteristic, if it is not followed by loss of virulence. For example, Sawyer (1929) reports that at first conidia of an *Empusa* sp. did not germinate on swordfish; but after months in culture, the conidia would germinate easily on this medium, showing an adaptation to saprophytic existence.

Steinkraus and Provvidenti (1958) found that *Bacillus popilliae* forms three types of spores, in axenic culture: (1) typical spores with a refractile parasporal body; (2) typical spores without parasporal body; and (3) abortive spores, which did not become refractile nor heat resistant. Spores of the second type had lost almost completely their virulence. The best strain so far examined by the two workers failed to produce new parasitic-type spores for more than four complete life cycles on artificial media. Generally, the ability to form typical spores was lost after the second transfer. The vegetative cells of these strains, however, formed spores when injected into the living larval host, even after 100 transfers on artificial media.

The preservation of cells of non-spore-forming bacteria presents many problems.

There is very little in the literature on the quantitative recovery of vegetative cells after long storage. Riley and Solowey (1958) reported results on quantitative recoveries of *Serratia marcescens* stored at 5° C as concentrates and as suspensions. The greatest recovery after 91 days of storage was obtained when the cells were suspended in gel phosphate diluent; the number of viable cells represented only 26·6 per cent of the viable cells in the original fresh concentrate. However, Steinhaus and Birkeland (1939) found that ageing broth cultures of *S. marcescens* contained remarkably high numbers of cultivable bacteria even after two years of incubation. Yurchenco, Piepoli, and Yurchenco (1954) were able to maintain unchanging virulence for cell pools of seven species of bacteria as long as two years. The cell pools are routinely prepared in 5 per cent hog gastric mucin and quickly frozen at −76° C. The sealed-glass ampoules are stored in a dry ice cabinet. Both freezing and thawing (at 37° C in a water bath) must be rapid. Gastric mucin has been used by Baird (1958a) to preserve the viability of *Pseudomonas aeruginosa* when used in field experiments against grasshoppers.

One of the main contributions of the Métalnikovs was the demonstration of the many advantages of spore-forming bacteria versus non-spore-forming bacteria, for the microbial control of insects (Métalnikov and Métalnikov 1935; Masera 1934). The problems encountered by d'Hérelle had created much scepticism towards the 'new' control method. Thanks to the spore-formers, the practicability of a magnificent idea was later demonstrated.

While in general the prolonged axenic culture of a micro-organism tends to decrease its virulence, in some instances an increase in virulence has been reported, as for *Beauveria bassiana* (= *B. globulifera*) (Masera 1935).

Further data concerning maintenance and loss of virulence of insect pathogens can be found in the valuable review of Tanada (1959a).

Micro-organisms pathogenic for insects are usually maintained in the collections of the laboratories where they have been isolated or where they are being studied (e.g., see Vago 1959b). In some instances they are sent to Type Culture Collection (Washington, D.C.; Lausanne, Switzerland). Recently, an effort towards the establishment of a comprehensive collection of entomogenous bacteria has been accomplished by Lysenko (1958b). Lysenko maintains the cultures chiefly as freeze-dried desiccates, in sealed, evacuated ampoules. All cultures listed in the catalogues are available for distribution. The Northern Utilization Research Branch of the United States Department of Agriculture has a collection devoted to micro-organisms of industrial importance. Haynes, Wickerham, and Hesseltine (1955) list the various methods and media used at the NURB collection for the propagation and maintenance of the major groups of micro-organisms. Vegetative cells of *Bacillus popilliae* Dutky and *Bacillus lentimorbus* Dutky have been preserved by lyophilization at the NURB collection (Haynes *et al.* 1961). Other bacteria and fungi with a potential as microbial insecticides could well be included in similar collections of industrially important micro-organisms.

CHAPTER 21

Use of Micro-organisms in Biological Control

IRVIN M. HALL

INTRODUCTION

THE MANIPULATION of entomogenous micro-organisms to bring about reductions in the populations of pest insects has long been the goal of entomologists interested in the study of insects and their diseases. It has been recognized for many years that the microbial control of insects is occurring continuously in nature. As part of the natural biological control complex, epizootics of disease often break out at intervals and aid in the suppression of insect populations. The rapid advance of the field of insect pathology in recent years has been followed by an increasing appreciation of the role played by insect pathogens in natural control, and there has developed a broadened interest by entomologists in the possibilities of the extensive utilization of micro-organisms to control insect pests.

There have been many attempts to use entomogenous micro-organisms for the control of economic infestations of insects. Some of these trials have resulted in successful microbial control, others have succeeded in bringing about only partial reductions of the pest populations, and some have been complete failures. These varied results have brought forth critical consideration of the potentialities of microbial control; in the past decade reports by Steinhaus (1949a, 1954), Bucher (1958), Baird (1958b), Bergold (1958), Tanada (1959a), and Hall (1961) have contributed to a better understanding of the fundamental factors concerning the use of micro-organisms in biological control.

Insect control through the use of pathogenic micro-organisms has long been considered a part of the complex pattern in insect ecology and many of the principles and laws governing the utilization of insect parasites and predators to control insects apply as well to control by the use of micro-organisms. However, microbial control has advanced rapidly by adopting many of the principles and methods of both biological control and chemical control. Tanada (1959a) states that the use of pathogens to control insect pests bears a close interrelationship with these two fields and the most successful applications of entomogenous micro-organisms in the future probably will be made in conjunction with these other agents of control. This should not be construed to imply that microbial control should be directed towards manipulation solely in the manner of chemical insecticides. As a matter of fact, many insect pathogens appear to be adaptable to development along with other biotic agents in programmes aimed towards the attainment of complete biological control of a pest species.

GENERAL CONSIDERATIONS

The successful utilization of diseases for insect control is dependent upon the biology and characteristics of both the host insects and the parasitic micro-organisms as well as the environment. Host insects must occupy habitats suitable for introduction of a pathogen and they must have habits that enhance the possibilities of infection. Since disease is a density-dependent factor of mortality, as stated by Bucher (1958), insects that live in aggregations or form large populations are more susceptible to epizootics than are those at low population densities. However, some pathogens have displayed the ability to control insect pests under conditions of very low host density (Hall 1953).

Mode of Infection

In general, parasitic micro-organisms may be divided into two groups according to the natural method of entry into their susceptible hosts. The first group, which has a contact type of action by normally infecting the host through the integument, includes the entomogenous fungi as well as certain of the entomophilic nematodes. The second group, which includes the bacteria, viruses, protozoa, rickettsiae, and many nematodes, contains organisms that must be ingested in order to cause infection.

Specificity of Organisms

There is a wide variation in the activity of entomogenous micro-organisms against different insects. Some organisms are specific in their activity while others show varying degrees of pathogenicity for many species of insects. The former group includes the viruses, many of which are considered to have specific hosts, while the latter category contains large numbers of pathogens including some of the fungi, the entomophilic nematodes, and the crystalliferous bacteria.

Advantages and Disadvantages of Microbial Control Methods

The various characteristics of the different groups of disease-producing micro-organisms tend to regulate the utilization of many insect pathogens and have indicated certain advantages and disadvantages of microbial control methods which have been documented by Steinhaus (1956c). The principal *advantages* of microbial control methods are:

1. The harmless and non-toxic nature of insect pathogens for other forms of life with the resultant absence of toxic residues.
2. The relatively high degree of specificity of most pathogens, which tends to protect beneficial insects.

3. The compatibility of many pathogens with many insecticides to the degree that the two may be used concurrently and, in some cases at least, synergistically, since infection may cause the insects to be more susceptible to chemical poisoning.

4. The ease and inexpensiveness with which some pathogens can be produced.

5. The high versatility of microbial pathogens in so far as methods of applying them are concerned. Some micro-organisms may be introduced and colonized with the result that the control brought about may be permanent. Other pathogens may be used as sprays or dusts in the same fashion as insecticides.

6. The apparent slowness by which a susceptible host develops resistance to a microbial pathogen.

7. The low dosages required in some instances to attain control.

The following *disadvantages* to microbial control methods have been recognized:

1. The necessity for careful and correct timing of the application of the pathogen with respect to the incubation period of the disease.

2. The relatively marked specificity of most pathogens sometimes narrows the spectrum of effectiveness to only one insect species in cases where several pests are involved, all of which might be destroyed by a single chemical insecticide.

3. The necessity of maintaining the pathogen in a viable condition and at a high virulence and in a durable or resistant state until the insect is contacted.

4. The difficulty of producing some pathogens either in large quantities or inexpensively, or both.

5. The tendency of some diseases to cause insects, or parts of the insects, to remain attached to the foliage of the host plant. This may be particularly objectionable with food crops on which insect parts cannot be tolerated.

6. The requirement of some pathogens of favourable climatic conditions in order to invade and infect their arthropod host.

Many of the points covered in the advantages and disadvantages will be discussed further in other sections of this chapter.

METHODS OF UTILIZATION

It has been pointed out by Baird (1958*b*) that entomogenous fungi may be utilized to control insects with three ends in view: (1) introduction where the fungus does not occur naturally; (2) application to initiate the disease before it would normally occur; and (3) distribution where the saturation point for a fungus and host has not been attained under natural conditions. These points also are applicable to the other groups of entomogenous micro-organisms and should be used as guides when programmes of biological control with the use of pathogens are being considered.

Introduction and Colonization vs. Direct Manipulation

Various means have been attempted for the utilization of micro-organisms in the biological control of insect pests. One method involves the introduction and colonization either singly or in combination with insect parasites, predators, or other entomogenous micro-organisms for the purpose of establishing pathogens, including exotic species, into an insect population. There is a similarity between this procedure and the foreign exploration and importation of entomophagous organisms discussed in chapters 9 to 14 inclusive and many of the same principles and precautions apply. Once colonized, successful establishment and the attainment of a satisfactory level of control will be up to the micro-organism. In this regard, Steinhaus (1954) has emphasized that if the economic level of the host density is higher than the threshold level of the disease, introduction and colonization of an insect pathogen can result in control that can be just as permanent as that accomplished by other agents of biological control. A second method involves the direct, and perhaps repeated, application of a pathogen, either singly or in combination with other micro-organisms or compatible chemical insecticides, for the temporary control of an economic pest population. The application of a pathogen acts to lower the threshold level of the disease (Steinhaus 1954), and if the economic level of the host density is lower than the disease threshold level, control will be of a temporary nature as with chemical insecticides. This method of periodic colonization of micro-organisms bears a relationship to the various means of manipulating parasites and predators discussed in chapter 15. It would be of value in situations where the degree of biological control was generally unsatisfactory or was subject to periodic upsets.

Although there have been many attempts to introduce and colonize exotic pathogens, with notable success in recent years in the case of the polyhedrosis virus of the European sawfly, *Neodiprion sertifer* (Geoffr.), in Canada (Bird 1953a), foreign exploration and importation of pathogens for the control of imported pest insects, in the manner developed for the detection and introduction of parasites and predators, has yet to receive thorough exploitation. There is the belief in some quarters that efforts along this line would be a waste of time and money since entomogenous micro-organisms could be obtained quite easily through contacts with insect pathologists and entomologists from other areas and from specimens received for diagnosis. However, considering the fact that many important pests are exotic species from parts of the world where knowledge and records of insect diseases are far from complete, it would appear that the potentialities of foreign exploration and importation of insect pathogens would be great, and expanded efforts should be made in this direction. It is possible that the results of efforts along this line could be as fruitful as those realized during past years in the exploration for parasites, predators, and weed-feeding insects.

The transfer of infective material from one area to another either in shipments from foreign explorers or exchanges from insect pathologists or entomologists should be made using packing and transportation procedures to ensure the arrival of the micro-organisms in a viable and usable condition. The handling of isolated micro-organisms under cultivation on artificial media offers few problems although the fastest means of transportation should be used and every effort should be made to comply with quarantine regulations to assure rapid delivery.

There are few restrictions pertaining to the transportation of dead insects, and diseased specimens may be sent through the mails or by express. To be safe, however, pathogens received at any location should be cleared if necessary with the proper governmental authorities and screened as required through adequate quarantine facilities (see chapter 10). In most cases, the fastest possible transportation (usually air mail) should be used. As outlined by Steinhaus (1958d), the insects should not be enclosed loosely in an ordinary letter envelope but should be placed in a cardboard or glass container and shipped in a small package or in a mailing tube. Small samples of small insects may be sent in an envelope if they are first enclosed in a smaller envelope and if there is no danger of their being crushed. Most diseased insects when shipped in pill boxes or in vials arrive at their destination in a satisfactory condition. In many instances the best procedure is to place the specimens individually in clean glass or plastic vials, unless the shipment includes a large quantity of material. The vials should be lightly stoppered in most instances to prevent or reduce the amount of desiccation, contamination, or loss of material. With fungus diseases, the use of cotton stoppers, or other porous plugs, will reduce the overgrowth of saprophytic organisms during transit. The disease material should not be placed in preservatives or chemical solutions of any kind, since such treatment prohibits success in attempting to culture or otherwise use the pathogens concerned.

It is of importance that specific information relative to the insect and the pathogen should accompany each shipment to permit proper handling when the material is received. In this regard, it is recommended that the following information be included: (1) common and scientific name (including authority citation) of the insect and the pathogen; (2) collector's accession or identification number, if any; (3) name of collector; (4) date and locality of collection; (5) name of host plant or animal, or nature of environment; (6) extent of the disease outbreak and condition under which it occurred; (7) abundance or prevalence of the insect; (8) abnormal behaviour and appearance of the affected insects; (9) insecticidal treatment, if any, or possibility of exposure to insecticidal treatment; and (10) general observations of an ecological or epizootiological nature.

Use of Resistive Stages

To assure the survival of infective material during the period between colonization or application and ingestion or contact with a susceptible host, the microorganisms usually are applied in their resistive stage: the viruses as polyhedra or capsules; the bacteria, fungi, and protozoa as spores (or inclusions of combinations of spores and inclusions of the crystalliferous bacteria); and the nematodes in the ensheathed dauer stage. Organisms which do not form resistant bodies have been used in some instances in combination with suitable protectants, such as casein, sucrose, and mucin (Stephens 1957c) that will preserve the viability of the infective stages for a reasonable length of time.

Application Techniques

In recent years, entomogenous micro-organisms have been successfully applied to all types of crops with the conventional ground and air equipment in widespread use for the control of insects (see figure 116, following p. 624). Because of the ease of preparation of suspensions from laboratory-produced and field-collected infective materials, most workers in the past emphasized the use of sprays. Various techniques have been used and the resistant stages of some pathogens have been applied in a number of instances at extremely high pressures of up to 1,000 pounds per square inch. Much less testing has been done with other types of microbial preparations although various crude dusts containing insect pathogens have been used experimentally at times in past years to control certain insect pests, and recently there has been some wide-scale testing of commercially produced dust and granular microbial materials. The fact that many insect pathogens may be processed into a variety of different formulations broadens the possibilities for successful experimentation with application techniques for the attainment of satisfactory microbial control of pest insects.

Dosage Determinations

With the development of reliable dosage levels of pathogenic materials for use especially in manipulation programmes involving direct and repeated applications, some method of standardization of infective stages is necessary to permit repetition of results. With the use of a commercially produced material this is not a difficult problem since the manufacturer will make an effort to standardize his own product and will give suggestions for successful use against susceptible insects in the field. In attempts to standardize preparations of laboratory-produced or field-collected micro-organisms for use in field trials, levels of dosage often have been established by utilizing the infective contents of a definite number of diseased insects per unit of test area. This method does give a rough idea of the amount of infective material being applied and is especially suitable in the initial testing of extremely pathogenic micro-organisms. However, a better method that has been widely employed in evaluations of concentration involves the use of a hemacytometer to determine the approximate number of resistant forms (spores of spore-forming organisms, and polyhedra of viruses) of the insect pathogen that are present in a unit of weight or volume. A similar technique for evaluating the concentration of suspensions of the capsules in granulosis virus infective material has been reported by Martignoni and Auer (1957), who made accurate determinations with a special counting chamber and a phase microscope.

Viable spore counts of spore-producing micro-organisms that grow readily on artificial media have been made by culturing known dilutions of spores on agar plates. However, recent work with *Bacillus thuringiensis* Berl. var. *thuringiensis* has indicated that the viable spore count of an organism that also produces a toxic product is not an accurate index to the pathogenicity of the species, since the insecticidal effect of the organism may be at least partly invested in the crystalline inclusions. Most workers dealing with crystal-bearing bacteria, therefore, are beginning to use a system of bioassay on susceptible laboratory insects in order to standardize the materials at uniform ratings of effectiveness prior to utilization against insects in the field.

Coverage

Since the effectiveness of many insect pathogens is limited to a great extent by their lack of mechanisms for dispersal, an important factor in the field manipulation of micro-organisms is the problem of proper coverage of the plant with infective material in order to obtain satisfactory kill of the susceptible pest insects. According to Hall and Andres (1959), many pathogens have a mode of action essentially like a stomach poison whereby the susceptible host must ingest enough of the infective stages to quickly sicken, cease to feed, and subsequently die. In order to attain a significant reduction of a susceptible pest population within a length of time short enough to prevent possible damage to the crop, it is evident that complete or good coverage of the feeding areas on the plant with the infective material is essential.

Timing of Application

In general, the timing of applications of sprays and dusts of most entomogenous micro-organisms when used for immediate control is more critical than with the relatively quick-acting chemical insecticides because of the time delay during the period of incubation of the disease from infection to the cessation of feeding of the insect host (Hall 1961). Since this may have a marked influence on the degree of control, it is an important factor to weigh when considering the use of micro-organisms to control insects on crops where even limited damage cannot be tolerated. A number of insect pathogens have very short incubation periods and their effect against specific insects can be compared favourably with many of the rapid-killing chemicals. On the other hand, the long incubation period inherent with some organisms may preclude their use as immediate control agents against susceptible hosts on certain high-value crops or force earlier treatment to allow for the delay in action in order to prevent excessive damage to the plants.

In most instances, timing is not too critical with the utilization of the crystal-liferous bacterium, *B. thuringiensis* var. *thuringiensis*, which against some insects compares favourably with many of the recommended chemical insecticides by causing death to susceptible hosts as quickly as one day after application. It has been reported by Stern, Hall, and Peterson (1959) that fourth- and fifth-instar larvae of the alfalfa caterpillar, *Colias eurytheme* Bdvl., ceased to feed and dropped from the foliage within 24 hours after application of low dosages of a commercially produced bacillus material. Their conclusion was that the speed of action of *B. thuringiensis* var. *thuringiensis* compared favourably with that of the best chemical insecticide currently recommended for use against the alfalfa caterpillar.

It is widely recognized that timing can be especially critical in the application of virus materials. With reference to the use of the polyhedrosis virus to control the alfalfa caterpillar, Thompson and Steinhaus (1950) have stated that the timing of application may be so critical that the average grower or commercial pest-control operator may experience difficulty in determining when to use the material. According to their findings, often when the virus should be applied to allow for the incubation period delay, the caterpillars have not yet begun to cause damage that can be noticed, and the grower may not even be aware of their presence. Once damage begins to show in the field, it is usually too late to use the polyhedrosis virus as a practical means of control since the larvae will continue to feed for at least four days after application of the material. In fields with extremely high populations, it may be necessary to apply the virus before the caterpillars hatch from the egg in order to attain control.

EFFECT OF PHYSICAL FACTORS

The principal physical factors that affect the activity of entomogenous micro-organisms against their hosts in the field are temperature and humidity. Tanada (1959a) states that these factors have a direct bearing on the pathogen (its survival and ability to infect), the host (its susceptibility or resistance, including activation of latent infections), and the progress of infection within the host. The roles played by these factors vary according to the responses of the different types of organisms. It is generally recognized that insect pathogens such as the fungi which infect their hosts through the integument are quite responsive to moisture con- ditions. Lack of adequate humidity can inhibit formation or germination of infective stages and thereby prevent infection even though the host may be highly susceptible. Because of this, Dresner (1949) has stated that entomogenous fungi can be depended upon to control insect infestations in zones of frequent rainfall or high humidity, but areas without this weather pattern should not expect insect control with the use of fungi. This is a widespread assumption that holds true in many instances, but, as mentioned by Hall (1961), the surprising ability of entomophthoraceous fungi to kill the spotted alfalfa aphid in irrigated fields in certain of the desert areas of the United States and Mexico in recent years suggests the importance of the microclimate surrounding the micro-organism and its host (see figure 117, following p. 624).

In contrast, a large number of insect pathogens, including the bacteria, the viruses, and the protozoa, that infect their hosts following ingestion, function irrespective of humidity conditions in the surrounding environment. These organisms have the capacity of remaining in their resistant stages until ingested, whereupon the tissues and body fluids of the susceptible hosts offer a suitable location for growth and development. In this situation, the environmental conditions favourable for the host are also favourable for the pathogen.

The successful utilization of micro-organisms in the control of insect pests is dependent in many instances on favourable temperature conditions. Although variations in temperature do not appear to have a great influence on the actions of pathogenic bacteria, temperature is known to have a marked effect upon the period of incubation of virus infections. According to Thompson and Steinhaus (1950), within the temperature range favourable for activity of the alfalfa caterpillar, susceptibility to infection by the polyhedrosis virus is independent of the temperature, but the length of time required for mortality decreases as the temperature rises. They recognized this as an important point to understand since relatively low temperatures during the period following treatment with a virus could result in poor control of the insect pest.

COMPATIBILITY WITH OTHER MATERIALS

Very little information is available on the effect of additives used in conjunction with applied preparations containing entomogenous micro-organisms. In the past, a number of the old standard wetting and sticking materials, such as flour, skim milk powder, and blood albumin spreader were used successfully in combination with microbial agents. In recent years, some of the new surface-active additives have been used in the application of sprays of insect pathogens, and 'built-in' dry wetting agents have been incorporated into some commercially produced wettable powder formulations containing B. thuringiensis var. thuringiensis to aid in the suspendibility of the materials. Although much is yet to be learned about the use of additives in the application of microbial materials, it is apparent that many of these agents should have no damaging effect on the organisms and that the effectiveness of the various microbial materials may be enhanced by the proper use of an additive to assure better application and retention on the foliage.

Although little is known of the effect of chemical pesticides on entomogenous micro-organisms, there is some evidence that some of these materials do not suppress the activities of certain pathogens. McEwen and Hervey (1958), in tests with a polyhedrosis virus against the cabbage looper, found that the addition of TEPP did not affect the activity of the virus in any way. The resistant-stage larvae of the nematode isolated from larvae of the codling moth, *Carpocapsa pomenella* (L.), are quite resistant to chemical insecticides (Anon. 1956). Hall and Dunn (1959) reported that several species of entomophthoraceous fungi displayed varied reactions to several pesticides in laboratory tests. However, they did not consider that the fungi would suffer seriously from insecticidal treatments of fields where they occurred, since the organisms would be in the inactive resting spore stage when chemicals were in general use.

RESISTANCE

The rapid development of resistance by insect pests to the various types of chemical insecticides has caused concern that similar problems of resistance to insect pathogens may appear as soon as microbial control is used on a broad scale. It is difficult at this time to anticipate the possibilities of the development of resistance to insect pathogens, since field observations and testing have been so limited in scope and so little is known about the natural or acquired resistance of insects to disease (Hall 1961). There is no positive evidence to date that insects have developed resistance to infection from applied pathogens or their by-products. However, it is realized that resistance is difficult to evaluate and could be even more difficult to recognize in its initial development if it did appear in any place where only small-scale microbial testing was undertaken. Broad field evaluation of resistance to entomogenous micro-organisms will have to await wide-scale testing and commercial utilization of insect pathogens.

PERSISTENCE IN THE FIELD: RESIDUAL EFFECT

The ability of an organism to carry over in the field at a level that can assure widespread infection of subsequent host generations can mean the difference between success or failure in attempts to utilize pathogens for the control of insects. This ability to survive often is referred to as persistence in the field in regard to micro-organisms colonized for long-range control and may be considered as residual activity in relation to pathogens applied for quick reduction of insect populations. Residual activity is not important when a highly pathogenic material is applied for control of a very susceptible insect that develops only one generation during the crop-growing period since the pest population once reduced does not build up again during the same cycle of plant growth (Hall 1961). Also, survival is not considered to be a factor controlling the efficiency of micro-organisms such as the crystal-bearing bacteria. These pathogens rely, in part at least, on the proteinaceous by-products for insecticidal activity and the organisms are not expected to perpetuate themselves in the field. As with chemical insecticides, the residual activity of the toxic by-products on the foliage is of major importance.

The ability of a pathogen to survive can be an important factor affecting its use on plants where continuous overlapping generations or a susceptible host may occur, since the necessity for additional treatments will depend upon the lasting effect of the organism. The viruses may have a lengthy residual activity since the remains of the virus-killed larvae usually stay on the foliage unless dislodged by physical agents (figure 118) and the amount of virus material may actually increase as the susceptible larvae become infected and die, subject to the effects of weathering action and the rate of plant growth. In contrast, the lasting effect of pathogens such as bacteria and protozoa may be expected to be of short duration since the insects killed by these organisms usually fall from the foliage and there can be no increase in the quantity of infective stages on the surfaces of the plant. Hall (1961) states that the period of effectiveness of an organism is dependent not only upon the host–parasite relationship but also upon the plant growth characteristics and the effect of the physical factors in the environment.

The practical utilization of any pathogen against a susceptible host will be dependent not only upon the other factors discussed heretofore, but also upon the amount of crop protection that is required and the level of control that the organism is capable of achieving. In the colonization of micro-organisms, a pathogen will become established if conditions are favourable and will function as a biological control agent to the extent permitted by the host–parasite relationship and the regulative activities of the physical factors in the environment. Some introduced organisms may be highly effective and give permanent microbial control of a pest while others may affect only a portion of the host population and thus operate only as part of a biological control complex.

In application of an insect pathogen for short-term control, the ease with which a micro-organism may be worked into a control programme will vary with the particular pest programme, the effectiveness of acceptable non-microbial insecticidal materials, the interest of the grower and the entomologist, and the availability of adequate supplies of microbial materials. If it is necessary to treat for only one insect pest, it is quite possible that applications of a single pathogen may bring about and maintain effective control (Hall 1961). On the other hand, if several pest populations are present on the same crop, it is quite possible that even a nonspecific pathogen may be unable to suppress all of the pest species. In that case, it will be necessary to try combinations of different microbial materials, mixtures of micro-organisms with compatible selective chemical insecticides, or supplemental applications of chemical materials by themselves in order to protect the crop.

SELECTION OF PATHOGEN FOR FIELD USE

The selection of an entomogenous micro-organism for use in manipulated microbial control of an insect pest will be dependent to a great extent upon the knowledge of the diseases of the particular insect, the characteristics of the pathogen, and the needs of the control programme. Some insects have no known infectious diseases, and unless a virulent micro-organism is discovered in laboratory infectivity tests with one of the non-specific pathogen, microbial control efforts will not be possible. Still other insects may be effectively killed in the laboratory by micro-organisms that cannot be adapted to the environment in the field or are unable to produce the amount of control needed to protect the crop. On the other hand, a large number of pest insects are subject to attack by a variety of different pathogens, thereby permitting the selection of an organism with characteristics that will enhance the chances of success.

If an attempt is to be made to achieve biological control through the importation and colonization of new and exotic pathogens, it would appear to be best (as has been suggested for entomophagous forms) to import and colonize as many promising, but untried, species as possible. Undoubtedly, some pathogens would not become established. However, the various species of micro-organisms with the capability of adjusting to the new environment within a reasonable time would become a permanent part of the over-all biological complex working against the pest insect.

EXAMPLES OF SUCCESSFUL USE OF ENTOMOGENOUS MICRO-ORGANISMS

Bacteria

Our knowledge of bacterial diseases, according to Steinhaus (1956a, 1958c) (see also chapter 18), dates back to the nineteenth century when Pasteur worked on diseases of the silkworm. However, it was not until d'Hérelle between 1911 and 1915 advocated the use of *Coccobacillus acridiorum* (d'Hérelle) (*Cloaca cloacae* var. *acridiorum* (d'Hérelle)) for the control of locusts that a general interest developed in the utilization of bacteria to destroy harmful insects. In subsequent years, there were numerous reports on the experimental use of bacteria to control some of the major insect pests. However, none of these attempts was ever developed to the point of becoming a part of established control programmes.

The discovery of *Bacillus popilliae* Dutky and *B. lentimorbus* Dutky, the causative agents of types A and B milky diseases in the Japanese beetle, *Popillia japonica* Newm., and the development of techniques for their use beginning in about 1940, gave added encouragement for the utilization of bacteria to control insects. This programme, in which spore dusts of these bacteria were distributed throughout the north-eastern part of the United States through the co-operation of federal and state agencies, has become one of the classic examples of effective microbial control by the colonization of a micro-organism. The mechanical dissemination of commercially produced spore powders of the milky disease bacteria has been utilized mainly on turf where quick control of the pest grubs is not deemed necessary and has resulted in permanent control of the Japanese beetle in many treated areas within three years after introduction. This successful microbial control effort in conjunction with the establishment of insect parasites and the judicious use of chemical insecticides, has resulted in wide-scale suppression of the pest insect.

During the past few years there has been a revival of interest in the use of bacteria as microbial control agents. At present most of the attention is focused on studies leading towards the commercial production and utilization of the spore-forming, crystal-bearing bacterium *Bacillus thuringiensis* Berl. var. *thuringiensis* in manipulation programmes. This organism was first isolated from diseased larvae of the Mediterranean flour moth, *Anagasta kühniella* (Zell.), in Europe in 1911. Since that time, it has been subjected to repeated tests to determine its potential as a microbial pathogen, and a large number of insect species, mostly Lepidoptera, have been found to be susceptible to it (Steinhaus 1957b; Heimpel and Angus 1958a; Hall and Dunn 1958a). However, it does not appear to persist in the field, hence it must be applied periodically like a chemical insecticide. Industry began to show an interest in the use of insect pathogens in 1956, after the publication of articles on microbial control and living insecticides by Steinhaus (1956b, c); and in the past few years a number of firms in the United States have undertaken research and development studies with the aforementioned bacterium. Mass production techniques have been developed and insecticidal products containing the bacillus have been distributed for wide-scale testing against susceptible insect pests throughout the world (see figure 119, facing p. 625).

Various aspects on the use of *B. thuringiensis* var. *thuringiensis* have been presented by Hall (1961). The bacterium was selected by industry as the first pathogen to be widely exploited as a manipulated microbial control agent because of characteristics that could make it suitable for adaptation into a large number of insect-control programmes. In addition to being specific for certain insect pests and having no effect on beneficial insects, the bacillus is easy to produce by modern fermentation processes and offers no storage problems since the final product appears to be indefinitely stable at moderate temperatures. The organism is one of a group of entomogenous bacteria that grows readily on artificial media and forms crystal-like proteinaceous inclusions during sporulation. The pathogenicity of the micro-organism against most susceptible insects is invested in the inclusions rather than in the germinating spores (Heimpel and Angus 1959). Therefore, the use of *B. thuringiensis* var. *thuringiensis* can be considered to be the application of a non-living stomach-poison insecticidal material which is the product of a living organism. Nevertheless, this type of utilization is considered by most insect pathologists as another form of biological control, but it is closely approaching chemical control, particularly in its action, lack of density-dependence, and failure to persist in the field.

The products containing *B. thuringiensis* var. *thuringiensis* that have been made available for testing against insects in the field have been composed of viable spores and inclusions blended with inert carriers. At this early stage of commercial development, the materials are being analysed for potency by the different companies on the basis of the number of viable spores per unit of dry weight, with the quantity of carrier being varied to attain a uniform spore count in the final product. This method is satisfactory when processing a spore-forming bacterium that does not produce toxic by-products. However, because of the recognized importance of the toxic inclusions, new methods are being developed for the determination of the concentration of these bodies for the proper establishment of accurate levels of insecticidal activity. When these techniques finally are established, the crystal counts probably will be checked by bioassays against standard test insects, such as larvae of the house fly, *Musca domestica* L., or the salt-marsh caterpillar, *Estigmene acrea* (Drury), and the preparations then will be adjusted during formulation to standard levels of activity. So far there has been no attempt by the various manufacturers for product standardization of microbial materials within the industry, and each company has selected spore-count concentrations for final formulations that would fit in with the method of production. With the wide variation of spore count and toxicity levels in the products appearing on the market, it is evident that industry-wide standardization must be forthcoming if a microbial material such as *B. thuringiensis* var. *thuringiensis* from more than one commercial source is to be utilized on a broad scale for the control of insect pests.

The first materials to be distributed in the United States, in 1958, for use in field trials were wettable-powder products for spray applications. However, a report by Hall and Andres (1959) suggested the desirability of microbial dust formulations for use when thorough coverage of under-leaf surfaces and other difficult-to-spray plant areas was necessary to obtain satisfactory kill with this stomach-poison material. As a result of these findings, some good dust formulations made their appearance in 1959 (see figure 126), and it appears that most of the various products containing *B. thuringiensis* var. *thuringiensis* that will be developed in the future will include preparations for both spraying and dusting to broaden the usefulness of the microbial material.

Although the list of insects susceptible to the bacillus is large, it should increase as the organism is subjected to wide-scale laboratory and field testing. Many of the susceptible insects are major pests of crops in various parts of the world. It is possible that as studies continue, *B. thuringiensis* var. *thuringiensis* may be found to be useful for the control of certain of these pests, particularly since it appears that the problem of poisonous residues on food products and in the soil is not involved as it is with so many of the modern chemical insecticides. However, to be successful the microbial material with its stomach-poison characteristic and resultant thorough coverage requirement will have to fit efficiently into present-day insecticidal control methods and will have to compete cost-wise with many of the acceptable chemical insecticides (Hall 1961).

Fungi

The possibilities of using entomogenous fungi for the control of insect pests were first considered in the latter part of the nineteenth century. The idea became quite popular during that period; and for a number of decades there were many attempts throughout the world to reduce insect populations through the artificial distribution of pathogenic fungi (see chapter 18). Some of these attempts were successful, indicating that fungus diseases could be used to advantage. However, a great many were listed as failures, no doubt because various investigators did not understand the conditions necessary for optimum activity of the fungi.

Baird (1958*b*) lists the factors that regulate the effectiveness of a fungus in biological control attempts. These include weather conditions, population density of the host, micro-habitat of the pathogen and the host, resistance of the host and virulence of the fungus, saturation point of the pathogen in the environment, ease of artificial propagation and distribution of the fungus, time of application, the ability of the fungus to survive and spread in an insect population, the effect of the pathogen on other biological control agents, and the economic value of such control measures.

Entomogenous fungi, in general, are able to produce highly resistant stages to assure survival during periods of unfavourable conditions in the environment, and they are capable of spreading rapidly in an insect population through the natural release of masses of wind-borne spores. Therefore, most successes in the use of fungi to control insects have involved introduction or colonization of pathogens into new areas where susceptible host populations occur. There have been a number of attempts over the years to enhance the natural spread of fungi with broad coverage applications of infective materials in sprays and dusts. However, none of these trials has ended in the continuous usage of fungi in insect control programmes since the problems encountered, particularly with unfavourable environmental conditions, have made the results from the use of these organisms quite unpredictable.

One of the important efforts in the history of microbial control was the attempt by early workers in the United States to use the white muscardine fungus, *Beauveria bassiana* (Bals.) Vuill. (= *B. globulifera* (Spegazzini) Picard), to control the chinch bug, *Blissus leucopterus* (Say). Following the first apparently successful attempt to distribute disease material, wide-scale programmes were initiated to disseminate the fungus throughout the area where the chinch bug was a pest. These programmes were abandoned subsequently when the artificial distribution of the fungus did not appear to have any material effect on the incidence of the disease in the chinch-bug populations or the effectiveness of the control brought about by the infection. The reasons for abandoning the use of the fungus in Kansas were discussed by Billings and Glenn (1911). Their far-reaching conclusions include the following important points: The chinch-bug fungus is present naturally in fields everywhere throughout the infected area in Kansas. It is present in such great abundance that any artificial distribution of infection in a field would be too insignificant, by comparison, to be of practical use. The fungus is distributed naturally through a field much more uniformly than it could be by any artificial distribution. It shows little tendency to spread from centres of artificial infection and the apparent rapid spread is due to favourable conditions bringing it into activity over considerable areas. Where the natural presence of the fungus is plainly evident, its effect on the bugs cannot be accelerated to any appreciable degree by the artificial introduction of spores. In fields where the fungus is not in evidence, spores introduced artificially have no measurable effect. Apparent absence of the fungus among chinch bugs in a field is evidence of unfavourable conditions rather than the lack of fungus spores. Moisture conditions have much to do with the activity of the fungus in the field—artificial infection nothing.

The findings of Billings and Glenn were given support by Packard and Benton (1937) who stated that *B. bassiana* probably is the most destructive natural enemy of the chinch bug; that it generally is present in fields but that its effectiveness depends upon the weather; and that its artificial dissemination is needless since the spores of the fungus are present wherever the host insects are common. The failure of the chinch bug fungus distribution programme to attain increased mortality has been cited often as an example of what may be expected from attempts to manipu-late entomogenous fungi. However, Fawcett (1944) and Steinhaus (1949a) state that the findings are concerned specifically with the chinch bug host, the particular fungus, and the general area in which the studies were made. Caution was suggested in making broad conclusions relating to fungus diseases in general since what was found with *B. bassiana* may not necessarily be true in the actions of other fungi.

There have been a number of successful attempts over the years to introduce and colonize species of entomophthoraceous fungi. Speare and Colley (1912)

FIGURE 114. Modern large-scale fermentation equipment. A battery of 4,000-gallon fermentor vessels. (Photograph courtesy of R. G. Dworschack, Industrial Products Investigations, Fermentation Laboratory, Agricultural Research Service, U.S. Department of Agriculture, Peoria, Illinois.)

FIGURE 115. Steel rack used to store culture trays during incubation for the mass production of *Neoaplectana glasseri* Steiner. Two trays are placed on each shelf. (From McCoy and Glaser 1936.)

FIGURE 116. Aerial application of a commercially produced insecticidal dust material containing *Bacillus thuringiensis* Berl. for the control of the cabbage looper on crucifers. (Photo courtesy of Bioferm Corp.)

FIGURE 117. Spotted alfalfa aphids killed by the entomogenous fungi, *Entomophthora exitialis* Hall and Dunn.

FIGURE 118. Alfalfa caterpillar (arrow) dead of a polyhedrosis virus applied in a spray with the larval remains attached to the foliage. From Steinhaus (1956*a*).

FIGURE 119. Commercial wettable powder and dust materials containing *Bacillus thuringiensis* var. *thuringiensis* Berl. released for experimentation during 1959.

FIGURE 120. Hand application of a commercial dust preparation containing *Bacillus thuringiensis* var. *thuringiensis* Berl. for the control of the cabbage looper on cabbage. (Photo courtesy of J. C. Elmore.)

reported on the successful utilization of the fungus *Entomophthora aulicae* (Reich.) against larvae of the brown-tail moth, *Nygmia phaeorrhoea* (Donov.) in Massachusetts. A few years later, Dustan (1924*a*, *b*; 1925) introduced species of Entomophthoraceae into populations of the green apple bug, *Lygus communis* var. *novascotiensis* Knight, and the apple sucker, *Psylla mali* (Schmdb.), in Nova Scotia, Canada. Much more recently, similar techniques were used by Hall and Dunn (1958*a*) to disseminate laboratory-reared and field-collected fungi for the control of the spotted alfalfa aphid, *Therioaphis maculata* (Buck.), in California. In these efforts, following successful introduction, the fungi spread gradually from the point of establishment depending upon the availability of host insects in successive generations as well as on favourable humidity and temperature conditions in the microenvironment. The entomophthoraceous fungi that have been successfully established show a remarkable ability to survive during periods of adversity, and in general additional colonization into an area are not necessary since the pathogens continually reappear when meteorological conditions become favourable for their growth and a population of a susceptible host is present (Hall 1961).

Viruses

The important role of virus diseases as natural control factors has long been recognized and the potentialities of entomogenous viruses to control insect pests have been investigated on many occasions in the past. However, only in the last few years have the viruses been used successfully in control programmes. As stated by Tanada (1959*a*), most of these efforts have been with the granulosis and nuclear polyhedrosis viruses. Much of the successful work on the introduction of viruses has been accomplished in Canada where efforts have resulted in the development of economical and efficient means for controlling major pests of forest trees. The first successful establishment of an exotic virus disease was accomplished by Balch (1946) who introduced the polyhedrosis virus of the European spruce sawfly, *Diprion hercyniae* (Htg.), into Newfoundland where it had never been observed in insect populations although the virus had given good control of outbreaks of the pest on the Canadian mainland in previous years. The first successful attempt to introduce a virus disease not present previously on the North American continent was made by Bird (1953*a*), who used both ground and air equipment to apply a polyhedrosis virus of the European pine sawfly, *Neodiprion sertifer*, obtained from Sweden, to heavily infested pine forests in Ontario, Canada. Dowden and Girth (1953) conducted similar studies against the same insect pest in the United States in 1951 and 1952. They obtained excellent control in Illinois when the virus was applied with ground equipment, and in New Jersey when the infective material was applied from an airplane. As an aftermath of these successes, the virus has gained wide usage in Canada and the United States for control of the European pine sawfly, replacing many of the other methods of control (Bergold 1958).

Although field studies have been limited, the results up to the present time indicate that the entomogenous viruses may prove to be useful in manipulated microbial control of insect pests of field and truck crops. One of the most successful attempts to obtain microbial control of an insect on a field crop has involved the use of a polyhedrosis virus for the control of the alfalfa caterpillar in California. According to Steinhaus and Thompson (1949) and also to Thompson and Steinhaus (1950), the virus is an important factor in the natural control of the insect pest; but these naturally developing epizootics cannot be depended upon to occur with any degree of regularity to assure satisfactory economic control of the caterpillar. Following a series of field tests in the Dos Palos area of California, they reported that the virus applied as a spray, by conventional ground and air equipment, is capable of initiating epizootics of disease, even in low density populations of caterpillars and can markedly reduce the numbers of worms in a field much earlier than would occur naturally, thereby reducing the amount of damage done to the crop by the insect. Under conditions usually encountered in the central California area, Thompson and Steinhaus considered that the application of a virus suspension containing 5-million polyhedra per millilitre at the rate of 5 gallons per acre would be adequate to assure infection of a field population of the alfalfa caterpillar and bring about its reduction to sub-economic levels. Since this study was completed, the recommendations for control of the alfalfa caterpillar in California have invariably included the application of the virus along with early cutting and chemical treatments. However, no virus material has been available through commercial pesticide outlets and the problem of supply has almost completely curtailed the use of the organism. In recent years, according to Hall (1961) the virus has been applied on only a few ranches in California where trained personnel have taken the time to collect or produce enough infective material for their own use.

There have been a number of recent studies on the use of a polyhedrosis virus to control the cabbage looper, *Trichoplusia ni* (Hbn.), in the United States. Hall (1957), in tests conducted in 1953 and 1954, demonstrated that when suspensions of the virus were sprayed on lettuce in California, the cabbage looper larvae feeding on the treated foliage contracted the disease and died. These findings were confirmed by McEwen and Hervey (1958) in tests against the cabbage looper on cabbage, cauliflower, and broccoli in New York. Additional information on the use of the polyhedrosis virus in commercial control practices against the cabbage looper on cotton and lettuce in Arizona has been furnished by Flood (personal communication, 1959), indicating that practical use of this virus may be near at hand.

Protozoa

As stated by Tanada (1959*a*), from a theoretical standpoint, the entomogenous protozoa offer considerable promise in microbial control because of the large number of parasitic species found in insects. However, because of production difficulties and other problems, few attempts have been made to utilize them in microbial control, and in recent years Weiser (1956) in Czechoslovakia has been the main supporter of the use of protozoa against pest insects. The protozoa have received only limited study because they generally cause chronic rather than acute infections, and although many entomogenous species are known to be highly virulent, their susceptible hosts often remain alive for long periods. However, reproduction of the host often is curtailed with resultant long-term reduction of the pest population. Therefore, effective biological control may be attained without high initial mortality to the host.

Nematodes

Very few field attempts have been made to utilize entomophilic nematodes for the control of insects. However, Tanada (1959a) suggests that the nematodes may eventually provide a significant number of effective agents because of the large numbers that are internal parasites of insects. There has been an increase in interest in the United States in the use of nematodes in insect control following the reports on a promising nematode parasite by Dutky and Hough (1955) and Anon. (1956). Although first observed in diseased larvae of the codling moth, the nematode has been found by Dutky, Thompson, and Hough (1956) to attack at least 35 other species of insects. According to Anon. (1956) the disease is primarily a septicaemia caused by a bacterium carried into the host by the nematode. The bacterium does not infect insects readily when ingested, but when introduced by the nematode into the body cavity of the host, it flourishes and not only kills the insect but also serves as food for the nematode. In addition, the bacterium produces an antibiotic that restricts other bacterial microflora in the killed insect, thus protecting the cadaver from decay that would interfere with the development and reproduction of the nematode.

The ensheathed second-stage nematodes can survive for long periods in the absence of suitable hosts and food. They seek out the host insect, enter usually through the mouth of the host, penetrate the intestinal wall, discard their sheaths, and inject the bacteria which multiply rapidly. A septicaemia occurs within 24 hours. The nematodes then feed on the bacteria and reproduce, and the young larvae emerge from the dead host ready to seek out a new host. The infective stages can migrate for considerable distances over a moist surface in search of a host insect and are capable of forming their own liquid film over dry areas when the humidity is high. They are able to migrate within a matter of hours into the centre of tightly headed vegetables. Although the need for moisture may limit the ability of the nematode to control insects that feed on the exposed portions of plants, this may be partially offset by the habit of the infective stages of staying in the host cadaver until free water becomes available. In the laboratory, the young nematodes have been observed to remain alive in partially dried host remains for up to two months. The nematodes were found to be most active at moderate temperatures (15 to 27° C). The life cycle takes 8 days at 24 to 30° C and at lower temperatures the time increases.

Although the nematode has been studied by a number of entomologists in the United States, very little information is available on its effectiveness against pest insects. The results of tests in the field by Dutky and his co-workers indicate that up to 60 to 70 per cent reduction of populations of the codling moth and the corn earworm, *Heliothis zea* (Boddie), can be achieved following application of the nematode. This would not be considered to be satisfactory control of these insect pests in many areas, according to Hall (1961), but it is possible that additional testing will reveal situations where the nematode can be used for successful control of a number of its susceptible hosts.

SECTION VII

Biological Control of Weeds

CHAPTER 22

Fundamentals of Biological Weed Control

C. B. HUFFAKER

In the biological control of weeds safety is the prime consideration

INTRODUCTION

A WEED is a plant in the wrong place. Weeds may be related to, or themselves may be, valuable plants in other situations. This fact is fundamental to a consideration of biological control. For this reason each weed subject must be considered from many points of view.

Economic Considerations, Objectives, and Approaches

Since the beginning of agriculture man has engaged in an endless struggle against weeds. Even today there are vast areas on which weeds flourish. Often weeds do not yield to chemicals used against them, or this method is impracticable. With some of the worst weeds known, where other measures have failed, biological control has been eminently successful. In fact, this method has usually been employed only after other methods have proved inadequate. Entomologists are surprised to learn that agriculturists sometimes rate weeds as much more destructive to agriculture than insects (Robbins, Crafts, and Raynor 1942, p. 12). The types of losses caused by weeds will illustrate the scope of ecological relations and of man's varied interests important in considering weeds subjects for biological control:

1. Crowding out or reducing the growth of desirable plants, causing losses in yield and quality.
2. Much of the cost of cultivation.
3. The need for special seed and grain cleaning.
4. Direct injury to man, livestock, or livestock products.
5. Depreciation of watershed and wild-life values.
6. The serving as alternative hosts for insect pests or plant pathogens.

The objective in this work is not eradication, but the reduction of densities to non-economic levels. This may be accomplished either by direct or indirect action of the natural enemies being used.

Biological methods of weed control have been reluctantly employed for two reasons: (1) the feeling that the risks are too great, compared with the chances of success, and (2) the conflict in acceptance of a given plant as a weed, coupled with the fact that introduced agents can move to other lands where the plant may be valuable. The first and most important reason is losing its validity before accumulating evidence of successes and greater assurances against disproportionate risk. There is no basis today for using this method only as a 'last resort.'

The theory of biological control of weeds is based upon a mutual dependence in the status of a weed and an insect or other agent capable of controlling it. It has usually been applied against alien weeds and, indeed, the abundance of such aliens is often due to their having escaped the natural enemies common to them in their native lands (discussed in chapter 4). Natural enemies of the type not having such mutual relations with the weed would either be ineffective, or would be dangerous to use because of risk to other plants as, for instance, unspecialized feeders.

Work in biological control of weeds has usually involved semi-natural grazing lands. On such lands, management practices may determine to a large degree whether specific weedy species become serious pests. Some weeds become serious only because of severe over-grazing or poorly timed grazing. Also, the process of deterioration undoubtedly could in some instances be reversed by use of chemical fertilizers or by seeding with legumes or other forage species.

While research in range managements contributes to an increasing realization along these lines, it is at the same time obvious that where practicable the introduction of natural enemies of weeds from foreign regions offers a solution to some problems which are not necessarily solvable by management methods. Furthermore, the method of biological control adds to, without detracting from, the possibilities to be realized from fundamental research along management lines (Huffaker 1959b).

Comparison with Biological Control of Insects

Tillyard (1929, 1930) and Sweetman (1936, 1958) refer to the biological control of weeds as the inverse of biological control of insects. They did not stress the more fundamental similarities. The principles are the same. In one instance plants are the objects being protected, whereas in the other, they are the pests to be controlled. Also, many of the procedures of biological control as applied to insect pests pertain in the control of weeds. Here, such questions are considered as are peculiar to, or need particular emphasis in, attempts to control weeds by this means.

Contrary interests in the two fields may exist. Pettey (1948) cites the example wherein the coccinellid *Cryptolaemus montrouzieri* Muls., previously introduced into South Africa for control of mealybugs, operated against control of the weed cacti, *Opuntia* spp. by feeding on *Dactylopius tomentosus* (Lamarck) (=*D. opuntiae* Ckll.), which was introduced there for control of the prickly pears (see also Anonymous 1954). Dodd (1953) reported that the parasite *Opius tryoni* (Cam.), previously introduced into Hawaii for control of the fruit fly, *Ceratitis capitata* (Wied.), was found parasitizing the pamakani gall fly, *Procecidochares utilis* (Stone), introduced for control of the weed *Eupatorium adenophorum* Sprengel.

H. S. Smith, in advocating biological control, often stated that weeds offer proportionately greater chances of success than use of the method against insect pests. Huffaker (1957, p. 133) listed the following possible reasons:

'(1) Weed subjects have been almost exclusively pests of relatively undisturbed, un-cropped range lands where human interferences are at a minimum. (2) Such weeds are also engaged in a more intense and more direct competition with other claimants of the requisites, many of which may become competitively superior at the site as a result of only slight destruction of the weed by a phytophagous insect, without actual mortality of individuals being occasioned by the insect's feeding. (3) Action of introduced insects may occasion additional damage to the weed by the encouragement of fungous, bacterial or other disease organisms (Dodd 1940; Wilson 1943). (4) With weeds, in contrast to insect pests, there seems to be no marked general deterrent to effective control by introduced agents in temperate regions compared with tropical. (5) Attempts made in this field have necessarily been restricted to examples where there are indications of promise, whereas with insect pests, this has not often been so, as Williams (1954) stated. (6) There is also introduced a new factor not at all similar to the situation with insect pests. Plants do not invariably, or even, usually, die from the attack of a single insect.'

Conflicting Interests in Weed Control

Physical, chemical, or cultural methods of weed control can be limited to the terrain to be cleared of a given weed. On the other hand, introduced phytophagous insects may on their own broaden their scope of activity beyond that intended. This may pose a problem, since a plant may be a pest in one place and useful in another, or in the same area it may be adverse to one interest and beneficial to another. Therefore, appraisal of the economic position of the subject everywhere it is found is necessary. Prospective future values must be considered as well as present ones (Miller 1936); minority as well as majority interests; neighbouring nations in the same land group; direct and indirect effects on other plants and animals and on the soil itself.

Two examples will illustrate the complexity:

1. Prickly pear or *Opuntia* spp. Regarding control of this weed in Australia by *Cactoblastis*, Dodd (1940) stated, 'The prickly pear territory has been transformed as though by magic from a wilderness [of 60 million acres of infested lands] to a scene of prosperous endeavour.' From Australia there seem to have been raised no dissenting voices. On the other hand, in Hawaii there were vigorous objections against the proposed programme of biological control of this plant. Fullaway (1954a) reported that cattlemen objected on the grounds that the tree cactus, *Opuntia megacantha* Salm-Dyck., is useful both as a feed and as a source of otherwise unavailable water on some ranges. Such a programme has also been opposed on the United States mainland largely because of similar sentiments in Mexico and parts of the United States and because of considerations of the value of the plant in relation to soil and wild-life conservation.

2. Yellowstar thistle, *Centaurea solstitialis* L. In California yellowstar thistle is a most complicated case. It involves the interests of cattlemen, beekeepers, and fruit and seed crop growers. The damage caused by the weed is to the grazing ranges and to grain and seed crops. This thistle is reported to be a key plant in the maintenance of the bee industry at a level commensurate with the requirements of bees in the pollination of the fruit and seed crops in the state. The predominant direct interest is the cattle industry.

Obviously, the more simplified the human economy and ecology of an area the better are the chances of attempting biological control of a weed without operating at cross purposes with self-interests.

CONCEPTS OF NATURAL CONTROL AS RELATED TO WEEDS

In considering natural or semi-natural vegetation, an understanding of the complex of forces which contribute to the abundance and composition of vegetation is necessary. While the climatic and edaphic factors are clearly recognized and the role of rodents and the large herbivores among the biotic factors have received much attention, the influence of insects or other invertebrates in determining plant cover has been largely neglected. Natural control, as detailed in chapter 4, involves the mechanics by which the balance of nature comes about.

Regarding vegetation, we cannot here describe the importance of light and light periods, wind, temperature, atmospheric moisture, rainfall, slope, exposure, and the chemical and physical properties of soils, for example. Such factors have been shown to bear a strong relation to the composition and structure of certain vegetations of the world. There are plants which are very aggressive or very intolerant under respective conditions pertaining to those factors. Some are light lovers and some shade lovers, while others differ in their optimal moisture requirements, etc.

However, it should be stressed that in natural areas a great many more species—regardless of their optima and ranges of tolerance—could successfully utilize the same sites in the absence of interspecific competition.

A poorly drained site may be the reason why some palustrine species is dominant there, but it undoubtedly must achieve that position in competition with other palustrine forms. Furthermore, the palustrine form which is dominant may not be competitively superior, intrinsically, to some other less common species which is unable to exert its advantage because some herbivore, phytophagous insects, or disease acts selectively against it. Thus, the environment acts as a complex or whole —the *holocoenotic principle*. This does not mean there are no dominant or principal causes which are demonstrable in their key roles under given conditions.

Disregarding the influence of animals for the moment, the competitive position of various plant species will be a function of the conditions for germination, seedling establishment, growth, production of seeds, and their viability over periods of adversity prior to germination. With annual-type vegetation the exacting conditions of temperature, rainfall, and substrate for germination may be dominant in determining the *potential* composition. As different species often vary markedly in their requirements and as the weather likewise varies from one year to another, the complex of seedlings present any one year would vary likewise. Therefore, the competitive stress encountered by a species would vary according to the assemblage of seedlings.

When the action of grazing animals, as well as that of seed gatherers, pollinators, and other animals related in significant ways, is considered the situation becomes much more complicated. Biological control has demonstrated that damage by some insect which does not appear to be significant may, neverthleess, be adequate in tipping the balance against a weedy species in favour of desirable plants (Simmonds 1934). Many other examples and suggested roles of insects are cited by Huffaker (1957), and are mentioned in this and the following chapter. The recent results of Tevis (1958) show that foraging of the harvester ant, *Veromessor pergandei* (Mayr), for seeds is highly selective. In the spring the three types especially favoured were *Malvastrum, Mentzelia,* and *Oenothera clavaeformis* Torr. and Frem., these comprising 90 per cent of the seeds the ants took to their nests, although they made up less than 8 per cent of the available seeds. *Plantago* made up 86 per cent of the available seed supply, but the ants did not gather these seeds during the spring. Tevis suggests that the accumulative effect of this selective action, in combination with other factors, could '. . . act against the preferred species to the advantage of *Plantago*.' Under the topic, 'The Nature of Controlling Action,' the direct or indirect forms which such selective action may take are considered.

Braun-Blanquet, Fuller, and Conard (1932) recognized that the climatic and edaphic requirements of plants are prerequisite to the manifold relationships that arise from the competitive utilization of the requisites by the plants of a community. These authors (p. 81) emphatically state that the action of temperature, light, water, soil, nutrients or other such factors can be studied by the autecologist in the garden or greenhouse under conditions where competition is eliminated, but that the underlying causes of natural community organization and composition can be learned only from field studies of relationships. Braun-Blanquet, Fuller, and Conard (p. 11) consider competition to be the universal and ever-present expression of such community relationships. They also explain the place of historical factors in making possible the existing floras (we would add—*faunas*).

According to Clements (1936) the concept of climax vegetation (cited from Cain 1939) is one of a tendency to stabilization under the ruling climate. Change is characteristic but in the absence of man it is within the fabric of the climax. The unity of the climax is characterized by the life form of its dominants and by certain characteristic genera and families of plants. Various separate expressions of the climax are linked together by the characteristic, wide-ranging species of lesser rank and importance. Edaphic factors are recognized but, given time and freedom, a climax vegetation of the same general type will be produced and stabilized, irrespective of earlier site differences.

Although there is a great general truth in this concept, the Clementsian philosophy has led to some mistaken ideas and approaches, perhaps not intended by Clements himself. Love (1959) took exception to a practice in range management research of setting as a goal the return of the range to a climax condition. He argued that recent range research in Australia and New Zealand and the history of progress in agriculture from primitive times is such that the goal should be the establishment of a range cover which would give the most productive and perpetuating returns, and that climax vegetation may, indeed, fall far short of this goal.

Gleason's (1939) argument may be used against the Clementsian concept of unquestioned, superior adaptation of the climax dominants. The existing flora and the other animals may affect the dominance status just as well as may the changed physical conditions. A point of importance here is the relation of superimposed adaptations or the pyramid of exploitation to effectiveness of insects used for weed control (see further, chapter 4).

The influence of the physical environment over the patterns of competition operating within the limits set by the physical conditions becomes very clear when considering annual vegetation which is dependent each year upon specific conditions for germination and establishment, in considering insects inhabiting very hazardous and widely fluctuating environments, or cases where the common ceilings to density are fixed, irrespective of density itself (see chapter 4). As an example of the complexity of control, the case of biological control of the perennial herb St. Johns Wort, *Hypericum perforatum* L., in California was cited in chapter 4.

An annual weed would be more subject than a perennial to effects of changes in weather; its potentials of germination and survival on which a controlling agent would depend would be more significant regarding its changes in abundance. Any mutually interdependent actions between such a weed and its controlling natural enemy would thus operate within these fluctuating potentials. The potentialities of recovery of animal populations from low positions following catastrophe or relaxed pressure from a given cause, are similarly more dependent upon patterns of weather and less so upon density relations, but in our concept the latter are nevertheless present, and increasingly so as density increases.

Brues (1946, chapter 3), discusses the importance of insects to plant abundance. He views the flowering plants and insects as having evolved in especial inter-relationship, and that to a far greater degree than is so with respect to the higher animals, insects fill selective roles of control of, and dependence upon, specific plants. Brues states, '. . . insects frequently multiply at such an excessive rate that they may destroy immense quantities of their food plants. This happens in spite of the large number of prolific animals and micro-organisms that prey in turn directly upon the insects and serve to check their multiplication. Under natural conditions insects are a prime factor in regulating the abundance of all plants, particularly the flowering plants as the latter are especially prone to insect attack.'

THE KINDS OF NATURAL ENEMIES

Insects

Beginning with the introduction of eight species of insects into Hawaii from Mexico in 1902 for the control of *Lantana camara* L., insects have been the principal agents used in biological control of weeds. Many species have been employed for this purpose (see chapters 23 and 24).

In the earlier years, emphasis was placed on insects which feed on their host plants in special ways—that is, those that bore in roots, stems, or seeds or which destroy the flowers, in contrast to those which feed only on the foliage. Experience has shown, however, not only that leaf feeders may be just as safe to use but also equally effective. Furthermore, the complexity of the total environment and the delicate balance of a given weed's superiority there, with respect to various factors in relation to the injury exerted by a given insect, are such that it is usually unwise to prejudge the merits of any prospective biological control agent. Nor is rate of reproduction a valid criterion.

Species of Lepidoptera (Phycitidae, Tortricidae), Homoptera (Coccidae), Hemiptera (Coreidae, Tingidae), Coleoptera (Cerambycidae, Chrysomelidae, Buprestidiae, Curculionidae, Galerucidae), and Diptera (Agromyzidae, Trypetidae) have been used successfully (Sweetman 1958, p. 451-2; Huffaker 1959b).

Other Organisms as Agents

Any organisms which curtail plant growth or reproduction may be used as biological weed control agents. Such could potentially include animals either higher or lower than the insects, and, as well, parasitic higher plants, fungi, bacteria, and viruses.

The spider mite, *Tetranychus desertorum* Banks (= *T. opuntiae* Banks), accidentally introduced into Australia with prickly pear insects from Texas, U.S.A., in 1922-23, was proving a useful agent in the control of *Opuntia stricta* Haw. (including form *inermis* DC.) in Australia before the general success by the moth *Cactoblastis cactorum* (Berg) eclipsed all other agents (Dodd 1940).

The carp fish, *Cyprinus carpio* L., has been used for control of aquatic weeds (Sweetman 1936, p. 382). It is possible that some snails might be used in a similar manner. As more is learned of the plant-feeding nematodes some of these may be found useful.

Vertebrates such as sheep, goats, and geese have been used for many years in control of weeds. This is more akin to mechanical control, since the densities and behaviour of the animals are held under the arbitrary control of man and they are not allowed to react, as populations, to changes in the densities of the weeds.

The fungi, *Gloeosporium lunatum* Ell. and Ev., *Phyllosticta concava* Seav. and *Montagnella opuntiarum* Speg. are reported by Dodd (1940, p. 47) to sometimes attack prickly pear as primary parasites. He considered the secondary parasites such as '. . . the bacterial soft rot or rots' more important than the primary parasites as an aid to *Cactoblastis* in the destruction of *Opuntia*. Fullaway (1954a) reported unsuccessful attempts to control *Opuntia megacantha* in Hawaii by spraying and inoculating with spores of *Fusarium oxysporum* Schlect., which cause a disease of the red-fruited form of *O. megacantha*.

Certain higher plants which are parasitic on other plants, for example the dodders, *Cuscuta* spp. and the broomrapes and witchweeds (e.g., *Orobanche*, *Boschniakia*, and *Striga*) might prove to have some usefulness.

THE NATURE OF CONTROLLING ACTION

The special interrelationship of insects to the flowering plants as quoted from Brues (1946) in the last section is fundamental to control of weeds by insects. This does not mean that it will be possible to control every serious weed by use of insects.

It is, however, important to realize that the injury caused to a plant by an insect may be either direct or indirect, obvious or quite subtle and unexpected. The result from injury of a given type and degree is relative to the total environment. A given degree of injury may cause death in one environment and not in another. The variable control of St. John's Wort by insects in various parts of the world is a good illustration of this (Clark 1953; Holloway and Huffaker 1951; Smith 1958).

It is well known that when an insect pest becomes established in a favourable new area it is frequently far more noxious than in its native home. The opinion is rather widespread that this condition is due primarily to a lack of natural enemies. The implication is that in its native country its innocuous status is maintained by natural enemies and that importations can be successful only against alien pests.

It is obvious that the greater the density of the weed the greater the chances of success. However, while aggressive alien weeds are good prospects for biological control, it does not follow that such aggressiveness in the new land is necessarily due to the absence of natural enemies, nor that native pests may not be controlled by this means. Full discussion of this question, applicable to insect or weed subjects, is presented in chapter 4.

Direct and Indirect Destruction

Natural enemies often destroy weeds through direct destruction of vital parts. Examples are the action of *Cactoblastis cactorum* on *Opuntia* (Dodd 1940) (see figure 121 D, chapter 23), or *Chrysolina quadrigemina* (Suffr.) on St. John's Wort (Holloway and Huffaker 1951). The weed may die quickly or die during another season of the year as a result of impairment of functions at a critical later time. Thus in California St. John's Wort plants, the primary roots of which are destroyed by *Agrilus hyperici* (Creutz.), do not die during the period of attack but during the long dry summer following attack (Holloway and Huffaker 1953).

An enemy may also destroy a weed indirectly through: (1) creating favourableness to infection by plant pathogens, and (2) disrupting the competitive advantage of the weed. The former is illustrated by Dodd (1940). Although directly destroying much tissue and many plants, *Cactoblastis cactorum* opens the tissues to secondary parasites previously listed and these aid in the destruction of the prickly pears. The control of *Clidemia hirta* (L.) D. Don in Fiji by *Liothrips urichi* Karny is an example of the latter (Simmonds 1934).

The Plant Parts Attacked

Great stress has been placed on the action of insects which attack seeds or flowers or which bore in the roots or stems. While safety has been the main reason according to Imms (1929), and Wilson (1943), those authors also felt that these forms were more effective. It has not been shown that they are safer or, indeed, more efficient. Too few examples are on record, and there are too many subtle ways in which control may be effected by forms which attack leaves or shoots, to draw the conclusion from the few experiences available.

The point of importance is that whatever the nature of the injury, a really good agent is one which, through direct or indirect action, causes the destruction of *existing stands*. We agree with Chater (1931) and Wilson (1949) that insects which damage only seeds or fruits of *long-lived perennials* are normally not very suitable for introduction. The host persists and control is unlikely, especially as vegetative reproduction is common and some flowering is likely to occur during periods when the insects are inactive.

However, it is of interest that in parts of California the feeding of adults of the imported seed weevil *Apion ulicis* (Forst.) on gorse, *Ulex europaeus* L., is sufficiently severe under the prevailing climate to cause death of some stands. This is a totally unexpected result from an introduction which was considered useful only as a means of reducing the weed's rate of spread.

Insects which attack seeds could prove highly efficient in the control of annual weeds, through preventing spread and replacement. Indeed, such weeds are now receiving attention in this field (see chapter 23).

Perkins and Swezey (1924) placed much importance on the action of fruit- and seed-destroying insects in the control of lantana in Hawaii, as did Miller (1936) in the control of ragwort, *Senecio jacobaea* L., by the seed-fly *Pegohylemyia seneciella* Meade. If spread is a vital factor and great quantities of seed are required, this type of injury is obviously important.

A given plant may be little damaged unless attacked by a large number of insects, or it may die from the attack of only one. Wilson (1943, p. 81) states that a stem or root borer which consumes or causes the death of large portions of a plant and is required in smaller numbers, to cause the plant's death, is more effective than a leaf-feeding insect which destroys smaller amounts of tissue and is required in greater numbers to effect destruction. It is obvious that, considered from the single viewpoint, this position is unsound (Huffaker 1957, p. 115). However, Wilson gave some valid reasons why insects which bore in vital plant parts are more likely to be successful:

'(*a*) the greater damage (per individual) caused to the host plant by virtue of the incidental death of tissues dependent on the eaten tissue.' [The significant point is that because of this, more such species do have the *capacity to destroy*; fewer of them would be of a valueless type—such as the hypothetical example of Wilson (1949) of a stem borer which attacks an annual weed too late to affect its seed-production or competitive power.]

'(*b*) the decay occurring in the host from the development of bacteria and fungi in the insect's frass.

'(*c*) their lesser likelihood of attack by native predators and parasites in the new country.'

The Relation of Climate to Control and the Choice of Agents

Wilson (1949) discussed the relation of climate in the selection of species for introduction. Some of his conclusions are:

'1. It is evident that different, but closely related species commonly play precisely the same role in relation to the host [plant] in different areas [where the plant has a wider distribution than any of its phytophagous enemies] and that the essential differences between the species consists in their special adaptations to particular climates.

'2. The climates of the regions of distribution of the weed in the invaded and in the native regions should be thoroughly studied as a basis of selection of subjects for introduction.

'3. The insect to be selected should be the species most numerous [rather, most effective] in the region climatically most resembling the climate of the invaded region; and conversely, superiority of an insect in an area dissimilar in climate to the invaded region, is no indication that it will prove of value [or that a form inferior to it may not prove of more value].

'4. When the phytophagous species becomes so numerous in local areas in the native region as to nearly eliminate the weed, and only one or two species survive in large numbers, these are the important ones. Since it is just such conditions of host plant control with resultant severe insect competition that is hoped to produce in countries where the weed has been introduced, it seems logical to introduce only those species that become dominant in the homoclime under conditions of local control of the host. This would improve the extreme slowness of such investigations and decrease the risk, if any, in introducing additional perhaps unnecessary species.'

However, we consider it rather problematical to predict an outcome, or to conclude in advance the best species for introduction, if based upon climatic analyses alone (see also Dodd 1940, p. 23), although climatic considerations are of great importance.

THE INTERRELATION OF THE INSECT AGENT AND ITS FOOD

In this section we are reminded of Darwin's (1859b, p. 90) classic inference of the interrelation of cats, mice, bumble bees, and red clover: 'Hence it is quite credible that the presence of a feline animal in large numbers in a district might determine, through the intervention first of mice and then of bees, the frequency of certain flowers in that district.'

The discussion in chapter 4 of the role of the introduced beetle in the control of Klamath weed in California, and the cycles of cylamen mite injury to strawberry plants (Huffaker and Kennett 1956) illustrate both the complexity of forces in the determination of vegetation and, as well, the fact that in some instances the densities of the regulating agents and the population regulated may be reciprocally geared.

Such theorists as Muir (1914), Thompson (1929a), Bodenheimer (1930), Smith (1935), and Imms (1937) agreed that phytophagous insects are only rarely limited by a shortage of their plant food. If this were true, then generally they do not vitally affect the success of their plant hosts, for if capable of affecting their hosts' success, they would reduce their hosts to such low levels that they themselves would in turn be limited by scarcity of food. The premise on which entomological control of weeds rests is the reverse of the earlier view. To be a useful agent, an insect must be capable of decisive destruction of its plant host, thus determining the latter's abundance; reciprocally, its own abundance is then adjusted to that of its plant host. The review of this important question as presented by Huffaker (1957) is restated here with some changes.

Bodenheimer (1930) opposed the thesis of a 'struggle for existence' with food as a limiting factor. Imms (1937) also stated, 'It must be recollected, as W. R. Thompson has pointed out, that although insects entail a vast amount of destruction to economic plants, they rarely cause sufficiently vital damage which will affect the survival of well-established species to a marked degree.' Smith (1935), stated, 'So far as actual starvation is concerned, I agree with Bodenheimer that this happens only in rare, borderline cases. Usually other environmental factors limit the density of a species before its food supply is exhausted, or it is exhausted only as a result of an oscillation of great amplitude, not because of a high average density.'

On the other hand, Nicholson (1933, 1954b), Uvarov (1931, p. 161), and Brues (1946), all of whom have made extensive studies of the importance of food, recognize that it is common for food to be limiting for a population.

There are a number of reasons why earlier workers disregarded plant food as limiting for phytophagous insects. In part they are correct. It seems that if natural selection had not previously produced many natural enemies which control phytophagous insects, the latter would have caused such drastically different selective pressure on their respective plant hosts, that the present assemblages in our vegetation, and the resulting assemblages of the higher animals, could hardly have resulted in the biomes as they exist today. For the phytophagous insects had a prior opportunity, and were in many cases, but not in all (for evolution is a many-sided and continuing thing), prevented from too severe pressure against their plant hosts by the origin of forms which check them.

On the other hand, there is much evidence that the impression that food is seldom limiting for phytophagous insects is misleading: First, the fact that host plants may be commonly present but not nearly so commonly suitable, or as suitable at all potential nourishing sites on a plant may have been one of the reasons why observers have often concluded that plant food in nature is seldom limiting for insect populations.

Another point of importance is the dispersion of the host plants at low densities. As pointed out in chapter 4, the balance of control by an effective phytophagous insect is struck at a level such that the host plants are widely dispersed, the insects have difficulty and are delayed in finding them, and other factors are of more importance than they would be at higher densities.

The work of Franz (1958b) illustrates the subtle way in which phytophagous insects may be checked by their food supply. The destruction of the phellogen and phelloderm cells in the plant by the feeding of the chermesid *Adelges piceae* (Ratz.) (in event that predators permit the population to reach high levels), sets an upper limit to density and duration of an infestation. Trees which have suffered attack for several years no longer maintain the chermesids, although a secondary phellogen develops in the deeper layers of the bark and this may in time give rise to a secondary population cycle.

Other studies have recently emphasized the importance of specific nutritive elements in the diets of insects and the dependence of many species not only upon adequate quantities of food, but food containing a precise balance of nutritive elements (Painter 1951; Rodriquez and Rodriquez 1952; Fleschner 1952.) Thus, the mere presence of a host plant is no assurance that *any* quantity of suitable nutriment is available for a phytophagous insect.

Secondly, the general impressions have been based upon the superficially obvious. This is often misleading. Plant hosts of insects at the time of being injured by the insects are also experiencing a resultant decreased ability to compete with adjacent plants. As the plant ecologist usually has not evaluated the role of the insects feeding on the plants, neither has the entomologist considered fully the complex of selective phytophagous insects along with and including the role of competition by other plants. A small advantage lost to a plant as a result of insect attack combined with the action of its plant competitors, may be enough to account for its low abundance. The low abundance, even as an indirect result, may be regulated by the insect and limiting for it in turn.

Thirdly, in most natural vegetation, balance already exists between such hosts and their significant phytophagous enemies. Action of the insects at such a time would not seem to affect the density of the stands appreciably, but, nevertheless, could be exerting the necessary action in holding the plant at its respective position, and capable of intensifying that action if the host were to increase appreciably. Paradoxically, it is at this low position that the insect (and also the weed) is markedly affected by weather adversity and difficulty of finding hosts, such that a balance is struck at a position where factors other than reciprocal dependence of the phytophagous insect and its food plant might well account for greater changes in intermediate, temporary fortunes of either the insect or its host. This explains the fallacious view of Uvarov (1931) and Bodenheimer (1930) that the proportionate kill of a population by a given factor is the measure of its importance as a regulating agent. Such importance cannot be ascertained in the absence of a series of data obtained under different levels of density (see chapter 4). But these causes and the changes themselves are secondary to the superimposed reciprocal, density-dependent control.

The case of Klamath weed is very pertinent. It is believed that in the absence of previous knowledge of this programme, and unless he made specific studies, an entomologist or ecologist viewing the current picture would conclude that what we know to be the key insect species, *Chrysolina quadrigemina*, is not a significant influent of the stand of vegetation and that the few plants of Klamath weed seen here and there are not primarily limited by this insect. He might also erroneously conclude that this plant is a shade-loving species, since the beetle checks it much less effectively under shade, hence more survive there.

The role which insects play in the destinies of their plant hosts is a potent argument that use of biological control of weeds is a sound procedure. Entomologists have pioneered here. Attention usually given by general ecologists to the role of insects has concerned pollination, the culture of fungus 'gardens' by ants, transmission of diseases, agents of seed dispersal, or as temporary destruction, in the form of 'outbreaks,' to forests or ranges. Little attention has been given to the role of insects in determining the composition and structure of vegetation.

As previously cited, Brues (1946, p. 90) stated that the insects are a prime factor in regulating the abundance of plants. This statement is the conclusion of a recognized authority on the food relation of insects.

Much consideration has been given to the disturbing influence of man, the large herbivores, and rodents on vegetation, in part by use of exclosures. Relatively no use has been made of insect exclusion methods (see chapter 14) in evaluating the influence of highly selective grazers among the insects which occur on the ranges. We have today many persistent, selective insecticide materials which should be tested as exclusive agents.

The evidence of the role of insects falls into two categories: (1) insect influence on natural vegetation, and (2) the results from introduction from other regions of insects for control of weeds. The latter is the subject of chapter 23.

In the scholarly work of Clements and Shelford (1939), the extreme paucity of statements relating to insects as influents of plant cover serves also to emphasize the great neglect of ecologists in this field.

The information available regarding the influence of insects on natural or semi-natural vegetation is far from conclusive in most instances. Yet, there is a strong suggestion from this evidence that long-term studies using insecticidal check methods for evaluating the role of host-selective phytophagous insects in the determination of plant cover could be startling (Huffaker 1959b). Here we cite only a few examples:

1. Chater (1931) reported studies of insects attacking gorse, *Ulex europaeus*, in England. He found a depressing action of the moth *Anarsia spartiella* Schr. which he considered would be of such greater influence were it not often severely attacked by its own entomophagous parasites.

2. Cameron (1935) made a thorough study of the factors which control the abundance of ragwort, *Senecio jacobaea* in England, and concluded that insects are an important element, particularly the moth *Tyria jacobaeae* L.

3. In isolated studies, Bugbee and Reigel (1945), Cook (1942), Pederson (1942), and Dameron and Smith (1939) concluded from studies in the Great Plains (U.S.A.) that the moth *Melitara dentata* (Grote) (= *M. doddalis* Dyar) is an important control factor of *Opuntia* spp. under favourable environmental conditions. They also concluded that other insects, particularly *Dactylopius confusus* (Ckll.), *Chelinidea vittiger* Uhler, and *Moneilema* spp., would be of much greater importance were they not attacked by their entomophagous enemies.

4. In western United States, Tisdale and Zappetini (1953) studied the causes of the recent invasion of range lands by the weed *Halogeton glomeratus* (Bieb.) C. A. Mey. Although they concluded that prolonged overgrazing by cattle appears to have been the principal factor, they also considered that invasions in areas of shadscale, *Atriplex confertifolia* (Torr. and Frem.) Wats., may be partially attributed to severe prolonged attack on shadscale by insects, two of which are a scale insect *Orthezia annae* Ckll. and a snout moth *Eumysia* sp.

5. Simmonds (1948a) demonstrated experimentally that the action of the entomophagous parasites *Tetrastichus* sp. and *Chaetonodexodes marshalli* Ald. prevented the galerucid *Schematiza cordiae* Barber from completely defoliating the shrub *Cordia macrostachya* (Jacquin) Roemer and Schultes in Trinidad. The galerucid, introduced into Mauritius in the absence of these parasites, has given good control of this pest shrub there. This type of evidence is inferential support of the claims of various authors that except for attack by their entomophagous enemies certain phytophagous insects would exert even greater control over the abundance of their plant hosts (see Huffaker 1957, 1959b, for a review of these observations).

6. Research on the southern pine beetle, *Dendroctonus frontalis* Zimm., indicates rather conclusively that pure pine stands in the Piedmont region, south-eastern United States, are

transformed to a mixed pine-hardwood composition because the hardwoods appear in the openings where the pines are killed by this beetle. This was the conclusion of St. George and Beal (1929) following a study of the extensive infestations by this insect in the 1920's. Detailed data obtained from plots after 22 years lapse in time were reported by Hoffman and Anderson (1945). The number of pines per plot dropped from 594 to 237 while the hardwoods increased from 435 to 1,019. In the other series maintained only 13 years, the pines reduced from 277 to 105 while the hardwood increased from 535 to 1,159. Balch (1928) also concluded that the activities of this insect change the type from pine to pine–oak to oak.

7. Many other examples are on record indicating influence of various insects on succession and composition of particular forest stands among which are: Craighead (1924), Ghent, Fraser, and Thomas (1957) on the role of the spruce budworm; Eaton (1941) and Evenden, Bedard, and Struble (1943) on the mountain pine beetle; Baker (1941) and Bess *et al.* (1947) on the gypsy moth; and Balch (1942) and Gobeil (1941) on the eastern spruce beetle, *Dendroctonus piceaperda* Hopk.

THE RISKS OF INTRODUCTION AND HOST SPECIFICITY

Biological weed control involves great potential risks. There is no absolute guarantee of safety. The risks are relative to: (1) the degree of host specificity and specialization of the agents to be introduced, and (2) the botanical position or special features of the weed. Tillyard (1929) stressed that the real risk is due to our ignorance of the nature of host specificity rather than in the method itself. Weeds far removed botanically from economic plants are generally better risks. Yet, as Thorsteinson (1958) stated, these relationships as such are not so basic as are the specific phagostimulants involved in the chemotactile sense relative to host plant acceptability. The works of Brues (1920), Dethier (1947a, 1954), Thorpe (1939), Thorsteinson (1953), Jolivet (1954), and others show that the essential oils and alkaloids are important determinants of the acceptability of host plants, together with secondary features such as hairiness of surfaces or physical condition.

Dethier (1954, pp. 40–43) stresses that the specific phagostimulants present may '... vary with the time of day, the seasons, the growth stage of the plant, the tissue, climate, and soil conditions.' He further emphasized that hybridization or polyploidy may alter these characteristics. Yet, he also stated that in studies of forced altering of diets, '... the more restricted a species is in its feeding the greater the difficulty in altering its feeding habits.'

Therefore, although recent work lends hope of eventually predicting which plants would be acceptable, this is far in the future. The method of conducting starvation tests on prospective host plants must be continued.

The examples of 'remarkable' changes in diet of insects customarily cited do not represent basic changes. The insects cited were not originally of demonstrated specificity (Huffaker 1957). Yet, the statement of Williams (1954) is a cornerstone of thinking: 'The critical phase of biological control work against weeds is the selection of species that will not harm other plants, or at least useful plants. All other considerations are subordinate ...'

While only insects of restricted habits may be introduced, it does not follow that such insects do not exist nor that it is unsafe to introduce phytophagous insects when full precautions are taken. The question is just how firm the assurance can be. There are two reasons for confidence—one based on academic consideration; the other on a record of results.

Evidence on the nature of specificity shows how unlikely it is that an introduced insect will become a pest if reasonable precautions are taken. The conclusion of recent research is not the promiscuous or changeable nature of phytophagy but rather the 'near immutability' and rigidity of such feeding habits (Brues 1946, pp. 94–96; Dethier 1947a). Although evolution from polyphagy to a restricted diet seems to have been more common, Dethier (1954) proposed that the course may also proceed from monophagy to secondary polyphagy. He considers that not only may the insects change their food habits by virtue of experience or mutation or both, altering either their behaviour or basic physiology, but also that unacceptable plants may undergo alteration, gaining qualities which make them acceptable.

Thus, either the potential hosts or the insect may change in a way causing a new plant to be accepted, but these changes are, as in evolution generally, rare, and they are the product usually of great periods of time. Constancy rather than change is the great rule of nature (Huxley 1954). Dethier (1954) suggests the possible transition of members of the host-restricted genus *Papilio* from *Citrus* to *Ruta*, which possess different oils by gradual steps through *Zanthoxylum*, which possesses the phagostimulants characteristic of both *Citrus* and *Ruta*.

Since specialization is a deepening rut in evolution it may be concluded that, while there can be no guarantee that an insect will not accept a new plant, those forms which have long progressed in the rut of high specificity are very unlikely to escape from it. Since the insects chosen for biological control are of this type only, the safety of the method is assured.

The folly of assuming that, since there is the *possibility* of an insect's adopting new hosts, phytophagous insects should not be introduced was well analysed by Miller (1936) and Wilson (1949). Miller stated that if we are to deny the utilization of specialized phytophagous insects for weed control because of this comparatively rare element of danger, and after all possible precautions have been taken, then we must be prepared to have our crops overrun by the many species of phytophagous insects as yet harmless. Wilson pointed out that the chance that a basic dietary change will cause an introduced species to adopt new hosts is no greater than the chance that such change will occur among our thousands of now innocuous native species.

The second reason for confidence is based on results. No insect introduced for weed control has become a pest (Dodd 1954). This excepts minor feeding on some crop plant [e.g., *Thecla echion* (L.) on eggplant in Hawaii] (Perkins and Swezey 1924) and the expected attack on spineless cactus in South Africa by insects introduced for control of other forms of these plants growing as pests. *T. echion* was not subjected to starvation tests prior to release in Hawaii. Starvation tests would have revealed such a capacity.

Aside from the chemicals present, a plant may be unsuitable in not possessing the physical characteristics necessary to release ovipositional responses or to serve as food and abode. Tinbergen (1953) shows that some complicated behaviour patterns of animals are set in motion only by a reception of some simple releaser stimulus. These may be either physical or chemical in nature or both. For insects, Currie (1932) showed that the peculiar seed-covering of *Xanthium* burs satisfies the requirement for oviposition of *Euaresta aequalis* (Loew). The females would likewise oviposit on artificial burs made of rubber and small recurved pins which simulated the physical structure of *Xanthium* burs.

Insects may also be restricted from using plants because of phenological asynchronization with special features of their life cycles or if an intimate insect/plant–hormone relation is involved.

Specificity Tests

Controversy exists in the interpretation of specificity tests. Decisions cannot be entirely objective. The urgency of each problem will alter the acceptability of an estimate of risk. It is obvious that the risk is greater and more involved in large continental areas of diversified agriculture (Sweetman 1936, p. 382). For obvious reasons, when possible the testing should be done in the country of origin.

It is unreasonable to insist that an insect be unable to engage in any feeding on some economic plant under forced or unnatural stress. The capacity to breed upon a given plant is the main criterion. However, feeding by adults or migrating larvae in an injurious manner on some economic plant on which they cannot reproduce may, under unusual conditions, be of secondary importance.

In nature many factors may prevent an insect from using a plant which is suitable nutritionally. Much weight is given to the host records of the insect in its native region and to whether it is known to depart from the normally restricted host range. This subject will be treated further in chapter 23.

Dodd (1940, p. 3) stated: 'In two or three instances, prickly-pear insects were able to feed and to develop on certain other plants or fruits, although all evidence pointed to their absolute restriction to cacti under field conditions in America.' Williams (1951*b*) stated that the leaf beetle, *Schematiza cordiae*, was subjected to starvation tests in both Trinidad and Mauritius prior to its release in the latter country against *Cordia macrostachya* (Jacquin). When confined in Petri dishes, it fed slightly on several unrelated plants, and appreciably so on the weed and its close allies, and also, surprisingly, on cabbage. However, under field conditions, this insect was entirely unable to breed on other species of *Cordia* or other plants.

Painter (1951) cited a number of examples showing that climatic and edaphic conditions, the types of cages used, phases of plant growth and other biological factors may be sufficient to alter the status of resistance of a given plant to attack by an insect.

It is therefore obvious that the greatest latitude must be used in conducting the tests and in interpreting the results. Dodd (1954) lists the following points as relevant to interpreting such tests and to the general question of introductions.

'(*a*) the importance of the weed, and the difficulty of its control by any method other than the biological;

'(*b*) the potential value of the insect for the control of the weed;

'(*c*) the value of the economic plant which may be attacked by the insect, weighed against the damage and loss of production caused by the weed;

'(*d*) the seriousness or otherwise of the damage that might be caused to the economic plant by the insect's attack;

'(*e*) the simplicity or otherwise of the insect's control by cultural, chemical or other means, if and when it attacked some particular economic plant.'

The Relative Safety of Different Types of Feeding

Imms (1929) emphasized the supposed greater safety in using root or stem borers or seed feeders for weed control. This contention does not seem to be well-founded, but it may eventually be proved correct. Dethier (1947*a*) stated, 'Nowhere is the role of attractants which guide insects to their proper food more complex and outstanding or the attractants more specific in action than in the lives of plant-feeding insects,' and, further, 'This is especially true as it relates to those insects which feed on leaves.' Wilson (1943) followed Imms in the view that insects which bore in roots, stems, fruits, or seeds are preferred because of greater safety and greater chances of success. Wilson later (1949) questioned the view that seed-infesting insects offer better prospects of success against perennials. The question of whether there is greater safety remains unanswered.

In this work the degree of specificity demonstrated by the particular examples, rather than the general dietary focus, is paramount. It is obvious that efforts to find insects which are specific to particular weeds should cover all possibilities without undue emphasis on the plant part attacked, and, by rigid starvation and ovipositional tests, to demonstrate the safety in introducing tested examples. The widest possible representation of test plants should be included.

THE NATURE OF INFESTATIONS AND THE PROSPECTS OF SUCCESS

Each weed considered as a subject for biological control must be viewed from many aspects, for biological control is applicable only under proper relations.

The Noxious Nature of the Weed

It is important whether a weed is noxious because of high toxicity to animals, because it displaces more desirable plants; serves as an alternative host of a plant pathogen or insect pest; is detrimental mainly because of its contamination of wool, for example, by its seeds; or is harmful to wild life or soil conservation. These factors may have a bearing on the chances of success. This is true, also, of the weed's habits of growth.

Successful control depends upon the continued presence of the weed, existing in small numbers and shifting in position with time. Biological control is a remote possibility in cases where near annihilation is required, such as might occur if a weed were so highly toxic that its presence at all on a range would be ruinous to livestock. With regard to insect pests, Carter (1935) pointed out that the degree of control necessary with an insect which is noxious by virtue of its role as a vector of plant disease may be too strict for attainment, particularly by use of natural enemies.

The Growth Habit of a Weed, Its Origin, and the Type of Land Infested

The special sphere of biological control of weeds is associated with the fact that responsible officials first try other feasible methods because of the element of risk in introducing phytophagous insects. Thus, the world's otherwise largely un-solvable weed problems have been the main subjects of this method of control. Land most commonly considered suitable to this method is either too inaccessible or too low in value for use of chemical or other methods, or on which weeds grow which do not yield to other methods. With advancing knowledge of host selection and specificity of phytophagous insects this reluctance to use biological control except as a last resort may be worn down.

As in the case of insect pests, alien weeds are the worst offenders. Examples are prickly pear, *Opuntia* spp., in Australia, South Africa, Asia, and Hawaii; and St. John's Wort, *Hypericum perforatum*, in Australia, the United States, Canada, and South America. Indeed, every weed subject of biological control has been an alien. As stated elsewhere, some authors (Currie and Garthside 1932; Williams 1954) consider that the theory of biological control of weeds is applicable only to alien species. However, as Sweetman (1936, p. 287) states, the control of the levuana moth, *Levuana iridescens* B–B., in Fiji is proof that native species of pests may be controlled by introduction of natural enemies of their near relatives. This has not been tried with weeds, but the possibilities should be explored. An example of the control by a natural enemy of a native plant, although not a weed, is the removal of chestnuts from the forests of eastern United States by the accidentally introduced fungus *Endothia parasitica* (Murr.) And. and And. In fact, this example shows that a native weed *may* be more readily controlled than an alien form. The Asiatic chestnuts possess a high degree of resistance to this pathogen (see Huffaker 1957).

Also, the control of prickly pears by *Cactoblastis cactorum* further illustrates this point. Although alien to Australia and endemic to southern North America, these cacti, *Opuntia stricta*, and other species do not occur in Argentina, the country from which *Cactoblastis* was imported to do its valuable work in Australia against these species, which are relatives of the insect's hosts in its native Argentina (Dodd 1940, p. 23).

Weeds of uncultivated lands have predominated as subjects of biological control. With such examples there is less interference which is detrimental to the introduced agents. Cultivation, removal of refuse, and the aspect of shifting locations of the weeds, the practices of crop rotation, and fallowed land would have indeterminate consequences. Also, weeds in cultivated areas are readily controlled by conventional means and such control is not prohibited by excessive cost.

However, the adaptability of insects attacking plants is such that many species which attack our crop plants are sufficiently resilient in their habits as to withstand man's row-crop interferences. These insects are major pests. Therefore, we cannot assume that insects may not be found which will be effective against weeds of cultivated areas.

Even in uncultivated areas, *annual* weeds are somewhat comparable with weeds of cultivated areas, but in less degree. The weed stand is removed at the end of each season. Continuity of host plants is dependent upon the vicissitudes of conditions for seed germination, establishment, growth, and reproduction. Adaptations of seeds to survive several years awaiting recurrence of conditions for germination, assures continuity of the plant host in a dormant state. The insects which attack them have no comparable capacities. They would not necessarily be in positions to respond quickly to increases in their hosts and thus to check them sufficiently soon. Because of these relations there is also probably a lessened chance (in contrast to perennials) that natural enemies attacking them will have evolved to monophagy or restricted oligophagy, which is a requirement for use of such agents. Thus, the requirements for annual weeds impose an added impediment but it does not preclude success. This is partially offset by the fact that insects which destroy seeds or flowers may be more effective in controlling annuals than perennials. Insects having high rates of reproduction and powers of flight or host-finding are the best prospects for control of annual weeds. At present, *Xanthium* spp. in Australia, *Tribulus terrestris* in California, and *Emex spinosa* (L.) Camp. in Hawaii are annual or short-lived perennial weeds which are subjects of biological control.

CHAPTER 23

Projects in Biological Control of Weeds

J. K. HOLLOWAY

INTRODUCTION

THE FIRST PUBLISHED REPORT on the deliberate use of insects to control an unwanted plant species, or the use of insects in the biological control of weeds, was made by Perkins and Swezey (1924). This was a report of work undertaken in 1902 in Hawaii, where *Lantana camara* L., an introduced ornamental plant, had escaped cultivation and had taken over such large areas of range land that it was causing great concern.

A survey of insects attacking *Lantana* in Hawaii had disclosed that an accidentally introduced scale insect, *Orthezia insignis* Dougl., was causing considerable damage in certain localities. Attempts made by ranchers to establish this scale insect in other localities met with a degree of success. Why not then go to the native home of the plant and seek other destructive insects? This thought was put into action in 1902 when the territorial government authorized investigations to be undertaken. Albert Koebele was sent by the territorial government on an exploratory trip to find insects destructive to *Lantana*, while Dr. R. C. L. Perkins remained in Hawaii to receive, test, propagate, and release the introduced insects.

Probably one of the most outstanding examples of biological control of weeds began in 1920 with initiation of the exploration for insects destructive to *Opuntia* sp.

In 1927, New Zealand became interested in this means of weed control which was shortly followed by work in Fiji.

Professor Harry S. Smith, when Chairman of the Department of Biological Control of the University of California and one of the leaders in biological control in the United States, became interested in the possibilities of the biological control of Klamath weed, *Hypericum perforatum* L., in 1922. However, the suggestion that a phytophagous insect be deliberately introduced was not acceptable. Not until 1944 was permission obtained to introduce insects for the control of this weed, and this project was the initial one on the mainland of the United States.

OUTSTANDING PROJECTS OF THE WORLD

Lantana — Lantana camara L.

This perennial shrub, a native of Central America, is used extensively throughout the world as an ornamental. On many occasions it has escaped cultivation and become a pest of range lands and coconut plantations, has hindered reforestation, and is a problem affecting to a lesser degree other agricultural interests.

HAWAII. The search by Albert Koebele in Mexico and Central America for insects destructive to *Lantana* ultimately resulted in the following introduced species becoming established in Hawaii: a seed fly, *Ophiomyia lantanae* (Frogg.); a lace bug, *Teleonemia scrupulosa* Stål (= *T. lantanae* Distant); an olethreutid, *Epinotia lantana* (Busck) (= *Crocidosema lantana* Busck); a plume moth, *Platyptilia pusillodactyla* (Wlkr.); a lepidopterous leaf miner, *Cremastobombycia lantanella* Busck; a gall fly *Eutreta xanthochaeta* Ald.; and two butterflies, *Thecla echion* (L.) and *T. bazochii* (Godart) (= *T. agra* Hewitson).

It is believed that the best results in the effort to control *Lantana* have been obtained from the activity of those insects which curtail production of viable seed by either preventing bloom or destroying already formed seed. The introduced insects greatly curtailed the spread of this plant. *Lantana* is not difficult to remove from the land, and cleared areas where the insects have been active have a better chance for continued control (Perkins and Swezey 1924).

Fifty years later further importation was attempted. Koebele had noted other insects occurring on *Lantana*, but in the early period transportation from Mexico to Hawaii took weeks and some of the species did not survive, while others arrived alive but in small numbers and poor condition. With lack of proper facilities, many of these died before releases could be made. With the beginning of air travel it was realized that some of these insects which failed to arrive alive could now be readily transported to Hawaii, and also, by the same token, more distant locales other than Mexico could be advantageously explored.

This renewed effort resulted in the importation and release of the following insects: a lace bug, *Teleonemia vanduzeii* Drake from Cuba and Florida (Krauss 1953); a cerambycid, *Aerenicopsis championi* Bates; noctuids, *Catabena esula* (Druce), *Diastema tigris* Guenée and *Hypena jussalis* Guenée (Davis 1958; Dodd 1957); pyraustids, *Syngamia haemorrhoidalis* Guenée, and *Blepharomastix acutangulalis* (Snell.). *H. jussalis* has been doing excellent work by completely defoliating all sizes of plants. It may well become an important factor.

The cerambycid has become established on the island of Hawaii while the noctuid, *Catabena*, is established on the islands of Hawaii, Maui, and Oahu. The pyraustid, *Syngamia*, has become well established, and Davis (personal correspondence to Huffaker, 1958) is of the opinion that this moth could become an important factor because it destroys regrowth which follows defoliation by *Teleonemia scrupulosa*.

A cerambycid, *Plagiohammus spinipennis* (Thoms.), imported from Mexico, was erroneously identified and destroyed in quarantine, but has been subsequently obtained and is being subjected to host specificity studies (Davis 1958). Two chrysomelids have been reported as having been released—*Octotoma scabripennis* (Guer.) from Mexico and *O. plicatula* (F.) from Honduras (Wilson 1954).

FIJI. *Lantana* was one of the first plants to be reported as a serious weed in Fiji.

Not only was it a problem on the ranges, but it was also a problem in the coconut plantations where it formed dense thickets.

Four species of the insects which had been previously established in Hawaii were introduced in Fiji and three of them—the seed fly, *Ophiomyia lantanae*, the lace bug, *Teleonemia scrupulosa*, and the butterfly, *Thecla bazochii*—became established. A material reduction in *Lantana* has been reported. Fiji recently joined Hawaii and Australia in their renewed efforts to introduce new species; the noctuid, *Diastema tigris*, and the pyraustid, *Blepharomastix acutangulalis*, have been introduced (Simmonds 1934).

INDIA. The biological control of *Lantana* was seriously considered but in making specificity tests it was found that *Teleonemia scrupulosa* would attack teak, a close relative of *Lantana*. In view of the value of this wood, the work was curtailed (Gardner 1944). However, ultimately it was found that *Ophiomyia lantanae* would be safe, and releases were made from insects originating in Hawaii (Fullaway 1954*b*).

AUSTRALIA. For many years *Lantana* has occurred abundantly in the tropical and subtropical areas of coastal Queensland and New South Wales. There is, however, a difference of opinion on its economic importance. Some believe it to be an important factor in preventing soil erosion, and others fear that the areas in which it occurs may be taken over by Crofton weed (*Eupatorium adenophorum* Sprengel). *Lantana* is looked upon with favour by operators of banana plantations because during the time the land is being rested, *Lantana* furnishes a cover crop which can be easily removed when the time comes to replant to banana. Nevertheless, the plant is a pest on ranges and hinders reforestation efforts. Because of these adverse effects, insects for control were introduced as early as 1914.

The early introductions via Hawaii and Fiji resulted in the establishment of *Ophiomyia lantanae* and *E. lantana* but the insects did not bring about satisfactory control. In 1935, *Teleonemia scrupulosa* was introduced into Australia from Fiji and by 1946 was accredited with various degrees of plant destruction up to complete defoliation and death of plants. Apparently this insect will survive only in the most tropical regions of Queensland (Cashmore and Campbell 1946).

Control has recently received further consideration. In 1957 Dodd reported that three species of Lepidoptera, *Syngamia haemorrhoidalis*, *Catabena esula*, and *Diastema tigris* were cleared for release but there has not been a report of establishment. Additional potential species are being investigated.

Prickly Pear — Opuntia spp.

Various species of *Opuntia* which originated in the Western Hemisphere have been transported by man around the world. Some species produce fruit which is used for human consumption—others, pads which are used for cattle food, and food for dye-producing insects. Among its other utilitarian aspects, it has been extensively used for hedge fences. In many places, it has escaped from cultivation and has become an extremely aggressive weed, occupying millions of otherwise productive acres.

AUSTRALIA. The work on prickly pear in Australia is truly an outstanding accomplishment in the field of biological control of weeds. As Wilson (1954) points out, the full repercussions of the work have yet to be felt in entomology and especially in the field of ecology.

This is one of the examples of the ability of insects to reduce the competitive value of a plant sufficiently to govern its abundance and distribution. The excellent results obtained have been responsible for attracting attention to the enormous potentialities in the use of insects to control unwanted plants.

This interesting problem, its progress and solution, has been well documented by Dodd (1940) from which only the highlights are brought out in this account. About six species of *Opuntia* had become established in Australia and of these, *Opuntia stricta* Haw. (= *O. inermis* De Candolle), was the one which had got out of hand and constituted the main problem. In 1900 it was causing considerable concern, as at that time it was reported to be occupying an estimated 10 million acres. As early as 1903, *Dactylopius indicus* Green was introduced but unfortunately did not become established. However, in 1913, establishment was successful and gave satisfactory control of a minor species, *Opuntia vulgaris* Mill. (= *O. monacantha* (Willd.) Haw.).

The other cacti continued to increase during the next two decades. Control by chemical or mechanical means was too costly to be feasible and with each year the problems became increasingly acute. In 1925 an estimated 60,000,000 acres had become infested; half of this total area had become so dense that it was practically impenetrable by man and large animals, so that the land had obviously become totally useless for agriculture.

In 1920, explorers were sent to the United States, Mexico, and Argentina seeking specific arthropods which potentially might bring about control. This effort resulted in studying some 50 species which could be used against *Opuntia*. However, of this number which were handled in quarantine, only 12 were introduced and established. The striking success of *Cactoblastis cactorum* (Berg) precluded further work with other species which had not been released prior to its introduction.

It is interesting to note that some of the arthropods which had been introduced and established before the dominance of *Cactoblastis cactorum* had shown considerable progress in the period from 1925 to 1927. These were *Chelinidea tabulata* (Burm.), *Dactylopius tomentosus* (Lam.), *Olycella junctolineela* (Hulst), and *Tetranychus desertorum* Banks (= *T. opuntiae* Banks).

The satisfactory but slow progress being made by these introductions was to be overshadowed in 1925 with the arrival of *Cactoblastis* eggs from Argentina. The first and only importation consisted of 2,750 eggs. The resulting larvae thrived on *Opuntia stricta*, which made it possible to increase the breeding stock so that by the second generation over 2·5 million eggs were obtained, and from this stock 2·25 million eggs were released in 20 locations in the field. The following year, 1927, 9 million eggs were available for release; however, by this time the insect was becoming so common in the field that it was no longer necessary to rely on a breeding stock, and the problem became one of redistribution of field colonies. The eggs of this moth are contained in slightly curved stalks readily seen with the unaided eye, and in this stage the moth can be advantageously moved to new locations. Following this procedure, from 1927 to 1929, 3 billion eggs were made available from field collections.

By 1930, the moth populations had increased to such great numbers that *Opuntia* destruction was no longer confined to individual plants and huge areas were killed off at one time. It was soon evident that this great depletion of food source would cause a drastic drop in *Cactoblastis* populations. In this process of food supply depletion there was a time when millions upon millions of starving larvae were in search of food, and it is most interesting that this already proved specific insect, under great stress for survival, was not observed attacking any plants other than *Opuntia*.

The great reduction in the moths presaged a resurgence of the *Opuntia* but fortunately *Cactoblastis* was able to increase with sufficient rapidity to lower the plant population again before the *Opuntia* reached alarming proportions. In the years that followed, the prickly pear receded and at present an occasional plant and a few larger patches can be found, but at no time has there been any alarming increase, nor have the moths had a change in diet and become pests of economic crops. Millions of acres formerly occupied by this pest have now been returned to useful agriculture brought about by an introduced insect, which in turn was fostered by the imagination, determination, and patience of all those associated with the undertaking.

INDIA AND CEYLON. Prickly pear had become a pest of importance in other places in the world, and naturally the great success obtained in Australia led to others attempting control. It is interesting to note the response of the various arthropods to the different species of *Opuntia* growing under climatic conditions other than those encountered in Australia.

Opuntia vulgaris (=*O. monacantha*) and *O. elatior* Mill. (=*O. nigricans* Haw.), according to David and Muthukrishnan (1953), were introduced into India about 1787 to be used in the culture of the commercial dye-producing cochineal insect. A third species, *O. dillenii* (Ker-Gawl) Haw., was in all probability introduced before the other two. In due time the *Opuntia* escaped cultivation and for more than a century and a half was recognized as a weed of importance. Fortunately, *O. vulgaris* did not become too serious a pest because of the action of *Dactylopius indicus*, which had been accidentally introduced with it or some other *Opuntia*.

During 1924, the cochineal insect, *Dactylopius tomentosus*, was introduced to Ceylon, and later, in 1926, to India. The scale became established and gave very good control of *Opuntia dillenii* and a lesser degree of control of *O. elatior*. According to Narayanan (1954), control of *O. dillenii* has been effected in over 100,000 acres.

CELEBES. During the early 1930's, *Opuntia elatior* was rapidly occupying abandoned rice fields and spreading to range lands in the Palu Valley of northern Clebes. *Dactylopius tomentosus* had, in Australia, shown promising results against this species of *Opuntia*. It was decided to make introductions, and the cochineal was released in 1935. Van der Goot (1940) reported that the first results of control were observed the next year, 1936, and by 1939 dense stands of cactus began to succumb and many fields were being tilled and pastured.

SOUTH AFRICA. Introduced *Opuntia*, of which there are some 20 species, has become a serious problem. The two species. *Opuntia megacantha* Salm-Dyck and *O. aurantiaca* Lind., have become established on the veld and it is reported that over 1 million acres are infested by *O. megacantha* alone.

Apparently *Opuntia aurantiaca* was introduced during the decade 1850–59, and in 1933 this species was considered to be the worst weed in South Africa (Pettey 1948). During the period 1934–38, government funds in the sum of £172,000 were spent in an eradication programme. Surveys revealed an estimated 420 thousand acres in eastern Cape Province and additional infestations in the Orange Free State and Natal. As was the experience in Australia it was ultimately considered too costly and impracticable to engage in a chemical or mechanical control programme, so in 1932 it was decided to attempt biological control and in that year *Cactoblastis* was introduced.

It became established, but the *Opuntia* appeared to be somewhat resistant to the insect's attack, and although quite successful on younger plants, the moth had difficulty with the older tougher ones. The *Cactoblastis* not only reduced existing stands but was somewhat effective in reducing spread by attacking new growth. Five additional species of insects were studied in the hope they might be used to supplement the work of *Cactoblastis*. The species under consideration were: *Cactoblastis doddi* Hein., *Dactylopius tomentosus*, *Lagochirus funestus* Thoms., *Moneilema ulkei* Horn, and *Cactophagus spinolae* (Gyll.). *C. doddi* and *M. ulkei* were not released in the field, which made a total in all of four species colonized, and of this number only *Cactoblastis cactorum* and *D. tomentosus* became established (Naude 1956; Pettey 1953; Sellers 1952).

Had it not been for the action of an indigenous coccinellid, *Exochomus flavipes* Thunb., and the previously imported *Cryptolaemus montrouzieri* Muls., which attack the cochineal, it is quite probable that the problem could have been solved by the scale insect alone. Even under such adverse conditions a large portion of *Opuntia megacantha* plants was killed off so that supplemental mechanical control at the proper time deterred regrowth. Pettey (1950) reports that by this method 90 per cent of areas originally infested by this *Opuntia* in the Karoo and in other parts of Cape Province was cleared and that most of the remaining infested areas are now located in a belt within 50 miles of the coast.

HAWAII. The tree cactus, *Opuntia megacantha*, introduced form Mexico about 1809, spread at an alarming rate, especially on the island of Hawaii. In the drier lowlands, large dense stands were encountered and it was spreading into the more valuable range lands at the higher elevations. From 1900 on it was recognized as a problem of ever-increasing importance. Biological control has been considered desirable but certain ranchers on Hawaii and on some of the other islands felt that the cactus was useful as cattle food, especially in times of drought. It was, however, ultimately agreed that insects with a potentially low rate of dispersal could be introduced into Hawaii. According to Fullaway (1954a), the importation of insects began in 1949 and was as follows: the California cochineal, *Dactylopius confusus* (Ckll.) (not established), *Chelinidea vittiger* Uhler, *Melitara prodenialis* Wlkr. and *M. dentata* (Grote) (= *doddalis* Dyar) (neither established); and borers, *Moneilema armata* LeC. (not recovered), *M. crassa* LeConte (questionable establishment), and *Lagochirus funestus* (probably established).

The introduced insects did not produce results and it was hoped that *Cactoblastis cactorum* from Australia could be brought in to solve the problem. Finally, objection to introduction was overruled, and in addition the cochineal from Australia was at the same time imported. Both insects became readily established with resulting effective control. The work of *Cactoblastis* in Hawaii may be seen in figure 121. Fullaway, in conversation, reported an interesting situation in that *Cactoblastis* is dominant in the higher elevations while *Dactylopius* is the major factor at the lower elevations.

MAURITIUS. The cactus causing trouble on this island is reported to be *Opuntia tuna* (L.) Mill. In 1927, *Dactylopius tomentosus* was introduced, established, and exerted considerable control. However, in 1938–39 *Cryptolaemus montrouzieri* was introduced to control the pineapple mealybug, with subsequent decline in control by *Dactylopius*. In 1950, *Cactoblastis cactorum* was obtained from South Africa, released, and became established. The multiplication and dispersion have been most satisfactory, and destruction of prickly pear is becoming apparent (Anonymous 1954).

St. John's Wort, Klamath weed, Hypericum perforatum L.

This plant has become widely distributed throughout the temperate zones of the world. Its minute seeds readily adhere to oily hair and hide of animals. In the United States its distribution is strongly associated with the movement of sheep herds, and it is also transferred with hay and seeds of other plants. It has many undesirable characteristics, among which is its effect on animals with unpigmented skin. An oil in the plant, when ingested, photosensitizes white-skin areas of the animals, and when exposed to sunlight causes these areas to become irritated and ultimately to form sore, scrubby patches on the hide. Ingestion of lesser amounts of the weed acts as an irritant in the mouth, and animals appear to experience considerable discomfort while drinking water. If very small amounts of the plant are included in the diet no drastic conditions result, but the animals do not maintain normal appetite and are naturally less thrifty. On ranges where annual plants predominate, this aggressive perennial has successfully crowded out useful range plants; at one time it was not uncommon to encounter large areas of almost pure stands of St. John's Wort in the coastal counties of California.

AUSTRALIA. *Hypericum perforatum* is reputed to have been introduced into Victoria, Australia, in about 1880, by a German woman who had received seeds from her homeland. In a very short time it escaped cultivation and at the turn of the century began to show unmistakable attributes of becoming a pest of importance; in 1916 it occupied an estimated 184 thousand acres in Victoria alone. In 1917 the

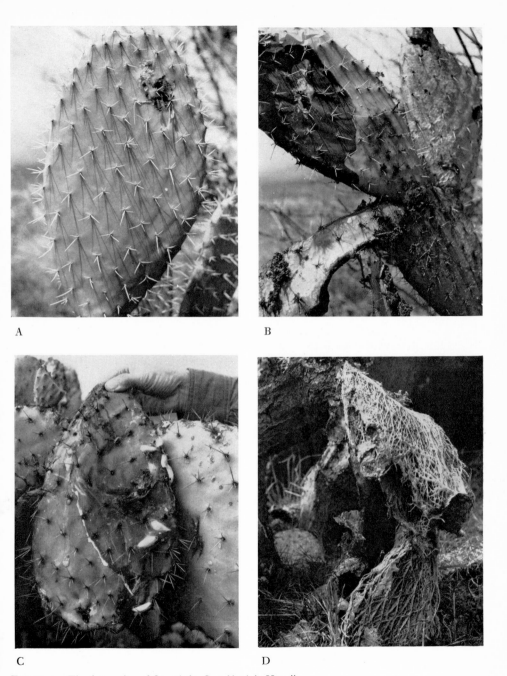

A

B

C

D

FIGURE 121. The destruction of *Opuntia* by *Cactoblastis* in Hawaii.

A. Appearance of pad shortly after larvae have entered.
B. Pad partially destroyed by larvae and wilt.
C. *Cactoblastis* cocoons attached to *Opuntia* pad.
D. Complete destruction.

FIGURE 122. *Emex* sp. on the Parker Ranch, Island of Hawaii.
A. *Emex* not yet attacked by *Apion*.

B. The destruction of *Emex* following a recent release of *Apion*.

A

B

FIGURE 123. The progressive destruction of Klamath weed at one of the original release sites in Humboldt County, California.

A. 1948, three years after release; foreground, viable weed not yet destroyed, in distance weed completely destroyed.

B. 1949, same location; foreground, the weed from previous season has been destroyed while in distance no evidence of weed remains and useful forage plants have returned.

problem was considered one of national importance, and preliminary investigations were initiated to look into the possibilities of entomological control. These investigations continued for several years, and in 1928 field work actually began in England and the next year in Australia. The completion of starvation tests in England and Australia resulted in the release of three species of *Chrysolina*, of which *Chrysolina hyperici* (Forst.) was the only one at that time to become established. The rate of increase and dispersion was slow and as a result it was decided to move the exploratory investigations from England to France (Currie and Garthside 1932).

Wilson (1943) worked with 37 species which were destructive to *Hypericum*. Many of these were of minor importance and were not introduced. The following from France became established: *Chrysolina quadrigemina* (Suffr.) and *Agrilus hyperici* (Creut.). In the 1950's, additional attempts were made to establish a gall midge, *Zeuxidiplosis giardi* (Kief.), as earlier attempts had not been successful. Parsons (1957) states that this midge might be of use in the wooded areas and every effort is being made to establish the insect in many new locations in Victoria.

The control exerted by the established insects has been quite good in localized areas, but some workers are of the opinion that it still leaves a lot to be desired as far as over-all control is concerned. The chrysomelid beetles seem to be slow to migrate to new areas and the adults are reluctant to oviposit in the shade, and unfortunately a great deal of infested land is in partial shade.

UNITED STATES. *Hypericum perforatum* has two common names in the West. In Washington and Oregon it is known as 'goat weed,' while in California it is called 'Klamath weed,' because it was first reported about 1900 in the northern part of the state in the vicinity of the Klamath River. From a meagre beginning in California it increased rapidly and soon began to show aggressive tendencies; in 1944 it was occupying in excess of 2 million acres of useful range land and had extended to 30 counties. The value of the heavily infested properties was greatly depreciated, so much so that it was almost impossible for ranchers to borrow money for improvements and the real estate value was about one-third that of uninfested lands.

The weed was susceptible to most of the weed killers used in 1944 but the cost and the inaccessibility of the land to be treated made large-scale control operations impracticable. The progress of the Australian experiment was followed in California with much interest, and about eight years after the later releases of *Chrysolina* in Australia, very encouraging results were reported by A. J. Nicholson in correspondence with Harry S. Smith of the University of California. Negotiations between the University of California and the then Bureau of Entomology and Plant Quarantine of the United States Department of Agriculture regarding the advisability of introducing the beetles into California resulted in an authorization to import *Chrysolina hyperici* (=*Chrysomela hyperici*), *C. quadrigemina*, and *Agrilus hyperici* with the proviso that feeding tests be made on the following plants: sugar beet, flax, hemp, sweet potato, tobacco, and cotton. A co-operative project for the importation and colonization was set up between the Bureau of Entomology and Plant Quarantine and the University of California.

The war made collections in Europe impossible but material available in Australia could be transported to California by the United States Army Transport Command. The Australian Council for Scientific and Industrial Research, through Dr. Nicholson, offered to collect and ship the needed material. The collection and preparation of the insects for shipment were under the immediate supervision of T. G. Campbell. Importations were begun in October, 1944, and the first problem encountered was to change timing of the life cycle so that the insects would be in phase with the seasons of the Northern Hemisphere. In the case of the two *Chrysolina*, it was found that the aestivating adults responded to fine sprays of water which resulted in their becoming active—feeding, mating, and laying eggs. Thus, it was possible within three weeks after the shipments were received to bring the adults out of aestivation and thus synchronize them with the Northern Hemisphere. Difficulty, however, was encountered with the *Agrilus* root borer due to heavy mortality while in transit and during pre-emergence retention. It was decided to wait until some later date, at which time the material could be obtained in the Northern Hemisphere and emergence could be more readily synchronized with California climate.

The *Chrysolina* readily passed all of the starvation tests by not feeding on any of the test plants. In fact, it was difficult to make the adults or larvae stay even momentarily on some of the plants; they showed no tendency to feed, there was a complete lack of interest, and ultimately they died of starvation (Holloway 1948). The first material available for release was *C. hyperici* in the spring of 1945, and the following February, *C. quadrigemina* was released. Both species became established, and two years after the first releases there was no further need for importations. Within a very short time, *C. quadrigemina* was obviously making a much greater rate of increase than was *C. hyperici*. After three generations in the field it was possible to collect thousands of beetles for redistribution from an original colony of only 5,000 adults and in this same location in 1950, more than 3 million adults were collected for redistribution.

The larvae of *Chrysolina* attack the winter basal growth of the *Hypericum* and after about three years in any one locality, they completely destroy all of the procumbent growth each year, which prevents flowering and seed production. Also, this destruction occurs at a critical time, because very shortly after beetle emergence the dry summer begins, and as a result the plant has no opportunity to recover. In about three years the root reserve is completely utilized and the weed, in competition with other plants, completely dies.

The success of *Chrysolina quadrigemina* as contrasted to *C. hyperici* is due to a better synchronization of the insect's life history with the climate and the growth phases of the plant. Both species are brought out of their summer aestivation by the autumn rains. *C. hyperici* requires a greater amount of rainfall than does *C. quadrigemina*, and as a result they do not begin laying eggs until December. This projects their life history further into the spring, at which time the plant is less suitable as food. Pupation conditions are also unfavourable. *C. quadrigemina* is unquestionably the dominant species because of its ready response to the early autumn rains, which in turn marks the beginning basal growth of the plant. Thus it is possible for the larvae to complete their full development at a time when food is abundant and suitable, and pupation conditions are more ideal. It also means that the plant is subjected to competition during the entire period of basal growth (Holloway and Huffaker 1951). The plant growth phases and the life history of *C. quadrigemina* are well synchronized.

In 1947, small importations of the root borer, *Agrilus*, were received from the United States Department of Agriculture, Entomology Research Division, Foreign Parasite Laboratory in Europe, from which sufficient material was obtained to complete the required starvation tests, which the root borers passed as they were unable to feed or multiply on any of the listed plants. It was not until 1950, however, that sufficient material was available to make large-scale releases. The borers became readily established, but they were overwhelmed by *Chrysolina quadrigemina* which ultimately moved into the colonization area. Before this occurred, *Agrilus* had demonstrated excellent ability to destroy Klamath weed, and it has persisted in limited numbers in several localities within California.

In 1949, permission was obtained to introduce the gall midge, *Zeuxidiplosis giardi*. Specificity tests were completed in March and April, 1950, and releases were made shortly thereafter. The midge was established but is extremely limited in its activities in California because it requires succulent foliage during the summer months, and this is difficult to find except in seepage areas. Even under these adversities, it has been observed to have excellent ability to migrate along the courses of irrigation ditches for several miles from the initial point of release. In fact, this very fragile insect has shown remarkable ability to disperse (Holloway and Huffaker 1953).

A third species of leaf-feeding beetle, *Chrysolina varians* (Schall.), was introduced in 1952. It failed to complete a generation in California. This, in all probability, was due to lack of rain which results in the foliage becoming unsuitable for food, as the larvae of this species feed on the late spring upright growth at the time of the blooming period. It did, however, persist for three or four generations in Idaho but has not been recovered since 1955.

Within a decade after release of the insects, Klamath weed was reduced from an extremely important pest of range lands to a road-side weed, with a resultant improvement in land-carrying capacity and land values. It is now less than one per cent of its former abundance and has been removed from the list of California's noxious weeds (Huffaker and Kennett 1959; Holloway and Huffaker 1951). Figure 123 illustrates the progressive destruction of Klamath weed in Humboldt County, California.

At about the time it became evident that the introduced insects were going to control Klamath weed in California, experimental releases were made in Washington, Oregon, Idaho, and Montana. *Chrysolina hyperici* and *C. quadrigemina* became established in all four states, and it is interesting to note that the dominant species there is also *C. quadrigemina*. *Zeuxidiplosis giardi* was introduced into Washington and Idaho and became established during the summer but failed to survive the winters. *Agrilus hyperici* became established in Idaho and Washington and has shown a reasonable rate of increase, but its ability to control the weed is still an unknown factor. In most localities in these states of the north-west the weed has been brought under satisfactory control.

CANADA. An attempt at biological control of Klamath weed was started in British Columbia in 1951 by the introduction of *Chrysolina hyperici* and *C. quadrigemina*. Both species became established, but to date the control has not been satisfactory. It seems that in one location *C. hyperici* made a terrific increase in population but it failed to control the weed. In 1955, the gall midge, *Zeuxidiplosis giardi*, and the root borer, *Agrilus hyperici*, were introduced but it is believed that they did not become established. Attempts are now being made to introduce *C. varians*; the results are not at present known (Smith 1958).

NEW ZEALAND. At about the time introductions were made into California, New Zealand was also attempting colonization. There are no published reports on the success of this endeavour, but it has been ascertained in conversation with visitors that in certain communities *Chrysolina quadrigemina* became established and has greatly reduced the weed.

CHILE. No published progress reports have become available but in conversation with workers from Chile they report that *Chrysolina quadrigemina* has become established and is apparently reducing the weed.

Gorse — Ulex europaeus L.

The genus *Ulex* in all probability had its origin in Western Europe and North Africa. It is used extensively as a hedge and an ornamental. In many places it has escaped cultivation and has become difficult to control, mainly because its thick, woody growth forms an impenetrable barrier and the older leaves form sharp pointed spines.

NEW ZEALAND. In 1927 the first attempt to control weeds in New Zealand by the biological method was initiated by Dr. R. J. Tillyard, and a portion of this early work was directed towards the control of gorse. Insect studies were begun in England in 1927, where host specificity tests were made with the gorse weevil, *Apion ulicis* (Forst). Other insects were studied but it was decided that an attempt would be made to retard the spread of the plant rather than to destroy existing stands.

The weevils were found not only to be highly specific to gorse, but in fact the life history of the insect is so tied in with the plant growth phases that it would be difficult for it to breed on another plant. The adult weevils are unable to make an exit from the gorse seed pod and are therefore dependent on the pod dehiscing at the proper time (Davies 1928).

The weevils were readily established in New Zealand where they have increased so greatly in numbers that seed production has been reduced by more than 98 per cent. It is, however, at present questioned if this reduction is sufficient to retard the spread (Miller's communication to Huffaker, 1958).

UNITED STATES. HAWAII. Gorse has in recent years become a problem of importance by forming dense thickets on range lands. *Apion ulicis* was introduced by the way of New Zealand. The weevils became established but after about five years it was felt that the progress being made was not satisfactory. Since the original New Zealand stock was from England, it was speculated that possibly insects from warmer areas of France might work better in Hawaii. Subsequently, introductions were made and the weevils from France are believed to have done better.

CALIFORNIA AND OREGON. This weed has so far been somewhat localized in the coastal areas of both these states. It is, however, quite a severe pest where it does occur and it could potentially occupy a much greater area.

Apion ulicis was introduced in 1953 and 1954 (Holloway and Huffaker 1957). It readily became established but for the first three years its spread was very slow. In 1959, however, it was recovered with ease several miles from release points, which would indicate that spread had been taking place previously, but due to the inconspicuousness of the adults and the great number of seed pods which were available it was difficult to detect small populations.

It is hoped that the seed weevil will assist in control operations in California, as a regular brush-control programme will handle the plant quite well on level accessible land, but in much of the coastal areas it also occurs in deep canyons where control operations are difficult and costly. If seed production can be greatly reduced in these inaccessible locations it might retard re-establishment in the cleared areas. It is too soon to obtain information on how successful this approach will be.

Both in Hawaii and on the mainland it is desired to obtain insects which will destroy the plant. Research on this phase at the present time is being pursued in the foreign field.

AUSTRALIA. In 1939, the seed weevils were introduced into Tasmania but no published progress reports have been located.

Tansy Ragwort — Senecio jacobaea L.

This very undesirable composite is a native of Europe. In England when it occurs in dairy pastures it is reputed to cause a heavy mortality in stock. Wherever it occurs, it is reported to be very toxic to cattle and horses, causing cirrhosis of the liver.

NEW ZEALAND. Tansy ragwort was introduced prior to 1874 and spread rapidly over wide areas. New Zealand took the initiative in biological control of the weed, with a preliminary research programme in England in 1927 concurrent with the gorse work. The studies in England revealed that over 60 insects were recorded from tansy ragwort and of these a moth, *Tyria jacobaeae* (L.), and a seed fly, *Pegohylemyia seneciella* Meade, were chosen for detailed studies with the thought of importation (Cameron 1935).

The choice was made because of their destructive ability and the fact that they were specific to *Senecio*. Both species became established in New Zealand. In the case of *Tyria jacobaeae* it is believed that general predation greatly reduced its effectiveness; in addition, there was also considerable parasite activity from species that had moved over from near relatives of *Tyria* which were already in existence in New Zealand.

The seed fly, *Pegohylemyia seneciella* Meade, became established and in 1954 was reported as destroying 98 per cent of the flowers in that year.

AUSTRALIA. This weed is of considerable importance in Victoria, where control has been attempted by the introduction of *Tyria jacobaeae* from New Zealand and England in the interval 1930 to 1937. Establishment was not successful following early releases, and attempts at establishment are to be tried again. Some work was done with the seed fly but was curtailed pending the outcome of the work in New Zealand (Currie and Fyfe 1938; Cashmore and Campbell 1946).

UNITED STATES. WASHINGTON, OREGON, AND CALIFORNIA. Tansy ragwort is of importance in the coastal areas of the western states. A trial release of *Tyria jacobaeae* was made in California in June, 1959, and in the spring of 1960 releases were made in Oregon and Washington.

Black Sage — Cordia macrostachya (Jacquin) Roemer and Schultes

MAURITIUS. Black sage was accidentally introduced into Mauritius with cane plants in about 1890. It invades pastures, forms dense clumps of scrub, and is a problem on sugar cane and hemp plantations.

The prospects of biological control were given consideration in 1939, and work actually began with investigations by the Commonwealth Institute of Biological Control in Trinidad in 1944. After thorough investigations, two leaf-feeding beetles were available for release in 1947. *Physonota alutacea* Boh. became established only temporarily. The other beetle, *Schematiza cordiae* Barb., released in 1948, took hold but the progress was slow during the dry spring. However, with the advent of winter they began to increase and by 1950 had brought the weed under subjugation. Williams (1951*b*) commented, 'The multiplication of *Schematiza* was so rapid that ascendency over the plant was achieved after the passage of one summer.'

Investigations continued in Trinidad, where it was decided to import a seed-destroying insect, *Eurytoma attiva* Bucks. It became established and soon accounted for a high percentage of seed destruction.

In Trinidad the possibility of obtaining stem- and root-destroying insects was being investigated, but in view of the success of the previous introductions it was decided not to continue.

It is anticipated that the present satisfactory control will be maintained as the competitive power of *Cordia* has been reduced by the vegetative destruction of *Schematiza* and the curtailment of seed production by *Eurytoma* (Simmonds 1958*c*).

Pamakani or Crofton Weed — Eupatorium adenophorum Sprengel

This shrub, a native of tropical America, is known as Pamakani in Hawaii and Crofton weed in Australia. Its spread is very rapid by means of buoyant seeds, and once started it will in a short time form dense thickets.

HAWAII. Pamakani was introduced about 1900 and subsequently became a range pest. At its maximum infestation level it had rendered 25,000 acres of land useless for grazing purposes. Considerable time and money had been utilized in mechanically removing the plant in an effort to reclaim the land. In 1945 a gall midge from Mexico, *Procecidochares utilis* (Stone), was introduced. In a matter of very few years after establishment the midge began to make inroads on the infestations and fortunately it is most effective in the areas of the better range lands (Bess and Haramoto 1958a).

AUSTRALIA. The gall midge, *Procecidochares utilis*, was introduced in 1951 and 1952 into Queensland and New South Wales, where Crofton weed is regarded as a serious threat to range lands. It now appears that the gall midge will slow down the spread and it is hoped it will ultimately be a solution to the problem (Wilson 1952, 1954).

Koster's Curse — Clidemia hirta (L.) D. Don

This undesirable shrub originates in tropical America, as do so many of the weeds in the Pacific area.

FIJI. Records indicate that the weed became established some time prior to 1890. By 1919 thousands of acres of pasture, coconut, and rubber lands were infested. In 1920 research began in an effort to obtain natural enemies. Many insects showed potentialities but only one, a thrips, *Liothrips urichi* Karny, proved to be specific in its habits. Releases of this insect were made in 1930, and within 18 months the numbers had increased and had shown a most satisfactory ability to disperse. Simmonds (1933) stated, '. . . the thrips can be definitely said to have brought the weed under control over large areas, not by directly killing it but by so inhibiting its growth that it was no longer able to compete with surrounding vegetation.' This is a very interesting accomplishment in weed control in that it demonstrates that some insects, even though not completely destroying the entire plant, do have the ability to reduce its competitive value. It is also interesting to note that in open pastures, where some of the taller plant competition is absent, the thrips alone do not exert sufficient stress on the plants; however, if the shrub is cut down, the young regrowth is then effectively retarded (Simmonds 1933).

HAWAII. The thrips, *Liothrips urichi*, was introduced via Fiji and became established in Hawaii. Fullaway (correspondence to Huffaker, 1958) stated in 1958 that it '. . . caused defoliation but seems to flourish best in sunny spots and doesn't do so well in the shade.'

Manuka Weed — Leptospermum scoparium Forster

This plant is native to New Zealand but has become a very undesirable weed in that country on low-value ranges. It was, however, believed to be of value by some in preventing erosion, so a difference of opinion existed as to the advisability of engaging in biological control.

In the early 1940's, it was noted that a mealybug, *Eriococcus* sp., was effectively killing plants. It was later identified as *E. orariensis* Hoy from Australia (Sewell 1949; Hoy 1949). The spread was fostered, and Miller reports it '. . . has literally wiped out thousands of acres of the scrub . . .' (Huffaker 1959*b*). This is an interesting example of the control of a native plant by an introduced insect, and it is possible that some native plants should receive more consideration than they have.

Noogoora Bur — Xanthium strumarium L. (=X. pungens Wallroth)

AUSTRALIA. The Noogoora bur has two undesirable characters: (1) it is an unpalatable plant, and (2) not the least of its undesirable attributes is the presence of the burs in wool. Chemical control is not advisable because of the economics of the problem, as the Noogoora bur occurs on land of low-production value.

Research was conducted in the United States and India in an effort to obtain insect enemies. Two cerambycids, *Nupserha antennata* Gahan, in India, and *Mecas saturnina* (LeConte), in the United States, showed promise. Unfortunately, however, these insects were found to develop in wild sunflowers and Jerusalem artichoke; therefore, no releases were made.

In the early 1940's a seed fly, *Euaresta aequalis* (Loew), from America was released and established (Cashmore and Campbell 1946). The fly has not so far given the desired results. It appears that almost total seed destruction will be required. Also, erratic seed production from year to year in certain localities curtails the effective build-up of the fly. Wilson (1952) commented on the cerambycids, 'The problem has arisen, therefore, whether the importance of attempting to control Noogoora bur should override the risks involved to a limited number of composites.' Dodd (1954) feels that further investigation is warranted, and should the borers attack only the plants mentioned they should be introduced.

Emex — Emex spinosa (L.) Camp.

HAWAII. This weedy herb is reputed to have been accidentally introduced in grass seed from Australia. The plant is prevalent on the islands of Hawaii, Oahu, Molokai, Maui, and Lanai.

In 1950 foreign investigations were initiated by searching for insect enemies in Italy and Sicily. *Lixus algirus* L. showed promise but it was found to feed on broad bean, which automatically ruled it out for possible introduction.

It was found that *Emex australis* Stein., a closely related species, was distributed in South Africa and Australia. Exploration in South Africa disclosed that *Apion antiquum* Gyll. caused considerable damage to *Emex* and that it was specific in its feeding habits. Upon release it became established at once and has begun to show considerable promise. It kills the vines completely and has a rapid rate of increase, approximately one generation a month (Fullaway 1958). The control of this weed is of interest as it is one of the first annuals to meet with any degree of success. Figure 122 shows the work of *Apion antiquum* on *Emex*.

Nutgrass — Cyperus rotundus L

Nutgrass is a perennial sedge which is difficult to control. It is well distributed throughout temperate and tropical climates. It is a pest in cultivated crops such as sugar cane and cotton and also causes trouble in irrigated pastures, especially in the low parts which retain moisture longer.

HAWAII. In Hawaii this tough sedge has invaded gardens, lawns, and sugar plantations. Two insects, a bulb borer, *Bactra truculenta* Meyr., and a weevil, *Athesapeuta cyperi* Marsh., were introduced from the Philippines (Fullaway 1954*b*). Releases were made in 1925 and subsequently both species became established. Williams (1931) stated that *B. truculenta* sometimes does effective work locally but is greatly hampered by the egg parasite, *Trichogramma minutum* Riley. The weevil is believed to effect no control at all.

AUSTRALIA. Nutgrass is a pest in cultivated fields, and the control practices which have given some relief have been crop rotation and soil sterilization. Introduction of *Bactra truculenta* and *Athesapeuta cyperi* was considered but the specificity test conducted from 1937 to 1940 showed that both insects would feed on related species of *Cyperus*, some of which had some forage value (Cashmore and Campbell 1946).

Piri-Piri or Bidi-Bidi — Acaena sanguisorbae Vahl

NEW ZEALAND. This native bur-producing plant causes great economic losses to the wool-producing interests. It is estimated that it reduces the annual wool crop value by £250,000. In the late 1920's, biological control was considered and this was the first attempt to introduce insects intentionally from other areas to control a native weed. The research began with studies of insects attacking *Acaena* in Chile.

Two flea beetles, *Altica virescens* Blanch., in Chile, and *Altica pagana* Black., which is somewhat effective in Australia, could not be introduced into New Zealand because the insects were not considered sufficiently specific (Sweetman 1936). It was deemed advisable to exercise caution in dealing with the plant as it is a member of the important *Rosaceae* family. However, a sawfly from Chile was later introduced but failed to become established. Miller (1936) says, 'It is quite possible that birds are responsible for the failure in the field, because at the time when sawfly larvae first emerge in the late winter and early spring, insect food is not particularly prevalent. . . .' It is interesting to note that at one time this plant was discovered in Hawaii, but fortunately it had not spread extensively and due to the foresight and perseverance of A. W. Carter the weed was successfully eradicated (Hosaka and Thistle 1954).

WEEDS BEING INVESTIGATED IN THE UNITED STATES FOR POSSIBILITIES OF CONTROL BY INSECTS

COMMON NAME	SCIENTIFIC NAME	PROBABLE ORIGIN
Alligator weed	*Alternanthera philoxeroides* (Mart.) Gris. (P)	South America
Arrow weed	*Pluchea sericea* (Nutt.) Cov. (P)	South-western U.S.A.
Bind weed	*Convolvulus arvensis* L. (P)	Eurasia
Canadian thistle	*Cirsium arvense* Scop. (P)	Europe, North Africa, Eastern Asia
Dwarf mistletoe	*Arceuthabium* (P) (p)	North America
Dalmatian toadflax	*Linaria dalmatica* (L.) Mill. (P)	Eastern Europe
Gorse	*Ulex europaeus* L. (P)	Europe
Halogeton	*Halogeton glomeratus* C. A. Meyer (A)	Western Asia
	Halogeton sativus (L.) C. A. Meyer (A)	Spain and North Africa
Hoary cress	*Cardaria draba* (L.) Scop. (P)	Central Europe Western Asia
Italian thistle	*Carduus pycnocephalus* Curt. (A)	Southern Europe
Leafy spurge	*Euphorbia esula* L. (P)	Europe
Mediterranean sage	*Salvia aethiopis* L. (P)	Eastern Europe
Medusa head	*Elymus caput-medusae* L. (A)	Europe
Nut grass	*Cyperus rotundus* L. (P)	Eurasia
Orobanche	*Orobanche* sp. (A) (p)	Europe
Pamakani	*Eupatorium adenophorum* Sprengel (P)	Tropical America
Puncture vine	*Tribulus terrestris* L. (A)	Southern Europe
Russian knapweed	*Centaurea repens* L. (P)	Near East
Scotch broom	*Cytisus scoparius* (L.) Link (P)	Europe
Spanish broom	*Spartium junceum* L. (P)	Southern Europe
Star thistle complex	*Centaurea* sp.	Mediterranean
Tansy ragwort	*Senecio jacobaea* L. (2A)	Europe
Water hyacinth	*Eichhornia crassipes* (Mart.) Solms (P)	Tropical America

(A)=Annual (2A)=Biannual
(P)=Perennial (p) =Parasitic

Of the weeds listed, the following are primarily range and pasture weeds.

Halogeton glomeratus has increased alarmingly in the last few years and is found most abundantly in the Great Salt Lake Basin areas of the intermountain states. This is truly an undesirable weed. In addition to its aggressiveness, it is very toxic to livestock.

Research on the possibilities of obtaining destructive insects has been under way since 1956 with the establishment of a research laboratory in Tehran, Iran. To the best of available information this plant originated in Russia just east of the Caspian Sea. Because of this, it was thought that infestations would be encountered in northern Iran; unfortunately this did not prove to be the case. *Halogeton sativus* (L) was recorded as existing in Spain and North Africa, and since this plant resembled *H. glomeratus* in so many ways and also grew in localities which were ecologically similar, it was decided to move the work to Morocco. Subsequently, the project leader, Dr. J. J. Drea, has found adequate infestations and the work has shown considerable progress. A moth, *Heterographis fulvolbasella* Rag., found in North Africa and Spain is very destructive to the vegetative growth, causing plants to be severely stunted and greatly reducing seed production. Host preference tests have shown that this insect is limited in its feeding preference and in all probability attempts will be made to introduce and establish this insect.

Centaurea spp., Star thistle complex. This group of unpalatable range weeds has, during the past ten years, shown a great increase in California and in some of the other western states. During the past several years, requests had been made for work on the yellow star thistle but no research could be initiated because of a conflict of interest. The main objection was on the part of beekeeping groups. This conflict was resolved in 1959 and research began during that year and will continue with increasing emphasis during 1960 and beyond.

Salvia aethiopis L., Mediterranean sage. This weed is becoming an increasing problem in Oregon and north-east California. Until recently, finding its native home was a problem, but it is now located in Greece, Turkey, and occasionally in Italy and France. Preliminary field work was started in 1959 and will be continued.

Cytisus scoparius (L.) Link, Scotch broom. During the autumn of 1959 all of the preliminary work was completed with a lepidopterous leaf and stem miner, *Leucoptera spartifoliella* Hübner. Laboratory preference tests have shown this insect to be specific. Permission was obtained to introduce this insect and initial releases were made in June, 1960. It became established and it is hoped that the colonies will increase so that in the near future it can be moved to the heavily infested areas.

Scotch broom is a pest on range lands and hinders reforestation by competing with seedling trees and it also increases the fire hazard among older trees. It is hoped that the introduction of the leaf and stem miner will lessen the competitive value of Scotch broom and thus give the seedling trees a better opportunity of establishment and growth. It is also hoped that a reduction in vegetative growth will diminish the damage caused by fires. Additional work is still being done in the foreign field where seed insects are being investigated.

Cardus spp., Italian thistle. This annual is a problem of long standing on ranges and dairy pastures in the coastal counties of California. Insect enemies are being sought in the Mediterranean area. The thistle group has quite a complement of insects and the dipterous species infesting seed heads appear to be an important factor in the abundance of the plants.

Alternanthera philoxeroides (Mart.) Griseb, alligator weed. This aquatic or semi-aquatic plant has become a severe pest of waterways and rice culture in the south and south-eastern states. Investigations are currently under way in South America, and a laboratory is being opened in Argentina for a study of the insects associated with this plant.

Eichhornia crassipes (Mart.) Solms, water hyacinth. This floating perennial clogs streams, impeding navigation and obstructing water flow (Robbins, Bellue, and Ball 1951). Preliminary plans are being made to investigate the insects of this weed.

Tribulus terrestris L., *puncture vine*. In Europe a stem weevil, *Microlarinus lypriformis* (Woll.), and a seed weevil, *M. lareynii* (J–D.), appeared to be important factors in regulating the abundance of puncture vine. It was found that both species were sufficiently specific to warrant introduction (Huffaker, Ricker, and Kennett 1961). Trial releases of both species are being made in Arizona, California, Nevada, Utah, and Washington. The seed weevil only has been released in Colorado.

Puncture vine has a great ecological amplitude in North America, and it will be interesting to see how well the introduced insects will be able to adapt themselves to the range of climatic conditions which will be encountered.

PROCEDURES

Successful biological control of weeds is dependent on the attack of phytophagous insects on the unwanted plants, and plant destruction must in some way lower the competitive value of the weed. This can be accomplished by various degrees of feeding on the vegetative process of the plant. It can be readily seen that by the nature of this requirement utmost precautions must be taken in investigation procedures and in interpretation of observations. Each problem could present conditions unique to the specific investigation; therefore, only the basic or fundamental procedures are brought out.

Conflict of Interest

When chemicals are used on weeds there is a reasonable amount of control over the geographical area covered by the operations so there need not be a conflict of interest in the event a plant is a weed to some and is a desirable plant to others. However, when considering the introduction of an insect to control a weed, it must be assumed that if the insect becomes established it could ultimately be found in all locations and situations in which the plant occurs. It is therefore necessary to determine if a weed is an unwanted plant in all the localities where it grows, or, if it is desired by some, how much loss would be sustained if it were attacked.

Conflicts of interest may exist in groups closely associated in agricultural interests. An example of this is the *Opuntia* spp. Some cattlemen classify it as a desirable plant while others consider it a scourge. In other instances the interests may be more diverse; bees thrive on yellow star thistle, which is a poor source of forage for domestic animals, but those interested in bees have for a long time opposed a biological control programme; Scotch broom is used for soil retention but conflicts with reforestation efforts. If conflicts do occur they must be settled before a research programme is organized, and this calls for considerable review of the economics involved so that arbitration can determine whose interests should be given precedence, and in some cases several years may elapse before an agreement is reached. It can be seen that this problem is a very important initial phase of a project in the biological control of weeds.

Foreign Exploration

Searching for the native home of plants can, on occasion, become an elusive occupation. This is especially true of some of the cosmopolitan weeds which have followed man and his domestic animals in their many centuries of migration over the face of the earth. The search for *Halogeton glomeratus* is an example. This species of *Halogeton* supposedly and very likely originated in the desert areas east of the Caspian Sea in Russia, and records are available which show it to exist at present in this location, an area inaccessible to collectors from the United States. Since the plant has scattered over large geographical areas in the United States, it was assumed that the weed could be found in north-east Iran, as this location is a continuation of the Caspian Sea and climatically similar to the slightly more northern location in Russia. Unfortunately, not a trace of *Halogeton* was to be found in Iran, and travellers to Russia have failed to observe this species not too distant from its recorded native home. Apparently the plant is much more restricted there than in the Great Salt Lake Basin of the United States.

Host Specificity of Insects

The necessity of finding host-specific insects is a very obvious one, as it would be unthinkable to consider introducing an insect which could potentially damage economic crops. Also, a monophagous insect obligated to its host plant should be able to reduce a plant to lower levels than one with a varied diet.

The desired degree of specificity would be provided by an insect, which, under natural conditions and during its life history, feeds and breeds on one plant species exclusively. Fortunately there are many species of insects which meet this requirement, and it has also been found that specialized life histories exist which further obligate an insect to a specific plant.

While experimenting with the two species of *Chrysolina* for *Hypericum* control, it was found that the ornamental St. John's Wort was chemically suitable as food for adult beetles. About 2,000 adults were released in a small patch and subsequently the plants were observed for injury. Within two months following release a small amount of injury was noted and an occasional egg was seen. The following year there were no beetles present and it was subsequently found that the first- and second-instar larvae, in order to feed successfully, had to be enclosed in a tender growing bud and it so happens that the ornamental plant does not produce tender buds during the period of early larval activity. Therefore, neither species of the introduced beetles could breed on a plant which had been found to be suitable food for adult beetles. There have been no reports of these beetles causing any difficulty by attacking the ornamental *Hypericum*.

Before an insect is to be considered for introduction it should be thoroughly tested in the country of origin to determine if it will feed and breed on plants closely related to the weed. Secondly, it should also be tested on representatives of other plant families which have as nearly as possible some physical or chemical attribute similar to the weed species. In addition to specificity, it is also advisable to search museum records and economic crop reports, and to make field surveys of the economic plants in the vicinity in which the weed and its insects naturally occur. It may be necessary on occasions to make additional tests under quarantine conditions after importation, but it is believed that testing at the destination should be avoided if possible, and under no conditions should such tests be made with an insect of known economic importance.

Quarantine Aspects

As mentioned earlier it is desirable to complete all specificity tests in the country of origin so that the only precaution upon arrival would be to guard against the inclusion of other phytophagous insects and to exclude parasites and predators of the desired insects. This work can be adequately handled in facilities normally used for the importation of entomophagous insects and with the same precautions. However, if experimental breeding on plants in quarantine is to be done, the problem is more complicated, as many plants will not survive under the lighting conditions encountered in an insect-tight quarantine room. To overcome this difficulty it is sometimes advisable to grow the plants in a greenhouse and bring in only small portions of plants free of soil for observational purposes. After completion of observation, the plant material can be safely disposed of without removal from quarantine.

The ideal condition would be to handle all the experimental work in an insect-tight glasshouse. Such facilities are available in Hawaii, which not only enjoys the reputation of engaging in the first attempted biological control of a weed but has continued its progressive work over the years.

Attempts to produce phytophagous insects for continuous mass-release purposes are, in most instances, too difficult to be economically feasible, especially if the insects have less than three generations a year. The main difficulties arise from the necessity of keeping the various greenhouse pest insects under control without harming the beneficial insects which are being reared.

When importing weed insects it has been found most desirable to ship them at a stage which is least susceptible to parasitization, e.g., with the exception of disease organisms, the adults are often found to be free of parasites. For detailed importation procedures see chapter 22.

SECTION VIII

Conclusion

CHAPTER 24

Successes, Trends, and Future Possibilities

PAUL DeBACH

EARLIER IN THIS BOOK many of the important successes in biological control were discussed to illustrate particular points. However, these are scattered and incomplete so a more or less complete list of the outstanding, substantial, or partial successes resulting from the *purposeful* introduction of insect parasites or predators to control insect pests was compiled for this chapter in order to analyse results and to draw some conclusions and generalizations regarding why, where, and how these came about. Recent trends in biological control also will be analysed, inasmuch as they tend to point out changes in lines of attack. Then conclusions, based on earlier work and recent trends, will emphasize the future possibilities in biological control and the means of enhancing their attainment.

SUCCESSES FOLLOWING IMPORTATION OF ENTOMOPHAGOUS INSECTS

Success is a relative thing, but here we shall measure it in an economic sense, hence outstanding successes refer to complete biological control being obtained and maintained against a major pest of a major crop over a fairly extensive area so that insecticidal treatment becomes rarely, if ever, necessary. Substantial successes will include cases where economic savings are somewhat less pronounced by reason of the pest or crop being less important, by the crop area being restricted (such as on a small island), or by the control being such that occasional insecticidal treatment is indicated.

Partial successes are those where chemical control measures remain commonly necessary but either the intervals between necessary applications are lengthened or results are improved when the same treatments are used or outbreaks occur less frequently. This category may also include cases where complete biological control is obtained only in a minor portion of the pest-infested area, or where entomophagous insects are only partially responsible for control results, as well as insufficiently substantiated cases. Some of these latter may include completely successful cases which merely have not been adequately documented in the literature. Partial successes tend to be overlooked or discounted but nonetheless they often represent a considerable savings as measured by reduction in damage or lessened need for treatment. Separation of the above-mentioned categories, one from the other, is, of course, arbitrary and open to interpretation, and additional information may necessitate changes. An extensive card file, which was made available to the author by C. P. Clausen, has been of great assistance in preparing the following tabulation of successes. It is emphasized that these successes resulted from importation projects. No cases of naturally occurring biological control are included; to attempt this would require another book. Neither are cases of biological control by micro-organisms or biological control of weeds included here, inasmuch as they have been thoroughly discussed in chapters 21 and 23. Also, the few cases of biological control by higher organisms, such as amphibians, birds, and mammals, are purposely omitted in order to restrict the analysis to the insect parasites and predators which have been responsible for the great majority of successes in biological control of insect pests.

The tabulation of biological control successes is given in three separate tables for purposes of analysis, clarity of presentation, and ease of discussion. Table 12 lists examples under the host (pest) species alone, regardless of the number of countries in which this has occurred but does not include cases of duplication of control of the same host by the same species of natural enemies for the four most commonly controlled species—*Aleurocanthus woglumi* Ashby, *Eriosoma lanigerum* (Hausm.), *Icerya purchasi* Mask., and *Pseudaulacaspis pentagona* (Targ.). Table 13 supports table 12 by showing the additional countries in which these four most commonly controlled pest species have been subjugated by their natural enemies; undoubtedly more countries remain to be included under biological control of *Icerya* and *Eriosoma*. Table 14 summarizes the total number of cases of biological control for each country regardless of previous occurrence (duplication) in other countries. In addition to the cases listed in table 12 there are several which have not been included there because of insufficient documentation or lack of data. Among these possible successes are: (1) the garden looper, several bruchid seed weevils, and the coconut and sugar-cane leaf rollers in Hawaii (Pemberton 1941); (2) the rice armyworm and the rice leaf roller in Fiji (Thompson 1958); (3) the citrophilus mealybug (H. Compere, personal communication), and the Sirex pine sawfly (Cottier, personal communication) in New Zealand; (4) the palmetto scale in Bermuda (Bennett and Hughes 1959); (5) the diamondback moth in Java and Sumatra (R. G. Sutardi, personal communication); (6) the European pine sawfly in Canada (Baird 1958); (7) a whitefly in Celebes (Voûte 1937); (8) the banana stem borer in Australia (Wilson 1953); (9) the golden oak scale in South Africa (Evans 1952); (10) the coconut rhinoceros beetle in various Pacific Islands (Gardner 1958); and (11) several pests, especially scales and mealybugs in South Russia, mentioned by Rubtsov (1957), Franz (1961*b*) in a review of the recent Russian and European work. Mellini (1958) also has reviewed the European and other work and discusses some of the same cases.

It would naturally be hoped that an analysis of the more than 220 cases involving about 110 species of pests being controlled to a greater or less degree by natural enemies in some 60-odd countries or islands might reveal one or several common denominators characterizing successful natural enemies which could point the way for future work. Such an idea is not new, and previous workers have presented various hypotheses as to why particular natural enemies controlled or failed to control particular hosts in particular countries or islands (see chapter 5). Some of these hypotheses stated in effect: (1) biological control works better on islands; (2) parasites are better than predators (or vice versa); (3) monophagous enemies are better than polyphagous enemies (or vice versa); (4) many species of enemies (attacking one host species) are better than one; (5) egg parasites acting alone are ineffective; (6) complete biological control following an introduction must occur rapidly (three years or three host generations) or else will not be complete; (7) biological control is most likely to be successful where the host plants are trees or other long-lived perennials; (8) sessile hosts—particularly Coccidae—are more amenable to biological control than other types; (9) the natural enemy should come from the same host in the country of origin; (10) natural enemies should be imported from areas ecologically equivalent ('ecological analogue' of Wilson (1960b)) to the area of introduction; and (11) immigrant pests offer the best opportunities for biological control. Various of these hypotheses (perhaps especially Nos. 3, 4, 9, 10, and 11) involve procedures or broad biological principles of considerable significance and therefore definitely indicate initial direction for research on new projects.

Although the weight of evidence may support many of these hypotheses as stated, I believe that the observed results have sometimes been attributed to the wrong causes. There are important exceptions or qualifications to each of the preceding hypotheses so that to generalize in advance regarding chances of success would be to risk the possibility of dooming a new project by precluding important trials of one sort or another. For example, complete biological control has occurred in all types of plant environments with many types (groups) of pests and has been brought about by egg parasites, larval parasites, or pupal parasites acting substantially alone, by predators acting substantially alone, as well as by various combinations of parasites and/or predators acting together. Actually, more biological control successes have occurred on continents than islands. Fairly monophagous species usually seem to do the best job, but there are important exceptions. Also, natural enemies obtained from other host species in the country of origin sometimes have been strikingly successful, as have natural enemies imported from areas not ecologically equivalent. Native pests also have been controlled by imported natural enemies. That a complete case of biological control will occur usually seems to be evident within two or three years, but exceptions to this, such as with *Gonipterus* in South Africa, occur. The chances of success with a new project are undoubtedly greater if we proceed with a scientifically planned programme, but this should not influence the eventual exploration of alternative possibilities if the first leads fail. As Wilson (1960b) says 'It is strange to reflect that although there are so many examples of successful biological control in the world, we cannot give an adequate account of why these particular examples were successful.'

At the risk of being anticipatory by presenting conclusions before discussing the evidence and for purposes of emphasis, the following broad summarization regarding the expectancy of success with new projects in biological control is presented.

TABLE 12

Cases of biological control of pest insects. (Only place of first success listed for Aleurocanthus woglumi, Eriosoma lanigerum, Icerya purchasi, and Pseudaulacaspis pentagona, except cases where different natural enemies are involved. Subsequent successes listed in table 13.)

Scientific name	Common name	Crop attacked	Place of infestation	Principal natural enemies			Control results C = complete S = substantial P = partial	Reference
				Name	Type	Place of origin and date		
				HOMOPTERA				
Aleurocanthus spiniferus (Quaint.)	spiny blackfly	citrus	Japan	Prospaltella smithi Silv.	parasite	China 1925	C	Kuwana, 1934; Watanabe, 1958
			Guam	Prospaltella smithi Silv.; Amitus hesperidum Silv.	parasites	Mexico 1952	S	Peterson, 1954a; Gardner, 1958
Aleurocanthus* woglumi Ashby	citrus blackfly	citrus	Cuba	Eretmocerus serius Silv.	parasite	Malaya 1930	C	Clausen, 1952a; 1958b
			Mexico	Amitus hesperidum Silv.; Prospaltella opulenta Silv.; Prospaltella clypealis Silv.	parasites	India and Pakistan 1949	C	Clausen, 1958b
Aleurodicus cocois Curt.	coconut white-fly	coconut, other palms	Barbados	Prospaltella sp.	parasite	Trinidad	P	Simmonds, 1958d
Aonidiella aurantii (Mask.)	California red scale	citrus	U.S.A. (Calif.)	Aphytis lingnanensis Comp; Aphytis melinus DeB.	parasites	S. China 1947; India and Pakistan	P	BeBach (unpublished data)
			Australia	Aphytis chrysomphali (Mercet)?	parasite	China 1905	P	Wilson, 1960a
Aonidiella citrina (Coq.)	yellow scale	citrus	U.S.A. (Calif.)	Comperiella bifasciata How.	parasite	Japan 1924-25	S	Clausen, 1956a; 1958a
Aphis sacchari Zhnt.	sugar cane aphis	sugar cane	U.S.A. (Hawaii)	a complex	parasite, various predators	various 1900-23	S	Pemberton, 1948a

Pest	Common name	Crop / habitat	Introduced to	Enemy type	Natural enemy	From	Result	Reference
Aspidiotus destructor Sign.	coconut scale	coconut, other palms	Fiji	predator	Cryptognatha nodiceps Mshll.	Trinidad 1928	C	Taylor, 1935
			Mauritius	predators	Chilocorus politus Muls.; Chilocorus nigritus Muls.	Java 1937, Ceylon 1939	C	Moutia and Mamet, 1946
			Port. W. Africa (Principe)	predator	Cryptognatha nodiceps Mshll.	Trinidad 1955	C	Simmonds, 1959
			Bali	parasite	Aspidiotiphagus citrinus (Craw)	Java 1934	P	Voûte, 1937
Asterolecanium pustulans (Ckll.)	bamboo (pustule) scale	forest, shade trees, ornamentals	Puerto Rico	predator	Chilocorus cacti (L.)	Cuba, Louisiana, Texas 1937	P	Wolcott, 1953; 1958
Asterolecanium variolosum (Ratz.)	golden oak scale	oak	New Zealand	parasite	Habrolepis dalmani (Westw.)	N. America	S	Miller, Clark, and Dumbleton, 1936; Thompson, 1958
			Tasmania	parasite	Habrolepis dalmani (Westw.)	New Zealand 1931–33	P	Miller, 1947; Wilson, 1960a
Brevicoryne brassicae (L.)	cabbage aphid	cabbage	Australia	parasite	unknown sp.	Ceylon 1907	P	Jenkins, 1948; Wilson, 1960a
Ceroplastes rubens Mask.	red wax scale	citrus persimmon tea	Japan (Honshu, Shikoku)	parasite	Anicetus beneficus Ishii and Yasumatsu	Japan (Kyushu) 1948	C	Yasumatsu, 1958
Chromaphis juglandicola (Kalt.)	walnut aphid	walnut	U.S.A. (Calif.)	parasite	Trioxys pallidus (Hal.)	France, Iran 1959	P	van den Bosch, Schlinger, and Hagen (except 1962)
Chrysomphalus aonidum (L.) (= ficus Ashm.)	Florida red scale	citrus	Israel	parasite	Aphytis holoxanthus DeB.	Hong Kong 1956	C	Cohen, I. (corres.)
			Seychelles	predator	Chilocorus nigritus (F.)	India 1938	S	Vesey-Fitzgerald, 1953
Eriococcus coriaceus Mask.	blue gum scale	eucalyptus	New Zealand	predator	Rhizobius ventralis (Er.)	Australia 1905	C	Miller, Clark, and Dumbleton, 1936; Thompson, 1958
Eriosoma* lanigerum (Hausm.)	woolly apple aphid	apple	New Zealand	parasite	Aphelinus mali (Hald.)	U.S.A. (northeast) 1921	C	Miller, Clark, and Dumbleton, 1936

* See additional cases in table 13.

TABLE 12—continued

Scientific name	Common name	Crop attacked	Place of infestation	Principal natural enemies Name	Type	Place of origin and date	Control results C = complete S = substantial P = partial	Reference
Eulecanium coryli (L.)	European fruit lecanium	forest trees ornamentals	Canada (Br. Columbia)	Blastothrix sericea (Dalm.)	parasite	England 1928–29	S	Glendenning, 1933; McLeod, 1954
Eulecanium persicae (F.)	vine scale	grapevine plum, etc.	Australia (western, etc.)	Aphycus timberlakei Ishii	parasite	U.S.A. (Calif.) 1907	S	Jenkins, 1948; Wilson, 1960a
Icerya aegyptiaca (Dougl.)	Egyptian mealy-bug or fluted scale	breadfruit avocado	Caroline Islands	Rodolia pumila (Weise)	predator	Mariana Islands 1947–49	S	Pemberton, 1954; Beardsley, 1955; Gardner, 1958
Icerya montserratensis Riley and Howard	fluted scale	citrus	Ecuador	Rodolia cardinalis (Muls.)	predator	U.S.A. 1941	S	Rodriguez L., 1942
Icerya palmeri Riley and Howard	fluted scale	citrus	Chile	Rodolia cardinalis (Muls.)	predator	U.S.A. (Calif.) 1931	P	Graf Marin and Cortes Peña, 1940
Icerya purchasi* Mask.	cottony-cushion scale	citrus	U.S.A. (Calif.)	Rodolia cardinalis (Muls.); Cryptochaetum iceryae (Will.)	predator parasite	Australia 1888–89 Australia 1888–89)	C	Clausen 1956a; 1958a
Icerya seychellarum (Westw.)	fluted scale	fruit and timber trees	Seychelles	Rodolia cardinalis (Muls.)	predator	Mauritius 1939	P	Vesey-Fitzgerald, 1953
Ischnaspis longirostris (Sign.)	black thread scale	coconut palm	Seychelles	Chilocorus nigritus (F.); Chilocorus distigma (Klug.)	predators	India 1938 E. Africa 1936	S	Vesey-Fitzgerald, 1953
Lepidosaphes beckii (Newm.)	purple scale	citrus	U.S.A. (Calif.)	Aphytis lepidosaphes Comp.	parasite	S. China and Formosa 1948–49	P	Clausen, 1956a; 1958b
			Mexico	Aphytis lepidosaphes Comp.	parasite	U.S.A. (Calif.) 1954–56	S	H. D. Smith (pers. comm.)
			U.S.A. (Texas)	Aphytis lepidosaphes Comp.	parasite	U.S.A. (Calif.) 1952	S	Dean, 1961

678

Pest	Common name	Plant	Locality	Natural enemy		Introduced from		Reference
Lepidosaphes ficus (Sign.)	fig scale	fig	U.S.A. (Calif.)	*Aphytis mytilaspidis* (LeB.)	parasite	France 1949	P	Clausen, 1956a
Lepidosaphes ulmi (L.)	oystershell scale	deciduous fruits	Canada (Br. Columbia)	*Hemisarcoptes malus* (Schimer)	predator	Canada (New Brunswick) 1917	P	McLeod, 1954; A. B. Baird, 1958
Macrosiphum pisi (Harris)	pea aphid	alfalfa	U.S.A. (Calif.)	*Aphidius smithi* Sharma and Rao	parasite	India 1958	S	Hagen, Schlinger and van den Bosch (unpublished data, 1961)
Myzocallis annulata (Hart.)	oak aphid	oak	Tasmania	*Aphelinus flavus* (Nees)	parasite	England 1937–38	P	Wilson, 1960a
Nipaecoccus (= *Pseudococcus*) *nipae* (Mask.)	avocado mealybug (coconut mealybug in Bermuda)	guava avocado fig mulberry, etc.	U.S.A. (Hawaii)	*Pseudaphycus utilis* Timb.	parasite	Mexico 1922	S	Pemberton, 1948a
Nipaecoccus (= *Pseudococcus*) *filamentosus* (Ckll.)	Lebbek mealybug	shade trees	Egypt	*Anagyrus aegyptiacus* Moursi; *Leptomastix phenacocci* Comp.	parasites	Java 1934–39	P	Kamal, 1951a
Orthezia insignis Dougl.	greenhouse orthezia	various plants	U.S.A. (Hawaii)	*Anagyrus dactylopii* Comp. (How.)	parasite	Hong Kong 1925	P	Swezey, 1934
		ornamentals	Kenya	*Hyperaspis jocosa* Muls.	predator	Hawaii 1948	S	LePelley, 1955
Parlatoria oleae (Colvée)	olive scale	olive, deciduous fruit trees, ornamentals	U.S.A. (Calif.)	*Aphytis maculicornis* (Masi)	parasite	Iran	S	Clausen, 1956a; Huffaker and Kennett, 1960
Perkinsiella saccharacida Kirk.	sugar cane leafhopper	sugar cane	U.S.A. (Hawaii)	*Cyrtorhinus mundulus* (Bredd.)	predator	Australia 1920	C	Pemberton, 1948a
Phenacoccus hirsutus Green	hibiscus mealybug	many ornamentals, crop plants	Egypt	*Leptomastix phenacocci* Comp.; *Anagyrus aegyptiacus* Moursi; *Achrysopophagus* sp.	parasites	Java 1934–39	S	Kamal, 1951a
Phenacoccus iceryoides Green	mealybug	coffee	Celebes	*Cryptolaemus montrouzieri* (Muls.)	predator	Java 1920	S	van der Vecht, 1953
Phenacoccus (= *Pseudococcus*) *aceris* Sign.	apple mealybug	apple	Canada (Br. Columbia)	*Allotropa utilis* Mues.	parasite	Canada (Nova Scotia) 1938	C	Marshall, 1953; McLeod, 1954; A. B. Baird, 1958

679

* See additional cases in table 13.

TABLE 12—continued

Scientific name	Common name	Crop attacked	Place of infestation	Principal natural enemies			Control results C = complete S = substantial P = partial	Reference
				Name	Type	Place of origin and date		
Pineus boerneri (Ann.)	pine chermid	Monterey pine	New Zealand	*Neoleucopis obscura* (Hal.)	predator	Europe 1932–34	P	Rawlings, 1958
Pinnaspis buxi (Bouché)	a coconut scale	coconut other palms	U.S.A. (Hawaii) Seychelles	*Telsimia nitida* Chapin	predator	Guam 1936	S	Pemberton, 1948a
				Chilocorus nigritus (F.)	predator	India 1938	S	Vesey-Fitzgerald, 1953; Wille, 1958
Pinnaspis minor (Mask.)	cotton white scale	cotton	Peru	a complex	parasites and predators	Barbados, Italy, Japan, U.S.A.	P	
Planococcus (= *Pseudococcus*) *citri* (Risso)	citrus mealybug	citrus	U.S.A. (Calif.)	*Cryptolaemus montrouzieri* (Muls.); *Leptomastidea abnormis* (Grlt.)	predator parasite	1904–12 Australia 1891–92 Sicily 1914	P	Clausen 1956a; 1958b
		citrus	Chile	*Cryptolaemus montrouzieri* (Muls.); *Leptomastidea abnormis* (Grlt.)	predator parasite	U.S.A. (Calif.) 1931 U.S.A. (Calif.) 1931	P	Graf Marin and Cortes Peña, 1940
		citrus etc.	U.S.A. (Hawaii)	*Leptomastidea abnormis* (Grlt.)	parasite	U.S.A. (Calif.) 1915	P	Swezey, 1934
Planococcus (= *Pseudococcus*) *kenyae* (LeP.)	coffee mealybug	coffee	Kenya	*Anagyrus* nr. *kivuensis* (Comp.)	parasite	Uganda 1938	C	LePelley, 1951; Thompson, 1958
*Pseudaulacaspis** (= *Diaspis*) *pentagona* (Targ.)	white peach scale	mulberry	Italy	*Prospaltella berlesei* (How.)	parasite	U.S.A. 1905	S	Malenotti, 1948
		mulberry	Puerto Rico	*Chilocorus cacti* (L.)	predator	Cuba 1938	S	Wolcott, 1958
		papaya, etc. oleander	Bermuda	*Aphytis diaspidis* (How.)	parasite	Italy 1924	P	Bennett and Hughes, 1959

680

Host species	Common name	Host plant	Location	Natural enemy	Type	Source & year	Result	Reference
Pseudococcus spp.	mealybugs	citrus	Australia (western)	*Cryptolaemus montrouzieri* (Muls.)	predator	New South Wales 1902	S	Wilson, 1960a
Pseudococcus citriculus Green	mealybug	citrus	Israel	*Clausenia purpurea* Ishii	parasite	Japan 1939	C	Rivnay, 1946; Clausen, 1958b; Cohen, I. (pers. comm.)
Pseudococcus adonidum (L.) (= *longispinus* (Targ.))	long-tailed mealybug	citrus avocado	U.S.A. (Calif.)	*Anarhopus sydneyensis* Timb.; *Tetracnemus peregrinus* Comp.	parasites	Australia 1933 Brazil 1934	P	Clausen, 1956a; 1958a
			Bermuda	*Tetracneuus peregrinus* Comp.; *Anagyrus fusciventris* (Grlt.)	parasites	U.S.A. (Calif.) 1951	P	Bennett and Hughes, 1959
Pseudococcus comstocki (Kuw.)	Comstock mealybug	apple	U.S.A. (eastern)	*Allotropa burrelli* Mues.; *Pseudaphycus malinus* Gah.	parasites	Japan 1939–41	C	Clausen, 1956a; 1958a
		apple and others	U.S.S.R. (Uzbekistan)	*Pseudaphycus malinus* Gah.	parasite	U.S.A. 1945	P	Rubtsov, 1957a
Pseudococcus gahani Green	citrophilus mealybug	citrus	U.S.A. (Calif.)	*Coccophagus gurneyi* Comp.; *Tetracnemus pretiosus* Timb.	parasites	Australia 1928	C	Clausen, 1956a; 1958a
			Chile	*Coccophagus gurneyi* Comp.	parasite	U.S.A. (Calif.) 1936	S	Graf Marin and Cortes Peña, 1940
Pulvinaria psidii Mask.	green shield scale	shade trees	Puerto Rico	*Cryptolaemus montrouzieri* (Muls.)	predator	U.S.A. (Calif.) 1911	P	Wolcott, 1948; 1958
			Bermuda	*Microterys kotinskyi* (Full.)	parasite	U.S.A. (Hawaii and Calif.)	P	Bennett and Hughes, 1959
Quadraspidiotus perniciosus (Comst.)	San Jose scale	deciduous fruit trees	U.S.A. (Calif.)	*Prospaltella perniciosi* Tow.	parasite	1953–55 Georgia 1933	P	Clausen, 1956a

* See additional cases in table 13.

681

TABLE 12—continued

Scientific name	Common name	Crop attacked	Place of infestation	Principal natural enemies			Control results C = complete S = substantial P = partial	Reference
				Name	Type	Place of origin and date		
Saissetia oleae (Bern.)	black scale	citrus olive citrus olive	U.S.A. (Calif.) Australia	Metaphycus helvolus (Comp.) Scutellista cyanea Mots.; Metaphycus lounsburyi (How.)	parasite parasites	S. Africa 1937 various	S P	Clausen, 1956a; 1958a Jenkins, 1948; Wilson, 1960a
		olive	Peru	Metaphycus lounsburyi (How.); Lecaniobius utilis Comp.; Scutellista cyanea Mots.	parasites	U.S.A. (Calif.) 1936	S	Wille, 1940
		olive	Chile	Metaphycus helvolus (Comp.)	parasite	Peru 1946	P	Isla Marco, 1959
Saissetia nigra (Nietn.)	nigra scale	citrus ornamentals	U.S.A. (Calif.)	Metaphycus helvolus (Comp.)	parasite	S. Africa 1937	S	Clausen, 1956a; 1958a
Siphanta acuta (Wlk.)	torpedo bug planthopper	coffee mango citrus and others	U.S.A. (Hawaii)	Aphanomerus pusillus Perkins	parasite	Australia 1904	S	Pemberton, 1948a
Tarophagus (= Megamelus) proserpina (Kirk.)	taro leafhopper	taro	U.S.A. (Hawaii)	Cyrtorhinus fulvus Knight	predator	Philippines	S	Pemberton, 1954
			Guam	Cyrtorhinus fulvus Knight	predator	Hawaii 1947	S	Pemberton, 1954
			Ponape	Cyrtorhinus fulvus Knight	predator	Guam 1947	P	Pemberton, 1954
Therioaphis maculata (Buck.)	spotted alfalfa aphid	alfalfa	U.S.A. (Calif.)	a complex of native predators, disease, and the imported parasites Praon palitans Mues., Trioxys utilis Mues., Aphelinus semiflavus How.	par., pred. and disease	par. from Middle East 1955–56	S for parasites	R. van den Bosch (pers. comm.)

682

Pest	Common name	Crop	Locality	Natural enemy	Status	Origin/date	S/P	Reference
Trialeurodes vaporariorum (Westw.)	greenhouse whitefly	tomatoes, etc.	Australia	Encarsia formosa Gah.	parasite	New Zealand 1934	S	Noble, 1938a; Wilson, 1953; 1960a
			Tasmania	Encarsia formosa Gah.	parasite	New Zealand 1934	S	Wilson, 1960a
Trionymus sacchari (Ckll.)	pink sugar-cane mealybug	sugar-cane	U.S.A. (Hawaii)	Anagyrus saccharicola Timb.	parasite	Philippines 1930	S	Pemberton, 1948a
Typhlocyba froggatti Baker (= australis Frogg.)	apple leaf-hopper	apple	Tasmania	Anagrus armatus nigriventris Grlt.	parasite	New Zealand 1935	P	Miller, 1947; Wilson, 1960a

LEPIDOPTERA

Pest	Common name	Crop	Locality	Natural enemy	Status	Origin/date	S/P	Reference
Bedellia orchilella Walsm.	leaf miner	sweet potato	U.S.A. (Hawaii)	Apanteles bedelliae Vier.	parasite	Kansas 1945	P	Pemberton, 1953
Chilo suppressalis (Wlk.)	asiatic rice borer	rice	U.S.A. (Hawaii)	Trichogramma japonicum Ashm.; Amyosoma chilonis Vier.; Dioctes chilonis Cush.	parasites	Japan, China, Formosa 1928	P	Pemberton, 1948a
Pseudaletia (= Cirphis) unipuncta (Haw.)	armyworm	sugar-cane, etc.	U.S.A. (Hawaii)	a complex	parasites	Mexico 1923–24	P	Pemberton, 1948b
Cnidocampa flavescens (Wlk.)	oriental moth	shade trees	U.S.A. (Mass.)	Chaetexorista javana B. and B.	parasite	Japan 1929–30	S	Clausen, 1956a; 1958b
Coleophora laricella (Hbn.)	larch case-bearer	larch	Canada	Agathis pumilus (Ratz.); Chrysocharis laricinellae (Ratz.)	parasites	England 1938 or 1939	S	Glen, 1954b; A. B. Baird, 1958
Diatraea saccharalis (F.)	sugar-cane borer	sugar-cane	West Indies (Antigua) (St. Kitts) (St. Lucia)	Lixophaga diatraeae (Tns.)	parasite		S	Simmonds, 1958d
				Metagonistylum minense Tns.	parasite		S	Simmonds, 1958d
			(Dominica)	Paratheresia claripalpis (v.d.W.)	parasite		S	Simmonds, 1958d
			(Guadeloupe)	Paratheresia claripalpis (v.d.W.); Lixophaga diatraeae (Tns.). Metagonistylum minense Tns.	parasites		S	Simmonds (pers. comm.)

TABLE 12—continued

Scientific name	Common name	Crop attacked	Place of infestation	Principal natural enemies			Control results C = complete S = substantial P = partial	Reference
				Name	Type	Place of origin and date		
Diatraea saccharalis (F.)	sugar-cane borer	sugar-cane	U.S.A. (Florida)	Lixophaga diatraeae (Tns.); Agathis stigmaterus (Cress.)	parasite	Cuba 1915	P	Clausen, 1952; 1956a
Grapholitha (Laspeyresia) molesta (Busck)	oriental fruit moth	peach	U.S.A. (other than New Jersey)	Macrocentrus ancylivorus Roh.	parasite	Peru 1929, 1932 U.S.A. (New Jersey)	P	Clausen, 1958a
			Canada	Macrocentrus ancylivorus Roh.	parasite	U.S.A. (New Jersey) 1929–30	S	A. B. Baird, 1958
Harrisina brillians B. and McD.	western grape leaf skeletonizer	grapevine	U.S.A. (Calif.)	Apanteles harrisinae Mues.; Sturmia harrisinae Coq.	parasites	U.S.A. (Arizona) 1950–52	S	Clausen, 1958a; 1961
Homona coffearia Nietn.	tea tortrix	tea	Ceylon	Macrocentrus homonae Nixon	parasite	Java 1935–36	C	Gadd, 1941; Evans, 1952
Laphygma exempta (Wlk.)	nutgrass armyworm	sugar-cane, pasture	U.S.A. (Hawaii)	a complex	parasites	U.S.A. (Calif., Texas) Mexico	P	Swezey, 1934; Pemberton, 1948b
Laspeyresia nigricana (Steph.)	pea moth	vegetables	Canada (Br. Columbia)	Ascogaster quadridentata Wesm.; Glypta haesitator Grav.	parasites	England 1937–39	S	McLeod, 1954; A. B. Baird, 1958
Levuana iridescens B.-B.	coconut moth	coconut	Fiji	Ptychomyia (= Bessa) remota Ald.	parasite	Malaya 1925	C	Tothill, Taylor and Paine, 1930
Lithocolletis messaniella Zell.	oakleaf miner	oak	New Zealand	Apanteles circumscriptus Nees	parasite	Europe 1958–59	P	W. Cottier (pers. comm.). Simmonds, 1959

684

Host	Common name	Crop/habitat	Introduced to	Natural enemy		Origin and date	Est.	Reference
Nygmia phaeorrhoea (Donov.)	brown tail moth	deciduous forest and shade trees	U.S.A. (north-east)	Apanteles lacteicolor Vier.; Townsendiellomyia nidicola (Tns.); and others	parasites	Europe 1905–11	S	Clausen, 1956a; 1958a
			Canada	Compsilura concinnata (Mg.); Apanteles lacteicolor Vier.; Meteorus versicolor (Wesm.)	parasites	U.S.A. (eastern) 1912–15	C	Baird, 1956
Pieris rapae (L.)	imported cabbage-worm	cruciferous crops	New Zealand	Pteromalus puparum (L.)	parasite	N. America 1933	S	Miller, Clark and Dumbleton, 1936; Clausen, 1958b; Thompson, 1958; Todd, 1959a; Wilson, 1960a
			Australia	Pteromalus puparum (L.); Apanteles glomeratus (L.)	parasites	New Zealand 1941; Canada 1942	P	Wilson, 1960a
			Tasmania	Pteromalus puparum (L.); Apanteles glomeratus (L.)	parasites	New Zealand 1942 Australia 1949	P	Wilson, 1960a
Plutella maculipennis (Curt.)	diamondback moth	cruciferous crops	New Zealand	Angitia (= Horogenes) cerophaga (Grav.)	parasite	England 1936–37	S	Thompson, 1958; Todd, 1959a
			Australia	Angitia (= Horogenes) cerophaga (Grav.)	parasite	New Zealand 1947	P	Wilson, 1960a
			Tasmania	Angitia (= Horogenes) cerophaga (Grav.)	parasite	New Zealand 1946–47	P	Wilson, 1960a
Porthetria dispar (L.)	gypsy moth	forest and shade trees	U.S.A. (New England)	Compsilura concinnata (Mg.); Blepharipoda scutellata (R–D.); Apanteles melanoscelus (Ratz.); and a complex of others	parasites	Europe 1905–14 Japan 1922–23	P	Clausen, 1956a; 1958a
Ostrinia nubilalis (Hbn.) (= Pyrausta)	European corn borer	corn	U.S.A.	Lydella stabulans grisescens R–D.; Macrocentrus gifuensis Ashm.; and others	parasites	France, Italy, Japan, Korea, 1920–38	P	Clausen, 1958a
Rhyacionia frustrana bushnelli (Busck)	pine tip moth	pine trees	U.S.A. (Nebraska)	Campoplex frustranae Cush.	parasite	U.S.A. (Virginia) 1925	P	Clausen, 1956a

TABLE 12—continued

Scientific name	Common name	Crop attacked	Place of infestation	Principal natural enemies			Control results C = complete S = substantial P = partial	Reference
				Name	Type	Place of origin and date		
Stilpnotia salicis (L.)	satin moth		U.S.A. (New England, Pac. N.W.)	Apanteles solitarius (Ratz.); Meteorus versicolor (Wesm.)	parasites	Europe 1927–34	S	Clausen, 1958a
			Canada (Br. Columbia)	Apanteles solitarius (Ratz.); Meteorus versicolor (Wesm.); Compsilura concinnata (Mg.)	parasites	Canada (New Brunswick) U.S.A. (Mass.) 1929–34	S	Baird and McLeod, 1953
			Canada (Maritime Prov.)	Apanteles solitarius (Ratz.); Compsilura concinnata (Mg.)	parasites	U.S.A. 1933 U.S.A. 1912	P	Reeks and Smith, 1956; A. B. Baird, 1958
Tirathaba trichogramma Meyrick	coconut spike moth	coconut	Fiji	Apanteles tirathabae Walk; Erycia basifulva Bezzi; Telenomus tirathabae Ferr.	parasites	Java 1930–34	P	Paine, 1935; Lever, 1943; Clausen, 1958b
				COLEOPTERA				
Adoretus sinicus Burm.	Chinese rose beetle	many plants	U.S.A. (Hawaii)	Campsomeris marginella modesta Sm.; Tiphia segregata Cwfd.	parasites	Philippines 1916–17	P	Pemberton, 1954
Anomala orientalis Waterh.	oriental beetle	sugar-cane	U.S.A. (Hawaii)	Campsomeris marginella modesta Sm.; Tiphia segregata Cwfd.	parasites	Philippines 1916–17	S	Pemberton, 1948a
Anomala sulcatula Burm.		sugar-cane	Mariana Islands (Saipan)	Campsomeris annulata Fabr.	parasite	Philippines 1940	C	Yasumatsu, et al., 1953
Brontispa longissima selebensis Gestro (= froggatti Sharp)	coconut leaf miner	coconut	Celebes	Tetrastichus brontispae (Ferr.)	parasite	Java 1929	S	Clausen, 1958b; Tjoa Tjien Mo (pers. comm.)

686

Pest	Common name	Host plant	Locality	Natural enemy	Role	Source and date	Status	References
Brontispa mariana Spaeth	Mariana coconut beetle	coconut	Mariana Islands	*Tetrastichus brontispae* (Ferr.)	parasite	Malaya, Java 1948	S	Gardner, 1958
Clemora (= Phytalis) smithi Ol.	white grub	sugar-cane	Mauritius	*Campsomeris phalerata* Sauss.; *Tiphia parallela* Sm.; *Campsomeris coelebs* Sic.; *Campsomeris pilosella* Sauss.	parasites	Java 1935–36; Barbados 1913–14; Madagascar 1917; Madagascar 1932	P	Moutia and Mamet, 1946
Cosmopolites sordidus Germ.	banana root borer	banana	Fiji	*Plaesius javanus* (Erich.)	predator	Java 1912	P	Lever, 1943; Pemberton, 1954; Gardner, 1958; Simmonds, 1958d
			Jamaica	*Plaesius javanus* (Erich.)	predator	Fiji 1942	P	
Crioceris asparagi (L.)	asparagus beetle	asparagus	U.S.A. (Washington)	*Tetrastichus asparagi* Cwfd.	parasite	Ohio 1937	P	Johansen, 1957
Epilachna philippinensis (Dke.)	Philippine ladybeetle	various solanaceous vegetables	Guam	*Pediobius (Pleurotropis) epilachnae* (Roh.)	parasite	Philippines 1954	P	Peterson, 1955b
Galerucella xanthomelaena (Schr.)	elm leaf beetle	elm	U.S.A. (Calif.)	*Erynnia nitida* R-D. *Tetrastichus brevistigma* Gah.	parasites	France 1939; U.S.A. (eastern) 1934	P	Clausen, 1956a
Gonipterus scutellatus Gyll.	eucalyptus weevil	eucalyptus	S. Africa	*Patasson nitens* (Grlt.)	parasite	Australia 1926	C	Tooke, 1953
			New Zealand	*Patasson nitens* (Grlt.)	parasite	Australia 1927	S	Miller, Clark, and Dumbleton, 1936; Thompson, 1958; Williams, Moutia, and Hermelin, 1951; Thompson, 1958
			Mauritius	*Patasson nitens* (Grlt.)	parasite	E. Africa 1946	C	
			Kenya	*Patasson nitens* (Grlt.)	parasite		S	Clausen, 1958b
			Madagascar	*Patasson nitens* (Grlt.)	parasite		S	Clausen, 1956a; 1958a
Hypera postica (Gyll.)	alfalfa weevil	alfalfa	U.S.A. (Calif., Utah)	*Bathyplectes curculionis* (Thoms.)	parasite	Italy 1911–13	S	
Oryctes tarandus Ol.	rhinoceros beetle	sugar cane	Mauritius	*Scolia oryctophaga* Coq.	parasite	Madagascar 1917	S	Moutia and Mamet, 1946
Popillia japonica Newm.	Japanese beetle	turf, pasture fruits	U.S.A. (eastern)	*Tiphia vernalis* Roh.	parasite	Korea; S. China 1924–33	P	Clausen 1956a; 1958a

TABLE 12—continued

Scientific name	Common name	Crop attacked	Place of infestation	Principal natural enemies			Control results C = complete S = substantial P = partial	Reference
				Name	Type	Place of origin and date		
Promecotheca papuana Cziki	leaf miner	coconut	New Britain	Pleurotropis parvulus Ferr.	parasite	Fiji 1938	S	Gressitt, 1958b; Wilson, 1960a
Promecotheca reichei Baly	coconut leaf-mining beetle	coconut	Fiji	Pleurotropis parvulus Ferr.	parasite	Java 1940 Java 1933	C	Taylor, 1937
Rhabdoscelus obscurus (Bdv.)	New Guinea sugar-cane weevil	sugar-cane	U.S.A. (Hawaii)	Ceromasia (= Microceromasia) sphenophori Vill.	parasite	New Guinea 1910	S	Pemberton, 1948a
Syagrius fulvitarsis Pasc.	fern weevil	tree ferns	U.S.A. (Hawaii)	Ischiogonus (= Doryctes) syagrii Full.	parasite	Australia 1921	P	Pemberton, 1948a
DIPTERA								
Ceratitis capitata (Wied.)	Mediterranean fruit fly	many fruits	U.S.A. (Hawaii)	Opius tryoni Cam.; Opius fullawayi Silv.	parasites	Australia 1913; S. Africa 1913	P	Willard and Mason, 1937
Dacus cucurbitae Coq.	melon fly	melons cucumber squash	U.S.A. (Hawaii)	Opius fletcheri Silv.	parasite	India 1916	P	Swezey, 1934
Dacus dorsalis Hendel	oriental fruit fly	many fruits	U.S.A. (Hawaii)	Opius oophilus Silv.	parasite	Malaya, India Borneo, etc. 1947	S	Clausen, 1956b; Bess and Haramoto, 1958b
Dasynerua mali Kieffer	apple leaf-curling midge	apple	New Zealand	Prosactogaster demades Walk.	parasite	France 1925–26	P	Todd, 1959b
Dasyneura pyri (Bouché)	pear-leaf midge	pear	New Zealand	Prosactogaster demades Walk.	parasite	France 1925–26	S	Miller, Clark, and Dumbleton, 1936
Phytomyza ilicis (Curt.)	holly-leaf miner	English holly	Canada (Br. Columbia)	Chrysocharis gemma (Walk.); Opius ilicis Nixon	parasites	England 1936–39	P	Baird and McLeod, 1953; McLeod, 1954
Musca domestica L.	housefly		Fiji	Pachylister chinensis (Quens.)	predator	Java 1938	P	H. W. Simmonds, 1958

688

Pest	Common name	Crop	Country	Natural enemy	Status	Locality and date	P/S	Reference
ORTHOPTERA								
Gryllotalpa africana P. de B.	African mole cricket	sugar-cane	U.S.A. (Hawaii)	*Larra luzonensis* Roh.	parasite	Philippines 1925	P	Pemberton, 1948a
Oxya chinensis (Thunb.)	Chinese grasshopper	sugar-cane	U.S.A. (Hawaii)	*Scelio pembertoni* Timb.	parasite	Malay Penin. 1930–31	S	Pemberton, 1948a
Periplaneta americana (L.) *Periplaneta australasiae* (F.)	cockroaches	household pest	U.S.A. (Hawaii)	*Ampulex compressa* (F.); *Dolichurus stantoni* (Ashm.)	parasites	New Caledonia 1940; Philippines 1917	P	Pemberton, 1948a; 1953
Sexava nubila (Stal)	coconut grasshopper	coconut	Celebes (Talaud Island)	*Leefmansia bicolor* Waterst.	parasite	Amboina 1924	P	Voûte, 1937
			Bismarck Archipelago	*Leefmansia bicolor* Waterst.	parasite	Amboina 1929–33	P	Wilson, 1960a
HYMENOPTERA								
Cephus pygmaeus (L.)	European wheat stem sawfly	wheat	Canada (Ontario)	*Collyria calcitrator* (Grav.); *Pleurotropis benefica* Gah.	parasites	England 1939–40	S	Glen, 1954b; A. B. Baird, 1958
Gilpinia (= *Diprion*) *hercyniae* Htg.	Spruce sawfly	spruce	Canada	*Drino bohemica* Mesn.; *Exenterus vellicatus* Cush.	parasites	Europe Japan 1934–39	S (C-along with virus)	Reeks, 1953; A. B. Baird, 1956, 1958
Pristiphora erichsonii (Htg.)	larch sawfly	larch	Canada	*Mesoleius tenthredinis* Morley	parasite	England 1910–13	S	A. B. Baird, 1958
			Canada (Br. Columbia)	*Mesoleius tenthredinis* Morley	parasite	Canada (Quebec, Ontario, New Brunswick) 1934–36	S	McLeod, 1954
DERMAPTERA								
Forficula auricularia L.	European earwig	garden and household pest	Canada (Br. Columbia) U.S.A. (Washington)	*Bigonicheta setipennis* (Fall.)	parasite	Oregon 1934	P	Baird and McLeod, 1953; McLeod, 1954 Johansen, 1957
				Bigonicheta setipennis (Fall.)	parasite	Europe 1931–35	P	
HEMIPTERA								
Nezara viridula (L.)	green tomato bug	vegetables	Australia	*Microphanurus basalis* (Woll.)	parasite	Egypt 1933	S	Jenkins, 1948; Wilson, 1960a

Over a period of time, the number of successes attained will be proportional to the amount of research and importation work carried out. It should go without saying that this carries the implication of work directed along lines which appear to be the most suitable both biologically and ecologically. The emphasis, however, is on the necessity for work and more work. Of course, with transfer projects, i.e., those involving previously demonstrated success in another country and the transshipment of the natural enemies responsible, chances of success are good with only a minimum of effort. The importance of the 'amount of effort expended' idea lies in the realization that there are no mystical or specifically peculiar features that make Hawaii or Fiji or California outstandingly favourable for biological control. Reference to table 14 shows that areas having cool temperature climates such as Canada, New Zealand, and Tasmania have had more than their share of successes. They have also done much more than their share of investigation and importation of

TABLE 13

Some countries, in addition to those of table 12, reporting biological control of:

Icerya purchasi Mask., the cottony-cushion scale, by *Rodolia cardinalis* (Muls.)*

Place of infestation	Date of import	Place of origin	Control results
Argentina	1932	Uruguay	C
Bahamas	1924	U.S.A.	S
Bermuda	1899	U.S.A.	S
Chile	1931	U.S.A.	C
Cyprus	1938	Egypt	C
Egypt	1892	U.S.A.	C
Greece	1927	France, Italy	C
Guam	1926	U.S.A. (Hawaii)	C
Hawaii	1890	U.S.A. (California)	C
India	1928	Australia	C
Israel	1912	Italy	C
Italy	1899	Australia	C
Japan	1910	Formosa	C
Madeira	1898	U.S.A.	C
Malta	1928	Italy	C
Morocco	1921	France	C
New Zealand	1892	U.S.A.	C
Peru	1932	U.S.A.	C
Portugal	1897–98	U.S.A.	C
Puerto Rico	1932–33	U.S.A.	C
South Africa	1891	U.S.A.	C
Spain	1922	Portugal	C
Tripoli	1920	Italy	S
Tunisia	?	France	C
Turkey	1932	Egypt, Palestine	C
Uruguay	1916	Portugal	C
U.S.A. (except California and Hawaii)	Various	U.S.A. (California)	C
U.S.S.R.	1931	Egypt	S
Venezuela	1941	U.S.A.	C

* *Cryptochaetum iceryae* (Will.) also is important in various countries.

TABLE 13—*continued*

Eriosoma lanigerum (Hausm.), the woolly apple aphid, by *Aphelinus mali* (Hald.)

Place of infestation	Date of import	Place of origin	Control results
Argentina	1922	Uruguay	C
Australia	1922–23	New Zealand	S
Brazil	1923	Uruguay	S
Canada (Br. Columbia)	1921	Canada (Ontario)	C
Chile	1921–22	U.S.A., Uruguay	C
Colombia	1933	U.S.A.	C
Costa Rica	1933, 1936	U.S.A.	C
Cyprus	1936	England	C
Germany	1923	Uruguay	P
	1926, 1933	Italy	
Israel	1935	Egypt	S
Italy	1921	Uruguay	S
	1921–23	France	
Japan	1931	U.S.A.	C
Kenya	1927–28	England	S
Malta	1933–34	Italy	S
Peru	1922	U.S.A.	S
Poland	1928	England	P
South Africa	1921–22	U.S.A.	S
Spain	1926	Italy, Uruguay	P
Tasmania	1924	Australia	S
U.S.A. (Pacific North-west)	1929–31	U.S.A. (New England States)	C
U.S.A. (California)	1935–39	U.S.A. (Pacific North-west)	S
Uruguay	1921	U.S.A.	C
U.S.S.R.	1930	Italy, England	S
Venezuela	1941	U.S.A.	P
Yugoslavia	1930	Italy	S

Pseudaulacaspis pentagona (Targ.), the white peach scale, by *Prospaltella berlesei* How.

Place of infestation	Date of import	Place of origin	Control results
Argentina	1908	U.S.A.	S
Austria	?	Italy	C
Brazil	1921	U.S.A.	C
Peru	1909–10	U.S.A., Italy	S
Uruguay	1912	U.S.A., Italy	C

Aleurocanthus woglumi Ashby, the citrus blackfly, by *Eretmocerus serius* Silv.

Bahamas	1932	Cuba	C
Costa Rica	1932	Cuba	C
Haiti	1932	Cuba	C
Jamaica	1932	Cuba	C
Panama	1932	Cuba	C
Seychelles	1958	Jamaica	C

TABLE 14

*Number of cases, by countries, of biological control of pest insects by imported entomophagous insects.**

Country of infestation	No. of cases—control results C=Complete S=Substantial P=Partial			
	C	S	P	Total
Antigua, W.I.		1		1
Argentina	2	1		3
Australia		5	5	10
Austria	1			1
Bahamas	1	1		2
Bali			1	1
Barbados			1	1
Bermuda		1	3	4
Bismarck Archipelago (incl. New Britain)		1	1	2
Brazil	1	1		2
Canada (British Columbia)	2	4	3	9
Canada (except British Columbia)	1	5	1	7
Caroline Islands		1		1
Celebes (incl. Talaud Island)		2	1	3
Ceylon	1			1
Chile	2	1	3	6
Colombia	1			1
Costa Rica	2			2
Cuba	1			1
Cyprus	2			2
Dominica, W.I.		1		1
Ecuador		1		1
Egypt	1	1	1	3
Fiji	3		3	6
Germany			1	1
Greece	1			1
Guadeloupe, W.I.		1		1
Guam	1	2	1	4
Haiti	1			1
India	1			1
Israel	3	1		4
Italy	1	2		3
Jamaica	1		1	2
Japan	4			4
Kenya	1	3		4
Madagascar		1		1
Madeira	1			1
Malta	1	1		2
Mariana Is.	1	1		2
Mauritius	2	1	1	4
Mexico	1	1		2
Morocco	1			1
New Zealand	3	6	2	11
Panama	1			1
Peru	1	3	1	5
Poland			1	1

* Includes total cases from tables 12, 13, and 14.

TABLE 14—*continued*

| Country of infestation | No. of cases—control results | | | |
| | C=Complete | S=Substantial | P=Partial | |
	C	S	P	Total
Ponape			1	1
Portugal	1			1
Port. W. Africa	1			1
Puerto Rico	1	1	2	4
St. Kitts, W.I.		1		1
St. Lucia, W.I.		1		1
Seychelles	1	3	1	5
South Africa	2	1		3
Spain	1		1	2
Tasmania		2	5	7
Tripoli		1		1
Tunisia	1			1
Turkey	1			1
U.S.A. (California)	2	9	8	19
U.S.A. (Hawaii)	2	10	12	24
U.S.A. (except California and Hawaii)	2	6	8	16
U.S.S.R.		2	1	3
Uruguay	3			3
Venezuela	1		1	2
Yugoslavia		1		1
Totals	66	88	71	225

natural enemies. Hawaii, which leads in recorded successes, has been continuously and very vigorously active in biological control research and has led in importation work since the 1890's; California, the runner-up in successes, is probably second in the number of importations carried out. It will also be noticed that the British Commonwealth's islands or possessions are prominent among areas having successes. This is because earlier Commonwealth and British colonial entomologists stressed biological control work, as Tothill, Taylor, and Paine did in Fiji. More recently the Commonwealth Institute of Biological Control and various governments have strongly supported such work. Were we to be more personal, many of the successes in biological control could be rather closely correlated with certain enthusiastic workers who have kept the work going and who have obtained support for their projects. Tables 12, 13, and 14 reveal that many of the countries listed as having only one or two successes have obtained these by the transhipment of natural enemies from countries which had already attained successes rather than having done the basic work themselves.

The theory that islands are appreciably more conducive to success in biological control no longer is tenable. About 31 islands and 34 countries on continents have reported successes. Some 55 per cent of these successes have occurred on continents and of the complete successes nearly 60 per cent have occurred on continents.

Additionally, perhaps the level of success on islands has been overemphasized with respect to those occurring on continents for as Wilson (1960b) points out 'It is no disparagement of the remarkable successes obtained in some islands to point out that similar control over an equal area on a large continental mass would usually be regarded as a partial success of little value.' What Wilson means is that complete control is less likely to occur over a geographically extensive and ecologically varied area than in a fairly local and ecologically uniform environment and he goes on to say 'It is unrealistic . . . to expect a single species of natural enemy to provide adequate control of its host over the whole area that the pest occupies in a continent.'

It is clear that most of the importation work in biological control has been done by a few countries, territories, islands, or states, and that successes have occurred more or less in proportion to the number of importations as exemplified by Hawaii, California, United States (aside from Hawaii and California), New Zealand, Australia (aside from Tasmania), British Columbia, Canada (aside from British Columbia), Tasmania, and British colonies or islands. One obvious reason why certain countries or areas have appeared to neglect biological control work is that they have not had so many problems from accidentally introduced pests. Really striking results are, of course, contingent upon a serious problem to start with, and the most serious problems often result from new pest immigrants.

Some other general conclusions emerging from a consideration of the various listed successes are: (1) about 40 per cent of the species controlled (41 out of 107) have been coccids (soft scales, armoured scales, and mealybugs), and the majority of the remainder have been Lepidoptera (21 species), Coleoptera (18 species), or Homoptera other than coccids (16 species); (2) usually control has been ascribed to one dominant natural enemy; (3) parasites have produced control about four times as frequently as predators; and (4) success has not occurred more frequently in tropical and subtropical (mild climate) areas, and the considerable number of cases in Canada, New Zealand, Tasmania, and parts of the United States emphasizes the possibilities in temperate areas. The proportion of successes to introductions or of introductions to establishment has probably been as high or higher in British Columbia (41 spp. imported against 21 pests with six complete and three partial successes, McLeod 1951; 1954) and New Zealand (24 spp. colonized against 12 pests with 11 spp. established, Miller, Clark, and Dumbleton 1936) as in any of the tropical areas. Various other conclusions can doubtless be drawn by the reader. These are left to him except for a discussion of the disproportionate number of cases that have occurred with coccids. Several reasons are seen for this: (1) coccids are easily transported and are among the most common of accidentally introduced pests, thus they have presented more problems to be solved; (2) they often have occurred on expensive crops and have defied easy chemical control; thus there has been considerable economic pressure and backing for biological control attempts; (3) the early success with the cottony-cushion scale led to continued emphasis on biological control of coccids, especially on citrus; and (4) coccids have certain biological attributes which may make them more susceptible than the average pest to control by natural enemies, such as: (a) their usual perennial host plants confer a degree of chronological host-population stability which is advantageous to parasites or predators, (*b*) mass immigration or emigration is not typical of coccid populations (many tend to be sessile); this also gives a tendency towards host-population stability, and (*c*) most coccids are exposed in all developmental stages to natural enemy attack. The fact that coccids occur commonly in mild climatic areas would not seem to be an important reason because this applies to many other pest groups as well. As far as the natural enemies themselves are concerned, there is no reason why those attacking coccids should be *inherently* more effective than those attacking many other groups of insects.

Because coccids are involved in such a large proportion of cases of successful biological control, naturally their particular groups of natural enemies would be proportionally heavy on a listing of the parasites and predators involved. Thus the Encyrtidae and Aphelinidae (Eulophidae) of the parasitic Hymenoptera and the Coccinellidae of the predatory Coleoptera would be strongly predominant in the list. This, it is re-emphasized, should not be taken to mean that the Encyrtidae and Aphelinidae contain most of the effective parasites. As more emphasis is brought to bear on other groups of pests, increasing numbers of parasites in other families will be found to be just as effective.

One of the most controversial and interesting papers dealing with the why and wherefore of successes in biological control is 'The Practice and Theory of Biological Control in Canada' (Turnbull and Chant, 1961). The authors thoroughly reviewed and summarized the work and results in Canada up to about 1960. Some of their general conclusions regarding the status of biological control as a science, as well as of some of the principles and practices involved could, however, be misleading to the casual reader. One of their statements, if it were generally subscribed to, might discourage future biological control work on a large proportion of pest insects; they say 'Indirect pests are suitable subjects for biological control; direct pests are not.' They list the codling moth as a direct pest and it will be interesting to see if biological control projects against this and other so-called direct pests will be dropped in accordance with their conclusion. As illustrated by the preceding example, certain of the conclusions of this paper could possibly, if taken too literally, be harmful to some aspects of future work in biological control even though they were certainly not so intended. On the other hand, the provocative issues raised may well act as a stimulant to research and progress. Serious students of biological control will want to analyse this paper carefully.

RECENT TRENDS IN BIOLOGICAL CONTROL

Since the Second World War there have been some notable shifts in emphasis, rapid development of particular phases and improved organization which are reflected in the development of international organizations, the expansion of insect pathology, an increased emphasis on biological control of weeds, and increased research on specific phases of biological control of insect pests.

World-wide Development of Organizations and International Co-operation

The idea of international co-operation in biological control work is not new, as is shown by Otanes' (1940) quotation of a 1924 resolution: '. . . And in this work, as well as in plant quarantine, the Philippines will seek the co-operation of other countries, particularly Pacific countries, along lines suggested by Resolution No. 25 of the Food Conservation Conference held at Honolulu, Hawaii, in 1924, as follows . . .

'*Whereas*, the excellent economic results that have been gained by the transportation of parasites and other natural enemies of injurious insects from one country to another as in Hawaii, on the mainland of the United States, in Italy, France, New Zealand, Uruguay, Chile, South Africa, the Islands of Mauritius, and other places have fully justified continued and broader work in this direction and therefore larger expenditures of funds by government and smaller organizations, and

'*Whereas*, the transportation and introduction of such beneficial insects, to be successful and free from danger, usually involves technical studies of an enormously complicated chain of interaction of organisms;

'*Resolved*, that this Conference urges all governments and organizations undertaking work of this character to provide for the most expert scientific supervision for such work, to include skilled biologists trained in the study of parasitic and predatory forms of life, and to assist so far as possible in the creation of a much larger number of such trained men by encouraging the study in the higher educational institutions of the very numerous problems of natural control;

'Resolved, further, that governments and institutions be advised to arrange their permanent stations intended for phytopathological and entomological investigations in such a way as to facilitate international exchange of parasites in every possible manner and to afford to the expert of other countries, who may be engaged in exploration work of this character, all possible facilities and assistance.' Thus, as early as 1924 the keynote was sounded, which is just coming into fruition today.

In 1948, a group of entomologists met in Stockholm, Sweden, under the auspices of the International Union of Biological Sciences (U.I.S.B.) to discuss international organization in biological control work. This led to publication of 'Les bases scientifiques d'une organization internationale pour la lutte biologique' by the U.I.S.B. in 1949 and later to the formation of the 'Commission Internationale de Lutte Biologique contre les ennemis des cultures' known as the C.I.L.B. The purpose and functions of the C.I.L.B. are discussed in detail by Franz (1958c). Briefly, this non-profit organization consists principally of biological control workers in various countries of Europe, the Mediterranean area, and Asia Minor, who co-operate in promoting basic and applied research in biological control. This involves carrying on projects of mutual interest, exchange of entomophagous organisms, and mutual planning. Each member country contributes a basic fee for fundamental operations and contributes, in addition, towards special projects in which they are interested. The C.I.L.B. is affiliated in the international framework of the U.I.S.B. and works co-operatively with other organizations such as the European and Mediterranean Plant Protection Organization, the Food and Agriculture Organization of the United Nations, the Committee on Study of Agricultural Zoology, the Commonwealth Institute of Biological Control, and the United States Department of Agriculture. The commission headquarters is in Zurich, and it has a taxonomic determination centre at the Museum of Natural History at Geneva as well as a documentation service which surveys and publishes each year a bibliography on biological control in its official journal, 'Entomophaga.' This journal originated in 1956 and is published by the Pasteur Institute in Paris. It contains original papers in all fields of biological control.

The C.I.L.B. is the first biological control organization which officially brings entomologists from foreign countries together in mutual co-operative effort. Of course, laboratories, institutions, and individuals in various countries have been co-operating informally for many years as is thoroughly attested, for instance, by the voluntary world-wide shipments of *Rodolia cardinalis* (Muls.) and *Aphelinus mali* (Hald.) for control of the cottony-cushion scale and the woolly apple aphid.

Two of the most outstanding world successes in biological control during the last decade were facilitated to a considerable extent by international co-operation. H. Compere, S. E. Flanders, and the author were fortunate in playing a small co-operative part in the recent outstanding success in Israel—the biological control of their major citrus pest, the Florida red scale, *Chrysomphalus aonidum* (L.), by *Aphytis holoxanthus* DeB. The details of the successful results in Israel have been furnished by Mr. I. Cohen, who initiated the project. Cohen first wrote to us in July, 1955, asking, among other things, for names of known parasites of the Florida red scale and where to seek for them. We suggested both Florida and Hong Kong as places known to have promising parasites. Hong Kong was selected, for one reason because the service of Mr. S. Cheng, an experienced part-time collector for the University of California Department of Biological Control, was available. Cheng's first shipments to Cohen early in 1956 contained the *Aphytis*, then thought to be *lingnanensis*. Early establishment followed and by 1959 control was complete. Mere exchange of information—albeit highly specialized and not available in the literature—played a very important role.

A similar instance, and also one of the world's outstanding—although poorly known—cases of biological control occurred in Israel during the 1940's. Again, Cohen and colleagues, through contacts with and co-operation of the U.S. Department of Agriculture and the University of California Department of Biological Control at Riverside, made the initial arrangements which resulted in the importation to Israel of *Clausenia purpurea* Ishii from Japan in 1940. This parasite soon controlled the mealybug *Pseudococcus citriculus* Green (then known as *Pseudococcus comstocki* (Kuw.)), which had become an extremely serious citrus pest from its discovery in Israel in 1937 until 1940 (figure 131). Control by insecticides was difficult, unreliable, and very costly. According to Rivnay (1946), 'After *Clausenia* had become well established in a citrus grove in Palestine, *Ps. comstocki* [= *P.*

citriculus] no longer rises to the degree of a pest . . . . Moreover, in many such groves it is difficult to find the host even when it is searched for diligently.'

Another classical example of biological control—that of the citrus blackfly, *Aleurocanthus woglumi* Ashby, by species of *Amitus* and *Prospaltella* in Mexico— was brought about by international co-operation between Mexican government officials and the U.S. Department of Agriculture. Dr. Paul Oman furnished the author with the details of this case. The citrus blackfly was first found in Mexico in 1935, and by 1952 this insect had spread to practically all the citrus-growing areas of Mexico where it had become the most damaging citrus pest. As such, it was also of grave concern to the citrus industry of the United States where this pest did not occur. This led to co-operative effort between the two countries to achieve biological control in Mexico. Co-operative early attempts from 1938 to 1945 with *Eretmocerus serius* Silv., which previously had produced excellent results in various Caribbean Islands and in Central America, failed of practical results because of poor parasite adaptation to climatic conditions in Mexico. Hence, the United States Department of Agriculture sent Herbert D. Smith to the Orient in 1948–49, where additional citrus blackfly parasites were known to occur. His shipments resulted in the establishment of *Amitus hesperidum* Silv., *Prospaltella clypealis* Silv., *P. opulenta* Silv., and *P. smithi* Silv. An elaborate co-operative re-distribution programme under the 'Comité National de Combate y Control de la Mosca Prieta de los Citricos' and guided by H. D. Smith translocated an estimated 400 million parasites throughout Mexico during the period 1951–57. By the end of this period biological control was virtually complete throughout Mexico.

The Commonwealth Institute of Biological Control, known as the C.I.B.C., with headquarters in Trinidad, B.W.I., and which originated in England in 1927 as Farnham House Laboratory, primarily serves its member British commonwealth countries in importation of new natural enemies. It represents a very large, well-conducted, co-operative effort in biological control. Each member country con-tributes toward basic support and makes additional contributions towards specifically requested projects. Other nations may take advantage of the C.I.B.C. facilities by covering the cost of requested projects. The C.I.B.C. maintains permanent laboratories in California, India, Switzerland, Pakistan, and Trinidad. Their staff is composed of permanent highly trained specialists in biological control. Various other countries or states maintain biological control laboratories or institutions which co-operate internationally on a volunteer basis. Many of their insectaries are shown in chapter 13. Notable among these stressing importation of natural enemies are the Canadian Department of Agriculture's Institute of Biological Control with headquarters at Ottawa and laboratories at Belleville and Vancouver; the United States Department of Agriculture's Insect Identification and Parasite Introduction Research Branch with headquarters in Washington and laboratories in Moorestown, New Jersey, Beltsville, Maryland, and in Paris, France; the Hawaii State Board of Agriculture and Forestry with headquarters and laboratory in Honolulu; and the University of California's Department of Biological Control with headquarters and laboratories at Berkeley (Albany) and Riverside.

A striking example of the recognition of need for international co-operation in biological control is given by the devotion of an entire symposium to the subject 'International Co-operation' in the Transactions (pp. 571–609) of the First International Conference of Insect Pathology and Biological Control held at Praha (Prague), Czechoslovakia, in 1958.

An illustration of the interest and need for co-operation on problems of biological control of medically important insects is seen in the 'Conference on the biological control of insects of medical importance' held in Washington, D.C., February 3–4, 1960. This was arranged by the American Institute of Biological Sciences (AIBS) and the proceedings are to be published. The AIBS is promoting international co-operation in all phases of biology and has proposed an IBY (International Biological Year), along the lines of the recent International Geophysical Year. The World Health Organization (WHO) of the United Nations in co-operation with the New Zealand government sponsored a pilot project, beginning in 1958, designed to establish a fungus parasitic on the mosquito vector of filariasis in the South Pacific (Laird 1959).

Expansion in Insect Pathology and Biological Control of Weeds

The most startling general development in the field of biological control in many years has been the amazing burst of interest in insect pathology following World War II. The spark was probably furnished by Professor H. S. Smith, then Chairman of the Department of Biological Control of the University of California, who visualized the need for increased work on insect pathogens and enlisted the services of E. A. Steinhaus in 1945. Steinhaus built the work in the department under the Laboratory of Insect Pathology and soon was stimulating interest nationally and internationally. Laboratories specializing in insect pathology were established in the Canadian Department of Agriculture at Sault Ste. Marie in 1946, by the United States Department of Agriculture at Beltsville, Maryland, in 1954, and more recently in the Institut für Biologische Schädlingsbekämpfung at Darmstadt, Germany. There is now a large number of European specialists, as was evidenced by the attendance and number of papers presented at the First International Conference of Insect Pathology and Biological Control at Praha, Czechoslovakia, in 1958 (see Trans. 1st Internatl. Conf. Insect Path. and Biol. Cont.; Praha, 1958). Franz (1961b) has reviewed the European work. Additional evidence of the interest in insect pathology is seen in the initiation of the 'Journal of Insect Pathology' in 1959. This periodical is published by Academic Press, Inc., New York.

Several substantial recent successes have resulted from the introduction of insect pathogens (see chapters 18 and 21), which, of course, have stimulated increased endeavours, but the use of pathogens applied periodically as sprays or dusts—the so-called 'microbial insecticides'—has received great emphasis during the last few years, particularly in the United States, perhaps because the possibility of commercial application has led several companies to undertake large-scale manufacture of formulations of micro-organisms such as *Bacillus thuringiensis* Berl. (see chapter 21). To the extent that such materials prove to be innocuous to other natural enemies, they may better fit into integrated control programmes than do chemical insecticides; otherwise they are utilized in the manner of, and act more like, chemical than biotic factors. In the author's opinion, the stress on this phase of insect pathology has led to a relative neglect of the classical procedure of importation and colonization; in this case, of new entomogenous micro-organisms. There is certainly much room for expansion of the introduction work and Laird (1960) has emphasized this with respect to biological control of mosquitoes.

The relatively great recent emphasis on insect pathology may lead to undue expectations of success. It should be borne in mind that because of the apparently restricted number of entomogenous species their use in biological control has little chance of producing the magnitude of results that has been and still is to be obtained with insect parasites and predators. Another restriction to bear in mind is that pathogens may have a low 'searching ability,' i.e., in general they may not operate efficiently at low host densities because of limited mechanisms for dispersal. While not over pessimistic, Bucher (1958) points out additional definite limitations to the use of diseases including ones common to disease organisms in general such as high cost of production, susceptibility to climatic factors, low pathogenicity and great variation in susceptibility displayed by individual hosts.

Research on biological control of weeds has expanded rapidly since World War II into new areas and countries. Notable successes have been obtained (see chapter 23) which have stimulated even more interest in new projects. There is no question but that continued intensive work in this field will produce additional great successes. Emphasis in the past has been on biological control of insect pests but there now seems little reason to assume that biological control should be less effective against plants than against insects provided equal effort is expended.

Research Trends

During the past ten to fifteen years there has been greatly increased emphasis on certain phases previously rather neglected. This includes studies on methods of evaluation of results of biological control, detailed field population studies, the extent of naturally occurring biological control, augmentation and conservation of natural enemies, and integrated pest control.

In California emphasis has been on methods (particularly experimental methods) of evaluating the effectiveness of natural enemies (see chapter 14). This is highly desirable for several reasons. Not all entomologists are willing to accept the biological control worker's word or observations that biological control of a certain pest is occurring or has been brought about. In order to ensure proper credit, results must be adequately demonstrated. Additionally, if manipulation of natural enemies is needed or contemplated, precise evaluation must be made in order to determine the most promising species. Likewise, adequate evaluation is needed in order to demonstrate the adverse effects of insecticides or other factors in order to develop better conservation and integration programmes. In the past, work of this nature has too often been by-passed.

Population studies have begun to pass more and more from the laboratory or from the realm of cerebration to the field. This is a very good trend. Few, if any, complete answers to specific field problems will come from generalized and necessarily highly controlled laboratory studies. Specific laboratory studies, however, often are necessary and are being used more to shed light on particular aspects of field problems. The recognition is coming that ecological relationships and interactions in the field, even between one host and one natural enemy, are so complicated that specific answers cannot be obtained anywhere but in the field.

The extent of naturally occurring biological control has been brought into focus for the average entomologist by the large numbers of upsets that have occurred in recent years from the often incautious use of the newer organic insecticides. It is, in a sense, just as important to recognize and perhaps thereby maintain a successful case of naturally occurring biological control as it is to bring another one to a successful conclusion. There is no doubt that many of the insects now causing trouble have adequate natural enemies. Field studies to demonstrate or evaluate natural control are being vigorously pursued in Russia and elsewhere. Fleschner (1960) has demonstrated that all insects and mites studied on avocados in California are usually under satisfactory natural biological control and that any one species can become a serious pest if its natural enemies are eliminated experimentally or by the injudicious use of chemicals. In addition to the value of such work in conservation or augmentation programmes, natural enemies for potential use in other areas are discovered.

The concepts of conservation and augmentation of natural enemies, while not new, have come to the forefront during the past decade or so. Again, the many upsets around the world from the use of insecticides have focused attention on the absolute necessity in many crops of protecting the natural enemies already present. Otherwise, problems may be compounded rather than alleviated. R. L. Metcalf, an eminent world authority on chemical control, recognized this in his statement (1959, p. 12) that, 'It is obvious that the most elegant use of insecticides lies in their selective use to conserve populations of beneficial insects . . . ' The rapidly expanding work along these lines is covered rather thoroughly in section V, chapters 15, 16, and 17. All this points to the necessity in many instances of careful integration of chemical with biological control. A good general discussion entitled 'The Integrated Control Concept' has recently been published by Stern et al. (1959).

FUTURE POSSIBILITIES IN BIOLOGICAL CONTROL

Recent developments in the field of insecticide utilization have clearly resolved the fact that insecticides will never permanently solve the great majority of pest problems as some enthusiasts once thought. These developments are, in fact, now bringing about ever-increasing support and interest in biological control. All phases of biological control will have to expand. Perhaps the few prophetic individuals who five to ten or more years ago pointed out what was happening helped bring this about. At least they started the ball rolling, but it is now going faster and faster of its own weight. Jacob (1958) has neatly summed this as follows:

'The first and rather superficial reaction to these new chemicals was rather like the popular reaction to penicillin in the medical field. They rendered possible the control of so many hitherto refractory pests that it seemed for a while that the future of economic entomology would consist of little more than the direction of spraying and dusting teams. There may still be some people who think that chemicals will provide the answer to all pest-control problems, but not many amongst right-minded economic entomologists, and the thought was never shared by some. The advent of DDT, for instance, was viewed with no little alarm by Wigglesworth and Strickland.

'The fears of these workers have to a large extent been confirmed by subsequent experience, and economic entomologists all over the world have realized that there is a real need to acquire a more profound knowledge of the purely biological problems of pest control, in order to make more rational use of the valuable aids put into their hands by the chemist. It may be of interest, therefore, briefly to examine some of the problems that have been brought into prominence by the changes of the last fifteen years or so, and to outline an approach to the most important problem of all—the future.

'The misuse of insecticides and other chemicals has emphasized three interesting and important problems: the effect of insecticides on the "balance of nature," the development of resistant strains of insects, and what is in effect a sociological problem, the effects of toxic residues on the user and the consumer.'

The latter problem, involving the effects of toxic residues on the user and consumer, has become perhaps the most important factor now regulating and restricting the use of insecticides and other chemicals, and it promises to become more restrictive in the future. The Public Health officials in many countries now drastically restrict the residues of toxic materials or suspect carcinogens on food and fodder, etc., to very small amounts. Some insecticide residues are prohibited entirely, and with certain crops, such as alfalfa, which in the United States is fed to cows to produce milk, no chlorinated hydrocarbon residues whatsoever are permitted. This sort of thing is reducing the number of new insecticides which were constantly being put on the market by agricultural chemical companies during the late 1940's and 1950's, and it means finding or utilizing other methods of control in many instances. Additional emphasis on such a trend is found in the following quote from Rollins (1960), 'Drift of pesticidal chemicals at the time of application is the biggest problem facing the agricultural aircraft business today . . . half the acreage treated with pesticides in California is treated by aircraft. . . . Drift of pesticides causes trouble in many ways. It may present a hazard to people. . . . Drift may present a hazard to livestock. . . . Drift presents hazards to honeybees and other beneficial insects on neighbouring crops or flowering weeds. . . . Drift also presents a hazard to fish and frog farms. . . . Drift presents a hazard to wild life. . . . Drift presents hazards to crops. It may damage the crop itself. . . . A particularly difficult problem is presented by the drift of pesticides onto feed and fodder crops and pasture. . . . Dairymen have been warned by creameries that milk will be rejected if it is found to contain any trace of pesticides, and mere suspicion of residue on hay may cause its rejection by a dairyman. . . . Somehow the drift problem must be solved if agricultural aircraft are going to stay in business. All these figures we have considered indicate that aircraft dusting and the concept of zero tolerances for a number of pesticides on a number of crops cannot coexist in many of the areas of diversified farming in California. No more than the Indians and buffalo could live with the railroads and farmers a hundred years ago, increasing restrictions seem inevitable. They may come from city, county, state, or federal regulations. They may come from prohibitive insurance rates. They may come from increased civil damage suits. In any event, the agricultural aircraft industry may have to reconcile itself to forgoing many of the jobs it has performed in the past, and has accepted as standard practice, because they are now incompatible with the requirement of no residue on neighbouring crops.' Jacob (1958) continues to say:

'Space does not permit a full discussion of all that has been written about the future of economic entomology, but the problems created by the rapid development of new chemicals have been so striking that during the last ten years or so a number of important papers have been written on this subject. The theme that is common to most of them is that there must be far more research into the ecology of insect communities that live in association with crops. This is not in fact a new idea. Pickett et al., for example, quote several writers going back to 1915, all of whom clearly recognized the importance to pest control of a deep understanding of the interrelationships of insect communities and their environment. Davis emphasized the need for a broadly biological approach to pest control. So did DeBach and Griffith in a symposium arranged by the American Association of Economic Entomologists, where, however, it was Ullyett who provided a careful theoretical analysis of the ecological approach to pest control. Ullyett stressed the "wholeness" of the environment in which man and animals live together and argued in favour of a rational approach to pest control, where all possible methods, including the use of insecticides, take their proper place. Chapman, Glen, English, Kennedy, and Strickland are other workers who have accepted pest control as an ecological problem. Nicholson takes the problem to its logical conclusion when he argues that, in fact, so is the whole of agriculture.

'No biologist would argue that this is not so, but the activities of many so-called economic entomologists would make it appear that they operate in the belief that salvation lies at the end of a spray nozzle. Furthermore, that when they have created problems of resurgence or resistance, or mammalian toxicity, the chemist will be ready with another pill. That view is not held here. If the experience of the last fifteen years has shown one thing more clearly than another it is our ignorance of what is going on in the lives of those animals we call pests. The fundamental need for the future is to extend biological research, with the corollary that fewer trained scientists should be wasted in the largely unproductive activity of screening chemicals. This is, however, a long-term outlook, founded in the faith that ultimately only the biologist will provide the answers to the basic problems of pest control.'

Gunther and Jeppson (1960), who are specialists on insecticide toxicology and utilization, recognize similar problems and trends resulting from intensive insecticidal usage. In their book, 'Modern Insecticides and World Food Production,' they state:

'Even though good initial kill is obtained at the time of treatment, insecticide applications sometimes cause an eventual tremendous increase in the population against which the insecticide has been applied, or in other plant-feeding species present in the field or orchard. . . .

'Extensive research around the world has been concerned with this complex phase of pest control. There is accumulating evidence that the effects of chemical control on the balance of insect and mite populations has not only caused a temporary "flare back" of populations of numerous insect pests, but also that some of our major pest problems would not be problems at all if the proper selective materials or techniques of application had been available and had been widely used. An outstanding example is shown by the increased difficulties encountered in controlling some of the well-known mite pests, as the common red spider mite and the European red mite.

'The world-wide increase in a number of other injurious tetranychid mite species is also noteworthy. Evidence has gradually accumulated to indicate that this increase is to a large extent a result of the extensive use of organic insecticides to control other plant infesting insects. The importance of each of the above-mentioned hypotheses on this major problem is conjectural, but there is no doubt that reduction of the natural enemies of phytophagous insects and mites is a major factor in the difficulties encountered in protecting man's food supply. . . .

'In addition to upsetting balances of nature, widespread and repeated uses of insecticides and acaricides cause many problems. Prominent among these are the possibilities of adverse effects upon soil treated either deliberately as for nematodes or inadvertently as from foliar applications on trees, vines, and other treated plants, and the possible hazards to be associated with residues from the chemical persisting in the commodity to the consumer.

'The long-term contamination of soils was briefly mentioned earlier. It can be a serious problem, for the soil may become sterilized, subsequent plant growth may be abnormal from effects on the root systems, or the chemicals in the soil may be translocated to growing crops. . . . This problem is currently receiving much attention, for there is accumulating evidence that the build-up in soil of insecticides in phytotoxic amounts can occur rather generally, that the insecticides may be altered chemically, and that translocation of the original chemical or its products from soil into growing plants is a distinct possibility. . . .

'From present information, the future of chemical pest-control agents would seem very bleak indeed. New developments of resistance among insect and mite species are increasing out of proportion with the rates of development of candidate chemicals. Control by chemicals can remain effective (1) if new types of chemicals are evolved, chemicals that will react upon entirely different physiological systems and to which the insects and mites cannot readily adapt, and (2) with improved understanding of the mechanisms of resistance so that specific chemicals could be tailored to circumvent the normal pathways of resistance.'

The preceding discussion has been admirably treated in a condensed manner by Wilson (1960b) who also neatly reviews the subjects of the following sections in his article 'The Future of Biological Control.'

Increased Recognition and Support by Science and Government

In the field of applied pest control, biological control has had something of the status of a stepchild. Granted, there are a few notable examples of support by federal, state, or local governmental, and private institutions and universities such as in the British Commonwealth organization (C.I.B.C.), and in Canada, California, and Hawaii, as well as the C.I.L.B. organization in Europe, but by and large the funds allotted to biological control work have been 'a drop in the bucket' compared with the support given to research on and utilization of insecticides, and this does not include the vast sums devoted to research development and promotion of insecticides by private industry. The people in responsible positions in government are coming to recognize that their departments need more support in areas of fundamental research, especially in ones such as biological control which obtains virtually no backing from private or commercial companies' funds. The limitations mentioned by Jacob to the use of insecticides, i.e., upsets in natural balance, development of resistance by pests to insecticides, and strict governmental regulation of the amount of chemical residues in foodstuffs, are bound to force more emphasis on biological control possibilities. Some good cases in point are the very substantial recent annual increase in the funds devoted by the United States Department of Agriculture to biological control work, the sponsorship by W.H.O. of work on biological control of insects of medical importance and the support of certain biological control projects by the F.A.O. of the United Nations organization and by the Rockefeller Foundation.

Increased International Co-operation

The discussion earlier in this chapter of international organizations and co-operation in biological control work has shown that substantial progress has been made. More is being developed and planned. There is as yet, however, no really international organization to promote co-operation and exchange on an equable basis from a world-wide standpoint, and this is what is needed. Wilson (1960b) has emphasized this point. Biological control is truly international, the natural enemies involved recognize no political boundaries, and I am happy to say that there is little evidence that the scientists do either. The voluntary and co-operative transfer from one country to another of many natural enemies attests to this, even though the agricultural industries thus protected may be in direct competition with each other. There is, however, an inequable aspect to this type of co-operation—it tends to be one way from the countries or institutions doing the largest share of the work. Not that complaints have been evident, but if recipient countries or institutions contributed through a world international organization towards projects on which they receive help, then much additional work could be financed. Additionally, there is still not enough liaison between workers around the world. Successful projects have been completed against a pest in one country, while another country having the same pest problem may fail to introduce for many years the natural enemy involved. Sometimes a shortage of interested workers in some countries is responsible; at other times it is a failure of those connected with a successful project to report upon it.

What is needed is a clearing-house type of organization which will grant and receive credit from members and which will facilitate transfer of natural enemies, provide scientific liaison of various sorts, underwrite a truly world-wide international journal of biological control with review and translation features, enable co-operative planning and development of projects of mutual interest, and at the same time remain free of politics. Organizations such as the C.I.L.B. and the C.I.B.C. already partially fill some of these needs but not on a broad enough scale. Such organizations could be benefited by—and would benefit as well—a world-wide organization. It is to be hoped that something of this nature can be brought about under the auspices of the United Nations.

Increased Emphasis on Importation Projects

This is the bread-and-butter work in biological control. It was pointed out earlier in this chapter that the countries having the most successes were the ones importing the greatest number of natural enemies. The pure and simple fact stands out that more and more emphasis is needed on importation, and that the greater the number of beneficial species imported and tested the more successes there will be. No country or state, with the possible exception of Hawaii, has begun to investigate in an adequate manner the biological control possibilities with more than a small proportion of their insect pests. In chapter 1, the author stressed that California, in spite of its continuing support of biological control work and the resultant enormous savings to agriculture, has barely scratched the surface in the importation of new natural enemies. Although biological control of citrus pests has been emphasized in California for seventy years, we are still finding promising new natural enemies of serious citrus pests. However, natural enemies and biological control of certain other serious pests of major crops in California have been virtually unstudied. Of the 10 most important crop pests of 1959 listed by the Bureau of Entomology of the California State Department of Agriculture, only two—the California red scale and the spotted alfalfa aphid—have been the objects of intensive importation of natural enemies, and about half of the 10 have been virtually unstudied from the biological control standpoint. Estimated losses from these and other leading major pests (a total of only 12), for which much could be tried in the way of importation of natural enemies, amounted to well over $65,000,000 for 1959. How much more, then, does this lack of effort apply to problems in other countries or states with lesser support? Although Australia has had a substantial number of successes, Wilson (1960b) emphasizes that 'the rate at which natural enemies of pests are introduced into new countries such as Australia is very slow by comparison with the number of pests requiring attention and the large numbers of natural enemies that could be introduced.'

From time to time it has been suggested that biological control work has reached the point of diminishing returns. Clausen (1958b) refutes this assertion as follows:

'Any analysis of the present status of biological control of insect pests and a projection of developments into the future are of much interest and reveal a wide divergence of opinion, even among experts in the field. A provocative discussion of the subject is that by Taylor who takes a definitely pessimistic viewpoint as to the possibility of worthwhile achievements in this field in the future, indicating that the cream has already been skimmed away and the point of diminishing returns has long since been reached. Simmonds presents a vigorous rebuttal to Taylor's thesis and cites many examples to illustrate the points at issue. Space limitations prevent an adequate review of these two articles, but a few points may be mentioned. Taylor states:

'"... I know it [biological control] to be the best of all methods of controlling pests when it works, but that it seldom works and that there is little future for it in continental areas."

'The successes in North America alone during the past 25 years are sufficient rebuttal to that statement. Systematic work on biological control of insect pests has hardly started in the great majority of continental countries, and there is every reason to expect results in those countries comparable to the successes achieved in North America and elsewhere. Accordingly, we may expect substantial progress in many areas in future years. Further, "... the present tendency to organize the moving of parasites and predators about the world on an ever-increasing scale, despite decreasing results, is unsound and is, therefore, to be regretted."

'A weighing of results of such recent work certainly refutes the assertion of decreasing returns.'

Simmonds (1959) also deals with the idea of diminishing returns. He states:

'Speedy and successful control of a number of insects and weed pests, which had spread into areas other than their original habitats, by biological methods may suggest that "the cream has been skimmed off" in the field of biological control. However, in many instances only comparatively superficial studies have been made and the most obvious and apparently promising natural enemies have been selected as biological control agents.

'The advent of increasingly frequent and speedy air services to wider and wider areas has opened up more possibilities for the use of the biological control method.

Increasing rigidity of quarantine laws and inspection services has not prevented the accidental introduction of exotic insects and weeds into new areas. Increased trade, and particularly facility and speed of air transport, have more than offset the effects of more stringent quarantine measures in this regard. The spread of pest species into new areas will continue and afford additional opportunity for the use of biological control methods.

'In the past a number of biological control projects have been abandoned as failures after the unsuccessful introductions of several exotic natural enemies of the pests in question, before any ecological studies have been carried out. Probably, in some of these, more detailed studies of these pests in their areas of origin might provide the answer to successful biological control. The results of the lack of such knowledge are shown in the difference between the success of *Eretmocerus serius* in controlling the citrus blackfly in Cuba and Jamaica, and its complete failure in ecologically different areas in western Mexico, and possibly also in the failure of introduced coccinellids to control several scale insects in Bermuda under apparently very favourable conditions. Here the influence of ants and possibly of predatory lizards has been investigated recently.

'In the various ways mentioned above there are possibilities for a wide expansion in the utilization of biological control methods in the future. This does not mean that it is a panacea for all problems on the control of insects, weeds, and other pests. It is not. The proportion of successes, partial successes and failures in future work will probably remain about the same as in the past, and spectacular successes will be few. It is hoped, however, that with increasing amounts of data on different types of problems available, particularly of an ecological nature, the assessment of the chances of success with individual problems will improve.

'There is therefore no justification for considering that the method of biological control is now of decreasing value as contended by Taylor. I have already discussed this paper elsewhere, but I think that the general contention that there will be a continued and probably increasing place for biological control methods in the future is clearly indicated. This is also suggested from a rather different standpoint in a recent book by Elton, "The Ecology of Invasions by Animals and Plants," in which he stresses the ever-increasing trend for many species to become more widespread within the limits of their climatic tolerance, and the explosive development of populations which may follow their introduction without normal natural enemies into new areas. This book gives the impression that, far from the cream having been skimmed off the general field of biological control work, we have hardly made a beginning.'

Even less emphasis has been placed on importation of natural enemies of weeds than of pests of agricultural crops. With respect to weed control there would seem to be a fertile field for investigation in the use of plant pathogens, i.e., weed diseases. Some certainly are highly specific. As already mentioned, the introduction of entomogenous micro-organisms in biological control projects has been relatively neglected and there remains a promising field here.

Research on biological control of insects of medical importance has been somewhat neglected in the past. Interest has increased considerably in recent years and there seem to be definite possibilities for success with some problems especially in the utilization of disease organisms. A rather complete discussion of the problems and possibilities in this field has been made by Laird (1959, 1960) who states (1959, p. 131) that 'It is hoped that this . . . will help pave the way for further introductions of mosquito pathogens, and specific predators too, from areas where they are endemic and in balance with host or prey populations to others in which they are not. . . . Detailed and integrated studies on a global basis are called for if this approach to mosquito control is to become, as it must become, more than a blundering meddling with natural economy.' Again Laird (1960, p. 345) says 'While some of these [parasitic and predacious] insects hold undoubted promise as biological control agents in special situations, and additional ones almost certainly await discovery, most suggestions thus far made for control by parasites in the public health field concern bacteria, fungi, protozoa or nematodes . . . all these groups include organisms with which economic entomologists are at present obtaining promising results. . . . Protozoa of the order Microsporidea and fungi of the genus *Coelomomyces* (Blastocladiales) offer fruitful research material. Muspratt . . . kept a Rhodesian study area under observation between 1941 and 1945, throughout this period the infection of *Anopheles gambiae* larvae by *Coelomomyces* spp. was responsible for a host mortality of 95 per cent.'

Biological control of forest insect pests has been emphasized in Canada and Europe, and to a lesser extent in the United States but has been neglected in most countries. Dowden (1957, 1959) reviews past work and stresses that importation of new natural enemies and the utilization of pathogens is needed along with basic ecological studies which may reveal means of manipulation to favour natural or biological control.

Increased emphasis in the field of taxonomy—particularly biosystematic studies (see chapter 9)—will lead to the recognition that in many cases several closely related species of natural enemies have been lumped under one name. Inasmuch as these will exhibit different climatic tolerances and capabilities, they will furnish more raw material for importation programmes.

Use of Biological Races

Just as the recognition of differences between closely related species will lead to increased possibilities in biological control, the recognition, biological evaluation, and utilization of naturally occurring races of the same species having different ecological requirements and capabilities will help to solve some problems. The artificial development of better adapted forms by selection offers much promise in particular cases. This subject has been covered in chapter 15. Races of natural enemies which attack different hosts will be discovered or developed by artificial selection, as will races which will be better adapted to the climatic range of their host.

Increased Use of Conservation and Manipulation In Augmentation Programmes

This field offers great opportunities to foster and obtain the maximum effectiveness from the natural enemies we already have. Opportunities here are numerous, as has already been demonstrated by the discussion in section V, chapters 15, 16, and 17 of this book. Recent trends, as mentioned earlier, show rapidly increasing emphasis on this general phase. According to Clausen (1954*a*):

'We need to know the intimate relationships between all elements of the pest complex, including their natural enemies, and their environment in the field or orchard, in order to make full use of the potentialities of these natural enemies. The various control programs now under way have a wide influence on the insect population as a whole. In order to make the fullest use of the natural enemies present in the field or orchard, we must know how they react, not only to insecticidal applications but to other elements in the environment that may have an influence, one way or another, upon them. With our present great concern regarding the fate of native parasites and predators of the so-called minor pests I feel that we can anticipate a marked expansion in work on this fundamental subject.'

As the problems with chemical control become more complex and costly the chances and need to employ manipulation, which also costs something, become greater. According to Simmonds (1959):

'With regard to the second point, the development of resistance, this is resulting in an increasing interest in the possibilities of biological control of several pests, even those where the chances of successful results seem rather remote. One might cite the example of the planthoppers, *Aeneolamia* spp., in Central and South America causing serious damage to sugar cane and pasture grasses. With developing resistance, chemical control is becoming increasingly expensive and less effective, and biological control investigations are being considered. The codling moth, *Carpocapsa pomonella* (L.), is another case in point. Thus even where chemical insecticides are used very effectively at present, it seems that biological control methods may still have a place in the future.'

Formal Training in Biological Control

One reason for the paucity of emphasis on the ecological approach to pest control problems has been the limited availability of personnel appropriately trained in this method. Most entomologists currently working in biological control are self-educated in this speciality, and since most are associated with research (non-teaching) institutes, the imparting of detailed knowledge has not been disseminated properly among undergraduate or graduate students at a large majority of schools which offer entomology courses in the United States.

In recent years to answer this need several universities and colleges in this country have been adding to their curricula new basic and advanced courses pertaining to ecology and biological control. In most of those educational institutions, however, space and facility shortages, not to mention lack of sufficient funds to offer scholarships or research assistantships are forcing the rejection of many promising graduate students annually.

The first college course in biological control *per se* taught in the United States was presented by Professor Harvey L. Sweetman at Massachusetts State College beginning in 1930 and his texts on the subject are well known.

A formal course in biological control was not offered at the University of California until 1947. However, during the twenty-four years immediately preceding that date graduate students were attracted to California to study and complete their dissertations under Professor Harry S. Smith, who had built a biological control research group of international renown.

In 1947 at Berkeley two courses, 'Biological control of insect and weed pests' (Ent. 129) and 'Insect pathology' (Ent. 131) were given by Professor Smith and Professor Edward A. Steinhaus, respectively. Professor Steinhaus has continued teaching and Professor R. L. Doutt has presented Ent. 129 following the retirement of Professor Smith in 1952. Both courses have been given annually at Berkeley since their inception and both are offered at the recently created College of Agriculture on the Riverside campus of the University of California, where Ent. 129, taught by the author, and Ent. 131, taught by Professor Irvin M. Hall, were initiated in the autumn of 1961 and spring of 1962, respectively. Other staff members on both campuses contribute lectures in Ent. 129 regarding their biological control specialities.

At present, courses in biological control and insect pathology are taught by members of the staffs of the Department of Biological Control and Laboratory of Insect Pathology within the curriculum of the Departments of Entomology. At Berkeley and Riverside the M.S. and Ph.D. degrees may be earned in Entomology with a field of major emphasis in biological control or insect pathology.

Expanded teaching of biological control as one of several ecology-oriented courses will assure that future entomologists will have the background necessary for a balanced approach to the resolution of pest control problems. Such training supplemented with training in the chemical methods of pest control will greatly enhance the possibility of establishing supervised pest control throughout agriculture.

Indeed, to assure general acceptance of ecology-oriented pest control procedures it now seems quite clear that recipients of such an education programme must include not only pest control specialists, but growers and consumers as well.

Altered Grower and Consumer Psychology

The average progressive modern farmer often tends to treat his crops by the calendar. This is sometimes dubbed 'insurance' treatment. When it's 'time' to spray for thrips, he sprays, regardless of whether thrips constitute a threat at that time in his field. When he operates this way, he usually doesn't check his pest populations, but even if he did it would be extremely unlikely that he would take into account the activities of natural enemies. The average farmer has been thoroughly 'sold' by insecticide salesmen, extension literature, and so-called economic entomologists. He has adopted the oft-repeated TV brainwashing slogan, 'The only good bug is a dead bug.' Now, obviously, this has to change, not because biological control workers think it's bad, but because it doesn't work. Resistance to pesticides has developed, upsets have occurred time and again, and toxic residues have become a public health problem. The grower's psychology towards pest control is being forced to change, and this will force him to try other methods which will mean greater support and use of biological control.

Meanwhile the consumer has aided and abetted the idea that 'the only good bug is a dead bug' by thoroughly accepting the advertising idea that shiny clean fruit, etc., are better fruit. No thrips scars, not a scale insect, must be present. Quality and taste are really forgotten to a large extent; appearance is of prime importance. The Public Health Service also says that only a certain very small amount of insect parts can be bottled up, for instance, with your catsup. People aren't supposed to like small bits of insects in their catsup even if they can't find them. Thus, Public Health, which is trying to keep poisonous residues out of foodstuffs, may be forcing the tomato grower to treat, with the result that the consumer has bug-free but not toxicant-free catsup.

Strict standardization procedures, which do not necessarily give the consumer food of better quality or taste, may force the grower to treat for a light infestation of a particular pest which would not be at all harmful to the crop. Thus, very strict standardization requirements may make the achievement of biological control a practical impossibility in particular instances. Even with the best examples of biological control, pest individuals are present. As food supplies become shorter during the coming decades and as consumers become more conscious of toxic residues in foods and less conscious of appearance only, certain highly artificial standardization procedures, which now make insecticidal treatment a virtual necessity, will be relaxed and more advantage will be taken of the biological control method.

The Ultimate in Integrated and Supervised Pest Control

The reader should not take this title to mean that integrated and supervised pest control is the ultimate objective. Complete biological control on a given crop is the rarely obtained ideal, but once this is attained the integration of chemical with biological control is unnecessary. With most crops, however, the most practical solution will be a thoroughly scientific integration of chemical and biological control. The trend to larger and larger farming operations will make integrated and supervised pest control more feasible for several reasons. Large-scale farming procedures tend towards uniformity of habitats and ecological interactions which make the development and application of manipulation and integration programmes easier and more reliable than if many small farms were involved. Further, the extension of ideas and practices is much easier with one large operator than with

20 small ones, and large-scale operators often more easily recognize the need for sound advice and consequently are more likely to support a well-trained supervising entomologist.

Obviously, integrated pest control is not something that one just goes out and tries. Successful results can be obtained only if (1) fairly effective natural enemies of most host insects are present in the complex, and (2) excessive and unmodifiable chemical treatments are not required for several major pests which lack effective enemies. The prime requisite for integrated pest control is basic ecological knowledge of the entire complex involved including the extent of biological control of each host insect that occurs in the absence of treatment. Basic studies may take several years in order to learn the best method of utilizing the chemicals that are found to be absolutely necessary, with the biological control that is known to occur if no chemicals are used. All this has been covered in chapter 17. In order to make it work effectively, however, it is likely that a supervising entomologist will have to be on the job. He will be a man with an ecological background and bias, whose decisions on pest control will be final. He will know how to use insecticides and which ones are least injurious in given situations, but best of all, he will know when not to use them.

Bibliography

Abarca, M., A. C. Iturbe, and S. F. Caceres. 1958. The sugarcane borers in Mexico. An attempt to control them through parasites. *Proc. 10th Internatl. Congr. Ent.*, 4: 827–834 (1956).

Acqua, C. 1919. Ricerche sulla malattia del giallume del baco da seta. *Rendiconti dell' Istituto Bac. del. R. Scuola Super. di Agric. in Portici*, 3: 243–56.

Adriaanse, A. 1947. *Ammophila campestris* Latr. und *Ammophila adriaansei* Wilcke. Ein Beitrag zur vergleichenden Verhaltensforschung. *Behaviour*, 1: 1–34.

Ahmed, Mostafa Kamal, L. D. Newsom, R. B. Emerson, and J. S. Roussel. 1954. The effect of systox on some common predators of the cotton aphid. *Jour. Econ. Ent.*, 47: 445–49.

Aizawa, K. 1958. Changement de forme des polyèdres de *Bombyx mori* par passage dans l'embryo de poulet. Second Colloquium of Insect Pathol. and Biological Control. *Comm. Internation. de Lutte Biologique*, Paris, Oct. 22–24, 1958, pp. 15–16.

Alam, S. M. 1952. A contribution on the biology of *Stenobracon deesae* Cameron (Braconidae, Hym.) and the anatomy of its pre-imaginal stages. *Zeitschr. Parasitenkunde*, 15: 159–82.

—— 1957. The biology of *Metaphycus taxi* Alam (Encyrtidae: Hymenoptera) in the constant temperature room, with notes on the anatomy of its pre-imaginal stages. *Indian Jour. Ent.*, 19: 231–40.

—— 1959. The life history and larval anatomy of *Euaphycus variolosus* Alam, an endoparasite of *Asterolecanium variolosum. Proc. Zool. Soc.*, 12: 35–40.

Albritton, E. C. 1953. Standard values in nutrition and metabolism. *Wright Air Development Center Tech. Rept.*, 52–301. 380 pp.

Alden, C. H., and J. E. Webb, Jr. 1937. Control of injurious insects by a beneficial parasite. *Georgia State Board Ent. Bull.* 79. 23 pp.

Alexandrov, N. 1948. *Eurygaster integriceps* Put. à Varamine et ses parasites. *Ent. et phytopath. Appl. Téhéran*, (5): 29–41; (6–7): 28–47; (8): 16–52 (In Iranian with French summary).

Allee, W. C. 1931. *Animal Aggregations. A Study in General Sociology.* Chicago, Univ. Chicago Press. 431 pp.

Allee, W. C., A. E. Emerson, O. Park, T. Park, and K. P. Schmidt. 1949. *Principles of Animal Ecology.* Philadelphia and London, W. B. Saunders. 837 pp.

Allee, W. C., and K. P. Schmidt. 1951. *Ecological Animal Geography*, 2nd ed. John Wiley & Sons, Inc. 715 pp.

Allen, H. W. 1925. Biology of the red-tailed tachina fly, *Winthemia quadripustulata* Fabr. *Mississippi Agric. Expt. Sta. Tech. Bull.*, 12. 32 pp.

—— 1932. Present status of oriental fruit moth parasite investigations. *Jour. Econ. Ent.*, 25: 360–67.

—— 1954a. Propagation of *Horogenes molestae*, an Asiatic parasite of the oriental fruit moth, on the potato tuberworm. *Jour. Econ. Ent.*, 47: 278–81.

—— 1954b. Nosema disease of *Gnorimoschema operculella* (Zeller) and *Macrocentrus ancylivorus* Rohwer. *Ann. Ent. Soc. America*, 47: 407–24.

—— 1958. Orchard studies on the effect of organic insecticides on parasitism of the oriental fruit moth. *Jour. Econ. Ent.*, 51: 82–87.

Allen, H. W., J. K. Holloway, and G. J. Haeussler. 1940. Importation, rearing and colonization of parasites of the oriental fruit moth. *U.S. Dept. Agric. Circ.*, 561. 61 pp.

Allen, H. W., and E. L. Plasket. 1958. Populations of the oriental fruit moth in peach and apple orchards in the eastern states. *U.S. Dept. Agric. Tech. Bull.*, 1182. 13 pp.

Allen, H. W., and A. J. Warren. 1932. The results from five years' experiments in mass liberations of *Trichogramma minutum* against the oriental fruit moth. *Jour. Econ. Ent.*, 25: 374–80.

Allen, W. W. 1958. The biology of *Apanteles medicaginis* Muesebeck (Hymenoptera: Braconidae). *Hilgardia*, 27: 515–41.

Allen, W. W., and R. F. Smith. 1958. Some factors influencing the efficiency of *Apanteles medicaginis* Muesebeck (Hymenoptera: Braconidae) as a parasite of the alfalfa caterpillar, *Colias philodice eurytheme* Boisduval. *Hilgardia*, 28: 1–42.

Andrewartha, H. G. 1957. The use of conceptual models in population ecology. In *Cold Spring Harbor Symposia on Quantitative Biology*, 22: 219–36.

Andrewartha, H. G., and L. C. Birch. 1948. Measurement of 'environmental resistance' in the Australian plague grasshopper. *Nature*, 161: 447–48.

—— 1954. *The Distribution and Abundance of Animals*. Univ. Chicago Press, Chicago. 782 pp.

Andrewes, C. H. 1954. Report of the subcommittee on viruses. *Internatl. Bull. Bact. Nomen. and Tax.*, 4: 109–14.

Angus, T. A. 1954. Some properties of a bacterial toxin affecting insect larvae. *Bi-Monthly Prog. Rept., Div. Forest Biol., Canada Dept. Agric.*, 10: 2–3.

—— 1956a. The reaction of certain lepidopterous and hymenopterous larvae to *Bacillus sotto* toxin. *Canadian Ent.*, 88: 280–83.

—— 1956b. Association of toxicity with protein-crystalline inclusions of *Bacillus sotto* Ishiwata. *Canadian Jour. Microbiol.*, 2: 122–31.

—— 1956c. Extraction, purification, and properties of *Bacillus sotto* toxin. *Canadian Jour. Microbiol.*, 2: 416–26.

Annecke, D. P. 1959. The effect of parathion and ants on *Coccus hesperidum* L. (Coccidae: Hemiptera) and its natural enemies. *Jour. Ent. Soc. So. Africa*, 22: 245–74.

Anonymous. 1954. Review of agricultural entomology during the period 1948–1954—Mauritius. Rept. Commonwealth Entomol. Conf., 6th Meeting. 281–84. London, England.

Anonymous. 1956. Nematode on our side. *U.S. Dept. Agric. Res.*, 4: 3–4.

Anonymous. 1959. Chemical plant internationally known. *Commerce and Industry*, 3: 18–20.

Aoki, K., and Y. Chigasaki. 1915. Ueber die Pathogenität der sog. Sotto-Bacillen (Ishiwata) bei Seidenraupen. *Mitt. Med. Fakult. Kaiser Univ. Tokyo*, 13: 419–40.

Aoki, K., K. Sasamoto, and Y. Nakasata. 1955. Studies on the relation between fungi and insects. (III) Flora of muscardines on various insects at Yamanasi-prefecture in 1953. *Jour. Seric. Sci. Japan*, 24: 231–39.

Arbuthnot, K. D., and W. A. Baker. 1938. Technique and equipment for handling two hymenopterous parasites of the European corn borer with particular reference to prolonging their hibernation. *U.S. Bur. Ent. Pl. Quar.*, E-460. 12 pp.

Arkell, W. J., and J. A. Moy-Thomas. 1940. Palaentology and the taxonomic problem, pp. 395–410. In *The New Systematics*, J. S. Huxley, editor.

Armitage, H. M. 1919. Controlling mealybugs by the use of their natural enemies. *Calif. Stat Hort. Com. Monthly Bulls.*, 8: 257–60.

Armitage, H. M. 1929. Timing field liberations of *Cryptolæmus* in the control of the citrophilus mealybug in the infested citrus orchards of southern California. *Jour. Econ. Ent.* 22: 910–15.

Armstrong, T. 1935. Two parasites of the white apple leafhopper (*Typhlocyba pomaria* McA.). *Ontario Dept. Agric. Ent. Soc. Ontario Rept.*, pp. 16–31.

Arnold, B. H., and R. Steel. 1958. Oxygen supply and demand in aerobic fermentations, pp. 149–81. In *Biochemical Engineering*, R. Steel, editor.

Arthur, D. R. 1945. The development of artificially introduced infestations of *Aphidius granarius* Marsh. under field conditions. *Bull. Ent. Res.*, 36: 291–95.

Arthur, A. P. 1958. Development, behaviour, and descriptions of immature stages of *Spilochalcis side* (Walk.) (Hymenoptera: Chalcididae). *Canadian Ent.*, 90: 569–632.

—— 1961. The cleptoparasitic habits and immature stages of *Eurytoma pini* Bugbee (Hymenoptera: Chalcidae), a parasite of the European shoot moth, *Rhyacionia buoliana* (Schiff.) (Lepidoptera: Olethreutidae). *Canadian Ent.*, 93, 655–60.

Arthur, A. P., and H. C. Coppel. 1953. Studies on dipterous parasites of the spruce budworm, *Choristoneura fumiferana* (Clem.) (Lepidoptera: Tortricidae). I. *Sarcophaga aldrichi* Park. (Diptera: Sarcophagidae). *Canadian Jour. Zool.*, 31: 374–91.

Aruga, H. 1957. Polyhedral diseases in the silkworm, *Bombyx mori* L. *Revue du Ver à Soie*, 8: 37–41.

Aruga, H., T. Hukuhara, N. Yoshitake, and Na Ayudhya Israngkul. 1961. Interference and latent infection in the cytoplasmic polyhedrosis of the silkworm, *Bombyx mori* (Linnaeus). *Jour. Insect Pathol.*, 3: 81–92.

Aubert, J. F. 1959. Les hôtes et les stades immatures des Ichneumonides *Pimpla* F., *Apechtis* Forst. et *Itoplectis* Forst. *Bull. Biol. de France et Belgique*, 93: 235–59.

Auclair, J. L. 1953. Amino acids in insects. *Canadian Ent.*, 85: 63–68.

—— 1958. Developments in resistance of plants to insects. *Ann. Rept. Ent. Soc. Ontario*, 88: 7–17.

Ayres, H. 1884. On the development of *Oecanthus nieveus* and its parasite *Teleas*. *Mem. Boston Soc. Natl. Hist.*, 3: 261–72.

Ayyar, P. N. 1940. Investigations on *Spathius critolaus* Nixon, an important braconid parasite of the cotton-stem weevil, *Pempheres affinis* Fst., of South India. *Indian Jour. Agric. Sci.*, 10: 879–900.

Baccetti, B. 1958. Ghiandole labialie fabbricazione del bozzolo negli Imenotteri Ricerche Ichneumonidi e Braconidi. *Redia*, 43: 215–93.

Bachmetjew, P. 1907. *Expèrimentelle entomologische studien vom physikalisch–chemischen standpunkt aus;* vol. II. *Einfluss der aüssern factoren auf insekten.* Leipzig, Engelmann. 108 pp.

Baer, W. 1920. Die Tachinen als Schmarotzer der schädlichen Inseckten. Ihre Lebensweise, wirtschafttiche Bedeutung und systematische Kennzeichnung. *Zeitschr. angew. Ent.*, 6: 185–246.

—— 1921. Die Tachinen als Schmarotzer der schädlichen Inseckten. Ihre Lebensweise wirtschaftliche bedeutung und systematiche Kennezeichung. *Zeitschr. angew. Ent.* 7: 97–163, 349–423.

Baerends, G. P. 1950. Specializations in organs and movement with a releasing function. *Symposia Soc. Exptl. Biol.*, IV: 337–60.

—— 1959. Ethological studies of insect behavior. *Ann. Rev. Ent.*, 4: 207–34.

Bagley, R. W. 1953. The biology and the parasite complex of the iris whitefly, *Aleyrodes spiraeoides* Quaintance. (Thesis M.S. Unpub.) Univ. Calif. Berkeley.

Bailey, L. 1956. Aetiology of European foul brood; a disease of the larval honeybee. *Nature*, 178: 1130.

Bailey, L. 1957a. European foul brood: a disease of the larval honeybee (*Apis mellifera* L.) caused by a combination of *Streptococcus pluton* (*Bacillus pluton* White) and *Bacterium eurydice* White. *Nature*, 180: 1214–15.

—— 1957b. The isolation and cultural characteristics of *Streptococcus pluton* and further observations on *Bacterium eurydice*. Jour. Gen. Microbiol., 17: 39–48.

—— 1959a. An improved method for the isolation of *Streptococcus pluton*, and observations on its distribution and ecology. *Jour. Insect Pathol.*, 1: 80–85.

—— 1959b. Recent research on the natural history of European foul brood disease. *Bee World*, 40: 66–70.

—— 1959c. The natural mechanism of suppression of *Nosema apis* Zander in enzootically infected colonies of the honey bee, *Apis mellifera* Linnaeus. *Jour. Insect. Path.*, 1: 347–50.

—— 1960. The epizootiology of European foulbrood of the larval honey bee, *Apis mellifera* Linnaeus. *Jour. Insect Pathol.*, 2: 67–83.

Bailey, V. A. 1931. The interaction between hosts and parasites. *Quart. Jour. Math.*, 2: 68–77.

Baird, A. B. 1935. Biological control of greenhouse insects. *Ontario Dept. Agric. Ent. Soc. 65th Ann. Rpt.*, 1934. pp. 72–73.

—— 1939. Laboratory propagation of parasites and its place in biological control programs. *Proc. 6th Pac. Sci. Congr.*, 4: 417–20.

—— 1956. Biological control. In *Entomology in Canada up to 1956*, by Robert Glen. *Canadian Ent.*, 88: 363–67.

—— 1958. Biological control of insect and plant pests in Canada. *Proc. 10th Internatl. Congr. Ent.*, 4: 483–85 (1956).

Baird, A. B., and J. H. McLeod. 1953. Biological control of insect pests in British Columbia. *Proc. 7th Pac. Sci. Congr.* 4: 232–36 (1949).

Baird, R. B. 1958a. Field experiments with *Pseudomonas aeruginosa* (Schroeter) Migula to control grasshoppers. *Canadian Ent.*, 90: 89–91.

—— 1958b. Use of fungous diseases in biological control of insects. *Proc. 10th Internatl. Congr. Ent.* (Montreal 1956), 4: 689–92.

Baker, W. A., W. E. Bradley, and C. A. Clark. 1949. Biological control of the European corn borer in the United States. *U.S. Dept. Agric. Tech. Bull.*, 983, 185 pp.

Baker, W. A., and L. G. Jones. 1934. Studies of *Exeristes roborator* (Fab.), a parasite of the European corn borer in the Lake Erie area. *U.S. Dept. Agric. Tech. Bull.*, 460, 26 pp.

Baker, W. L. 1941. Effect of gypsy moth defoliation on certain forest trees. *Jour. Forest.*, 39: 1017–22.

Bakkendorf, O. 1934. Biological investigations on some Danish hymenopterous egg-parasites, especially in homopterous and heteropteron eggs, with taxonomic remarks and descriptions of new species. *Ent. Meddel.*, 19: 1–134.

Balch, R. E. 1928. The influence of the southern pine beetle on forest composition in western North Carolina. Unpub. thesis. New York State College of Forestry.

—— 1942. On the estimation of forest insect damage with particular reference to *Dendroctonus piceaperda* (Hopk.). *Jour. Forest.*, 40: 621–29.

—— 1946. The disease of the European spruce sawfly. Canada Dept. *Agric. Bi-Monthly Prog. Rept.*, 2: 1.

—— 1958. Control of forest insects. *Ann. Rev. Ent.*, 3: 449–68.

Balch, R. E. and F. T. Bird. 1944. A disease of the European spruce sawfly, *Gilpinia hercyniae* (Htg.), and its place in natural control. *Sci. Agric. Ottawa*, 25: 65–80.

Balch, R. E., R. C. Clark, and N. R. Brown. 1958. *Adelges picea* (Ratz.) in Canada with reference to biological control. *Proc. 10th Internatl. Congr. Ent.*, 4: 807–17 (1956).

Balduf, W. V. 1926a. The bionomics of *Dinocampus coccinellae* Schrank. *Ann. Ent. Soc. America*, 19: 465–89.

—— 1926b. *Telenomus cosmopeplae* Gahan, an egg parasite of *Cosmopeplae bimaculatus* Thomas. *Jour. Econ. Ent.*, 19: 829–41.

—— 1928. Observations on the buffalo tree hopper *Ceresia bubalus* Fabr. (Membracidae, Homoptera), and the bionomics of an egg parasite, *Polynema striaticorne* Girault (Mymaridae, Hymenoptera). *Ann. Ent. Soc. America*, 21: 419–35.

—— 1935. *The Bionomics of Entomophagous Coleoptera.* John S. Swift Co., Inc. St. Louis, Chicago, New York, Indianapolis. 220 pp.

—— 1939a. Food habits of *Phymata pennsylvanica americana* Melin (Hemiptera). *Canadian Ent.*, 71: 66–74.

—— 1939b. *The bionomics of entomophagous insects.* Part II. John S. Swift Co. Inc. St. Louis, Chicago, New York, Cincinnati. 384 pp.

—— 1941. Quantitative dietary studies on *Phymata. Jour. Econ. Ent.*, 34: 614–20.

—— 1947a. The weights of *Phymata pennsylvanica americana* Melin. *Ann. Ent. Soc. America*, 40: 576–87.

—— 1947b. The weights of *Sinea diadema* (Fabr.). *Ann. Ent. Soc. America*, 40: 588–97.

—— 1948. A summary of studies on the ambush bug *Phymata pennsylvanica americana* Melin (Phymatidae, Hemiptera). *Trans. Illinios State Acad. Sci.*, 41: 101–06.

Baldwin, W. F., and H. C. Coppel. 1947. Observations on the emergence of *Phorocera hamata* A. and W. (Tachinidae). *Canadian Ent.*, 79: 221–23.

Ball, G. H., and E. W. Clark. 1953. Species differences in amino acids of *Culex* mosquitoes. *Systematic Zool.*, 2: 138–41.

Baltensweiler, W. 1958. Zur kenntnis der Parasiten des Grauen Lärchenwicklers (*Zeiraphera griseana* Hübner) im Oberengadin. Ihre Biologie und Bedeutung während der Gradation, von 1949 bis 1958. *Mitteil. schweiz. Anst. forst. Versuchswesen*, 34: 399–478.

Banks, C. J. 1958. Effects of the ant, *Lasius niger* (L.), on the behavior and reproduction of the black bean aphid, *Aphis fabae* Scop. *Bull. Ent. Res.*, 49: 701–14.

Barber, H. S. 1951. North American fireflies of the genus *Photuris. Smithsonian Misc. Coll.*, 117, 58 pp.

Barclay, J. M. 1938. The oviposition habits of some of the species of the genus *Exenterus* parasitic on sawfly larvae. *69th Ann. Rept. Ent. Soc. Ontario*, pp. 29–31.

Bardner, R., and Joyce Kenten. 1957. Notes on the laboratory rearing and biology of the wheat bulb fly, *Leptohylemyia coarctata* (Fall.). *Bull. Ent. Res.*, 48: 821–31.

Barnes, H. F. 1929. Gall midges as enemies of aphids. *Bul. Ent. Res.*, 20: 433–42.

—— 1930. Gall midges (Cecidomyidae) as enemies of the Tingidae, Psyllidae, Aleurodidae and Coccidae. *Bull. Ent. Res.*, 21: 319–29.

Barnes, O. L. 1944. Feeding experiments with the range caterpillar egg parasite *Anastatus semiflavidus* Gahan. *Jour. Econ. Ent.*, 37: 544.

Bartlett, Blair. 1951. Effect of parathion on parasites of *Coccus hesperidum. Jour. Econ. Ent.*, 44: 344–47.

Bartlett, B. R. 1951a. A new method for rearing *Drosophila* and a technique for testing insecticides with this insect. *Jour. Econ. Ent.*, 44: 621.

—— 1951b. The action of certain 'inert' dust materials on parasitic Hymenoptera. *Jour. Econ. Ent.*, 44: 891–96.

—— 1957. Biotic factors in natural control of citrus mealybugs in California. *Jour. Econ. Ent.*, 50: 753–55.

—— 1958. Laboratory studies on selective aphicides favoring natural enemies of the spotted alfalfa aphid. *Jour. Econ. Ent.*, 51: 374–78.

Bartlett, B. R. 1961. The influence of ants upon parasites, predators, and scale insects. *Ann. Ent. Soc. America*, 54: 543–51.

Bartlett, Blair R., and T. W. Fisher. 1950. Laboratory propagation of *Aphytis chrysomphali* for release to control California red scale. *Jour. Econ. Ent.*, 43: 802–06.

Bartlett, B. R., and C. F. Lagace. 1960. Interference with the biological control of cottony-cushion scale by insecticides and attempts to re-establish a favorable natural balance. *Jour. Econ. Ent.*, 53: 1055–58.

Bartlett, Blair R., and J. C. Ortega. 1952. Relation between natural enemies and DDT-induced increases in frosted scale and other pests of walnuts. *Jour. Econ. Ent.*, 45: 783–85.

Bartlett, K. A., and C. L. Lefebvre. 1934. Field experiments with *Beauveria bassiana* (Bals.) Vuill., a fungus attacking the European corn borer. *Jour. Econ. Ent.*, 27: 1147–57.

Bassi, A. 1835. *Del mal del segno, calcinaccio o moscardino, malattia che affligge i bachi da seta e sul modo di liberarne le bigattaie anche le piu infestate*. Parte I: Teoria. Orcesi, Lodi. pp. i–ix, 1–67.

Bates, M., and P. S. Humphrey (Editors). 1956. *The Darwin Reader*. Charles Scribner's Sons, New York, 470 pp.

Beard, R. L. 1942. On the formation of the tracheal funnel in *Anasa tristis* DeGeer induced by the parasite *Trichopoda pennipes* Fabr. *Ann. Ent. Soc. Amer.*, 35: 68–73.

—— 1944. Susceptibility of Japanese beetle larvae to *Bacillus popilliae*. *Jour. Econ. Ent.*, 37: 702–08.

—— 1945. Studies on the milky disease of Japanese beetle larvae. *Connecticut Agric. Expt. Sta. Bull.*, 491: 505–83.

—— 1946. Competition between two entomogenous bacteria. *Science*, 103: 371–72.

—— 1952. The toxicology of *Habrobracon* venom: a study of a natural insecticide. *Connecticut Agric. Expt. Sta. Bull.*, 562. 27 pp.

—— 1956. Two milky diseases of Australian Scarabaeidae. *Canadian Ent.*, 88: 640–47.

Beardsley, John W., Jr. 1955. Fluted scales and their biological control in United States administered Micronesia. *Proc. Hawaiian Ent. Soc.*, 15: 391–99.

Beacher, J. H. 1947. Studies of pistol case-bearer parasites. *Ann. Ent. Soc. America.*, 40: 530–44.

Beck, S. D. 1956a. The European corn borer, *Pyrausta nubilalis* (Hubn.), and its principal host plant. I. Orientation and feeding behavior of the larva on the corn plant. *Ann. Ent. Soc. America.*, 49: 552–58.

—— 1956b. The European corn borer, *Pyrausta nubilalis*, and its principal host plant. II. The influence of nutritional factors on larval establishment and development of the corn plant. *Ann. Ent. Soc. America*, 49: 582–88.

—— 1957. The European corn borer, *Pyrausta nubilalis* (Hubn.), and its principal host plant. VI. Host plant resistance to larval establishment. *Jour. Insect Physiol.*, 1: 158–177.

Beck, S. D., C. A. Edwards, and John T. Medler. 1958. Feeding and nutrition of the milk-weed bug, *Oncopeltus fasciatus* (Dallas). *Ann. Ent. Soc. America*, 5: 283–88.

Beck, S. D., J. H. Lilly, and J. F. Stauffer. 1949. Nutrition of the European corn borer, *Pyrausta nubialis* (Hbn.). I. Development of a satisfactory purified diet for larval growth. *Ann. Ent. Soc. America*, 42: 483–96.

Beck, S. D., and J. F. Stauffer. 1950. An aseptic method for rearing European corn borer larvae. *Jour. Econ. Ent.*, 43: 4–6.

Becker, A. 1949. Beiträge zur Ökologie der Hausbockkäfer-Larven. *Zeitschr. angew. Ent.*, 31: 135–74.

Beckley, W. C. 1956. Biological control for 1955–56. *29th Ann. Rept. of Associates Insectary*, Santa Paula, Calif.

—— 1959. *Report of manager.* Biol. Div. Associates Insectary 32nd Ann. Rpt., 1958–59. 2 pp.

Beckman, H. F., S. M. Bruckart, and R. Reiser. 1953. Laboratory culture of the pink bollworm on chemically defined media. *Jour. Econ. Ent.*, 46: 627–30.

Bedford, E. C. G. 1956. The automatic collection of mass-reared parasites into consignment boxes, using two light sources. *Jour. Ent. Soc. So. Africa*, 19: 342–53.

Beeson, C. F. C., and S. N. Chatterjee. 1939. Further notes on the biology of parasites of teak defoliators in India. *Indian Forest Rec. Ent.*, 5: 357–67.

Begg, M., and F. W. Robertson. 1948. Nutritional requirements of *Drosophila*. *Nature*, 161: 769–70.

—— 1950. The nutritional requirements of *Drosophila melanogaster*. *Jour. Exptl. Biol.*, 26: 380–87.

Béguet, M. 1916. Campagne d'expérimentation de la méthode biologique contre les *Schistocerca peregrina* en Algérie, de Décembre 1914 à Juillet 1915 et en particulier dans la région de Barika (département de Constantine). *Ann. Inst. Pasteur [Paris]*, 30: 225–42.

Beingolea, O. 1957. El sembrio del maiz y la fauna benefica del algodonero. Estacion Experimental Agricola de 'La Molina', Lima. *Informe No. 104*, 19 pp.

Beirne, B. P. 1941. A consideration of the cephalic structures and spiracles of the final instar larvae of the Ichneumonidae (Hym.). *Trans. Soc. Brit. Ent.*, 7: 123–190.

—— 1942a. Observations on the life history of *Praon volucre* Haliday (Hym.: Braconidae) a parasite of the mealy plum aphis (*Hyalopterus arundinis* Fab.). *Proc. Roy. Ent. Soc. Lond.*, 17: 42–47.

—— 1942b. Observations on the developmental stages of some Aphidiinae (Hym. Braconidae). *Ent. Monthly Mag.*, 78: 283–86.

—— 1946. Notes on the biology of some hymenopterous parasites of the beech weevil (*Rhynchaenus fagi* L.) (Col.). *Proc. Roy. Ent. Soc. London A*, 21: 7–11.

—— 1955. Collecting, preparing and preserving insects. *Canada Dept. Agric. Sci. Serv. Div. Ent., Processed Publ.*, 932, 133 pp.

Bellevoye, Ad. and J. Laurent. 1897. Plantations de pins dans la Marne et les parasites que les attaquent. *Soc. d'étude des sci. nat de Reims.* 7ᵉ année, Tome VI, pp. 59–111.

Benassy, C. 1958a. Remarques sur l'écologie de *Quadraspidiotus perniciosus* Comst. dans le Midi méditerranean (Hom. Diaspidinae). *Entomophaga*, 3: 93–108.

—— 1958b. Etude bio-écologique de *Pseudaulacaspis pentagona* Targ. et de son parasite spécifique *Prospaltella berlesei* Howard, en France. *Ann. des Epiphyt.*, 4: 425–96.

Benassy, C., and A. Burgerjon. 1955. Méthode d'élevage au laboratoire de *Prospaltella perniciosi* Tow. *Ann. Epiphyt.*, 6: 5–10, illus.

Benedict, R. G., H. J. Koepsell, H. M. Tsuchiya, E. S. Sharpe, J. Corman, C. B. Kemp, G. B. Meyers, and R. W. Jackson. 1957. Studies on the aerobic propagation of *Serratia marcescens*. *Appl. Microbiol.*, 5: 308–13.

Bennett, F. 1960. Parasites of *Ancylostomis stercorea* (Zell.) (Pyralidae, Lepidoptera) a pod borer attacking pigeon pea in Trinidad. *Bull. Ent. Res.*, 50: 737–57.

Bennett, F. D., and I. W. Hughes. 1959. Biological control of insect pests in Bermuda. *Bull. Ent. Res.*, 50: 423–36.

Benson, R. B. 1944. Swarming flights of *Blacus tripudians* (Hym., Braconidae). *Ent. Monthly Mag.*, 80: 208.

Berg, V. L. 1940. The external morphology of the immature stages of the bee fly, *Systoechus vulgaris* Loew (Diptera, Bombyliidae), a predator of grasshopper egg pods. *Canadian Ent.*, 72: 169–78.

Berger, E. W. 1910. Whitefly control. *Florida Agric. Expt. Sta. Bull.*, 103, 28 pp.

—— 1911. Report of entomologist. *Florida Agric. Expt. Sta. Report for fiscal year ending June 30, 1911.* Pp. 40–57.

—— 1919. Work of the Entomological Department State Plant Board. *Florida State Hort. Soc. Quart., Proc. 32nd Ann. Meeting.* Pp. 160–70.

—— 1921. Natural enemies of scale insects and whiteflies in Florida. *Florida State Plant Board Quart. Bull.*, 5: 141–54.

Bergold, G. 1947. Die Isolierung des Polyeder-Virus und die Natur der Polyeder. *Zeitschr. Naturforsch.*, 2b: 122–43.

Bergold, G. H. 1950. The multiplication of insect viruses as organisms. *Canadian Jour. Res.*, 28: 5–11.

—— 1951. The polyhedral disease of the spruce budworm, *Choristoneura fumiferana* (Clem.) (Lepidoptera: Tortricidae). *Canadian Jour. Zool.*, 29: 17–23.

—— 1953a. Insect viruses. *Advances in Virus Res.*, 1: 91–139.

—— 1953b. On the nomenclature and classification of insect viruses. *Ann. New York Acad. Sci.*, 56: 495–516.

—— 1958. Viruses of insects. *Handbuch der Virusforschung*, 4: 60–142.

Berlese, A. 1913. Intorno alle metamorphosi degli insetti. *Redia.*, 9: 121–136.

Berliner, E. 1911. Über die Schlaffsucht der Mehlmottenraupe. Zeitschr. *Gesamte Getreidewesen*, 3: 63–70.

—— 1915. Über die Schlaffsucht der Mehlmottenraupe (*Ephestia kühniella*, Zell.) und ihren Erreger *Bacillus thuringiensis*, n. sp. *Zeitschr. angew. Ent.*, 2: 29–56.

Bess, H. A. 1939. Investigations on the resistance of mealybugs (Homoptera) to parasitization by internal hymenopterous parasites, with special reference to phagocytosis. *Ann. Ent. Soc. America*, 32: 189–226.

—— 1945. A measure of the influence of natural mortality factors on insect survival. *Ann. Ent. Soc. America*, 38: 472–81.

—— 1958. The green scale, *Coccus viridis* (Green) (Homoptera: Coccidae), and ants. *Proc. Hawaiian Ent. Soc.*, 16: 349–55.

Bess, H. A., and F. H. Haramoto. 1958a. Biological control of pamakani, *Eupatorium adenophorum*, in Hawaii by a tephritid gall fly, *Procecidochares utilis*. I. The life history of the fly and its effectiveness in the control of the weed. *Proc. 10th Internatl. Congr. Ent.*, 4: 543–48 (1956).

—— 1958b. Biological control of the oriental fruit fly in Hawaii. *Proc. 10th Internatl. Congr. Ent.*, 4: 835–40 (1956).

—— 1959. Biological control of Pamakani, *Eupatorium adenophorum*, in Hawaii by a tephritid gall fly, *Procecidochares utilis*. 2. Population studies of the weed, the fly, and the parasites of the fly. *Ecology*, 40: 244–49.

Bess, H. A., S. H. Spurr, and E. W. Littlefield. 1947. Forest site conditions and the gypsy moth. *Harvard Forest Bull.*, 22. 56 pp.

Bessey, E. A. 1950. *Morphology and Taxonomy of Fungi.* Blakiston Co., Philadelphia. 791 pp.

Billiotti, E. 1955. Survie des larves endophages de Tachinaires à une mort prématurée de leur hôte par maladie. *Compt. Rend. Acad. Sci.*, 240: 1021–23.

—— 1956a. Entomophages et maladies des insectes. *Entomophaga*, 1: 45–53.

—— 1956b. Relations entre agents pathogènes et entomophages. *Entomophaga*, 1: 101–03.

—— 1958. Eléments de la spécificité parasitaire chez les Tachinaries. *Proc. Xth Internatl. Congr. Ent.*, 4: 751–57.

Biliotti, E. and P. Delanoue. 1959. Contribution à l'étude biologique d'*Opius concolor* Saepl. (Hym. Braconidae) en élevage de laboratoire. *Entomophaga*, 4: 7–14.

Billings, Frederick H., and Pressley A. Glenn. 1911. Results of the artificial use of the white-fungus disease in Kansas: with notes on approved methods of fighting chinch bugs. *U.S. Dept. Agric. Bur. Ent. Bull.*, **107**. 58 pp.

Bioferm Corporation, Wasco, California. 1959. (Personal communication.)

Birch, L. C. 1945. The influence of temperature, humidity, and density on the oviposition of the small strain of *Calandra oryzae* L. and *Rhizopertha dominica* Fab. (Coleoptera). *Australian Jour. Expt. Biol. and Med. Sci.*, **23**: 197–203.

—— 1948. The intrinsic rate of natural increase of an insect population. *Jour. Animal Ecol.*, **17**: 15–26.

—— 1954. Experiments on the relative abundance of two sibling species of grain weevils. *Australian Jour. Zool.*, **2**: 66–74.

—— 1955. Selection in *Drosophila pseudoobscura* in relation to crowding. *Evolution*, **9**: 389–99.

—— 1957. The role of weather in determining the distribution and abundance of animals. In *Cold Spring Harbor Symposia on Quantitative Biology*, **22**: 203–18.

Bird, F. T. 1953a. The use of a virus disease in the biological control of the European pine sawfly, *Neodiprion sertifer* (Geoffr.). *Canadian Ent.*, **85**: 437–46.

—— 1953b. The effect of metamorphosis on the multiplication of an insect virus. *Canadian Jour. Zool.*, **31**: 300–03.

—— 1954. The use of a virus disease in the biological control of the European spruce sawfly, *Diprion hercyniae* (Htg.). *Canada Dept. Agric. Sci. Serv., Div. Forest Biol., Bi-Monthly Progress Rept. Jan.–Feb.*, **10**: 2–3.

—— 1955. Virus diseases of sawflies. *Canadian Ent.*, **87**: 124–27.

—— 1959. Polyhedrosis and granulosis viruses causing single and double infections in the spruce budworm, *Choristoneura fumiferana* Clemens. *Jour. Insect Pathol.*, **1**: 406–30.

Bird, F. T., and D. E. Elgee. 1957. A virus disease and introduced parasites as factors controlling the European spruce sawfly, *Diprion hercyniae* (Htg.), in central New Brunswick. *Canadian Ent.*, **89**: 371–78.

Bird, F. T., and M. M. Whalen. 1953. A virus disease of the European pine sawfly *Neodiprion sertifer* (Geoffr.). *Canadian Ent.*, **85**: 433–37.

Bischoff, H. 1927. *Biologie der Hymenopteren.* Berlin, 571 pp.

Bissell, T. 1945. *Mylophasia globosa* (Tns.), tachinid parasite of the cowpea curculio. *Ann Ent. Soc. America*, **38**: 417–40.

Bissert, G. A. 1938. Larvae and pupae of Tachinids parasitizing *Pieris rapae* L. and *P. brassicae* L. *Parasitology*, **30**: 111–22.

Blackwelder, R. E., and A. Boyden. 1952. The nature of systematics. *Systematic Zool.*, **1**: 26–33,

Blanchard, R. A., and C. B. Conyer. 1932. Notes on *Prodenia praefica* Grote. *Jour. Econ. Ent.*, **25**: 1059–70.

Blunck, H. 1951. Zur Kenntnis der Hyperparasiten von *Pieris brassicae* L. 4. Beitrag: *Gelis* cf. *transfuga* Forst. *Zeitschr. angew. Ent.*, **33**: 217–67.

—— 1952a. Zur Kenntnis der Hyperparasiten von *Pieris brassicae* L. 5 Beitrag: *Hemiteles simillimus sulcatus* die Metamorphose. *Zeitschr. angew. Ent.* **33**: 421–59.

—— 1952b. Ueber die bei *Pieris brassicae* L., ihren Parasiten und Hyperparasiten schmarotzenden Mikrosporidien. *Proc. 9th Internatl. Congr. Ent.*, **1**: 432–38.

—— 1954. Mikrosporidien bei *Pieris brassicae* L., ihren Parasiten und Hyperparasiten. *Zeitschr. angew. Ent.*, **36**: 316–33.

Bobb, M. L. 1939. Parasites of the oriental fruit moth in Virginia. *Jour. Econ. Ent.*, **32**: 605–07.

Bobb M. L. 1942. Parasites of the oriental fruit moth and of certain weed-infesting larvae. *Virginia Agric. Expt. Sta. Bull.*, 79. 23 pp.

Bodenheimer, F. S. 1928. Welche factoren regulieren die individuenzahl einer insektenart in die natur? *Biol. Zentrabl.*, 48: 714–39.

—— 1930. Über die grundlagen einer allgemeinen epidemiologie der insektenkalamitäten. *Zeitschr. angew. Ent.*, 16: 433–50.

—— 1931. Der massenwechsel in der tierwelt. Grundriss einer allgemeinen tierischen bevolkerungslehre. *Arch. Zool. Ital.*, 16: 98–111. Napoli.

—— 1938. *Problems of Animal Ecology.* Oxford University Press. 183 pp.

Bodenheimer, F. S., and M. Guttfeld. 1929. Über die Möglichkeiten einer biologischen Bekämpfung von *Pseudococcus citri* Risso (Rhy. Cocc.) in Palästina. *Zeitschr. angew Ent.*, 15: 67–136.

Bodenheimer, F. S., and M. Schiffer. 1952. Mathematical studies in animal populations. I. A mathematical study of insect parasitism. *Acta Biotheoretica*, 10: 23–56.

Bohart, R. M. 1941. A revision of the Strepsiptera with special reference to the species of North America. *Univ. Calif. Publ. Ent.*, 7: 91–160.

Bohart, G. E., W. P. Stephen, and R. K. Eppley. 1960. The biology of *Heterostylum robustum* (Diptera: Bombyliidae), a parasite of the alkali bee. *Ann. Ent. Soc. America*, 53: 425–35.

Boldaruev, V. O. 1956. The development of *Telenomus gracilis* Mayr (Hymenoptera, Scelionidae) and *Ooencyrtus pinicola* (Mats.) (Hymenoptera, Encyrtidae) parasites of eggs of *Dendrolimus sibiricus* Tshetv. *Ent. obozrenie Moscow*, 35: 101–08.

—— 1958. *Rhogas dendrolimi* Mats. (Hymenoptera, Braconidae) an efficient parasite of *Dendrolimus sibiricus* Tshetv. (Lepidoptera, Lasiocampidae). A translation of *Ent. Rev. (Ent. Obozr.)* by *Amer. Instit. Biol. Sci.*, 37: 716–22.

Bonar, J. 1931. *Theories of Population from Raleigh to Arthur Young.* London, George Allen and Unwin. 253 pp.

Bond, E. J., and H. A. Monro. 1954. Rearing the cadelle *Tenebroides mauritanicus* (L.) as a test insect for insecticidal research. *Canadian Ent.*, 86: 402–08.

Bonnet, C. 1779. *Oeuvres d'histoire et de philosophie.* I. *Traité d'insectologie.* Neuchâtel.

Borgmeier, T. 1957. Basic questions of systematics. *Systematic Zool.*, 6: 53–69.

Borror, D. J., and D. M. Delong. 1954. *An Introduction to the study of insects.* Rhinehart and Co., New York. 1030 pp.

Botero, G. 1588. *A treatise concerning the causes of the magnificency and greatness of cities.* Trans. by Robert Peterson, 1606. Reprinted in 1956. London, Routledge and Kegan Paul.

Botta, P. E. 1841. *Relation d'un voyage dans l'Yemen.* (Duprat, Paris. 1841.).

Bottger, G. T. 1940. Preliminary studies of the nutritive requirements of the European corn borer. *Jour. Agric. Res.*, 60: 249–58.

—— 1942. Development of synthetic food media for use in nutrition studies of the European corn borer. *Jour. Agric. Res.*, 65: 493–500.

Bottimer, L. J. 1945. Roach rearing and testing. *Soap and Sanitary Chem.*, 21: 151–57.

Boucek, Z. 1956. A contribution to the biology of *Eucharis adscendens* (F.) (Hymenoptera). *Acta Soc. Zool., Bohemosl. Praha*, 20: 97–99.

Bovien, P. 1937. Some types of associations between nematodes and insects. *Vidensk. Meddel. Dansk. Naturhist. For. Köbenhavn.*, 101: 1–114.

Boving, A. G., and F. C. Craighead. 1931 (1930). An illustrated synopsis of the principal larval forms of the order Coleoptera. *Ent. Amer.*, 11: 1–351.

BIBLIOGRAPHY 725

Box, H. E. 1925. Porto Rican cane-grubs and their natural enemies with suggestions for the control of Lamellicorn larvae by means of wasp-parasites (Scoliidae). *Jour. Dept. Agric. Porto Rico*, 9: 291–356.

—— 1952a. Discussion part of Szumkowski's paper: Observations on Coccinellidae. II. Experimental rearing of *Coleomegilla* on a non-insect diet. *Trans. 9th Internatl. Congr. Ent.*, 1: 784–85.

—— 1952b. Investigaciones sobre los Taladradores de la cana de azucar (*Diatraea* spp.) en Venezuela. El proyecto del combate biologico. Informe del progresso durante 1949–51. *Inst. Nacl. Agric. Venezuela, Bol. Tec.*, 5. 52 pp.

—— 1956. The biological control of moth borers (*Diatraea*) in Venezuela. Battle against Venezuela's cane borer. Part 1. Preliminary investigations and the launching of a general campaign. *Sugar* (*New York*), 51: 25–27, 30, 45.

Boyce, A. M. 1950. Entomology of citrus and its contribution to entomological principles and practices. *Jour. Econ. Ent.*, 43: 741–66.

Boyce, H. R., and G. G. Dustan. 1958. Prominent features of parasitism of twig-infesting larvae of the oriental fruit moth, *Grapholitha molesta* (Busck) (Lepidoptera: Olethreutidae), in Ontario, Canada. *Proc. 10th Internatl. Congr. Ent.*, 4: 493–96 (1956).

Boyden, A. 1943. Serology and animal systematics. *Amer. Nat.*, 77: 234–55.

Boyles, W. A., and R. E. Lincoln. 1958. Separation and concentration of bacterial spores and vegetative cells by foam flotation. *Appl. Microbiol.*, 6: 327–34.

Bradley, William G. 1941. Methods of breeding *Chelonus annulipes* on the Mediterranean flour moth for use against the European corn borer. *U.S. Dept. Agric. Circ.*, 616, 22 pp.

Bradley, W. G., and K. D. Arbuthnot. 1938. The relation of host physiology to development of the braconid parasite, *Chelonus annulipes* Wesmael. *Ann. Ent. Soc. America*, 31: 359–65.

Bradley, W. G., and E. D. Burgess. 1934. The biology of *Cremastus flavoorbitalis* (Cameron), an Ichneumonid parasite of the European corn borer. *U.S. Dept. Agric. Techn. Bull.*, 441, 15 pp.

Branigan, E. J. 1916. A satisfactory method of rearing mealybugs for use in parasite work. *California State Hort. Comm. Monthly Bull.*, 5: 304–06.

Braun-Blanquet, J., G. D. Fuller, and H. S. Conard. 1932. *Plant Sociology*. New York and London. McGraw-Hill Co. 439 pp.

Breland, O. P. 1941. *Podagrion mantis* Ashmead and other parasites of praying mantid egg cases (Hym: Chalcidoidea, Dipt.: Chloropidae). *Ann. Ent. Soc. America*, 34: 99–113.

Brennan, J. M., and G. A. Mail. 1954. A technique for shipping live mosquitoes with particular reference to *Culex tarsalis. Science* (*n.s.*), 119: 443–44.

Brian, M. V. 1958. Interaction between ant populations. *Proc. 10th Internatl. Congr. Ent.*, 2: 781–84. Montreal, 1956.

Brickhill, D. D. 1958. Biological studies of two species of tydeid mites from California. *Hilgardia*, 27: 601–20.

Briggs, J. D. 1958. Humoral immunity in lepidopterous larvae. *Jour. Exptl. Zool.*, 138: 155–88.

—— 1960. Reduction of adult house-fly emergence by the effects of *Bacillus* spp. on the development of immature forms. *Jour. Insect Pathol.*, 2: 418–32.

—— 1962. *Commercial production of insect pathogens. In Insect pathology, an advanced treatise*. E. A. Steinhaus, editor. Academic Press, New York and London. (In press.)

Bronskill, Joan F. 1959. Embryology of *Pimpla turionellae* (L.) (Hymenoptera: Ichneumonidae). *Canadian Jour. Zool.*, 37: 655–88.

Bronskill, Joan F. 1960. The capsule and its relation to the embryogenesis of the ichneu-monid parasitoid *Mesoleius tenthredinis* Morl. in the larch sawfly, *Pristiphora eriohsonii* (Htg.) (Hymenoptera: Tenthredinidae). *Canadian Jour. Zool.*, 38: 769–75.

Bronskill, Joan F., and H. L. House. 1957. Notes on rearing a pupal endoparasite, *Pimpla turnionellae* (L.) (Hymenoptera: Ichneumonidae), on unnatural food. *Canadian Ent.*, 89: 483.

Brooks, A. R. 1952. Identification of bombyliid parasites and hyperparasites of Phalaenidae of the prairie provinces of Canada with descriptions of six other bombylid pupae (Diptera). *Canadian Ent.*, 84: 357–73.

Brown, A. W. A. 1951. *Insect Control by Chemicals*. John Wiley and Sons, New York, 817 pp.

Brown, N. R. 1946a. Studies on parasites of the spruce budworm *Archips fumiferana* (Clem.) 1. Life history of *Apanteles fumiferanae* Viereck (Hymenoptera, Braconidae). *Canadian Ent.*, 78: 121–29.

—— 1946b. Studies on parasites of the spruce budworm, *Archips fumiferana* (Clem.) 2. Life history of *Glypta fumiferanae* (Viereck) (Hymenoptera, Ichneumonidae). *Canadian Ent.*, 78: 138–147.

Brown, W. J. 1959. Taxonomic problems with closely related species. *Ann. Rev. Ent.*, 4: 77–98.

Brues, C. T. 1908. The correlation between habits and structural characters among para-sitic Hymenoptera. *Jour. Econ. Ent.*, 1: 123–28.

—— 1920. The selection of food-plants by insects, with special reference to lepidopterous larvae. *Amer. Nat.*, 54: 313–32.

—— 1921. Correlation of taxonomic affinities with food habits in Hymenoptera, with special reference to parasitism. *Amer. Nat.* 55: 134–64.

—— 1929. Present trends in systematic entomology. *Psyche*, 36: 13–20.

—— 1939. Some adaptive responses of taxonomy to a changing environment. *Jour. New York Ent. Soc.*, 47: 145–54.

—— 1946. *Insect Dietary*. Harvard Univ. Press, Cambridge, Mass., 146 pp.

Brues, C. T., A. L. Melander, and F. M. Carpenter. 1954. Classification of insects: keys to the living and extinct families of insects, and to the living families of other terres-trial arthropods. *Bull. Mus. Comp. Zool. Harvard Univ.*, 108: 1–917, illus.

Brunson, M. H. 1940. Mass liberation of parasites of the oriental fruit moth for immediate reduction of infestation. *Jour. Econ. Ent.*, 33: 346–49.

Brunson, M. H., and H. W. Allen. 1944. Mass liberation of parasites for immediate re-duction of oriental fruit moth injury to ripe peaches. *Jour. Econ. Ent.*, 37: 411–16.

Brust, M. and G. Frankel. 1955. The nutritional requirements of the larvae of the blowfly, *Phormia regina*. *Physiol. Zool.*, 28: 186–204.

Bryden, J. W., and M. W. H. Bishop. 1945. *Perilitus coccinellae* (Hym., Braconidae) in Cambridgeshire. *Ent. Monthly Mag.*, 81: 51–2.

Bucher, G. E. 1958. General summary and review of utilization of disease to control in-sects. *Proc. 10th Internatl. Congr. Ent. (Montreal 1956)*, 4: 695–701.

—— 1959. The bacterium *Coccobacillus acridiorum* d'Herelle: its taxonomic position and status as a pathogen of locusts and grasshoppers. *Jour. Insect Path.*, 1: 331–46.

—— 1960. Potential bacterial pathogens of insects and their characteristics. *Jour. Insect Pathol.*, 2: 172–95.

Bucher, G. E., and J. M. Stephens. 1957. A disease of grasshoppers caused by the bacter-ium *Pseudomonas aeruginosa* (Schroeter) Migula. *Canadian Jour. Microbiol.*, 3: 611–25.

Buckner, C. H. 1955a. Small mammal populations on a changing site. *Canada Dept. Agric. Sci. Serv., Div. Forest Biol., Bi-monthly Prog. Rept.*, 11: 2.

Buckner, C. H. 1955*b*. Small mammals as predators of sawflies. *Canadian Ent.*, 87: 121–23.

Buffon, L. L. de. 1756. *Histoire naturelle générale et particulière*. Paris, Plonteaux.

Bugbee, R. E., and A. Reigel. 1945. The cactus moth, *Melitara dentata* (Grote), and its effect on *Opuntia macrorrhiza* in western Kansas. *Amer. Midland Nat.*, 33: 117–27.

Bünzli, G. H., and W. W. Büttiker. 1959. Fungous diseases of lamellicorn larvae in Southern Rhodesia. *Bull. Ent. Res.*, 50: 89–96.

Burgess, A. F., and S. S. Crossman. 1929. Imported insect enemies of the gypsy moth and the brown-tail moth. *U.S. Dept. Agric. Tech. Bull.*, 86. 148 pp.

Burke, H. R. and Dial F. Martin. 1956. The biology of three chrysopid predators of the cotton aphid. *Jour. Econ. Ent.*, 49: 698–700.

Burkill, I. H. 1914. The Sirangoon outbreak (1913) of *Brachartona catoxantha*. *Gardens' Bull. [Singapore]*, 1: 207–08.

Burnett, T. 1948. Modal temperatures for the greenhouse white-fly *Trialeurodes vaporariorum* and its parasite *Encarsia formosa*. *Ecology*, 29: 181–89.

—— 1949. The effect of temperature on an insect host-parasite population. *Ecology*, 30: 113–34.

—— 1956. Effects of natural temperatures on oviposition of various numbers of an insect parasite (Hymenoptera, Chalcididae, Tenthredinidae). *Ann. Ent. Soc. America*, 49: 55–59.

—— 1958*a*. Effect of host distribution on the reproduction of *Encarsia formosa* Gahan (Hymenoptera: Chalcidoidea). *Canadian Ent.*, 90: 179–91.

—— 1958*b*. Effect of area of search on reproduction of *Encarsia formosa* Gahan (Hymenoptera: Chalcidoidea). *Canadian Ent.*, 90: 225–29.

Bussart, J. E. 1937. The bionomics of *Chaetophleps setosa* Coquillett (Diptera: Tachinidae). *Ann. Ent. Soc. America*, 30: 285–95.

Busse, K. 1953. Beobachtungen an der Ilexminierfliege *Phytomyza ilicis* Curtis (Diptera, Agromyzidae) und ihrem Parasiten *Opius ilicis* Nixon (Hymenoptera, Braconidae). *Publ. Ent. Mitteil. Zool. Sta.-institut. Zool. Mus. Hamburg No. 3*, 16 pp.

Butschli, O. 1874. Ein beitrag zur kenntnis des stoffwechsels, insbesondere bei den insekten. *Arch. Anat. Physiol., Leipzig*, 1874: 348–61.

Cain, A. J. 1953. Geography, ecology and coexistence in relation to the biological definition of the species. *Evolution*, 7: 76–83.

Cain, S. A. 1939. The climax and its complexities. *Amer. Midland Nat.*, 21: 146–81.

Caldwell, A. H. 1949. Mass rearing *Drosophila. Jour. Econ. Ent.*, 42: 707.

Calhoun, E. H. 1953. Notes on the stages and the biology of *Baryodma ontarionis* Casey (Coleoptera: Staphylinidae), a parasite of the cabbage maggot, *Hylemya brassicae* Bouche (Diptera: Anthomyiidae). *Canadian Ent.*, 85: 1–8.

Caltagirone, L. E. 1959. The biology of *Pontania pacifica* Marlatt (Hymenoptera, Tenthredinidae), and its parasites and inquilines. Ph.D. Thesis, Univ. Calif.

Cameron, Ewen. 1935. A study of the natural control of ragwort (*Senecio jacobaea* L.). *Jour. Ecol.*, 23: 265–322.

Cameron, E. 1938. A study of the natural control of the pea moth, *Cydia nigricana* Steph. *Bull. Ent. Res.*, 29: 277–313.

—— 1939. The holly leaf-miner, *Phytomyza ilicis* Curt. and its parasites. *Bull. Ent. Res.*, 30: 173–208.

—— 1941. The biology and post-embryonic development of *Opius ilicis* n. sp., a parasite of the holly leaf-miner (*Phytomyza ilicis* Curt.). *Parasitology*, 33: 8–38.

—— 1950. The biology and economic importance of *Alomya debellator* (F.), a remarkable parasite of the swift moth, *Hepialus lupulinus* (L.). *Bull. Ent. Res.*, 41: 429–38.

Cameron, E. 1951. On the identity of an ichneumonid parasite of *Hepialus lupulinus* (L.). *Bull. Ent. Res.*, 41: 637.

—— 1957. On the parasites and predators of the cockroach II. *Evania appendigaster* (L.). *Bull. Ent. Res.*, 48: 199–209.

Campbell, F. L., and F. R. Moulton. 1943. Laboratory procedures in studies of the chemical control of insects. *American Assoc. Adv. Sci. Publ. No. 20*, 206 pp.

Candolle, A. de. 1855. *Géographie botanique raisonée ou exposition des faits principaux et des lois concernant la distribution géographique des plantes de l'époque actuelle.* 2 vol. Paris–Geneve.

Canizo, J. del. 1957. Parasitos de la langosta en Espana, II. Los Trichodes (Col. Cleridae). *Bol. Pat. Veg. Ent. Agric.*, Madrid, 22: (1955–56) 297–312.

Canning, E. U. 1953. A new microsporidian, *Nosema locustae* n. sp., from the fat body of the African migratory locust, *Locusta migratoria migratorioides* R. & F. *Parasitology*, 43: 287–90.

Carnes, E. K. 1912. Collecting ladybirds (Coccinellidae) by the ton. *Calif. State Hort. Comm. Monthly Bull.*, 1: 71–81.

Carter, W. 1935. Studies on biological control of *Pseudococcus brevipes* (Ckll.) in Jamaica and Central America. *Jour. Econ. Ent.*, 28: 1037–41.

Cashmore, A. B., and T. G. Campbell. 1946. The weed problem in Australia: A review. *Australia Council Sci. and Indust. Res. Jour.*, 19: 16–31.

Cazier, M. A., and A. Bacon. 1949. Introduction to quantitative systematics. *Bull. Amer. Mus. Hist.*, 93: 347–88.

Ceballos, G., and E. Zarco. 1952. Ensayo de lucha biologica contra una plaga de *Diprion pini* (L.) en masas de *Pinus silvestris*, de la Sierra de Albarracin. *Madird, Inst. Esp. Ent.* 1–38.

Cendaña, S. M. 1937. Studies on the biology of *Coccophagus* (Hymenoptera) a genus parasitic on nondiaspidine Coccidae. *Univ. California Publ. Ent.*, 6: 337–400.

Chamberlin, F. S., and S. R. Dutky. 1958. Tests of pathogens for the control of tobacco insects. *Jour. Econ. Ent.*, 51: 560.

Chant, D. A. 1958. On the ecology of typhlodromid mites in southeastern England. *Proc. 10th Internatl. Congr. Ent.*, 4: 649–58.

—— 1959. Phytoseiid mites (Acarina: Phytoseiidae). Part I. Bionomics of seven species in southeastern England. Part II. A taxonomic review of the family Phytoseiidae, with descriptions of 38 new species. *Canadian Ent. Suppl.*, 12 of Vol. 91, 164 pp.

Chapman, R. N. 1928a. The quantitative analysis of environmental factors. *Ecology*, 9: 111–22.

—— 1928b. Temperature as an ecological factor in animals. *Amer. Nat.*, 62: 298–310.

—— 1931. *Animal Ecology, with Especial Reference to Insects.* New York, McGraw-Hill. 464 pp.

Chapman, J. A., and J. W. Wilson. 1956. The use of impregnated paper as an approach to nutritional studies with the Douglas fir beetle. *Jour. Econ. Ent.*, 49: 426–27.

Chater, E. H. 1931. A contribution to the study of the natural control of gorse. *Bull. Ent. Res*, 22: 225–35.

Chauvin, R. 1956. *Physiologie de l'insecte.* Institut Nat. Recherch. Agron. Paris. 917 pp.

Chen, S. H. 1946. Evolution of the insect larva. *Trans. Roy. Ent. Soc. London*, 97: 381–404.

Cheshire, F. R., and W. W. Cheyne. 1885. The pathogenic history and the history under cultivation of a new bacillus (*B. alvei*), the cause of a disease of the hive bee hitherto known as foul brood. *Jour. Roy. Microsc. Soc.*, 5: 581–601.

Chiang, H. C., and Holdaway, F. G. 1960. Relative effectiveness of resistance of field corn to the European corn borer, *Pyrausta nubilalis*, in crop protection and in population control. *Jour. Econ. Ent.*, 53: 918–24.

Chitty, D. 1957. *Self-regulation of numbers through changes in viability*. In *Cold Spring Harbor Symposia on Quantitative Biology*, 22: 277–80.

Christenson, L. D., S. Maeda, and J. R. Holloway. 1956. Substitution of dehydrated for fresh carrots in medium for rearing fruit flies. *Jour. Econ. Ent.*, 49: 135–36.

Chrystal, R. N. 1930. Studies of the *Sirex* parasites. The biology and post-embryonic development of *Ibalia leucospoides* Hochenw. (Hymenoptera-Cynipoidea). *Oxford Forest. Mem.*, 11: 1–63.

Chu, H. F. 1949. *How to know the immature insects*, 234 pp. Wm. C. Brown Co., Dubuque, Iowa.

Clancy, D. W. 1944. Biology of *Allotropa burrelli*, a gregarious parasite of *Pseudococcus comstocki*. *Jour. Agric. Res.*, 69: 159–67.

—— 1946. The insect parasites of the Chrysopidae (Neuroptera). *Univ. California Publ. Ent.*, 7: 403–96.

Clark, C. A. 1934. The European corn borer and its controlling factors in the Orient. *U.S. Dept. Agric. Tech. Bull.*, 455. 37 pp., illus.

Clark, Edger W. 1958. A review of literature on calcium and magnesium in insects. *Ann. Ent. Soc. America.*, 51: 142–54.

Clark, E. C. 1955. Observations on the ecology of a polyhedrosis of the great basin tent caterpillar *Malacosoma fragile*. *Ecology*, 36: 373–76.

—— 1956. Survival and transmission of a virus causing polyhedrosis in *Malacosoma fragile*. *Ecology*, 37: 728–32.

—— 1958. Ecology of the polyhedroses of tent caterpillars. *Ecology*, 39: 132–39.

Clark, E. C., and C. G. Thompson. 1954. The possible use of microorganisms in the control of the Great Basin tent caterpillar. *Jour. Econ. Ent.*, 47: 268–72.

Clark, L. R. 1953. The ecology of *Chrysomela gemellata* Rossi and *C. hypepici* Forst. and their effect on St. John's wort in the Bright District, Victoria. *Australian Jour. Zool.*, 1: 1–69.

Clausen, C. P. 1915. Mealybugs of citrus trees. *Calif. Agric. Expt. Sta. Bull.*, 258: 19–48.

—— 1923. The biology of *Schizaspidia tenuicornis* Ashm., a Eucharid parasite of *Camponotus*. *Ann. Ent. Soc. America*, 16: 195–219.

—— 1928. *Hyperalonia oenomaus* Rond., a parasite of *Tiphia* larvae. (Dipt., Bomblyiidae.) *Ann. Ent. Soc. America*, 21: 461–72, 642–59.

—— 1929. Biological studies on *Poecilogonalos thwaitesii* (Westw.), parasitic in the cocoons of *Henicospilus*. *Proc. Ent. Soc. Washington*, 31: 67–79.

—— 1931*a*. Biological notes on the Trigonalidae. *Proc. Ent. Soc. Washington*, 33: 72–81.

—— 1931*b*. Biological observations on *Agriotypus*. *Proc. Ent. Soc. Washington*, 33: 29–37.

—— 1932*a*. The citrus blackfly in Asia, and the importation of its natural enemies into tropical America. *U.S. Dept. Agric. Tech. Bull.*, 320. 58 pp., illus.

—— 1932*b*. The early stages of some Tryphonine Hymenoptera parasitic on sawfly larvae. *Proc. Ent. Soc. Washington*, 34: 49–60.

—— 1932*c*. The biology of *Encyrtus infidus* Rossi, a parasite of *Lecanium kunoensis* Kuw. *Ann. Ent. Soc. America*, 25: 670–84.

—— 1936. Insect parasitism and biological control. *Ann. Ent. Soc. America*, 29: 201–23.

—— 1940*a*. *Entomophagous insects*. McGraw-Hill Book Co., Inc., New York and London. 688 pp.

—— 1940*b*. The immature stages of the Eucharidae. *Proc. Ent. Soc. Washington*, 42: 161–70.

Clausen, C. P. 1940c. The oviposition habits of the Eucharidae (Hymenoptera). *Jour. Washington Acad. Sci.*, 30: 504–16.

—— 1941. Some factors relating to colonization, recovery and establishment of insect parasites. *Proc. 6th Pac. Sci. Congr. (1939)*, 4: 421–28.

—— 1942. The relation of taxonomy to biological control. *Jour. Econ. Ent.*, 35: 744–48.

—— 1950. Respiratory adaptations in the immature stages of parasitic insects. *Arthropoda* 1: 197–224.

—— 1951. The time factor in biological control. *Jour. Econ. Ent.*, 44: 1–9.

—— 1952a. Parasites and predators. In *Insects. U.S. Dept. Agric., Yearbook of Agric.* 1952. Pp. 380–88.

—— 1952b. Biological control of insects: California's subtropical climate favors establishment of natural enemies of agricultural pests. *California Agriculture*, 6: 10.

—— 1954a. Biological antagonists in the future of biological control. *Jour. Agric. and Food Chem.*, 2: 12–18.

—— 1954b. The egg-larval host relationship among the parasitic Hymenoptera. *Boll. del Lab. di Zool. Gen. Agr., Portici*, 33: 119–33.

—— 1956a. Biological control of insect pests in the continental United States. *U.S. Dept. Agric. Tech. Bull. No. 1139*, 151 pp.

—— 1956b. Biological control of fruit flies. *Jour. Econ. Ent.*, 49: 176–78.

—— 1958a. The biological control of insect pests in the continental United States. *Proc. 10th Internatl. Congr. Ent.*, 4: 443–47 (1956).

—— 1958b. Biological control of insect pests. *Ann. Rev. Ent.*, 3: 291–310.

—— 1961. Biological control of western grape leaf skeletonizer (*Harrisina brillians* B. and McD.) in California. *Hilgardia*, 31: 613–38.

—— 1962. *Entomophagous insects.* McGraw-Hill Book Co., Inc., New York and London. 688 pp. Reprint Edition, Hafner Pub. Co., New York.

Clausen, C. P., and P. A. Berry. 1932. The citrus blackfly in Asia and the importation of its natural enemies into tropical America. *U.S. Dept. Agric. Tech. Bull.* 320. 58 pp.

Clausen, C. P., H. A. Jaynes, and T. R. Gardner. 1933. Further investigations of the parasites of *Popillia japonica* in the Far East. *U.S. Dept. Agric. Tech. Bull.* 366. 58 pp.

Clausen, C. P., J. L. King, and C. Teranishi. 1927. The parasites of *Popillia japonica* in Japan and Chosen (Korea) and their introduction into the United States. *U.S. Dept. Agric. Bull.* 1429, 55 pp.

Cleare, L. D., Jr. 1929. Moth borer in British Guiana. *Trans. 4th Internatl. Congr. Ent.*, 2: 131–37.

—— 1934. Sugar-cane moth borer investigations in British Guiana: The present position. *Agric. Jour. [British Guiana]*, 5: 13–21.

Clements, F. E. 1936. Nature and structure of the climax. *Jour. Ecol.*, 24: 252–84.

Clements, F. E., and V. E. Shelford. 1939. *Bioecology.* New York, John Wiley and Sons. 425 pp.

Cloudsley-Thompson, J. L. 1957. Some comments on the natural control of animal populations with especial reference to insects. *Entomologist*, 90: 195–203.

Cobb, N. A. 1904. Parasites as an aid in determining organic relationship. *Agric. Gaz. N. South Wales*, 15: 845–48.

Cochrane, V. W. 1958. *Physiology of fungi.* John Wiley and Sons, New York. 524 pp.

Cockerell, T. D. A. 1934. 'Mimicry' among insects. *Nature*, 133: 329–30.

Cohen, A. L. 1953. Rapid and simple methods for the harvesting of mass cultures of microorganisms. *Appl. Microbiol.*, 1: 168–71.

Cohn, F. A. 1855. *Empusa muscae* und die Krankheit der Stubenfliegen. *Nova Acta Acad. Caes. Leop. Carol. Germ. Nat. Cur.*, 25: 301–60.

Cole, L. C. 1955. Review: Andrewartha, H. G., and L. C. Birch. 1954. The distribution and abundance of animals. Univ. Chicago Press. *Ecology*, 36: 538–39.

—— 1957. *Sketches of general and comparative demography*. In *Cold Spring Harbor Symposia on Quantitative Biology*, 22: 1–15.

Cole, L. R. 1959. On the defences of lepidopterous pupae in relation to the oviposition behaviour of certain Ichneumonidae. *Jour. Lepidopt. Soc.*, 12: 1–10.

Coleman, E. 1929. Pollination of an Australian orchid, *Cryptostylis leptochila* F. Muell. *Jour. Bot. London*, 67: 97–100.

Colyer, C. N. 1952. Notes on the life history of the British species of *Phalacrotophora* Enderlein (Dipt., Phoridae). *Ent. Monthly Mag.*, 88: 135–39.

Compere, H. 1925. New Chalcidoid (Hymenopterous) parasites and hyperparasites of the black scale, *Saissetia oleae* Bernard. *Univ. California Publ. Ent.*, 3: 295–326.

—— 1931. A revision of the species of Coccophagus, a genus of hymenopterous coccid-inhabiting parasites. *Proc. U.S. Nat. Mus.*, 78: 1–132.

—— 1940. Parasites of the black scale, *Saissetia oleae*, in Africa. *Hilgardia*, 13: 387–425.

—— 1961. The red scale, *Aonidiella aurantii* (Mask.), and its insect enemies. *Hilgardia*, 31: 173–278.

Compere, H., and H. S. Smith. 1932. The control of the citrophilus mealybug, *Pseudococcus gahani*, by Australian parasites. *Hilgardia*, 6: 585–618.

Comstock, J. H. 1880. *Introduction of the 1880 Report of the U.S. Dept. Agric.* pp. 289–90.

—— 1940. *An Introduction to Entomology*, 9th rev. ed. Comstock Publishing Co., Inc. Ithaca, 1064 pp.

Cook, C. W. 1942. Insects and weather as they influence growth of cactus on the Central Great Plains. *Ecology*, 23: 209–14.

Cook, E. F. 1949. The evolution of the head in the larvae of the Diptera. *Micro-entomology* 14: 1–57.

Cook, W. C. 1930. Field studies of the pale western cutworm (*Porosagrotis orthogonia* Morr.). *Montana Agric. Expt. Stat. Bull.*, 225.

—— 1931. Notes on predicting the probable future distribution of introduced insects. *Ecology*, 12: 245–47.

Cooper, K. W. 1954. Biology of Eumenine wasps. IV. A Trigonalid wasp parasitic on *Rygchium rugosum* (Saussure). *Proc. Ent. Soc. Washington*, 56: 280–88.

Coppel, H. C. 1958. Studies on dipterous parasites of the spruce budworm, *Choristoneura fumiferana* (Clem.) (Lepidoptera: Tortricidae). VI. *Phorocera incrassata* Smith (Diptera: Tachinidae). *Canadian Jour. Zool.*, 36: 453–62.

Coppel, H. C., and K. Leius. 1958. Morphological variations in populations of the larch sawfly, *Pristiphora erichsonii* (Htg.) (Hymenoptera: Tenthredinidae), from Canada, Great Britain, and Japan. *Proc. 10th Internatl. Congr. Ent.*, 1: 231–38 (1956).

Coppel. H. C., and M. G. Maw. 1954a. Studies on dipterous parasites of the spruce budworm (*Choristoneura fumiferana* (Clem.)) (Lepidoptera: Tortricidae). IV. *Madremyia saundersii* (Will.) (Diptera: Tachinidae). *Canadian Jour. Zool.*, 32: 314–23.

—— 1954b, Studies on dipterous parasites of the spruce budworm *Choristoneura fumiferana* (Clem.) III. *Ceromasia auricaudata* Tns. *Canadian Jour. Zool.*, 32: 144–56.

Coppel, H. C., H. L. House, and M. G. Maw. 1959. Studies on dipterous parasites of the spruce budworm, *Choristoneura fumiferana* (Clem.) (Lepidoptera: Tortricidae). VII. *Agria affinis* (Fall.) (Diptera: Sarcophagidae). *Canadian Jour. Zool.* 37: 817–30.

Coppel, H. C., and B. C. Smith. 1957. Studies on dipterous parasites of the spruce bud-worm, *Choristoneura fumiferana* (Clem.) (Lepidoptera: Tortricidae). V. *Omotoma fumiferanae* (Tot.) (Diptera: Tachinidae). *Canadian Jour. Zool.*, 35: 581–92.

Corman, J., H. M. Tsuchiya, H. J. Koepsell, R. G. Benedict, S. B. Kelly, V. H. Feger, R. G. Dworschack, and R. W. Jackson. 1957. Oxygen absorption rates in laboratory and pilot plant equipment. *Appl. Microbiol.*, 5: 313–18.

Cornalia, E. 1856. Monografia del bombice del gelso (*Bombyx mori* Linneo). *Mem. dell' I. R. Istituo Lonbardo di Scienze, Lettere ed Arti.*, 6: 1–387.

Couch, J. N. 1945. Revision of the genus *Coelomomyces*, parasitic in insect larvae. *Jour. Elisha Mitchell Sci. Soc.*, 61: 124–36.

Couch, J. N., and H. R. Dodge. 1947. Further observations on *Coelomomyces*, parasitic on mosquito larvae. *Jour. Elisha Mitchell Sci. Soc.*, 63: 69–79.

Couturier, A. 1950. Biologie d'un *Hexamermis* (Nematodes Mermithidae) parasite des insectes défoliateurs de l'osier. *Ann. Inst. natl. Recherches agron. Sér. C. Ann. épiphyt.*, 1: 13–37.

Cowles, H. C. 1901. The physiographic ecology of Chicago and vicinity; a study of the origin, development, and classification of plant societies. *Bot. Gaz.*, 31: 73–182.

Cowperthwaite, Jean, M. M. Weber, L. Packer, and S. H. Hutner. 1953. Nutrition of *Herpetomonas (Strigomonas) culicidarum*. *Ann. New York Acad. Sci.*, 56: 972–81.

Cox, James A. 1932. *Ascogaster carpocapsae* Viereck, an important larval parasite of the codling moth and oriental fruit moth. *New York State Agric. Expt. Sta. Tech. Bull.* 188, 26 pp.

Craig, R., and W. M. Hoskins. 1940. Insect biochemistry. *Ann. Rev. Biochem.*, 9: 617–40.

Craighead, F. C. 1924. Studies on the spruce budworm *Cacaecia fumiferana* Clem., Part II. General bionomics and possibilities of prevention and control. *Dominion Dept. Agric. Bull.*, 37.

Crandell, H. A., 1939. The biology of *Pachycrepoideus dubius* Ashmead (Hymenoptera), a pteromalid parasite of *Piophila casei* Linne (Diptera). *Ann. Ent. Soc. America*, 32: 632–54.

Crawford, A. W. 1933. *Glypta rufiscutellaris* Cresson, an ichneumonid larval parasite of the oriental fruit moth. *New York State Agric. Expt. Sta. Tech. Bull.*, 217. 29 pp.

Creager, D. B., and F. J. Spruijt. 1935. The relation of certain fungi to larval development of *Eumerus tuberculatus* Rond. *Ann. Ent. Soc. America*, 28: 425–36.

Criddle, N. 1922. The western wheat stem sawfly and its control. *Canada Dept. Agric. Pamphlet*, 6, N. S. 8 pp.

Crouzel, I. S. de, 1944. First instar larva of *Acridiophaga caridei* (Brethes) (Diptera: Sarcophagidae). *Proc. Ent. Soc. Washington*, 46: 239–46.

Crouzel, I. S. de, and R. G. Salavin. 1943. Contribucion al estudio de los *Neorhyncho-cephalus argentinos* (Diptera: Nemestrinidae). *Argentina An. Soc. Cient.*, 136: 145–77.

Cumber, R. A. 1949. Humblebee parasites and commensals found within a thirty mile radius of London. *Proc. Roy. Ent. Soc. London A.*, 24: 119–27.

Curran, C. H. 1934. *The Families and Genera of North American Diptera*. The Ballou Press, New York, 512 pp.

Currie, G. A. 1932. Ovipositional stimuli of the burr-seed fly, *Euaresta aequalis* Loew. (Diptera: Trypetidae). *Bull. Ent. Res.*, 23: 191–99.

Currie, G. A., and R. V. Fyfe. 1938. The fate of certain European insects introduced into Australia for the control of weeds. *Australia Council Sci. and Indust. Res. Jour.*, 11: 289–301.

Currie, G. A., and S. Garthside. 1932. The possibility of the entomological control of St. John's wort in Australia—Progress report. *Australia Council Sci. and Indust. Res. Pamph.* 29. 28 pp.

Cushman, R. A. 1926*a*. Location of individual hosts versus systematic relation of host species as a determining factor in parasitic attack. *Proc. Ent. Soc. Washington*, 28: 5–6.

—— 1926*b*. Presidential address. *Proc. Ent. Soc. Washington*, 28: 25–51.

Dahm, Paul A. 1955. A convenient method for rearing large cockroaches. *Jour. Econ. Ent.*, 48: 480–82.

Dameron, W. H., and H. P. Smith. 1939. Control of *Opuntia* by insects. *Texas Agric. Expt. Sta. Bull.* 575. 55 pp.

Daniel, D. M. 1932. *Macrocentrus ancylivorus* Rohwer, a polyembryonic braconid parasite of the oriental fruit moth. *New York Agric. Expt. Sta. Tech. Bull.* 187. 101 pp.

—— 1936*a*. Mass liberation of an oriental fruit moth parasite. *Jour. Econ. Ent.*, 29: 459–61.

—— 1936*b*. Utilizing parasites in controlling the oriental fruit moth. *Ann. Ent. Soc. America.*, 29: 640–44.

Darlington, C. D. 1940. *Taxonomic species and genetic systems*, pp. 137–60. In *The New Systematics*, J. S. Huxley, editor.

Darlington, P. J., Jr. 1957. *Zoogeography: the Geographical Distribution of Animals.* John Wiley & Sons, New York, 675 pp.

Darwin, C. 1859*a*. *On the Origin of Species.* Reprinted by Cassell & Co., Ltd., London, 1909. 430 pp.

—— 1859*b*. *On the Origin of Species.* New York and London. D. Appleton. Sixth Edition (Author's edition) 1872. 365 pp.

David, A. L., and T. S. Muthurkrishnan. 1953. Summaries of *Opuntia* control by insects. The prickly pear cochineal: observations on its natural hosts and enemies in South Africa. *Indian Jour. Ent.*, 15–16: 219–24.

David, W. A. L. 1957. Breeding *Pieris brassicae* L. and *Apanteles glomeratus* L. as experimental insects. *Zeitschr. Pflkrankh. und Pflanzenschutz*, 64: 572–77.

David, W. A. L., and B. O. C. Gardiner. 1952. Laboratory breeding of *Pieris brassicae* L. and *Apanteles glomeratus* L. *Proc. Roy. Ent. Soc. London Ser. A.*, 27: 54–56.

—— 1960. A *Pieris brassicae* (Linnaeus) culture resistant to a granulosis. *Jour. Insect Pathol.*, 2: 106–114.

Davidson, J., and H. G. Andrewartha. 1948*a*. The influence of rainfall, evaporation and atmospheric temperature on fluctuations in the size of a natural population of *Thrips imaginis* (Thysanoptera). *Jour. Animal Ecol.*, 17, 200–22.

—— 1948*b*. Annual trends in a natural population of *Thrips imaginis* (Thysanoptera). *Jour. Animal Ecol.*, 17: 193–99.

Davidson, W. M. 1919. The convergent ladybird beetle (*Hippodamia convergens* Guerin) and the barley-corn aphis (*Aphis maidis* Fitch). *Calif. State Hort. Com. Monthly Bull.*, 8: 23–26.

—— 1924. Observations and experiments on the dispersion of the convergent ladybeetle (*Hippodamia convergens* Guerin) in California. *Trans. Amer. Ent. Soc.*, 50: 163–75.

Davies, D. M., and B. V. Peterson. 1956. Observations on the mating, feeding, ovarian development, and oviposition of adult black flies. *Canadian Jour. Zool.*, 34: 615–55.

Davies, W. M. 1928. The bionomics of *Apion ulicis* (gorse weevil) with special reference to its role in the control of *Ulex europaeus* in New Zealand. *Ann. Appl. Biol.*, 15: 263–85.

Davis, C. J. 1958. Recent introductions for biological control in Hawaii—IV. *Proc. Hawaiian Ent. Soc.*, 17: 62–68.

Davis, C. S. et al. 1957. The spotted alfalfa aphid and its control in California. *California Agric. Ext. Service* (mimeo.). 43 pp.

Davis, E. G. 1944. *Apanteles diatraeae*, a braconid parasite of the southwestern corn borer. *U.S. Dept. Agric. Tech. Bull.* 871. 19 pp.

Davis, G. R. F. 1956. Amino acid requirements of *Oryzaephilus surinamensis* (L.) (Coleoptera: Silvanidae) for pupation. *Canadian Jour. Zool.*, 34: 82–85.

—— 1959. A method for rearing larvae of *Ctenicera aeripennis destructor* (Brown) (Coleoptera: Elateridae) aseptically in test tubes. *Ann. Ent. Soc. America*, 52: 173–75.

Day, M. F., and T. D. C. Grace. 1959. Culture of insect tissues. *Ann. Rev. Ent.*, 4: 17–38.

Dean, H. A. 1961. *Aphytis lepidosaphes* (Hymenoptera: Chalcidoidea), an introduced parasite of purple scale. *Ann. Ent. Soc. America*, 54: 918–20.

Dean, R. W. 1938. Experiments on rearing apple maggot adults. *Jour. Econ. Ent.*, 31: 241–44.

DeBach, Paul. 1940. Experimental studies on quantitative relations between parasite and host populations. Ph.D. Thesis, Univ. California, Berkeley.

—— 1942. A simple method of obtaining standardized houseflies. *Jour. Econ. Ent.*, 35: 282.

—— 1943a. The effect of low storage temperature on reproduction in certain parasitic Hymenoptera. *Pan-Pacific Ent.*, 19: 112–19.

—— 1943b. The importance of host-feeding by adult parasites in the reduction of host populations. *Jour. Econ. Ent.*, 36: 647–58.

—— 1946. An insecticidal check method for measuring the efficacy of entomophagous insects. *Jour. Econ. Ent.*, 39: 695–97.

—— 1947a. Cottony-cushion scale, vedalia and DDT in central California. *California Citrograph*, 32: 406–07.

—— 1947b. Predators, DDT, and citrus red mite populations. *Jour. Econ. Ent.*, 40: 598.

—— 1949. Population studies of the long-tailed mealybug and its natural enemies on citrus trees in southern California, 1946. *Ecology*, 30: 14–25.

—— 1951. The necessity for an ecological approach to pest control on citrus in California. *Jour. Econ. Ent.*, 44: 443–47.

—— 1953. The establishment in California of an Oriental strain of *Prospaltella perniciosi* Tower on the California red scale. *Jour. Econ. Ent.*, 46: 1103.

—— 1954. Relative efficacy of the red scale parasites *Aphytis chrysomphali* Mercet and *Aphytis* 'A' on citrus trees in southern California. *Bol. Lab. Zool. Gen. e Agraria 'Filippo Silvestri' Portici*, 33: 134–51.

—— 1955. Validity of the insecticidal check method as a measure of the effectiveness of natural enemies of diaspine scale insects. *Jour. Econ. Ent.*, 48: 584–88.

—— 1958a. Selective breeding to improve adaptations of parasitic insects. *Proc. 10th Internatl. Congr. Ent.*, 4: 759–68 (1956).

—— 1958b. The role of weather and entomophagous species in the natural control of insect populations. *Jour. Econ. Ent.*, 51: 474–84.

—— 1958c. Application of ecological information to control of citrus pests in California. *Proc. 10th Internatl. Congr. Ent.*, 3: 187–94 (1956).

—— 1959. New species and strains of *Aphytis* (Hymenoptera, Eulophidae) parasitic on the California red scale, *Aonidiella aurantii* (Mask.), in the Orient. *Ann. Ent. Soc. America*, 52: 354–62.

—— 1960. The importance of taxonomy to biological control as illustrated by the cryptic history of *Aphytis holoxanthus* n. sp. (Hymenoptera: Aphelinidae), a parasite of *Chrysomphalus aonidum*, and *Aphytis coheni* n. sp., a parasite of *Aonidiella aurantii*. *Ann. Ent. Soc. America*, 53: 701–05.

DeBach, Paul, and Blair Bartlett. 1951. Effects of insecticides on biological control of insect pest of citrus. *Jour. Econ. Ent.*, 44: 372–83.

DeBach, Paul, E. J. Dietrick, and C. A. Fleschner. 1949. A new technique for evaluating the efficiency of entomophagous insects in the field. *Jour. Econ. Ent.*, 42: 546.

DeBach, Paul, E. J. Dietrick, C. A. Fleschner, and T. W. Fisher. 1950. Periodic colonization of *Aphytis* for control of the California red scale. Preliminary tests, 1949. *Jour. Econ. Ent.*, 43: 783–802.

DeBach, Paul, E. J. Dietrick, and C. A. Fleschner. 1951. Ants vs. biological control of citrus pests. *California Citrograph*, 36: 312, 347–48.

—— 1953. Natural control of the California red scale in untreated citrus orchards in southern California. *Proc. 7th Pac. Sci. Congr.*, 4: 236–48.

DeBach, Paul, and T. W. Fisher. 1956. Experimental evidence for sibling species in the oleander scale, *Aspidiotus hederae* (Vallot). *Ann. Ent. Soc. America*, 49: 235–39.

DeBach, Paul, T. W. Fisher, and J. Landi. 1955. Some effects of meteorological factors on all stages of *Aphytis lingnanensis*, a parasite of the California red scale. *Ecology*, 36: 743–53.

DeBach, Paul, C. A. Fleschner, and E. J. Dietrick. 1949. California red scale. *California Agric.*, 3: 12, 14.

—— 1950. Studies of the efficacy of natural enemies of citrus red mite in southern California. *Jour. Econ. Ent.*, 43: 807–19.

—— 1951. A biological check method for evaluating the effectiveness of entomophagous insects. *Jour. Econ. Ent.*, 44: 763–66.

DeBach, Paul, and John Landi. 1959a. New parasites of California red scale. *California Citrograph*, 44: 290, 301, 303–04.

—— 1959b. Integrating chemical, biological control by strip treatment. *California Citrograph*, 44: 324, 345–47, 352.

DeBach, Paul, J. H. Landi, and E. B. White. 1955. Biological control of red scale. *California Citrograph*, 40: 254, 271–72, 274–75.

DeBach, Paul, C. E. Kennett, and R. J. Pence. 1958. Species of *Thysanus* as primary parasites. *Jour. Econ. Ent.*, 51: 114–15.

DeBach, Paul and P. Sisojevic. 1960. Some effects of temperature and competition on the distribution and relative abundance of *Aphytis lingnanensis* and *A. chrysomphali* (Hymenoptera: Aphelinidae). *Ecology*, 41: 153–160.

DeBach, Paul, and H. S. Smith. 1947. Effects of parasite population density on rate of change of host and parasite populations. *Ecology*, 28: 290–98.

DeBach, Paul, and E. B. White. 1960. Commercial mass culture of the California red scale parasite *Aphytis lingnanensis*. *California Agric. Expt. Sta. Bull.* 770. 58 pp.

DeBach, Paul, E. White, R. Orth, S. Warner, and R. Morrison. 1960. Artificial selection of climate-tolerant strains of *Aphytis lingnanensis* Comp. Unpublished data, on file Dept. of Biological Control, Univ. California, Riverside.

de Beer, G. R. 1940. *Embryology and taxonomy*, pp. 365–94. In *The New Systematics*, J. S. Huxley, Editor.

De Fluiter, H. H. 1939. Het witte luis-vraagstuk bu de koffie. (The white mealybug question in relation to coffee). *Bergcultures*, 13, 760–65 [Batavia]. *Abs. in R.A.E.*, A. 28: 397–98.

De Geer, C. (Degeer, K.). 1776. *Mémoires pour servir à l'histoire des insectes*. Vol. 6. Pierre Hesselberg, Stockholm.

—— 1782. *Abhandlungen zur Geschichte der Insekten*. (Translated from the French by J. A. E. Goeze), Vol. 6, 200 pp.

de Groot, A. P. 1953. *Protein and amino acid requirements of the honeybee (Apis mellifica* L.). Dr. W. Junk, Publishers. The Hague, Netherlands.

d'Herelle, F. 1911. Sur une épizootie de nature bactérienne sévissant sur les sauterelles au Mexique. *Compt. Rend. Acad. Sci.*, **152**: 1413–15.

—— 1912. Sur la propagation, dans la République Argentine, de l'épizootic des sauterelles du Mexique. *Compt. Rend. Acad. Sci.*, **154**: 623–25.

—— 1914. Le coccobacille des sauterelles. *Ann. Inst. Pasteur [Paris]*, **28**: 280–328, 387–407.

—— 1915. Sur le procédé biologique de destruction des sauterelles. *Compt. Rend. Acad. Sci.*, **161**: 503–05.

—— 1916. Campagne contre les *Schistocerca peregrina* en Tunisie par la méthode biologique (avril–juillet 1915). *Arch. Inst. Pasteur [Tunis]*, **9**: 135–48.

Delaporte, B., and S. Béguin. 1955. Étude d'une souche de *Bacillus* pathogène pour certains insectes, identifiable à *Bacillus thuringiensis* Berliner. *Ann. Inst. Pasteur [Paris]*, **89**: 632–43.

DeLeon, D. 1935. A study of *Medetera aldrichii* Wh. (Diptera: Dolichopodidae) a predator of the mountain pine beetle (*Dendroctonus monticolae* Hopk. (Coleoptera: Scolytidae)). *Entomol. Americana (New Series)*, **15**: 59–91.

Delucchi, V. 1950. The mass rearing of *Apanteles rubecula* Marsh., a braconid endoparasite of *Pieris rapae* L. (English summary). *Redia*, **35**: 205–24.

—— 1953. *Aphidecta obliterata* L. (Coleoptera, Coccinellidae) als Räuber von *Dreyfusia (Adelges) piceae* Ratz. *Pflanzenschutz-Berich.*, **11**: 73–83.

—— 1954. *Pullus impexus* (Muls.) (Coleoptera, Coccinellidae) a predator of *Adelges piceae* (Ratz.) (Hemiptera, Adelgidae), with notes on its parasites. *Bull. Ent. Res.*, **45**: 243–78.

—— 1958. Biological control methods (rearing and shipping methods). *Proc. 10th Internatl. Congr. Ent.*, **4**: 891–94 (1956).

Delucchi, V., M. Tadic, and M. Bogavac. 1954. L'elevage en masse de *Apanteles plutellae* Kurdj. (Hym., Braconidae) et de *Angitia tibialis* Grav. (Hym.) Ichneumonid parasites endophages de *Plutella maculipennis* Curt. et notes biologiques sur ces parasites. *Plant Prot.*, **21**: 20–41.

De Saeger, H. 1942. Les *Apanteles* Hyménoptèra, braconides, parasites de lépidoptères. *Bull. Agric. Congo Belge*, **33**: 234–88.

Dethier, V. G. 1947*a*. *Chemical Insect Attractants and Repellents*. Philadelphia, The Blakiston Co. 289 pp.

—— 1947*b*. The response of hymenopterous parasites to chemical stimulation of the ovipositor. *Jour. Exptl. Zool.*, **105**: 199–207.

—— 1953. Host plant perception in phytophagous insects. *Proc. 9th Internatl. Congr. Ent., Symposia*. Pp. 81–89. Dr. W. Junk, Publishers, The Hague, Netherlands.

—— 1954. Evolution of feeding preferences in phytophagous insects. *Evolution*, **8**: 33–54.

Dexter, Raquel. 1932. The food habits of the imported toad, *Bufo marinus*, in the sugar cane sections of Porto Rico. *Internatl. Soc. Sugar Cane Technologists, 4th Cong., San Juan Puerto Rico, Bull.*, **74**. 6 pp.

Dice, L. R. 1952. Quantitative and experimental methods in systematic zoology. *Systematic Zool.*, **1**: 97–104.

Dickson, R. C. 1949. Factors governing the induction of diapause in the oriental fruit moth. *Ann. Ent. Soc. America*, **42**: 511–37.

Dietrick, E. J., E. I. Schlinger, and M. J. Garber. 1960. Sampling insect populations. *California Agric.*, **14**: 9–11.

Dietrick, E. J., E. I. Schlinger, and R. van den Bosch. 1959. A new method for sampling arthropods using a suction collecting machine and modified Berlese funnel separator. *Jour. Econ. Ent.*, **52**: 1085–91.

Dietrick, E. J., and R. van den Bosch. 1957. Insectary propagation of the squash bug and its parasite *Trichopoda pennipes* Fabr. *Jour. Econ. Ent.*, **50**: 627–29.

Difco manual of dehydrated culture media and reagents for microbiological and clinical laboratory procedures. Ninth edition, reprinted. 1953. Difco Laboratories, Inc. Detroit. 350 pp.

Dimond, J. B., A. O. Lea, and D. M. De Long. 1958. Nutritional requirements for reproduction in insects. *Proc. 10th Internatl. Congr. Ent.*, **2**: 135–37 (1956).

Diver, C. 1940. *The problem of closely related species living in the same area*, pp. 303–328. In *The New Systematics*, J. S. Huxley, editor.

Dobzhansky, T. 1937. *Genetics and the origin of species.* Columbia Univ. Press, New York. 364 pp.

—— 1943. Genetics of natural populations. IX. Temporal changes in the composition of populations of *Drosophila pseudoobscura*. *Genetics*, **28**: 162–86.

—— 1947. Genetics of natural populations. XIV. A response to certain gene arrangements in the third chromosome of *Drosophila pseudoobscura* to natural selection. *Genetics*, **32**: 142–60.

—— 1948. Genetics of natural populations. XVI. Altitudinal and seasonal changes produced by natural selection in certain populations of *Drosophila pseudoobscura* and *Drosophila persimilis*. *Genetics*, **33**: 158–76.

—— 1950. Evolution in the tropics. *Amer. Scientist*, **38**: 209–21.

—— 1951. *Genetics and the Origin of Species*, 3d ed. Columbia Univ. Press, New York, 364 pp.

—— 1955. *Evolution, Genetics, and Man.* Chapman and Hall, Ltd., London, 398 pp.

—— 1956. Genetics of natural populations. XXV. Genetic changes in populations of *Drosophila pseudoobscura* and *Drosophila persimilis* in some localities in California. *Evolution*, **10**: 82–92.

Dobzhansky, T., and B. Spassky. 1947. Evolutionary changes in laboratory cultures of *Drosophila pseudoobscura*. *Evolution*, **1**: 191–216.

Dobrovsky, T. M. 1954. Laboratory observations on *Conoderus vagus* Candece. *Florida Ent.*, **37**: 123–31.

Dodd, A. P. 1912. Some remarkable ant-friend Lepidoptera of Queensland. *Ent. Soc. London Trans. (1911)*, **59**: 577–90.

—— 1940. *The biological campaign against prickly pear.* Commonwealth Prickly Pear Board, Brisbane, Australia, 177 pp.

—— 1953. Observations on the stem gall-fly of pamekani, *Eupatorium glandulosum*. *Proc. Hawaiian Ent. Soc.*, **15**: 41–44.

—— 1954. Biological control of weeds. Weed Control Conf., Roseworthy *Agric. College, Session 5*, Aug. 1954. Pp. 121–23.

—— 1957. Recent developments in the biological control on lantana. Minutes Ent. Soc. Queensland, Brisbane (November).

Dodge, H. R. 1941. Observations on *Sandalus niger* Knoch, its egg, and first instar larva. *Ann. Ent. Soc. America*, **34**: 458–66.

Domenichini, G., and C. Vago. 1955. Contributo al problema della limitazione naturale delle popolazioni acridiche. *Boll. Zool. Agraria Bachicoltura*, **21**: 83–86.

Dondale, C. D. 1954. Biology of *Agathis laticinctus* (Cress.) (Hymenoptera: Braconidae), a parasite of the eye-spotted bud moth, in Nova Scotia. *Canadian Ent.*, **86**: 40–44.

Donisthorpe, H. 1944. The dancing habits of some Braconidae (Hym.). *Ent. Month. Mag.*, 80: 72.

Dorman, S. C., W. C. Hale, and W. M. Hoskins. 1938. The laboratory rearing of flesh flies and the relations between temperature, diet and egg production. *Jour. Econ. Ent.*, 31: 44–51.

Doten, S. B. 1911. Concerning the relation of food to reproductive activity and longevity in certain hymenopterous parasites. *Univ. Nevada Agric. Expt. Sta. Tech. Bull.* 78. 30 pp.

Doubleday, T. 1841. *The true law of population shown to be connected with the food of the people.* London, Smith, Elder.

Doucette, C. F., and P. M. Eide. 1955. Influence of sugars on oviposition of narcissus bulb fly. *Ann. Ent. Soc. America*, 48: 343–44.

Dougherty, E. C. 1959a. Introduction to 'Axenic culture of invertebrate metazoa: a goal.' *Ann. New York Acad. Sci.*, 77: 27–51.

—— 1959b. A nomenclature for media of known or partly known composition. *Ann. New York Acad. Sci.*, 77: 51–54.

Dougherty, E. C. et al. (34 authors). 1959. Axenic culture of invertebrate metazoa: a goal. *Ann. New York Acad. Sci.*, 77: 25–406.

Doutt, R. L. 1947. Polyembryony in *Copidosoma koehleri* Blanchard. *American Naturalist*, 81: 435–53.

—— 1948. Effect of codling moth sprays on natural control of the Baker mealybug. *Jour. Econ. Ent.*, 41: 116.

—— 1951a. Biological control quarantine. *California Agric.*, 5: 3, 14.

—— 1951b. Biological control of mealybugs infesting commercial greenhouse gardenias. *Jour. Econ. Ent.*, 44: 37–40.

—— 1952a. Biological control of *Planococcus citri* on commercial greenhouse *Stephanotis*. *Jour. Econ. Ent.*, 45: 342.

—— 1952b. The teratoid larva of polyembryonic Encyrtidae (Hymenoptera). *Canadian Ent.*, 84: 247–50.

—— 1952c. A comparative study of spermatozoa in relation to the classification of mealybugs. *Proc. Hawaiian Ent. Soc.*, 14: 391–7.

—— 1954a. An evaluation of some natural enemies of the olive scale. *Jour. Econ. Ent.*, 47: 39–43.

—— 1954b. Biological control of fig scale. *California Agric.*, 8: 13.

—— 1957. Biology of *Solenotus begini* (Ashmead). *Jour. Econ. Ent.*, 50: 373–74.

—— 1958. Vice, Virtue and the Vedalia. *Bull. Ent. Soc. Amer.*, 4: 119–23.

—— 1959. The biology of parasitic Hymenoptera. *Ann. Rev. Ent.*, 4: 161–82.

Doutt, R. L., and G. L. Finney. 1947. Mass culture technique for *Dibrachys cavus*. *Jour. Econ. Ent.*, 40: 577.

Doutt, R. L., and K. S. Hagen. 1949. Periodic colonization of *Chrysopa californica* as a possible control of mealybugs. *Jour. Econ. Ent.*, 42: 560.

—— 1950. Biological control measures applied against *Pseudococcus maritimus* on pears. *Jour. Econ. Ent.*, 43: 94–96.

Doutt, R. L., and R. A. Smith. 1950. Males and intersexes in a normally thelyotokous insect, *Tropidophryne melvillei* Compere (Hymenoptera, Encyrtidae). *Canadian Ent.*, 82: 165–70.

Dowden, P. B. 1933. *Lydella nigripes* and *L. piniariae*, fly parasites of certain tree-defoliating caterpillars. *Jour. Agric. Res.*, 46: 963–95.

—— 1934. *Zenillia libatrix* Panzer, a tachinid parasite of the gypsy moth and the brown-tail moth. *Jour. Agr. Res.*, 48: 97–114.

Dowden, P. B. 1935. *Brachymeria intermedia* (Nees), a primary parasite, and *B. compsilurae* (Cwfd.), a secondary parasite, of the gypsy moth. *Jour. Agric. Res.*, 50: 495–523.

—— 1938. *Rogas unicolor* (Wesm.), a braconid parasite of the satin moth. *Jour. Agric. Res.*, 56: 523–36.

—— 1941. Parasites of the birch leaf-mining sawfly (*Phyllotoma nemorata*). *U.S. Dept. Agric. Tech. Bull.* 757. 55 pp.

—— 1952. The importance of coordinating applied control and natural control of forest insects. *Jour. Econ. Ent.*, 45: 481–3.

—— 1957. Biological control of forest insects in the United States and Canada. *Jour. Forest.*, 55: 723–6.

—— 1959. What about biological control? *Jour. Forest.*, 57: 267–70.

Dowden, P. B., V. M. Carolin, C. O. Dirks. 1950. Natural control factors affecting the spruce budworm in the Adirondacks during 1946–48. *Jour. Econ. Ent.*, 48: 774–83.

Dowden, P. B., and H. B. Girth. 1953. Use of a virus disease to control European pine sawfly. *Jour. Econ. Ent.*, 46: 525–6.

Dowden, P. B., H. A. Janes,' and V. M. Carolin. 1953. The role of birds in a spruce budworm outbreak in Maine. *Jour. Econ. Ent.*, 46: 307–12.

Dresner, E. 1949. Culture and use of entomogenous fungi for the control of insect pests. *Boyce Thompson Inst. Plant Res., Inc.*, 15: 319–35.

Driggers, B. F. 1930. Recent experiments on oriental peach moth control in New Jersey. *Jour. Econ. Ent.*, 23: 209–15.

—— 1940. Oriental fruit moth larval parasitism as related to infestation. *Jour. Econ. Ent.*, 33: 353–7.

—— 1941. Three years' survey and liberation of oriental fruit moth parasites in peach orchards in northern New Jersey. *Jour. Econ. Ent.*, 34: 239–44.

Driggers, B. F., and B. B. Pepper. 1936. Effect of orchard practices on codling moth and leaf hopper parasitism. *Jour. Econ. Ent.*, 29: 477–80.

Dubinin, N. P., and G. G. Tiniakov. 1945. Seasonal cycles and the concentration of inversions in populations of *Drosophila funebris*. *Amer. Naturalist*, 79: 570–2.

Duddington, C. L. 1961. *Micro-organisms as allies. The industrial use of fungi and bacteria.* Macmillan, New York. 256 pp.

Dugas, A. L. 1940. Present status of *Trichogramma* spp. as a parasite of the sugar cane borer, *Diatraea saccharalis* (F.) in Louisiana. *Louisiana Agric. Expt. Sta. Bull.* 323. 29–31.

Dumbleton, L. J. 1936. IV. The biological control of fruit pests in New Zealand. Symposium 'Biological Control of noxious insects and weeds in New Zealand,' Fifth Sci. Congr. Roy. Soc. N.Z., Dunedin, 1935. *New Zealand Jour. Sci. and Tech.*, 18: 588–92.

Dunn, J. A. 1952. The effect of temperature on the pea aphid-ladybird relationship. *Natl. Veg. Res. Sta. Wellesbourne; 2nd Rept.*, pp. 21–3.

Dupont, P. R. 1913. Notes sur quelques cochenilles (vulgairement appelées poux) qui attaquent le cocotier et autres plantes de grande culture à Mahé (Seychelles). *Agric. pratique Pays chauds*, 13: 164–7.

DuPorte, M. E., and J. Vanderleck. 1917. Studies on *Coccobacillus acridiorum* d'Herelle, and on certain intestinal organisms of locusts. *Ann. Ent. Soc. America*, 10, 47–62.

Dupuis, C. 1947. Nouvelles données biologiques et morphologiques sur les Diptères Phasiinae parasites d'Hemiptères Hétéroptères. *Ann. Parasitol. Humaine et Comp.*, 22: 201–32, 397–441.

—— 1948. Notes à propos des *Eurygaster* (Hemip., Pentatomidae) (Fam. Scutelleridae) Systématique, Biologie, Parasites. *L'entomologiste*, 4: 202–5.

Dupuis, C. 1949a. Observations biologiques sur les parasites d'Hémiptères Hétéroptères à Richelieu (Indre-et-Loire) en 1946, 1947, 1948. *Ann. Parasitol. Humaine et Comp.*, 24: 211–42.

—— 1949b. Contributions à l'étude des Phasiinae cimicophages VIII. Notes biologiques et de morphologie larvaire sur la sous-tribu Allophorina. *Ann. Parasitol. Humaine et Comp.*, 24: 503–46.

—— 1953. Contributions à l'étude des Phasiinae cimicophages XV. Données sur les Leucastomatina et, en particulier, *Leucostoma analis* (Meigen) s. str. *Ann. Parasitol. Humaine et Comp.*, 28: 64–97.

Dustan, A. G. 1924a. Studies on a new species of *Empusa* parasitic on the green apple bug (*Lygus communis* var. *novascotiensis* Knight) in the Annapolis Valley. *Proc. Acadian Ent. Soc.*, 9: 14–36.

—— 1924b. The control of the European apple sucker by means of a parasitic fungus. *Sixtieth Ann. Rept. Fruit Growers' Assoc., Nova Scotia*, pp. 100–24.

—— 1925. A study of the method used in growing entomophthorous fungi in cages prior to their artificial dissemination in the orchards. Fifty-fifth Ann. Rept. Ent. Soc. Ontario, 1924: 63–7.

Dutky, S. R. 1937. Investigation of the diseases of the immature stages of the Japanese beetle. Ph.D. Thesis, Rutgers University, New Brunswick, New Jersey.

—— 1940. Two new spore-forming bacteria causing milky diseases of Japanese beetle larvae. *Jour. Agric. Res.*, 61: 57–68.

—— 1942. Method for the preparation of spore-dust mixtures of type A milky disease of Japanese beetle larvae for field inoculation. *U.S. Dept. Agric. Bur. Ent. Plant. Quar.*, ET 192. 15 pp.

—— 1956. Nematodes on our side. *U.S. Dept. Agric., Agric. Res.*, 4: 3–4.

—— 1959. Insect microbiology. *Advances Appl. Microbiol.*, 1: 175–200.

Dutky, S. R., and E. L. Gooden. 1952. *Coxiella popilliae*, n. sp., A rickettsia causing blue disease of Japanese beetle larvae. *Jour. Bact.*, 63: 743–50.

Dutky, S. R., and W. S. Hough. 1955. Note on a parasitic nematode from codling moth larvae, *Carpocapsa pomonella* (Lepidoptera, Olethreutidae). *Proc. Ent. Soc. Washington*, 57: 244.

Dutky, S. R., J. Thompson, and W. Hough. 1956. A new nematode parasite of codling moth showing promise in insect control. *U.S. Dept. Agric.* Mimeo, 3 pp.

Dworschack, R. G., A. A. Lagoda, and R. W. Jackson. 1954. Fermentor for small-scale submerged fermentations. *Appl. Microbiol.*, 2: 190–97.

Dworschack, R. G., A. A. Lagoda, and R. W. Jackson. 1956. The control and recording of pH in small scale fermentations. *U.S. Dept. Agric., Fermentation Section, Northern Utilization Research Branch, Peoria, Ill.* Paper No. 56–17–1. 8 pp.

Earle, N. W., R. C. Gaines, and J. S. Roussel. 1959. A larval diet for the boll weevil containing an acetone powder of cotton squares. *Jour. Econ. Ent.*, 52: 710–12.

Eastham, L. E. S. 1929. The post-embryonic development of *Phaenoserphus viator* Hal. a parasite of the larva of *Pterostichus niger* (Carabidae). *Trans. Fourth Internatl. Congr. Ent., 1928*, 2: 546–51.

Eaton, C. B. 1941. Influence of the mountain pine beetle on the composition of mixed pole stands of ponderosa pine and white fir. *Jour. Forest.*, 39: 710–13.

Ebeling, Walter. 1959. *Subtropical fruit pests*. University of California, Press, Berkeley, 436 pp.

Eddy, C. O. 1939. An attempt to colonize *Hippodamia convergens* Guer. Proc. Internatl. Soc. Sugar Cane Tech. Congr., 6: 385–6. In *Abs. Rev. Appl. Ent. A* 28: 245 (1940).

Edington, D. 1899. Locust fungus. *Cape of Good Hope Bacteriological Institute Ann. Rept., 1898.* Grahamstown, Cape of Good Hope. Pg. 9–10, 84–90.

Edmunds, L. R. 1952. The oviposition of *Prosevania punctata* (Brullé): a hymenopterous parasite of cockroach egg capsules. *Ohio Jour. Sci.,* 26: 29–30.

—— 1954. A study of the biology and life history of *Prosevania punctata* (Brullé) with notes. on additional species (Hymenoptera: Evaniidae). *Ann. Ent. Soc. America,* 47: 575–92.

Edwards, G. A. 1953. *Respiratory mechanisms. In: Insect Physiology.* Ed. by Roeder, 55–95. John Wiley & Sons, Inc., New York.

Edwards, J. G. 1954. A new approach to infraspecific categories. *Systematic Zool.,* 3: 1–20.

Edwards, R. L. 1954. The host-finding and oviposition behavior of *Mormoniella vitripennis* (Walker) (Hym., Pteromalidae), a parasite of muscoid flies. *Behaviour,* 7: 88–112.

—— 1955. How the hymenopteran parasite *Mormoniella vitripennis* (Walker) finds its host. *Brit. Jour. Animal Behaviour,* 3: 37–38.

Elliott, K. R. 1955. Studies on the nutrition of the southern armyworm *Prodenia eridania* Cramer. *Ann. Rept. Ent. Soc. Ontario,* 86: 17–19.

Elton, C. S. 1947. *Animal Ecology.* Sidgwick and Jackson, Ltd., London. 209 pp.

—— 1958. *The Ecology of Invasions by Animals and Plants.* Methuen and Co. Ltd., London. 181 pp.

Emerson, A. E. 1935. Termitophile distribution and quantitative characters as indicators of physiological speciation in British Guiana termites. *Ann. Ent. Soc. America,* 28: 369–95.

Enock, F. 1895. Abstract of proceedings. *South London Ent. Nat. Hist. Soc.,* p. 47.

Errington, P. L. 1946. Predation and vertebrate populations. *Quart. Rev. Biol.,* 21: 144–77.

—— 1954. On the hazards of overemphasizing numerical fluctuations in studies of 'cyclic' phenomena in muskrat populations. *Jour. Wildlife Management,* 18: 66–90.

Esaki, T. and S. Miyamoto. 1958. The Strepsiptera parasitic on Heteroptera. *Proc. 10th Inter. Congr. Ent.,* 1: 373–81.

Escherick, K., and M. Miyajima. 1911. Studien über die Wipfelkrankheit der Nonne. *Naturwiss. Z. Forst- u. Landw.,* 9: 381–402.

Essig, E. O. 1931. *A History of Entomology.* The Macmillan Company, New York. 1029 pp.

—— 1934. *Insects of Western North America.* The Macmillan Company, New York. 1035 pp.

—— 1942a. *College Entomology.* The Macmillan Co., New York, 900 pp.

—— 1942b. The significance of taxonomy in the general field of economic entomology. *Jour. Econ. Ent.,* 35: 739–43.

Evans, A. C. 1933. Comparative observations on the morphology and biology of some hymenopterous parasites of carrion-infesting Diptera. *Bull. Ent. Res.,* 24: 385–405.

Evans, H. E. 1953. Comparative ethology and systematics of spider wasps. *Systematic Zool.,* 2: 155–72.

—— 1957. *Comparative Ethology of Digger Wasps of the Genus Bembix.* Comstock Publishing Associates, Ithaca, New York, 248 pp.

—— 1959. The larvae of Pompilidae (Hymenoptera). *Ann. Ent. Soc. America,* 52: 430–44.

Evans, J. W. 1933. Thrips investigation. I. The seasonal fluctuations in numbers of *Thrips imaginis* Bagnall and associated blossom Thrips. *Jour. Counc. Sci. and Ind. Research,* August, 1933, pp. 145–59.

—— 1952. *The injurious insects of the British Commonwealth.* Commonwealth Inst. Ent. London. 242 pp.

Evenden, J. C., W. D. Bedard, and G. R. Struble. 1943. The mountain pine beetle, an important enemy of western pines. *U.S. Dept. Agric. Circ.* 664.

Evenhuis, H. H. 1958. *Een oecologish Onderzoek over de Appelbloedluis, Eriosoma lanigerum* (Hausm.), *en haar Paraseit Aphelinus mali (Hald.) in Nederland.* H. Veenman and Zonen, Wageningen. 103 pp.

Fawcett, H. S. 1944. Fungus and bacterial diseases of insects as factors in biological control. *Bot. Rev.,* 10: 327–48.

Fawcett, H. S. 1908. Fungi parasitic upon *Aleyrodes citri.* Master of Science Thesis, Univ. Florida, Special studies No. 1. 41 pp.

Fallis, A. M. 1942. The life-cycle of *Apanteles carpatus* (Say), a parasite of the webbing clothes moth, *Tineola biselliella* Húm. *Canadian Jour. Res.,* 20: 13–19.

Feron, M., P. Delanoue, and F. Soria. 1958. L'élevage massif artificiel de *Ceratitis capitata* Wied. *Entomophaga,* 3: 45–53.

Ferris, G. F. 1928. The principles of systematic entomology. *Stanford Univ. Publ. Univ. Ser. Biol. Sci.,* 5: 103–269.

—— 1942. The needs of systematic entomology. *Jour. Econ. Ent.,* 35: 732–38.

—— 1954. *The contribution of natural history to human progress.* In *A Century of Progress in the Natural Sciences,* 1853–1953, pp. 75–87, E. L. Kessel, Editor. California Acad. Sci, San Francisco. 807 pp.

Finlayson, T. 1960. Taxonomy of cocoons and puparia, and their contents, of Canadian parasites of *Neodiprion sertifer* (Geoff.) (Hymenoptera: Diprionidae). *Canadian Ent.,* 92: 20–47.

Finlayson, L. R., and Thelma Finlayson. 1957. Influence of adult food on viability of early stages of *Aptesis basizonia* (Grer.) (Hymenoptera: Ichneumonidae) a parasite of pine sawflies. *Canadian Ent.,* 89: 507–9.

Finney, G. L. 1948. Culturing *Chrysopa californica* and obtaining eggs for field distribution. *Jour. Econ. Ent.,* 41: 719–21.

—— 1950. Mass-culturing *Chrysopa californica* to obtain eggs for field distribution. *Jour. Econ. Ent.,* 43: 97–100.

—— 1953. A technique for mass-culture of the six-spotted mite. *Jour. Econ. Ent.,* 46: 712–13.

—— 1956. A fortified carrot medium for mass-culture of the oriental fruit fly and certain other tephritids. *Jour. Econ. Ent.,* 49: 134.

—— 1960. A ventilation unit for aerating insectary sleeve cages. *Jour. Econ. Ent.,* 53: 959.

Finney, G. L., S. E. Flanders, and H. S. Smith. 1947. Mass culture of *Macrocentrus ancylivorus* and its host, the potato tuber moth. *Hilgardia,* 17: 437–83.

Fisher, R. C. 1959. Life history and ecology of *Horogenes chrysostictas* Gmelin (Hymenoptera, Ichneumonidae), a parasite of *Ephestia sericarium* Scott (Lepidoptera, Phycitidae). *Canadian Jour. Zool.,* 37: 429–46.

Fisher, R., and L. Rosner. 1959. Toxicology of the microbial insecticide Thuricide. *Jour. Agric. and Food Chem.,* 7: 686–88.

Fisher, T. W. 1959. Use of flashed opal glass for detecting parasitized coccids. *Jour. Econ. Ent.,* 52: 782.

—— 1961. Biology of *Physcus* sp. (Eulophidae, Aphelininae) from Burma. *Jour. Econ. Ent.,* 54: 444–46.

Fisk, F. W. 1958. *Feeding and drinking methods.* In *Methods of testing chemicals on insects.* (Ed. H. H. Shepard.) Ch. 9, pp. 114–29. Burgess Publ. Co., Minneapolis, Minn.

Fiske, W. F. 1910. Superparasitism: an important factor in the natural control of insects. *Jour. Econ. Ent.,* 3: 88–97.

Fitch, Asa. 1856. Sixth, seventh, eighth and ninth reports on the noxious, beneficial and other insects of the state of New York. Albany, N.Y. 259 pp.

Fitz-James, P. C. 1957. Cytological changes occurring during germination. Discussion. In *Spores. Amer. Inst. Biol. Sci., Publ. No.* 5: 85–92.

Flanders, S. E. 1929. The mass production of *Trichogramma minutum* Riley and observations on the natural and artificial parasitism of the codling moth egg. *Trans. 4th Internatl. Congr. Ent.*, 2: 110–30.

—— 1930a. Notes on *Trichogramma minutum. Pan. Pac. Ent.*, 6: 180–1.

—— 1930b. Mass production of egg parasites of the genus *Trichogramma. Hilgardia*, 4: 465–501.

—— 1930c. Evaluation of *Trichogramma* liberations. *Jour. Econ. Ent.*, 23: 886–7.

—— 1931. The temperature relationships of *Trichogramma minutum* as a basis for racial segregation. *Hilgardia*, 5: 395–406.

—— 1934. *Sitotroga* production. *Jour. Econ. Ent.*, 27: 1197.

—— 1935. An apparent correlation between the feeding habits of certain pteromalids and the condition of their ovarian follicles. (Pteromalidae, Hymenoptera) *Ann. Ent. Soc. America*, 28: 438–44.

—— 1936. A biological phenomenon affecting the establishment of Aphelinidae as parasites. *Ann. Ent. Soc. America*, 29: 251–5.

—— 1937a. Ovipositional instincts and developmental sex differences in the genus *Coccophagus. Univ. California Publ. Ent.*, 6: 401–22.

—— 1937b. Notes on the life history and anatomy of *Trichogramma. Ann. Ent. Soc. America*, 30: 304–8.

—— 1938a. Identity of the common species of American *Trichogramma. Jour. Econ. Ent.*, 31: 456.

—— 1938b. Cocoon formation in endoparasitic chalcidoids. *Ann. Ent. Soc. America*, 31: 167–80.

—— 1939. Environmental control of sex in hymenopterous insects. *Ann. Ent. Soc. America*, 32: 11–26.

—— 1940. Environmental resistance to the establishment of parasitic Hymenoptera. *Ann. Ent. Soc. America*, 33: 245–53.

—— 1942a. Oösorption and ovulation in relation to oviposition in the parasitic Hymenoptera. *Ann. Ent. Soc. America*, 35: 251–66.

—— 1942b. *Metaphycus helvolus*, an encyrtid parasite of the black scale. *Jour. Econ. Ent.*, 35: 690–8.

—— 1942c. Propagation of black scale on potato sprouts. *Jour. Econ. Ent.*, 35: 687–9.

—— 1942d. Sex differentiation in the polyembryonic proclivity of the Hymenoptera. *Jour. Econ. Ent.*, 35: 108.

—— 1942e. The larval meconium of parasitic Hymenoptera as a sign of the species. *Jour. Econ. Ent.*, 35: 456–7.

—— 1943a. Indirect hyperparasitism and observations on three species of indirect hyperparasites. *Jour. Econ. Ent.*, 36: 921–6.

—— 1943b. Mass production of the California red scale, and its parasite, *Comperiella bifasciata. Jour. Econ. Ent.*, 36: 233–5.

—— 1943c. The role of mating in the reproduction of parasitic Hymenoptera. *Jour. Econ. Ent.*, 36: 802–3.

—— 1944a. Observations on *Comperiella bifasciata*, an endoparasite of diaspine coccids. *Ann. Ent. Soc. America*, 37: 365–71.

—— 1944b. *Acerophagus notativentris*, an important parasite of the grape mealybug. *Jour. Econ. Ent.*, 37: 541.

—— 1944c. Diapause in the parasitic Hymenoptera. *Jour. Econ. Ent.*, 37: 408–10.

Flanders, S. E. 1945*a*. Coincident infestations of *Aonidiella citrina* and *Coccus hesperidium*, a result of ant activity. *Jour. Econ. Ent.*, 38: 711–2.

—— 1945*b*. Uniparentalism in the Hymenoptera and its relation to polyploidy. *Science*, 100: 168–9.

—— 1945*c*. A barrier for confining crawling organisms. *Jour. Econ. Ent.*, 38: 495.

—— 1946*a*. Control of sex and sex-limited polymorphism in the Hymenoptera. *Quart. Rev. Biol.*, 21: 135–43.

—— 1946*b*. The role of the spermatophore in the mass propagation of *Macrocentrus ancylivorus*. *Jour. Econ. Ent.*, 38: 323–7.

—— 1947. Elements of host discovery exemplified by parasitic Hymenoptera. *Ecology*, 28: 299–309.

—— 1948. A host-parasite community to demonstrate balance. *Ecology*, 29: 123.

—— 1949*a*. Culture of entomophagous insects. *Canadian Ent.*, 81: 257–74.

—— 1949*b*. Using black scale as a 'foster host.' *California Citrograph*, 34: 222–4.

—— 1950*a*. Regulation of ovulation and egg disposal in the parasitic Hymenoptera. *Canadian Ent.*, 82: 134–40.

—— 1950*b*. Races of apomictic parasitic Hymenoptera introduced into California. *Jour. Econ. Ent.*, 43: 719–20.

—— 1951. Mass culture of California red scale and its golden chalcid parasites. *Hilgardia* 21: 1–42.

—— 1953*a*. Variations in susceptibility of citrus-infesting coccids to parasitization. *Jour. Econ. Ent.*, 46: 266–9.

—— 1953*b*. Aphelinid biologies with implications for taxonomy. *Ann. Ent. Soc. America*, 46: 84–94.

—— 1953*c*. Predatism by the adult hymenopterous parasite and its role in biological control. *Jour. Econ. Ent.*, 46: 541–4.

—— 1955. Principles and practices of biological control utilizing entomophagous insects. [Extract from series of lectures presented at the University of Naples, Italy.] Deposited in Univ. California libraries at Davis and Riverside, California.

—— 1956. The mechanisms for sex-ratio regulation in the (parasitic) Hymenoptera. *Insectes Sociaux*, 3: 325–34.

—— 1958. The role of the ant in the biological control of scale insects in California. *Proc. 10th Internatl. Cong. Ent.*, 4: 579–82 (1956).

—— 1959*a*. The employment of exotic entomophagous insects in pest control. *Jour. Econ. Ent.*, 52: 71–5.

—— 1959*b*. Differential host relations of the sexes in parasitic Hymenoptera. *Ent. Exp. and appl.*, 2: 125–42.

Flanders, S. E., B. R. Bartlett, and T. W. Fisher. 1961. *Coccophagus basalis* (Hymenoptera: Aphelinidae); its introduction into California with studies of its biology. *Ann. Ent. Soc. Amer.*, 54: 227–36.

Flanders, S. E., and Harold Compere. 1934. *Anarhopus sydneyensis* Timb., an encyrtid parasite of *Pseudococcus longispinus* Targ. recently introduced into California from Australia. *Jour. Econ. Ent.*, 27: 966–73.

Flanders, S. E., J. L. Gressitt, and T. W. Fisher. 1958. *Casca chinensis*, an internal parasite of California red scale. *Hilgardia*, 28: 65–91.

Fleming, W. E. 1958. Biological control of the Japanese beetle with special reference to entomogenous diseases. *Proc. 10th Internatl. Congr. Ent.*, 3: 115–25 (1956).

Fleschner, C. A. 1950. Studies on searching capacity of the larvae of three predators of the citrus red mite. *Hilgardia*, 20: 233–65.

Fleschner, C. A. 1952. Host-plant resistance as a factor influencing population density of citrus red mites on orchard trees. *Jour. Econ. Ent.*, **45**: 687–95.

—— 1958. Field approach to population studies of tetranychid mites on citrus and avocado in California. *Proc. 10th Interntl. Congr. Ent.*, **2**: 669–74 (1956).

—— 1959. Biological control of insect pests. *Science*, **129**: 537–44.

—— 1960. Parasites and predators for pest control. *In* Biological and Chemical Control of Plant and Animal Pests. L. P. Reitz, editor. *Amer. Assoc. Adv. Sci.*, **61**: 183–99.

Fleschner, C. A., J. C. Hall, and D. W. Ricker. 1955. Natural balance of mite pests in an avocado grove. *Calif. Avocado Soc. Yearbook*, **39**, 155–62.

Fleschner, C. A., and D. W. Ricker. 1953. Food habits of coniopterygids on citrus in southern California. *Jour. Econ. Ent.*, **46**: 458–61.

Flitters, N. E., P. S. Messenger, and C. N. Husman. 1956. Bioclimatic cabinets used in studies on the Mexican fruit fly and the pink bollworm. *U.S. Dept. Agric. ARS*-33-33. 12 pp.

Flock, R. A. 1941. Biological control of the brown-banded roach. *Bull. Brooklyn Ent. Soc.*, **36**: 178–81.

Fluke, C. L. 1937. *The culture of aphidophagous syrphid flies.* In: Galtsoff *et al.*, *Culture Methods for Invertebrate Animals.* Comstock Publishing Co., Inc. Ithaca, New York. 590 pp.

Fluke, C. L., and T. C. Allen. 1931. The role of yeast in life history studies of the apple maggot, *Rhagoletis pomonella* Walsh. *Jour. Econ. Ent.*, **24**: 77–80.

Folsom, J. W., and F. F. Bondy. 1930. Calcium arsenate dusting as a cause of aphid infestation. *U.S. Dept. Agric. Circ.* **116**. 11 pp.

Foott, W. H. 1954. The biology of the adults of *Hylemya brassicae*. *Ann. Rept. Ent. Soc. Ontario*, **85**: 42–53.

Forbes, E. 1843. Report on the molluscs and radiata of the Aegean Sea and on their distribution considered as bearing on geology. *Rept. Brit. Acad. Adv. Sci.*, **13**: 130–93.

Forbes, S. A. 1880. On some interactions of organisms. *Bull. Illinois Nat. Hist. Surv.*, **1**: 1–17.

—— 1883. The food relations of the Carabidae and Coccinellidae. *Bull. Illinois Nat. Hist. Sur.*, **1**: 33–60.

—— 1890. Studies on the chinch bug (*Blissus leucopterus*, Say). II. *Sixteenth Rept. State Entomol. on Noxious and Beneficial Insects of the State of Illinois.* Pp. 1–57.

—— 1895. On contagious disease in the chinch-bug (*Blissus leucopterus* Say). *Illinois State Ent. 19th Rept.* Pp. 16–176.

Ford, E. B. 1954. *Problems in the evolution of geographical races.* Pp. 99–108. *In* Evolution as a Process, J. S. Huxley, A. C. Hardy, and E. B. Ford, editors.

Forskål, P. 1775. *Descriptiones animalium, avium, amphibiorum, piscium, insectorum, vermium; quae in itinere orientali observavit P. Forskål, post mortem auctoris edidit, Carsten Niebuhr.* Hauniae, Moeller (pt. 3).

Fraenkel, G. S. 1940. Utilization and digestion of carbohydrates by the adult blow-fly. *Jour. Exptl. Biol.*, **17**: 18–29.

—— 1953. The nutritional value of green plants for insects. *Proc. 9th Internatl. Congr. Ent., Symposia.* Pp. 90–100. Dr. W. Junk, Publisher, The Hague, Netherlands.

—— 1959. The raison d'être of secondary plant substances. *Science*, **129**: 1466–70.

Fraenkel, G. S., and M. Blewett. 1943. The basic food requirements of several insects. *Jour. Exptl. Biol.*, **20**: 28–34.

Frank, F. 1954. Die Kausalität der Nagatier-zyklen im Lichte neuer populationsdynamischer Untersuchungen an deutschen Microtinen. *Zeitschr. f. Morph. u. Ökol. d. Tiere*, **43**: 321–56.

Franklin, B. 1751. *Concerning the increase of mankind, peopling of countries, etc.* In the Writings of Benjamin Franklin. New York, Macmillan, 3: 63–73.

Franz, J. M. 1949. Über die genetischen Grundlagen des Zusammenbruches einer Massenvermehrung aus inneren Ursachen. *Zeitschr. angew. Ent.*, 31: 228–60.

—— 1951. Möglichkeiten und Grenzen der biologischen Schädlingsbekämpfung. *Pflanzenschutz.*, 3. *Jahrgang, Nr. 8*, pp. 100–02.

—— 1952. Observations on collecting parasites of *Cacoecia histrionana* (Froel.) (Lep. Tortricidae). *Bull. Ent. Res.*, 43: 1–19.

—— 1961. Definitionen in der biologischen Schädlingsbekämpfung. *Zeit. Pflanzenkrankheiten und Pflanzenschutz.*, 68: 321–29.

—— 1956. Der Einfluss der Passage durch den Darm von Raubinsekten und Vögeln auf die Infektiosität insektenpathogener Viren. *Entomophaga*, 1: 103–4.

—— 1958a. Biological control in Germany. *Proc. 10th Internatl. Congr. Ent.*, 4: 461–4 (1956).

—— 1958b. The effectiveness of predators and food in limiting gradations of *Adelges* (*Dreyfusia*) *piceae* (Ratz.) in Europe. *Proc. 10th Internatl. Congr. Ent.*, 4: 781–7 (1956).

—— 1958c. Die Internationale Kommission für biologische Schädlingsbekämpfung (C.I.L.B.), pp. 605–9. In *Trans. 1st Internatl. Conf. Insect Pathol. and Biol. Control, Praha, 1958.* 653 pp.

—— 1961a. *Biologische Schädlingsbekämpfung.* In 'Handbuch der Pflanzenkrankheiten' (H. Richter, editor), 2nd ed., Vol. 6, No. 3, pp. 1–302. Paul Parey, Berlin.

—— 1961b. Biological control of pests insects in Europe. *Ann. Rev. Ent.*, 6: 183–200.

—— 1962. Definitions in biological control. *XI. Intl. Kong. Entom. Wien (1960).* Verhandl Band II., Sect. XIII, 670–4.

Franz, J. M., and A. Krieg. 1957. Virosen europäischer Forstinsekten. *Zeitschr. Pflanzenkrankh. u. Pflanzenschutz*, 64: 1–9.

Franz, J. M., A. Krieg, and R. Langenbuch. 1955. Untersuchungen über den Einfluss der Passage durch den Darm von Raubinsekten und Vögeln auf die Infektiosität insektenpathogener Viren. *Zeitschr. f. Pflanzenkrankh. u. Pflanzenschutz*, 62: 721–6.

Freeman, C. C., and F. E. Guyton. 1957. A method for rearing leaf-mining Agromyzidae. *Jour. Econ. Ent.*, 50: 829–31.

Friederichs, K. 1927. Die Bedeutung der Biocönosen für den Pflanzenschutz gegen Tiere. *Zeitschr. angew. Ent.*, 12: 385–411.

Friend, W. G. 1955. Problems in nutritional studies of phytophagous insects. *Ann. Rept. Ent. Soc. Ontario*, 86: 13–17.

—— 1958a. Nutritional requirements of phytophagous insects. *Ann. Rev. Ent.*, 3: 57–74.

—— 1958b. The nutrition of phytophagous insects with special reference to *Hylemya antiqua* (Mg.). *Proc. 10th Internatl. Congr. Ent.*, 2: 145–9 (1956).

Friend, W. G., R. H. Backs, and L. M. Cass. 1957. Studies on amino acid requirements of larvae of the onion maggot, *Hylemya antiqua* (Meig.), under aseptic conditions. *Canadian Jour. Zool.*, 35: 535–43.

Friend, W. G., and R. L. Patton. 1956. Studies on vitamin requirements of larvae of the onion maggot, *Hylemya antiqua* (Meig.), under aseptic conditions. *Canadian Jour. Zool.*, 34: 152–62.

Friend, W. G., E. H. Salkeld, and R. J. McClanahan. 1958. A chemically defined diet and axenic rearing method for larvae of the seed-corn maggot, *Hylemya cilicrura* (Rond.) (Diptera: Anthomyiidae). *Canadian Jour. Zool.*, 36: 931–6.

Friend, W. G., E. H. Salkeld, and I. L. Stevenson. 1959. Nutrition of maggots, larvae of *Hylemya antiqua* (Meig.), with reference to other members of the genus *Hylemya*. *Ann. New York Acad. Sci.*, 77: 384–93.

Frings, H. 1947. A simple method for rearing blowflies without meat. *Science*, **105**: 482.
—— 1948. Rearing houseflies and blowflies on dog biscuit. *Science*, **107**: 629–30.
Frings, H., and Mabel Frings. 1953. Dog biscuit as a larval medium for *Scarcophaga bullata*. *Jour. Econ. Ent.*, **46**: 185.
Frison, T. H. 1942. The significance of economic entomology in the field of insect taxonomy. *Jour. Econ. Ent.*, **35**: 749–52.
Frühaufie. 1924. Legeapparat und Eiablage bei Gallwespen (Cynipidae). *Zeitschr. f. wiss. Zool.*, **121**: 656–723.
Fullaway, D. T. 1954a. Biological control of cactus in Hawaii. *Jour. Econ. Ent.*, **47**: 696–700.
—— 1954b. Fifty years' progress in the biological control of weeds—a review. Board of Agric. and Forestry, Honolulu, Hawaii. (Mimeo. report, circa 1954.)
—— 1958. Importations of natural enemies of the weed, *Emex spinosa* Campd. *Proc. Hawaiian Ent. Soc.*, **16**: 359–60.
Fullaway, D. T., and N. L. Krauss. 1945. *Common Insects of Hawaii*. Tongg Publ. Co., Honolulu. 228 pp.
Fulton, B. B. 1933. Notes on *Habrocytus cerealellae*, parasite of the angoumois grain moth. *Ann. Ent. Soc. America*, **26**: 536–53.
—— 1940. The hornworm parasite, *Apanteles congregatus* Say, and the hyperparasite *Hypopteromalus tabacum* (Fitch). *Ann. Ent. Soc. America*, **33**: 231–44.
Gäbler, H. 1948. Vorteile der Frühbestaübung bei der Nonne unter besonderer Berücksichtigung der Tachinenvermehrung. *Zeit. angew. Ent.*, **31**: 441–54 (*Abs. Rev. Appl. Ent.*, **40**: 49).
Gabriel, B P. 1959. Fungus infection of insects via the alimentary tract. *Jour. Insect Pathol.*, **1**: 319–30.
Gadd, C. H. 1941. The control of tea tortrix by its parasite, *Macrocentrus homonae*. *Tea Quart.*, **15**: 93–7.
Gadd, C. H., and W. T. Fonseka. 1945. *Neoplectrus maculatus* Ferriere a predator and parasite of *Natada nararia* Mo. and other nettlegrubs. *Ceylon Jour. Sci.*, *Sect. B. Zoo.*, **32**: 9–18.
Gadd, C. H., W. T. Fonseka, and D. J. W. Ranaweeva. 1946. Parasites of tea nettle grubs with special reference to *Platyplectrus natadae* Ferriere and *Autoplectrus taprobanes* Gadd. *Ceylon Jour. Sci.*, *Sect B. Zoo.*, **23**: 81–94.
Gahan, A. B. 1923. The role of the taxonomist in present day entomology. *Proc. Ent. Soc. Wash.*, **25**: 69–78.
Galtsoff, P. S., F. E. Lutz, P. S. Welch, and J. G. Needham. 1937. *Culture methods for invertebrate animals*. Comstock Publishing Co., Inc., Ithaca, New York. 590 pp.
Ganhão, J. F. P. 1956. *Cephalosporium lecanii* Zimm. um fungo entomógeno de cochonilhas. *Revista Brotéria Série Ciências Naturais*, **25**: 71–136.
Ganin, M. 1869. Beiträge zur Erkenntniss der Entwickelungsgeschichte bei den Insecten. *Zeitschr. f. wiss. Zool.*, **19**: 381–451.
Gardner, J. C. M. 1940. The puparia of some Indian Tachinidae (Diptera). *Indian Forest Rec.*, *Ent.*, **6**: 227–51.
—— 1944. A note on the imported lantana bug (*Teleonemia scrupulosa* Stal). *Indian Forester*, **70**: 139–40.
Gardner, T. R. 1938. Influence of feeding habits of *Tiphia vernalis* on the parasitization of the Japanese beetle. *Jour. Econ. Ent.*, **31**: 204–07.
—— 1958. Biological control of insect and plant pests in the Trust Territory and Guam. *Proc. 10th Internatl. Congr. Ent.*, **4**: 465–9 (1956).
Garman, P. 1917. The oriental peach pest. *Maryland Agric. Expt. Sta. Bull.* **209**.

Garman, P. 1936. Control of apple aphids with California ladybeetles. *Connecticut Agr. Exp. Sta. Bull.* 383: 356–57.

Garman, P., and W. T. Brigham. 1933. Studies on parasites of the oriental fruit moth. II. *Macrocentrus*. *Connecticut Agric. Exp. Sta. Bull.* 356: 73–116.

Gatenby, J. B. 1919. Note on *Apanteles glomeratus* a braconid parasite of the larva of *Pieris brassicae*. *Ent. Monthly Mag.*, 55: 19–26.

Gater, B. A. R. 1925. Some observations on the Malaysia coconut zygaenid (*Artona catoxantha* Hamps). *Malayan Agric. Jour.*, 13: 92–115.

Gause, G. F. 1934. *The Struggle for Existence*. Baltimore, Williams and Wilkins. 163 pp.

Gause, G. F., N. P. Smaragdova, and A. A. Witt. 1936. Further studies of interaction between predators and prey. *Jour. Animal Ecol.*, 5: 1–18.

Gay, F. J. 1938. A nutritional study of the larva of *Dermestes vulpinus* F. *Jour. Exptl. Zool.*, 79: 93–107.

Gemmill, A. V. 1960. Flask-tank setup now turns out first 'bug-kill-bug' insecticide. *Chem. Engineer.*, 67: 42–4.

Génieys, P. 1925. *Habrobracon brevicornis* Wesm. *Ann. Ent. Soc. America*, 18: 143–202.

Gerhardt, R. W. 1955. Further studies during 1954 on blue-green algae—A possible anti-mosquito measure for rice fields. *Proc. and Papers 23rd Ann. Conf. California Mosquito Control Assoc.*, pp. 120–23.

Gerig, L. 1960. Zur Morphologie der Larvenstudien einiger parasitischer Hymenopteren des Grauen Lärchenwicklers (*Zeiraphera griseana* Hübner). *Zeitschr. angew. Ent.*, 46: 121–77.

Gerolt, P. 1957. Method of breeding, handling and sexing adults of *Drosophila melanogaster* as a test insect for bioassay. *Bull. Ent. Res.*, 48: 311–15.

Gershenson, S. M. 1956. Phenomenon on latency in polyhedral viruses. *Compt. Rend. Acad. Sci.* Ukranian R.S.R. 3: 295–7.

—— 1959a. The variability of polyhedral viruses. *Trans. First International Conf. Insect Pathol. and Biol. Control. Prague 1958*. Pp. 197–200. (In Russian with English summary.)

—— 1959b. Mutation of polyhedrosis viruses. *Doklady Akad. Nauk SSSR*, 128: 622–5. (In Russian.)

—— 1960. A bibliography of Soviet works on virus diseases of insects. *Ent. Rev.*, 39: 334–40.

Getzendaner, C. W. 1936. Parasitizing European earwig with *Bigonicheta setipennis* Fall. *Jour. Econ. Ent.*, 29: 1105–14.

Getzin, L. W. 1961. *Spicaria rileyi* (Farlow) Charles, an entomogenous fungus of *Trichoplusia ni* (Hübner). *Jour. Insect Pathol.*, 3: 2–10.

Ghent, A. W., D. A. Fraser, and J. B. Thomas. 1957. Studies of regeneration in forest stands devastated by the spruce budworm. I. Evidence of trends in forest succession during the first decade following budworm devastation. *Forest Sci.*, 3: 184–208.

Ghouri, A. S. K., and J. E. McFarlane. 1958. Observations on the development of crickets. *Canadian Ent.*, 90: 158–65.

Giard, A. 1892. L'*Isaria densa* (Link) Fries, champignon parasite du hanneton commun (*Melolontha vulgaris* L.). *Bull. Sci. France Belgique*, 24: 1–112.

Gibbs, A. J. 1948. The tolerance of the metacyclic and flagellate forms of *Leptomonas ctenocephali* Fantham to variations of humidity and salinity. *Trans. Roy. Soc. Trop. Med. and Hyg.*, 42: 89–93.

—— 1957. *Leptomonas serpens* n. sp., parasitic in the digestive tract and salivary glands of *Nezara viridula* (Pentatomidae) and in the sap of *Solanum lycopersicum* (tomato) and other plants. *Parasitology*, 47: 297–303.

Gibbs, A. J. 1958. Predation by tits and squirrels on the eucosmid *Ernarmonia conicolana* (Heyl.). *Jour. Animal Ecol.*, **27**: 375–96.

Gilmore, J. U. 1938. Notes on *Apanteles congregatus* (Say) as a parasite of tobacco hornworms. *Jour. Econ. Ent.*, **31**: 712–15.

Gilmour, J. S. L. 1940. *Taxonomy and philosophy*, pp. 461–74. In *The New Systematics*, J. S. Huxley, editor.

Giordani, G. 1959. Amoeba disease of the honey bee, *Apis mellifera* Linnaeus, and an attempt at its chemical control. *Jour. Insect Pathol.*, **1**: 245–69.

Girault, A. A. 1907. Hosts of insect egg-parasites in North and South America. *Psyche*, **14**: 27–39.

Girth, H. B., E. E. McCoy, and R. W. Glaser. 1940. Field experiments with a nematode parasite of the Japanese beetle. *New Jersey Dept. Agric. Circ.* 317. 21 pp.

Given, B. B. 1944. The anatomy of the final larval instar of *Diadromus* (*Thyraeella*) *collaris* Grav. (Ichneumonidae) with notes on structural changes through the prepupal and pupal stages. *Trans. Roy Soc. New Zealand*, **74**: 297–301.

Glaser, R. W. 1918. A systematic study of the organisms distributed under the name of *Coccobacillus acridiorum* d'Herelle. *Ann. Ent. Soc. America*, **11**: 19–42.

—— 1923. The effect of food on longevity and reproduction in flies. *Jour. Exptl. Zoo.*, **38**: 383–412.

—— 1924. Rearing flies for experimental purposes with biological notes. *Jour. Econ. Ent.*, **17**: 486–96.

—— 1926. The isolation and cultivation of *Herpetomonas muscae-domesticae*. *Amer. Jour. Trop. Med.*, **6**: 205–16.

—— 1931. The cultivation of a nematode parasite of an insect. *Science*, **73**: 614–15.

—— 1932. Studies on *Neoaplectana glaseri*, a nematode parasite of the Japanese beetle (*Popillia japonica*). *New Jersey Dept. Agric. Bur. Plant Indust. Circ.* 211. 34 pp.

—— 1940. The bacteria-free culture of a nematode parasite. *Proc. Soc. Exptl. Biol. and Med.*, **43**: 512–14.

Glaser, R. W., and J. W. Chapman. 1913. The wilt disease of gypsy moth caterpillars. *Jour. Econ. Ent.*, **6**: 479–88.

Glaser, R. W., and C. C. Farrell. 1935. Field experiments with the Japanese beetle and its nematode parasite. *Jour. New York Ent. Soc.*, **43**: 345–71.

Glaser, R. W., and H. Fox. 1930. A nematode parasite of the Japanese beetle (*Popillia japonica* Newm.). *Science*, **71**: 16–17.

Glaser, R. W., E. E. McCoy, and H. B. Girth. 1940. The biology and economic importance of a nematode parasitic in insects. *Jour. Parasitol.*, **26**: 479–95.

—— 1942. The biology and culture of *Neoaplectana chresima*, a new nematode parasitic in insects. *Jour. Parasitol.*, **28**: 123–6.

Gleason, H. A. 1939. The individualistic concept of the plant association. *Amer. Midland Nat.*, **21**: 92–110.

Glen, Robert. 1954*a*. Factors that affect insect abundance. *Jour. Econ. Ent.*, **47**: 398–405.

—— 1954*b*. Canada—Review of Economic Entomology, 1948–1954. *Rept. 6th Commonw. Ent. Conf., London*: 188–205.

Glendenning, R. 1933. A successful parasite introduction into British Columbia. *Canad. Ent.*, **65**: 169–71.

Gobeil, A. R. 1941. *Dendroctonus piceaperda*: A detrimental or beneficial insect. *Jour. Forest.*, **39**: 632–40.

Gochnauer, T. A. 1958. The use of bacteriophages in the analysis of the foulbrood diseases. *Proc. 10th Internatl. Congr. Ent.*, **4**: 1091–6 (1956).

750   BIBLIOGRAPHY

Gordon, H. T. 1959a. Effect of amino acid balance on growth of *Tetrahymena*. *Ann. New York Acad. Sci.*, 77: 338–51.

—— 1959b. Minimal nutritional requirements of the German roach, *Blattella germanica* L. *Ann. New York Acad. Sci.*, 77: 290–351.

Gösswald, Karl. 1935. Zur Biologie und Ökologie von *Parasetigena segregata* Rond. und *Sarcophaga schützei* Kram. (Dipt.) nebst Bemerkungen über die forstliche Bedeutung der beiden Arten. *Ztschr. angew. Ent.*, 21: 1–23.

—— 1940. Die Massenzucht von Königinnen der roten Waldameise im laboratorium. *Mitteil. aus Forstwirtschaft und Forstwissenschaff.* Pp. 283–91.

—— 1951. *Die rote Waldameise im dienste der Waldhygiene*. Metta Kinau Verlag, Wolf u. Täuber, Lüneburg, Germany. 160 pp.

Gough, L. H. 1911. Results obtained in the study of the froghopper during the wet season of 1910. *Trinidad Dept. Agric. Circ.* 8: 46 pp.

Graber, V. 1887. Thermische Experimente an das Küchenschabe (*Periplaneta orientalis*). *Arch. ges. Physiol.*, 41: 240–56.

Grace, T. D. C. 1958. Induction of polyhedral bodies in ovarian tissues of the tussock moth in vitro. *Science*, 128: 249–50.

Grady, A. G. 1928. Studies for breeding insects throughout the year for insecticide tests. *Jour. Econ. Ent.*, 21: 598–604.

Graf Marin, Alberto, and Raul Cortes Peña. 1940. Introducción de hiperparasitas en Chile: Resumen de las importaciones hechas y de sus resultados. *Proc. 6th Pac. Sci. Congr.*, 4: 351–53 (1939).

Graham, A. J., and F. H. Dudley. 1959. Culture methods for mass rearing of screw-worm larvae. *Jour. Econ. Ent.*, 52: 1006–8.

Graham, S. A. 1929. *Principles of Forest Entomology*. McGraw Hill Book Co., Inc. New York and London, 339 pp.

Grandi, G. 1951. *Introduzione allo studio dell' Entomologia*. Vol. 2, 1332 pp. (In Italian.) Edizioni Agricole, Bologna.

—— 1954. Contributi alla conoscenza degli Imenotteri Aculeati *XXVI. Boll. Ist. Ent. Univ. Bologna*, 20: 81–255.

—— 1958. Contributi alla conscenza degli Imenotteri Aculeati XXVII. *Boll. Ist. Ent. Univ. Bologna*, 22 (1957): 307–98.

—— 1959. Contributi alla conoscenza degli Imenotteri Aculeati XXVIII. *Boll. Ist. Ent. Univ. Bologna*, 23 (1957): 239–92.

Grandori, R. 1911. Contributo all' embriologia alla biologia dell' *Apanteles glomeratus* (L.) Reinh. *Redia*, 7: 363–428.

Grange, W. B., and W. L. McAtee. 1934. Improving the farm environment for wild life. *U.S. Dept. Agric. Farmers' Bull.* 1719. 61 pp.

Greene, C. T. 1921. An illustrated synopsis of the puparia of 100 Muscoid flies (Diptera). *Proc. U.S. Natl. Mus.*, 60: 1–39.

—— 1925a. The puparia and larvae of Sarcophagid flies. *Proc. U.S. Natl. Mus.*, 66: 1–26.

—— 1925b. A tentative arrangement of the muscoid flies based on the puparia. *Proc. Ent. Soc. Wash.*, 27: 157–63.

Greenshields, F. 1936. Tetraploidy and Hymenoptera. *Nature*, 138: 330.

Grelet, N. 1957. Growth limitation and sporulation. *Jour. Appl. Bact.*, 20: 315–24.

Gressitt, J. L. 1958a. Zoogeography of insects. *Ann. Rev. Ent.*, 3: 207–30.

—— 1958b. Ecology of *Promecotheca papuana* Csiki, a coconut beetle. *Proc. 10th Internatl. Congr. Ent.*, 2: 747–53 (1956).

Grisebach, A. H. R. 1838. Ueber den Einfluss des Klimas auf die Begrenzung der natür-lichen Floren. *Linnaea*, 12: 159–200.

Grison, P. 1948. Alimentation artificielle des insectes phytophages. *Ann. Sci. Nat. Zool.*, 10: 59–65.

—— 1951. Emploi des méthodes d'alimentation artificielle des insectes dans les études toxicologiques. *Proc. 2nd Internatl. Congr. Crop Protection, London.* Pp. 162–4.

Grison, P., M. Feron, and K. Sacantanis. 1950. Développement de la Mouche des fruits (*Ceratitis capitata* Wied.) en milieu nutritif synthétique. *Compt. Rend. Acad. Sci.*, 23: 996–8.

Grison, P., and C. Vago. 1953. La régulation des infestations de chenilles processionnaires du pin par les maladies à virus. *Compt. Rend. Acad. Agric. France*, 39: 485–87.

Groff, G. W., and C. W. Howard. 1924. The cultured citrus ant of South China. *Lingnan Agric. Rev.*, 2: 108–14.

Grosch, D. S. 1948. Growth in *Habrobracon*. *Growth*, 12: 243–54.

Grosch, D. S., L. E. La Chance, and R. L. Sullivan. 1955. Notes on the feeding preferences of *Habrobracon* adults (*Microbracon hebetor* (Say): Hymen: Braconidae). *Ann. Ent. Soc. America*, 48: 415–16.

Guthrie, F. E., R. L. Rabb, and T. G. Bowery. 1959. Evaluation of candidate insecticides and insect pathogens for tobacco hornworm control, 1956–1958. *Jour. Econ. Ent.*, 52: 798–804.

Guyénot, E. 1917. Recherches experimentales sur la vie aseptique et le développement d'un organisme *Drosophila ampelophila* en fonction du milieu. *Bull. Biol. France Belgique*, 51: 1–330.

Günther, S. 1956. Zur Infektion des Goldafters (*Euproctis chrysorrhoea* L.) mit *Plistophora schubergi* Zwölfer (Microsporidia). *Zeitschr. angew. Zool.*, 43: 397–405.

—— 1958. Forschungsarbeiten über Infektionskrankheiten bei Forstinsekten als Ergänzung zu gradologischen Untersuchungen. *Forst und Jagd*, 8: 208.

—— 1959. Über die Auswirkung auf die Infektiosität bei der Passage insektenpathogener Mikrosporidien durch den Darm von Vögeln und Insekten. *Nachrichtenbl. deutsch. Pflanzenschutzdienst [Berlin].* 13: 19–21.

Gunther, F. A., and L. R. Jeppson. 1960. *Modern Insecticides and World Food Production.* Chapman and Hall Ltd. London. 284 pp.

Haden, W. R. 1935. Parasitism of the oriental fruit moth with special reference to the importance of certain alternate hosts. *Univ. Delaware Agric. Expt. Sta. Bull.* 194. 42 pp.

Hadley, C. H. 1938. Progress of Japanese beetle investigations. *Jour. New York Ent. Soc.*, 46: 203–16.

Haeussler, G. J. 1930. Parasites of the oriental peach moth, *Laspeyresia molesta* Busck, in North America. *Jour. Agric. Res.*, 41: 365–77.

—— 1932. *Macrocentrus ancylivorus* Roh. an important parasite of the oriental fruit moth. *Jour. Agric. Res.*, 45: 79–100.

—— 1940. Parasites of the oriental fruit moth in Japan and Chosen and their introduction into the United States. *U.S. Dept. Agric. Tech. Bull.* 728. 62 pp.

Hafez, Mostafa. 1947. The biology and life-history of *Apanteles ruficrus* Hal. *Bull. Soc. Fouad Ier Entom.*, 31: 225–49.

—— 1949. A simple method for breeding the housefly, *Musca domestica* L., in the laboratory. *Bull. Ent. Res.*, 39: 385–86.

—— 1951. Notes on the introduction and biology of *Microplitis demolitor* Wilk. *Bull. Soc. Fouad Ier Entom.*, 35: 107–21.

—— 1953. Studies on *Tachina larvarum* L. (Diptera, Tachinidae). *Bull. Soc. Fouad. Ier Entom.*, 37: pp. 255–335.

Hafez, Mostafa. 1961. *Seasonal fluctuations of population density of the cabbage aphid, Brevicoryne brassicae (L.), in the Netherlands and the role of its parasite, Aphidius (Diaeretiella) rapae (Curtis).* H. Veenman and Zonen N.V.—Wageningen—1961. 5–104.

Hafez, M., and R. L. Doutt. 1954. Biological evidence of sibling species in *Aphytis maculicornis* (Masi). (Hymenoptera, Aphelinidae.) *Canadian Ent.*, 86: 90–6.

Hagen, K. S. 1950. Fecundity of *Chrysopa californica* as affected by synthetic foods. *Jour. Econ. Ent.*, 43: 101–4.

—— 1952. Influence of adult nutrition upon fecundity, fertility and longevity of three fruit flies (Diptera: Tephritidae). Ph.D. Thesis, Univ. California, Berkeley.

—— 1953. A premating period in certain species of the genus *Opius* (Hymenoptera: Braconidae). *Proc. Hawaiian Ent. Soc.*, 15: 115–16.

—— 1958. Honeydew as an adult fruit fly diet affecting reproduction. *Proc. 10th Internatl. Congr. Ent.*, 3: 25–30 (1956).

Hagen, K. S., and G. L. Finney. 1950. A food supplement for effectively increasing the fecundity of certain tephritid species. *Jour. Econ. Ent.*, 43: 735.

Hagen, K. S., and E. I. Schlinger. 1960. Imported Indian parasite of pea aphid established in California. *California Agric.*, 14: 5–6.

Hairston, N. G. 1957. Discussion: Nelson G. Hairston. In *Cold Spring Harbor Symposia on Quantitative Biology*, 22: 327.

Hale, M. 1677. *The primitive origination of mankind.* London, Shrowsbery.

Hall, I. M. 1953. The role of virus diseases in the control of the alfalfa looper. *Jour. Econ. Ent.*, 46: 1110–11.

—— 1954. Studies of microorganisms pathogenic to the sod webworm. *Hilgardia*, 22: 535–65.

—— 1957. Use of a polyhedrosis virus to control the cabbage looper on lettuce in California. *Jour. Econ. Ent.*, 50: 551–53.

—— 1961. Some fundamental aspects of applied insect pathology. *Advances in Pest Control Res.*, 4: 1–32.

Hall, I. M., and L. A. Andres. 1959. Field evaluation of commercially produced *Bacillus thuringiensis* used for control of lepidopterous larvae on crucifers. *Jour. Econ. Ent.*, 52: 877–80.

Hall, I. M., and M. E. Badgley. 1957. A rickettsial disease of larvae of species of *Stethorus* caused by *Rickettsiella stethorae* n. sp. *Jour. Bact.*, 74: 452–55.

Hall, I. M., and P. H. Dunn. 1957a. Entomophthorous fungi parasitic on the spotted alfalfa aphid. *Hilgardia*, 27: 159–81.

—— 1957b. Fungi on spotted alfalfa aphid. *California Agriculture*, 11: 5, 14.

—— 1958a. Artificial dissemination of entomophthorous fungi pathogenic to the spotted alfalfa aphid in California. *Jour. Econ. Ent.*, 51: 341–44.

—— 1958b. Susceptibility of some insect pests to infection by *Bacillus thuringiensis* Berliner in laboratory tests. *Jour. Econ. Ent.*, 51: 296–98.

—— 1959. The effect of certain insecticides and fungicides on fungi pathogenic to the spotted alfalfa aphid. *Jour. Econ. Ent.*, 52: 28–30.

Hall, I. M., and J. C. Halfhill. 1959. The germination of resting spores of *Entomophthora virulenta* Hall and Dunn. *Jour. Econ. Ent.*, 52: 30–35.

Hallez. P. 1886. Loi de l'orientation de l'embryon chez les insectes. *Compt. rend.*, 103: 606–8.

Halvorson, H. O., editor. 1957a. Spores. *American Inst. Biol. Sci.*, 5: 164 pp.

—— 1957b. Rapid and simultaneous sporulation. *Jour. Appl. Bact.*, 20: 305–14.

Hambleton, E. J. 1944. *Heliothis virescens* as a pest of cotton, with notes on host plants in Peru. *Jour. Econ. Ent.*, 37: 660–66.

Hamilton, W. J., Jr., and D. B. Cook. 1940. Small mammals and the forest. *Jour. Forest.*, 38: 468–78.

Hamlin, John C. 1924. The Australian Prickly Pear Problem. *Jour. Econ. Ent.*, 17: 60–4.

Hamlin, J. C., F. V. Lieberman, R. W. Bunn, W. C. McDuffie, R. C. Newton, and L. J. Jones. 1949. Field studies of the alfalfa weevil and its environment. *U.S. Dept. Agric. Tech. Bull.* 975. 84 pp.

Hammen, C. S. 1956. Nutrition of *Musca domestica* in single-pair culture. *Ann. Ent. Soc. America*, 49: 365–8.

—— 1957. A growth-promoting effect of cholesterol in the diet of larvae of the house fly, *Musca domestica* L. *Ann. Ent. Soc. America*, 50: 125–7.

Handschin, E. 1932. A preliminary report on investigations on the buffalo fly (*Lyperosia exigua* de Meij.) and its parasites in Java and northern Australia. *Australian Council Sci. and Indust. Res. Pamph.* 31. 24 pp.

Hanna, A. D. 1947. Studies on the Mediterranean fruit fly, *Ceratitis capitata* Wied. *Bull. Soc. Fouad Ier Ent.*, 31: 251–85.

Hannay, C. L. 1953. Crystalline inclusions in aerobic sporeforming bacteria. *Nature*, 172: 1004.

—— 1956. *Inclusions in Bacteria. Bacterial Anatomy*, 6: 318–40. (E.T.C. Spooner and B.A.D. Stocker, editors). Cambridge Univ. Press, N.Y.

Hannay, C. L., and P. Fitz-James. 1955. The protein crystals of *Bacillus thuringiensis* Berliner. *Canadian Jour. Microbiol.*, 1: 694–710.

Hanson, H. S. 1937. Notes on the ecology and control of pine beetles in Great Britain. *Bull. Ent. Res.*, 28: 185–242.

Harned, R. L. 1954. The production of prodigiosin by submerged growth of *Serratia marcescens*. *Appl. Microbiol.*, 2: 365–8.

Hart, M. P., and D. M. MacLeod. 1955. An apparatus for determining the effects of temperature and humidity on germination of fungous spores. *Canadian Jour. Bot.*, 33: 289–92.

Harvey J. L. 1960. Exemption from requirement of tolerance for residues of viable spores of microorganism *Bacillus thuringiensis* Berliner. *Federal Register*, 25: 3207–8.

Harville, J. P. 1955. Ecology and population dynamics of the California oak moth *Phryganidia californica* Packard (Lepidoptera: Dioptidae). *Microentomology*, 20: 83–166.

Hassett, C. C., V. G. Dethier, and J. Gans. 1950. A comparison of nutritive values and taste thresholds of carbohydrates for the blowfly. *Biol. Bull.*, 99: 446–53.

Hastings, J. J. H. 1958. *Present trends and future developments*. In *Biochemical engineering*. R. Steel, editor. 1958. Macmillan Co., New York. Pp. 297–318.

Haub, J. G., and D. F. Miller. 1932. Food requirements of blowfly cultures used in the treatment of osteomyelitis. *Jour. Exptl. Zool.*, 64: 51–6.

Haviland, M. D. 1921a. On the bionomics and development of *Lygocerus testaceimanus* Kieffer and *Lygocerus cameroni* Kieffer (Prototrypoidea-Ceraphronidae) parasites of *Aphidius* (Braconidae). *Quart. Jour. Micros. Sci.*, 65: 101–27.

—— 1921b. On the bionomics and postembryonic development of certain Cynipid hyperparasites of aphids. *Quart. Jour. Micros. Sci.*, 65: 451–78.

—— 1922. On the larval development of *Dacnusa areolaris* Nees (Braconidae), a parasite of Phytomyzinae (Diptera), with a note on certain chalcid parasites of phytomyzids. *Parasitol.*, 14: 167–73.

Hawboldt, L. S. 1947. *Bessa selecta* (Meigen) (Diptera: Tachinidae) as a parasite of *Gilpinia hercyniae* (Hartig) (Hymenoptera: Diprionidae). *Canadian Ent.*, 79: 84–104.

Hawkes, O. A. M. 1920. Observations on the life-history, biology and genetics of the lady-bird beetle, *Adalia bipunctata* (Mulsant). *Proc. Zool. Soc. London*, 4: 475–90.

Hawley, I. M., and G. F. White. 1935. Preliminary studies on the diseases of larvae of the Japanese beetle (*Popillia japonica* Newm.). *Jour. New York Ent. Soc.*, 43: 405–12.

Haydak, M. H. 1936. A food for rearing laboratory insects. *Jour. Econ. Ent.*, 29: 1026.

—— 1942. Rearing grasshoppers under laboratory conditions. *Science*, 95: 657–8.

—— 1943. A basic diet., p. 56. In laboratory procedures in studies of the chemical control of insects. (Ed., F. L. Campbell and F. R. Moulton.) *Amer. Assoc. Adv. Sci.*, 20: 206 pp.

—— 1947. Rearing clothes moth and black carpet beetle in the laboratory. *Jour. Econ. Ent.*, 40: 279–80.

—— 1949. Causes of deficiency of soybean flour as a pollen substitute for honeybees. *Jour. Econ. Ent.*, 42: 573–9.

—— 1958. Pollen substitutes. *Proc. Tenth Internatl. Congr. Ent.*, 4: 1053–6 (1956).

Haydak, M. H., and M. C. Tanquary. 1942. Various kinds of soybean flour as pollen substitutes. *Jour. Econ. Ent.*, 35: 317–18.

Haynes, W. C., G. St. Julian, Jr., Margaret C. Shekleton, H. H. Hall, and H. Tashiro. 1961. Preservation of infectious milky disease bacteria by lyophilization. *Jour. Insect Pathol.*, 3: 55–61.

Haynes, W. C., L. J. Wickerham, and C. W. Hesseltine. 1955. Maintenance of cultures of industrially important microorganisms. *Appl. Microbiol.*, 3: 361–8.

Hazelhoff, E. H. 1927. Biological control of the sugar-cane aphid by transferring its native parasite from old to young fields. *Trans. 4th Internatl. Congr. Ent.*, 2: 55–61.

Headlee, Thomas J. 1914. Some data on the effect of temperature and moisture on the rate of insect metabolism. *Jour. Econ. Ent.*, 7: 413–17.

Heimburger, C. C. 1945. Comment on the budworm outbreak in Ontario and Quebec. *Forest. Chron.*, 21: 114–26.

Heimpel, A. M. 1955. The pH in the gut and blood of the larch sawfly, *Pristiphora erichsonii* (Htg.), and other insects with reference to the pathogenicity of *Bacillus cereus* Fr. and Fr. *Canadian Jour. Zool.*, 33: 99–106.

Heimpel, A. M., and T. A. Angus. 1958a. Recent advances in the knowledge of some bacterial pathogens of insects. *Proc. 10th Internatl. Congr. Ent.* 4: 711–22 (1956).

—— 1958b. The taxonomy of insect pathogens related to *Bacillus cereus* Fr. and Fr. *Canadian Jour. Microbiol.*, 4: 531–41.

—— 1959. The site of action of crystalliferous bacteria in Lepidoptera larvae. *Jour. Insect Pathol.*, 1: 152–70.

—— 1960. Bacterial insecticides. *Bact. Revs.*, 24: 266–88.

Heinrich, G. H. 1960. Synopsis of Nearctic Ichneumoninae Stenopheusticae with particular reference to the Northeastern region (Hymenoptera). Part I. *Canadian Ent. 92, Suppl. 15*, 87 pp.

Henderson, C. F. 1941. Apparatus and technique for the study of the egg parasites of the beet leafhopper. *U.S. Dept. Agric. Circ.* 593, 18 pp.

—— 1955. Overwintering, spring emergence and host synchronization of two egg parasites of the beet leaf hopper in southern Idaho. *U.S. Dept. Agric. Circ.* 967. 16 pp.

Henderson, C. F., and J. K. Holloway. 1940–43. Manuscript reports. Effect of artificial control practices on natural enemies of insect pests. (On file *U.S. Bur. Ent. and Plant Quar., Div. Foreign Parasite Introduction, Washington, D.C.*)

Hennig, W. 1948 to 1952. *Die Larvenformen der Dipteren.* Teil 1, 184 pp. (1948); Teil 2, 458 pp. (1950); Teil 3, 628 pp. (1952). Akademie-Verlag, Berlin.

Henson, H. 1946. The theoretical aspect of insect metamorphosis. *Biol. Rev.*, 21: 1–14.

Hering, E. M. 1953. Probleme der Xenophobia und Xenophilie bei der Wirtswahl phytophager Insekten. *Trans. 9th Internatl. Congr. Ent.*, 1: 507–13.

Hesse, R., W. C. Allee, and K. P. Schmidt. 1937. *Ecological Animal Geography.* New York, John Wiley and Sons Inc., London, Chapman and Hall, Ltd. 597 pp.

Hidaka, T. 1958. Biological investigation on *Telenomus gifuensis* Ashmead (Hym.: Scelionidae), an egg-parasite of *Scotinophara lurida* Burmeister (Hem.: Pentatomidae) in Japan. *Acta Hymenopterologica*, 1: 75–93.

Hill, C. C. 1923. *Platygaster vernalis* Myers, an important parasite of the Hessian fly. *Jour. Agric. Res.*, 25: 31–42.

—— 1926. *Platygaster hiemalis* Forbes, a parasite of the Hessian fly. *Jour. Agric. Res.*, 22: 261–75.

Hill, C. C., and W. T. Emery. 1937. The biology of *Platygaster herrickii*, a parasite of the Hessian fly. *Jour. Agric. Res.*, 55: 199–213.

Hill, C. C., and J. S. Pinckney. 1940. Keys to the parasites of the hessian fly based on remains left in the host puparium *U.S. Dept. Agric. Tech. Bul.* 715: 13 pp.

Hill, C. C., and H. D. Smith. 1931. *Heterospilus cephi* Rohwer, a parasite of the European wheat sawfly, *Cephus pygmaeus* (L.). *Jour. Agric. Res.*, 43: 597–609.

Hill, D. L., V. A. Bell, and L. E. Chadwick. 1947. Rearing of the blowfly, *Phormia regina* Meigen, on a sterile synthetic diet. *Ann. Ent. Soc. America*, 40: 213–16.

Hills, O. A., and E. A. Taylor. 1951. Parasitization of dipterous leaf miners in cantaloups and lettuce in the Salt River Valley, Arizona. *Jour. Econ. Ent.*, 44: 759–62.

Hinds, W. E., B. A. Osterberger, and A. L. Dugas. 1933. Review of six seasons' work in Louisiana in controlling the sugar cane moth borer by field colonizations of its egg parasite *Trichogramma minutum* Riley. *Louisiana Agric. Expt. Sta. Bull.* 248. 34 pp.

Hinds, W. E., and H. Spencer. 1928. Utilization of *Trichogramma minutum* for control of the sugarcane borer. *Jour. Econ. Ent.*, 21: 273–9.

—— 1930. Progress in the utilization of *Trichogramma minutum* in cane borer control in Louisiana during 1929. *Jour. Econ. Ent.*, 23: 121–7.

Hinton, H. E. 1948. On the origin and function of the pupal stage. *Trans. Roy. Ent. Soc. London*, 99: 395–409.

—— 1956. Dietary requirements of insects. Amino acids and vitamins. *Sci. Progress*, 44: 292–309.

Hinton, T., D. T. Noyes, and J. Ellis. 1951. Amino acids and growth factors in a chemically defined medium for *Drosophila*. *Physiol. Zool.*, 24: 335–53.

Hitzman, D. O., H. O. Halvorson, and T. Ukita. 1957. Requirements for production and germination of spores of anaerobic bacteria. *Jour. Bact.*, 74: 1–7.

Hodgson, E., V. H. Cheldelin, and R. W. Newburgh. 1956. Substitution of choline by related compounds and further studies on amino acid requirements in nutrition of *Phormia regina* (Meig.). *Canadian Jour. Zool.*, 34: 527–31.

Hodson, A. C., and H. C. Chiang. 1948. A new method for rearing *Drosophila*. *Science*, 107: 176–7.

Hoffman, C. H., and R. F. Anderson. 1945. Effect of southern pine beetle on timber losses and natural restocking. *Jour. Forest.*, 43: 436–9.

Hofmaster, R. N., and L. P. Ditman. 1961. Utilization of a nuclear polyhedrosis virus to control the cabbage looper on cole crops in Virginia. *Jour. Econ. Ent.*, 54: 921–3.

Hogben, L. 1940. *Problems of the origins of species*, pp. 269–86. In *The New Systematics*, J. S. Huxley, editor.

Holling, C. S. 1958. A radiographic technique to identify healthy, parasitized, and diseased sawfly prepupae within cocoons. *Canadian Ent.*, 90: 59–61.

Holling, C. S. 1959. The components of predation as revealed by a study of small mammal predation of the European pine sawfly. *Canadian Ent.*, 91: 293–320.

—— 1961. Principles of insect predation. *Ann. Rev. Ent.*, 6: 163–82.

Holloway, J. K. 1939. An agar preparation for feeding adult parasite insects. *Jour. Econ. Ent.*, 32: 154.

—— 1948. Biological control of Klamath weed—Progress report. *Jour. Econ. Ent.*, 41: 56.

Holloway, J. K., C. F. Henderson, and H. V. McBurnie. 1942. Population increase of citrus red mite associated with the use of sprays containing inert granular residues. *Jour. Econ. Ent.*, 35: 348–50.

Holloway, J. K., and C. B. Huffaker. 1951. The role of *Chrysolina gemellata* in the biological control of Klamath weed. *Jour. Econ. Ent.*, 44: 244–7.

—— 1953. Establishment of a root borer and a gall fly for control of Klamath weed. *Jour. Econ. Ent.*, 46: 65–7.

—— 1957. Establishment of the seed weevil, *Apion ulicis* Forst., for suppression of gorse in California. *Jour. Econ. Ent.*, 50: 498–9.

Holloway, T. E. 1929. Local conditions as influencing recommendations for the control of sugar-cane insects. *Trans. 4th Internatl. Cong. Ent.*, 2: 448–51.

Holmes, F. O. 1948. *Borrelinaceae*. In *Bergey's Manual of Determinative Bacteriology*, 6th Edition, pp. 1225–8. Williams and Wilkins, Baltimore.

Hopkins, A. D. 1918. Periodic events and natural law as guides to agricultural research and practice. *U.S. Mon. Weather Rev. Suppl.*, 9: 1–42.

Horn, W. 1929a. The future of insect taxonomy. *Trans. 4th Internatl. Congr. Ent.*, 2: 34–51.

—— 1929b. On the splitting influence of the increase of entomological knowledge and on the enigma of species. *Trans. 4th Internatl. Congr. Ent.*, 2: 500–7.

Hosaka, E. Y., and A. Thistle. 1954. Noxious plants of the Hawaiian ranges. *Univ. Hawaii Exten. Bull.* 62. 39 pp.

Hoskins, W. M., H. P. Bloxham, and M. W. Van Ess. 1940. The insecticidal effects of organic compounds. *Jour. Econ. Ent.*, 33: 875–81.

House, H. L. 1947. The laboratory propagation of *Sturmia* sp., a parasite of sawflies. *Rept. Quebec Soc. Protection Plants*, 30: 60–2.

—— 1951. Notes on the laboratory propagation of *Pseudosarcophaga affinis* (Fall.), a sarcophagid parasite of the spruce budworm, *Choristoneura fumiferana* (Clem.). *31st Rept. Quebec Soc. Protection Plants (1948–49)*. Pp. 134–7.

—— 1954a. Nutritional studies with *Pseudosarcophaga affinis* (Fall.), a dipterous parasite of the spruce budworm, *Choristoneura fumiferana* (Clem.). I. A chemically defined medium and aseptic-culture technique. *Canadian Jour. Zool.*, 32: 331–41.

—— 1954b. II. Effects of eleven vitamins on growth. *Canadian Jour. Zool.*, 32: 342–50.

—— 1954c. III. Effects of nineteen amino acids on growth. *Canadian Jour. Zool.*, 32: 351–7.

—— 1954d. IV. Effects of ribonucleic acid, Glutathione, dextrose, a salt mixture, cholesterol, and fats. *Canadian Jour. Zool.*, 32: 358–65.

—— 1955. Nutritional requirements and artificial diets for insects. *Ann. Rept. Ent. Soc. Ontario*, 86: 5–9, 21–3.

—— 1958a. The nutrition of insects with particular reference to entomophagous parasites. *Proc. 10th Internatl. Congr. Ent.*, 2: 139–43 (1956).

—— 1958b. Nutritional requirements of insects associated with animal parasitism. *Exper. Parasit.*, 7: 555–609. (Parasitological reviews section.)

House, H. L., and J. S. Barlow. 1956. Nutritional studies with *Pseudosarcophaga affinis* (Fall.), a dipterous parasite of the spruce budworm, *Choristoneura fumiferana* (Clem.). V. Effects of various concentrations of the amino acid mixture, dextrose, potassium ion, the salt mixture, and lard on growth and development; and a substitute for lard. *Canadian Jour. Zool.*, **34**: 182–9.

—— 1958. Vitamin requirements of the housefly *Musca domestica*. *Ann. Ent. Soc. America*, **51**: 299–302.

House, H. L., and M. G. Traer. 1949. An artificial food for rearing *Pseudosarcophaga affinis* (Fall.), a parasite of the spruce budworm *Choristoneura fumiferana* (Clem.). *Ann. Rept. Ent. Soc. Ontario*, **79**: 1–4.

Hovanitz, W. 1958. *Distribution of butterflies in the new world*, pp. 321–68. In *Zoogeography*, C. L. Hubbs, Editor.

Howard, L. O. 1893. *The correlation of structure and host-relations among the Encyrtinae.* Wilder Quarter-Century Book, pp. 177–85.

—— 1897. A study in insect parasitism: a consideration of the parasites of the white-marked tussock moth, with an account of their habits and interrelations and with descriptions of new species. *U.S. Dept. Agric. Tec. Ser.* **5**: 1–57.

—— 1910. On the habit with certain Chalcidoidea of feeding at the puncture holes made by the ovipositor. *Jour. Econ. Ent.*, **3**: 257–60.

—— 1924. Retarded establishment of introduced parasites of injurious insects. *Nat. Acad. Sci.*, **10**: 16–18.

—— 1925. Albert Koebele, an obituary. *Jour. Econ. Ent.*, **18**: 556–62.

—— 1930. A history of applied entomology. *Smithsonian Misc. Coll.*, **84**: 1–564.

—— 1931. An apologetic correction. *Science*, **73**: 342.

Howard, L. O., and W. F. Fiske. 1911. The importation into the United States of the parasites of the gipsy moth and the brown-tail moth. *U.S. Dept. Agric. Bur. Ent. Bull.* **91**: 1–312.

Howe, R. W. 1953. Studies on beetles of the family, Ptinidae. VIII. The intrinsic rate of increase of some ptinid beetles. *Ann. Appl. Biol.*, **40**: 121–34.

Howe, R. W., and H. D. Burges. 1951. Studies on beetles of the family Ptinidae. VI. The biology of *Ptinus fur* (L.) and *P. sexpunctatus* Panzer. *Bull. Ent. Res.*, **42**: 499–511.

Hoy, J. M. 1949. Control of manuka by blight. *New Zealand Jour. Agric.*, **79**: 321–4.

—— 1954. The biology and host range of *Neoaplectana leucaniae*, a new species of insect-parasitic nematode. *Parasitology*, **44**: 392–99.

Hubbell, T. H. 1954. The naming of geographically variant populations. *Systematic Zool.*, **3**: 113–21.

—— 1956. Some aspects of geographic variation in insects. *Ann. Rev. Ent.*, **1**: 71–88.

Hubbs, C. L. (Editor). 1958. Zoogeography. *Amer. Assoc. Adv. Sci. Publ.* **51**, 509 pp.

Hueck, H. J. 1953. *The population-dynamics of the fruit tree red spider (Metatetranychus ulmi Koch 1836, Acari, Tetranychidae) with special reference to the influence of DDT.* N. V. Grafisch Bedrijf en Uitgeverij De Jong-Leiden. 148 pp.

Huff, C. G. 1928. Nutritional studies on the seed corn maggot, *Hylemya cilicrura* (Rond.). *Jour. Agric. Res.*, **36**: 625–30.

Huffaker, C. B. 1941. Egg parasites of the harlequin bug in North Carolina. *Jour. Econ. Ent.*, **34**: 117–18.

—— 1956. Spread and activity of imported parasites of fig. scale. *Proc. 10th Ann. California Fig. Inst.*, p. 23.

—— 1957. Fundamentals of biological control of weeds. *Hilgardia*, **27**: 101–57.

Huffaker, C. B. 1958a. The concept of balance in nature. *Proc. 10th Internatl. Congr. Ent.*, 2: 625–36 (1956).

—— 1958b. Experimental studies on predation: Dispersion factors and predator-prey oscillations. *Hilgardia*, 27: 343–83.

—— 1959a. Notes on entomology in the U.S.S.R. *Unpublished.* Taken as a member of the U.S. Agricultural and Technical Exchange Delegation in Entomology in U.S.S.R., 1959.

—— 1959b. Biological control of weeds with insects. *Ann. Rev. Ent.*, 4: 251–76.

Huffaker, C. B., and C. E. Kennett. 1953. Developments toward biological control of cyclamen mite on strawberries in California. *Jour. Econ. Ent.*, 46: 802–12.

—— 1956. Experimental studies on predation: predation and cyclamen-mite populations on strawberries in California. *Hilgardia*, 26: 191–222.

—— 1959. A ten-year study of vegetational changes associated with biological control of Klamath weed. *Jour. Range Management*, 12: 69–82.

—— 1960. Control of olive scale. *California Agric.*, 14: 4–8.

Huffaker, C. B., D. W. Ricker, and C. E. Kennett. 1961. Biological control of puncture vine with imported weevils. *California Agric.*, 15: 11, 12.

Huffaker, C. B., and C. H. Spitzer, Jr. 1951. Data on the natural control of the cyclamen mite on strawberries. *Jour. Econ. Ent.*, 44: 519–22

Huger, A. 1959. Histological observations on the development of crystalline inclusions of the rickettsial disease of *Tipula paludosa* Meigen. *Jour. Insect. Pathol.*, 1: 60–6.

Hughes, K. M. 1957. An annotated list and bibliography of insects reported to have virus diseases. *Hilgardia*, 26: 597–629.

Hunter-Jones, P. 1956. *Instructions for rearing and breeding locusts in the laboratory.* Anti-Locust Res. Centre, London. Pp. 1–9.

Hunter, S. J., and P. A. Glenn. 1909. The green bug and its enemies. *Univ. Kansas Bull.* 9. 221 pp.

Hurpin, B. 1955. Sur une 'maladie laiteuse' des larves de *Melolontha melolontha* L. (Coléopt. Scarabeidae.) *Compt. Rend. Soc. Biol.*, 149: 1966–7.

Husz, B. 1931. Experiments during 1931 on the use of *Bacillus thuringiensis* Berliner in controlling the corn borer. *Internatl. Corn Borer Invest.*, *Sci. Rept.*, 4: 22–3.

Hutchinson, G. E. 1954. Theoretical notes on oscillatory populations. *Jour. Wildlife Management*, 18: 107–9.

Hutner, S. H., and W. Trager (Conference Chairmen), *et al.* 1953. Growth of protozoa. *Ann. New York Acad. Sci.*, 56: 815–1093.

Huxley, J. S. 1939. Clines: an auxiliary method in taxonomy. *Bijdr. Dierk.*, 27: 491–520, 624, 626–7.

—— 1940. *Toward the new systematics*, 1–46. In *The New Systematics*, J. Huxley, editor. Oxford Univ. Press 583 pp.

—— 1943. *Evolution, the Modern Synthesis.* Harper and Bros., Publishers, New York and London, 645 pp.

—— 1954. *The evolutionary process.* In *Evolution as a Process*, J. S. Huxley, A. C. Hardy, and E. B. Ford, editors.

Huxley, J. S., A. C. Hardy, and E. B. Ford (editors). 1954. *Evolution as a Process.* George Allen and Unwin Ltd., London, 367 pp.

Huzimatsu, K. 1940. The life history of a new cynipid fly, *Kleidotoma japonica*, n. sp. *Tohoku Imperial Univ. Sci. Rept. Ser. 4, Biol.*, 15: 457–80.

Imms, A. D. 1916. Observations on the insect parasites of some Coccidae. I. On *Aphelinus mytilapidis* Le Baron, a chalcid parasite of the mussel scale (*Lepidosaphes ulmi* L.). *Quart. Journ. Microscop. Sci.*, 61: 217–74.

Imms, A. D. 1918. Observations on *Pimpla pomorum* Ratz., a parasite of the apple blossom weevil (including a description of the male by Claude Morley, F.Z.S.). *Ann. Appl. Biol.*, 4: 211–27.

—— 1925. *A General Textbook of Entomology.* Methuen & Co. Ltd. London. 698 pp.

—— 1929. Remarks on the problem of the biological control of noxious weeds. *Trans. 4th Internatl. Congr. Ent.* pp. 10–17 (1928).

—— 1931. *Recent Advances in Entomology.* J. and A. Churchill, London. 374 pp.

—— 1937. *Biological control of noxious weeds.* In *Recent Advances in Entomology.* Philadelphia, E. Blakiston and Sons. Pp. 410–19.

—— 1948. *A General Textbook of Entomology Including the Anatomy, Physiology, Development and Classification of Insects.* 7th ed. Methuen and Co., Ltd., London, 727 pp.

—— 1957. *A General Textbook of Entomology Including the Anatomy, Physiology, Development and Classification of Insects.* Ninth ed. revised by O. W. Richards and R. G. Davies. Methuen and Co. Ltd., London. 886 pp.

Isakova, N. P. 1954. *The use of the pathogenic properties of insecticidal bacteria under conditions of mixed cultures.* In *Infectious and Protozoan Diseases of Insects.* Editors V. I. Poltev, L. V. Alexandrova, A. A. Yevlakhova, and M. S. Pavelyeva. *All-Union Order of Lenin Academy of Agric. Sciences named for V. L. Lenin,* abstracts, 76 pp. (in Russian).

Ishii, S. 1956. Culture of phytophagous insects on artificial diet. (Translated by E. R. Hope of the Canadian Scientific Information Center.) *Shokubutsu Boeki,* 10: 7–10.

Ishii, S., and C. Hirano. 1955. Qualitative studies on the essential amino acids for the growth of the larva of the rice stem borer, *Chilo simplex* Butler, under aseptic conditions. *Bull. Natl. Inst. Agric. Sci.,* 5: 35–47.

Ishii, S., and H. Urushibara. 1954. On fat and water soluble growth factors required by the rice stem borer, *Chilo simplex* Butler. *Natl. Inst. Agric. Sci. Bull.,* Ser. C., 4: 109–33.

Ishii, T. 1928. *Enargopelte ovivora,* a new chalcid-fly from Japan. *Kontyû Insect.,* 2: 205–8.

Ishimori, N. 1934. Contribution à l'étude de la grasserie du ver à soie, *Bombyx mori. Compt. Rend. Soc. Biol., Soc. Franco–Japonaise Biolog.,* 116: 1169.

Ishiwata, S. 1905. Concerning 'Sotto-Kin' a bacillus of a disease of the silkworm. *Rept. Assoc. Seric. Japan.* Pp. 160–61.

—— 1906. Sur 'Sottokin' un bacille de la maladie des vers à soie. *Sta. Seric. Kyoto,* 10: 1–20.

Isla Marco, Ricardo. 1959. Notes on the biological control of pests of agriculture in Chile. *FAO Plant Prot. Bull.,* 8: 25–30.

Ivanova-Kazas, O. M. 1948. 'Characteristics of embryonic development of parasitic Hymenoptera in connection with parasitism.' [In Russian.] *Uspekhi Sovremennoi Biol.,* 25: 123–42.

—— 1950. 'Adaptation to parasitism in the embryonic development of the Ichneumon *Prestwichia aquatica.*' (Hymenoptera.) [In Russian.] *Zool. Zhr.,* 29: 630–44.

—— 1952a. 'Embryonic development of *Mestocharis militaris* R.-Kors.' (Hymenoptera, Chalcididae.) [In Russian.] *Ent.-Obozrenie, Moscow,* 32: 160–6.

—— 1952b. 'Postembryonic development of *Prestwichia aquatica* Lubb.' [In Russian.] *Trudy Lening. Obshsch. Estestvoisp.,* 71: 165–213.

—— 1954a. 'The effect of parasitism on the embryonic development of *Caraphractus reductus* R.-Kors." (Hymenoptera.) [In Russian.] *Trudy Leningrad Obschestra Estestro,* 72: 57–73.

—— 1954b. 'On the evolution of embryonic development of Hymenoptera.' [In Russian.] *Trudy Vsesoyuz. Ent. Obschch., Moscow,* 44: 301–35.

Ivanova-Kazas, O. M. 1954c. 'On the evolution of the embryonic development in Hymenoptera.' [In Russian.] *Doklady Akad. Nauk S.S.S.R., Moscow (n.s.)*, 96: 1269–72.

—— 1956. Comparative study of embryonal development in aphidiids (*Aphidius* and *Ephedrus*). [In Russian, with summary in German.] *Ent. Obozernie*, 35: 245–61.

—— 1958. Biology and embryonic development of *Eurytoma aciculata* Ratz. (Hymenoptera, Eurytomidae.) [In Russian with summary in English.] *Entomol. obozrenie* [Transl. Ent. Rev.], 37: 1–18.

Iwata, K. 1942. Biology of some Japanese *Polysphincta*. *Mushi*, 14: 98–102.

—— 1942. Comparative studies on the habits of solitary wasps. *Tenthredo*, 4: 1–146.

—— 1958. Ovarian eggs of 233 species of the Japanese Ichneumonidae (Hymenoptera). *Acta Hymenopterologica*, 1: 63–74.

—— 1959. The comparative anatomy of the ovary in Hymenoptera. Part IV. Proctotrupoidea and Agriotypidae (Ichneumonoidea) with description of ovarian eggs. *Kontyû*, 27: 18–20.

—— 1960. The comparative anatomy of the ovary in Hymenoptera. Part V. Ichneumonidae. *Acta Hymenopterologica*, 1: 115–69.

Iwata, K., and A. Nagatomi. 1954. Biology of Tachinid, *Phorocerosoma forte* Townsend, parasitic on *Oxya japonica* Willemse in Japan. *Mushi*, 26: 23–34.

Jackson, D. J. 1928. The biology of *Dinocampus (Perilitus) rutilus* Nees, a braconid parasite of *Sitona lineata* L. Part I. *Proc. Zool. Soc. London (1928)*, 597–630.

—— 1937. Host selection in *Pimpla examinator* F. (Hymenoptera). *Proc. Roy. Ent. Soc. London (A)*, 12: 81–91.

—— 1956. Notes on hymenopterous parasitoids bred from eggs of Dytiscidae in Fife. *Jour. Soc. Brit. Ent.*, 5: 144–9.

—— 1958a. Observations on the biology of *Caraphractus cinctus* Walker (Hymenoptera: Myrmaridae), a parasitoid of the eggs of Dytiscidae—I. *Trans. Roy. Ent. Soc. London*, 110: 533–54.

—— 1958b. A further note on *Chrysocharis* (Hym.: Eulophidae) parasitizing the eggs of *Dytiscus marginalis* L., and a comparison of its larva with that of *Caraphractus cinctus* Walker (Hym.: Mymaridae). *Jour. Soc. Brit. Ent.*, 6: 15–22.

Jackson, T. 1958. *Development of aerobic fermentation processes: penicillin*, pp. 185–221. In *Biochemical Engineering*, R. Steel, editor.

Jacob, F. H. 1958. Some modern problems in pest control. *Science Progress*, 181: 30–45.

Jacobi, E. F. 1939. Ueber Lebensweise, Auffinden des Wirtes und Regulierung des Individuanzahl von *Mormoniella vitripennis* Walker. *Arch. Neerland. Zool.*, 3: 197–282.

Jacobs, S. E. 1950. Bacteriological control of the flour moth, *Ephestia kuehniella* Z. *Proc. Soc. Appl. Bact.*, 13: 83–91.

James, M. T. 1947. The flies that cause myiasis in man. *U.S. Dept. Agric. Misc. Pub.* 631, 175 pp.

Janisch, E. 1938. Untersuchungen uber den Massenwechsel von Schadinsekten. *Zeitschr. Pflanzenkrankh*, 48: 435–48.

—— 1939. Die Bedeutung des Optimums fur den Massenwechsel forstschädlicher Insekten. Verhandl. 7 *Internatl. Kongr. Ent.* 3: 1974–89. (1938.)

—— 1958. Nachträge zum Problem des Polyedervirus bei Insektenkrankheiten. *Zeitschr. angew. Ent.*, 42: 292–306.

Janvier, H. 1956. Hymenopterous predators as biological control agents. *Jour. Econ. Ent.*, 49: 202–5.

Jaynes, H. A. 1933. The parasites of the sugarcane borer in Argentina and Peru, and their introduction into the United States. *U.S. Dept. Agric. Tech. Bull.* 363. 27 pp.

Jaynes, H. A., and E. K. Bynum. 1941. Experiments with *Trichogramma minutum* as a control of the sugarcane borer in Louisiana. *U.S. Dept. Agric. Tech. Bull.* 743. 42 pp.

Jenkins, C. F. H. 1948. Biological control in western Australia. *Jour. Roy. Soc. Western Australia*, 32: 1–17. (1945–46.)

Jenni, W. 1951. Beitrag zur Morphologie und Biologie der Cynipide *Pseudeucoila bochei* Weld, eines Larvenparasiten von *Drosophila melanogaster* Meig. *Acta. Zool.*, 32: 177–254.

Jepsen, G. L., E. Mayr, and G. G. Simpson. 1949. *Genetics, Paleontology and Evolution.* Princeton Univ. Press, Princeton, 474 pp.

Jepson, W. F. 1954. *A Critical Review of the World Literature on the Lepidopterous Stalk Borers of Tropical Graminaceous Crops.* London, Commonwealth Inst. Ent. 127 pp.

Jensen, D. D. 1957. Parasites of the Psyllidae. *Hilgardia*, 27: 71–99.

Johannsen, O. A., and F. H. Butt. 1941. *Embryology of Insects and Myriapods.* 462 pp. McGraw-Hill Book Co., Inc. New York and London.

Johansen, C. A. 1957. *History of Biological Control of Insects in Washington.* Northwest Sci. 31: 57–79.

Johansson, A. S. 1951. Studies on the relation between *Apanteles glomeratus* L. (Hym., Braconidae) and *Pieris brassicae* L. (Lepid., Pieridae). *Norsk Ent. Tidsskr. B.*, 7: 145–86.

Johnston, F. A. 1915. Asparagus-beetle egg parasite. *Jour. Agric. Res.*, 4: 303–13.

Jolivet, P. 1954. *Phytophagie et selection trophique.* Volume Jubilaire, Victor Van Straelen. Inst. Roy. Sci. Nat. Belgique. Tome II.

Juillet, J. A. 1959. Morphology of immature stages, life-history, and behaviour of three hymenopterous parasites of the European pine shoot moth, *Rhyacionia buoliana* (Schiff.) (Lepidoptera: Olethreutidae). *Canadian Ent.*, 91: 709–19.

Kadner, C. G., and F. M. LeFleur. 1951. The vitamin requirements of *Phaenicia sericata* larvae. *Wasmann Jour. Biol.*, 9: 129–36.

Kamal, A. D. 1954. Ecological and nutritional studies on the cherry fruit fly. *Jour. Econ. Ent.*, 47: 959–65.

Kamal, M. 1938. *Brachymeria femorata* Panz. (Hymenoptera-Chalcididae) a primary parasite of the cabbage worm *Pieris rapae* L. *Bull. Soc. Roy. Ent. d'Egypte*, 21: 5–27.

―― 1939. Biological studies on some hymenopterous parasites of aphidophagous Syrphidae. *Egypt Min. Agric. Tech. and Sci. Serv. Bull.*, 207. 110 pp.

―― 1951a. Biological control projects in Egypt, with a list of introduced parasites and predators. *Bull. Soc. Fouad Ier Ent.*, 35: 205–20.

―― 1951b. The biological control of the cotton leaf-worm (*Prodenia litura* F.) in Egypt. *Bull. Soc. Fouad. Ier Ent.*, 35: 221–70.

Karpova, A. I. 1950. The prospect of controlling the pea bruchid by the biological method with the aid of the egg-parasite *Lathromeris senex* Grese (Hymenoptera, Trichogrammatidae). *Ent. Obozrenie*, 31: 54–62. (In Russian.) [R.A.E., 41: 163–64, 1953.]

Kaussari, M. 1946. Coastal citrus pests (Iran). *Ent. Phytopath. Appl. Teheran*, 1: 32–38.

Kearns, H. G. H. 1931. The larval and pupal anatomy of *Stenomalus micans* Ol. (Pteromalidae), a chalcid endo-parasite of the gout-fly of barley (*Chlorops taeniopus* Meig.) with some details of the life history of the summer generation. *Parasitology*, 23: 380–95.

Keen, F. P. 1952. Insect Enemies of Western Forests. *U.S. Dept. Agric. Misc. Publ.* 273 (1st revision). 280 pp.

Keifer, H. H. 1944. Applied entomological taxonomy. *Pan-Pacific Ent.*, 20: 1–6.

Keilin, D. 1915. Recherches sur les larves de Diptères Cyclorrhaphes. *Bull. Sci. France Belg.*, 49: 15–198.

Keilin, D. 1919. On the life history and larval anatomy of *Melinda cognata* Meig., parasitic in *Helicella virgata* Costa, etc. *Parasitology*, 11: 430–55.

—— 1921*a*. On a new ciliate, *Lambornella stegomyiae* n.g., n.sp., parasitic in the body cavity of the larvae of *Stegomyia scutellaris* Walker (Diptera, Nematocera, Culicidae). *Parasitology*, 13: 216–24.

—— 1921*b*. On a new type of fungus: *Coleomomyces stegomyiae* n.g., n.sp., parasitic in the body cavity of the larva of *Stegomyia scutellaris* Walker (Diptera, Nematocera, Culicidae). *Parasitology*, 13: 225–34.

—— 1944. Respiratory systems and adaptations in Diptera. *Parasitology*, 36: 1–66.

Keilin, D., and C. Baume-Pluvinel. 1913. Formes larvaires et Biologie d'un Cynipide, entomophage, *Eucoila keilini* Kieffer. *Bull. Sci. de la France et Belgique*, 47: 88–104.

Keilin, D., and C. Picado. 1913. Evolution et formes larvaires du *Diachasma crawfordi* n.sp. Braconide parasite d'une Mouche des fruits (*Anastrepha striata* Schin.). *Bull. Sci. de la France et Belgique.*, 47: 203–14.

Keilin, D., and W. R. Thompson. 1915 Sur le cycle évolutif des Pipunculides (Diptères), parasites intracoelomiques des *Typhocybes* (Homoptères). *Soc. de Biol. (Paris) Compt. Rend.*, 78: 9–12.

Kelly, E. O. G. 1914. A new sarcophagid parasite of grasshoppers. *Jour. Agric. Res.*, 2: 435–45.

Kennedy, J. S. 1953. *Host plant selection in Aphididae*. Proc. 9th Internatl. Congr. Ent., Symposia. Pp. 106–13. Dr. W. Junk, Publisher, The Hague, Netherlands.

Kennedy, J. S., and T. E. Mittler. 1953. A method of obtaining phloem sap via the mouth-parts of aphids. *Nature*, 171: 528.

Kenneth, J. H. 1953. *A Dictionary of Scientific Terms: Pronunciation, Derivation, and Definitions of Terms in Biology, Botany Zoology, Anatomy, Cytology, Genetics, Embryology, Physiology*. Fifth Edition. Oliver and Boyd Ltd., Edinburgh, 506 pp.

Kerner, A. 1863. Das Pflanzenleben der Donauländer Innsbruck. [See transl. by Konard, H.S. 1951. The background of plant ecology. Iowa State College Press, Ames, Iowa. 238 pp.]

Kerr, R. W. 1954. Rearing *Drosophila melanogaster* Mg. for insecticide investigations. *Bull. Ent. Res.*, 45: 313–16.

Kerr, T. W., and D. L. McLean. 1956. Biology and control of certain Lathridiidae. *Jour. Econ. Ent.*, 49: 269–70.

Kerrich, G. J. 1936. Notes on larviposition in *Polyblastus* (Hym. Ichn. Tryphaniae). *Proc. Roy. Ent. Soc., London Ser. A.*, 11: 108–10.

—— 1960. The state of our knowledge of the systematics of the Hymenoptera Parasitica, with particular reference to the British fauna. *Trans. Soc. British Ent.*, 14: 1–18.

King, J. C. 1958. Some light on population dynamics provided by lines of *Drosophila melanogaster* selected for resistance to DDT. *Proc. 10th Internatl. Congr. Ent.*, 2: 811–19 (1956).

King, J. L. 1916. Observations on the life history of *Pterodentia flavipes* Gray. *Ann. Ent. Soc. America*, 9: 309–21.

—— 1937. *Methods for rearing tiphiids and scoliids*, pp. 502–8. In Galtsoff et al: *Culture Methods for Invertebrate Animals*. Comstock. Publ. Co., N.Y. 590 pp.

King, J. L., and H. C. Hallock. 1925. A report on certain parasites of *Popillia japonica* Newm. *Jour. Econ. Ent.*, 18: 351–6.

King, J. L., and J. K. Holloway. 1930. *Tiphia popilliavora* Rohwer, a parasite of the Japanese beetle. *U.S. Dept. Agric. Circ.* 145. 11 pp.

King, J. L., and L. B. Parker. 1950. The spring *Tiphia*, an important enemy of the Japanese beetle. *U.S. Dept. Agric., A.R.S., Ser. E* 799. 8 pp.

King, K. M., and N. J. Atkinson. 1928. The biological control factors of the immature stages of *Euxoa ochrogaster* Gn. (Lepidoptera, Phalaenidae) in Saskatchewan. *Ann. Ent. Soc. America*, 21: 167–88.

King, R. L., and A. B. Taylor. 1936 *Malpighamoeba locustae*, n.sp. (Amoebidae), a protozoan parasitic in the malpighian tubes of grasshoppers. *Trans. Amer. Microsc. Soc.*, 55: 6–10.

King, P. B. 1958. *Evolution of Modern Surface Features of Western North America*, pp. 3–60, C. L. Hubbs, editor.

Kirby, W., and W. Spence. 1815. *An Introduction to Entomology*. Longman, Brown, Green and Longmans, London. 285 pp.

—— 1826. *Diseases of insects. Letter (chpt.)* XLIV (pp. 197–232). In *An Introduction to Entomology: or Elements of the Natural History of Insects.* Longman, *et al.*, London. Vol. 4. 634 pp.

—— 1856. *An Introduction to Entomology.* 7th Edition. 607 pp.

Kirkpatrick, T. W. 1937. Studies on the ecology of coffee plantations in East Africa. II. The autecology of *Antestia* spp. (Pentatomidae) with a particular account of a strepsipterous parasite. Part I. The bionomics and control of *Antestia*. *Trans. Roy. Ent. Soc. London*, 86: 247–81.

—— 1947. Notes on a species of Epipyropidae (Lepid.) parasite on *Metaphaena* species (Hemip.: Fulgoridae) at Amani Tanganyika. *Proc. Roy. Ent. Soc. London*, A, 22: 61–4.

Klomp, H. 1958*a*. On the theories of host-parasite interaction. *Arch. Néerland Zool.*, 13: 134–45.

1958*b*. On the synchronization of the generations of the Tachinid *Carcelia obesa* Zett. (*Brutilla* B.B.) and its host *Bupalus piniarius* L. *Zeit. Angew. Ent.*, 42: 210–17.

Knipling, E. F. 1936. A comparative study of the first-instar larvae of the genus *Sarcophaga* (Calliphoridae, Diptera) with notes on the biology. *Jour. Parasitol.*, 22: 417–54.

Knowlton, G. F., C. F. Smith, and F. C. Harmston. 1938. Pea aphid investigations. *Proc. Utah Acad. Sci.*, 15: 71–80.

Koebele, A. 1893. *Studies of Parasitic and Predaceous Insects in New Zealand, Australia and Adjacent Islands.* U.S. Dept. Agric., Govt. Print. Office, Washington D.C. 39 pp.

Koidsumi, K. 1957. Antifungal action of cuticular lipids in insects. *Jour. Insect Physiol.*, 1: 40–51.

Kollar, Vincent. 1837. In *Loudon's Gardner's Magazine*. 1840. (English translation.)

Kornhauser, S. J. 1919. The sexual characteristics of the membracid *Thelia bimaculata* (Fab.). I. External changes induced by *Apelopus theliae* (Gahan). *Jour. Morphol.* 32: 531–635.

Koyama, T. S., S. Yasuda, and S. Ishii. 1951. On the rearing method of rice stem borer by artificial media. *Oyo-Kontyu*, 6: 198–201. In Japanese with English summ.

Kovačević, Z. 1954. Značaj poliedrije za masovnu pojavu nekih insekata. *Zashtita Bilja*, 23: 3–20.

—— 1956. Die Nahrungswahl und das Auftreten der Pflanzenschädlinge. *Anz. Schädlingsk.*, 29: 97–101.

Kovaleva, M. F. 1954. Means of increasing the effectiveness of *Trichogramma* in the campaign against agricultural pests. [In Russian.] *Zoologicheskii Zhurnal*, 33: 77–86.

—— 1957. The effectiveness of Trichogramma in the control of the codling moth. [In Russian.] *Zoologicheskii Zhurnal*, 36; 225–9. Moscow. [*Abs. in R.A.E.*, 47: 146.]

Kramer, J. P. 1959*a*. Some relationships between *Perezia pyraustae* Paillot (Sporozoa, Nosematidae) and *Pyrausta nubilalis* (Hübner) (Lepidoptera, Pyralidae). *Jour. Insect Pathol.*, 1: 25–33.

Kramer, J. P. 1959*b*. Observations on the seasonal incidence of microsporidiosis in European corn borer populations in Illinois. *Entomophaga*, 4: 37–42.

Krassilstschik, I. M. 1888. La production industrielle des parasites végétaux pour la destruction des insectes nuisibles. *Bull. Sci. France Belgique*, 19: 461–72.

Krauss, N. L. H. 1953. Notes on insects associated with lantana in Cuba. *Proc. Hawaiian Ent. Soc.*, 15: 123–5.

Kreokhin, G. 1947. *Subtropical plant pests of Iran and the methods of controlling them.* Dept. Plant Pest Control, Ministry of Agric. Teheran (In Persian). 132 pp.

Krogh, A. 1941. *The Comparative Physiology of Respiratory Mechanisms.* Univ. Penn. Press. Philadelphia, Pa. 172 pp.

Krieg, A. 1956. 'Endogene Virusentstehung' und Latenzproblem bei Insektenviren. *Arch. ges. Virusforsch.*, 6: 472–81.

—— 1957*a*. Über die Möglichkeit einer Bekämpfung des Kohlweisslings (*Pieris brassicae*) durch künstliche Verbreitung einer Bakteriose. *Zeitschr. Pflanzenkrank.*, 64: 321–7.

1957*b*. 'Toleranzphänomen' und Latenzproblem. *Arch. ges. Virusforsch.*, 7: 212–19.

—— 1958. Vergleichende taxonomische, morphologische und serologische Untersuchungen an insekten-pathogenen Rickettsien. *Zeitschr. Naturforsch.*, 13b: 555–7.

—— 1961. *Grundlagen der Insektenpathologie. Viren-, Rickettsien- und Bakterien-Infektionen.* Dr. D. Steinkopff Publisher. Darmstadt. 304 pp.

Kudo, R. R. 1924. A biologic and taxonomic study of the Microsporidia. *Illinois Biol. Monogr.*, 9: 85–344.

Kutter, H. 1934. Weitere Untersuchungen über *Kakothrips robustus* Uzel und *Contarinia pisi* Winn., sowie deren Parasiten, insbesondere *Pirene graminea* Hal. *Mitteil., schweiz. Ent. Ges.*, 16: 1–82.

Kuwana, Inokichi. 1934. Notes on a newly imported parasite of the spiny whitefly attacking citrus in Japan. *Proc. 5th Pac. Sci. Congr.* (5): 3521–3 (1933).

Labeyrie, V. 1957. Remarques sur la mise au point d'un élevage semi-industriel de *Macrocentrus ancylivorus* Roh. *Entomophaga*, 2: 271–81.

Lack, D. 1944. Ecological aspects of species-formation in passerine birds. *Ibis*, 86: 260–86.

—— 1954. *The Natural Regulation of Animal Numbers.* Clarendon Press, Oxford, England. 343 pp.

Laing, J. 1937. Host-finding by insect parasites. 1. Observations on the finding of hosts by *Alysia manducator*, *Mormoniella vitripennis*, and *Trichogramma evanescens*. *Jour. Animal Ecol.*, 6: 298–317.

Laird, Marshall. 1959. Biological solutions to problems arising from the use of modern insecticides in the field of public health. *Acta Tropica*, 16: 331–55.

—— 1960. Microbiology and mosquito control. *Mosquito News*, 20: 127–33.

Lal, K. B. 1934. Insect parasites of Psyllidae. *Parasitology*, 26: 325–34.

Lal, Rattan, and Ejazul Hague. 1955. Effect of nutrition under controlled conditions of temperatures and humidity on longevity and fecundity of *Sphaerophoria scuttellaris*. Efficacy of its maggots as aphid predators. *Indian Jour. Ent.*, 17: 317–20.

Lamborn, W. A. 1915. Second report on *Glossina* investigations in Nyasaland. *Bul. Ent. Res.*, 6: 249–65.

—— 1921. A protozoan pathogenic to mosquito larvae. *Parasitology*, 13: 213.

Lamore, D. H. 1960. Cases of parasitism of the basilica spider, *Allepeira lemniscafa* (Walckenaer), by the dipteran endoparasite, *Ogcodes dispar* (Macq.). *Proc. Ent. Soc. Wash.*, 62: 65–85.

Landis, B. J., and N. F. Howard. 1940. *Paradexodes epilachnae*, a tachinid parasite of the Mexican bean beetle. *U.S. Dept. Agric. Tech. Bull.* 721. 31 pp.

Langford, G. S., R. H. Vincent, and E. N. Cory. 1942. The adult Japanese beetle as host and disseminator of type A milky disease. *Jour. Econ. Ent.*, 35: 165–9.

La Rivers, I. 1949. Entomic nematode literature from 1926 to 1946. Exclusive of medical and veterinary titles. *The Wasmann Collector*, 7: 177–206.

Larson, A. O., and C. K. Fisher. 1924. Longevity and fecundity of *Bruchus quadrimaculatus* Fab. as influenced by different foods. *Jour. Agric. Res.*, 29: 297–305.

Lathrop, G. H., and R. C. Newton. 1933. The biology of *Opius melleus* Gahan, a parasite of the blueberry maggot. *Jour. Agric. Res.*, 46: 143–60.

Latreille, P. A. 1805. *Histoire naturelle, générale et particulière des crustacés et des insectes.* F. Dufart, Paris, 14. 432 pp.

Lawson, F. A. 1954. Observation on the biology of *Comperia merceti* (Compere), (Hymenoptera: Encyrtidae). *Jour. Kansas Ent. Soc.*, 27: 128–42.

Lawson, F. R. 1958. Some features of the relation of insects to their ecosystems. *Ecology*, 39: 515–21.

Lawson, F. R., J. C. Chamberlin, and G. T. York. 1951. Dissemination of the beet leafhopper in California. *U.S. Dept. Agric. Tech. Bull.* 1030. 59 pp.

Lawson, F. R., R. L. Rabb, F. E. Guthrie, and T. G. Bowery. 1961. Studies of an integrated control system for hornworms on tobacco. *Jour. Econ. Ent.*, 54: 93–7.

LeBaron, Dr. Wm. 1870. The chalcideous parasite of the apple-tree Bark-louse (*Chalcis* [*Aphelinus*] *mytilaspidis*, n.sp.*). *Amer. Ent. and Bot.*, 2: 360–2.

Leclercq, J., N. Magis, and C. Rey. 1954. Sur les besoins nutritifs du *Gnathocerus cornutus* F. Recherche de l'optimum glucidique et de l'optimum protidique dans un régime alimentaire artificiel. *Arch. Internatl. Physiol.*, 62: 264–71.

Le Corroller, Y. 1958. A propos de la transformation de souches banales de *B. cereus* Frank. et Frank. en souches cristallophores pathogènes pour les insectes. *Ann. Inst. Pasteur* [*Paris*], 94: 670–73.

Lees, A. D. 1955. *The Physiology of Diapause in Arthropods.* Cambridge Univ. Press. 151 pp.

—— 1956. The physiology and biochemistry of diapause. *Ann. Rev. Ent.*, 1: 1–16.

Leiby, R. W. 1922. The polyembryonic development of *Copidosoma gelechiae*, with notes on its biology. *Jour. Morphol.*, 37: 195–285.

—— 1929. Polyembryony in insects. *Trans. Fourth Internatl. Congr. Ent.*, 2: 873–87 (1928).

Leiby, R. W., and C. C. Hill. 1923. The twinning and monembryonic development of *Platygaster heimalis*, a parasite of the Hessian fly. *Jour. Agric. Res.*, 25: 337–50.

—— 1924. The polyembryonic development of *Platygaster vernalis*. *Jour. Agric. Res.*, 28: 829–40.

Lennox, F. G. 1939. Studies of the physiology and toxicology of blow-flies. I. The development of a synthetic medium for aseptic cultivation of larvae of *Lucilia cuprina*. *Council Sci. and Industrial Res. Pamphlet* 90. 24 pp. Melbourne, Australia.

le Pelley, R. H. 1934. Report on questionnaire on *Antestia* control 1933–34. *Colony and Protectorate of Kenya, Dept. Agric. Bull.*, 5. 32 pp.

le Pelley, R. 1951. Annual report of the senior entomologist, 1950. *Ann. Rept. Dept. Agric. Kenya (1950)*, 2: 60–70.

—— 1955. Annual report of the senior entomologist, 1954. *Ann. Rept. Dept. Agric. Kenya (1954)*, 2: 1–12.

Lever, R. J. A. W. 1943. Entomological services in Fiji. *Fiji Dept. Agric. Jour.*, 14: 92–7.

Levin, M. D., and M. H. Haydak. 1958. Comparative value of different pollens in the nutrition of *Osmia lignaria* Say. *Proc. Tenth Internatl. Congr. Ent.*, 4: 1079–84 (1956).

Levine, M., and H. W. Schoenlein. 1930. *A Compilation of Culture Media for the Cultivation of Microorganisms.* Williams and Wilkins Co. Baltimore. 969 pp.

Levinson, Z. H. 1955. Nutritional requirements of insects. *Rev. Parasitol.*, 16: 113–38, 183–204.

Lewallen, L. L. 1954. Biological and toxicological studies of the little housefly. *Jour. Econ. Ent.*, 47: 1137–41.

Lewis, F. B. 1960. Factors affecting assessment of parasitization by *Apanteles fumiferanae* Vier. and *Glypta fumiferanae* (Vier.) on spruce budworm larvae. *Canadian Ent.*, 92: 881–91.

Lewis L. F., and W. C. Rothenbuhler. 1961. Resistance to American foulbrood in honey bees: III. Differential survival of the two kinds of larvae from two-drone matings. *Jour. Insect Pathol.*, 3: 197–215.

L'Heritier, Ph. 1958. The hereditary virus of *Drosophila*. In *Advances in Virus Research*, 5: 195–245.

Lichtenstein, J. L. 1920. Le parasitisme d'*Aphiochaeta* (*Phora*) *fasciata* Fallen. [*Paris*] *Acad. des Sci. Compt. Rend.*, 170: 531–4.

—— 1921. Le déterminisme de la ponte chez un chalcidien, *Habrocytus cionicida*. *Compt. Rend. Acad. Sci.*, 173: 1416–17.

Lindroth, C. H. 1957. *The Faunal Connections Between Europe and North America*. John Wiley & Sons, Inc., New York. 344 pp.

Linsley, E. G. 1944. The naming of infra-specific categories. *Ent. News*, 55: 225–32.

—— 1958. *Geographical origins and phylogenetic affinities of the cerambycid beetle fauna of western North America*, pp. 299–320. In *Zoogeography*, C. L. Hubbs, editor. American Assoc. Adv. Sci. Publ. 51, 509 pp.

Linsley, E. G., and J. W. MacSwain. 1941. The bionomics of *Ptinus californicus* a de-predator in the nests of bees. *Bull. So. Calif. Acad. Sci.*, 40: 126–37.

—— 1942. The parasites, predators and inquiline associate of *Anthophora linsleyi*. *Amer. Midland Nat.*, 27: 402–17.

—— 1943. Observations on the life history of *Trichodes ornatus* (Coleoptera, Cleridae), a larval predator in the nests of bees and wasps. *Ann. Ent. Soc. America*, 26: 589–601.

—— 1946. Longevity of *Trichodes* and *Pelonium* larvae. *Pan-Pacific Ent.*, 22: 18.

—— 1952. Notes on the biology and host relationships of some species of *Nemognatha* (Coleoptera: Meloidae). *Wasmann Jour. Biol.*, 10: 91–102.

—— 1955. Two new species of *Plega* from Mexico (Neuroptera, Mantispidae). *Pan. Pacific Ent.*, 31: 15–19.

—— 1957. Observations on the habits of *Stylops pacifica* Bohart. *Univ. Calif. Pub. Ent.*, 11: 395–430.

Linsley, E. G., J. W. MacSwain, and R. F. Smith. 1952a. The bionomics of *Diadasia consociata* Timberlake and some biological relationships of emphorine and antho-phorine bees. *Univ. California Pub. Ent.*, 9: 267–90.

—— 1952b. The life history and development of *Rhipiphorus smithi* with notes on their phylogenetic significance (Coleoptera, Rhipiphoridae). *Univ. California Pub. Ent.*, 9: 291–314.

Lipa, J. J. 1957. Observations on development and pathogenicity of the parasite of *Aporia crataegi* L. (Lepidoptera)—*Nosema aporiae* n. sp. *Acta Parasitol. Polonica*, 5: 559–84.

Lipke, H., and G. Fraenkel. 1956. Insect nutrition. *Ann. Rev. Ent.*, 1: 17–44.

Liu Chung-Lo. 1959. Contribution to generic definition of *Telenomus* by two new Chinese species. *Acta Soc. Ent. Chechoslovenical*, 56: 155–60.

Lloyd, J. T. 1919. An aquatic Dipterous parasite, *Ginglymyia acrirostris* Towns., and additional notes on its Lepidopterous host, *Elphila fulicalis*. *Jour. N.Y. Ent. Soc.*, 27: 263–5.

Lloyd, D. C. 1938. A study of some factors governing the choice of hosts and distribution of progeny by the chalcid *Ooencyrtus kuvanae* Howard. *Phil. Trans. Roy. Soc. London, Ser. B : Biol. Sci.*, **229**: 275–322.

—— 1940. Host selection by hymenopterous parasites of the moth *Plutella maculipennis* Curtis. *Proc. Roy. Soc. London Ser. B.: Biol. Sci.*, **128**: 451–84.

—— 1951. A survey for grasshopper parasites in temperate South America. *Canadian Ent.*, **83**: 213–30.

—— 1952. Biological observations on some thinnids of western Patagonia. *Bull. Ent. Res.*, **42**: 707–19.

—— 1956. Studies of parasite oviposition behaviour. I. *Mastrus carpocapsae* Cushman (Hymenoptera: Ichneumonidae). *Canadian Ent.*, **88**: 80–9.

—— 1958. Studies of parasite oviposition behavior. II. *Leptomastix dactylopii* Howard (Hymenoptera, Encyrtidae). *Canadian Ent.*, **90**: 450–61.

Löcher, F. G. 1958. Der Einfluss von Dichlordiphenyltrichlormethylmethane (DDT) auf einige Tetranychiden (Acari, Tetranychidae). *Zeit. eng. Zool.*, **45**: 201–48.

Loeb, J. 1915. The simplest constituents required for growth and the completion of the life cycle in an insect (*Drosphila*). *Science*, **41**: 169–70.

Long, D. B. 1958. Observations on oviposition in the wheat bulbfly, *Leptohylemyia coarctata*. *Bull. Ent. Res.*, **49**: 355–66.

Lord, F. T. 1956. The influence of spray programs on the fauna of apple orchards in Nova Scotia. IX. Studies on means of altering predator populations. *Canadian Ent.*, **88**: 129–37.

Lord, F. T., and A. W. MacPhee. 1953. The influence of spray programs on the fauna of apple orchards in Nova Scotia. VI. Low temperatures and the natural control of the oystershell scale, *Lepidosaphes ulmi* (L.) (Homoptera:Coccidae). *Canadian Ent.*, **85**: 282–91.

Lotka, A. J. 1923. Contribution to the mathematical theory of capture. I. Conditions for capture. *Proc. Natl. Acad. Sci.*, **18**: 172.

—— 1925. *Elements of Physical Biology*. Baltimore, Williams and Wilkins. 460 pp.

Lotmar, R. 1941. Die Polyederkrankheit der Kleidermotte (*Tineola biselliella*). *Mitteil. schweiz. Ent. Ges.*, **18**: 372–3.

Love, R. M. 1959. New frontiers in range improvement. *Proc. Grassland Council, Tulsa, Okla.* January 1959. Pp. 7–20.

Lower, H. F. 1954. A morphological interpretation of postembryonic insect development. *Arch. Zool. Exptl. et Gen Notes et Revue*, **91**: 51–72.

Lucchese, E. 1941. Contributi alla conoscenza dei Lepidotteri del melo. III *Acroclita naevana* Hb. *Bol. R. Lab. di Ent. Agrar., Portici*, **5**: 1–60.

Luckey, T. D. 1954. A single diet for all living organisms. *Science*, **120**: 396–8.

Lukefahr, M., and J. A. Griffin, 1956. The effects of food on the longevity and fecundity of pink bollworm moths. *Jour. Econ. Ent.*, **49**: 876–7.

Lund, H. O. 1934. Some temperature and humidity relations of two races of *Trichogramma minutum* Riley (Hym. Chalcididae). *Ann. Ent. Soc. America*, **27**: 324–40.

Lund, H. O., and R. J. Bushnell. 1939. The relation of nutritional levels to the growth of populations of *Tribolium confusum*. II. Egg production in patent flour and in patent flour supplemented with yeast. *Jour. Econ. Ent.*, **32**: 640–2.

Lundgren, D. G., and R. T. Russell. 1956. An air-lift laboratory fermentor. *Appl. Microbiol.*, **4**: 31–3.

Lung, C. T., Y. P. Wang, and P. G. Tang. 1960. Investigations on the biology and utilization of *Aphelinus mali* Hald., the specific parasite of the woolly apple aphis, *Eriosoma lanigerum* Hausm. [In Chinese with English summ.] *Acta Ent. Sinica*, **10**: 1–39.

Lysenko, O. 1958a. Contribution to the taxonomy *Coccobacillus acridiorum* d'Herelle. *Folia Biol. (Prague)*, 4: 342–47.

—— 1958b. *Catalogue of strains of bacteria deposited in the collection of the Laboratory.* Czechoslovak Academy of Sciences, Institute of Biology, Laboratory of Insect Pathology, Prag. February, 1958; Supplement, July, 1958.

Lysenko, O., and K. Slama. 1959. The relation between oxygen consumption and bacterial infection in sawflies. *Jour. Insect Pathol.*, 1: 184–8.

MacArthur, R. 1955. Fluctuations of animal populations and a measure of community stability. *Ecology*, 36: 533–6.

MacArthur, W. P. 1922. A holotrichus ciliate pathogenic to *Theobaldia annulata* Schrank. *Jour. Roy. Army Med. Corps*, 38: 83–92.

MacDonald, D. R. 1959. Biological assessment of aerial forest spraying against spruce budworm in New Brunswick. III. Effects on two overwintering parasites. *Canadian Ent.*, 91: 330–6.

MacGinitie, H. D. 1958. *Climate since the late cretaceous*, pp. 60–81. In *Zoogeography*, C. L. Hubbs, editor. *American Assoc. Adv. Sci. Publ.* 51, 509 pp.

Machay, M. L. 1957. About the ovarial transmission of the *Nosema bombycis* Naegeli. *Acta Veterinaria Acad. Sci. Hungary*, 7: 11–18.

Machiavelli, N. 1521. *History of Florence.* Transl. by C. E. Detmold. Boston, Osgood. 1882. (Orig. ed. 1521–25).

MacKenzie, J. M. D. 1951. Control of forest populations. *Quart. Jour. Forest.*, 42: 95–102.

Mackerras, M. J. 1933. Observations on the life histories, nutritional requirements and fecundity of blow-flies. *Bull. Ent. Res.*, 24: 353–62.

MacLellan, C. R. 1958. Role of woodpeckers in control of the codling moth in Nova Scotia. *Canadian Ent.*, 90: 18–22.

MacLeod, D. M. 1954a. Investigations on the genera *Beauveria* Vuill. and *Tritirachium* Limber. *Canadian Jour. Bot.*, 32: 818–90.

—— 1954b. Natural and cultural variation in entomogenous Fungi, Imperfecti. *Ann. New York Acad. Sci.*, 60: 58–70.

—— 1959a. Nutritional studies on the genus *Hirsutella*. I. Growth response in an enriched liquid medium. *Canadian Jour. Bot.*, 37: 695–714.

—— 1959b. Nutritional studies on the genus *Hirsutella*. II. Nitrogen utilization in a synthetic medium. *Canadian Jour. Bot.*, 37: 819–34.

MacSwain, J. W. 1956. A classification of the first instar larvae of the Meloidae (Coleoptera). *Univ. California Publ. Ent.*, 12: 1–182.

Maeda, S., K. S. Hagen, and G. L. Finney. 1953. Artificial media and the control of microorganisms in the culture of tephritid larvae (Diptera: Tephritidae). *Proc. Hawaiian Ent. Soc.*, 15: 177–85.

Maestri, A. 1856. *Frammenti anatomici, fisiologici e pathologici sul baco da seta (Bombyx mori* Linn.). Fratelli Fusi, Pavia. 172 pp.

Malenotti, E. 1948. La *Prospaltella berlesei* How. *Italia Agric.*, 85: 729–35.

Mally, C. W. 1916. On the selection and breeding of desirable strains of beneficial insects. *S. African Jour. Sci., Cape Town*, 13: 191–5.

Malthus, T. R. 1803. *An Essay on the Principle of Population as It Affects the Future Improvement of Society.* London, J. Johnson. 2nd ed. 610 pp.

Maple, J. D. 1937. The biology of *Ooencyrtus johnsoni* (Howard) and the role of the egg shell in the respiration of certain encyrtid larvae (Hymenoptera). *Ann. Ent. Soc. America*, 30: 123–54.

—— 1947. The eggs and first instar larvae of Encyrtidae and their morphological adaptation for respiration. *Univ. California Publ. Ent.*, 8: 25–122.

Marchal, P. 1898. Le cycle évolutif de l'*Encyrtus fusicollis*. *Bull. Soc. Ent. de France (1898)*: 109–11.

—— 1904. Recherches sur la biologie et le développement des hyménoptères parasites. I. La Polyembryonie spécifique ou germinogonie. *Arch. de Zool. Exp. et Gen.*, 2: 257–335.

—— 1905. Observations biologiques sur un parasite de la galeruque de L'orme, le *Tetrastichus xanthomelaenae* (Rond.). *Bull. Ent. Soc. France (1905)*: 64–8.

—— 1906. Recherches sur la biologie et le développement des Hyménoptères parasites. Les Platygasters. *Arch. Zool. Exp. et Gen. IV ser 4*: 485–640.

—— 1908. The utilization of auxiliary entomophagous insects in the struggle against insects injurious to agriculture. *Ann. Inst. Natl. Agron.* English translation 1908. In: *Pop. Sci. Mon.*, 72: 352–70, 406–19.

—— 1927a. Contribution à l'étude génotypique et phénotypique des Trichogrammes. *Compt. Rend. Acad. Sci.*, 185: 489–93.

—— 1927b. Les lignées naturelles de Trichogrammes. *Compt. Rend. Acad. Sci.*, 185: 521–3.

—— 1936. Recherches sur la biologie et le développement des Hyménoptères parasites: les Trichogrammes. *Ann. Epiphyties, Paris* 2 (n.ser.): 447–550.

Marcovitch, S. 1958. Some climatic relations of armyworm outbreaks. *Jour. Tennessee Acad. Sci.*, 33: 348–50.

Marion, A. F. 1880. *Application du sulfure de carbone au traitement des vignes phylloxérées.* Rapport sur les travaux de l'année 1879. Vol. 4. Compagnie des Chemins de Fer de Paris à Lyon et à la Méditerranée. Paul Dupont, Paris. 118 pp.

Marlatt, C. L. 1901. *The Scale Insect and Mite Enemies of Citrus Trees.* U.S. Dept. Agric. Yearbook (1900). Pp. 247–90.

Marlowe, R. H. 1934. An artificial food medium for the Mediterranean fruit fly (*Ceratitis capitata*). *Jour. Econ. Ent.*, 28: 1100.

Marshall, J. 1953. A decade of pest control in British Columbia orchards. *Proc. Ent. Soc. Brit. Columbia*, 49: 7–11.

Martignoni, M. E. 1957. Contributo alla conoscenza di una granulosi di *Eucosma griseana* (Hübner) (Tortricidae, Lepidoptera) quale fattore limitante il pullulamento dell'insetto nella Engadina alta. *Mitteil. schweiz. Anst. forst. Versuchswesen*, 32: 371–418.

—— 1959. Preparation of glass needles for microinjection. *Jour. Insect Path.* 1: 294–6.

—— 1960. Problems of insect tissue culture. *Experentia*, 16: 125–8.

Martignoni M. E., and C. Auer. 1957. Bekämpfungsversuch gegen *Eucosma griseana* (Hübner) (Lepidoptera, Tortricidae) mit einem Granulosis-Virus. *Mitteil. schweiz. Anst. forst. Versuchswesen*, 33: 73–93.

Martignoni, M. E., and R. L. Langston. 1960. Supplement to an annotated list and bibliography of insects reported to have virus diseases. *Hilgardia*, 30: 1–40.

Martignoni, M. E., and J. E. Milstead. 1962. Trans-ovum transmission of the nuclear polyhedrosis virus of *Colias eurytheme* Boisduval through contamination of the female genitalia. *Jour. Insect Pathol.* 4: 113–21.

Martignoni, M. E., and R. J. Scallion. 1961a. Multiplication *in vitro* of a nuclear polyhedrosis virus in insect amoebocytes. *Nature*, 190: 1133–4.

—— 1961b. Preparation and uses of insect hemocyte monolayers *in vitro*. *Biol. Bull.*, 121: 507–20.

Martignoni, M. E., and P. Schmid. 1961. Studies on the resistance to virus infections in natural populations of Lepidoptera. *Jour. Insect Pathol.*, 3: 62–74.

Martin, C. H., and G. L. Finney. 1946. Factors involved in the separation of *Macrocentrus ancylivorus* cocoons from tuber worm pupae. *Jour. Econ. Ent.*, 39: 29–35.

Martin, F. 1914. Zur Entwicklungsgeschichte des polyembryonalen Chalcidiers *Ageniaspis (Encyrtus) fuscicollis* Dalm. Ph.D. *Dissertation Zool. Inst. Univ. Leipzig*, pp. 419–79.

Martin, J. C. 1956. A taxonomic revision of the Triaspidine Braconid wasps of Nearctic America (Hymenoptera). *Canada Dept. of Agric., Ottawa Pub.* 965.

Martin, P. S. 1958. *Pleistocene ecology and biogeography of North America*, pp. 375–420. In *Zoogeography*, C. L. Hubbs, editor. *American Assoc. Adv. Sci. Publ.* 51, 509 pp.

Martouret, D., and G. Dusaussoy. 1959. Multiplication et extraction des corps d'inclusion de la virose intestinale de *Thaumetopoea pityocampa* Schiff. *Entomophaga*, 4: 253–9.

Marucci, P. E., and D. W. Clancy. 1950. The artificial culture of fruit flies and their parasites. *Proc. Hawaiian Ent. Soc.*, 14: 163–6.

Masera, E. 1934. Esperimenti moderni di lotta biologica agli insetti e conoscenze attuali sulle loro malattie batteriche. *L'Italia Agricola*, 71: 949–53. (Also in *Annu. Staz. bacol. sper. Padova, 1936*, 48: 351–9.)

—— 1935. Contributo allo studio della virulenza e patogenicità di alcuni entomomiceti. *Annu. Staz. bacol. sper. Padova*, 48: 477–91.

—— 1937. L'andamento della concentrazione idrogenionica nei terreni di coltura durante lo sviluppo di miceti. *Annu. Staz. bacol. sper. Padova*, 49: 220–31.

—— 1948. Rapporti fra *Apanteles glomeratus* Reinh. e *Pieris brassicae* L. infette di pebrina. *Actes 7 Internatl. Seric. Congr.*: 551–5.

—— 1954. Sul contenuto microbico intestinale del baco da seta e sull'etiologia della flaccidezza. *Agricoltura delle Venezie*, 8: 714–35.

—— 1957. Transmissione delle nosemiasi degli insetti al baco da seta. *L'Agricoltura italiana*, 57 (12 n.s.) 8 pp.

Mason, A. C. 1934. Some methods for shipping, feeding and rearing fruit-fly parasites. *Jour. Econ. Ent.*, 27: 891–6.

Mason, W. R. M. 1956. A revision of the Nearctic Cteniscini (Hymenoptera: Ichneumonidae). *Canadian Jour. Zool.*, 34: 120–51.

Matheson, R., and A. G. Ruggles. 1907. The structure of the silk glands of *Apanteles glomeratus* L. *The American Naturalist*, 41: 567–85.

Matsumoto, Y. 1954. An aseptic rearing of the oriental fruit moth, *Grapholitha molesta* Busck, on synthetic food media. *Ber. Chara Inst. Kuraschiki*, 10: 66–71.

Mattes, O. 1927. Parasitäre Krankheiten der Mehlmottenlarven und Versuche über ihre Verwendbarkeit als biologisches Bekämpfungsmittel. *Sitzungsber. Ges. Bedförder. Ges. Naturw. Marburg*, 62: 381–417.

Matuka, St. 1959. Importance de la nourriture larvaire dans l'étiologie de la Loque américaine. *Bulletin Apicole*, 2: 46.

Maurizio, A. 1954. Pollenernährung und Lebensvorgänge bei der Honigbiene (*Apis mellifica* L.). *Landw. Jahrbuch der Schweiz*, 68: 115–82.

Maw, M. G., and H. C. Coppel. 1953. Studies on dipterous parasites of the spruce budworm, *Choristoneura fumiferana* (Clem.). II. *Phryxe pecosensis* (Tns.). *Canadian Jour. Zool.*, 31: 392–403.

Maxwell, D. E. 1955. The comparative internal larval anatomy of sawflies (Hymenoptera: Symphyta). *Canadian Ent.*, 87, Supplement 1. 132 pp.

Maybee, G. E. 1955. Observations, life-history, immature stages, and rearing of *Loxotropa tritoma* (Thoms.) (Hymenoptera: Proctotrupoidea) a parasite of the carrot rust fly, *Psila rosae* (F.) (Diptera: Psilidae). *Ann. Rept. Ent. Soc. Ontario*, 86: 53–8.

Mayer, K. 1955. Das *Trichogramma* Problem. *Nachrichtenbl. deutsch. Pflanzenschutz.*, 7: 131–3.

Mayr, E. 1942. *Systematics and the Origin of Species from the Point of View of a Zoologist.* Columbia Univ. Press, New York, 334 pp.

—— 1947. Ecological factors in speciation. *Evolution*, 1: 263–88.

—— 1948. The bearing of new systematics on genetical problems. The nature of species. *Advances in Genetics*, 2: 205–37.

—— 1954. *Change of genetic environment and evolution*, pp. 157–180. In *Evolution as a Process*, J. S. Huxley, A. C. Hardy, and E. B. Ford, editors. George Allen and Unwin Ltd., London, 367 pp.

—— 1957a. The Species Problem. *Amer. Assoc. Adv. Sci. Publ.* 50, 395 pp. (Editor).

—— 1957b. *Species concepts and definitions*, pp. 1–22. In *The Species Problem. Amer. Assoc. Adv. Sci. Publ.* 50, 395 pp.

—— 1957c. *Difficulties and Importance of the Biological Species*, pp. 371–88. In *The Species Problem*, E. Mayr, editor. *Amer. Assoc. Adv. Sci. Publ.* 50, 395 pp.

—— 1958. *Behavior and systematics*, pp. 341–62. In *Behavior and Evolution*, Roe and Simpson, editors. Yale Univ. Press, 557 pp.

Mayr, E., E. G. Linsley, and R. L. Usinger. 1953. *Methods and Principles of Systematic Zoology.* McGraw-Hill Book Co., Inc., New York, 328 pp.

McAtee, W. L. 1940. *A venture in song bird management. Jour. Wildlife Management*, 4: 85–9.

McClanahan, R. J., and L. A. Miller. 1958. Laboratory rearing of the seed-corn maggot, *Hylemya cilicrura* (Rond.). *Canadian Ent.*, 90: 372–4.

McColloch, J. W. 1923. The Hessian fly in Kansas. Kansas State Agric. *Coll., Agric. Expt. Sta. Tech. Bull.* 11. 96 pp.

McConnell, E., and A. G. Richards. 1959. The production by *Bacillus thuringiensis* Berliner of heat-stable substance toxic for insects. *Canadian Jour. Microbiol.*, 5: 161–8.

McCook, H. 1882. Ants as beneficial insecticides. *Proc. Acad. Nat. Sci. Philadelphia*, pp. 263–71.

McCoy, E. E., and C. W. Carver. 1941. A method for obtaining spores of the fungus *Beauveria bassiana* (Bals.) Vuill. in quantity. *Jour. New York Ent. Soc.*, 49: 205–10.

McCoy, E. E., and H. B. Girth. 1938. The culture of *Neoaplectana glaseri* on veal pulp. *New Jersey Dept. Agric. Bur. Plant Indust. Circ.* 285. 12 pp.

McCoy, E. E., and R. W. Glaser. 1936. Nematode culture for Japanese beetle control. *New Jersey Dept. Agric. Bur. Plant Indust. Circ.* 265. 9 pp.

McEwen, F. L., and G. E. R. Hervey. 1958. Control of the cabbage looper with a virus disease. *Jour. Econ. Ent.*, 51: 626–31.

—— 1959a. Microbial control of two cabbage insects. *Jour. Insect Path.*, 1: 86–94.

—— 1959b. And now—'living' insecticide. *Farm Res., New York Agric. Expt. Sta.*, 25: 8–9.

McGuire Jr., J. V., and W. W. Wirth. 1958. The discriminant function in taxonomic research. *Proc. 10th Internatl. Congr. Ent. (1956)*, 1: 387–93.

McKeown, K. C., and V. H. Mincham. 1948. The biology of an Australian Mantispid (*Mantispa vittata* Guerin). *Australian Zool. Jour.*, 11: 207–24.

McLeod, J. H. 1938. The control of the greenhouse whitefly in Canada by the parasite *Encarsia formosa* Gahan. *Sci. Agric., Ottawa*, 18: 529–35.

—— 1951. Biological control investigations in British Columbia. *Proc. Ent. Soc. Brit. Columbia*, 47: 27–36.

—— 1954. Statuses of some introduced parasites and their hosts in British Columbia. *Proc. Ent. Soc. British Columbia*, 50: 19–27.

McLimans, W. F., F. E. Giardinello, E. V. Davis, C. J. Kucera, and G. W. Rake. 1957. Submerged culture of mammalian cells: the five liter fermentor. *Jour. Bact.*, 74: 768–74.

Meier, N. F. 1940. The theoretical basis of the biological control method against injurious insects. (In Russian.) *Bull. Plant Prot.*, Leningrad No. 1–2, 143–52. [*RAE*. A. 30: 144].

Meijere, J. C. H. de, 1904. Beiträge zur Kenntnis der Biologie und der systematischen Verwandtschaft der Conopiden. *Tijdschr. Ent.*, 46: 144–224.

—— 1912. Neue Beiträge zur Kenntnis der Conopiden. *Tijdschr. Ent.*, 55: 184–207.

—— 1916. Beiträge zur Kenntnis der Dipterenlarven und-puppen. *Zool. Jahrb. Syst.*, 40: 177–322.

Mellini, E. 1956. Studi sui Ditteri Larvevoridi. III. *Sturmia bella* Meig. su *Inachis io* L. (Lepidoptera Nymphalidae). *Boll. Inst. Ent. Univ. Bologna*, 22: 70–98.

—— 1957. Studi sui Ditteri Larvevoridi. IV. *Ptilosina nitens* Zett., parassita di *Plagiodera versicolar* Laich. (Coleoptera: Chrysomelidae). *Boll. Inst. Ent. Univ. Bologna*, 22: 135–76.

—— 1958. Nozioni sulla lotta biologica contro gli Insetti dannosi all'Agricoltura. *Osser. Fitopat. Inst. Ent. Univ. Bologna.*, 11: 1–27.

—— 1959. Studi sui Ditteri Larvevoridi. V. *Macquartia chalconota* Meig. su *Chrysomela fastuosa* Scop. (Coleoptera: Chrysomelidae). *Boll. Inst. Ent. Univ. Bologna*, 23: 1–34.

Melvin, R., and R. C. Bushland. 1940. The nutritional requirements of screw-worm larvae. *Jour. Econ. Ent.*, 33: 850–2.

Menozzi, C. 1927. Contributo alla biologia della *Phalacrotophora fasciata* Fall. Parassita di coccinellidi. *Soc. Ent. Ital. Bol.*, 59: 72–8.

Merrian, C. H. 1894. Laws of temperature control of the geographic distribution of terrestrial animals and plants. *Natl. Geogr. Mag.*, 6: 229–38.

Mesnil, L. 1939. *Essai sur les Tachinaires (Larvaevoridae) Monographies stat. et Lab. de Recher.* Agronomiques, Paris, 66 pp.

—— 1950. Larvaevorinae (Tachininae). In Lindner: Die Fliegen der Palaearktischen Region, 164: 105–60. E. Schweizerbart, Stuttgart.

—— 1953. 'Monograph of the Palaeardk Tachinids.' *Lindner, Fasc.*, 172, pp. 257–304.

—— 1955. Larvaevorinae (Tachininae). In Lindner: Die Fliegen der Palaearktischen Region, 186: 417–64. E. Schweizerbart, Stuttgart.

—— 1956. Larvaevorinae (Tachininae). In Lindner: Die Fliegen der Palaearktischen Region, 192: 513–60. E. Schweizerbart, Stuttgart.

Messenger, P. S. 1959. Bioclimatic studies with insects. *Ann. Rev. Ent.*, 4: 183–206.

Messenger, P. S., and N. E. Flitters. 1954. Bioclimatic studies of three species of fruit flies in Hawaii. *Jour. Econ. Ent.*, 47: 756–65.

—— 1957. Bioclimatic studies of the Mexican fruit fly. *Calif. Avocado Soc. Yearbook*, 41: 119–27.

Métalnikov, S., and S. S. Métalnikov. 1935. Utilisation des microbes dans la lutte contre les insectes nuisibles. *Ann. Inst. Pasteur [Paris]*, 55: 709–60.

Metcalf, M. M. 1929. Parasites and the aid they give in problems of taxonomy, geographical distribution and palaeogeography. *Smithsonian Misc. Coll.*, 81: 1–36.

Metcalf, Robert L. 1957. The role of systemic insecticides in world agriculture. *Proc. 2nd Internatl. Conf. Plant Protection, Fernhurst, England (1956)*. Butterworth Sci. Publ. 1957. pp. 129–42.

—— 1959. The impact of the development of organophosphorus insecticides upon basic and applied science. *Bull. Ent. Soc. America*, 5: 3–15.

Metchnikoff, E. 1879. *Diseases of the larvae of the grain weevil. Insects harmful to agriculture* (*series*). *Issue III. The grain weevil.* Published by the Commission attached to the Odessa Zemstvo Office for the investigation of the problem of insects harmful to agriculture. Odessa. 32 pp. (In Russian; seen in translation only.)

—— 1880. Zur Lehre über Insectenkrankheiten. *Zool. Anz.*, 3: 44–7.

Meyer, N. F., and Z. A. Meyer. 1946. The formation of biological forms in *Chrysopa vulgaris* Schr. (Neuroptera, Chrysopidae). *Zool. Zhurnal, Moscow*, 25: 115–20.

Michelbacher, A. E. 1940. Effect of *Bathyplectes curculionis* on the alfalfa-weevil population in lowland middle California. *Hilgardia*, 13: 81–99.

—— 1954. Natural control of insect pests. *Jour. Econ. Ent.*, 47: 192–4.

Michelbacher, A. E., W. M. Hoskins, and W. B. Herms. 1932. The nutrition of flesh fly larvae, *Lucilia sericata* (Meig.). *Jour. Exptl. Zool.*, 64: 109–31.

Michelbacher, A. E., and W. W. Middlekauff. 1950. Control of the melon aphid in northern California. *Jour. Econ. Ent.*, 43: 444–7.

Michelbacher, A. E., and R. F. Smith. 1943. Some natural factors limiting the abundance of the alfalfa butterfly. *Hilgardia*, 15: 369–97.

Michener, C. D. 1953a. Comparative morphological and systematic studies of bee larvae with a key to the families of hymenopterous larvae. *Univ. Kansas Sci. Bull.*, 35: 987–1102.

—— 1953b. Life history studies in insect systematics. *Systematic Zool.*, 2: 112–18.

—— 1957. Some bases for higher categories in classification. *Systematic Zool.*, 6: 160–73.

—— 1958. Morphologically meaningful vs. descriptive terminologies for use by taxonomists, with comments on interordinal homologies of male genitalia. *Proc. 10th Internatl. Congr. Ent.*, 1: 583–6 (1956).

Micks, D. W. 1956. Paper chromatography in insect taxonomy. *Ann. Ent. Soc. America*, 49: 576–81.

Micks, D. W., and F. J. Gibson. 1957. The characterization of insects and ticks by their free amino acid patterns. *Ann. Ent. Soc. America*, 50: 500–5.

Middlekauff, W. W. 1959. Some biological observations on *Sarcophaga falciformis*, a parasite of grasshoppers (Diptera: Sarcophagidae). *Ann. Ent. Soc. America*, 52: 724–8.

Miles, H. W., and M. Miles. 1948. *Insect Pests of Glasshouse Crops.* Crosby Lockwood and Son, Ltd., London. 200 pp.

Miller, C. A. 1959. The interaction of the spruce budworm, *Choristoneura fumiferana* (Clem.), and the parasite *Apanteles fumiferanae* Vier. *Canadian Ent.*, 91: 457–77.

—— 1960. The interaction of the spruce budworm, *Choristoneura fumiferana* (Clem.), and the parasite *Glypta fumiferanae* (Vier.). *Canadian Ent.*, 92: 839–50.

Miller, D. 1936. Biological control of noxious weeds. *New Zealand Jour. Sci. and Technol.*, 18: 581–4.

Miller, D., A. F. Clark, and L. J. Dumbleton. 1936. Biological control of noxious insects and weeds in New Zealand. *New Zealand Jour. Sci. and Technol.*, 18: 579–93.

Miller, Frank E. 1940. A rearing method for the mass production of *Microplectron fuscipennis* (Zett.), cocoon parasite of the European sawfly, *Gilpinia polytoma* (Htg.). *U.S. Dept. Agric. Bur. Ent. Mimeo. Ser. ET* 161. 5 pp.

Miller, L. W. 1947. The biological control of insect pests in Tasmania. *Tasmanian Jour. Agric.*, 18: 117–19.

Milliron, H. E. 1940. A study of some factors affecting the efficiency of *Encarsia formosa* Gahan, an aphelinid parasite of the greenhouse whitefly, *Trialeurodes vaporariorum* (Westw.). *Michigan Agric. Expt. Sta. Tech. Bull.* 173: 1–23.

—— 1950. The identity of a cleptid egg parasite of the common walking stick, *Diapheromera femorata* Say. *Proc. Ent. Soc. Wash.*, 52: 47.

Millot, J. 1938. Le développement et la biologie larvaire des oncodides (Cyrtides), Diptères parasites d'araignées. *Bull. Soc. Zool. France*, 63: 162–81, 183–97.

Mills, H. B. 1942. Montana insect pests, 1941 and 1942. Twenty-ninth report of the State Entomologist. *Bull. Montana Agric. Expt. Sta.* 408. 36 pp.

Milne, A. 1957a. The natural control of insect populations. *Canadian Ent.*, 89: 193–213.

—— 1957b. Theories of natural control of insect populations. In *Cold Spring Harbor Symposia on Quantitative Biology*, 22: 253–71.

—— 1958. Perfect and imperfect density dependence in population dynamics. *Nature*, 182: 1251.

Miner, J. R. 1933. Pierre-François Verhulst, the discoverer of the logistic curve. *Human Biol.*, 5: 673–89.

Mittler, T. E. 1958. Studies on the feeding and nutrition of *Tuberolachnus salignus* (Gmelin). III. The nitrogen economy. *Jour. Exptl. Biol.*, 35: 626–38.

Mobius, K. 1877. The oyster and oyster culture. Translation in *Rept. U.S. Fish Comm. 1880.* Pp. 683–751.

Mokrezecki, S. A., and A. P. Bragina. 1916. The rearing of *Trichogramma semblidis* and *T. fasciatum* P. in the laboratory and temperature experiments on them. Salgir Expt. Pomological Station, Simferopol, Crimea (Text Russian). [Abs. in *R.A.E.. Ser. A.*, 5: 155–6, 1917.]

Monro, R. E. 1961. Protein turnover and the formation of protein inclusions during sporulation of *Bacillus thuringiensis*. *Biochem. Jour.*, 81: 225–32.

Monteith, A. E. 1956. *Phygadeuon trichops* Thoms. (Hymenoptera: Ichneumonidae) an occasional parasite of *Hylemya* spp. (Diptera: Anthomyiidae). *Canadian Ent.*, 88: 69–73.

Monteith, L. G. 1956. Influence of host movement on selection of hosts by *Drino bohemica* Mesn. (Diptera: Tachinidae) as determined in an olfactometer. *Canadian Ent.*, 88: 583–6.

—— 1958. Influence of host and its food plant on host-finding by *Drino bohemica* Mesn. (Diptera: Tachinidae) and interaction of other factors. *Proc. 10th Inter. Congr. Ent. (1956)*, 2: 603–6.

Moore, E. 1946. Nutrition of Attagenus (?) sp. II. *Ann. Ent. Soc. America*, 39: 513–21.

Moore, I. 1959. A method for artificially culturing the olive fly (*Dacus oleae* Gmel.) under aseptic conditions. *Ktavim*, 9: 295–6.

Moreland, C. R., and W. S. McLeod. 1957. Studies on rearing the house fly on a bran-alfalfa medium. *Jour. Econ. Ent.*, 50: 146–50.

Morrill, A. W. 1931. A discussion of Smith and Flanders' Trichogramma fad query. *Jour. Econ. Ent.*, 24: 1264–73.

Morris, K. R. S. 1937. The prepupal stage in Ichneumonidae, illustrated by the life-history of *Exenterus abruptorius* Thb. *Bull. Ent. Res.*, 28: 525–34.

—— 1938. *Eupelmella vesicularis* Retz. (Chalcididae) as a predator of another chalcid, *Microplectron fuscipennis* Zett. *Parasitology*, 30: 20–32.

Morris, K. R. S., E. Cameron, and W. F. Jepson. 1937. The insect parasites of the spruce sawfly, *Diprion polytomum*, in Europe. *Bull. Ent. Res.*, 28: 341–93.

Morris, R. F. 1957. The interpretation of mortality data in studies on population dynamics. *Canadian Ent.*, 89: 49–69.

—— 1958a. A review of the important insects affecting the spruce-fir forest in the maritime provinces. *Forest. Chron.*, 34: 159–89.

—— 1958b. The population dynamics of the spruce budworm in eastern Canada. *Proc. 10th Internatl. Congr. Ent.*, 4: 137–49 (1956).

—— 1959. Single-factor analysis in population dynamics. *Ecology*, 40: 580–88.

Morris, R. F. 1960. Sampling insect populations. *Ann. Rev. Ent.*, **5**: 243–64.

Morris, R. F., W. F. Cheshire, C. A. Miller, and D. G. Mott. 1958. The numerical response of avian and mammalian predators during a gradation of the spruce budworm. *Ecology*, **39**: 487–94.

Moser, J. C. 1956. A new species of *Torymus* (Hymenoptera: Torymidae) parasitic on *Pachypsylla celtidis-vesicula* Riley (Chermidae) with notes on its biology and other parasitoids attacking the same host at Columbus, Ohio. *Jour. Kansas Ent. Soc.*, **29**: 57–62.

Moursi, A. A. 1948*a*. *Anagyrus kamali* Moursi, a parasite of the *Hibiscus* mealybug, *Phenacoccus hirsutus* Green. *Bull. Soc. Fouad Ier Entom.*, **32**: 9–16.

—— 1948*b*. *Leptomastix phenacocci* Compere, a parasite of the Lebbek mealybug *Pseudococcus filamentosus*. *Bull. Soc. Fouad Ier Entom.*, **32**: 33–40.

Moutia, A. L., and C. M. Courtois. 1952. Parasites of moth-borers of sugar-cane in Mauritius. *Bull. Ent. Res.*, **43**: 325–59.

Moutia, A. L. and R. Mamet. 1946. A review of 25 years of economic entomology in the Island of Mauritius. *Bull. Ent. Res.*, **36**: 439–72.

Muesebeck, C. F. W. 1918. Two important introduced parasites of the brown-tail moth. *Jour. Agric. Res.*, **15**: 191–206.

—— 1942. Fundamental taxonomic problems in quarantine and nursery inspection. *Jour. Econ. Ent.*, **35**: 753–8.

—— 1956. A braconid parasite of a psocid. *Proc. Ent. Soc. Wash.*, **58**: 148–9.

Muesebeck, C. F. W., and S. M. Dohanian. 1927. A study of hyperparasitism with particular reference to the parasites of *Apanteles melanoscelus* (Ratzeburg). *U.S. Dept. Agric. Bull.* 1487. 35 pp.

Muesebeck, C. F. W., K. V. Krombein, and H. K. Townes. 1951. Hymenoptera of Americ north of Mexico. Synoptic catalog. *U.S. Dept. Agric., Agric. Monogr.*, **2**: 1–1420.

Muesebeck, C. F. W., and P. L. Parker. 1933. *Hyposoter disparis* Viereck, an introduced ichneumonid parasite of the gypsy moth. *Jour. Agric. Res.*, **46**: 335–47.

Muir, F. 1914. Presidential address. *Proc. Hawaiian Ent. Soc.*, **3**: 28–42.

Muir, F. 1931. *Introduction*—In *The Insects and Other Invertebrates of Hawaiian Sugar Cane Fields*, by Francis X. Williams. Expt. Sta. Hawaiian Sugar Planters' Assoc. 400 pp.

Muir, F., and O. H. Swezey. 1916. The cane borer beetle in Hawaii and its control by natural enemies (with appendices A–G). *Rept. Hawaiian Sugar Planters' Expt. Sta. Ent. Ser. Bull.* **13**. 102 pp.

Mukerji, S., and T. V. Venkatraman. 1948. Studies on *Epipyrops melanolenca* Fletcher (Lepidoptera: Epipyropidae), an ectoparasite of the sugar cane leaf-hopper, *Pyrilla* spp. (Homoptera: Fulgoridae). *Proc. Zoo. Soc. Bengal*, **1**: 91–102.

Muldrew, J. A. 1953. The natural immunity of the larch sawfly (*Prestiphora erichsonii* (Htg.)) to the introduced parasite *Mesoleius tenthredinis* Morley, in Manitoba and Saskatchewan. *Canadian Jour. Zool.*, **31**: 313–32.

Muller, H. J. 1940. *Bearings of the 'Drosophila' work on systematics*, pp. 185–268. In *The New Systematics*, J. S. Huxley, editor.

Müller-Kögler, E. 1958 Eine Rickettsiose von *Tipula paludosa* Meig. durch *Rickettsiella tipulae* nov. spec. *Naturwissenschaften*, **45**: 248.

—— 1959. Zur Isolierung und Kultur insektenpathogener Entomophthoraceen. *Entomophaga*, **4**: 261–74.

—— 1960. Niedrige Keimprozente der Sporen insektenpathogener Pilze: eine mögliche Fehlerquelle bei ihrer Anwendung. *Zeitschr. Pflanzenkrank.*, **67**: 663–8.

Muma, M. H. 1955. Factors contributing to the natural control of citrus insects and mites in Florida. *Jour. Econ. Ent.*, 48: 432–8.

—— 1961. The influence of cover crop cultivation on populations of indigenous insects and mites in Florida citrus groves. *Florida Ent.*, 44: 61–8.

Munger, Francis. 1955. Rearing citrus red mites in the laboratory. *Jour. Econ. Ent.*, 48: 72–4.

Myers, G. S. 1952. The nature of systematic biology and of a species description. *Systematic Zool.*, 1: 106–11.

Myers, J. G. 1931. *A Preliminary Report on an Investigation into the Biological Control of West Indian Insect Pests.* His Majesty's Stationery Office, London. 178 pp.

—— 1935. Second report on an investigation into the biological control of West Indian pests. *Bull. Ent. Res.*, 26: 181–252.

Narayanan, E. S. 1954. Discussion of 'The Biological Control of Weeds,' J. R. Williams 95–8. *Rep. Commonwealth Ent. Conf., 6th Meeting,* 100 (London, England).

—— 1957. The phenomena of insect parasitism and their practical utilisation in the biological control of insect pests. *Proc. 44th Indian Sci. Congr.: Part 2.* 22 pp.

Narayanan, E. S., and R. P. Chaudhuri. 1954. Studies on *Stenobracon deesae* (Cam.), a parasite of certain lepidopterous borers of graminaceous crops in India. *Bull. Ent. Res.*, 45: 647–59.

Narayanan, E. S., and P. B. Mookherjee. 1956. Effect of nutrition on the longevity and rate of reproduction in *Trichogramma evanescens minutum* Riley. *Indian Jour. Ent.*, 17 (1955) Pt. 3: 376–82.

Narayanan, E. S., B. R. Subba Rao, and G. A. Gangrade. 1956. The biology and rate of reproduction and the morphology of the immature stages of *Apanteles angaleti* Muesebeck (Hymenoptera: Braconidae). *Beitr. Ent.*, 6: 296–320.

Narayanan, E. S., B. R. Subba Rao, and R. B. Kauv. 1956. Studies on the biology of the parasites of the pea leaf miner *Phytomyza atricornis* (Meigen). *Proc. Indian Acad. Sci.*, 64 (Sect. B): 137–47.

Naude, T. J. 1956. Biological control of the prickly pear. *World Crops*, 8: 401–2.

Neff, R. J. 1957. Purification, axenic cultivation, and description of a soil amoeba, *Acanthamoeba* sp. *Jour. Protozool.*, 4: 176–82.

Neilson, M. M. 1956. Disease in spruce budworm adults. *Canada Dept. Agric. Sci. Serv., Div. Forest Biol., Bi-monthly Progress Rept.*, Nov.-Dec., 12: 1–2.

Nelson, W. A., and C. W. Farstad. 1953. Biology of *Bracon cephi* (Gahan) (Hymenoptera: Braconidae) an important native parasite of the wheat stem sawfly, *Cephus cinctus* Nort. (Hymenoptera: Cephidae), in western Canada. *Canadian Ent.*, 85: 103–7.

Neumark, S. 1952. *Chrysopa carnea* St. and its enemies in Israel. *Ilanoth Forest Res. Sta. No. 1*, p. 127.

Newell, W. 1921. Report of the plant commissioner for the biennium ending April 30, 1920, and supplemental reports. *Florida State Plant Board Quart. Bull.*, 5: 37–126.

—— 1923. Report of the plant commissioner for the period from May 1, 1920 to June 30, 1922. *Florida State Plant Board Quart. Bull.*, 7: 75–143.

Neyman, J., T. Park, and E. L. Scott. 1956. Struggle for existence. The *Tribolium* model: biological and statistical aspects. *3rd Berkeley Symposium on Math. Stat. and Prob., Dec., 1954 and June and July, 1955.* Univ. Calif. Press. pp. 41–79.

Nicholson, A. J. 1933. The balance of animal populations. *Jour. Animal Ecol.* Supplement to Vol. 2, No. 1: 132–78.

—— 1940. Indirect effects of spray practice on pest populations. *Proc. 7th Internatl. Congr. Ent.*, 4: 3022–8.

—— 1951. A simple method of disintegrating cells. *Nature*, 167: 563.

Nicholson, A. J. 1954*a*. Compensatory reactions to stresses and their evolutionary significance. *Australian Jour. Zool.*, 2: 1–8.

—— 1954*b*. An outline of the dynamics of animal populations. *Australian Jour. Zool.*, 2: 9–65.

—— 1957. The self-adjustment of populations to change. In *Cold Spring Harbor Symposia on Quantitative Biology*, 22: 153–73.

—— 1958. Dynamics of insect populations. *Ann. Rev. Ent.*, 3: 107–36.

Nicholson, A. J., and V. A. Bailey. 1935. The balance of animal populations. *Proc. Zool. Soc. London. Part I.* 551–98.

Nickels, C. B., W. C. Pierce, and C. C. Pinkey. 1950. Parasites of the pecan nut casebearer in Texas. *U.S. Dept. Agric. Tech. Bull.* 1011. 21 pp.

Nicolet, H. 1841. Recherches pour servir à l'histoire des podurelles. *N. Denkschr. Schweiz. Ges. Naturw.*, 6: 1–88.

Nielsen, J. C. 1909. Jagtlagelser over entoparasitiske Muscidelarver has Arthropoder. *Ent. Meddel.*, 4: 1–126.

—— 1911. Undersgelser over entoparasitiske Muscidelarver has Arthropoder I. *Vidensk. Meddel. Dansk Naturhist. For. Copenhagen*, 63: 1–26.

—— 1912. Undersgelser over entoparasitiske Muscidelarver has Arthropoder II. *Vidensk. Meddel Dansk Naturhist. For. Copenhagen*, 64: 215–48.

—— 1913. Undersgelser over entoparasitiske Muscidelarver has Arthropoder III. *Vidensk. Meddel Dansk Naturhist. For. Copenhagen*, 65: 301–04.

—— 1914. Undersgelser over entoparasitiske Muscidelarver has Arthropoder IV. *Vidensk. Meddel Dansk Naturhist. For. Copenhagen*, 66: 211–20.

—— 1915. Undersgelser over entoparasitiske Muscidelarver has Arthropoder V. *Vidensk. Meddel Dansk Naturhist. For. Copenhagen*, 67: 9–24.

—— 1916. Undersgelser over entoparasitiske Muscidelarver has Arthropoder VI. *Vidensk. Meddel Dansk Naturhist. For. Copenhagen*, 68: 23–36.

—— 1918. Undersgelser over entoparasitiske Muscidelarver has Arthropoder VII. *Vidensk. Meddel Dansk Naturhist. For. Copenhagen*, 70: 1–3.

Niklas, O. F. 1939. Zum Massenwechsel der Tachine *Parasetigena segregata* Rond. (*Phorocera agilis* R.-D) in der Rominter Heide. (Die Parasitierung der Nonne durch Insekten. Teil II). *Zeitschr. angew. Ent.*, 26: 63–103.

—— 1956*a*. Untersuchungen über das Auftreten von Krankheiten und Schädigungen, insbesondere über die 'Lorscher Seuche' (*Rickettsia melolonthae* Krieg) in Freiland-Populationen des Maikäfer-Engerlings (*Melolontha spec.*). *Zeitschr. f. Pflanzenkrank. u. Pflanzenschutz*, 63: 81–95.

—— 1956*b*. Die Erzwespe *Tetracampe diprioni* Ferrière als Eiparasit der Kiefernblattwespe *Neodiprion sertifer* Geoffr. *Beiträge Ent.*, 6: 320–32.

—— 1960. Standorteinflüsse und natürliche Feinde als Begrenzungsfaktoren von *Melolontha*-Larvenpopulationen eines Waldgebietes (Forstamt Lorsch, Hessen) (Coleoptera: Scarabaeidae). *Mitteilungen aus der Biologische Bundesanstalt für Land- und Forstwirtschaft. Berlin-Dahlem. No. 101.* 60 pp.

Nishida, T. 1956. An experimental study of the ovipositional behavior of *Opius fletcheri* Silvestri (Hymenoptera: Braconidae), a parasite of the melon fly. *Proc. Hawaiian Ent. Soc.*, 16: 126–34.

Noble, N. S. 1932. Studies of *Habrocytus cerealellae* (Ashmead), a pteromalid parasite of the angoumois grain moth, *Sitotroga cerealella* (Olivier). *Univ. Calif. Publ. Ent.*, 5: 311–54.

—— 1937. An egg parasite of the green vegetable bug. *Agric. Gaz. N. South Wales Misc. Pub. No. 3094*: 337–41.

Noble, N. S. 1938a. The greenhouse white fly. Control by the parasite, *Encarsia formosa*. *Agric. Gaz. N. South Wales*, 49: 253–5.

—— 1938b. *Euplectrus agaristae* Craw., a parasite of the grape vine moth (*Phalaenoides glycine* Lew.). *N. South Wales Dept. Agric. Bull. No. 63*. 27 pp.

—— 1938c. *Epimegastigmus* (*Megastigmus*) *brevivalvus* Girault. *Dept. Agric. New South Wales Sci. Bull. No. 65*. 46 pp.

Noland, J. L. 1956. An improved method for rearing cockroaches. *Jour. Econ. Ent.*, 49: 411–12.

Norris, M. J. 1933. Contributions towards the study of insect fertility. II. Experiments on the factors influencing fertility in *Ephestia kuhniella* Z. (Lepidoptera: Phycitidae). *Proc. Zool. Soc., London*, 4: 903–34.

—— 1934. Contributions towards the study of insect fertility. III. Adult nutrition, fecundity, and longevity in the genus *Ephestia* (Lepidoptera: *Phycitidae*). *Proc. Zool. Soc. London*, 2: 333–60.

Novoa-Zanartu, A. O. 1956. The biology of *Prospaltella peltatus* (Cockerell) (Hymenoptera: Aphelinidae). Master's Thesis Univ. of Calif. 70 pp.

O'Connor, B. A. 1950. Premature nutfall of coconuts in the British Solomon Islands Protectorate. *Agric. Jour. [Fiji]*, 21: (1–2). 22 pp.

—— 1953. Biological control of insects and plants in Fiji. *Proc. 7th Pacific Sci. Congr., New Zealand*, 4: 278–93 (1949).

Odum, E. P. 1953. *Fundamentals of Ecology*. W. B. Saunders Co. Philadelphia and London. 384 pp.

Odum, E. P., and W. C. Allee. 1954. A note on the stable point of populations showing both intraspecific cooperation and disoperation. *Ecology*, 35: 95–7.

Oettinger, A. J. von. 1879. Phanologie der dorpater lignosen. *Arch. Naturk. Liv.-Est.-u. Kurlands*, 8: 241–352.

Ogloblin, A. A. 1913. [Contribution to the biology of the Coccinellidae.] *Russ. Ent. Obozr.* (*Rev. Russe d'Ent.*), 13: 27–43.

—— 1924. Le rôle du blastoderme extra-embryonaire du *Dinocampus cerminalis* Nees, pendant l'état larvaire. *Čes Koslov. Spoléc. Ent. Casopis*, 3, 27 pp.

—— 1939. The Strepsipterous parasites of ants. *Verh. VII. Kongr. Ent.*, 2: 1277–84.

Oldroyd, H. 1958. *Collecting, Preserving and Studying Insects*. The MacMillan Co. New York, 327 pp.

Oman, Paul. 1959. Personal communication.

Oman, P. W., and A. D. Cushman. 1946. Collection and preservation of insects. *U.S. Dept. Agric. Misc. Publ. 601*, 42 pp.

Osborne, P. 1960. Observations on the natural enemies of *Meligethes aeneus* (F.) and *M. viridescens* (F.) (Coleoptera: Nitidulidae). *Parasitology*, 50: 91–110.

Osburn, M. R., and W. Mathis. 1946. Effect of cultivation on Florida red scale populations. *Jour. Econ. Ent.*, 39: 571–4.

Ossowski, L. L. J. 1957a. Über *Kotochalia junodi* (Heyl.)—Psychidae-einen Grossschädling in Schwarzakazienwäldern von Südafrika. *Zeitschr. angew. Ent.*, 41: 139–52.

—— 1957b. The biological control of the wattle bagworm (*Kotochalia junodi* Heyl.) by a virus disease. I. Small-scale pilot experiments. *Ann. Appl. Biol.*, 45: 81–9.

—— 1958. Occurrence of strains of the nuclear polyhedral virus of the wattle bagworm. *Nature*, 181: 648.

—— 1960. Variation in virulence of a wattle bagworm virus. *Jour. Insect Pathol.*, 2: 35–43.

Otanes, F. Q. 1940. A survey of Philippine entomology, with special reference to applied or economic work. *Proc. 6th Pac. Sci. Congr.*, 4: 383–96 (1939).

Packard, C. M., and C. Benton. 1937. How to fight the chinch bug. *U.S. Dept. Agric. Farmers' Bull.* 1780. 21 pp.

Packard, C. M., and R. E. Campbell. 1926. The pea aphid as an alfalfa pest in California. *Jour. Econ. Ent.*, 19: 760–1.

Paillot, A. 1924. Sur une nouvelle maladie des chenilles de *Pieris brassicae* et sur les maladies du noyau chez les insectes. *Compt. Rend. Acad. Sci.*, 179: 1353–6.

—— 1925. Le problème de l'équilibre naturel chez les insectes phytophages. *Rev. générale des sciences pures et appliquées*, 36: 206–11.

—— 1926a. Contribution à l'étude des maladies à virus filtrant chez les insectes. Un nouveau groupe de parasites ultramicrobiens: les *Borrellina*. *Ann. Inst. Pasteur*, 40: 314–52.

—— 1926b. Sur une nouvelle maladie du noyau ou grasserie des chenilles de *Pieris brassicae* et un nouveau groupe de micro-organismes parasites. *Compt. Rend. Acad. Sci.*, 182: 180–2.

—— 1930a. Influence des infections microbiennes secondaires sur le développement des ultravirus chez le *Bombyx* du Murier. *Compt. Rend. Soc. Biol.*, 104: 585–6.

—— 1930b. *Traité des maladies du ver à soie*. G. Doin et Cie., Paris. 279 pp.

—— 1933. *L'infection chez les insectes*. G. Patissier, Trévoux, 535 pp.

—— 1937. Sur le développement polyembryonaire d'*Amicroplus collaris* Spin. Parasite des chenilles d'*Euxoa segetum* Schiff. *Compt. Rend. Acad. Sci. (Paris)*, 204: 810–12.

Paine, R. W. 1935. The control of the coconut spike moth (*Tirathaba trichogramma* Meyr.) in Fiji. *Fiji Dept. Agric. Bull.* 18: 1–30.

Painter, R. H. 1951. *Insect Resistance in Crop Plants*. The Macmillan Co., New York. 520 pp.

—— 1953. The role of nutritional factors in host plant selection. *Symposia 9th Internatl. Congr. Ent.*, pp. 101–5. Dr. W. Junk, Publishers, The Hague, Netherlands.

Painter, R. H., and J. C. Hall. 1960. A monograph of the genus *Poecilanthrax*. *Kans. St. Univ. Tech. Bull.* 106. pp. 1–132.

Pampel, W. 1914. Die Weiblichen Geschlechtsorgane der Ichneumoniden. *Ztschr. f. Wiss. Zool.*, 108: 290–357.

Pantel, J. 1898. Le *Thrixion halidayanum* Rond. Essai monographique sur les caractères extérieurs, la biologie et l'anatomie d'une larve parasite du groupe des Tachinaries. *Cellule*, 15: 1–290.

—— 1910. Recherches sur les Diptères à larves entomobies. I. Caractères parasitiques aux points de vue biologique, éthologique et histologique. *Cellule*, 26: 27–216.

Paoli, G. 1937. Richerche sulla morfologia e anatomia del capo delle larve dei Ditteri Bombiliidi. *Redia*, 23: 5–16.

Park, T. 1955. *Experimental competition in beetles, with some general implications*. Pp. 69–82. In: *The numbers of man and animals*. Institute of Biology. Oliver and Boyd Ltd.

Parker, D. L. E. 1935. *Apanteles solitarius* (Ratzeburg), an introduced braconid parasite of the satin moth. *U.S. Dept. Agric. Tech. Bull. No. 477*. 17 pp.

—— 1936. *Chrysis shanghaiensis* Smith, a parasite of the oriental moth. *Jour. Agric. Res.*, 52: 449–58.

Parker, H. L. 1923. Contribution à la connaissance de *Chalcis fonscolombei* Dufour (Hym.). *Bull. Soc. Entomol. France 1923*: 238–40.

—— 1924. Recherches sur les formes post embryonaires des Chalcidiens. *Ann. Soc. Ent. de France*, 93: 261–379.

—— 1931a. Notes on *Meteorus (Zemiotes) nigricollis* Thomson, an occasional parasite of the European corn borer. *Proc. Ent. Soc. Washington*, 33: 93–103.

Parker, H. L. 1931b. *Macrocentrus gifuensis* Ashmead, a polyembryonic braconid parasite in the European corn borer. *U.S. Dept. Agric. Tech. Bull.* 230: 1–62.

—— 1949. The handling, transporting, packing and shipping of insects, particularly parasites and predators. *Internatl. U. Biol. Sci. Ser. B.*, 5: 121–7.

—— 1959. Studies of some Scarabaeidae and their parasites. *Boll. Lab. Ent. Agraria, Portici*, 17: 29–50.

Parker, H. L., and H. D. Smith. 1933. *Eulophus viridulus* Thoms., a parasite of *Pyrausta nubilalis* Hubn. *Ann. Ent. Soc. America*, 26: 21–39.

Parker, H. L., and W. R. Thompson. 1925. Notes on the larvae of the Chalcidoidea. *Ann. Ent. Soc. America*, 18: 384–95.

Parman, D. C. 1928. Experimental dissemination of the tabanid egg parasite *Phanurus emersoni* Girault and biological notes on the species. *U.S. Dept. Agric. Circ.* 18. 6 pp.

Parsons, W. T. 1957. St. John's wort in Victoria—history, distribution, control. *Jour. Dept. Agric., Victoria (Dec.)* 55: 781–8.

Pascalet, P. 1939. La lutte biologique contre *Stephanoderes hampei* un scolyte du caféier au Cameroun. *Revue de Bot. appl. et Agric. tropic.*, 19: 753–64.

Pasteur, L. 1870. *Études sur la maladie des vers à soie*. Gautherie-Villars, Paris, I: 322 pp.; II: 327 pp.

Pastrana, J. A., and H. Gahan. 1950. The mass breeding of *Macrocentrus ancylivorus* Roh., a natural parasite of *Cydia molesta* in Argentina. (*Publ. Inst. Sanid. veg.*) *Minist. Agric. Argent.*, (*B*), 6: 22 pp.

Patterson, J. T. 1915. Observations on the development of *Copidosoma gelechiae*. *Biol. Bull.*, 29: 291–305.

—— 1917. Studies on the biology of *Paracopidosomopsis*. I. Data on the sexes. *Biol. Bull.*, 32: 291–305.

Patterson, J. T., and W. S. Stone. 1952. *Evolution in the Genus Drosophila*. The Macmillan Co., New York, 610 pp.

Patterson, T. L., and W. F. Fiske. 1911. Investigations into the habits of certain Sarcophagidae. *U.S. Dept. Agric. Tech. Ser.*, 19: 25–32.

Payne, N. M. 1933a. The differential effect of environmental factors upon *Microbracon hebetor* Say (Hymenoptera: Braconidae) and its host *Ephestia kuhniella* Zeller (Lepidoptera: Pyralidae). *I. Biol. Bull.*, 65: 187–205.

—— 1933b. A parasitic hymenopteron as a vector of an insect disease. *Ent. News*, 44: 22.

—— 1934. The differential effect of environmental factors upon *Microbracon hebetor* Say (Hymenoptera: Braconidae) and its host *Ephestia kuhniella* Zeller (Lepidoptera: Pryalidae) II. *Ecol. Monog.*, 4: 1–46.

Pearl, R. 1925. *The Biology of Population Growth*. New York, A. A. Knopf. 260 pp.

—— 1932. The influence of density of population upon egg production in *Drosophila melanogaster*. *Jour. Exptl. Zool.*, 63: 57–84.

Pearl, R., and L. J. Reed. 1920. On the rate of growth of the population of the United States since 1790 and its mathematical representation. *Proc. Natl. Acad. Sci.*, 6: 275–88.

Pederson, M. W. 1942. A survey of biological destruction of cactus on Nebraska range land. *Jour. Amer. Soc. Agron.*, 34: 769–70.

Pelczar, M. J., Chairman, *et al.* 1957. *Manual of Microbiological Methods* (Society of American Bacteriologists, Committee on Bacteriological Technic). McGraw-Hill Book Co., Inc., New York, Toronto, and London. x–315 pp.

Pemberton, C. E. 1941. Contribution of the entomologists to Hawaii's welfare. *Hawaiian Planters' Rec.*, 45: 107–19.

Pemberton, C. E. 1948a. History of the entomology department experiment station, H.S.P.A., 1904–1945. *Hawaiian Planters' Rec.*, **52**: 53–90.

—— 1948b. The control of the grass armyworm, *Laphygma exempta* (Walker), in Hawaii by parasites. *Hawaiian Planters' Rec.*, **52**: 181–200.

—— 1953. The biological control of insects in Hawaii. *Proc. 7th Pac. Sci. Congr.*, **4**: 220–3.

—— 1954. Invertebrate Consultants Committee for the Pacific, Report for 1949–1954. *Pac. Sci. Bd., Natl. Acad. Sci., Natl. Res. Counc.* 56 pp.

Pemberton, C. E., and J. S. Rosa. 1940. Notes on the life history of *Baeus californicus* Pierce, an egg parasite of the black widow spider. *Hawaii Planters Rec.*, **44**: 73–80

—— 1946. Life history of a new parasite of the black widow spider in Hawaii. *Hawaii Planters Rec.*, **50**: 29–37.

Pemberton, C. E., and H. F. Willard. 1918. A contribution to the biology of fruit-fly parasites in Hawaii. *Jour. Agric. Res.*, **15**: 419–65.

Pepper, B. B., and B. F. Driggers. 1934. Non-economic insects as intermediate hosts of parasites of the oriental fruit moth. *Ann. Ent. Soc. America*, **27**: 593–8.

Pepper, J. H. 1955. The ecological approach to management of insect populations. *Jour. Econ. Ent.*, **48**: 451–6.

Perkins, R. C. L. 1906. Leaf-hoppers and their natural enemies (Introduction). *Report of work of the Expt. Sta. Hawaiian Sugar Planters' Assn. Bull.* 1. 32 pp.

—— 1907. Parasites of leaf-hoppers. *Hawaii Sugar Plant. Agric. Sta. Bull.* 4, 1–59.

Perkins, R. C. L., and O. H. Swezey. 1924. The introduction into Hawaii of insects that attack lantana. *Hawaiian Sugar Planters' Assoc. Expt. Sta. Ent. Ser. Bull.* 16. 83 pp.

Person, H. L. 1940. The clerid *Thanasimus lecontei* (Wolc.) as a factor in the control of the western pine beetle. *Jour. Forest.*, **38**: 390–6.

Peterson, A. 1930. A biological study of *Trichogramma minutum* Riley as an egg parasite of the oriental fruit moth. *U.S. Dept. Agric. Tech. Bull.* 215. 21 pp.

—— 1947. *A Manual of Entomological Equipment and Methods.* Parts I and II. Edwards Bros., Inc., Ann Arbor, Michigan. Approx. 200 pp.

—— 1951a. *Larvae of Insects Part I. Lepidoptera and Plant-infesting Hymenoptera.* Columbus, Ohio. 315 pp.

—— 1951b. *Larvae of Insects.* Part II. *Coleoptera, Diptera, Neuroptera, Siphonaptera, Mecoptera, Trichoptera.* Columbus, Ohio. 416 pp.

—— 1953. *A Manual of Entomological Techniques.* Edwards Brothers, Inc. Ann Arbor, Mich. 7th ed. 367 pp.

Peterson, G. D., Jr. 1955a. Biological control of the orange spiny whitefly in Guam. *Jour Econ. Ent.*, **48**: 681–3.

—— 1955b. Biological control of *Epilachna philippinensis* Dieke in Guam. *Jour. Econ. Ent.* **48**: 758–9.

Pettey, F. W. 1948. The biological control of prickly pears in South Africa. *Union S. Africa Dept. Agric. Sci. Bull.* 271. 163 pp.

—— 1950. The cochineal (*Dactylopius opuntiae*) and the problem of its control in spineless cactus plantations. Part I. Its history, distribution, biology and what it has accomplished in the control of prickly pear in South Africa. Part II. The control of cochineal in spineless cactus plantations. *Union S. Africa Dept. Agric. Sci. Bull.* 296. 34 pp.

—— 1953. The boring beetles of prickly pear in South Africa and their importance in the control of *Opuntia megacantha. Union S. Africa Dept. Agric. Sci. Bull.* 340. 36 pp.

Phillips, W. J. 1927. *Eurytoma parva* (Girault) Phillips and its biology as a parasite of the wheat jointworm, *Harmolita tritici* (Fitch). *Jour. Agric. Res.*, **34**: 743–58.

Phillips, D. H., and M. J. Johnson. 1961. Aeration in fermentations. *Jour. Biochem. Microbiol. Technol. Engineer*, **3**: 277–309.

Picard, F., and E. Rabaud. 1914. Sur le parasitisme externe des Braconides (Hym.). *Bull. Ent. Soc. France 1914:* 266–9.

Pickett, A. D. 1959. Utilization of native parasites and predators. *Jour. Econ. Ent.*, 52: 1103–5.

Pickett, A. D., and N. A. Patterson. 1953. The influence of spray programs on the fauna of apple orchards in Nova Scotia. IV. A review. *Canadian Ent.*, 85: 472–8.

Pickett, A. D., W. L. Putman, and E. J. LeRoux. 1958. Progress in harmonizing biological and chemical control of orchard pests in eastern Canada. *Proc. 10th Internatl. Congr. Ent.*, 3: 169–74. (1956).

Pickles, A. 1931. Entomological contributions to the study of the sugar cane frog hopper I. *Trop. Agric. [Trinidad]*, 10: 222–33.

Pielou, D. P., and R. F. Glasser. 1952. Selection for DDT resistance in a beneficial insect parasite. *Science*, 115: 117–18.

—— 1953. Survival of *Macrocentrus ancylivorus* Roh., a parasite of the oriental fruit moth on different concentrations of various sugar solutions. *Canadian Jour. Zool.*, 31: 121–4.

—— 1954. Thermal tolerance in *Macrocentrus ancylivorus* Roh. *Canadian Jour. Zool.*, 34: 30–8.

Pierce, W. D. 1912. The insect enemies of the cotton boll weevil. *U.S. Dept. Agric. Bur. Ent. Bull. 100.* 99 pp.

Pierce, W. D., and T. E. Holloway. 1912. Notes on the biology of *Chelonus texanus* Cress. *Jour. Econ. Ent.*, 5: 425–8.

Pimentel, D. 1961. The influence of plant spacial patterns on insect populations. *Ann. Ent. Soc. America*, 54: 61–9.

Pimentel, R. A. 1958. Taxonomic methods, their bearing on subspeciation. *Systematic Zool.*, 7: 139–56.

Pirt, S. J., and D. S. Callow. 1958. Observations on foaming and its inhibition in a bacterial culture. *Jour. Appl. Bact.*, 21: 211–16.

Plank, H. K. 1929. A summary of investigations of the sugar cane moth stalkborer in Cuba. *Trop. Plant Res. Foundation. Bull. 8.* Cuba Sugar Club Expt. Sta. 16 pp.

Plomley, N. J. B. 1947. Some notes on the biology of the Cyrtidae (Diptera) with special reference to the genus *Oncodes*. *Rec. Queen Vict. Mus. and Art Gallery*, 2: 23–30.

Polivka, J. B. 1956. Effectiveness of milky disease in controlling Japanese beetle in Ohio. *Jour. Econ. Ent.*, 49: 4–6.

Pospelov, V. P. 1926. The influence of temperature on the maturation and general health of *Locusta migratoria* L. *Bull. Ent. Res.*, 16: 363–7.

—— 1940. *Biological methods of controlling the beet weevil.* In *Kulagin.* (Eds. N. M. and G. K. Pyatnitzkii.) *The beet weevil and its control.* (In Russian.) 151 pp. Moscow, Vsesoyuzn. Akad. s.-kh. Nauk Lenina. Pp. 45–6 [*R.A.E. A.*, 30: 66–7].

Poyarkoff, E. 1914. Essai—d'une theorie de la nymphe des insectes holometaboles. *Arch. Zool. Exptl. et Gén.*, 54: 221–65.

Prell, H. 1915. Zur Biologie der Tachinen *Parasetigena segregata* Rond. und *Panzeria rudis* Fall. *Zeitschr. Angew. Ent.*, 2: 57–148.

Prescott, H. W. 1955. *Neorhynchocephalus sackenii* and *Trichopsidea clausa*, Nemestrinid parasites of grasshoppers. *Ann. Ent. Soc. America*, 48: 392–402.

—— 1961. Respiratory pore construction in the host by the nemestrinid parasite *Neorhynchocephalus sackenii* (Diptera), with notes on respiratory tube characters. *Ann. Ent. Soc. America*, 54: 557–66.

Prescott, S. C., and C. G. Dunn. 1959. *Industrial Microbiology*. 3rd edition. McGraw-Hill Book Co., Inc., New York, Toronto, London. 945 pp.

Principi, M. M. 1947. Contributi allo studio dei 'Neurotteri' Italiani V. Ricerche su *Chrysopa formosa* Brauer e su alcuni suoi parassiti. *Boll. Istit. Ent. Univ. Bologna*, 16: 134–75.

Pritchard, A. E. 1949. California greenhouse pests and their control. *California Agric. Expt. Sta. Bull.* 713. 71 pp.

Proper, A. B. 1931. *Eupteromalus nidulans*, a parasite of the brown-tail and satin moths. *Jour. Agric. Res.*, 43: 37–56.

Provasoli, L. (Chairman). 1958. A catalogue of laboratory strains of free-living and parasitic protozoa (with sources from which they may be obtained and directions for their maintenance). *Jour. Protozool.*, 5: 1–38.

Pschorn-Walcher, H. 1956. *Aphanogmus nigrofornicatus* nov. spec. (Ceraphronid) ein Parasit der räuberisch an Adelgiden lebenden Gallmuckenlarven von *Aphidoletes thompsoni* Moehn. *Mitteil. Schweiz. ent. Ges.* 29: 353–62.

Puttler, B. 1961. *Hyposoter exiguae* (Hymenoptera: Ichneumonidae), a parasite of lepidopterous larvae. *Ann. Ent. Soc. America*, 54: 25–30.

Puttler, B., and R. van den Bosch. 1959. Partial immunity of *Laphygma exigua* (Hübner) to the parasite *Hyposoter exiguae* Viereck. *Jour. Econ. Ent.*, 52: 327–9.

Pyatnitzkiĭ, G. K. 1940. *Agrotechnical methods of controlling the beet-weevil*. In *Kulagin*. (Eds. N. M. and G. K. Pyatnitzkiĭ) The beet weevil and its control. (In Russian.) 151 pp. Moscow, Vsesoyuzn. Akad. s.-kh. Nauk Lenina. Pp. 25–37. [*R.A.E. A.*, 30: 64–5].

Quayle, H. J. 1911. The black scale. *California Agric. Expt. Sta. Bull.* 223: 150–200.

Quednau, W. 1955. Über einige *Trichogramma*-Wirte und ihre Stellung im Wirt-Parasit-Verhältnis. Ein Beitrag zur Analyse des Parasitismus bei Schlupfwespen. *Nachrichtenbl. deutsch. Pflanzenschutz.*, 7: 145–8.

—— 1956a. Die biologischen Kriterien zur Unterschiedung von Trichogramma-Arten. *Zeitschr. Pflanzen. krankh.*, 63: 334–44.

—— 1956b. Der Wert des physiologischen Experiments für die Artsystematik von *Trichogramma* (Hym. Chalcididae)—*Ber. Hundertjahrfeier Deutsch. Ent. Ges. Berlin*, 30: 87–92.

—— 1957. Über den Einfluss von Temperatur und Luftfeuchtigkeit auf den Eiparasiten, *Trichogramma cacoeciae* Marchal. *Mitteil. Biol. Bundesanstalt Land. u. Forstwirtschaft.*, 90: 1–63.

Radha, K., K. K. Nurula, and K. P. V. Menon. 1956. The green muscardine disease of *Oryctes rhinoceros* L. II. The causal organism. *Indian Coconut Jour.*, 9: 83–9.

Raff, J. W. 1934. Observations on sawflies of the genus *Perga*, with notes on some reared parasites of the families Trigonalidae, Ichneumonidae, and Tachinidae. *Proc. Roy. Soc. Victoria*, 47: 53–77.

Ramachandran, S. 1950. *Cyphorcera varia* Fabr., a tachinid parasite on *Spodoptera mauritia* Bolsd. in South India. *Indian Jour. Ent.*, 12: 107–12.

Rasmussen, Steen. 1956a. Nutritional preference experiments with larvae of house longhorn beetle *Hylotrupes bajulus*. *Oikos*, 7: 82–97.

—— 1956b. On the significance of cholesterol and yeast extract in the diet of larvae of house longhorn beetle (*Hylotrupes bajulus*). *Oikos*, 7: 243–50.

—— 1957. Simultaneous analysis of several growth factors in *Hylotrupes* larvae. *Oikos*, 8: 65–82.

Rasso, S. C., and G. Fraenkel. 1954. The food requirements of the adult female blow-fly, *Phormia regina* (Meigen), in relation to ovarian development. *Ann. Ent. Soc. America*, 47: 636–45.

Ratzeburg, J. T. C. 1844a. *Die Ichneumonen der Forstinsekten in forstlicher und entomologischer Beziehung; ein Anhang zur Abbildung und Beschreibung der Forstinsekten.* Berlin, Theile. 3 vol.

—— 1844b. *Die Ichneumonen der Forstinsekten*, Vol. 1, Berlin.

Rawlings, G. B. 1958. Problems of forest entomology in exotic forests in New Zealand. *Proc. 10th Internatl. Congr. Ent.*, 4: 241–6 (1956).

Rawlins, W. A. 1953. A method for rearing the onion maggot in insectary cultures. *Jour. Econ. Ent.*, 46: 1101.

Readio, P. A. 1931. Dormancy in *Reduvius personatus* (Linnaeus). *Ann. Ent. Soc. America*, 24: 19–39.

Réaumur, M. de. 1726. Remarques sur la plante appellée à la Chine Hia Tsao Tom Tchom, ou plante ver. *Mem. Acad. Roy. Sci. (21 Aug. 1726)*, pp. 302–5.

Réaumur, R. A. F. de. 1735. Observations du thermomètre. *Mem. Acad. Roy. Sci. Paris*, 545–76.

Reeks, W. A. 1953. The establishment of introduced parasites of the European spruce sawfly (*Diprion hercyniae* (Htg.)) (Hymenoptera: Diprionidae) in the Maritime Provinces. *Canad. Jour. Agric. Sci.*, 33: 405–29.

Reeks, W. A., and C. C. Smith. 1956. The satin moth, *Stilpnotia salicis* (L.), in the maritime provinces and observations on its control by parasites and spraying. *Canadian Ent.*, 88: 565–79.

Rehn, J. A. G. 1958. *The origin and affinities of the Dermaptera and Orthoptera of western North America*, pp. 253–98. In *Zoogeography. Amer. Assoc. Adv. Sci. Publ.* 51, 509 pp. C. L. Hubbs, Editor.

Reynoldson, T. B. 1957. *Population fluctuations in Urceolaria mitra* (Peritricha) and *Enchytraeus albidus* (*Oligochaeta*) *and their bearing on regulation.* In *Cold Spring Harbor Symposia on Quantitative Biology*, 22: 313–27.

Rhode, R. H. 1957. A diet for Mexican fruit flies. *Jour. Econ. Ent.*, 50: 215.

Ribbands, C. R. 1953. *The Behavior and Social Life of Honeybees.* Bee Research Assoc., Ltd., London, 352 pp.

Richards, A. G., and M. A. Brooks. 1958. Internal symbiosis in insects. *Ann. Rev. Ent.*, 3: 37–56.

Richards, O. W. 1955. Review: 'Andrewartha, H. G. and L. C. Birch. The distribution and abundance of animals. Chicago, Univ. Chicago Press. 782 pp.' *Jour. Animal Ecol.*, 24: 465.

Richardson, C. H. 1913. Studies on the habits and development of a hymenopterous parasite *Spalangia muscidarum* Rich. *Jour. Morphol.*, 24: 513–57.

Richardson, H. H. 1932. An efficient medium for rearing house flies through the year. *Science*, 76: 350–1.

Riemann, H., and Z. J. Ordal. 1961. Germination of bacterial endospores with calcium and dipicolinic acid. *Science*, 133: 1703–4.

Riherd, P. T. 1950. Biological notes on *Anagyrus antoninae* Timberlake (Hymenoptera: Encyrtidae) and its host *Antonina graminis* (Maskell) (Homoptera: Coccidae). *Florida Entom*, 33: 18–22.

Riley, C. V. 1893. Parasitic and predaceous insects in applied entomology. *Insect Life*, 6: 130–41.

Riley, J. M., and M. Solowey. 1958. Survival of *Serratia marcescens* in concentrates and suspensions stored at 5° C. *Appl. Microbiol.*, 6: 233–5.

Riley, W. A. 1931. Erasmus Darwin and the biologic control of insects. *Science*, 73: 475–6.

Ripley, L. B., G. A. Hepburn, and J. Dick. 1939. Mass breeding of false codling-moth *Argyroplace leucotreta* Meyr., in artificial media. *Union S. Africa Dept. Agric. Sci. Bull.* 207. 17 pp.

Ripper, W. E. 1956. Effect of pesticides on balance of arthropod populations. *Ann. Rev. Ent.*, 1: 403–38.

Ripper, W. E., R. M. Greenslade, J. Heath, and K. Barker. 1948. New formulation of D.D.T. with selective properties. *Nature*, 161: 484.

Risco Briceno, S. H. 1954. The indigenous fly, *Paratheresia claripalpis* W., in the biological control of *Diatraea saccharalis* Fabr., in Peru. Observations on its biology, artificial rearing, and natural parasitism in the sugar-cane fields. *Soc. nac. Agrar., Com. Prod. Azuc., Lima*, 32 pp.

Rivas, A. M., and W. D. Buchanan. 1958. A new technique for rearing carpenterworms. *Jour. Econ. Ent.*, 51: 406–7.

Rivers, C. F. 1959. Virus resistance in larvae of *Pieris brassicae* (L.). *Trans. 1st Internatl. Conf. Insect Pathol. and Biol. Control, Prague, 1958.* Pp. 205–10.

Rivnay, E. 1939. Studies in the biology and control of *Pseudococcus comstocki* Kuwana, on citrus in Palestine. *Hadar*, 12: 1–16.

—— 1946. The status of *Clausenia purpurea* Ishii and its competition with other parasites of *Pseudococcus comstocki* Kuw. in Palestine. [Hymenoptera: Chalcidoidea-Encyrtidae, and Hemiptera-Homoptera: Coccoidea]. *Bull. Soc. Fouad Ier Entom.*, 30: 11–19.

Roberts, R. A. 1933. The biology of *Brachymeria fonscolombei* (Dufour), a hymenopterous parasite of blowfly larvae. *U.S. Dept. Agr. Tech. Bull.* 365. 22 pp.

—— 1935. Some North American parasites of blowflies. *Jour. Agric. Res.*, 50: 479–94.

Robertson, A. 1960. A theory of limits in artificial selection. *Proc. Roy. Soc. Ser. B.*, 153: 234–49.

Robbins, W. W., M. K. Bellue, and W. S. Ball. 1951. *Weeds of California.* Calif. State Dept. Agric. Publ. 547 pp.

Robbins, W. W., A. S. Crafts, and R. N. Raynor. 1942. *Weed Control.* McGraw-Hill Book Co. New York and London. 543 pp.

Robson, G. C. 1928. *The Species Problem. An Introduction to the Study of Evolutionary Divergence in Natural Populations.* Oliver and Boyd, London, 283 pp.

Rockwood, L. P. 1950a. Entomogenous fungi of the family Entomophthoraceae in the Pacific Northwest. *Jour. Econ. Ent.*, 43: 704–7.

—— 1950b. Entomogenous fungi of the genus *Metarrhizium* on wireworms in the Pacific Northwest. *Ann. Ent. Soc. America*, 43: 495–8.

Rödel, H. 1886. Über das vitale Temperaturminimum wirebelloser Tiere. *Zeitschr. Naturw.*, 59: 183–214.

Rodriguez, J. G., and L. D. Rodriguez. 1952. The relation between minerals, B-complex vitamins and mite populations in tomato foliage. *Ann. Ent. Soc. America*, 45: 331–8.

Rodriguez Lopez, L. 1942. La 'Icerta' plaga de los citricos. *Bol. Dep. Agric. Ecuador No. 17.*

Roe, Anne, and G. G. Simpson (Editors). 1958. *Behavior and Evolution.* Yale Univ. Press, New Haven. 557 pp.

Roegner-Aust, S. 1949. Der Infektionsweg bei der Polyederepidemie der Nonne. *Zeitschr. angew. Ent.*, 31: 1–37.

Rollins, Robert Z. 1960. Drift of pesticides. *California Dept. Agric. Bull.* 49: 34–9.

Romanova, V. P., and L. Il'Inskaya. 1938. Methods for large-scale rearing of *Lariophagus distinguendus* Forst. and its hosts. *Lenin Acad. Sci., Leningrad.*, 3: 55–8. [*R.A.E.*, 27: 304].

Romney, V. E., and T. P. Cassidy. 1945. *Anaphes ovijentatus*, an egg-parasite of *Lygus hesperus. Jour. Econ. Ent.*, 38: 497–8.

Ronna, A. 1936. Observacoes biologicas sabre dois dipteros parasitas de *Apis mellifica* L. *Rev. d'Ent.*, 6: 1–9.

—— 1937. *Melaloncha ronnai* Brgm. 1935. (Phoridae) endoparasita de *Apis mellifica* L. *Rev. de Indus. Anim.*, 4: 113–6.

Rorer, J. B. 1910. The green muscardine of froghoppers. *Proc. Agric. Soc. Trinidad and Tobago*, 10: 467–82.

—— 1913*a*. The use of the green muscardine in the control of some sugar cane pests. *Phytopath.*, 3: 88–92.

—— 1913*b*. The green muscardine fungus and its use in cane fields. *Board of Agric., Trinidad and Tobago, Circ.* 8. 15 pp.

Rosenberg, H. T. 1934. The biology and distribution in France of the larval parasites of *Cydia pomonella* L. *Bull. Ent. Res.*, 25: 201–56.

Ross, D. A. 1952. Key to the puparia of the dipterous parasites of *Choristoneura fumiferana* Clem. *Canadian Ent.*, 84: 108–12.

Ross, E. S. 1953. *Insects Close Up: a Pictorial Guide for the Photographer and Collector.* Univ. Calif. Press. 80 pp.

—— 1954. *Systematic entomology: Introduction.* In *A Century of Progress in the Natural Sciences, 1853–1953,* pp. 485–95, E. L. Kessel, editor. California Acad. Sci., San Francisco. 807 pp.

Ross, H. H. 1958*a*. The relationships of systematics and the principles of organic evolution. *Proc. 10th Internatl. Congr. Ent.*, 1: 423–9 (1956).

—— 1958*b*. *Affinities and origins of the northern and montane insects of western North America,* pp. 231–52. In *Zoogeography. Amer. Assoc. Adv. Sci. Publ.* 51, 509 pp. C. L. Hubbs, editor.

Ross, J. 1835. *Narrative of a Second Voyage in Search of a Northwest Passage.* London. (Appendix: p. lxxi.) [Cited in Uvarov 1931.]

Roth, L. M., and E. R. Willis. 1954. *Anastatus floridanus* (Hymenoptera: Eupelmidae), a new parasite on the eggs of the cockroach *Eurycotis floridana. Trans. American Ent. Soc.*, 80: 29–41.

—— 1960. The biotic associations of cockroaches. *Smithsonian Misc. Coll.*, 141. 470 pp.

Roubaud, E. 1922. Recherches sur la Fécondité et la Longévité de la Mouche Domestique. *Ann. Inst. Pasteur*, 36: 765–83.

Rubtzov, I. A. 1947. On the state and outlook of the biological control of insects. (In Russian—English summary.) *Rev. Ent. U.S.S.R.*, 29: 1–11.

—— 1957a. Etat et problèmes de l'étude et de l'utilisation en U.R.S.S. des entomophages dans la lutte biologique contre les insectes nuisibles. *Entomophaga*, 2: 125–8.

—— 1957b. Conference on problems of biological pest control methods. *Entomol. Oboz.* (Translated: *Entomological Review* by A.I.B.S. Washington, D.C.), 37: 174–8.

—— 1959. Biological control of insect pests. (In Russian with English summary.) *Izvestia, Acad. Nauk. U.S.S.R. Ser. Biol.* 4: 558–76.

—— 1960. Variability and selection of entomophages. *Zool. Zurn. Acad. Nauk U.S.S.R.*, 39: 641–54 [Russian with English summary].

Russo, G. 1938. Contributo alla conoscenza dei coleotteri scolitidi Fleotribo: *Phloestribus scarabaeoides* (Bern.) *Fauv. Bol. Lab. Ent. Agr. Portici*, 2: 3–419.

Ryan, Roger B. 1961. A biological and developmental study of *Coelorides brunneri* Vier., a parasite of the Douglas-fir beetle, *Dendroctonus pseudotsugae* Hopk. Ph.D. thesis, Oregon State Univ.

Ryivkin, B. V. 1950. *Telenomus verticillatus* Kieffer (Hymenoptera: Scelionidae)—a parasite of the eggs of *Dendrolimus pini* (L.). *Ent. Obozereine, Moscow*, **31**: 71–76. (In Russian.) [*R.A.E.*, **41**: 165–6. 1953.]

Sabrosky, C. W. 1950. Taxonomy and ecology. *Ecology*, **31**: 151–2.

—— 1955. The interrelations of biological control and taxonomy. *Jour. Econ. Ent.*, **48**: 710–14.

Sager, S. M. 1960. On the transtadial transmission of insect viruses. *Jour. Insect Pathol.*, **2**: 307–9.

Sailer, R. I. 1954. Interspecific hybridization among insects with a report on cross breeding experiments with stink bugs. *Jour. Econ. Ent.*, **47**: 377–83.

Salavin, R. J. 1958. Notas biologicas sobre la mosca *Servaisai* (*Protodexia*) *arteagai* (Blanch) Rob. (Diptera: Sarcophagidae) parasito de la tucura. *Rev. Invest. Agric. Buenos Aires*, **12**: 299–310. [*R.A.E.*, **48**: 319.]

Salkeld, E. H. 1959. Notes on anatomy, life-history, and behaviour of *Aphaereta pallipes* (Say) (Hymenoptera: Braconidae), a parasite of the onion maggot, *Hylemya antiqua* (Meig.). *Canadian Ent.*, **91**: 93–7.

Salt, G. 1931. Parasites of the wheat-stem sawfly, *Cephus pygmaeus* Linnaeus, in England. *Bull. Ent. Res.*, **22**: 479–545.

—— 1932. Superparasitism by *Collyria calcitrator* Grav. *Bull. Ent. Res.*, **23**: 211–15.

—— 1934. Experimental studies in parasitism. II. Superparasitism. *Proc. Roy. Soc. London Ser. B: Biol. Sci.*, **114**: 455–76.

—— 1935. Experimental studies in insect parasitism. III. Host selection. *Proc. Roy. Soc. London Ser. B: Biol. Sci.*, **117**: 413–35.

—— 1937. The sense used by *Trichogramma* to distinguish between parasitized and unparasitized hosts. *Proc. Roy. Soc. London Ser. B: Biol. Sci.*, **122**: 57–75.

—— 1938. Experimental studies in insect parasitism. VI. Host suitability. *Bull. Ent. Res.*, **29**: 223–46.

—— 1941. The effects of hosts upon their insect parasites. *Biol. Rev.*, **16**: 239–364.

—— 1961. Competition among insect parasitoids. *Symposia Soc. Exper. Biol.*, **15**; *Mechanisms in Biol. Competition*, pp. 96–119.

Sampson, A. W., and K. W. Parker. 1930. St. Johnswort on range lands of California. *California Agric. Expt. Sta. Bull.* **503**. 48 pp.

Sanderson, E. D. 1908. The influence of temperature in the northern distribution of insects. *Jour. Econ. Ent.*, **1**: 245–62.

Sandner, H. 1958. Biological control in Poland. *Proc. 10th Internatl. Congr. Ent.*, **4**: 471–4 (1956).

Sang, J. H. 1956. The quantitative nutritional requirements of *Drosophila melanogaster*. *Jour. Exptl. Biol.*, **33**: 45–72.

—— 1959. Circumstance affecting the nutritional requirements of *Drosophila melanogaster*. *Ann. New York Acad. Sci.*, **77**: 352–65.

Sang, J. H., and G. A. Clayton. 1957. Selection for larval development time in *Drosophila*. *Jour. Heredity*, **48**: 265–70.

Sasaki, C. 1886. On the life history of *Ugimyia sericaria* Rondani. *Tokyo Jour. Col. Sci.*, **1**: 1–46.

Saunders, D. S. 1960. On the stages in the development of *Syntomosphyrum albiclavus* Kerrich (Hym.: Eulophidae), a parasite of Tsetse flies. *Bull. Ent. Res.*, **51**: 25–31.

Saunders, W. 1882. Address of the President of the Entomological Society of Ontario. *Canadian Ent.*, **14**: 147–50.

Sawyer, W. H. 1929. Observations on some entomogenous members of the Entomophthoraceae in artificial culture. *American Jour. Bot.*, **16**: 87–121.

Sawyer, W. H. 1931. Studies on the morphology and development of the insect-destroying fungus, *Entomophthora sphaerosperma. Mycologia*, 23: 411–32.

Schaefer, E. E. 1936. The white fungus disease (*Beauveria bassiana*) among red locusts in South Africa, and some observations on the grey fungus disease (*Empusa grylli*). *Union S. Africa, Dept. Agric. Sci. Bull., Plant Industry Ser., 18*, No. 160. 28 pp.

Schaerffenberg, B. 1952. Die Möglichkeiten einer Maikäferbekämpfung mit Hilfe von Mykosen. I. *Beauveria densa* Link, ein Hauptparasit von *Melolontha* sp. *Anz. Schädlingsk.*, 25: 166–70.

—— 1957. *Beauveria bassiana* (Vuill.) Link als Parasit des Kartoffelkäfers (*Leptinotarsa decemlineata* Say). *Anz. Schädlingskunde*, 30: 69–74.

—— 1959. Zur Biologie und Oekologie des insektennötenden Pilzes *Metarrhizium anisopliae* (Metsch.) Sorok. (Entwicklung, Kultur, Lebensanspruche, Infektionsverlauf, praktische Bedeutung). *Zeitschr. angew. Ent.*, 44: 262–71.

Scheel, C. A., S. Beck, and J. T. Medler. 1957. Nutrition of plant-sucking Hemiptera. *Science*, 125: 444–5.

—— 1958. Feeding and nutrition of certain Hemiptera. *Proc. 10th Internatl. Congr. Ent.*, 2: 303–8 (1956).

Schell, S. C. 1943. The biology of *Hadronotus ajax* Girault (Hymenoptera: Scelionidae) a parasite in the eggs of squash-bug (*Anasa tristis* DeGeer). *Ann. Ent. Soc. America*, 36: 625–35.

Schenk, E. T., and J. H. McMaster. 1956. *Procedure in taxonomy: including a reprint of the International Rules of Zoological Nomenclature, with summaries of opinions rendered to the present date*. Stanford, California, and Oxford Univ. Press, London, 72 pp.

Schlabritzky, E. 1955. Das Stuttgarter Insektarium zur Zucht von *Prospaltella perniciosi* Tow. (Hymenoptera). *Zeitschr. Pflanzenkrank. (Pflanzenpath.) u. Pflanzenschutz*, 62: 440–5.

Schlinger, E. I. 1952. The emergence, feeding habits, and host of *Opsebius diligens* Osten Sacken. *Pan-Pacific Ent.*, 28: 7–12.

—— 1957. A generic revision and catalogue of the Acroceridae. Ph.D. thesis, Univ. of California. 317 pp.

—— 1960a. Diapause and secondary parasites nullify the effectiveness of rose-aphid parasites in Riverside, California, 1957–1958. *Jour. Econ. Ent.*, 53: 151–4.

—— 1960b. A revision of the genus *Ogcodes* Latreille with particular reference to species of the Western Hemisphere. *Proc. U.S. Natl. Mus.*, 111: 227–36.

—— 1960c. A review of the genus *Eulonchus* Gerstaeker. Part I. The species of the *Smaragdinus* group (Diptera: Acroceridae). *Ann. Ent. Soc. America*, 53: 416–22.

Schlinger, E. I., and E. J. Dietrick. 1960. Biological control of insect pests aided by strip-farming alfalfa in experimental program. *California Agriculture*, 14: 8–9, 15.

Schlinger, E. I., and J. C. Hall. 1959. A synopsis of the biologies of three imported parasites of the spotted alfalfa aphid. *Jour. Econ. Ent.*, 52: 154–7.

—— 1960. The biology, behavior, and morphology of *Praon palitans* Muesebeck, and internal parasite of the spotted alfalfa aphid, *Therioaphis maculata* (Buckton) (Hymenoptera; Braconidae, Aphidiinae). *Ann. Ent. Soc. America*, 53: 144–60.

—— 1961. The biology behavior, and morphology of *Trioxys* (*Trioxys*) *utilis*, an internal parasite of the spotted alfalfa aphid, *Therioaphis maculata* (Hymenoptera: Braconidae, Aphidiinae). *Ann. Ent. Soc. America*, 54: 34–45.

Schlinger, E. I., R. van den Bosch, and E. J. Dietrick. 1959. Biological notes on the predacious earwig *Labidura riparia* (Pallas) a recent immigrant to California [Dermaptera: Labiduridae]. *Jour. Econ. Ent.*, 52: 247–9.

Schmeider, R. G. and P. W. Whiting. 1947. Reproductive economy in the Chalcidoid wasp *Melittobia*. *Genetics*, **32**: 29–37.

Schmieder, R. G. 1939*a*. On the dimorphism of cocoons of *Sphecophaga burra* (Cresson). *Ent. News*, **50**: 91–7.

—— 1939*b*. The significance of the two types of larvae in *Sphecophaga burra* (Cresson) and the factors conditioning them (Hymenoptera: Ichneumonidae). *Ent. News*, **50**: 125–31.

Schmidt, K. P. 1954. *Animal Geography*. In *A Century of Progress in the Natural Sciences, 1853–1953*, pp. 767–94, E. L. Kessel, editor. California Acad. Sci., San Francisco, 807 pp.

Schmidt, L. 1956. Utjecaj hrane na razvoj gubara (*Lymantria dispar* L.). *Ann. Exp. for.*, *Zagreb*, **12**: 105–66.

Schmidt, L., and G. Philips. 1958. Granuloza—Nova virusna bolest na dudovcu *Hyphantria cunea* Drury. Poljoprivredno—Sùmarski Fakultet, Zavod za entomologiju, Zagreb., No. 1, mimeo. rept. 27 pp.

Schneider, F. 1939. Ein Vergleich von Urwald und Monokultur in Bezug auf ihre Gefährdung durch phytophage Insekten, auf Grund einiger Beobachtungen an der Ostküste von Sumatra. *Schweiz. Zeitschr. Forstw.*, **90**: 82–9.

—— 1948. Beitrag zur Kenntnis der Generationsverhältnisse und Diapause räuberischer Schwebefliegen (Syrphidae). *Mitteil., Schweiz. Ent. Ges.*, **21**: 249–85.

—— 1950. Die Entwicklung des Syrphidenparasiten *Diplazon fissorius* Grav. *Mitteil., Schweiz. ent. Ges.*, **23**: 155–94.

Schneidermann, H. A., and J. Horwitz. 1958. The induction and termination of facultative diapause in the chalcid wasps *Mormoniella vitripennis* (Walker) and *Tritneptis klugii* (Ratzeburg). *Jour. Exptl. Biol.*, **35**: 520–51.

Schread, J. C. 1932. Behaviour of *Trichogramma* in field liberations. *Jour. Econ. Ent.*, **25**: 370–4.

—— 1935. Cooperative European corn borer egg parasitism investigation. *Conn. Agric. Expt. Sta. Bull.* 383: 344–6.

Schread, J. C., and P. Garman. 1933. Studies on parasites of the oriental fruit moth. I. *Trichogramma*. *Bull. Connecticut Agric. Expt. Sta.* 353: 691–756.

Schultz, O. 1900. Filarien in paläarktischen Lepidopteren. *Illustr. Zeitschr. Ent.*, **5**: 148–52; 164–6; 183–5; 199–201; 264–5; 279–80; 292–7.

Schultz, J., P. St. Lawrence, and D. Newmeyer. 1946. A chemically defined medium for the growth of *Drosophila melanogaster*. *Anat. Record*, **96**: 540 (abstr.).

Schulz-Langner, E. 1958. Über das Vorkommen hoher Körpertemperaturen bei der Honigbiene mit entwicklungshemmender Wirkung auf den Parasiten *Nosema apis* (Zander). *Zeitschr. f. Bienenforsch.*, **4**: 67–86.

Schvester, D. 1957. Contribution à l'étude écologique des Coléoptères Scolytides. Essai d'analyse des facteurs de fluctuation des populations chez *Ruguloscolytus rugulosus* Müller 1818. *Ann. inst. natl. recherches agron. Sér. C. Ann. épiphyt. Numéro Hors Série 8*. 162 pp.

Schweizer, G. 1936. Der Pilz *Empusa muscae* und seine Bedeutung bei der Fliegenbekämpfung. *Natur und Kultur (München)*, **33**: 149–52.

—— 1947. Ueber die Kultur von *Empusa muscae* Cohn und anderen Entomophthoraceen auf kalt sterilisierten Nährböden. *Planta*, **35**: 132–76.

Schwenke, W. 1958. Local dependence of parasitic insects and its importance for biological control. *Proc. 10th Internatl. Congr. Ent.*, **4**: 851–4 (1956).

Schwerdtfeger, F. 1941. Über die Ursachen des Massenwechsels der Insekten. *Zeitschr. angew. Ent.*, **28**: 254–303.

Schwerdtfeger, F. 1958. Is the density of animal populations regulated by mechanisms or by chance? *Proc. 10th Internatl. Congr. Ent.*, 4: 115–22. (1956.)

Scoggin, J. K., and O. E. Tauber. 1950. Survey of literature on insect lipids. *Iowa State Coll. Jour. Sci.*, 25: 99–124.

—— 1951. The bionomics of *Dermestes maculatus* Deg. II. Larval and pupal development at different moisture levels and on various media. *Ann. Ent. Soc. America*, 44: 544–50.

Seamans, H. L. 1926. The pale western cutworm. *Canada Dept. Agric. Pamph.* 71. N.S. 8 pp.

Sekhar, P. S. 1957. Mating, oviposition, and discrimination of host by *Aphidius testaceipes.* (Cresson) and *Praon aguti* Smith, primary parasites of aphids. *Ann. Ent. Soc. America*, 50: 370–5.

Sellers, W. F. 1952. The collection of the cactus weevil, *Cactophagus spinolae* (Gylh.) and its dispatch to South Africa. *Bull. Ent. Res.*, 43: 43–50.

—— 1953. A critique on the time factor in biological control. *Bull. Ent. Res.*, 83: 230–40.

Semper, K. G. 1881. *Animal Life as Affected by the Natural Conditions of Existence.* New York, Appleton. 472 pp.

Sergeant, T. P., C. E. Lankford, and R. W. Traxler. 1957. Initiation of growth of *Bacillus* species in a chemically defined medium. *Jour. Bact.*, 74: 728–36.

Sergent, E. 1916. Campagne d'expérimentation de la méthode biologique contre les *Schistocerca peregrina* dans la vallée de la haute Tafna, commune mixte de Sebdou (Département d'Oran). Existence d'une épizootie autochtone vaccinante (mai, juin, juillet 1915). *Ann. Inst. Pasteur [Paris]*, 30: 209–24.

Sergent, E., and A. Lheritier. 1914. Essai de destruction des sauterelles en Algérie par le 'Coccobacillus acridiorum' de d'Herelle. *Ann. Inst. Pasteur [Paris]*, 28: 408–19.

Seurat, M. 1899. Contributions à l'étude des Hyménopterès entomophages. Ph.D. Thèses à la Faculté des sci. de Paris ser. A. No. 329. 159 pp.

Severin, H. H. P., H. C. Severin, and W. Hartung. 1915. The stimuli which cause the eggs of the leaf-ovipositing Tachinidae to hatch. *Psyche*, 22: 132–7.

Sewell, T. G. 1949. Manuka blight survey. *New Zealand Jour. Agric.*, 79: 101–4.

Shafer, G. D. 1949. *The Ways of a Mud Dauber.* Stanford Univ. Press. 78 pp.

Shanor, L. 1936. The production of mature perithecia of *Cordyceps militaris* (Linn.) Link in laboratory culture. *Jour. Elisha Mitchell Sci. Soc.*, 52: 99–104.

Shelford, V. E. 1913. Animal communities in temperate America. *Bull. Geogr. Soc. Chicago*, 5: 1–368.

—— 1929. Laboratory and Field Ecology. *The Responses of Animals as Indicators of Correct Working Methods.* Baltimore, Williams and Wilkins. 56 pp.

Shepetilnikova, V. A. 1960. Results of the studies on use of parasites in the insect control in the Soviet Union. *Trans. 1st Intern. Conf. Ins. Path. Bio. Contr., Prague 1958.* 441–53. [Russian with English summary.]

Sherwood, R. C., and D. D. Pond. 1954. A simple method of rearing *Hylemya brassicae* (Bouche). *Canadian Ent.*, 86: 178–9.

Short, J. R. T. 1952. The morphology of the head of larval Hymenoptera with special reference to the head of Ichneumonoidea, including a classification of the final instar of the Braconidae. *Trans. Roy. Ent. Soc. Lond.*, 103: 27–84.

—— 1953. A grouping by larval characters of some species of the genus *Apanteles* (Hymenoptera: Braconidae). *Bull. Ent. Res.*, 44: 327–32.

—— 1959. A description and classification of the final instar larvae of the Ichneumonidae (Insecta, Hymenoptera). *Proc. U.S. Natl. Mus.*, 110: 391–511.

Shough, W. W. 1940. The feeding of ground beetles. *Amer. Midland Nat.*, 24: 336–44.

Shvetsova, O. I. 1950. The polyhedrosis disease of the greater wax moth (*Galleria mellonella* L.) and the role of the nutritional factor in virus diseases of insects. *Mikrobiologiia*, 19: 532–42.

—— 1954. *The role of the nutritive factor in the development of virus epizootics of insects.* In: *Infections and protozoan diseases of insects.* V. I. Poltev, L. V. Alexandrova, and A. A. Yevlakhova, editors. Plenary Session of the Sericulture and Apiculture, Plant Protection, and Veterinary Science Sections. Leningrad. All-Union Order of Lenin Academy of Agric. Sciences named for V. I. Lenin. (Vesoiuznaia akademiia sel. skokhoziaĭstvennykh nauk imeni V. I. Lenina). Abstracts of Reports, 76 pp. (In Russian.)

Sidor, C. 1959. Susceptibility of larvae of the large white butterfly (*Pieris brassicae* L.) to two virus diseases. *Ann. Appl. Biol.*, 47: 109–13.

Sidrovnina, E. P. 1938. A field experiment with *Trichogramma* for control of the codling moth in Azerbaidzhan. *Lenin Acad. Agric. Sci., Leningrad,* 111: 60–3. [Abs. in *R.A.E.*, 27: 305, 1939.]

Sieburth, J. F., and M. G. Bonsall. 1951. A simplified biological assay method using the cockroach, *Periplaneta americana* (Linn.), for protein utilization. *Ann. Ent. Soc. America,* 44: 463–8.

Silvestri, F. 1906. Contribuzioni alla conoscenza biologica degli imenotteri parassiti. I. Biologia del *Litomastix truncatellus* (Dalm.). *Bol. Lab. Zoo. Gen. e Agr. Portici,* 1: 17–64.

—— 1909a. A survey of the actual state of agricultural entomology in the United States of North America. Extracts from *Reprint from the Bulletin of the Society of Italian Agriculturalists.* Vol. XIV, No. 8, April 30, 1909. Translated from the Italian by J. Rosenstein. In *The Hawaiian Forester and Agriculturalist,* 6: 287–336.

—— 1909b. Squardo allo stato attuale dell' entomologica agraria negli statiuniti del Nord America e ammastramenti che possono derivarne per l'agricoltura Italiana. *Boll. Soc. Agric. Ital. Roma,* 14: 1–65.

—— 1914. Report of an expedition to Africa in search of the natural enemies of fruit flies (Trypaneidae). *Hawaii Board of Agric. and Forestry, Div. of Ent. Bull.* 3, 176 pp.

—— 1916. Contribuzione alla conoscenza del genere *Poropoea* Forster. *Bol. Lab. Zool. Gen. Agr., Portici,* 11: 120–35.

—— 1919. Contribuzioni alla conoscenza degli insetti dannosi e dei loro simbionti. IV. La cocciniglia del prugno (*Sphaerolecanium prunastri* Fonsc.). V. La cocciniglia del Nocciuolo (*Eulecanium coryli* L.). *Boll. Lab. Zool. Gen. e Agr., Portici,* 13: 70–126, 127–92.

—— 1921. Contribuzioni alla conoscenza biologica degli Imenotteri parassiti. V. Sviluppo del *Platygaster dryomyiae* Silv. *Bol. Lab. Zool Gen. e Agr., Portici,* 11: 299–326.

—— 1923. Contribuzioni alla conoscenza dei Tortricidi delle querce. *Bol. Lab. Zool. Gen. e Agr., Portici.* 17: 41–107.

—— 1929. The relation of taxonomy to other branches of entomology. *Trans. 4th Internatl. Congr. Ent.,* 2: 52–4.

—— 1937. Insect polyembryony and its general biological aspects. *Bull. Mus. Comp. Zool., Cambridge, Mass.,* 81: 469–98.

—— 1941a. Contribuzioni alla conoscenza degli insetti dannosi e dei loro simbionti: VI. La Falena Bramlae o la brumale (*Operophthera brumata* L.). *Boll. Lab. Ent. Agr., Portici,* 5: 61–120.

—— 1941b. Studi sugli 'Strepsiptera' (Insecta). I. Ridescrizione e ciclo dell' *Eoxenos laboulbenei* Peyerimoff. *Boll. Lab. Zool. Gen. e Agr., Portici,* 31: 311–42.

Silvestri, F. 1943. Studi sugli 'Strepsiptera' (Insecta). III. Descrizione e biologia di 6 specie italiane di *Mengenilla*. *Boll. Lab. Zool. Gen. e Agr., Portici*, **32**: 197–283.

—— 1949. Le problème de la lutte biologique en Europe Continentale. *Int. U. Biol. Sci., Ser. B*, **5**: 106–20.

Simmonds, F. J. 1943. The occurrence of superparasitism in *Nemeritis canescens* Grav. *Rev. Canadienne Biol.*, **2**: 15–58.

—— 1944*a*. Observations on the parasites of *Cydia pomonella* L. in southern France. *Sci., Agric.*, **25**: 1–30.

—— 1944*b*. The propagation of insect parasites on unnatural hosts. *Bull. Ent. Res.*, **35**: 219–26.

—— 1947*a*. Improvement of the sex-ratio of a parasite by selection. *Canadian Ent.*, **79**: 41–4.

—— 1947*b*. The biology of the parasites of *Loxostege sticticalis* L. in North America— *Bracon vulgaris* (Cress.) (Braconidae, Agathinae). *Bull. Ent. Res.*, **38**: 145–55.

—— 1947*c*. The biology of the parasites of *Loxostege sticticalis* L. in North America— *Meteorus loxostegei* Vier. (Braconidae, Meteorinae). *Bull. Ent. Res.*, **38**: 373–9.

—— 1947*d*. The biology of *Phytodietus pulcherrimus* (Cress.) (Ichneumonidae, Tryphoninae) parasitic on *Loxostege sticticalis* L. in North America. *Parasitology*, **38**: 150–6.

—— 1948*a*. The effective control by parasites of *Schematiza cordiae* Barber, in Trinidad. *Bull. Ent. Res.*, **39**: 217–20.

—— 1948*b*. Some difficulties in determining by means of field samples the true value of parasitic control. *Bull. Ent. Res.*, **39**: 435–40.

—— 1948*c*. The biology of parasites of *Loxostege sticticalis* L. in North America. IV. *Cryptus inornatus* Pratt (Ichneumonidae, Cryptinae). *Proc. Roy. Ent. Soc. London Ser. A.*, **23**: 71–9.

—— 1948*d*. The influence of maternal physiology on the incidence of diapause. *Phil. Trans. Roy. Soc. London. Ser. B : Biol. Sci.*, **233**: 385–414.

—— 1952. Parasites of the frit-fly, *Oscinella frit* (L.), in eastern North America. *Bull. Ent. Res.*, **43**: 503–42.

—— 1953. Observations on the biology and mass-breeding of *Spalangia drosophilae* Ashm. (Hymenoptera: Spalangiidae), a parasite of the frit-fly, *Oscinella frit* (L.). *Bull. Ent. Res.*, **44**: 773–8.

—— 1956*a*. Superparasitism by *Spalangia drosophilae* Ashm. *Bull. Ent. Res.*, **47**: 361–76.

—— 1956*b*. The successful breeding of *Palpozenillia palpalis* (Ald.) (Diptera: Tachinidae) a parasite of *Diatraea* spp. *Trop. Agric.*, **35**: 218–24.

—— 1958*a*. The effect of lizards on the biological control of scale insects in Bermuda. *Bull. Ent. Res.*, **49**: 601–12.

—— 1958*b*. The control of *Cordia macrostachya* (Boraginaceae) in Mauritius. *Proc. 10th Internatl. Congr. Ent.*, **4**: 553–5 (1956).

—— 1958*c*. Recent work on biological control in the British West Indies. *Proc. 10th Internatl. Congr. Ent.*, **4**: 475–8 (1956).

—— 1959. Biological control—past, present and future. *Jour. Econ. Ent.*, **52**: 1099–1102.

—— 1960. Biological control of the coconut scale, *Aspidiotus destructor* Sign., in Principe, Portuguese West Africa. *Bull. Ent. Res.*, **51**: 223–37.

Simmonds, H. W. 1933. The biological control of the weed *Clidemia hirta* D. Don., in Fiji. *Bull. Ent. Res.*, **24**: 345–8.

—— 1934. Biological control of noxious weeds, with special reference to the plants *Clidemia hirta* (The Curse) and *Stachytarpheta jamaicensis* (Blue Rat Tail). *Fiji Dept. Agric. Jour.*, **7**: 3–10.

Simmonds, H. W. 1958. Housefly problem in Fiji and Samoa. *S. Pacific Comm. Quart. Bull.*, 8: 29–30, 47.

Simpson, G. G. 1943. Criteria for genera, species, and subspecies in zoology and paleozoology. *Ann. New York Acad. Sci.*, 44: 145–78.

—— 1945. The principles of classification and a classification of mammals. *Bull. Amer. Mus. Nat. Hist.*, 85: 1–350.

—— 1951. The species concept. *Evolution*, 5: 285–98.

—— 1953. *Evolution and Geography*. Oregon State System of Higher Education, Eugene. 64 pp.

Slobodkin, L. B., and S. Richman. 1956. The effect of removal of fixed percentages of the newborn on size and variability in populations of *Daphnia pulicaria* (Forbes). *Limnology and Oceanography*, 1: 209–37.

Smart, J. 1940. *Entomological systematics examined as a practical problem*, pp. 475–92. In *The New Systematics*, J. S. Huxley, editor. Oxford Univ. Press, 583 pp.

Smirnoff, W. A. 1958. An artificial diet for rearing coccinellid beetles. *Canadian Ent.*, 90: 563–5.

—— 1959. Predators of *Neodiprion swainei* Midd. (Hymenoptera: Tenthredinidae) larval vectors of virus diseases. *Canadian Ent.*, 9: 246–8.

—— 1961. A virus disease of *Neodiprion swainei* Middleton. *Jour. Insect Pathol.*, 3: 29–46.

Smirnov, B. A. 1954. *An experiment in using white muscardine in the control of Aradus cinnamomeus* Panz. In *Infections and protozoan diseases of insects.* (V. I. Poltev, L. V. Alexandrova, A. A. Yevlakhova, and M. S. Pavelyeva, editors.) All-Union Order of Lenin Academy of Agricultural sciences named for V. I. Lenin. Abstracts. 76 pp. (In Russian.)

Smith, C. G., and M. J. Johnson. 1954. Aeration requirements for the growth of aerobic microorganisms. *Jour. Bact.*, 68: 346–50.

Smith, F. 1942. Effect of reduced food supply upon the stature of *Camponotus* ants. *Ent. News*, 53: 133–5.

—— 1944. Nutritional requirements of *Camponotus* ants. *Ann. Ent. Soc. America*, 37: 401–8.

Smith, F. E. 1961. Density dependence in the Australian thrips. *Ecology*, 42: 403–7.

Smith, H. D. 1932. *Phaeogenes nigridens* Wesmael, an important Ichneumonid parasite of the pupa of the European corn borer. *U.S. Dept. Agr. Tech. Bull.* 331. 45 pp.

Smith, H. G. V., and D. W. Empson. 1955. Note on the courtship and predaceous behaviour of *Poecilobothrus nobilitatus* L. (Dipt.: Dolichopodidae). *Brit. Jour. Animal Behaviour*, 3: 32–4.

Smith, H. S. 1912. The Chalcidoid genus *Perilampus* and its relations to the problem of parasite introduction. *U.S. Dept. Agric. Tech. Ser.*, *19*, Pt. IV: 33–69.

—— 1916. An attempt to redefine the host relationships exhibited by entomophagous insects. *Jour. Econ. Ent.*, 9: 477–86.

—— 1919. On some phases of insect control by the biological method. *Jour. Econ. Ent.*, 12: 288–92.

—— 1921. Biological control of black scale in California. *California Dept. Agric. Monthly Bull.*, 10: 127–37.

—— 1929a. Multiple parasitism: its relation to the biological control of insect pests. *Bull. Ent. Res.*, 20: 141–9.

—— 1929b. The utilization of entomophagous insects in the control of citrus pests. *Trans. 4th Internatl. Congr. Ent.*, 2: 191–8.

Smith, H. S. 1933. The influence of civilization on the insect fauna through purposeful introductions. *Ann. Ent. Soc. America*, **26**: 518–25.

—— 1935. The role of biotic factors in the determination of population densities. *Jour. Econ. Ent.*, **28**: 873–98.

—— 1939. Insect populations in relation to biological control. *Ecol. Monogr.*, **9**: 311–20.

—— 1941. Racial segregation in insect populations and its significance in applied entomology. *Jour. Econ. Ent.*, **34**: 1–13.

—— 1942*a*. Biological control of the black scale. *California Citrograph*, **27**: 266, 290–1.

—— 1942*b*. A race of *Comperiella bifasciata* successfully parasitizes California red scale. *Jour. Econ. Ent.*, **35**: 809–12.

—— 1946. The biological control program in relation to California agriculture. *California Citrograph*, **31**: 414, 452.

—— 1955. *Ecological aspects of insect population dynamics.* Unpublished manuscript. Presented as a symposium paper before the Entomological Society of America, Cincinnati, 1955.

Smith, H. S., and H. M. Armitage. 1920. Biological control of mealybugs in California. *California Dept. Agric. Monthly Bull.*, **9**: 104–58.

—— 1931. The biological control of mealybugs attacking citrus. *California Agric. Expt. Sta. Bull.* **509**. 74 pp.

Smith, H. S., and H. Compere. 1928. A preliminary report on the insect parasites of the black scale, *Saissetia olea* (Bern.). *Univ. California Pub. Ent.*, **4**: 231–334.

—— 1931. Notes on *Ophelosia crawfordi* Riley. *Jour. Econ. Ent.*, **24**: 1109–10.

Smith, H. S., and P. DeBach. 1942. The measurement of the effect of entomophagous insects on population densities of their hosts. *Jour. Econ. Ent.*, **35**: 845–9.

—— 1953. Artificial infestation of plants with pest insects as an aid in biological control. *Proc. 7th Pacific Sci. Congr.*, **4**: 255–9. (1949.)

Smith, H. S., and S. E. Flanders. 1913. Is *Trichogramma* becoming a fad? *Jour. Econ. Ent.*, **24**: 666–72.

Smith, J. M. 1957. Effects of the food plant of California red scale, *Aonidiella aurantii* (Mask.), on reproduction of its hymenopterous parasites. *Canadian Ent.*, **89**: 219–30.

—— 1958. Biological control of Klamath weed, *Hypericum perforatum* L., in British Columbia. *Proc. 10th Internatl. Congr. Ent.*, **4**: 561–5. (1956.)

Smith, K. M. 1959. *The insect viruses* (Chapter 13: 369–92). In *The Viruses 3.* 428 pp. (F. M. Burnet and W. M. Stanley, editors.) New York, Academic Press.

Smith, K. M., and R. C. Williams. 1958. Insect viruses and their structure. *Endeavor*, **17**: 12–21.

Smith, O. J. 1952. Biology and behavior of *Microctonus vittatae* Muesebeck (Braconidae). *Univ. Calif. Publ. Ent.*, **9**: 315–44.

Smith, O. J., A. G. Diboll, and J. H. Rosenberger. 1955. Laboratory studies of *Pelecystoma harrisinae* (Ashmead) an adventive braconid parasite of the western grape leaf skeletonizer. *Ann. Ent. Soc. America*, **48**: 232–7.

Smith, O. J., P. H. Dunn, and J. H. Rosenberger. 1955. Morphology and biology of *Sturmia harrisinae* Coquillett (Diptera), a parasite of the western grape leaf skeletonizer. *Univ. California Publ. Ent.*, **10**: 321–58.

Smith, O. J., K. M. Hughes, P. H. Dunn, and I. M. Hall. 1956. A granulosis virus disease of the western grape leaf skeletonizer and its transmission. *Canadian Ent.*, **88**: 507–15.

Smith, O. J., and R. L. Langston. 1953. Continuous laboratory propagation of the western grapeleaf skeletonizer and parasites by prevention of diapause. *Jour. Econ. Ent.*, **46**: 477–84.

Smith, R. C. 1922. The biology of the Chrysopidae. *Cornell Univ. Agric. Expt. Sta. Mem.*, 58: 1287–1372.

—— 1923. The life histories and stages of some hemerobiids. *Ann. Ent. Soc. America*, 16: 129–48.

—— 1927. Observations on *Euplectrus plathypenae* How. (Chalcidae), a parasite of noctuid larvae. *Bull. Brooklyn Ent. Soc.*, 22: 128–34.

—— 1942. *Guide to the Literature in the Zoological Sciences.* Burgess Publ. Co., Minneapolis, 128 pp.

—— 1956. Upsetting the balance of nature, with special reference to Kansas and the Great Plains. *Science*, 75: 649–54.

Smith, R. F. 1954. The importance of the microenvironment in insect ecology. *Jour. Econ. Ent.*, 47: 205–9.

Smith, R. F., and K. S. Hagen. 1956. Predators of the spotted alfalfa aphid. *California Agric.*, 10: 8–10.

Smith, R. W. 1952. Another method of rearing grasshoppers in the laboratory. *Canadian Ent.*, 84: 269–71.

—— 1958. Parasites of nymphal and adult grasshoppers (Orthoptera: Acrididae) in western Canada. *Canadian J. Zool.*, 36: 217–62.

Smith, R. W., and T. U. Finlayson. 1950. Larvae of dipterous parasites of nymphal and adult grasshoppers. *Canadian Jour. Res. (D)*, 28: 81–117.

Smith, S. G. 1955. Cytogenetics of obligatory parthenogenesis. *Canadian Ent.*, 87: 131–5.

—— 1959. The cytogenetic basis of speciation in Coleoptera. *Proc. 10th Internatl. Congr. Ent.*, 1: 444–50. (1956.)

Smyth, E. G. 1939. *Trichogramma* proves itself in sugar cane borer. *Proc. Internatl. Congr. Sugar Cane Technol. Soc.*, 6: 367–77.

Smyth, H. F., and W. L. Obold. 1930. *Industrial Microbiology.* Williams and Wilkins Co., Baltimore. 313 pp.

Snodgrass, R. E. 1935. *Principles of Insect Morphology.* McGraw-Hill Book Co., Inc., New York, 667 pp.

—— 1952. *A Textbook of Arthropod Anatomy.* Comstock Publ. Associates, New York, 363 pp.

—— 1954. Insect metamorphosis. *Smithsonian Misc. Coll.*, 122, 124 pp.

—— 1956. *Anatomy of the Honey Bee.* Comstock Publ. Associates, New York, 334 pp.

Snow, F. H. 1891. Experiments for the destruction of chinch bugs. *21st Ann. Rept. Ent. Soc. Ontario.* Pp. 93–7.

—— 1896. Contagious diseases of the chinch-bug. *Fifth Annual Report of Director, Kansas Univ. Agric. Expt. Sta. for 1895.* 55 pp.

Sokal, R. R. 1958. Quantification of systematic relationships and of phylogenetic trends. *Proc. 10th Internatl. Congr. Ent.*, 1: 409–15. (1956.)

Solomon, M. E. 1949. The natural control of animal populations. *Jour. Animal Ecol.*, 18: 1–35.

—— 1953. The population dynamics of storage pests. *Trans. 9th Internatl. Congr. Ent.* 2: 235–48. (1951.)

—— 1955. Review: 'Nicholson, A. J. 1954. An outline of the dynamics of animal populations. *Australian Jour. Zool.*, 2: 9–65.' *Jour. Animal Ecol.*, 24: 463.

—— 1957. Dynamics of insect populations. *Ann. Rev. Ent.*, 2: 121–42.

—— 1958a. Meaning of density-dependence and related terms in population dynamics. *Nature*, 181: 1778–80.

—— 1958b. Perfect and imperfect density dependence in population dynamics. *Nature*, 182: 1252.

Solomon, M. E. 1959. (A review.) A symposium on population ecology. *Ecology*, 40: 325–6.

Somsen, H. W., and P. Luginbill, Jr. 1956. *Bracon lissogaster* Mues., a parasite of the wheat stem sawfly. *U.S. Dept. Agric. Tech. Bull.* 1153. 7 pp.

Speare, A. T. 1912. Fungi parasitic upon insects injurious to sugar cane. Hawaiian Sugar Planters' Experiment Station. *Path. Ser. Bull.*, 12. 62 pp.

Speare, A. T., and R. H. Colley. 1912. *The Artificial Use of the Brown-tail Fungus in Massachusetts, with Practical Suggestions for Private Experiment, and a Brief Note on a Fungous Disease of the Gypsy Caterpillar*. Wright and Potter Printing Co., Boston. 29 pp.

Spector, W. S. 1956. *Handbook of Biological Data*. W. B. Saunders Co., Philadelphia and London. 584 pp.

Speicher, K. G., and B. R. Speicher. 1938. Diploids from unfertilized eggs in *Habrobracon*. *Biol. Bull.*, 74: 247–52.

Spencer, G. J. 1958. On the Nemestrinidae of British Columbia dry range lands. *Proc. 10th Internatl. Congr. Ent.*, 4: 503–9 (1956).

Spencer, H. 1852, A theory of population, deduced from the general law of animal fertility. *Westminster Rev.*, 57: 468–501.

—— 1897a. *First Principles*. New York, D. Appleton and Co. 612 pp.

—— 1897b. *The Principles of Biology*. New York, D. Appleton and Co. Vol. 1, 470 pp.; Vol. 2, 536 pp.

Spencer, Herbert. 1926. Biology of the parasites and hyperparasites of aphids. *Ann. Ent. Soc. America*, 19: 119–57.

Spencer, H., L. Brown, and A. M. Phillips. 1935. New equipment for obtaining host material for the mass production of *Trichogramma minutum*, an egg parasite of various insect pests. *U.S. Dept. Agric. Circ.* 376. 17 pp.

—— 1949. Use of the parasite *Trichogramma minutum* for controlling pecan insects. *U.S. Dept. Agric. Circ.* 818. 17 pp.

Spencer, W. P. 1950. *Collection and laboratory Culture*. In: *Biology of Drosophila*, pp. 535–90, M. Demerec, editor. John Wiley and Sons, Inc. New York.

Speyer, E. R. 1927. An important parasite of the greenhouse white-fly (*Trialeurodes vaporariorum* Westwood). *Bull. Ent. Res.*, 17: 301–8.

Spieth, H. T. 1958. Behavior and isolating mechanisms, pp. 363–89. In: *Behavior and Evolution*, Roe and Simpson, editors. Yale Univ. Press, New Haven, Conn.

Stallybrass, C. O. 1931. *The Principles of Epidemiology and the Process of Infection*. George Routledge and Son, Ltd., London. 696 pp.

Stanley, J. 1953. Studies on the autotrephon. II. The analysis of autotrephon data. *Ecology*, 34: 29–43.

Starrett, A. 1958. What is the subspecies problem? *Systematic Zool.*, 7: 111–15.

Stearns, L. A. 1919. Some recently recorded parasites of the oriental peach moth. *Jour. Econ. Ent.*, 12: 347–8.

Stearns, L. A., and J. M. Amos. 1941. Ten-year record of oriental fruit moth parasitism in Delaware. *Jour. Econ. Ent.*, 34: 245–8.

Steel, R. (editor). 1958. *Biochemical Engineering*. Macmillan Co. New York. 328 pp.

St. George, R. A., and J. A. Beal. 1929. The southern pine beetle; a serious enemy of pines in the South. *U.S. Dept. Agric. Farmer's Bull.* 1586. 18 pp.

Stein, Wolfgang. 1960. Versuche zur biologischen Bekämpfung des Apfelwicklers (*Carpocapsa pomonella* (L.)) durch Eiparasiten der Gattung *Trichogramma*. *Entomophaga*, 5: 237–59.

Stein, W., and J. Franz. 1960. Die Leistungsfähigkeit von Eiparasiten der Gattung *Trichogramma* (Hym. Trichogrammatidae) nach Aufzucht unter verschiedenen Bedingungen. *Naturwiss.*, 11: 262–3.

Steiner, H. M. 1938. Effects of orchard practices on natural enemies of the white apple leafhopper. *Jour. Econ. Ent.*, 31: 232–40.

Steinhaus, E. A. 1946. *Insect Microbiology*. Comstock Publishing Co., Inc., Ithaca, New York. 763 pp.

—— 1949a. *Principles of Insect Pathology*. McGraw-Hill Book Co., Inc., New York. 757 pp.

—— 1949b. Polyhedrosis ('wilt disease') of the alfalfa caterpillar. *Jour. Econ. Ent.*, 41: 859–65.

—— 1949c. Nomenclature and classification of insect viruses. *Bact. Rev.*, 13: 203–23.

—— 1951a. Report on diagnoses of diseased insects 1944–1950. *Hilgardia*, 20: 629–78.

—— 1951b. Possible use of *Bacillus thuringiensis* Berliner as an aid in the biological control of the alfalfa caterpillar. *Hilgardia*, 20: 359–81.

—— 1953a. Taxonomy of insect viruses. *Ann. New York Acad. Sci.*, 56: 517–37.

—— 1953b. Diseases of insects reared in the laboratory or insectary. *Univ. California, Div. Agric. Sci. Leaflet* 9. 26 pp.

—— 1954. The effects of disease on insect populations. *Hilgardia*, 23: 197–261.

—— 1956a. Microbial control—the emergence of an idea. A brief history of insect pathology through the nineteenth century. *Hilgardia*, 26: 107–60.

—— 1956b. Living insecticides. *Sci. Amer.*, 195: 96–100, 102, 104.

—— 1956c. Potentialities for microbial control of insects. *Agric. and Food Chem.*, 4: 676–80.

—— 1957a. New records of insect-virus diseases. *Hilgardia*, 26: 417–30.

—— 1957b. List of insects and their susceptibility to *Bacillus thuringiensis* and closely related bacteria. Mimeo. Ser. 4, Lab. Insect Path., Dept. Biol. Cont., Univ. California.

—— 1957c. New horizons in insect pathology. *Jour. New York Ent. Soc.*, 65: 113–21.

—— 1957d. Concerning the harmlessness of insect pathogens and the standardization of microbial control products. *Jour. Econ. Ent.*, 50: 715–20.

—— 1958a. The diagnosis of insect diseases. *No. 2, Mimeo. Series, Lab. Insect Pathol., Univ. Calif.*, 4 pp.

—— 1958b. Stress as a factor in insect disease. *Proc. 10th Internatl. Congr. Ent.*, 4: 725–30 (1956).

—— 1958c. Crowding as a possible stress factor in insect disease. *Ecology*, 39: 503–14.

—— 1958d. Bacteria as microbial control agents. *Trans. 1st Internatl. Conf. Insect. pathol. and biol. control, Praha, 1958*. Pp. 37–50.

—— 1959a. On the improbability of *Bacillus thuringiensis* Berliner mutating to forms pathogenic for vertebrates. *Jour. Econ. Ent.*, 52: 506–8.

—— 1959b. *Serratia marcescens* Bizio as an insect pathogen. *Hilgardia*, 28: 351–80.

—— 1960a. Insect pathology: challenge, achievement, and promise. *Bull. Ent. Soc. America*, 6: 9–16.

—— 1960b. Symposium: Selected topics in microbial ecology. II. The importance of environmental factors in the insect-microbe ecosystem. *Bacteriol. Rev.*, 24: 365–73.

Steinhaus, E. A., and J. M. Birkeland. 1939. Studies on the life and death of bacteria. I. The senescent phase in aging cultures and the probable mechanisms involved. *Jour. Bact.*, 38: 249–61.

Steinhaus, E. A., and E. A. Jerrel. 1954. Further observations on *Bacillus thuringiensis* Berliner and other sporeforming bacteria. *Hilgardia*, 23: 1–23.

Steinhaus, E. A., and C. G. Thompson. 1949. Preliminary field tests using a polyhedrosis virus to control the alfalfa caterpillar. *Jour. Econ. Ent.*, 42: 301–5.

Steinkraus, K. H. 1957. Studies on the milky disease organisms. II. Saprophytic growth of *Bacillus popilliae*. *Jour. Bact.*, 74: 625–32.

Steinkraus, K. H., and M. L. Provvidenti. 1958. Studies on the milky disease organisms. III. Variability among strains of *Bacillus popilliae* sporulating on artificial media. *Jour. Bact.*, 75: 38–42.

Steinkraus, K. H., and H. Tashiro. 1955. Production of milky-disease spores (*Bacillus popilliae* Dutky and *Bacillus lentimorbus* Dutky) on artificial media. *Science*, 121: 873–4.

Stejskal, M. 1959. Correlation entre les maladies des abeilles et les conditions atmosphèriques. *Bull. Apicole*, 2: 103–6.

Stelfox, A. W. 1944. The swarming flights of *Blacus* (Hym.: Braconidae). *Ent. Month. Mag.*, 80: 208.

Stephen, W. P. 1958. Hemolymph proteins and their use in taxonomic studies. *Proc. 10th Internatl. Congr. Ent.*, 1: 395–400 (1956).

Stephens, J. M. 1952. Disease in codling moth larvae produced by several strains of *Bacillus cereus*. *Canadian Jour. Zool.*, 30: 30–40.

—— 1957a. Survival of *Pseudomonas aeruginosa* (Schroeter) Migula suspended in various solutions and dried in air. *Canadian Jour. Microbiol.*, 3: 995–1000.

—— 1957b. Spore coverage and persistence of *Bacillus cereus* Frankland and Frankland sprayed on apple trees against the codling moth. *Canadian Ent.*, 89: 94–6.

—— 1959a. Mucin as an agent promoting infection by *Pseudomonas aeruginosa* (Schroeter) Migula in grasshoppers. *Canadian Jour. Microbiol.*, 5: 73–7.

—— 1959b. Immune responses of some insects to some bacterial antigens. *Canadian Jour. Microbiol.*, 5: 203–28.

—— 1959c. Note on effects of feeding grasshoppers two pathogenic species of bacteria simultaneously. *Canadian Jour. Microbiol.*, 5: 313–15.

Stern, V. M., I. M. Hall, and G. D. Peterson. 1959. The utilization of *Bacillus thuringiensis* Berliner as a biotic insecticide to suppress the alfalfa caterpillar. *Jour. Insect Path.*, 1: 142–51.

Stern, V. M., R. F. Smith, R. van den Bosch, and K. S. Hagen. 1959. The integration of chemical and biological control of the spotted alfalfa aphid. The integrated control concept. *Hilgardia*, 29: 81–101.

Stevenson, J. P. 1959. Epizootiology of a disease of the desert locust, *Schistocerca gregaria* (Forskål), caused by nonchromogenic strains of *Serratia marcescens* Bizio. *Jour. Insect Pathol.*, 1: 232–44.

Steyn, J. J. 1958. The effect of ants on citrus scales at Letaba, South Africa. *Proc. 10th Internatl. Congr. Ent.*, 4: 589–94 (1956).

Stoll, N. R. 1953. Axenic cultivation of the parasitic nematode, *Neoaplectana glaseri*, in a fluid medium containing raw liver extract. *Jour. Parasitol.*, 39: 422–44.

—— 1959. Conditions favoring the axenic culture of *Neoplectana glaseri*, a nematode parasite of certain insect grubs. *Ann. New York Acad. Sci.*, 77: 126–36.

Strickland, E. H. 1923. Biological notes on parasites of prairie cutworms. *Canada Dept. Agric. Ent. Branch Bull.* 22, 40 pp.

Stride, G. O. 1953. On the nutrition of *Carpophilus hemipterus* L. *Trans. Roy. Ent. Soc., London*, 104: 171–94.

Struble, G. R. 1942. Laboratory propagation of two predators of the mountain pine beetle. *Jour. Econ. Ent.*, 35: 841–4.

Stuart, A. M. 1957. *Ephialtes brevicornis* (Grav.) as an external parasite of the diamond-back moth, *Plutella maculipennis* Curt. *Bull. Ent. Res.*, 48: 477–88.

Stunkard, H. W. 1940. Life history studies and development of parasitology. *Jour. Parasitol.*, 26: 1–15.

Sussman, A. S. 1951. Studies of an insect mycosis. I. Etiology of the disease. *Mycologia*, 43: 338–50.

—— 1952. Studies of an insect mycosis. IV. The physiology of the host-parasite relationship of *Platysamia cecropia* and *Aspergillus flavus*. *Mycologia*, 44: 493–505.

Swain, R. B. 1952. *How Insects Gain Entry*. The Yearbook of Agriculture, pp. 350–5. U.S. Govt. Printing Office, 800 + pp.

Sweetman, H. L. 1936. *The Biological Control of Insects*. Comstock Publ. Co., Inc., Ithaca, N.Y. 461 pp.

—— 1956. Rearing successive generations of the carpet beetle under controlled conditions. *Jour. Econ. Ent.*, 49: 277–8.

—— 1958. *The Principles of Biological Control*. Wm. C. Brown Co., Dubuque, Iowa. 560 pp.

Swezey, O. H. 1909. Army worms and cut worms on sugar cane in the Hawaiian Islands. *Rept. Exp. Sta. Hawaii. Sugar Plant. Assoc. Div. Ent. Bull.*, 7: 1–32.

—— 1925. Records of introduction of beneficial insects into the Hawaiian Islands. *Hawaiian Planters' Rec.*, 29: 368–78.

—— 1934. Biological control of insect pests in Hawaii. *Proc. 5th Pac. Sci. Congr.*, 5: 3531–6. (1933.)

Sysoev, A. T. 1953. The possibility of combining biological and chemical methods in the control of pests of agricultural crops. [In Russian.] *Dokl. vsesoyuz. Akad. sel.-khoz. Nauk Lenina*, 18(7): 26–31, Moscow, 1953. [*R.A.E.*, 42: 147, 1954.]

Szirmai, J. 1957. Biologische Abwehr mittels Virus zur Bekämpfung der *Hyphantria cunea* Drury. *Acta Microbiol. Acad. Scient. Hungaricae*, 4: 31–42.

Szumkowski, W. 1952a. Observations on Coccinellidae. I. Coccinellids as predators of lepidopterous eggs and larvae in Venezuela. *Trans. 9th Internatl. Congr. Ent.*, 1: 778–81.

—— 1952b. Observations on Coccinellidae. II. Experimental rearing of *Coleomegilla* on a non-insect diet. *Trans. 9th Internatl. Congr. Ent.*, 1: 781–5.

Tadic, M. D. 1958. *Apanteles hyphantriae* Riley, an egg parasite of the fall webworm. *Proc. Xth Internatl. Congr. Ent.*, 4: 859–86. (1956.)

Talalaev, E. V. 1956. Septicemia of the caterpillars of the Siberian silk-worm. *Microbiology U.S.S.R.*, 25: 99–102.

Tamashiro, M. 1960. The susceptibility of *Bracon*-paralyzed *Corcyra cephalonica* (Stainton) to *Bacillus thuringiensis* var. *thuringiensis* Berliner. *Jour. Insect Pathol.*, 2: 209–19.

Tanada, Y. 1953. Description and characteristics of a granulosis virus of the imported cabbageworm. *Proc. Hawaiian Ent. Soc.*, 15: 235–60.

—— 1955a. Field observations on a microsporidian parasite of *Pieris rapae* (L.) and *Apanteles glomeratus* (L.). *Proc. Hawaiian Ent. Soc.*, 15: 609–16.

—— 1955b. Susceptibility of the imported cabbageworm to fungi: *Beauveria* spp. *Proc. Hawaiian Ent. Soc.*, 15: 617–22.

—— 1956a. Some factors affecting the susceptibility of the armyworm to virus infections. *Jour. Econ. Ent.*, 49: 52–7.

—— 1956b. Microbial control of some lepidopterous pests of crucifers. *Jour. Econ. Ent.*, 49: 320–9.

—— 1959a. Microbial control of insect pests. *Ann. Rev. Ent.*, 4: 277–302.

Tanada, Y. 1959*b*. Synergism between two viruses of the armyworm, *Pseudaletia unipuncta* (Haworth) (Lepidoptera: Noctuidae). *Jour. Insect Pathol.*, 1: 215–31.

—— 1961. The epizootiology of virus diseases in field populations of the armyworm, *Pseudaletia unipuncta* (Haworth). *Jour. Insect Pathol.*, 3: 310–23.

Tanada, Y., and G. Y. Chang. 1960. A cytoplasmic polyhedrosis of the armyworm, *Pseudaletia unipuncta* (Haworth) (Lepidoptera: Noctuidae). *Jour. Insect Pathol.*, 2: 201–8.

Tanaka, M. 1953. The settlement of the red scale and the horned wax scale on the potato tubers. I. The study of mass production of the important hym. parasite (*Anicetus ceroplastis* Ishii). (English summary.) *Kyushu Agric. Expt. Sta. Bull.*, 2: 55–63.

Tardrew, C. G. 1951. The biological control of the Karoo caterpillar. *Farming in So. Africa*, reprint No. 33, pp. 1–4. (May.)

Tashiro, H. 1957. Susceptibility of European chafer and Japanese beetle larvae to different strains of milky disease organisms. *Jour. Econ. Ent.*, 50: 350–2.

Tashiro, H., and R. T. White. 1954. Milky diseases of European chafer larvae. *Jour. Econ. Ent.*, 47: 1087–92.

Tateishi, I. 1957. On the relation between the green muscardine disease of the late autumn silkworm and *Naranga aenescens* Moor. *Jour. of Plant Protection (Japan)*, 11: 65–7.

Tateishi, I., T. Murata, and S. Hirano. 1954. On the relation between the silkworm and the green muscardine disease of *Naranga aenescens* Moor and the hardening diseases of outdoor insects collected in Fukuoka Prefecture. *Fukuoka Prefectural Agric. Expt. Sta. Res. Rept. No. 8*: 49–56.

Taylor, A. B., and R. L. King. 1937. Further studies on the parasitic amebae found in grasshoppers. *Trans. Amer. Microsc. Soc.*, 56: 172–6.

Taylor, T. H. C. 1935. The campaign against *Aspidiotus destructor* Sign. in Fiji. *Bull. Ent. Res.*, 26: 1–102.

—— 1937. *The Biological Control of an Insect in Fiji. An account of the coconut leaf-mining beetle and its parasite complex.* Imp. Inst. Ent., London. 239 pp.

—— 1955. Biological control of insect pests. *Ann. Appl. Biol.*, 42: 190–6.

Taylor, W. L. 1938. Birds and British forestry. *Forestry*, 12: 1–9.

Telenga, N. A. 1956. Investigations on *Trichogramma evanescens* Westw. and *T. pallida* Meyer (Hymenoptera: Trichogrammatidae) and their use for the control of injurious insects in the U.S.S.R. *Rev. Ent. U.S.S.R.*, 35: 599–610 Moscow (in Russian). [Abs. *R.A.E.*, Ser. *A*, 45: 474–75.

—— 1958. Biological method of pest control in crops and forest plants in the U.S.S.R. *9th Internatl. Conf. Quarantine and Plt. Protect. against Pests and Diseases.* Moscow, 1958. Pp. 1–15.

Telford, A. D. Features of the lodgepole needle miner parasite complex in California. *Canadian Ent.*, 93: 394–402.

Terao, A., and T. Tanaka. 1928. Population growth of the water flea *Moina macrocopa* Strauss. *Proc. Imper. Acad. (Japan)*, 4: 550–2.

Tevis, L. Jr. 1958. Interrelations between the harvester ant *Vermoessor pergandei* (Mayr) and some desert ephemerals. *Ecology*, 39: 695–704.

Théodoridès, J. 1952. Remarques sur l'écologie de certains Mermithidés (Nematoda). *Vie et Milieu*, 3: 288–91.

Theron, P. P. A. 1945. Rearing *Euxoa* on artificial media. *Jour. Ent. Soc. So. Africa*, 8: 65.

—— 1947. Studies on the provision of hosts for the mass-rearing of colding moth parasites. *Union S. Africa. Dept. Agric. Sci. Bull.* 262. 45 pp.

Thomas, W. J., D. W. Ziegler, S. A. Schepartz, and W. F. McLimans. 1958. Use of arginine to eliminate medium changes in tissue culture systems. *Science*, 127: 591–2.

Thompson, C. G. 1959. Thermal inhibition of certain polyhedrosis virus diseases. *Jour. Insect. Pathol.*, 1: 189–90.

Thompson, C. G., and E. A. Steinhaus. 1950. Further tests using a polyhedrosis virus to control the alfalfa caterpillar. *Hilgardia*, 19: 411–45.

Thompson, W. R. 1910. Notes on the pupation and hibernation of Tachinid parasites. *Jour. Econ. Ent.*, 3: 283–95.

—— 1915a. Sur la biologie de deux tachinaires à state intramusculaire (*Plagia trepida* Meig. et *Sturmia scutellata* Rond.). *Soc. de Bio. (Paris) Compt. Rend.*, 78: 717–21.

—— 1915b. Contribution à la connaissance de la larvae planidium. *Bull. Sci. de la France et Belg.*, 48: 319–49.

—— 1920. Note sur *Rhacodineura antiqua* Fall., Tachinaire parasite des forficules. *Soc. Ent. France Bull.* 1920, pp. 199–201.

—— 1921. Recherches sur les Diptères parasites. I. Les larves des Sarcophagidae. *Bull. Biol. de la France et Belg.*, 54: 313–463.

—— 1922a. On the taxonomic value of larval characters in tachinid parasites (Dipt.). *Proc. Ent. Soc. Wash.*, 24: 85–93.

—— 1922b. Biologie—Théorie de l'action des parasites entomophages. Les formules mathématiques du parasitisme cyclique. *C. R. Acad. Sci. Paris*, 174: 1201–4.

—— 1922c. Entomologie—Étude mathématique de l'action des parasites entomophages. Durée du cycle parasitaire et accroissement de la proportion d'hôtes parasites. *C. R. Acad. Sci. Paris*, 174: 1433–5.

—— 1922d. Parasitologie—Étude de quelques cas simples de parasitisme cyclique chez les insectes entomophages. *C. R. Acad. Sci. Paris*, 174: 1647–9.

—— 1922e. Parasitisme—Théorie de l'action des parasites entomophages. Accroissement de la proportion d'hôtes parasites dans le parasitisme cyclique. *C. R. Acad. Sci. Paris*, 175: 65–8.

—— 1923a. A criticism of the 'sequence' theory of parasitic control. *Ann. Ent. Soc. America*, 16: 115–28.

—— 1923b. Recherches sur la biologie des Diptères parasites. *Bull. Biol. de la France et Belg.*, 57: 174–237.

—— 1923c. Recherches sur les Diptères parasites. Les larves primaires des Tachinidae du groupe des Echinomyiinae. *Ann. Epiphyties*, 9: 137–201.

—— 1924. Les larves primaires des Tachinaires à œufs microtypes. *Ann. Parasitol. Humaine et Comp.*, 2: 185–201, 279–306.

—— 1926. Recherches sur les larves des Tachinaires *Sturmia*, *Winthemia*, *Carcelia* et *Exorista*. *Ann. Parasitol. Humaine et Comp.*, 4: 111–25.

—— 1927. On the effects of methods of mechanical control on the progress of introduced parasites of insect pests. *Bull. Ent. Res.*, 18, 13–16.

—— 1928a. A contribution to the study of the Dipterous parasites of the European earwig (*Forficula auricularia* L.). *Parasitology*, 20: 123–58.

—— 1928b. A contribution to the study of biological control and parasite introduction in continental areas. *Parasitology*, 20: 90–112.

—— 1929a. On natural control. *Parasitology*, 21: 269–81.

—— 1929b. On the relative value of parasites and predators in the biological control of insect pests. *Bull. Ent. Res.*, 19: 343–50.

—— 1930a. The utility of mathematical methods in relation to work on biological control. *Ann. Appl. Biol.*, 17: 641–8.

—— 1930b. The biological control of insect and plant pests. *Publ. Empire Marketing Board, No. 29.* 124 pp.

Thompson, W. R. 1939. Biological control and the theories of the interactions of populations. *Parasitology*, 31: 299–388.

—— 1943 to 1958. *A Catalogue of the Parasites and Predators of Insect Pests*. Section 1, parts 1–11, and section 2, parts 1–5. Commonwealth Inst. Biol. Control, Ottawa, Ont., Canada. 16 volumes.

—— 1948. Can economic entomology be an exact science? *Canadian Ent.*, 80: 49–55.

—— 1951*a*. The specificity of host relations in predaceous insects. *Canadian Ent.*, 83: 262–9.

—— 1951*b*. The time factor in biological control. *Canadian Ent.*, 83: 230–40.

—— 1952. The philosophical foundations of systematics. *Canadian Ent.*, 84: 1–16.

—— 1953. The tachinid parasites of *Archips cerasivorana* Fitch (2) *Eusisyropa blanda* O.S. (Diptera). *Canadian Ent.*, 85: 393–404.

—— 1954. Biological control work on cedar scales in Bermuda. *Rept. 6th Commonwealth Ent. Conf.*, pp. 89–93.

—— 1955. Mortality factors acting in sequence. *Canadian Ent.*, 87: 264–75.

—— 1956. The fundamental theory of natural and biological control. *Ann. Rev. Ent.*, 1: 379–402.

—— 1958. Biological control in some commonwealth countries. *Proc. 10th Internatl. Congr. Ent.*, 4: 479–82 (1956).

Thompson, W. R., and H. L. Parker. 1927. The problem of host relations with special reference to entomophagous parasites. *Parasitology*, 19: 1–34.

—— 1928. The European corn borer and its controlling factors in Europe. *U.S. Dept. Agric. Tech. Bull.* 59. 62 pp.

—— 1930. The morphology and biology of *Eulimneria crassifemur*, an important parasite of the European corn borer. *Jour. Agric. Res.*, 40: 321–45.

Thomsen, M. 1927. Some observations on the biology and anatomy of a cocoon-making chalcid larva, *Euplectrus bicolor* Swed. *Vidensk. Meddel. Dansk. Naturhist. For.*, 84: 73–89.

Thomson, H. M. 1958. Some aspects of the epidemiology of a microsporidian parasite of the spruce budworm, *Choristoneura fumiferana* (Clem.). *Canadian Jour. Zool.*, 36: 309–16.

Thorpe, W. H. 1929. Biological races in *Hyponomeuta padella* L. *Linn. Soc. London Jour. Zool.*, 36: 621–34.

—— 1930*a*. Biological races in insects and allied groups. Cambridge . *Phil. Soc. Biol. Rev.*, 5: 177–212.

—— 1930*b*. Observations on the parasites of the pine-shoot moth, *Rhyacionia buoliana* Schiff. *Bull. Ent. Res.*, 21: 387–412.

—— 1931*a*. The biology, post-embryonic development, and economic importance of *Cryptochaetum iceryae* (Diptera: Agromyzidae) parasitic on *Icerya purchasi* (Coccidae: Monophlebini). *Proc. Zool. Soc. London*, 60: 929–70.

—— 1931*b*. Biological races in insects and their significance in evolution. *Ann. Appl. Biol.*, 18: 406–14.

—— 1932*a*. The primary larvae of three Ophionine ichneumonids, parasitic on *Rhyacionia buoliana*. *Parasitology*, 24: 107–10.

—— 1932*b*. Experiments upon respiration in the larvae of certain parasitic Hymenoptera. *Proc. Roy. Soc. London Ser. B.*, 109: 450–71.

—— 1934. The biology and development of *Cryptochaetum grandicorne* (Diptera), an internal parasite of *Guerinia serratulae* (Coccidae). *Quart. Jour. Micros. Sci.*, 77: 273–304.

Thorpe, W. H. 1936. On a new type of respiratory interrelation between an insect (chalcid) parasite and its host (Coccidae). *Parasitology*, **28**: 517–40.

—— 1939. Further studies on pre-imaginal olfactory conditioning in insects. *Proc. Roy. Soc. London Ser. B.*, **127**: 424–33.

—— 1940. *Ecology and the future of systematics*, pp. 341–64. In *The New Systematics*, J. S. Huxley, editor. Oxford Univ. Press. 583 pp.

Thorpe, W. H., and H. B. Caudle. 1938. A study of the olfactory responses of insect parasites to the food plant of their host. *Parasitology*, **30**: 523–8.

Thorpe, W. H., and F. G. W. Jones. 1937. Olfactory conditioning in a parasitic insect and its relation to the problem of host selection. *Proc. Roy. Soc. London Ser.*, *B.*, **124**: 56–81.

Thorsteinson, A. J. 1953. The role of host selection in the ecology of phytophagous insects. *Canadian Ent.*, **85**: 276–82.

—— 1955. The experimental study of the chemotactic basis of host specificity in phytophagous insects. *Canadian Ent.*, **87**: 49–57.

—— 1958. Acceptability of plants for phytophagous insects. *Proc. 10th Internatl. Congr. Ent.*, **2**: 599–602. (1956.)

Tiegs, O. W. 1922. Researches on the insect metamorphosis. I. On the structure and postembryonic development of a chalcid wasp, *Nasonia*. II. On the physiology and interpretation of the insect metamorphosis. *Trans. Roy. Soc. S. Australia*, **46**: 319–527.

Tillyard, R. J. 1929. The biological control of noxious weeds. *Proc. Roy. Soc. [Tasmania]*. Pp. 51–86.

—— 1930. The biological control of noxious weeds. *Trans. 4th Internatl. Congr. Ent.*, **2**: 4–9. (1928.)

Timberlake, P. H. 1910. Observations on the early stages of two Aphidiine parasites of aphids. *Psyche*, **17**: 125–30.

—— 1912. Technical results from the gipsy moth parasite laboratory. V. Experimental parasitism: a study of the biology of *Limnerium validum* (Cresson). *U.S. Dept. Agric. Bur. Ent. Tech. Ser. No. 19*: 71–92.

Timofeeff-Ressovsky, N. 1940. *Mutations and geographical variation*, pp. 73–136. In *The New Systematics*, J. S. Huxley, editor. Oxford Univ. Press. 583 pp.

Tinbergen, N. 1950. The hierarchical organization of nervous mechanisms underlying instinctive behaviour. *Symposia Soc. Exptl. Biol.*, **4**: 305–12.

—— 1951. *The Study of Instinct*. The Clarendon Press, Oxford, 228 pp.

—— 1953. *Social Behavior in Animals*. John Wiley, New York. 150 pp.

Tisdale, E. W., and G. Zappetini. 1953. *Halogeton* studies on Idaho ranges. *Jour. Range Management*, **6**: 225–36.

Todd, D. H. 1959a. Incidence and parasitism of insect pests of cruciferous crops in the North Island. Evaluation of data, 1955–58 seasons. *New Zealand Jour. Agric. Res.*, **2** 613–22.

—— 1959b. The apple leaf-curling midge, *Dasyneura mali* Kieffer, seasonal history, varietal susceptibility and parasitism, 1955–58. *New Zealand Jour. Agric. Res.*, **2**: 859–69.

Tooke, F. G. C. 1953. The eucalyptus snout-beetle, *Gonipterus scutellatus* Gyll. A study of its ecology and control by biological means. *Union S. Africa, Dept. Agric. Ent. Mem.*, **3**: 282 pp.

Toplin, I., and E. L. Gaden, Jr. 1961. The chemical sterilization of liquid media with beta-propiolactone and ethylene oxide. *Jour. Biochem. Microbiol. Technol. Engineer*, **3**: 311–23.

Torre-Bueno, J. R. de la. 1937. *A Glossary of Entomology*. The Science Press Printing Co., Lancaster, 336 pp.

Tothill, J. D. 1922. The natural control of the fall webworm (*Hyphantria cunea* Drury), in Canada together with an account of its several parasites. *Canada Dept. Agric. Tech. Bull. No. 3*, 107 pp.

—— 1958. Some reflections on causes of insect outbreaks. *Proc. 10th Internatl. Congr. Ent.*, 4: 525–31 (1956).

Tothill, J. D., T. H. C. Taylor, and R. W. Paine. 1930. *The Coconut Moth in Fiji. A history of its control by means of parasites*. Publ. Imp. Bur. Ent., London. 269 pp.

Toumanoff, C. 1950. À propos d'une infection à Protozoaire des Fausses Teignes et du rôle de *Dibrachys boucheanus* Ratzb. dans la destruction de ces insectes. *Rev. Francaise d'Apiculture*, 2: 251–4.

—— 1956. Virulence expérimentale d'une souche banale de *Bacillus cereus* Frank. et Frank. pour les chenilles de *Galleria mellonella* L. et *Pieris brassicae*. *Ann. Inst. Pasteur [Paris]*, 90: 660–5.

—— 1959. Observation concernant le rôle probable d'un prédateur dans la transmission d'un bacille aux chenilles de *Pieris brassicae*. *Ann. Inst. Pasteur [Paris]*, 96: 108–10.

Toumanoff, C., and M. Lapied. 1954. L'effet des antibiotiques sur les souches entomophytes ou non de *Bacillus cereus* Frank. et Frank. *Ann. Inst. Pasteur [Paris]*, 87: 370–4.

Toumanoff, C., and Y. Le Corroller. 1959. Contribution à l'étude de *Bacillus cereus* Frank. et Frank. cristallophores et pathogènes pour les larves des lépidoptères. *Ann. Inst. Pasteur [Paris]*, 96: 680–8.

Toumanoff, C., and C. Vago. 1951. L'agent pathogène de la flacherie des vers à soie endémique dans la région des Cévennes: *Bacillus cereus* var. *alesti* var. nov. *Compt. Rend. Acad. Sci.*, 233: 1504–6.

—— 1952a. La nature de l'affection des vers à soie due à *Bacillus cereus* var. *alesti* Toum. et Vago, et les modalités d'action de ce bacille. *Ann. Inst. Pasteur*, 83: 421–2.

—— 1952b. L'effet de l'alcalinité du milieu de culture sur la virulence de *Bacillus cereus* var *alesti* Toum. et Vago, pour les vers à soie. *Compt. Rend. Acad. Sci.*, 235: 1715–17.

—— 1953. Etude histopathologique des vers à soie atteints de *Bacillus cereus* var. *alesti*. *Ann. Inst. Pasteur*, 84: 376–86.

Tower, D. G. 1915. Biology of *Apanteles militaris*. *Jour. Agric. Res.*, 5: 495–508.

Townsend, C. H. T. 1908. A record of results from rearings and dissections of Tachinidae. *U.S. Bur. Ent. Tech. Ser. 12*, 6: 95–118.

—— 1934. *Manual of Myiology*. I. Development and structure. Escolas Profissionais Salesianas São Paulo, Brasil. 1–280.

—— 1935. *Manual of Myiology*. II. Muscoid classification and habits. Escolas Profissionais Salesianas São Paulo, Brasil. 1–296.

—— 1936a. *Manual of Myiology*. III. Oestroid classification and habits. Gymnosomatidae to Tachinidae. Escolas Profissionais Salesianas São Paulo, Brasil. 1–255.

—— 1936b. *Manual of Myiology*. IV. Oestroid classification and habits. Dexiidae and Exoristidae. Escolas Profissionais Salesianas São Paulo, Brasil. 1–309.

—— 1937. *Manual of Myiology*. V. Muscoid generic diagnoses and data. Glossinini to Agriini. Escolas Profissionais Salesianas São Paulo, Brasil. 1–234.

—— 1938a. *Manual of Myiology*. VI. Muscoid generic diagnoses and data. Stephanostomatini to Moriniini. Escolas Profissionais Salesianas São Paulo, Brasil. 1–246.

—— 1938b. *Manual of Myiology*. VII. Oestroid generic diagnoses and data. Gymnosomatini to Senostomatini. Escolas Profissionais Salesianas São Paulo, Brasil. 1–428.

Townsend, C.H.T. 1939a. *Manual of Myiology*. VIII. Oestroid generic diagnoses and data. Microtropesini to Voriini. Escolas Profissionais Salesianas São Paulo, Brasil, 1–405.

—— 1939b. *Manual of Myiology*. IX. Oestroid generic diagnoses and data. Thelairini to Clythoini. Escolas Profissionais Salesianas São Paulo, Brasil, 1–270.

—— 1940. *Manual of Myiology*. X. Oestroid generic diagnoses and data. Anacamptomyiini to Frontinini. Escolas Profissionais Salesianas São Paulo, Brasil, 1–334.

—— 1941. *Manual of Myiology*. XI. Oestroid generic diagnoses and data. Goniini to Trypherini. Escolas Profissionais Salesianas São Paulo, Brasil, 1–342.

—— 1942. Manual of Myiology. XII. General consideration of the Oestromuscaria. Geologic history and geographic distribution—environment and response—relations to man—hosts and flowers—bibliography and plates. Escolas Profissionais Salesianas São Paulo, Brasil.

Townes, H. 1956. The Nearctic species of *Trigonalid* wasps. *Proc. U.S. Natl. Mus.*, 106: 295–304.

—— 1958. Some biological characteristics of the Ichneumonidae (Hymenoptera) in relation to biological control. *Jour. Econ. Ent.*, 51: 650–2.

Townes, H., and M. Townes. 1959. Ichneumon-flies of America north of Mexico. 1. Subfamily Metopiinae. *U.S. Nat. Mus. Bull.* 216. 318 pp.

—— 1960. Ichneumon-flies of America north of Mexico; 2. Subfamilies Ephialtinae, Xoridinae, Acaenitinae. *Bull. U.S. Nat. Mus.* 216. 676 pp.

Trager, W. 1935. Cultivation of the virus of grasserie in silkworm tissue cultures. *Jour. Exptl. Med.*, 61: 501–13.

—— 1941. The nutrition of invertebrates. *Physiol. Revs.*, 21: 1–35.

—— 1947. Insect nutrition. *Physiol. Revs.*, 22: 148–77.

—— 1953a. Further studies on the extracellular cultivation of an avian malaria parasite. *Ann. New York Acad. Sci.*, 56: 1074–80.

—— 1953b. *Nutrition.* In *Insect Physiology*, K. D. Roeder, editor. Pp. 350–86. John Wiley and Sons, Inc. New York.

—— 1957. The nutrition of an intracellular parasite (Avian malaria). *Acta Tropica*, 14: 289–301.

Tripp, H. A. 1960. *Spathimeigenia spinigera* Townsend (Diptera:Tachinidae), a parasite of *Neodiprion swainei* Middleton (Hymenoptera: Tenthredinidae). *Canadian Ent.*, 92: 345–59.

—— 1961. The biology of a hyperparasite, *Euceros frigidus* Cress. (Ichneumonidae) and description of the planidial stage. *Canadian Ent.*, 93: 40–58.

Trotter, A. 1908. Due precursori nell' applicazione degli insetti carnivori a difesa delle plante coltivate. *Redia*, 5: 126–32.

Tucker, R. W. E. 1931. The mass breeding of *Trichogramma minutum* to control *Diatraea saccharalis* in Barbados during 1930. *Trop. Agric. [Trinidad]*, 8: 281–8.

—— 1939a. Some aspects of the control of the sugarcane moth borer, *Diatraea saccharalis* F. *Proc. Internatl. Congr. Sugar Cane Technol. Soc.*, 6: 240–3.

—— 1939b. Introduction of dry area race of *Metagonistylum minense* into Barbados. *Barbados Dept. Sci. and Agric., Agric. Jour.*, 8: 113–31.

Turnbull, A. L., and D. A. Chant. 1961. The practice and theory of biological control of insects in Canada. *Canad. Jour. Zool.*, 39: 697–753.

Tuxen, S. L. (Editor). 1956. *Taxonomist's Glossary of Genitalia in Insects*. Ejnar Munksgaard, Copenhagen, 284 pp.

Ueda, K., Y. Okimoto, H. Sakai, K. Arima, H. Yonehara, and Y. Sakagami. 1955. An antibiotic against silkworm jaundice virus, grasseriomycin, produced by *Streptomyces* species. *Jour. Antibiot., Ser. A, [Tokyo]*, 8: 91–5.

32*

806 BIBLIOGRAPHY

Ullyett, G. C. 1936. Host selection by *Microplectron fuscipennis* Zett. Hymenoptera. Chalcididae). *Proc. Roy. Soc. London Ser. B.*, 120: 253–91.

—— 1943. Some aspects of parasitism in field populations of *Plutella maculipennis* Curt. *Jour. Ent. Soc. So. Africa*, 6: 65–80.

—— 1944. On the function of the caudal appendage in primary larvae of parasitic Hymenoptera. *Jour. Ent. Soc. So. Africa*, 7: 30–7.

—— 1945. Distribution of progeny by *Microbracon hebetor* Say. *Jour. Ent. Soc. So. Africa*, 8: 123–31.

—— 1947. Mortality factors in populations of *Plutella maculipennis* Curtis (Lep. Tineidae), and their relation to the problems of control. *Union S. Africa, Dept. Agric. Ent. Mem.*, 2: 77–202.

—— 1953. Biomathematics and insect population problems. A critical view. *Mem. Ent. Soc. So. Africa*, 2: 1–89.

Ullyett, G. C., and A. H. DeVries. 1940. Observations on the natural control of sheep blowflies in South Africa. Part I. Predatory wasps of the genus *Bembix* Fabr. *Union So. Africa Dept. Agric. Sci. Bull.* 224. 23 pp.

Ullyett, G. C., and J. S. V. D. Merwa. 1947. Some factors influencing population growth of *Ephestia kuhniella* Zell. *Jour. Ent. Soc. So. Africa*, 10: 46–63.

Ullyett, G. C., and D. B. Schonken. 1940. A fungus disease of *Plutella maculipennis* Curt., with notes on the use of entomogenous fungi in insect control. *Union So. Africa, Dept. Agric. Sci. Bull.* 218. 24 pp.

Urquijo, Pedro 1946. Selección de estirpes de *Trichogramma minutum* Riley de máxima efectividad parasitaria. *Bol. Patol. Veg. y Ent. Agric. (Madrid)*, 14: 199–216.

—— 1951. Aplicación de la Genética al aumento de la eficacia del *Trichogramma minutum* en la lucha biológica. *Bol. Patol. Veg. y Ent. Agric. (Madrid)*, 18: 1–12.

—— 1956. Aplicación de la genética a la selección de insectos utiles. *Bol. Lab. Zoo. Gen. Agr. Portici*, 33: 594–602.

Urquijo, Pedro, and J. M. Dadin. 1943. Ensayo de los parásitos útiles *Trichogramma minutum* y. *T. pretiosum* en la lucha biológica contra la *Cydia pomonella*. *Bol. Patol. Veg. y Ent. Agric. (Madrid)*, 12: 411–25.

Utida, Syunro. 1950. On the equilibrium state of the interacting population of an insect and its parasite. *Ecology*, 31: 165–75.

—— 1953a. Interspecific competition between two species of bean weevil. *Ecology*, 34: 301–7.

—— 1953b. Effect of host density upon the population growth of interacting two species of parasites. Experimental studies on synparasitism. Second report. *Oyo-Kontyu*, 9: 102–7.

—— 1955. Fluctuations in the interacting populations of host and parasite in relation to the biotic potential of the host. *Ecology*, 36: 202–6.

—— 1957. Population fluctuation, an experimental and theoretical approach. In *Cold Spring Harbor Symposia on Quantitative Biology*, 22: 139–51. Biol. Lab., Long Island, N.Y.

Uvarov, B. P. 1928. Insect nutrition and metabolism. *Trans. Ent. Soc. London*, 76: 255–343.

—— 1931. Insects and climate. *Trans. Ent. Soc. London*, 79: 1–247.

—— 1957. The aridity factor in the ecology of locusts and grasshoppers of the old world. *Human and Animal Ecology, Reviews of Research*. Paris, UNESCO. Arid Zone Research Part 8. Pp. 164–98.

Vachon, M. 1955. Contribution à l'étude de la biologie de l'Hyménoptère *Baeus semilunum* (Hal.) parasite des œufs d'Araignées [Hym. Serphidae (= Proctotrypidae)]. *Ann. Soc. Ent. France*, 124: 141–6.

Vago, C. 1951. Phénomènes de 'Latentia' dans une maladie à ultravirus des insectes. *Rev. Canadienne Biol.*, 10: 299–308.

—— 1952. Maladies latentes et tolérance symbiotique chez les invertébrés. 6ᵐᵉ *Congreso Internacional de Patología Comparada, Madrid*, 1: 121–33.

—— 1953a. Facteurs alimentaires et activation des viroses latentes chez les insectes. *Proc. 6th Internatl. Congr. Microbiol.*, 5: 556–64.

—— 1953b. La polyédrie de *Thaumetopoea pityocampa*. *Ann. Inst. natl. Recherches agron. Sér. C. Ann. épiphyt.*, 4: 319–32.

—— 1956. Actions virusales indirectes. *Entomophaga*, 1: 82–7.

—— 1958. Sur la nomenclature des virus d'insectes. *Entomophaga*, 3: 331–2.

—— 1959a. On the pathogenesis of simultaneous virus infections in insects. *Jour. Insect Pathol.*, 1: 75–9.

—— 1959b. Première liste de souches de germes entomopathogènes. *Entomophaga*, 4: 286–8.

Vago, C., and P. Atger. 1961. Multiplication massive des virus d'insectes pendant la mue nymphale. *Entomophaga*, 6: 53–6.

Vago, C., and R. Cayrol. 1955. Une virose à polyèdres de la noctuelle gamma *Plusia gamma* L. (Lépidoptera). *Ann. Inst. natl. Recherches agron. Ser. C. Ann. épiphyt.*, 6: 421–32.

Vance, A. M. 1931. *Apanteles thompsoni* Lyle, a braconid parasite of the European corn borer. *U.S. Dept. Agric. Tech. Bull.* **233**. 28 pp.

—— 1932. The biology and morphology of the braconid *Chelonus annulipes* Wesm., a parasite of the European corn borer. *U.S. Dept. Agric. Tech. Bull.* **294**. 48 pp.

—— 1949. Some physiological relationships of the female European corn borer moth in controlled environments. *Jour. Econ. Ent.*, **42**: 474–84.

Vance, A. M., and H. D. Smith. 1933. The larval head of parasitic Hymenoptera and nomenclature of its parts. *Ann. Ent. Soc. America*, **26**: 86–94.

van den Bosch, R. 1950. The bionomics of *Prodenia praefica* Grote in California. Doctorate thesis, Univ. Calif., Berkeley.

van den Bosch, R., and E. J. Dietrick. 1959. The interrelationships of *Hypera brunneipennis* (Coleoptera: Curculionidae) and *Bathyplectes curculionis* (Hymenoptera: Ichneumonidae) in southern California. *Ann. Ent. Soc. America*, **52**: 609–16.

van den Bosch, R., and F. H. Haramoto. 1951. *Opius oophilus* Fullaway, an egg-larval parasite of the oriental fruit fly discovered in Hawaii. *Proc. Hawaii Ent. Soc.*, **14**: 251–5.

—— 1953. Competition among parasites of the oriental fruit fly. *Proc. Hawaiian Ent. Soc.*, **15**: 201–6.

van den Bosch, R., E. I. Schlinger, E. J. Dietrick, K. S. Hagen, and J. K. Holloway. 1959. The colonization and establishment of imported parasites of the spotted alfalfa aphid in California. *Jour. Econ. Ent.*, **52**: 136–41.

van den Bosch, R., E. I. Schlinger, E. J. Dietrick, and I. M. Hall. 1959. The role of imported parasites in the biological control of the spotted alfalfa aphid in southern California in 1957. *Jour. Econ. Ent.*, **52**: 142–54.

van den Bosch, R., E. I. Schlinger, and K. S. Hagen. 1962. Initial field observations in California on *Trioxys pallidus* (Haliday) a recently introduced parasite of the walnut aphid. *Jour. Econ. Ent.*, **55**: 857–62.

Van Den Brande, J. 1939. Een belangrijke parasiet (*Encarsia formosa* Gahan) van de Witte Motjes (*Trialeurodes vaporariorum* Ww.). *Mededel. Landbouwhoogesch Opzoekingssta. Gent.*, 7: 280–7 [Abs. in *R.A.E.* A28: 234.]

Van der Goot, P. 1940. Biological control of prickly pear in the Palu Valley (N. Celebes). *Overdruk uit Landbouw*, 16: 413–29.

van der Merwe, J. S. 1943. Investigations on the biology and ecology of *Mormoniella vitripennis* Walk. (Pteromalidae, Hym.). *Jour. Ent. Soc. South Africa*, 6: 48–64.

van der Vecht, J. 1953. Agricultural entomology of Indonesia 1939–1948. *Proc. 7th Pac. Sci. Congr.* (4): 100–8. (1949.)

Vanderzant, E. S., and T. B. Davich. 1958. Laboratory rearing of the boll weevils, a satisfactory larval diet and oviposition studies. *Jour. Econ. Ent.*, 51: 288–91.

Vanderzant, E. S., K. Kerur, and R. Reiser. 1957. The role of dietary fatty acids in the development of the pink bollworm. *Jour. Econ. Ent.*, 50: 606–8.

Vanderzant, E. S., and R. Reiser. 1956a. Aseptic rearing of the pink bollworm on synthetic media. *Jour. Econ. Ent.*, 49: 7–10.

—— 1956b. Studies of the nutrition of the pink bollworm using purified casein media. *Jour. Econ. Ent.*, 49: 454–8.

Vanderzant, E. S., R. Reiser, and E. E. Ivy. 1956. Methods for the mass rearing of the pink bollworm. *Jour. Econ. Ent.*, 49: 559–60.

van Emden, F. I. 1942. A key to the genera of larval Carabidae (Col.). *Trans. Royal Ent. Soc. London*, 92: 1–99.

—— 1950. Dipterous parasites of Coleoptera. *Ent. Month. Magazine*, 86: 182–206.

—— 1954. Handbooks for the identification of British insects. Diptera Cyclorrhapha Calyptrata (1) Section (a) Tachinidae and Calliphoridae. *Royal Ent. Soc. Lond.*, 10, 133 pp.

—— 1957. The taxonomic significance of the characters of immature insects. *Ann. Rev. Ent.*, 2: 91–106.

Vankova, J. 1959. Kultivierung von *Bacillus thuringiensis* im Versuchsbetriebmassstab. *Trans. 1st Internatl. Conf. Insect Pathol. and Biol. Control, Prag., 1958.* Pp. 59–64.

van Lith, J. P. 1955. Biologie van *Melittobia acasta* Walker (Hymenoptera, Chalcididae). *Tijdschr. Ent.*, 98: 29–42.

van Zwaluwenburg, R. H. 1928. The interrelationships of insects and roundworms. *Bull. Expt. Sta. Hawaiian Sugar Planters' Assoc. Entomol. Ser. Bull.* 20. 68 pp.

Varley, G. C. 1937. Description of the eggs and larvae of four species of Chalcidoid Hymenoptera parasitic on the knapweed gallfly. *Proc. Roy. Ent. Soc., London, Ser. B,* 6: 122–30..

—— 1941. On the search for hosts and the egg distribution of some chalcid parasites of the knapweed gall-fly. *Parasitology*, 33: 47–66.

—— 1947. The natural control of population balance in the knapweed gall-fly (*Urophora jaceana*). *Jour. Animal Ecol.*, 16: 139–87.

—— 1958. Meaning of density-dependence and related terms in population dynamics. *Nature*, 181: 1780–1.

Varley, G. C., and R. L. Edwards. 1957. The bearing of parasite behaviour in the dynamics of insect host and parasite populations. *Jour. Animal Ecology*, 26: 471–7.

Varley, G. C., and G. R. Gradwell. 1958. Balance in insect populations. *Proc. 10th Internatl. Congr. Ent.*, 2: 619–24. (1956.)

Vassiliev, I. V. 1913. *Eurygaster integriceps* Put. and new methods of fighting it by aid of parasites. *Trav. Bur. Ent. Minist. Agric. St. Petersbourg* 4. 3rd ed. 81 pp.

Velu, H., and A. Bouin. 1916. Essai de destruction du *Schistocerca peregrina* au Maroc. *Ann. Inst. Pasteur [Paris]*, 30: 389–421.

Verhulst, P. F. 1838. Notice sur la loi que la population suit dans son accroissement. *Corresp. Math. et Phys.*, 10: 113–21.

Vesey-Fitzgerald, D. 1953. Review of biological control of coccids on coconut palms in the Seychelles. *Bull. Ent. Res.*, 44: 405–13.

Vevai, E. J. 1942. On the bionomics of *Aphidius matricariae* Hal., a Braconid parasite of *Myzus persicae* Sulz. *Parasitology*, 34: 141–51.

Vodjdani, S. 1954. Contribution à l'étude des punaises des céréales et en particulier d'*Eurygaster integriceps* Put. (Hemiptera, Pentatomidae, Scutellerinae). *Ann. Epiphyt.* No. 2, pp. 105–160.

Volterra, V. 1926. Variazioni e fluttuazioni del numero d'individui in speci animali conviventi. *Mem. accad. Lincei*, 2: 31–113.

von Frisch, K. 1950. *Bees: Their Vision, Chemical Senses, and Language*. Cornell Univ. Press, Ithaca, 119 pp.

von Prowazek, S. 1907. Chlamydozoa. II. Gelbsucht der Seidenraupen. *Arch. Protistenk.*, 10: 358–64.

—— 1912. Untersuchungen über die Gelbsucht der Seidenraupen. *Zentr. Bakt., Parasitenk. Infekt.*, 67: 268–84.

Vouk, V., and Z. Klas. 1931. Conditions influencing the growth of the insecticidal fungus *Metarrhizium anisopliae* (Metsch.) Sor. *Internatl. Corn Borer Invest., Sci. Rept.*, 4: 24–45.

Voûte, A. D. 1937. Die biologische Bekämpfung der Insekten in Niederd. Indien. *Niederl. Natur. Tijdschr. Ned.-Ind.*, 97: 28–34.

—— 1946. Regulation of the density of the insect populations in virgin forests and cultivated woods. *Archives Néerlandaises de Zoologie*, 7: 435–70.

Walker, D. L., R. P. Hanson, and A. S. Evans. 1958. *Symposium on Latency and Masking in Viral and Rickettsial Infections*. Burgess, Mineapolis. 202 pp.

Walker, M. G. 1943. Notes on the biology of *Dexia rustica* F. a dipterous parasite of *Melolontha melolontha* F. *Proc. Zool. Soc. London*. À, 113: 126–76.

Wallace, A. R. 1876. *The Geographical Distribution of Animals with a Study of the Relations of Living and Extinct Faunas as Elucidating the Past Changes of the Earth's Surface*. 2 vols. MacMilland and Co., London, vol. 1, 503 pp; vol. 2, 607 pp.

—— 1880. *Island Life: or, the Phenomena and Causes of Insular Faunas and Floras, Including a Revision and Attempted Solution of the Problem of Geological Climates*. MacMillan and Co., London, 526 pp.

Wallace, F. G. 1956. Cultivation of *Trypanosoma ranarum* on a liquid medium. *Jour. Protozool.*, 3: 47–9.

Wallace, G. E. 1942. Observations on the life history of a new Chalcidoid wasp, an internal parasite of ant-lion larvae. *Ann. Carnegie Mus.*, 29: 31–40.

Wallin, I. E. 1927. *Symbionticism and the Origin of Species*. The Williams and Wilkins Co., Baltimore, 171 pp.

Wallis, R. C. 1957. Incidence of polyhedrosis of gypsy-moth larvae and the influence of relative humidity. *Jour. Econ. Ent.*, 50: 580–3.

Walsh, B. D. 1864. On phytophagic varieties and phytophagic species. *Proc. Ent. Soc. Philadelphia*, 3: 403–30.

—— 1865. On the phytophagic varieties of phytophagous species, with remarks on the unity of coloration in insects. *Proc. Ent. Soc. Philadelphia*, 5: 194–216.

—— 1866. *Practical Entomologist*. June 1866, p. 101.

Walter, E. V., and D. W. La Hue. 1939. Notes on food for corn earworm adults. *Jour. Econ. Ent.*, 32: 156.

Walz, A. J. 1957. Observations on the biologies of some hymenopterous parasites of the cabbage seedpod weevil in northern Idaho. *Ann. Ent. Soc. America*, 50: 219–20.

Warming, J. E. B. 1895. *Plantesamfund. grundträk of den ökologiske plantegeografi*. Copenhagen. (German translation 1896 by Knoblauch.)

Warren III, F. W., and D. R. King. 1959. The biotic effect of insecticides on populations of aphids and mites of pecans. *Jour. Econ. Ent.*, 52: 163–5.

Warren, G. L. 1958. A method of rearing bark and cambium feeding beetles with particular reference to *Hylobius warreni* Wood. *Canadian Ent.*, 90: 425–8.

Wasser, H. B. 1952. Demonstration of a new insect virus not associated with inclusion bodies. *Jour. Bact.*, 64: 787–92.

Watanabe, Chihisa. 1958. Review of biological control of insect pests in Japan. *Proc. 10th Internatl. Congr. Ent.*, 4: 515–17 (1956).

Waters, Harold. 1937. Methods and equipment for laboratory studies of insects. *Jour. Econ. Ent.*, 30: 179–203.

Watson, J. R. 1915. Report of entomologist. *Florida Agric. Expt. Sta. Report for fiscal year ending June 30th, 1914.* Pp. 46–56.

Watt, K. E. F. 1955. Studies on population productivity. I. Three approaches to the optimum yield problem in populations of *Tribolium confusum*. *Ecol. Monogr.*, 25: 269–90.

—— 1959. A mathematical model for the effect of densities of attacked and attacking species on the number attacked. *Canadian Ent.*, 91: 129–44.

—— 1961. Mathematical models for use in insect pest control. *Canad. Ent. Suppl. 19*, 93, 62 pp.

—— 1962. Use of mathematics in population ecology. *Ann. Review Ent.*, 7: 243–60.

Way, M. J. 1958. The influence of other ant species on biological control of *Oecophylla longinoda* (Latr.). *Proc. 10th Internatl. Congr. Ent.*, 4: 595–6 (1956).

Way, M. J., and C. J. Banks. 1958. The control of *Aphis fabae* Scop. with special reference to biological control of insects which attack annual crops. *Proc. 10th Internatl. Congr. Ent.*, 4: 907–9 (1956).

Weaver, N. 1955. Rearing of honeybee larvae on royal jelly in the laboratory. *Science*, 121: 509–10.

—— 1958. Rearing honeybee larvae in the laboratory. *Proc. 10th Internatl. Congr. Ent.*, 4: 1031–6. (1956.)

Weaver, N., and K. A. Kuiken. 1951. Quantitative analysis of the essential amino acids of royal jelly and some pollens. *Jour. Econ. Ent.*, 44: 635–8.

Webber, R. T., and J. V. Schaffner, Jr. 1926. Host relations of *Compsilura concinnata* Mg., *an important tachinid parasite of the gypsy moth and the brown-tail moth*. *U.S. Dept. Agric. Bull.* 1363. 31 pp.

Webster, L. T. 1946. Experimental epidemiology. *Medicine*, 25: 77–109.

Weems, H. V. 1953. Notes on collecting syrphid flies (Diptera: Syrphidae). *Florida Ent.*, 36: 91–8.

Weiser, J. 1946. Studie o mikrosporidiích z larev hmyzú našich vod. (The mikrosporidia of insect larvae.) *Vestník Českoslov Zool. Společnosti*, 10: 245–72.

—— 1947. Klíc kurcovaní Mikrosporidií. *Acta Soc. Sci. Naturalium Moravicae*, 18: 1–64.

—— 1951. Příspěvek k poznání plísní cizopasících v hmyzu. *Entomologicke Listy*, 14: 130–5.

—— 1954. Zur systematischen Stellung der Schizogregarinen der Mehlmotte, *Ephestia kuhniella* Z. *Arch. f. Protistenkunde*, 100: 127–42.

—— 1955a. *Neoaplectana carpocapsae* n. sp. (Anguillulata, Steinernematinae), nový cizopasník housenek obaleče jablečneho, *Carpocapsa pomonella* L. *Véstník Českoslov. Zool. Spolecnosti.*, 19: 44–52.

—— 1955b. A new classification of the Schizogregarine. *Jour. Protozool.*, 2: 6–12.

—— 1956. Protozoäre Infektionen im Kampfe gegen Insekten. *Zeitschr. f. Pflanzenkrankh. u. Pflanzenschutz*, 63: 625–38.

Weiser, J. 1957a. Mikrosporidien des Schwammspinners und Goldafters. *Zeitschr. angew. Ent.*, 40: 509–21.

—— 1957b. Možnosti biologického boje s přástevníčkem americkým (*Hyphantria cunea* Drury)—III. *Československá Parasitologie*, 4: 359–67.

—— 1958a. Protozoan diseases in insect control. *Proc. 10th Internatl. Congr. Ent.*, 4: 681–5. (1956.)

—— 1958b. Zur Taxonomie der Insektenviren. *Československá Parasitologie*, 5: 203–211.

Weiser, J., and O. Lysenko. 1956. Septikemie bource moruůového. *Československá Mikrobiologie*, 1: 216–22.

Weiser, J., and J. Veber. 1955. Možnosti biologického boje s přástevníčkem americkým (*Hyphantria cunea* Drury) II. *Československá Parasitologie*, 2: 191–9.

—— 1957. Die Mikrosporidie *Thelohania hyphantriae* Weiser des weissen Bärenspinners und anderer Mitglieder seiner Biocönose. *Zeitschr. angew. Ent.*, 40: 55–70.

Weismann, A. 1864. *Die Entwicklung der Dipteren ein Beitrag zur Entwicklungsgeschichte der Insekten.* 263 pp. Leipzig.

Welch, H. E. 1958. A review of recent work on nematodes associated with insects with regard to their utilization as biological control agents. *Proc. 10th Internatl. Congr. Ent.*, 4: 863–8. (1956.)

Weldon, G. F. 1914. Insect notes. *California Hort. Comm. Monthly Bull.*, 3: 296.

Wellington, E. F. 1949. Artificial media for rearing some phytophagous Lepidoptera. *Nature*, 163: 574.

Wellington, W. G. 1957. The synoptic approach to studies of insects and climate. *Ann. Rev. Ent.*, 2: 143–62.

West, A. S., and B. De Long. 1955. Notes on the biology and laboratory rearing of a predatory insect, *Zelus exsanguis* (Stahl) (Hemiptera: Reduviidae). *Ann. Rept. Ent. Soc. Ontario*, 86: 97–101.

Wheeler, E. W. 1923. Some braconids parasitic on aphids and their life-history (Hym.). *Ann. Ent. Soc. America*, 16: 1–29.

Wheeler, W. M. 1923. *Social Life Among the Insects.* Harcourt, Brace. New York. 375 pp.

Whitcomb, W. D. 1940. Biological control of mealybugs in greenhouses. *Massachusetts Agric. Expt. Sta. Bull.* 375. 22 pp.

White, G. F. 1923. Hornworm septicemia. *Jour. Agric. Res.*, 26: 477–86.

—— 1923. Cutworm septicemia. *Jour. Agric. Res.*, 26: 487–95.

White, M. J. D. 1949. Cytological evidence on the phylogeny and classification of Diptera. *Evolution*, 3: 252–61.

—— 1954. *Animal Cytology and Evolution*, 2nd Ed. Cambridge Univ. Press, Cambridge, 454 pp.

—— 1957. Cytogenetics and systematic entomology. *Ann. Rev. Ent.*, 2: 71–90.

White, R. T. 1940. Survival of type A milky disease of Japanese beetle larvae under adverse field conditions. *Jour. Econ. Ent.*, 33: 303–6.

—— 1943. Effect of milky disease on *Tiphia* parasites of Japanese beetle larvae. *Jour. New York Ent. Soc.*, 51: 213–18.

—— 1946. Effect of the sun's rays upon the viability of spores of *Bacillus popilliae* Dutky, the organism causing milky disease of Japanese beetle larvae. *U.S. Dept. Agric. Bur. Ent. and Plant Quar.*, E-703. 4 pp.

—— 1947. Milky disease infecting *Cyclocephala* larvae in the field. *Jour. Econ. Ent.*, 40: 912–14.

White, R. T., and S. R. Dutky. 1940. Effect of the introduction of milky diseases on populations of Japanese beetle larvae. *Jour. Econ. Ent.*, 33: 306–9.

White, R. T., and P. J. McCabe. 1943. Colonization of the organism causing milky disease of Japanese beetle larvae. *U.S. Dept. Agric., Bur. Ent. Plant Quarantine, E-605.* 7 pp.

Whiting, P. W. 1935. Sex determination in bees and wasps. *Jour. Heredity,* 26: 263–78.

—— 1945. The evolution of male haploidy. *Quart. Rev. Biol.,* 20: 231–60.

Wigglesworth, V. B. 1931. Respiration. *Biol. Rev.,* 6: 181–220.

—— 1939. *The Principles of Insect Physiology.* E. P. Dutton and Company Inc., New York. 434 pp.

—— 1954. *The Physiology of Insect Metamorphosis.* Cambridge Monographs in Experimental biology No. 1, Cambridge at the University Press. 152 pp.

Wikén, T. 1956. Möglichkeiten der Produktionssteigerung in der schweizerischen Landwirtschaft durch neuzeitliche bakterielle Impfverfahren. *Schweiz. Landwirtschaftl. Monatshefte,* 34: 480–93, 536–51.

Wikén, T., and H. Wille. 1953. Über den Wuchsstoffbedarf eines Sporenbildenden, fur den Engerling von *Melolontha vulgaris* Fabr. pathogenen Bakteriums. *Zentralbl. Bakt. Abt. II.* 107: 259–71.

—— 1955. Über den Wuchsstoffbedarf und die Virulenz einer sporenbildenden pathogenen Bakterie des Engerlings von *Melolontha vulgaris* Fabr. *Proc. 6th Internatl. Congr. Microbiol.,* 6: 348–9. (Also in *Riassunti delle Comunicazioni,* 3: 156.)

Wikén, T., P. Bovey, H. Wille, and T. Wildbolz. 1954. Über die Ergebnisse der in der Schweiz im Jahre 1953 durchgeführten Freilandversuche zur mikrobiologischen Bekämpfung des Engerlings von *Melolontha melolontha* L. (= *Melolontha vulgaris* F.). *Zeitschr. angew. Ent.,* 36: 1–19.

Wilkes, A. 1942. The influence of selection on the preferendum of a chalcid (*Microplectron fuscipennis* Zett.) and its significance in the biological control of an insect pest. *Proc. Roy. Soc. Ser. B.: Biol. Sci.,* 130: 400–15.

—— 1947. The effects of selective breeding on the laboratory propagation of insect parasites. *Proc. Roy. Ent. Soc. London Ser. B.,* 134: 227–45.

Willard, H. F., and T. L. Bissell. 1926. Work and parasitism of the Mediterranean fruit fly in Hawaii in 1921. *Jour. Agric. Res.,* 33: 9–15.

Willard, H. F., and A. C. Mason. 1937. Parasitization of the Mediterranean fruit fly in *Hawaii,* 1914–33. *U.S. Dept. Agric. Circ.* 439. 17 pp.

Wille, H. 1954. Neue Versuchsergebnisse über die mikrobiologische Engerlingsbekämpfung. *Zentrale für Maikäfer-Bekämpfungsaktionen, Bericht,* 48. 9 pp.

Wille, H., and M. E. Martignoni. 1952. Vorläufige Mitteilung über einen neuen Krankheitstypus beim Engerling von *Melolontha vulgaris* F. *Schweiz. Zeitschr. allg. Path. u. Bakt.,* 15: 470–4.

Wille, J. E. 1940. Resumen de las diferentes labores ejecutadas en el Peru para combatír insectos dañinos por el 'Metodo Biologico.' *Proc. 6th Pac. Sci. Congr.,* 4: 369–71 [Univ. Calif. Press (1939)].

—— 1951. Biological control of certain cotton insects and the application of new organic insecticides in Peru. *Jour. Econ. Ent.,* 44: 13–18.

—— 1958. El control biológico de los insectos agrícolas en el Peru. *Proc. 10th Internatl. Congr. Ent.,* 4: 519–23 (1956).

Williams, C. B. 1957. Insect migration. *Ann. Rev. Ent.,* 2: 163–80.

—— 1958. *Insect Migration: the New Naturalist Series.* The MacMillan Co., New York, 235 pp.

Williams, F. X. 1931a. *The Insects and Other Invertebrates of Hawaiian Sugar Cane Fields.* Advertizer Co., Honolulu, Hawaii. 400 pp.

Williams, F. X. 1931b. *Handbook of the Insects and Other Invertebrates of Hawaiian Sugar Cane Fields*. Hawaiian Sugar Planters' Assoc., Honolulu. 400 pp.

—— 1932. *Exallonyx philonthiphagous*, a new proctotrypid wasp in Hawaii, and its host. *Proc. Hawaii Ent. Soc.*, 8: 205–8.

Williams, J. R. 1951a. The factors which promote and influence the oviposition of *Nemeritis canescens* Grav. (Ichneumonidae, Ophioninae). *Proc. Roy. Ent. Soc. London Ser. A*, 26: 49–58.

—— 1951b. The control of the black sage in Mauritius by *Schematiza cordiae* Barb. (Col. Galerucid.). *Bull. Ent. Res.*, 42: 455–63.

—— 1954. The biological control of weeds. *Rept. 6th Commonwealth Entom. Conf. London, July*. Pp. 95–8.

Williams, J. R., L. A. Moutia, and P. R. Hermelin. 1951. The biological control of *Gonipterus scutellatus* Gyll. (Col.: Curculionidae) in Mauritius. *Bull. Ent. Res.*, 42: 23–8.

Wilson, E. D., and W. L. Brown. 1953. The subspecies concept and its taxonomic application. *Systematic Zool.*, 2: 97–111.

Wilson, F. 1943. The entomological control of St. John's wort (*Hypericum perforatum* L.) with special reference to the weed in southern France. *Australia Council Sci. and Indust. Res. Bull.* 169. 87 pp.

—— 1949. The entomological control of weeds. *Internatl. Union Biol. Sci., Ser. B.*, 5: 53–64.

—— 1950. *Biological control of weeds*. In *New Biology*. Penguin Books 8: 51–74.

—— 1952. The biological control of weeds in Australia. *Proc. 6th Internatl. Grassland Congr.*, 6: 567–72. (University Park, Pa.).

—— 1954. Some aspects of the biological control of weeds in Australia, 105–13. Weed Control Conf., Roseworthy Agric. Col., Roseworthy, So. Australia, Session 5 (August).

—— 1953. Some aspects of Australian entomological research since 1939. *Proc. 7th Pac. Sci. Congr.*, 4: 113–18 (1949).

—— 1960a. A Review of the Biological Control of Insects and Weeds in Australia and Australian New Guinea. *Tech. Com. 1, Comm. Inst. Bio. Cont., Ottawa, Canada*. 102 pp.

—— 1960b. *The Future of Biological Control*. 7th Commonwealth Ent. Conf. Rept. London. 72–9.

Wilson, G. S., and A. A. Miles. 1946. *Topley and Wilson's Principles of Bacteriology and Immunity*. Williams and Wilkins Co., Baltimore. Vol. 2, 3rd ed. 2054 pp.

Wishart, G. 1945. *Aplomya caesar* (Aldrich), a Tachinid parasite of the European corn borer. *Canadian Ent.*, 77: 157–67.

—— 1946. Laboratory rearing of *Macrocentrus gifuensis* Ashm., a parasite of the European corn borer. *Canad. Ent.*, 78: 78–82.

—— 1948. The biology of *Melanichneumon rubicundus* (Cress.) (Hymenoptera: Ichneumonidae). *Canadian Ent.*, 80: 118–37.

—— 1949. Biological control of the European corn borer. *Quebec Soc. Prot. Pl. Rpt.*, 31: 1–2.

—— 1956. Effects of hydrogen ion concentration on hatching of eggs of *Aplomya caesar* (Ald.) (Diptera: Tachinidae). *Canadian Ent.*, 88: 655–6.

Woglum, R. S., J. R. La Follette, W. E. Landon, and H. C. Lewis. 1947. The effect of field-applied insecticides on beneficial insects of citrus in California. *Jour. Econ. Ent.*, 40: 818–20.

Wolcott, G. N. 1934. The present status of white grub parasites in Puerto Rico. *Jour. Agric., Univ. Puerto Rico.*, 18: 436–41.

33—I.P.W.

Wolcott, G. N. 1941. The establishment in Puerto Rico of *Larra americana* Saussure. *Jour. Econ. Ent.*, 34: 53–6.

—— 1942. The requirements of parasites for more than hosts. *Science*, 96: 317–18.

—— 1948a. Collecting parasites of white grubs for Puerto Rico: then and now. *Jour. Econ. Ent.*, 41: 813.

—— 1948b. The Insects of Puerto Rico. *Jour. Agric. Univ. Puerto Rico* 32: 1–416.

—— 1953. Biological control of the pustule scale in Puerto Rico. *Jour. Agric. Univ. Puerto Rico.*, 37: 228–33.

—— 1958. The evanescence of perfect biological control. *Proc. 10th Internatl. Congr. Ent.*, 4: 511–13 (1956).

Wolcott, G. N., and L. F. Martorell. 1943a. Natural parasitism by *Trichogramma minutum* of the eggs of the sugar cane moth borer, *Diatraea saccharalis*, in the cane fields of Puerto Rico. *Jour. Agric. Univ. Puerto Rico*, 27: 39–83.

—— 1943b. Control of the sugar cane borer in Puerto Rico by laboratory-reared parasites. *Jour. Econ. Ent.*, 36: 460–4.

Wolf, J., and S. A. Z. Mahmoud. 1957. The effects of l- and d-alanine on the germination of some *Bacillus* spores. *Jour. Appl. Bact.*, 20: 373–83.

Woodruff, L. C. 1929. *Eupelmus popa* Girault, a parasite of the sorghum midge, *Contarina sorghicola* Coquillett. *Jour. Econ. Ent.*, 22: 160–7.

Wright, D. W., Q .A. Geering, D. G. Ashby. 1947. The insect parasites of the carrot fly *Psila rosae* Fab. *Bull. Ent. Res.*, 37: 507–29.

Wright, D. W., R. D. Hughes, and J. Worrall. 1960. The effect of certain predators on the numbers of cabbage root fly (*Erioischia brassicae* (Bouche)) and on the subsequent damage caused by the pest. *Ann. Appl. Bio.*, 48: 756–63.

Wright, S. 1940. *The statistical consequences of Mendelian heredity in relation to speciation*, pp. 161–84. In *The New Systematics*, J. S. Huxley, editor. Oxford Univ. Press, 583 pp.

Wright, S., and T. Dobzhansky. 1946. Genetics of natural populations. XII. Experimental reproduction of some of the changes caused by natural selection in certain populations of *Drosophila pseudoobscura. Genetics*, 31: 125–56.

Wylie, H. G. 1958a. Factors that affect host finding by *Nasonia vitripennis* (Walk.) (Hymenoptera: Pteromalidae). *Canadian Ent.*, 90: 597–608.

—— 1958b. Observations on *Aphidecta obliterata* (L.) (Coleoptera: Coccinellidae), a predator of conifer-infesting Aphidoidea. *Canadian Ent.*, 90: 518–22.

Wynne-Edwards, V. C. 1955. The dynamics of animal populations. *Discovery*, 16: 433–6.

Xeros, N. 1954. A second virus disease of the leather jacket, *Tipula paludosa. Nature*, 174: 562.

Yakhontov, V. V. 1937. Coccinellid control of *Hypera variabilis. Vuisshaya Shkola*, 1: 77–81. [Abs. in *R.A.E.* A 26: 238, 1938.]

Yamafuji, K. 1957. Discussion on biochemistry of virogenesis. *Rept. Agric. Biochem. Kyushu Univ.*, 17: 1–12.

—— 1958. Induction and latency of virus. *Report of Agricultural Biochemistry, Kyushu University, No. 18*, pp. 12–15.

Yasumatsu, Keizo. 1958. An interesting case of biological control of *Ceroplastes rubens* Maskell in Japan. *Proc. 10th Internatl. Congr. Ent.*, 4: 771–5 (1956).

Yasumatsu, K., K. Nomura, S. Utida, and T. Yamasaki. 1953. *Applied Entomology*. Asakura Publ. Co. Ltd. Tokyo. 296 pp. [In Japanese.]

Yetter, W. P., Jr., and H. W. Allen. 1940. Effect of larval parasitization of the oriental fruit moth on infestation. *Jour. Econ. Ent.*, 33: 349–53.

York, G. T. 1958. Field tests with the fungus *Beauveria* sp. for control of the European corn borer. *Iowa State Coll. Jour. Sci.*, 33: 123–9.

York, G. T., and H. W. Prescott. 1952. Nemestrinid parasites of grasshoppers. *Jour. Econ. Ent.*, **45**: 5–10.

Young, I. E., and P. C. Fitz-James. 1959. The formation of parasporal protein crystals in *Bacillus cereus* var. *alesti*. *Bact. Proc.*, **59**: 38.

Yuill, J. S., and R. Craig. 1937. The nutrition of the flesh fly larvae, *L. sericata* Meig. *Jour. Exptl. Zool.*, **75**: 169–78.

Yurchenco, J. A., C. R. Piepoli, and M. C. Yurchenco. 1954. Low temperature storage for maintaining stable infectious bacterial pools. *Appl. Microbiol.* **2**: 53–5.

Zaazou, H. 1948. Oviposition of the bean weevil. *Bull. Soc. Fouad Ier Ent.*, **32**: 343–61.

Zhdanov, V. M. 1953. Determination of viruses in man and animals. *Acad. Med. Sci. U.S.S.R., Moscow.* 348 pp.

Ziegler, D. W., E. V. Davis, W. J. Thomas, and W. F. McLimans. 1958. The propagation of mammalian cells in a 20-liter stainless steel fermentor. *Appl. Microbiol.*, **6**: 305–10.

Zimmack, H. L., K. D. Arbuthnot, and T. A. Brindley. 1954. Distribution of the European corn borer parasite *Perezia pyraustae*, and its effect on the host. *Jour. Econ. Ent.*, **47**: 641–5.

Zimmack, H. L., and T. A. Brindley. 1957. The effect of the protozoan parasite *Perezia pyraustae* Paillot on the European corn borer. *Jour. Econ. Ent.*, **50**: 637–40.

Zimmerman, E. C. 1948. *Insects of Hawaii. Introduction.* Vol. 1. Univ. Hawaii Press Honolulu. 206 pp.

Zinna, Giulio. 1959. Richerche sugli insetti entomofagi. 1. Specializzazione entomoparassitica negli Encrytidae: Studio morfologico etologico e fisiologico del *Leptomastix dactylopii* Howard. *Bol. Lab. Ent. Agr. 'Filippo Silvestri,' Portici*, **18**: 1–150.

—— 1961. Richerche sugli insetti entomofagi. II. Specializzazione entomoparassitica negli Aphelinidae: Studio morfologico, etologico e fisiologico del *Coccophagus bivittatus* Compere, nuovo parassita del *Coccus hesperidum* L. per l'Italia. *Boll. Lab Ent. Agraria 'Filippo Silvestri' Portici*, **19**: 301–58.

Zoebelein, Gerhard. 1956. Der Honigtau als Nahrung der Insekten. Teil I. *Zeitschr. angew Ent.*, **38**: 369–416. Teil. II. *Ibid.*, **39**: 129–67.

—— 1957. Die Rolle des Waldhonigtaus im Nahrungshaushalt forstlich nützlicher Insekten. *Forstw. Cbl.* 76 Jg. (1957): 1–64.

Zwolfer, H., and M. Kraus. 1957. Biocoenotic studies on the parasites of two fir- and two oak-tortricids. *Entomophaga*, **2**: 173–96.

Index to Scientific Names

This index includes all scientific names cited in the book. Page references for all species are given only after the full scientific name, i.e., *Abella subflava* Girault, page 477, but reference to any particular specific name can be made in case the genus is unknown by locating the associated generic name in the index. For example, under *abietis* (*Cephalcia*) refer to *Cephalcia abietis* Linnaeus, which the index shows is referred to on page 553 of the text. For an index to subject matter, the reader is referred to the Table of Contents.